S0-AJY-967

Human Physiology

Human Physiology

Functions of the Human Body

Ross M. Durham

University of Tennessee at Chattanooga

wcb

Wm. C. Brown Publishers
Dubuque, Iowa

Book Team

Editor *Edward G. Jaffe*
Developmental Editor *Carol Mills*
Designer *Ben Neff*
Production Editor *Kevin Campbell*
Art Editor *Barbara J. Grantham*
Photo Research Editor *Carol M. Smith*
Permissions Editor *Vicki Krug*
Visuals Processor *Vickie Werner*

wcb

Chairman of the Board *Wm. C. Brown*
President and Chief Executive Officer *Mark C. Falb*

wcb

Wm. C. Brown Publishers, College Division

President *G. Franklin Lewis*
Vice President, Editor-in-Chief *George Wm. Bergquist*
Vice President, Director of Production *Beverly Kolz*
Vice President, National Sales Manager *Bob McLaughlin*
Director of Marketing *Thomas E. Doran*
Marketing Communications Manager *Edward Bartell*
Marketing Manager *Craig S. Marty*
Executive Editor *Edward G. Jaffe*
Manager of Visuals and Design *Faye M. Schilling*
Production Editorial Manager *Colleen A. Yonda*
Production Editorial Manager *Julie A. Kennedy*
Publishing Services Manager *Karen J. Slaght*

Cover Image

An artist's view of a successful sperm's assault on the ramparts of the human ovum. Some artistic license has been taken, but the basic idea is accurate: one sperm, one ovum.

Cover and section openers image: © Francis Leroy.

Cover and interior design by Tara L. Bazata

The credits section for this book begins on page C1, and is considered an extension of the copyright page.

Library of Congress Catalog Card Number: 88-72245

ISBN 0-697-00395-7

Printed in the United States of America by Wm. C. Brown Publishers
2460 Kerper Boulevard, Dubuque, IA 52001

10 9 8 7 6 5 4 3 2 1

*To my beloved wife,
Valerie. Not for a
moment did she doubt
that I would write this
book. Without her
unwavering confidence,
I might not have.*

Contents

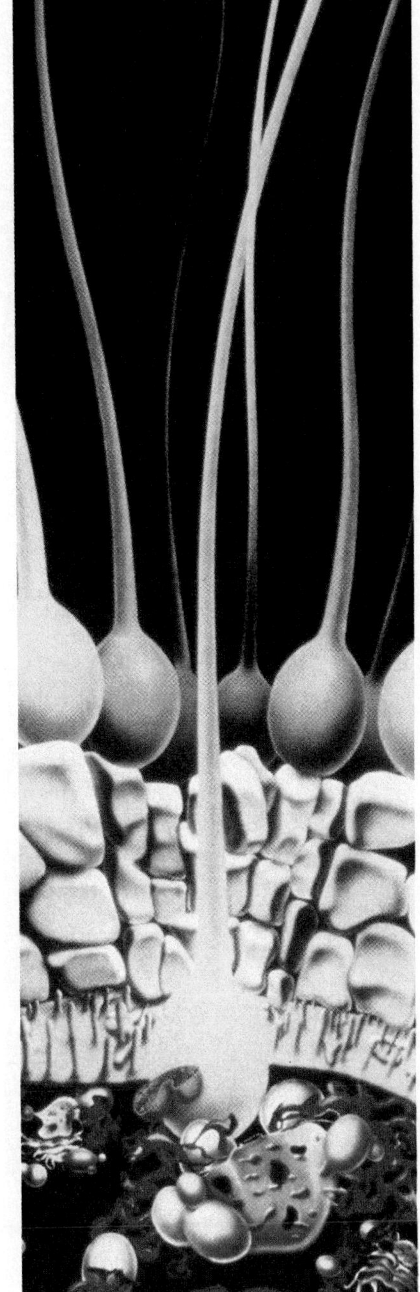

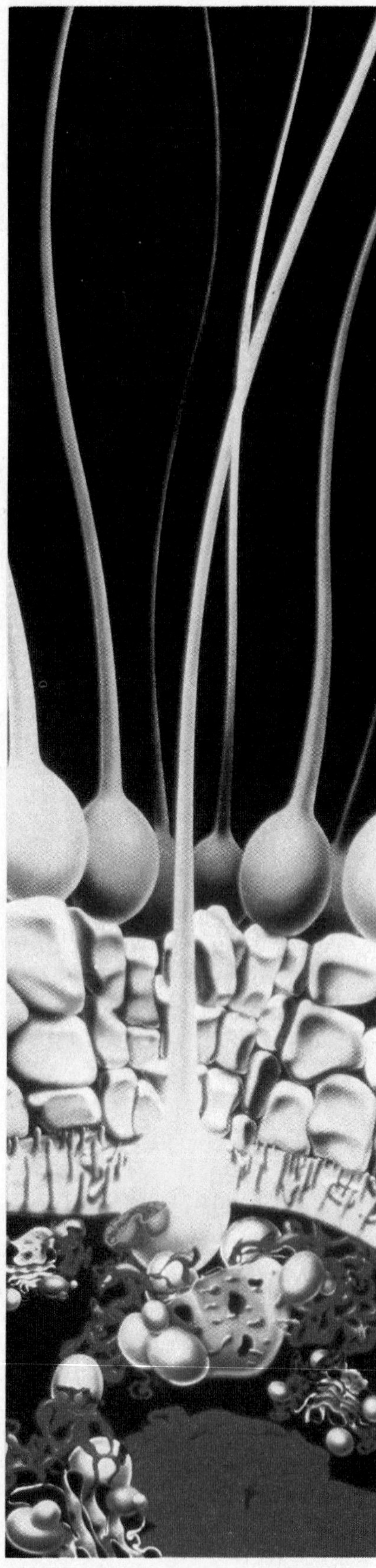

Section II

The Control Systems 137

Section III

Motion and Motor Control 351

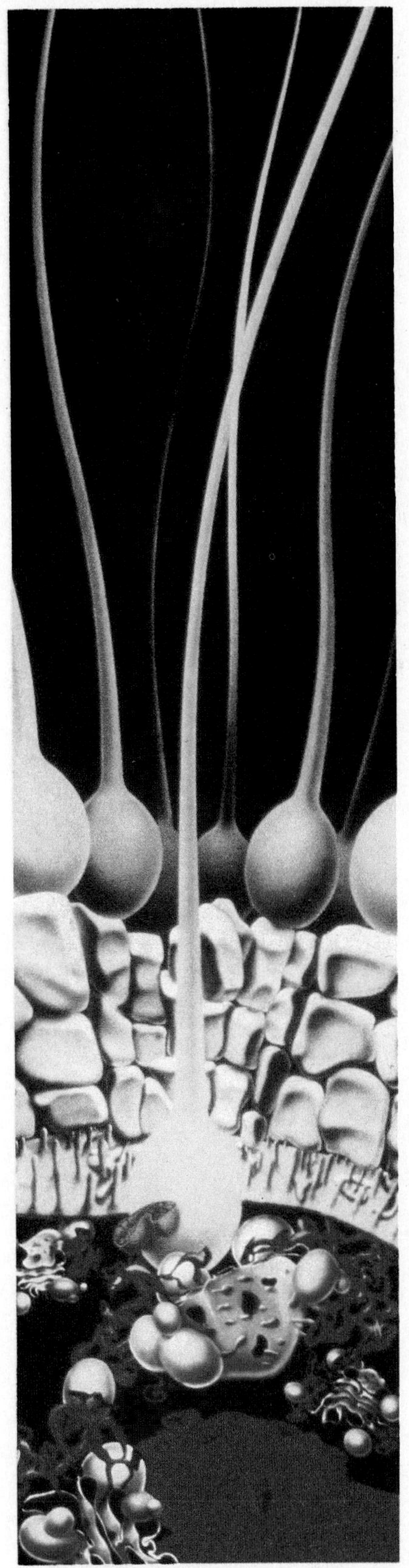

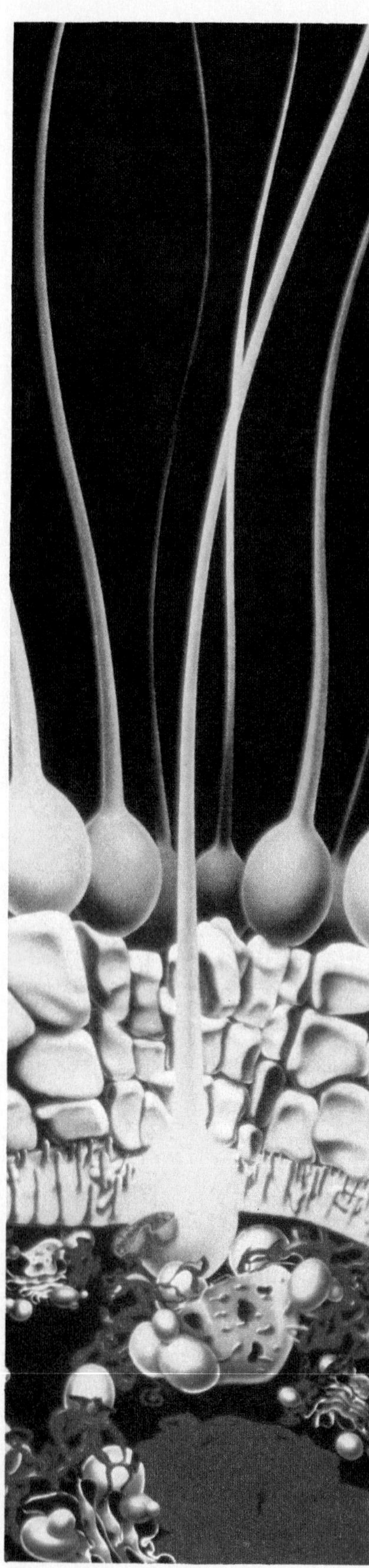

Preface

This textbook was written to fill a gap. The current market abounds with books covering much the same material, but most offer it in concentrated doses and present it as tersely as possible. Not everyone can digest it that way. Many of the students taking college physiology lack a science background. Some are taking the course only to fulfill a degree requirement, while others may be considering careers in allied health but still have not had a great deal of science in high school. Most have never read any scientific literature, and so they are ill-prepared for the terse, rather cold and factual style they find in many textbooks.

This book was written for those students . . . students who have never read much about science and who have little or no scientific background. It is written in narrative fashion; occasional digressions and descriptive adjectives give the readers a chance to mentally collect themselves before being confronted by the next group of facts . . . and there are plenty of those. This is a rigorous textbook. There is no stinting of information, as a read-through will quickly demonstrate.

Wherever it seems natural, I have included bits of information that are peripheral to the main flow of thought yet are definitely related to the subject matter. They associate facts with everyday experience. To avoid interrupting the narrative, they are isolated on the textbook pages, in small boxes. Concepts that seem to be unusually difficult are often presented in analogy to help student comprehension. Larger panels appear occasionally to enhance the text and provide additional information. I firmly believe that students who have difficulty reading other texts will read this one thoroughly and learn from it.

Homeostasis is featured as the absolute goal of all physiological mechanisms, and this attitude is emphasized throughout, even to the extent of pointing out that behavior is directed at giving our bodies what they need to retain internal constancy. While I do not necessarily relate every physiological mechanism directly to homeostasis, it nevertheless should be present as a powerful undercurrent on whatever tide is running, and the student needs to be reminded of it often.

I have included some chapters that are not common in physiology textbooks. Chapter 6 deals exclusively with the fundamentals of electricity, and of necessity it presents some elementary physical principles that go along with electrical theory. In this, my textbook is unique. I know of no other in which these principles are explained, and yet students who are going to encounter neurophysiology for the first time *must* know the difference between an ampere and a volt. How can they otherwise comprehend the movement of an action potential along a nerve fiber, or the crosswise flow of current in the neuronal axon? If you find this chapter unnecessary, you can bypass it.

Chapter 20 deals with some of the drugs most abused by today's society. This problem is so acute and so ubiquitous that a book of this sort should not ignore it. Our students will need to understand the subject when they begin their careers.

I have not provided information in depth, but I have dealt with the drugs most popularly used at the time of this writing, and what information I have offered is accurate and in sufficient detail to satisfy the informed layperson. Chapter 21 is included for the same reason—it is the kind of knowledge that an informed medical or allied health professional should have, and will be expected to have by the general public.

Each chapter begins with a short introduction, often including a brief history of the subject. Unfamiliar or jargonesque words appearing for the first time are in boldface, and where it is necessary I have also provided the Latin or Greek roots and a pronunciation guide. A complete glossary is also included.

Each chapter also features its own list of study hints. These are essentially notes to the student regarding chapter content—specifically, which core items must be learned if the chapter is to be understood. A list of objectives is also included as a learning aid.

Years of experience have shown me that students have a difficult time finding out what it is that they do *not* know, even after several hours of study. To help provide this information, each chapter ends with a comprehensive list of questions. These are not the kinds of questions one would expect to encounter on an examination, and they are not intended to be. They are designed to make the student aware of areas of information that need more study, and in this, I feel they will succeed.

A complete ancillary package is available to instructors who adopt this text. The ancillaries include an Instructor's Manual; a Student Study Guide by T. Daniel Kimbrough; over fifty acetate transparencies; **wcb** TestPak, a computerized testing service; and **wcb** QuizPak, a computerized student self-testing program. I would like to thank the reviewers of this manuscript: Galen E. Clothier, Sonoma State University; Patrick G. Coyle, Jr., Grossmont College; Darrell Davies, Kalamazoo Valley Community College; Charles F. Denny, University of South Carolina, Sumter Campus; Dale A. Des Lauriers, Chaffey College; H. Lee Fairbanks, Pennsylvania State University, Beaver Campus; Howard M. Fuld, Bronx Community College; Robert E. Gatten, Jr., University of North Carolina, Greensboro; Lynda Gordon, San Diego City College; T. Daniel Kimbrough, Virginia Commonwealth University; E. Keith Michal, The Ohio State University; Raymond A. Miller, Somerset Community College and University of Kentucky; C. Wayne Simpson, University of Missouri, Kansas City; and Robert B. Tallitsch, Augustana College. They were very thorough, and in most cases I altered the manuscript to conform to their wishes. Nevertheless, I did not acquiesce to all their suggestions, and for that I accept full blame.

It is hard to overstate the importance of the assistance provided by Dr. Charles Nelson, the chairman of the biology department at the University of Tennessee, Chattanooga, and the cooperation of the entire departmental faculty. The writing of this book would have been infinitely more difficult and time-consuming had it not been for their willingness to tolerate my occasional absences and weird hours. And finally, the entire publishing team with which I worked was pleasant, patient, and often more tolerant than I would have been in their position. Thank you all.

Ross Durham, Professor of Biology
University of Tennessee
Chattanooga, TN 37405

Human Physiology

Section I

Introduction to Physiology

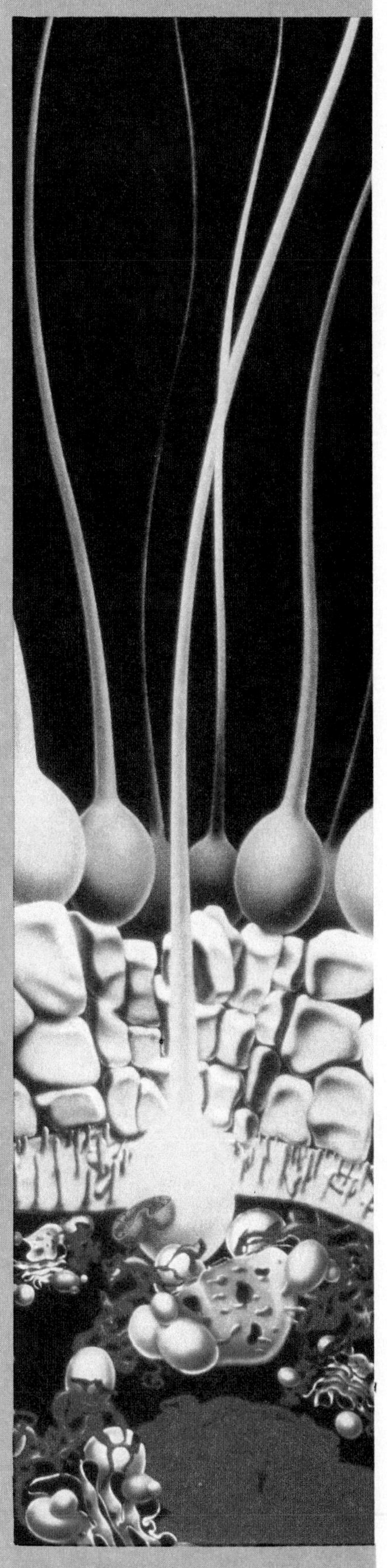

Chapter 1 Physiology—The Fundamentals

Study Hints

This chapter is intended to be introductory. When reading it, try to grasp the underlying purposes of our physiological operations and relate them to the systems that are mentioned. See if you can't, during your reading, think of mechanisms that are not mentioned here but that you can clearly relate, through personal experience, to the concept of homeostasis.

The study of the human body has a long history, as indicated by this illustration from the second book of *De Humani Corporis Fabrica* by Andreas Vesalius, issued in 1543.

Introduction

Most people handle their bodies the same way as they do a car. When it needs fuel, they fuel it up. When it needs water or air, that is easy to identify and easy to handle. But few people understand the mechanisms underlying these requirements. Health addicts and auto buffs are exceptions, of course, but they are rare, and in any case they are amateurs, not professionals. When some really serious malfunction troubles a valued car, the amateur surrenders. Then the professional is consulted, and it's the professional who must do the repair. Good mechanics have been carefully trained and have detailed knowledge of what each part of the car is supposed to do and how it contributes to keeping the whole thing running properly. They can recognize signs and symptoms and pinpoint the source of trouble as the entire automobile grinds away; thanks to their careful training they can often go straight to the malfunctioning part.

Elementary physiology offers basic, detailed knowledge to those who are interested in finding out how their bodies work. You need not be a potential health professional. Just as auto buffs spend time in auto mechanic's classes, people who are concerned about their health often study physiology so that they, too, can benefit from their knowledge of body mechanics. It seems there is no end of dangers in the environment (even water, we are told, can cause cancer if it's rubbed on the skin long enough), and the most intimate contacts with other people can present a mortal danger. It is becoming important to investigate our life-style, to examine our sexual habits—even to avoid sunbathing. Television and radio bombard listeners with warnings of threats to their health, usually in an effort to sell something. How can worthless medicines be distinguished from vital ones? How can imaginary illnesses be distinguished from those that might be life-threatening? Where is there danger? What can you do with impunity and when are you taking a deadly chance?

It is too expensive to visit the doctor every week, and in any case, it helps to know what you are doing. When you buy a medicine, it's nice to *know* where it's working and how. When you give up pie and cake or eat more of a certain kind of food, it's an enormous advantage to *understand* why you will benefit. Learning how a human body functions when healthy will help you to keep it that way.

Homeostasis and the Body's Internal Environment

Just like the driver who drives his car in blissful ignorance of how it all works, people tend to use their bodies without thinking very much about the thousands of little parts that are interacting and doing their tiny but important jobs minute by minute. The human body is a beautifully orchestrated instrument composed of highly tuned and specialized engines. Each one contributes to the efficient operation of the whole machine. Yet the body is more than a collection of solitary parts that do their jobs and ignore their biological neighbors. The activity of individual parts is subordinate to the proper function of the whole body, and activities of neighbors *cannot* be ignored. In this respect, the living organism is greater than the sum of its parts. That concept has been at the foundation of physiology for more than a century.

Claude Bernard, arguably the greatest biological scientist of the 19th century, gave us many scientific bricks to add to this foundation, but probably his best-known contribution is the concept of the **milieu interieur**—the body's internal environment. Bernard suggested that large organisms have a free and independent life because their body parts live in a carefully controlled internal environment. This internal environment is liquid. It takes the form of several specialized fluids, and there is no doubt that large organisms, including humans, can only retain their independent existence if these fluids remain constant. Thus the body's prime directive is *resist change*!

The healthy existence of large organisms depends on maintaining internal constancy. The body's parts—the cells, tissues, and organs, and the internal oceans that bathe them—operate within limits established by heredity. If the internal environment is changed a little bit too much, the parts won't work quite as well. If it changes a lot, the parts will not work at all.

Regulation of the internal environment, then, becomes the goal of all the coordinated systems of the human body, and this internal constancy, or more accurately, this variation within established tolerance limits, has been given a name—**homeostasis**. Harvard professor Walter B. Cannon coined this term in 1930 to describe the goal of all the body's physiological processes. The term means that proper environmental conditions are maintained in the body regardless of what enters or how the outside environment may vary. It does not imply a firm, never-changing state. Internal conditions vary constantly, but the amount of variation is limited. The limits are established by the genetic makeup of the organism and, barring injury or disease, they are never exceeded. Mammals and birds, for instance, can maintain their body temperatures within variations of no more than a degree or so either way, despite environmental temperature changes. All kinds of mechanisms are involved in this. If, for example, things get too cool, animals will first try to correct the situation behaviorally. Birds head for shelter and rabbits for their burrows. Humans put on heavy clothing. If that doesn't correct the situation, then other mechanisms begin to increase or conserve body heat. Furry animals fluff up their coats; birds puff up their feathers. If the cooling persists, internal physiological mechanisms begin operation—such things as the uncontrollable muscle movements known as shivering, small muscle contractions that produce extra heat. When humans reach this stage, if they're smart, they go indoors. Indoors, they might stand next to a warm fire or jump into a hot tub. Everyone has done something like this at one time or another and without giving it much thought. It makes people feel comfortable, so they do it. What they don't usually realize is that they were uncomfortable in the first place because a homeostatic parameter had passed a little beyond tolerance limits. By climbing into the hot bath, they exhibited, without knowing it, a simple behavioral homeostatic response.

Body Systems and Homeostasis

The human body has a basic organizational plan. All of the body's requirements are established and each zone, no matter how small, is monitored constantly by control systems designed to maintain homeostasis. Change anywhere is detected and translated into a specialized code. The code can be electrical or chemical, but whatever it may be, it results in signals that the body can uderstand, and the information can be used to activate specific control mechanisms. Minor adjustments are made at the rate of dozens a second, usually without any conscious awareness. But they are neither automatic nor magic. Each depends on the proper functioning of a barrage of mechanisms that act at many different levels within the body. Throughout the person's lifetime, these mechanisms continue to operate, bringing into play organs, tissues, cells, molecules, and even the atoms that lie at the base of everything material. Each mechanism has its own level at which it operates. Atoms readjust wayward atoms, molecules operate on molecules, and cells attend to homeostatic problems at cellular levels (figure 1.1). The goal of each mechanism is to maintain the entire organism in a state of dynamic equilibrium—homeostasis. The major systems and their specific roles are described in table 1.1.

Figure 1.1 The human body is a collection of smaller functioning entities.

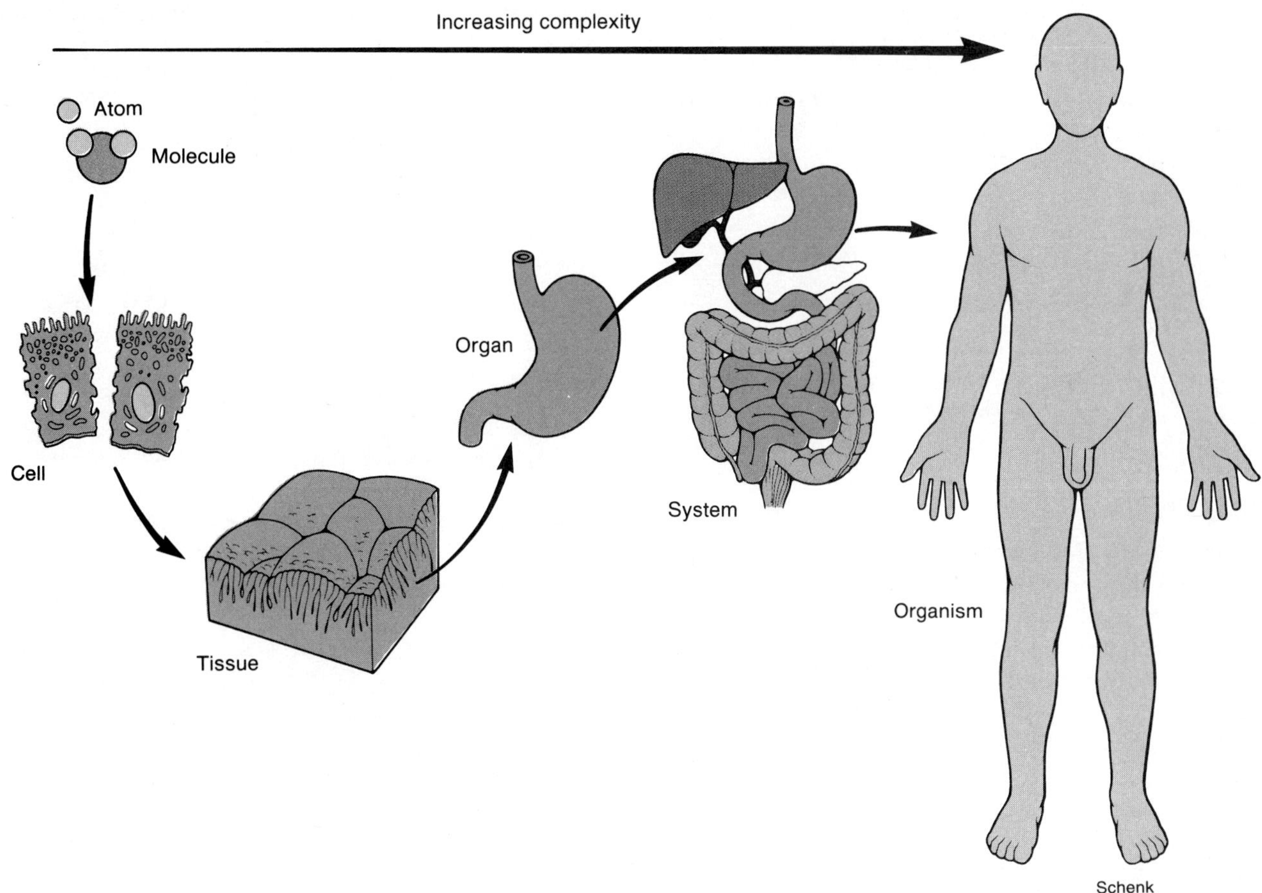

Table 1.1 Major Physiological Systems		
System	**Principal Organs**	**Function**
Nervous	Brain and spinal cord	Maintains control over many body functions, including behavior
Endocrine	Many, scattered widely	Maintains control over diverse body functions (in conjunction with nervous system)
Muscle	Diverse. Includes heart and internal musculature	Permits movement of and movement within whole organism
Circulatory	Heart	Transport and communication within organism
Respiratory	Lungs, respiratory tree	Removes carbonaceous wastes and recharges blood with O_2
Digestive	Stomach, intestinal tract	Provides energy and raw materials for organic synthesis
Excretory	Kidneys	Maintains homeostasis in body fluids
Immune system	Various blood cells	Prevents loss of homeostasis due to attack from without
Reproductive	Female and male genitalia	To maintain the species

Figure 1.2 A simplified feedback control system (loop).

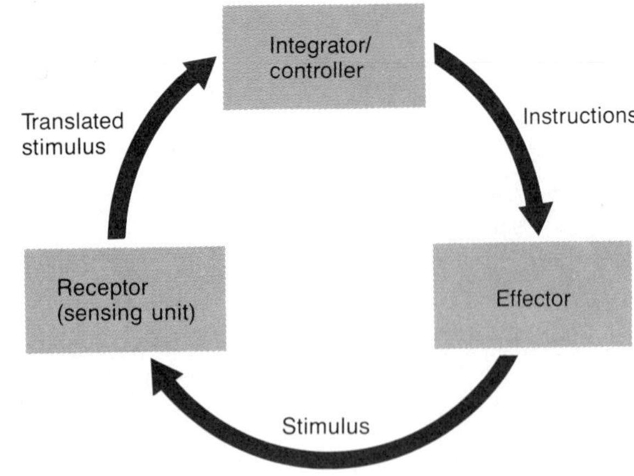

Figure 1.3 (*a*) The home air conditioner: A typical negative feedback system. Negative feedback systems reduce the original stimulus and tend to produce stable conditions. They are self-limiting. (*b*) Pregnancy: A positive feedback loop. Positive feedback systems reinforce the original stimulus and are not self-limiting. Unless shut off by something external to the loop, they tend to go completely out of control.

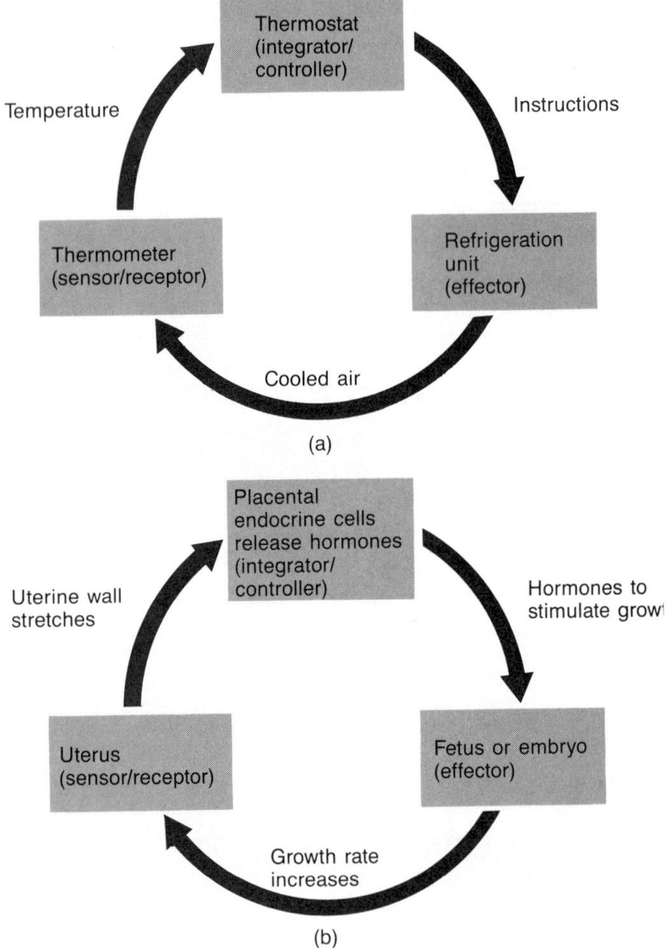

Homeostatic Systems

Self-regulating devices form the backbone of electronic and engineering designs, and the same principles apply to physiological regulation. Figure 1.2 is a general schematic that can be applied to any such system, whether it be electronic, hydraulic, or physiological.

As you can see, these devices usually form a cycle or **loop.** Within this loop, information in the form of a **stimulus** is obtained from the environment by a **receptor** and is converted into a signal—usually an electrical one—that the system can read. This encoded signal (input) then travels along a clearly defined pathway to an area where it can be interpreted and evaluated. Here in the **integrator/controller,** the information is considered, and if necessary, instructions are coded and sent out along a second defined pathway, heading for an **effector.** These instruction codes may be electrical signals traveling along various nerve fibers or they may take the form of a specific chemical released by specialized cells. However they are sent, the effector, in obedience to the instructions, will produce responses that either reverse or support the original stimulus. If it reverses (subtracts from) the original stimulus, it is a **negative feedback loop,** if it supports (adds to) the original stimulus, it is a **positive feedback loop.**

Negative feedback loops tend to retain stability in whatever system they are operating and are able to control their own oscillations. A home temperature control system is a common example of how these negative feedback loops operate (figure 1.3*a*). The air inside the house represents the environment people wish to maintain, and the thermal requirements are established by setting the thermostat (integrator/controller) at the desired temperature. The thermometer, to which the thermostat is electrically connected, functions as the receptor. As the temperature in the house fluctuates, the thermometer notes the change (stimulus) and converts the information into an electrical signal that the thermostat can comprehend. Signals from the thermometer are fed to the thermostat in a steady stream, and as long as the air temperature inside the house is within tolerance limits, the information produces no response. Nevertheless, the thermostat continues to compare air temperatures with its instructions, and the moment that the air temperature gets too high, the thermostat produces a signal of its own—a command to the refrigeration unit (effector) to switch on. As cooled air pours into the house, the thermometer keeps the thermostat informed of falling temperatures, and when things are cool enough, the compressor is shut off.

The original stimulus (the rising temperature) is *opposed* by action of the effector (the cooling unit), and the falling temperature eventually limits the effector's activity by turning it off. Since the goal is stability within desired limits—or homeostasis—this is clearly a negative feedback system.

Positive feedback loops must be shut off by some mechanisms outside the loop or they will either run out of control or begin to oscillate wildly, either of which could lead to disaster. Since the prime goal of physiological systems seems to be to resist change, it is logical to assume that negative loops would be more abundant in biological systems than positive loops, and they are. Nevertheless, positive loops do exist. Pregnancy is an example of an endocrine-controlled process that is positive in nature. As the fetus grows, increasing amounts of hormones are produced, and these hormones increase placental mass and circulation. This permits increased growth of the fetus which in turn increases hormonal flow again . . . and so on (figure 1.3*b*).

All of the mechanisms of the body are apparently aimed at achieving homeostasis. But there are two specialized control systems that are designed to oversee the operations of all the others. They are the **nervous system** and the **endocrine system,** and they operate both independently and cooperatively, whichever is necessary to achieve their goal.

Generally, the two systems work through different structures, often serving as redundant "safety valves" in case one of them should fail. But they monitor similar parameters, use the same kinds of feedback loops, and sooner or later they meet and share information, thus providing living systems with a remarkable means of maintaining equilibrium. Our admiration for these systems is reflected in the myriad electronic instruments that copy biological feedback loops—products of a field known as **bionics.** This is a relatively new discipline that weds precision engineering to the science of physiology. It involves copying organic control systems and structural designs to produce mechanisms that will do what living systems can do. For example, cybernetic engineers are deeply engrossed in the study of animal nervous communications and are currently trying to discover the brain's methods of processing information. By learning all they can about this, they hope to increase both the learning capacities and the miniaturization of modern computers.

Figure 1.4 The main nerve bundles of the peripheral nervous system.

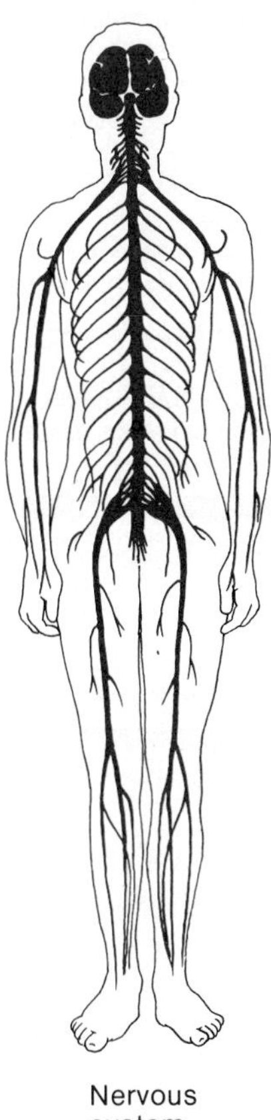

The Nervous System: Electrical Communication and Control

The nervous system is separated both anatomically and functionally. The anatomical separation—into the **central nervous system** (CNS) and the **peripheral nervous system**—is a fairly obvious one. The brain and spinal cord are the CNS, and everything else is peripheral. The functional separation of the **autonomic nervous system** from the **somatic nervous system** is not nearly as obvious to beginning students. Both are discussed in considerable detail in chapter 8.

The organs that comprise the central system—the brain and spinal cord—integrate all the activities of the living body. These activities can be consciously controlled (drinking a glass of water to replenish depleted water supplies) or they can involve processes over which there is *no* conscious control (absorption of the water by the digestive system).

The cranial and spinal nerves (figure 1.4) emerge from the central trunks and spray into the body in an incredibly complex fan. These are the elements of the peripheral nervous system, and while they do have

Figure 1.5 This is the simplest of nervous reflexes. A stimulus such as a hot plate is detected, coded, and sent as an electrical impulse to the spinal cord, where instructions are encoded and relayed to muscles to move the hand. The reflex can be inhibited if the brain chooses to do so, but often such inhibitory signals arrive too late to stop the reflex.

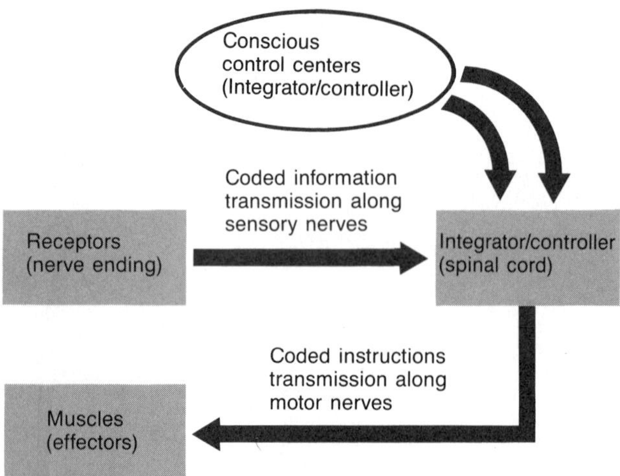

The brain can override reflex responses if it is given enough time. In the case of simple reflexes, however, there is seldom enough warning given, and sometimes the uncontrolled reflex can produce damage. Consider the person who is working on his car engine when a child suddenly blows the horn. The reflex response produces a sudden movement that usually results in a badly banged head. If, however, the mechanic is aware that a child is in the car and is about to blow the horn, when the noise occurs, the brain is able to override the tendency to suddenly leap away from the engine. The power of the simple reflex is illustrated by the observation that even when you know the noise is coming, it's hard to inhibit *all* reflex movement—there's usually a little jump in response.

special functions, fundamentally they are all extensions of the CNS and are designed to do only one thing: carry information. One part utilizes specialized receptors to obtain bits of information from the environment. Another part carries this information *to* the central system. Still others take instructions *from* the central system out to effectors, such as muscles or glands (figure 1.5).

Wherever this information goes in the nervous system, it travels in the form of coded electrical signals along nerve fibers that look and function somewhat like telephone lines. These fibers are long, hair-fine extensions of nerve cells, and in the periphery, they are classified according to where they carry their information. They are considered **sensory** if they carry information *to* the central nervous system. For example, an animal in the woods may be seen or heard (stimulus) by an uneasy camper, and this information is coded and carried along the optic and/or auditory nerves into the brain (integrator), where it may register consciously as fear. Unconsciously, however, neural comparisons are made. What the person knows about the current situation is compared with memories of earlier experiences, and conclusions are drawn. The integrator may decide the fear is unwarranted and may calm the camper down. Or it may decide to act, in which case **motor nerves** carry instructions *from* the central nervous system out into the periphery. The result—a quick dash away from the campfire and into the car, where all the doors are promptly locked.

Routine body processes usually operate below the conscious level, and when they are invoked, they follow their programing, regardless of conscious attempts to stop them or speed them up. For instance, once the swallow reflex has been invoked, the conscious brain no longer has any control over what happens. Instead, a branch of the nervous system—the autonomic—swings into action, stimulating muscles that propel the swallowed material down the throat and into the stomach.

Receptors, integrators, and effectors are common features of all control systems and are explained in more detail in later chapters.

The Endocrine System: Chemical Control

Endocrine control systems also function, for the most part, as negative feedback loops. But instead of using electrical impulses as nerves do, they use chemicals as their information carriers. These blood-borne chemicals are called **hormones,** and they serve mainly to control and maintain homeostatic mechanisms. They help maintain body fluids by regulating levels of physiologically important substances like glucose, sodium, and calcium, they assist in energy accumulation, and they help with routine operations like food digestion, growth, and reproduction. Figure 1.6 shows the location of the principal endocrine glands.

Interplay between the nervous system and the endocrine system is common. Neural receptors may monitor blood levels of a particular hormone or other chemical; when its levels drop too low, the neural receptors encode this information and transmit it. Thus a typical endocrine control loop may start with neural signals. This neurally derived information may stimulate an endocrine gland (receptor) to synthesize and secrete its hormone into the blood. The hormone (coded information) travels in the blood to the appropriate target tissue (effector), where its instructions are followed and a response is elicited (figure

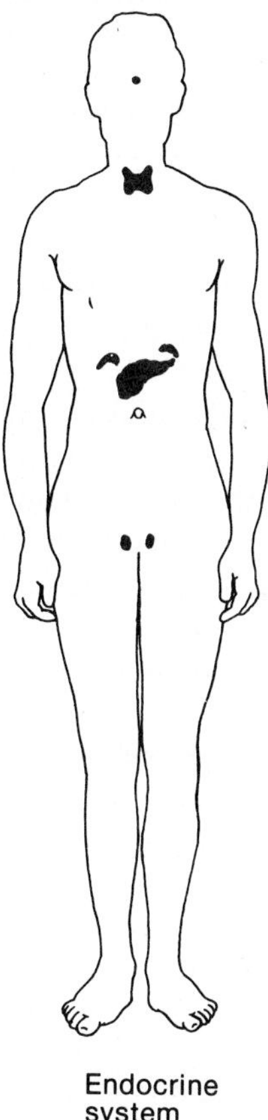

Figure 1.6 The principal glands of the endocrine system.

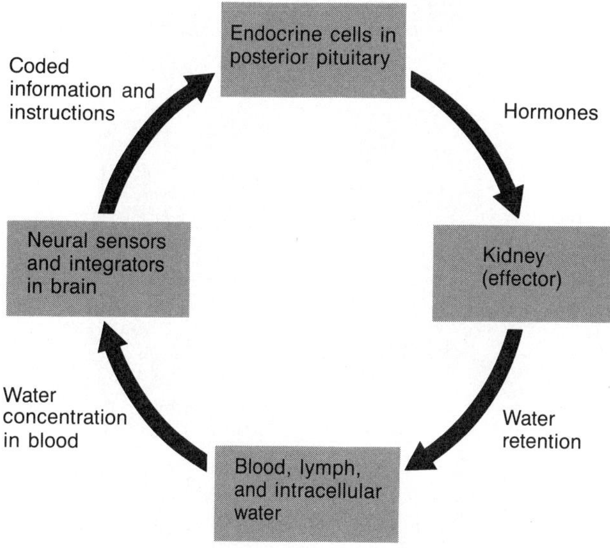

Figure 1.7 Schematic diagram of a neuroendocrine feedback loop.

1.7). If the feedback loop is a negative one (and nearly all are, as we know), the response will produce conditions that offset or oppose the original stimulus.

Some endocrine loops are so complex that they have never been worked out. Nerves are often incorporated, usually as sensing mechanisms, but they are not always involved; there are several endocrine loops that can function without any discernable neural intervention. For instance, the principal control system for regulating insulin output, although it receives and accepts neurally derived information, doesn't require it. It can operate quite well solely as an endocrine control loop. The pathway is as follows: As a person begins to absorb sugars from the intestinal tract, the rising plasma glucose concentration is detected by endocrine cells in the pancreas (receptors). These receptors also function as integrator-secretory cells, and the result is an increased secretion of the hormone insulin. Insulin is carried by the blood to its target tissues (effectors), where it speeds up the utilization of glucose by these tissues. The accelerated glucose utilization takes glucose out of the blood, and the lowered blood sugar reduces the original stimulus.

Muscles and Movement

Muscle cells are unique among body cells in that they are able to shorten with power. The stimuli that produce this shortening process are chemical in nature and are usually the result of a special nerve impulse that activates the muscle. Muscle is an *effector* in that it represents the final element in a control loop and responds to instructions given by an integrator/controller.

There are three kinds of muscle in humans.

Skeletal Muscles

Taken all together, skeletal muscles are known as *the muscular system* in humans (figure 1.8). Skeletal muscle is the meat of our bodies, and its healthy red color reflects the presence of a huge blood supply. Each fiber in a skeletal muscle has its own neuronal fiber to supply it with necessary instructions. As large motor nerves approach a skeletal muscle, they diffuse into sprays of fine fibrils, each one heading into a muscle cell. This arrangement forms the basis of graded, voluntary response to instructions. An individual motor nerve and the muscle fibers it innervates are known as a **motor unit,** and the strength of a muscle contraction depends on how many motor units are used for a given job. If we want to pick up a pencil, we just use a couple of motor units; to pick up a log, we may use nearly all of them.

Figure 1.8 The muscle system: free movement.

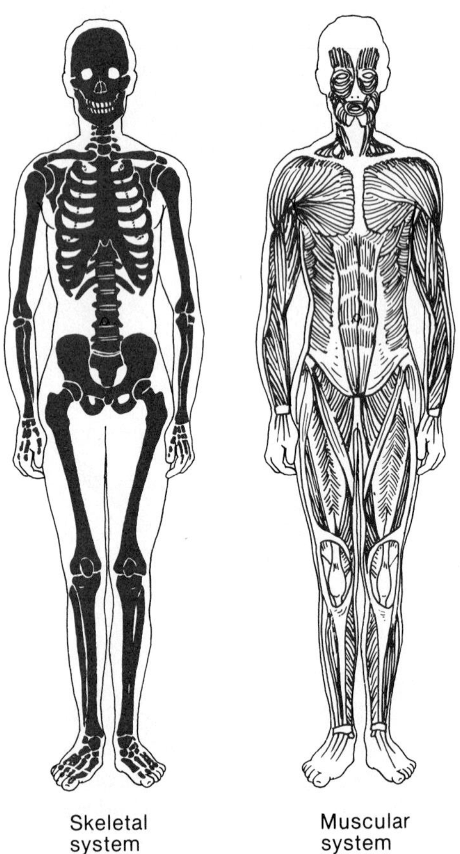

The recruitment of skeletal motor units is believed to remain always well short of 100 percent. This means that people, even when straining hard to lift something, never actually recruit *all* of their motor units. To recruit all motor units in a muscle is thought to require a type of unpredictable emotional input—an input that produces incredible neural instructions. This sort of neural bombardment apparently is limited to extreme emergency and results in a frenzied recruitment of motor neurons and their associated muscle fibers. It occurs as an unconscious effort born of desperation and produces what is often thought of as "insane strength." It is the kind of thing that gives a father the power to lift the rear end of a car that is crushing his son or permits a frantic mother to tear open a locked door in a burning house to get to her baby. Often it results in serious muscle or tendon tears because of the unusual stress that is placed on supporting structures.

If asked what the function of skeletal muscles might be, most people would promptly answer "motion!" and that is, of course, their main role. But it is not their only job. They are involved in respiration and in maintaining body posture, they provide protection for some body areas, and they supply the circulatory system with the energy necessary to move venous blood from the legs to the heart. Through the process of shivering, they even provide emergency heat to prevent the body from getting too cold.

Smooth Muscle

There is muscle in the digestive tract and around all of the tubes and glands in the body, but it is not skeletal muscle. It was given the name *smooth* muscle because of its appearance, and the name is functionally appropriate because of the way this muscle contracts. When stimulated, this muscle shortens with an even, sustained pressure, and it can stay contracted without the huge expenditures of energy so characteristic of the more explosive skeletal muscles. The slow but relentless contractions of smooth muscle sheets are responsible for the rhythmic, wavelike movement of the digestive tract, for changes in blood flow and pressure in selected portions of the circulatory system, and for the sustained pressure of the uterus during the final stages of childbirth.

Cardiac (Heart) Muscle

Cardiac muscle contracts as skeletal and smooth muscles do, but its control mechanisms and structure are unique. The synchronous contractile pattern of the human heart is due more to heart structure than to the physiology of the muscle cells. The cells are interwoven in such a way as to form a single cooperative unit, and cardiac contractions are (barring malfunction) a communal process. They have to be, because the heart must operate as a single unit to pump blood throughout the body. All the cells must take part simultaneously in the activity, and while the heart generally provides its own basic stimulus, both neural and endocrine mechanisms are involved in adjusting its rate and force (figure 1.9).

The Circulatory System: Communications, Protection, and Transport

Whenever body parts wear out or break and have to be replaced, there must be raw materials available from which to make new parts. Fuel is required, too, because fuel provides energy; without energy, nerves can't send messages, muscles can't contract, and cells can't assemble their raw materials. Cellular machinery requires a constant flow of fuel and material, but the cells cannot get it for themselves because they are too small and the supply depots are too far away. The **circulatory system** supplies these needs through the media of blood and lymph.

Figure 1.9 Some aspects of neural and endocrine control over heart rate and blood flow. Volume and pressure receptors feed information to both control systems. If such information suggests volume and pressure are low, accelerator nerves increase pressure while endocrine mechanisms increase water retention in the kidneys. If the reverse is indicated, inhibitory nerves will reduce the force of the heartbeat while kidney mechanisms release more water into the urinary bladder.

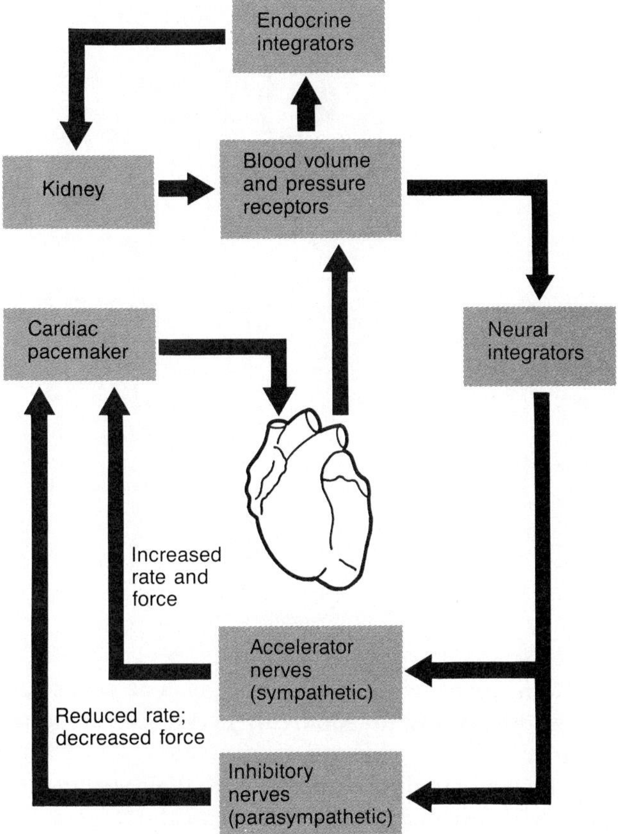

The blood is thrust into all parts of the body by the muscle of the heart. Specialized vessels carry blood to each organ, to its tissues, and ultimately to within 50 micrometers or so of the organ's cells. Here, in the tiny vessels known as **capillaries,** materials vital to the cellular machinery are released from the blood, and metabolic debris is picked up for disposal. The body does not pollute its own environment.

During its travels through the various organs and tissues of the body, the blood's depleted fuel and spare parts are replenished, and the waste it carries is carefully treated to remove undesirable materials. The overall plan of the blood circulation is diagrammed in figure 1.10.

The blood does more than function as a supply house and sewage disposal system. It maintains temperature homeostasis throughout the body and, through its built-in self-sealing mechanisms and armies of defensive cells, it provides protection for

Figure 1.10 The circulatory plan in the human body.

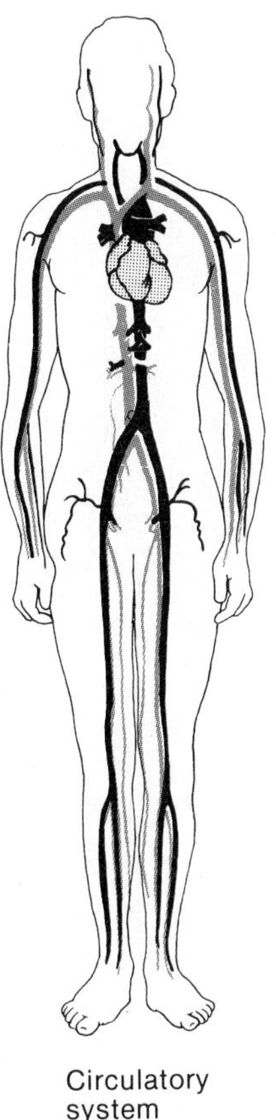

the deep tissues. Its importance was recognized by early humans long before its properties or functions were identified. Inviolable pacts were often "sealed in blood," and "blood brothers" were honor-bound to each other forever.

The Lymphatic System

The lymphatic system is an important auxiliary to blood circulation (figure 1.11), and the fluid that fills it is an ultrafiltrate of the blood. All of the water and minerals and most of the organic compounds that are filtered through the capillaries into the fluids outside ultimately find their way into the lymphatic circulation. Enclosed within the lymphatic vessels, they are carried to the main lymph ducts. Scattered along the pathway followed by the lymphatic vessels are the **lymph nodes,** which offer important protective functions. They are arranged in the lymphatic circulation in such a way that no lymphatic fluid can return to the blood without passing through at least one of them, and they are super-efficient filters. Their job is to prevent potentially harmful materials from going any further through the system. The lymphatic fluid, filtered and cleansed, returns to the blood as the lymph rejoins the cardiovascular circulation.

Figure 1.11 The lymphatic system in humans.

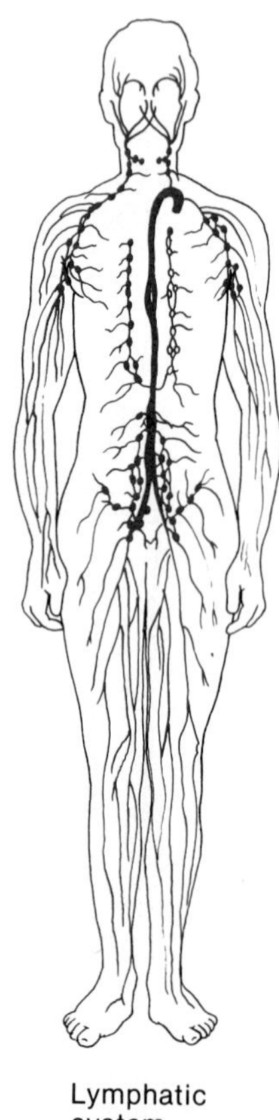

Figure 1.12 The human digestive system.

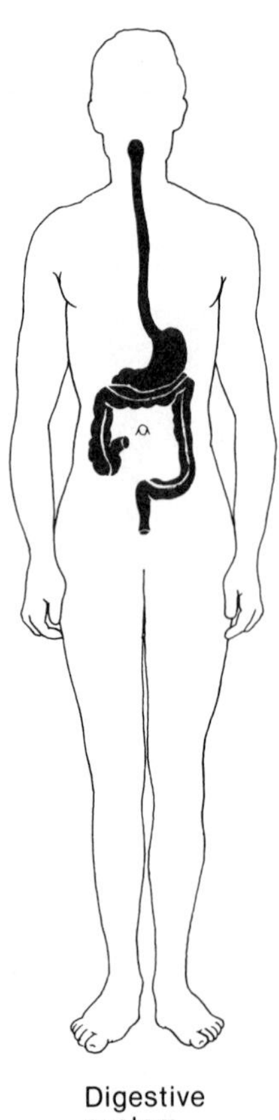

The condition of the lymph nodes and analysis of their contents is an important tool in the diagnosis of disease. Swollen lymph nodes in the groin often indicate an infection in a leg or foot, and the presence of malignant cells in the lymph nodes of the thorax and abdomen is an indication to a cancer specialist that a breast cancer has spread and is probably lethal.

The supplies carried by the blood do not materialize out of thin air. Every fuel molecule or vitamin it hands out must be replaced. When wastes are picked up and carried away from the cells and tissues, they must be dumped or treated before they can do any damage. In other words, the *blood has a homeostasis of its own* that must be maintained. And as we have seen, other systems contribute. Nerves and endocrine glands regulate blood flow throughout the body, and the **digestive system** provides the unrefined fuel and raw materials (figure 1.12).

The Digestive System: Fuel and Spare Parts

This system does more than merely function as a supply dump. It processes the raw materials and refines the fuels before they are offered to the blood. Certain parts of the digestive system serve as a dumping ground for some things the body no longer wants.

Raw materials are presented to the digestive tract as large chunks of mixed food, and the system must process this organic ore thoroughly before it can be passed into body fluids. It is helped in this task by two organs within the body cavity that are not part of the digestive system *per se* but contribute mightily to its operations: the **pancreas** and the **liver**. These organs provide chemicals that help break the food particles into pieces small enough to squeeze across the intestinal walls and into the blood. As digestion proceeds, fuel and spare parts pour into the blood in ever-increasing quantities until so much accumulates that the blood's homeostasis is threatened by an overabundance of nutrients. Obviously, whatever isn't immediately used has to be stashed somewhere, or the blood's homeostatic mechanisms will dump it. The liver functions as a warehouse for many of these nutrients, including glucose, the body's major fuel molecule. As long as food is being digested, nutrient molecules continue to stream into the blood, yet their concentrations never stay high for more than a few moments. Specialized cells in the liver remove them

Figure 1.13 The lungs and respiratory tree.

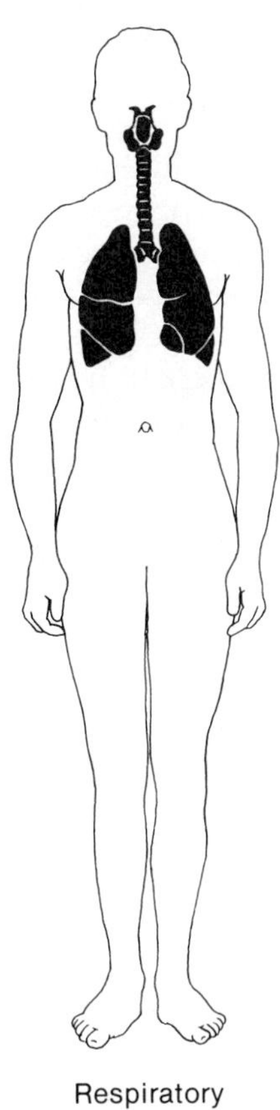

Figure 1.14 The kidneys and excretory structures.

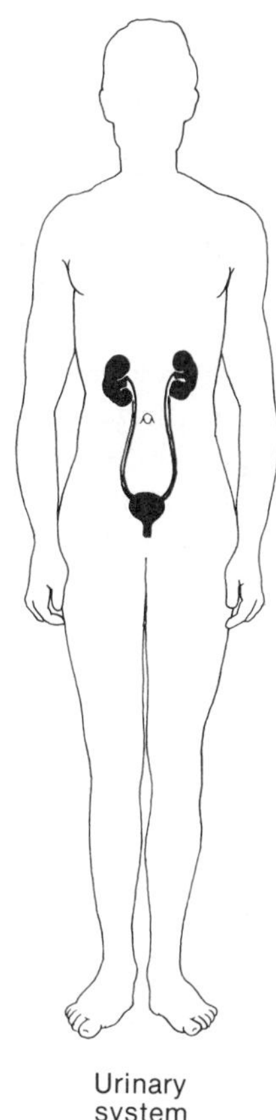

as fast as they can, package them in special containers, then store them away for use at night or during a long afternoon when the gut is empty and fuel becomes scarce.

The lower part of the digestive system, the large intestine, takes care of what is left after all digestible material has been pretty well withdrawn. In this region, indigestible food particles and any other undesirable materials present are prepared for disposal. While the materials are in the lower gut, water is withdrawn, and the chunks of waste are assembled into **feces,** which are packed away until the nervous system signals that conditions are right for disposal.

The Respiratory System: Ventilation and Gas Exchange

The lungs (figure 1.13), like the digestive tract, remove a waste product from the blood and add certain critical supplies to it. In this case, both the supplies and the wastes are in the form of gases, for this is where oxygen and carbon dixoide (CO_2) diffuse into and out of the blood. In this case, the atmosphere represents both the external supply house and the dumping grounds. The nose and mouth, open to the atmosphere, inhale its gases, and tubular air passageways from these openings carry the mixture to the lung tissues.

Each of these gases, according to its concentration, exerts a pressure or force in these closed areas, and movement back and forth is a result of the pressure differences. Since the pressure of oxygen is higher in the lungs than it is in the blood, oxygen moves into the blood for transportation to the cells. The reverse is the case with CO_2, and it shifts from the blood into the lungs, whence it is breathed out into the atmosphere as a waste product.

The process of breathing in and out (ventilation) is regulated by mechanisms that originate in a portion of the brain. These systems are very sensitive to CO_2 levels in the blood, and they regulate ventilation according to its concentration. If, for instance, prolonged exercise results in an accumulation of CO_2 in the body fluids, an increase in the rate and depth of breathing quickly occurs to prevent homeostatic upset.

The Kidneys: Fluid Homeostasis

The kidneys and their associated blood vessels (figure 1.14) function much like a modern sewage treatment plant in that a large quantity of fluid is treated, waste is removed, and most of the original fluid is returned to the source.

In the kidneys, large quantities of blood are filtered into tiny biological treatment vats, where the filtrates are analyzed and adjusted. Waste products are removed, acidity is regulated, and all materials are manipulated so that their concentration is neither too high nor too low. When the kidneys are finished, the newly scrubbed filtrate is returned to the circulatory system. Collected wastes along with just enough water to dissolve them are excreted from the body as urine.

Excretion of urine is an important job, since it represents a homeostatic control mechanism, but for the kidneys it is an ancillary operation. More important is the scrubbing and refining they give the blood. This may represent the most significant maintenance the blood gets, and it helps maintain proper pressure, volume, and acid-base balance in fluids throughout the body.

How important are the kidneys? They are so efficient that the loss of just one of the paired organs doesn't usually throw an intolerable load on the remaining one. But if both kidneys are removed or both malfunction, *death is inevitable.* In many parts of the world there is no hope at all for such patients. In this country, dialysis machines can mimic many of the kidney's blood-scrubbing functions. Dialysis may extend life for years, but it is often a poor quality life, requiring overnight stays in the hospital every three days or so. If the patient has the funds, home dialysis machines are available, and there is hope that in the near future, compact solid-state units will be offered at much lower cost. Right now, however, unless an appropriate donor can be located and a kidney transplanted, life is likely to be short and generally unpleasant. Even with a transplant, survival is uncertain, for the new kidney may not work or may be rejected by the recipient's body.

Homeostasis in Action

Sustained Activity

Constant, sustained activity is one of the most popular forms of exercise. Aerobic exercises have attracted people to commercial spas and public gymnasiums in swarms. Still more buy videotapes or audio cassettes so they can bounce and leap to aerobic programs at home. The roads are covered with joggers, sweat bands around their heads and earphones securely in place as they plod through their routines several times a week. Races like the Boston Marathon draw runners from all over the world, and 15,000 people will sometimes burst out of the starting gates to compete with people they have never seen before but with whom they share a passion for running.

Sustained, aerobic exercise produces unique results. It develops long, gracile skeletal muscles and lean bodies. A runner who covers miles with each workout and the seemingly tireless professional dancer look very much the same. Each seems to be composed of hard, thin-fleshed bands of shapely steel cable. The term *wiry* was coined to describe their build.

Internally, they are as conditioned to their lifestyle as they are externally, and they have developed abilities in response to the demands they have placed on their bodies. As their training sessions gradually increased the demands for fuel and oxygen, the body responded—slowly at first, then accelerating with each workout. In the beginning, the dancer would have to stop and pant after only a few leaps or swirls, and aching muscles would sometimes make sleep difficult. But as training progressed, pauses to pay off this "oxygen debt" became less and less frequent, and the sore muscles became better able to withstand the stress. Finally the dance can proceed for several hours without anyone having to quit. The body has responded to the increased demands by rearranging internal priorities and adapting homeostatic controls throughout. Even the heart has changed. When fully adapted, it is able to pump more blood per beat than it used to, so that during vigorous aerobic exercise, dancing or running, it won't be banging away at a rate impossible to maintain. Instead, it speeds up only a little. Respiratory capacity has increased, and the capillary beds within the lungs hold more blood at any given time so that efficiency of gas exchange is maximal . . . all this in an effort to maintain homeostasis even during periods of heaviest demand. When our dancer finally lands an important part and is forced to place unusually heavy demands on her body, if she has trained long enough and hard enough, it will not let her down.

Even so, she cannot spend energy at a frenzied pace without paying a price. Despite months of conditioning, before her performance is over she will have placed enough stress on her skeletal muscles to accumulate a considerable oxygen debt—a debt that she will have to pay off to regain internal homeostasis.

The Football Player

The football player requires a very different set of homeostatic adjustments. He has conditioned his body differently by making different demands. He has to move fast—faster than the dancer or long-distance runner—but only in short bursts. He must twist his body into unusual positions, accelerate like a flash, shift directions while traveling at full speed, and frequently absorb crushing physical impacts. No runner's build could live with the intermittent, pounding demands that a game of football makes. The football player needs muscles that can contract explosively and do so with tremendous power. These contractions do not have to last very long, but while they exist, energy expenditure must be maximal. So the footballer's muscles are thick and chunky, able to contract with full power in a fraction of a second, then relax almost as quickly. They must also have enough bulk to absorb considerable shock. The demands are not steady, as they are in the dancer or the distance runner, but during the brief period that they exist, everything else is subordinate. During a furious, 40-yard dash downfield, the football player may not even breathe.

His body is adapted to these demands, and all internal mechanisms try to adjust so they can maintain homeostasis no matter what. A football player would fall flat on his face if he tried to dance a two-hour ballet, but he'll play sixty minutes of slam-bang football featuring repeating periods of activity and collisions so intense that the distance-runner would tear a lean muscle trying to keep up with him.

As with the dancer, our footballer pays a price—sometimes a very big one indeed. The bigger his muscles are, the better able they are to absorb impact and to push obstacles out of the way, so the athlete tries to increase muscle mass. It is possible to build powerful, enormous muscles by concentrated weight lifting—"pumping iron" as it is known today. For a while, the tendons and ligaments associated with the muscles are able to match the increasing power, but researchers are finding out that the tolerance limits of ligaments and tendons are reached before those of skeletal muscle are. It is apparently not possible to strengthen them to match muscle development, and this is probably the biggest cause of knee and shoulder injuries today. The muscles of these athletes are getting too big, too strong, and the connective tissues they are involved with just cannot keep up—an example of how things can go awry when homeostasis is lost.

The Addict

She cannot sleep on her back because when she does, she coughs so much it wakes her up. She can hear the railing inside her lungs when she breathes, and chest colds seem to hang onto her longer than they do to her nonsmoking friends, but she cannot stop. She is addicted to smoking. Her body is doing all it can to adjust to it, but it never will, and the cost of trying is terrible.

Nicotine is probably the most addictive drug used in American society today. Few things in this world can match it. People will pick up cigar and cigarette butts from a filth-filled gutter to placate their habit, and there are reliable reports that starving Jews in Nazi concentration camps would trade infrequent, meager meals for a half-cigarette. Like all drugs, nicotine forces changes on certain cells in the brain. The drug forces a homeostatic shift away from equilibrium and into a pleasure zone. In the beginning, this feels good. But while the nicotine is present, this thrust away from homeostasis forces the body to push against it in order to reestablish the healthy equilibrium. When the nicotine is gone, sometimes the rebound pushes feelings into the unpleasant zone. This feeling of dissatisfaction does not last very long to start with, and the smoker doesn't feel particularly hard pangs when she is not smoking. But eventually, exposure to nicotine in the blood is so routine and the thrust away from healthy equilibrium so consistent that the backlash increases its power. Before long the euphoric feeling vanishes and the smoker finds she must inhale her smoke not to feel good, but to avoid feeling dissatisfaction. Now she's hooked! She smokes so often now that nicotine is almost always present, so the homeostatic mechanisms are pushing constantly against its effects. Should it disappear completely for any length of time, the homeostatic thrust becomes so hard, dissatisfaction becomes so intense that tremors, anxiety—all the symptoms of drug withdrawal—crop up and drive her into her purse for another cigarette. This is the final, most unpleasant phase of addiction, when the system has achieved the most unpleasant equilibrium of all. It's one in which much of the fun has gone, but she can't quit because now she feels rotten when she is *not* smoking.

And the price she is paying is prohibitive. By now, delicate lung tissues have been assaulted by the smoke long enough to reduce the efficiency of gas exchange. Hair-producing cells in the respiratory tract have shriveled into dysfunction, and dust particles of all kinds are able to invade the respiratory tree without these filters working to remove them. Much of the mucus that normally moistens the windpipe is missing because the cells that make it are weakened or destroyed. So our smoker coughs. She coughs to get rid of the fluids that the lungs are secreting in self-defense, and she coughs to get rid of the dust particles that are finding their way inside in increasing numbers. Ultimately, if statistics are correct (and there is no reason to doubt them), she will contract cancer or arteriosclerosis as a direct result of her habit and will die many years before she should.

The Astronaut

Space is intriguing and is truly, as a famous television show maintains, the "final frontier." We are only now beginning to "get our feet wet" in this new environment. The adjustments are probably going to be far more profound than most people today can imagine.

A tremendous number of adjustments will have to be made in order to adapt humans to space, but we can get some idea of the complexity of the problem by considering only the lack of gravity. No earthly organisms have ever experienced a time when there was no gravity. Those organisms alive today and all that preceded them have lived in earth's gravitational field—in what is called a "one-G" environment. No one really knows all the things that might happen when people are placed in a "zero-G" environment, but thanks to early research, exobiologists have some ideas.

The human homeostatic mechanisms may never have encountered a zero-G condition before, but they respond pretty quickly to a lack of gravity. Just as skeletal muscles grow larger or more durable in response to the unusual strains placed on them by prolonged, vigorous aerobics, muscles in zero G respond to the *lack* of stress by losing power and getting smaller. The heart adapts to great stress by strengthening itself, and when there is a lack of stress, it adapts to that, too. It gets weaker. No one really *knows* what will happen to it after extended periods in zero G, but we can guess, and none of the speculations are pleasant. The bones that normally support body weight decalcify slightly after a few days in zero G. It is suspected that over a period of several months in space, bones might actually get rubbery. It is not known what extended periods in space might do to the central nervous system, but it is hard to believe that it will not do something unusual—maybe something humanity has never experienced before.

All these alterations are a direct result of the body's homeostatic mechanisms trying to adapt to a new environment. Since nothing that ever lived on this earth has encountered such an environment before, there is really no way to predict all of the things that might happen.

The big problem is that the body does not really know what to do. It must be disastrous to leech so much calcium out of the bones that they cannot support the weight of a person returning from space to earth. It must be equally disastrous to weaken the muscles to a similar extent, but the body mechanisms can only do what their evolutionary background and genetic instructions have fitted them for. Throughout evolutionary history, physiological mechanisms have always sought the most economical way to keep their bodies alive and healthy. When people *need* heavier muscles and a stronger skeleton, they let their homeostatic mechanisms know by making greater demands. When such demands are removed, they save energy by removing the extra muscle tissue and bone salts and utilizing the raw materials somewhere else. In space, where almost *none* is needed, the body's homeostatic mechanisms do the same thing—they remove the energy-consuming excess. It is not hard to predict what would happen to people returning to earth in such a weakened condition. Whether or not they could continue to survive in space is anyone's guess.

Summary

Homeostasis and the Body's Internal Environment

The purpose of all our physiological efforts is to resist change. Change is resisted first of all through behavior, then through physiological operations.

Body Systems and Homeostasis

Each of the body's major systems works to maintain homeostasis.

Homeostatic Systems

I. Homeostatic systems usually operate as closed loops. Each loop has a receptor or sensor, an integrator/controller, and an effector.
   A. Sensors obtain stimuli from the environment (internal or external) and encode them.
   B. Integrator/controllers evaluate the coded messages and, if necessary, send coded instructions to the effector.
   C. The effector obeys these instructions, producing an effect that either reinforces the original stimulus or opposes it—usually the latter.
   D. Negative feedback systems oppose the original stimulus. They are self-limiting—they tend to produce stability in a given parameter.
   E. Positive feedback systems reinforce the original stimulus. They tend to run wild if not carefully controlled.

II. The Nervous System. Special transmission lines convey both information and instructions, in the form of coded electrical impulses, to target organs.

III. The Endocrine System. Information and instructions are in the form of highly specialized chemicals that are transported via the bloodstream.

IV. Muscles and Movement
   A. Skeletal Muscles
      1. Provide us with independent motility and hence are responsible for most behavioral homeostatic operations.
      2. Also provide protection for abdominal organs, provide energy for venous return, and supply much of our body heat.

B. Smooth Muscle
   1. Surrounds gastrointestinal tract and provides movement that propels food and fluids through the gut.
   2. Surrounds all blood vessels. Provides acute ability to alter blood flow through certain body areas by expanding or constricting local blood vessels.
   3. Wraps most glandular tissue, providing both protection and energy for active secretion.

C. Cardiac Muscle. Restricted to the vertebrate heart. It operates as a unit.

V. The Circulatory System. There are two circulatory systems within the human body: the blood and the lymphatic system.
   A. They serve as systemic transportation systems.
   B. They carry nutrients to all parts of the body.
   C. They transport waste products to various organs where disposal takes place.
   D. They offer protection.
   E. They serve as communications systems.
      1. The blood carries chemical instructions throughout the body.
      2. The lymphatic system disseminates them to the individual cells.

VI. The Digestive System. The source of the body's nutrients.
   A. It receives large, unprocessed chunks of nutrition from the environment.
   B. It breaks these food particles down into compounds that can be absorbed.
   C. It eliminates indigestible particles and certain systemic waste products.

VII. The Respiratory System. Recharges the blood with oxygen and eliminates carbon dioxide waste.

VIII. The Kidneys. Maintain homeostasis in body fluids. They also eliminate nitrogenous waste products and help maintain proper water and electrolyte balance.

Homeostasis in Action

I. Sustained Activity. Adaptations to the active life of the jogger/runner.

II. The Football Player. Adaptations to an active life of short bursts of furious activity.

III. The Addict. Homeostatic adaptations to tobacco.

IV. The Astronaut. Adaptations to a zero-G environment.

Review Questions

1. Who was Claude Bernard and what was his contribution to the science of physiology? Describe the *milieu interieur*.
2. Define *homeostasis*.
   a. What is its significance to the science of physiology?
   b. Suggest some examples of homeostasis.
3. Name the nine principal body systems, the organs associated with them, and their functions.
4. Name the main elements in a feedback loop. Describe how each of these contributes to the overall operation of the loop.
5. Name the two control systems of the body.
6. Describe the operation of a typical nervous feedback loop. Be sure to mention:
   a. How instructions and information are coded.
   b. The types of nerves that perform each function.
7. Describe the operation of a typical endocrine feedback loop.
8. Name the three types of muscle in a human being. Be sure to mention:
   a. The characteristics that make each type unique.
   b. The primary function(s) of each type.
   c. Where each type is found in greatest abundance.
9. Name the two circulatory systems in human beings. Mention:
   a. The distinguishing characteristics of each.
   b. The primary function of each.
10. Name at least two organs that are not actually part of the digestive system but contribute mightily to its proper function. What *is* its proper function?
11. Discuss the operations of the respiratory system in detail.
12. What is the main purpose of the kidneys and their associated structures?

Chapter 2 Chemistry of the Cell

Study Hints

For those who have recently had a chemistry course, this chapter will serve mainly as a cursory review and will be easy reading. Those not familiar with chemistry should read it with care and much patience. To grasp the principles of physiology, you must clearly understand the fundamentals outlined in this chapter.

Everyone today knows what atoms are, but not everyone knows the difference between the nucleus and the orbital particles. Be sure that you do. One *extremely* important point: Organic compounds are profoundly influenced by the so-called organic radicals or functional groups that always seem to show up. Learn them and their characteristics thoroughly. You will encounter them again and again in biochemistry.

Objectives

When you have finished reading this chapter, you should:

1. be able to describe *precisely* the difference between an element, a compound, and a mixture.
2. be able to describe a dispersion and know the differences between colloids, solutions, and temporary suspensions.
3. know the chemical symbols of the eleven elements that are abundant in organic compounds and know what the numbers involved with each element mean.
4. know which characteristics of matter are physical and which are chemical.
5. understand the significance of the "stable octet."
6. be able to describe the difference between ionic bonds and covalent bonds.
7. be able to name the so-called organic radicals and describe how they affect the materials they are part of.
8. be able to describe the distinguishing molecular characteristics of the four major organic compound types and know the primary functions of each type.

Uric acid crystal from dialysis filter.

Introduction

Chemistry deals with **matter** and how matter can change under various conditions. How easily, for example, will one chunk of matter combine with another? Does combining two types of matter always produce the same result, or are variations possible? What does it take to reverse the process and disrupt the combination—what energy alterations occur when materials combine or disperse?

Matter is that which has **mass** and occupies a point in space that cannot be occupied by other matter at the same time. It seems to be essentially eternal—it can neither be created nor destroyed—so the matter that the universe began with is still around, somewhere. It is not merely the inanimate things that are involved—plants and animals, even people, are matter. Everything we can see, hear, and touch is matter.

The greatest problem that confronted early scientists was the apparently limitless variety of form and substance matter can assume. Wood, iron, leather, water, air, sand, cloth—there's no apparent limit to the variation, and scientists were understandably afraid that each species of matter would turn out to be unique. The English mathematician and physicist Sir Isaac Newton (1642–1727) expressed the fears of all when he wrote:

> To tell us that every species of things is endowed with an occult specifick quality by which it acts and produces manifest effects is to tell us nothing.

He knew what a breakthrough it would be to discover a single principle that would ally all matter. That principle arrived in the 19th century with the confirmation of the existence of the **atom.** Its discovery provided the symmetry that Newton had lacked and science had been searching for—the "common denominator" of matter.

The main problem experienced by students confronting the atomic theory for the first time is the limits of their own senses. No one can see, feel, or hear atoms, and there is nothing to suggest that breaking a comb or a piece of wood into smaller and smaller pieces would ultimately produce a bunch of atoms. So understanding consists first of accepting the statement of mathematicians and other scientists that the theory is true. Atoms are everywhere in the universe. Everything that is material is composed of atoms, so that brings in all the planets and stars, and even in the deepest reaches of interstellar space there are probably one or two atoms vibrating quietly to themselves within every cubic kilometer or so of emptiness.

How small are atoms? That question, which actually requests quite fundamental information, necessitates an answer that is almost impossible to comprehend. It is doubtful that anyone can fully grasp how infinitesimal they are. In just two ounces of iron there are more than 600 hexillion atoms. The exact number is 602 hexillion, 209 quintillion, 400 quadrillion plus some change, and that number has no meaning to anyone. Even a person who knows what a hexillion or a quintillion is cannot really appreciate its enormity. Rounded off and written out, it looks like this:

600,000,000,000,000,000,000,000

If atoms were the size of buckshot pellets, that many pellets would cover the entire earth to a depth of six hundred feet. It is a number that is essentially beyond comprehension, yet there are that many atoms in just two ounces of iron. Obviously, estimating the number of atoms present in the human body would be like estimating the number of sand grains on every beach in the world—it cannot be done with any accuracy.

To people familiar with the national debt, numbers in the billions and even the trillions are pretty familiar, yet it is not likely any of us have a real appreciation of how many units they actually refer to. To get an idea of how incomprehensibly vast some of these numbers are, consider the following:

If you were to begin counting at 8 o'clock in the morning on January 1 and continued to count twelve hours a day without pausing for anything except to go to the bathroom; if you restricted eating to periods before and after the daily counting stint and took no days off, you might, by the next December 31, have counted up to 50 million—that's 50,000,000. However, there is an important proviso: You would have to count very quickly—at a rate of seven or eight numbers per second at least—and curb bathroom excursions severely. Working that hard for *two years*, you could only count to a hundred million.

Figure 2.1 The hydrogen atom, showing the electron cloud on the left. The densest zone of the cloud is where the electron is found most often, and its statistical average is the electron's "orbital."

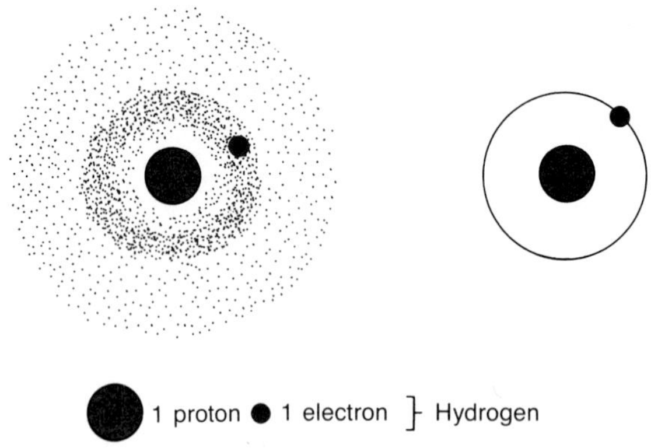

1 proton 1 electron } Hydrogen

Atoms: The Indivisible Units

Atoms have been described as the indivisible units of matter, and in a sense they are, but they are not indivisible in the strictest meaning of the word because they can, if enough energy is used, be broken apart into three smaller units: the **proton,** the **electron,** and the **neutron.** These three particles are not present in atoms in a random arrangement; despite the variety of form that matter can manifest, the tiny atoms of which it is composed reflect neither wild disorder nor boundless diversity.

A Tiny "Solar System"

Internal atomic arrangement is regular and seems to fit an established blueprint—in fact, an atom is very like a tiny planetary system in which things are vastly speeded up (figure 2.1). The center of the system is the **nucleus.** It is comparable in position to the sun, and like its full-sized counterpart, it contains most of the system's mass. Atomic nuclei consist of protons and neutrons, particles that are nearly identical to each other in mass and linear dimensions but are dissimilar in charge. Protons have a positive charge, whereas neutrons have no charge at all.

Electrons, the atomic "planets," are much smaller, having an actual mass of less than 1/1,800 the mass of a proton. Electrons are tiny, but they share one very important characteristic with the larger protons—they also have an electrical charge. No electrostatic charge smaller than that present on a single electron or a single proton has ever been detected, so both particles are assigned a value of 1, the smallest whole value possible. Because they are opposite in effect, the charge on the electron is said to be minus one (−1), while that on the proton is plus one (+1).

Comparing atoms to astronomical solar systems is a convenient way to think of atomic structure, but the systems differ in some important respects. For one thing, the velocity of electrons is tremendous. The earth lumbers along at 25,000 miles an hour, which is faster than the family car but just a crawl compared to the electron. Electrons whizz around their nucleus at staggering velocity . . . they can cover 25,000 miles in fifteen or twenty seconds. Also, the orbits are irregular to the point of being spasmodic, unlike any plant or star that is known. One moment they'll be diving toward the nucleus, barely scraping past, and a split second later they'll be plunging toward interatomic space out in the "orbit of Jupiter." Because of this combination of speed and fitful movement, electrons are said to form "clouds" around their nucleus. Nevertheless, for the sake of convenience, they are viewed as belonging in a single orbit that sits a fixed distance from the nucleus. Statistically, this is correct. If it were possible to freeze electron motion as animal motion is frozen on film, each electron would be found in one discrete orbit more often than it would appear anywhere else, and unlike galactic solar systems, it is the rule rather than the exception for several electron "planets" to occupy the same orbit.

Considering the teeming diversity of matter, it is hard sometimes for us to understand how it can all be composed of just three particles. The individual particles themselves do not reflect any diversity at all. But they are arranged in specific, predictable ways, and it is the variety of arrangement that seems to produce the diversity. This suggests that the basic structure of matter depends not so much on the particles themselves as on the way they *interact* with each other, and that the key to understanding matter lies in studying the nature of the interaction rather than the nature of the individual particles.

Figure 2.2 If a proton were the size of a golf ball, the electron in a hydrogen atom would be smaller than a BB, but it would have an orbital approximately 597 yards in circumference with a radius of 95 yards (88 meters). Such an orbit would enclose an area of more than 28,000 square yards (24,000 square meters), which is greater than the area of four football playing fields linked together. The solid material in the atom would occupy less than one cubic inch of space and less than a square inch of area.

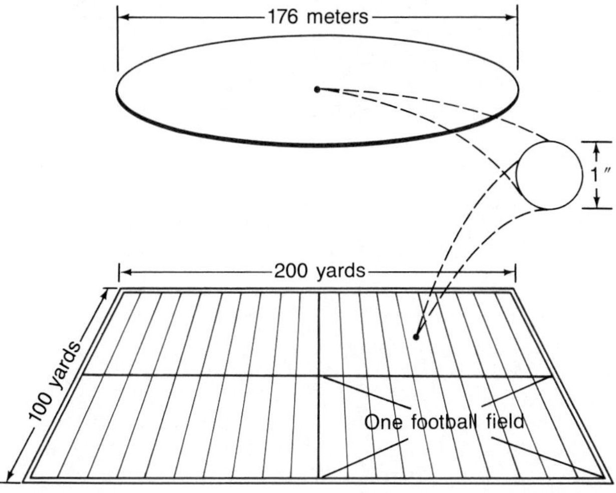

One rather shocking fact leaps at us when we compare atoms to planetary systems. If the analogy is good, then matter, like solar systems, must be mostly empty space. This is hard to accept for many people. Looking at something like a rock—knocking on it and hurting our knuckles—makes it hard to believe that the rock is mostly nothing, but it's true. Consider hydrogen: The nucleus of the hydrogen atom consists of one proton with an electron in orbit around it. If that proton were the size of a golf ball and the rest of the atom were to scale, the orbit of the electron would be 110 yards away from the proton. The proton in the center, however, is only the size of a golf ball, and the electron is 1/1,800 the size of that. In an atom that covers more than eight acres, the total amount of matter would probably not exceed two cubic inches (figure 2.2).

Categories of Matter

The interaction of these three subatomic particles has resulted in the various forms of matter that we are all familiar with. For the sake of order, they are grouped into three basic categories: the *element*, the *compound*, and the *mixture*. These classes tend to have rather hazy meanings in everyday usage, but to chemists and medical professionals they have very specific meanings.

Elements

An **element** is any substance composed of atoms all of which have the same number of protons in their nuclei. And there are not as many as you might think. There are 106 known elements making up the entire material universe. Twenty-one of them are man-made, produced from other elements by nuclear bombardment; they don't exist in free form on the earth. Those that do are here in varying amounts. Gold, silver, lead, iron, carbon, and oxygen are all examples of elements.

When we consider that there are more than one hundred elements, it is rather sobering to realize that the material of which life is made utilizes only twenty-three. In fact, nearly all organic material is made up of just eleven—and the smallest elements at that. Hydrogen (H), oxygen (O), carbon (C), and nitrogen (N) are the primary ones while Calcium (Ca), phosphorus (P), potassium (K), sodium (Na), chlorine (Cl), magnesium (Mg), and sulfur (S) are secondary. There may not be many of them involved, yet they comprise more than 99 percent of the human body, and their arrangement is extremely complex. As was suggested, it is particle interaction and the orchestration of the elements that is important in the synthesis of material things.

The twelve other elements that are involved in living systems are present in very small amounts. Since they each consitute less than 0.01 percent of the body's total mass, they are considered **trace elements,** but their abundance doesn't reflect their importance. Iron, for instance, is responsible for carrying oxygen into the tissues and cells. Without it, we would need 136 times as much blood as we have. Iodine is also present only in trace amounts, yet it's a vital part of a compound that regulates the body's overall use of energy.

The chemical composition of the human body is outlined in table 2.1. Chemical symbols are included for each of the elements mentioned.

Chemical Symbols

Every element has its own special symbol, one that belongs to that element and no other. Centuries ago, these symbols consisted of "secret" planetary or astrological characters. But by the early nineteenth century the secret designs were discarded in favor of universally recognizable devices, in this case one or two letters of the alphabet.

Table 2.1 The Chemical Composition of the Typical Adult Human (ranked according to the percentage molarity)

Element	Symbol	%	Comments
Primary Elements			
Hydrogen	H	63	Required for water and all organic compounds.
Oxygen	O	25.5	Required for water and most organic compounds.
Carbon	C	9.5	Required for all organic compounds.
Nitrogen	N	1.4	Required for certain organic compounds.
Secondary Elements			
Calcium	Ca	0.31	Major component of bone. Necessary for proper functioning of many physiological systems.
Phosphorous	P	0.22	Essential for biochemical synthesis and energy transfer.
Potassium	K	0.06	Principle intracellular mineral.
Sulfur	S	0.05	Required for proteins and other biological compounds.
Sodium	Na	0.03	A major extracellular mineral.
Chlorine	Cl	0.03	A major extra- and intracellular element.
Magnesium	Mg	0.01	Required for enzymes.
*Trace Elements**			
Chromium	Cr	Each is less than 0.01% of the total	Essential element. Related to action of insulin.
Cobalt	Co		Required for enzyme activity. Present in vitamin B_{12}.
Copper	Cu		Essential for proper enzyme activity.
Fluorine	F		Growth factor. Possible constituent of bone and teeth.
Iodine	I		Essential constituent of thyroid hormones.
Iron	Fe		Essential for blood pigment and many enzymes.
Manganese	Mn		Required for proper activity of some enzymes.
Molybdenum	Mo		Required for proper activity of some enzymes.
Selenium	Se		Essential for proper function of liver.
Zinc	Zn		Required for proper activity of many enzymes.

*Listed alphabetically.
From "The Chemical Elements of Life" by Earl Frieden.

Sometimes chemical symbols are easy to remember. For example, as you have seen, C refers to carbon, Cl to chlorine, O to oxygen, and N to nitrogen. In these cases, the symbol reflects the English name of the element. But that's not always the case, and when it is not, the symbols are harder to remember. For example, sodium (Na) and potassium (K) get their symbols from their Latin names *natrium* and *kalium*. This is true also of gold (Au), silver (Ag), mercury (Hg), lead (Pb), and a host of others.

Chemical symbols are more than simple abbreviations, and they're useful for more than merely indicating the presence of an element. For example, in chemical shorthand the symbol H doesn't just mean that hydrogen is present. It means it is present by itself, as a pure element. Adding numbers can increase the information, and shifting them around can vary it. For instance, 2H means that there are two atoms of elemental hydrogen. On the other hand, H_2 means that while there are two atoms of hydrogen present, they are not in elemental form. Instead the two atoms are joined together chemically to form a *molecule* of hydrogen, which is the only way hydrogen is ever found as a pure gas. If these two variations are combined ($2H_2$), the meaning changes to indicate there are now four atoms of hydrogen present in the form of two molecules. There is another rule regarding the use of these symbols, and it is very important. The first letter is always capitalized, while the second letter never is. This may seem trifling, but it is not. For example, the symbol for the element cobalt is Co. If convention were not followed, and the symbol were mistakenly written as CO, the writer would have designated two elements, carbon and oxygen, instead of cobalt. As you can see, there's a lot of information that can be transmitted through the use of symbols, and the code really is not complicated. Like any jargon, it becomes less confusing the more it is used.

Properties of Matter

Just as each element has its own distinctive atomic configuration and symbol, it also has definite characteristics that mark it as unique and can be used to identify it. Such characteristics are known as that element's **properties,** and there are two types: **physical** and **chemical.**

Physical Properties

Physical properties are qualities that are characteristic of the element but are not involved in altering basic structure. Things like density, odor, mass, texture, color, and boiling and freezing points are all physical properties.

Physical properties can be used to identify elements, but not all are of equal value. A property that can be precisely measured and expressed in standardized units is more valuable than one that must be evaluated subjectively. As an example, consider the relative merits of texture and freezing point. Texture is determined by feeling or viewing, and there are no units one can use to express a degree of texture. As a result, observers are forced to resort to subjective terms like "very smooth" or "relatively smooth," and such evaluations are not quantifiable. What is smooth to a laborer may be like sandpaper to a bank clerk. Freezing point, on the other hand, can be expressed in units that are standardized throughout the world. When we write down that mercury freezes at −38°C, the temperature is precise and can be understood by anyone, anywhere. Since it provides clearer information about the element than does texture, freezing point is, from an analytical point of view, a more valuable physical property.

Within the limits of physical properties, matter can exist in three different phases—**solid, liquid,** or **gas.** We are familiar with all of these, and depending on the element involved, we expect one or the other at normal earth temperatures.

The Gas Phase

The gas phase is the high-energy phase. When an element is present as a gas, its atoms move randomly and very rapidly through wide ranges. Because of this rapid, aimless motion, a gas has no predetermined shape or size. Gas released from an automobile tire is not shaped like a doughnut, and no one expects it to be. It will assume the shape of whatever container it is placed in and will expand or compress to fill it, exerting equal pressure at every point. Oxygen and carbon dioxide, the respiratory gases, are present in the lungs and in the air, and they assume the shape of lung or atmosphere, exerting pressure that is directly proportionate to their individual concentrations.

The Liquid Phase

In the liquid phase, the atoms are closer together than they are in a gas. There is less energy in the system, hence molecular movement is less vigorous and attractive forces that exist between molecules (which we will discuss shortly) are able to get a grip. As a result, the volume of a liquid is constant. A small amount of liquid won't expand to fill a larger container the way that gases do, but the attractive forces between the molecules are rubbery and are able to flex and stretch a great deal. Liquid surfaces may always be flat and level, but below the surface there is no definite shape, and the liquid assumes the contours of the bottom and sides of the container.

Cooling a liquid reduces the energy content of the molecules, slowing their movement until the interatomic attractions are powerful enough to lock them into a rigid configuration. At this point, their state changes and they become solids.

The Solid Phase

In the solid state, the atoms are firmly arranged in whatever alignment is characteristic of the substance. Like liquids, the volume of solids is constant, but *unlike* liquids, solids have a definite shape. Placing a square block of solid iron in a round box will not change the shape of the iron.

One very important point, and one that should be remembered, is that shifts in phase will not alter a substance's basic characteristics. Copper is copper and oxygen is oxygen whether they are solid, liquid, or gas. They may look and feel like different substances as they shift phases, but they are not different.

Chemical Properties

Chemical properties are quite unlike physical properties. They don't deal with individual elements as do the latter. Instead, chemical properties of an element describe how it will interact with other elements. Some elements collaborate vigorously with others and hence are considered extremely active chemically. Others won't combine even with other atoms of their own species and so remain perpetually in the elemental state. *Helium (He), Argon (Ar), Krypton (Kr),* and *Neon (Ne)* belong to this latter category. They are incapable of combining with anything and as a result have been given the title the **noble gases**—not because they are particularly awe-inspiring, but because they are "aloof" and will not associate with any other elements. On the other hand, elements like sodium and hydrogen are so reactive that certain combinations will produce explosive force.

The reactivity of an element depends on the number, arrangement, and interaction of its subatomic particles. To understand this, we should investigate these particles and how they arrange themselves within atoms. We will begin with hydrogen. Because it's the smallest of all the elements, hydrogen is extremely light. In the atmosphere, it promptly floats to the top where gravity is too weak to hold it, and it vanishes into space. Hydrogen is composed of a single nuclear particle (a proton) and an electron in orbit. The electron is held in orbit around the proton by a force similar to the one that holds the earth in orbit around the sun. It is called **electromagnetism,** and it results from the charges that exist on the proton and electron. As we know, electrons and protons each have a charge, and these charges affect each other in very specific ways. If two particles are positively charged, they will repel each other. So will two particles that are negatively charged. But two particles with opposite charges—one negative and the other positive—have a powerful attraction for one another. This has led to a simple rule of thumb when dealing with electromagnetism: *like charges repel, and unlike charges attract.* In a hydrogen atom, therefore, the proton is attracted to the electron because each possesses a different charge. Adding their charges together results in cancellation: $(+1) + (-1) = 0$. The charge across the whole atom is zero, and this zero charge is characteristic of atoms, for neutrality appears to be the desired state in nature.

With the exception of hydrogen, the smallest element is helium. One might expect it to be just twice as massive as hydrogen, but in fact it is four times as large, since it contains both protons and neutrons in the nucleus. The neutrons are necessary because two protons could not exist side-by-side in an atomic nucleus. Two positively charged particles would repel each other with considerable force, so for an atomic nucleus with more than a single proton to stay together, there has to be something besides protons in the nucleus, something that is relatively negative. Neutrons have approximately the same mass as protons, but they have no charge at all; hence they represent an unlike charge to which the positively charged protons can be attracted. The nucleus of the helium atom contains one more proton than the hydrogen atom does, and that makes it a different element. The two neutrons are present to keep the nucleus from flying apart (figure 2.3).

Figure 2.3 The hydrogen and helium atoms compared.

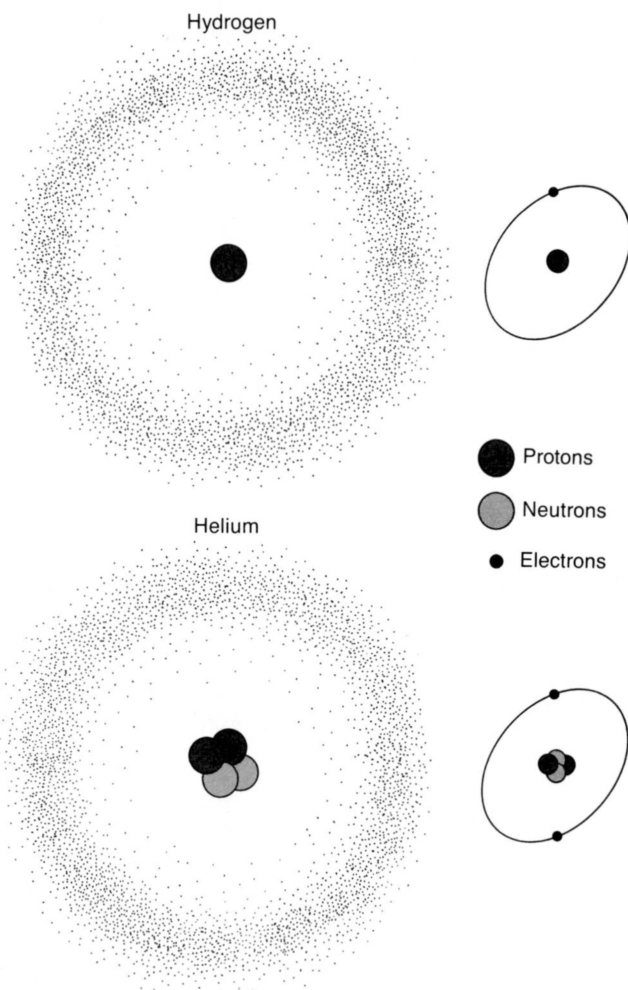

Helium, like hydrogen, is lighter than air, and when it is free in the atmosphere, it floats, like hydrogen, to the upper layers and is easily lost into space. Within the atmosphere, it has less than a quarter of the lifting power of hydrogen because of its relative mass, but it has one characteristic that is overwhelmingly important in this regard. Helium is a noble gas; it will not combine with anything and that means it won't burn. Major accidents involving lighter-than-air transports such as the Hindenburg and the Graf Zeppelin would never have occurred if the gas in the huge bags had been helium instead of the highly combustible hydrogen. But nearly all of the world's available helium is found in the United States. When the great airships were being built in the early decades of this century, the U.S. was reluctant (for political reasons) to export the gas to Germany and other European nations.

Figure 2.4 The carbon atom. In the diagram on the left, only the outer orbital is heavily shaded. The inner orbital is not shown.

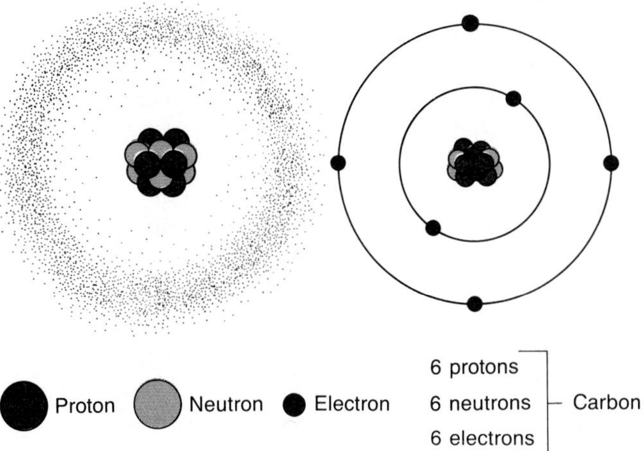

In determining the chemical properties of a given element, atomic nuclei are not terribly important. However, it is the atomic nucleus with its set number of protons that determines what the element *is.* Hydrogen, for instance, has one proton in its nucleus, and if it has more, then it's not hydrogen. Carbon, the prime element in living substances, has six protons in its nucleus (figure 2.4).

The number of electrons or neutrons, however, can vary without affecting the identity of the element. For instance, the most abundant form of carbon (called *carbon-12*) contains six protons and six neutrons, but there is another form of carbon known as *carbon-14* that has six protons and eight neutrons. Carbon-12 is a stable (unchanging) element, while carbon-14 is radioactive and unstable. Large lumps of carbon-14 emit detectable energy in the form of neutrons at a steady rate, yet the only difference between carbon-12 and carbon-14 is the number of neutrons in their nuclei. They both have similar physical properties, and chemically their behavior is identical. Technically, they are both carbon atoms, yet they are not *exactly* the same. They have, therefore, been given a name that clearly stipulates their relationship, yet simultaneously indicates that they are different. ^{12}C and ^{14}C are two separate **isotopes** of carbon, and carbon is not the only element with isotopes.

There is nothing rare or unusual about isotopes, radioactive or otherwise. Isotopes of all the elements are found in nature. Often, radioactive ones like ^{14}C occur in predictable ratios with their nonradioactive isotopes, a fact that has made possible a highly accurate technique of determining the age of archaeological finds. The technique is called **radioactive dating** and is the only reliable means of determining the absolute ages of many historical and paleontological finds. Radioactive isotopes of elements found in living systems have many uses. In medical research and practice they have greatly enhanced our knowledge of body functions and have helped us to diagnose and treat disease.

Hydrogen has two familiar isotopes. The isotope with one proton and one neutron is called deuterium (D), and the other, an atom with one proton and *two* neutrons, is known as tritium (T). Both of these atoms combine with oxygen in exactly the same ratio and configuration as regular hydrogen does and when they do, like normal hydrogen, they form water. Since both D_2O and T_2O contain hydrogen atoms that are two or three times as massive as regular hydrogen, the water that is formed is known as **heavy water.** Heavy water is an important research tool in nuclear physics.

Atomic nuclei have a relatively minor role in the interaction of elements. To students of chemistry and physiology, the most important particles are the electrons—the "planets" of the atom. The number and arrangement of the orbiting electrons determine how and to what extent a given element will react with any other. The outermost orbit is the key, because elements may combine with each other according to how these electrons are arranged. Whole atoms tend to be neutral, meaning that they possess equal numbers of electrons and protons. Carbon, with six protons, should therefore have six electrons in orbit around it, and in its free state, it does. Hydrogen, with a single proton, has one electron, and so on. These electrons don't whirl around their nuclei randomly. Even the most convulsive have orbital boundaries that are clearly defined and are seldom exceeded.

Electron Orbits

The orbit closest to the nucleus is called the **K-shell,** and it is full when it contains two electrons. No matter how big the element is or how many electrons there are in orbit, the orbit closest to the nucleus will never contain more than two electrons. Obviously, this means that any element with more than two electrons will have to have more than one orbital shell. The next orbital level is known as the **L-shell,** and it is full when it contains eight electrons. The third orbit is the **M-shell,** and it can hold up to eighteen electrons. The **N-shell** and the **O-shell** can hold a maximum of thirty-two each; then the capacities begin to come back down again. The **P-shell** holds eighteen and the **Q-shell** just two. The maximum numbers are important, of course, but since filled P and Q shells occur only in the larger elements, they won't concern us very much. The elements involved in living systems are all pretty small.

The outermost shell is known as the **valence shell.** This shell is of vital concern to the chemist, because when elements react with each other, it is their valence shells that change. Sometimes there is a loss or a gain of electrons, and sometimes the distribution of the electrons changes, but no matter what the change is, it takes place in the valence shell.

Each element is different from its neighbor. Each has its own proton pattern and number; hence each will have its own electron number and orbital configuration. Since the electron patterns in the valence shell determine just how a given element will react with another, we can assume that each element will have its own unique reaction characteristics. Some will react with other elements with tremendous speed, while others react only slowly. Some, it turns out, don't react at all.

The Stable Octet

Atoms that have very little or no tendency to react are said to be **chemically stable.** It seems that there are basic valence patterns that produce such stability. For reasons not clearly understood, stability occurs with the greatest power when the outermost shell of an atom contains eight electrons. Obviously, if they are to remain electrically neutral, not many atoms will be able to attain such a valence configuration. The few that can are the noble gases, so called because of their tendency to remain "aloof" from the "common" elements. Their valence profiles are worth tabulating (table 2.2). Helium is the only one that lacks the "stable eight" or **stable octet** configuration, and that's because it is so small. Its outermost orbit—the K-shell—holds the atom's only two electrons and for helium, that two-electron valence shell obviously constitutes a stable contour.

Table 2.2 Electronic Configuration of Some Noble Gases

Element	K-Shell	L-Shell	M-Shell	N-Shell
Helium	**2e**	0	0	0
Neon	2e	**8e**	0	0
Argon	2e	8e	**8e**	0
Krypton	2e	8e	18e	**8e**

Electrons in the valence shell are indicated by boldface type. Note that with the exception of helium, the valence shell—the outermost energy level—contains the so-called *stable octet*, a chemically inert profile.

Ions — the Charged Particles

Chemical introversion seems to be unique to the noble gases, but the tendency of atoms of other elements to assume this "noble gas configuration" is common, and it results in the formation of particles known as **ions.** *An ion is an atom or array of atoms possessing a net charge.* It is the result of the loss or gain of electrons, often in an effort by the atom to attain the noble gas profile.

Sodium

Consider, for example, the element sodium. Sodium is a metal. Physically it is medium-soft, malleable, silver-white in color, and smooth in texture. Chemically, it is extremely unstable, which means it is tremendously reactive. Sodium has eleven protons, and so has eleven electrons orbiting the nucleus—two in the K-shell, eight in the L-shell, and one in the M-shell. In order to attain the stable octet in its valence shell, sodium must either lose its single outermost electron or gain seven. The latter alternative would upset the electrical nature of the atom tremendously, and in any case the energy needed to cram extra electrons onto the sodium atom is simply not available. How much easier to simply give up a single electron and achieve the configuration of neon . . . that would upset the atom's electrical dispostion by only a single charge instead of by seven. So that is what happens. Sodium readily gives up its outermost electron in order to attain the stable contour, and since it has given up a negative particle, it now has a surplus of one positive charge, thereby becoming the *sodium ion,* designated Na^+. The energy required to separate the outermost electrons from their atoms is known as **ionization energy,** and metals characteristically have very low *ionization potentials,* which means very little energy is required to remove these electrons.

Chlorine

Most of the nonmetallic elements, on the other hand, have extremely high ionization potentials. Yet like sodium, they all have a tendency to try to attain the structure of a noble gas. Chlorine is a good example. Chlorine has seventeen protons, hence seventeen electrons, all in their proper shells. With seven electrons present in the valence shell, the easiest way for chlorine to achieve the octet configuration would be to add an electron, and chlorine has a high electron affinity. So do bromine and fluorine. And unlike the metallic ions, which must acquire energy to pry electrons loose, the nonmetallic ions release energy because they add an electron. The addition of an electron to chlorine's outermost orbit increases the negativity of the atom, resulting in the chloride ion (Cl^-).

Compounds

This tendency of many elements to form ions is very important, because knowing what charge an ion has tells how it will combine, and with what. If one element loses a charge while another gains, the resultant ions will be attracted to each other and will lock together (unlike charges attract, remember). The result is a **compound,** and when compounds form, old physical and chemical properties disappear and new ones take their place. A compound has characteristics that are unique and quite different from those of the elements of which it is made. The indivisible unit of the compound is the **molecule.** The molecules of a given compound must be left intact if its characteristics are to be retained, because these characteristics are unique. The process of combining separate elements into a compound invariably results in the complete loss of identity of the elements involved. Consider, for example, sodium chloride, which is ordinary table salt.

Pure sodium is one of the most reactive of all the metallic elements. Its potential for violence is so great that if a chunk of pure sodium metal the size of a child's marble were dropped into a gallon of water in the kitchen sink, the resulting explosion would probably blow the sink apart. Sodium reacts with water so violently, in fact, that it is customarily stored under kerosene to avoid accidental contact with moisture in any form. It is not an element one handles casually.

Chlorine is a nonmetal and at normal temperatures it is a greenish-yellow gas as unpleasant to smell as it is to see. A good noseful will choke a person half to death. Mixed with water, it can bleach clothing and rust iron with equal facility. In mild concentrations it will kill bacteria and other small organisms, and we use it in swimming pools and in city reservoirs to keep our water pure. In higher concentrations it is deadly to large animals, including humans. During World War I it was the major toxic ingredient in the poison gases that killed thousands on both sides of the struggle.

Both sodium and chlorine are dangerous to handle and hazardous to life, yet when combined into sodium chloride—common table salt—unique and different characteristics appear. Salt is not merely inoffensive, it is essential in living systems. Nothing about table salt is like either chlorine gas or sodium metal. It won't react with explosive violence when placed in water and has never been used in poisonous gases. It is ingested perhaps a little too much by Americans who like to eat fast food, but generally speaking it's harmless and very useful. Its historic importance was enormous, and the esteem in which it was held is reflected in the fact that in many cultures, once persons had "eaten their salt" they were accepted as bona fide guests and could be done no mischief.

Figure 2.5 Ion arrangement when sodium chloride dissolves in water.

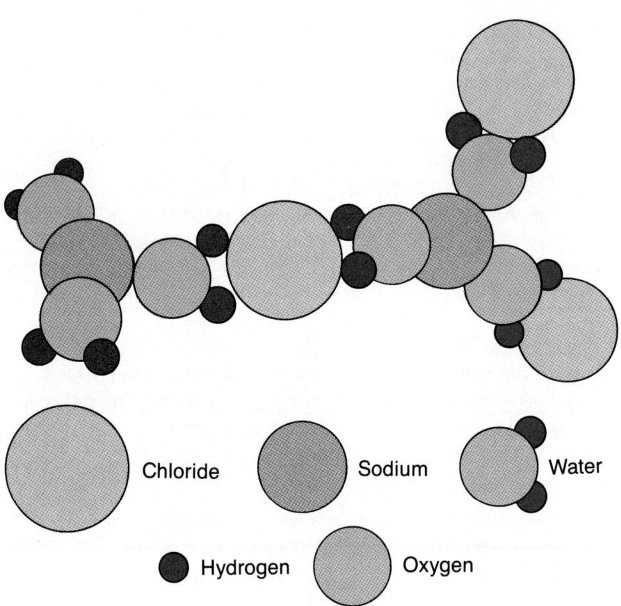

Chemical Bonds

Ionic Bonding

In the formation of sodium chloride, sodium and chlorine exchange an electron. Sodium becomes the sodium ion (Na^+) through the loss of an electron, and chlorine becomes chloride (Cl^-) when it grips the errant particle. Once exposed to each other, they are attracted by the charges that exist on the two ions—the same kind of electrostatic attraction that keeps the universe from flying apart. Because they combine as ions, the attraction that holds them together is termed **ionic bonding.** Such electron transfer between elements is common and is the way metallic and nonmetallic ions normally interact to form compounds.

Usually, ionic bonds are the most powerful of all chemical bonds. In water, however, many of these ions separate from each other, because the charge on the water molecules is powerful enough to attract them away from their molecular structure. Once separated, they snuggle against the water molecules, with the chloride ion nestled against the positive end and the sodium adjacent to the negative zone produced by the oxygen atom (figure 2.5). As a result, polar compounds like salt exist in ionic rather than molecular form when in aqueous solution.

Salt dissolves in water because the charges on the water molecule are stronger than the charges on salt's ions, so the water molecules have a stronger attraction for sodium and chloride ions than the two ions have for each other. However, becoming ions in water doesn't change them back to their elemental form. Taste a solution of salt and water and it tastes like salty water. The salt is still there, and it's still there as salt. If the water were to be boiled away, the sodium and chloride ions would attract each other and promptly form salt crystals again.

Reactions that result in ionic bonds all feature a transfer of electrons from one element to the other, and there are some important rules. One of the most important is that in these reactions, *the number of electrons lost by one element must exactly equal the number of electrons gained by the other.* When sodium chloride forms, sodium loses one electron and chlorine gains one, so the number of sodium ions is equal to the number of chloride ions, and the combining ratio of the two elements is one-to-one (1:1). When other elements are involved, this ratio does not necessarily hold. Calcium, for example, must lose two electrons to attain the stable octet, so when it combines with chlorine it is in a 1:2 ratio, and the compound that forms has the formula $CaCl_2$. Each element has its own capacity for reacting, and this *reaction capacity* is known as the element's **valence.** Its value depends on the number of electrons that a given element loses or gains when it becomes an ion.

Once the valence of a given element is known, it is easy to work out its combining ratio with other elements, and it is not hard to figure out the molecular formulas of the compounds that will form. Magnesium, with its +2 valence, when reacting with chlorine (−1) will form magnesium chloride ($MgCl_2$). Potassium (+1), when reacting with oxygen (−2), forms potassium oxide, K_2O, and so on.

These ionic interactions apply to all reactions involving metals and nonmetals, and so compounds held together by ionic bonds are usually metal/nonmetal combinations. The exchange of electrons by reacting atoms results in particles with opposite charges being created adjacent to each other. The attractive force that holds such compounds together, therefore, is electrostatic. Elements that form ionic bonds are the central figures in the study of **inorganic chemistry,** and they play an important role in biology. When they occur in living systems they are classified under the heading **minerals,** and most are metal/nonmetal compounds that separate into ions in body water. Although most of us don't realize it, our bodies contain a lot of metal. Some metals, like potassium, sodium, and calcium, are present in abundance, while others such as tin, nickel, vanadium, chromium, zinc, copper, and magnesium are present only in trace amounts.

Figure 2.6 The chlorine molecule (schematically rendered). Lone chlorine atoms do not have the noble gas configuration and so are very unstable, tending to easily ionize and form ionic compounds. Chlorine is able to exist in the pure state only by sharing valence electrons with another chlorine atom. The molecule that results is still reactive but, since each chlorine atom has the stable configuration for 50 percent of the time, the chlorine molecule is less reactive than elemental chlorine.

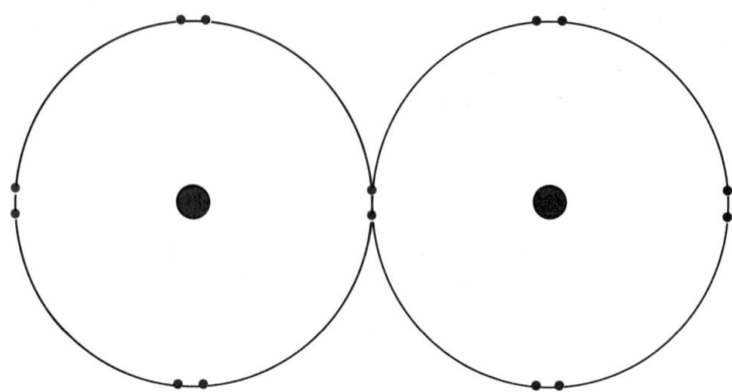

Covalent Bonding

Naturally, not all compounds are metal/nonmetal combinations. There are myriad compounds composed exclusively of nonmetallic elements, and such compounds are not held together by ionic bonds. When nonmetals get together to form compounds, electrons are not *transferred* from one element to another, but instead are *shared* by the elements involved (figure 2.6).

The formation of chlorine gas molecules (Cl_2) is shown in figure 2.6 and demonstrates why two atoms share electrons. The same principle is also true of hydrogen. Hydrogen atoms are tremendously reactive and exist for only split seconds before combining—sometimes violently—with another element. In order to exist for any length of time in the pure state, such an atom must link up with another hydrogen atom to form a hydrogen molecule. The formation is much the same as that of chlorine. Individual hydrogen atoms move to obtain an extra electron in their valence shells in order to achieve the stable configuration of helium, the smallest noble gas. However, when two hydrogen atoms encounter one another, how is it possible for one to get the extra electron and the other to wind up two short? Since the two atoms are identical, neither is able to remove an electron from the other. The problem is solved by sharing electrons, one from each atom, so that 50 percent of the time they both possess the stable configuration. In such molecules the shared electrons circle the whole molecule instead of either single atom, forming H_2 gas. It is still not stable, but it is a lot less reactive than lone hydrogen atoms. Many gases exist this way, including the two most abundant—nitrogen (N_2) and oxygen (O_2).

Since there is no ion formation, there are no charges on the atoms involved, and without opposite charges to provide attraction, what is it that holds the

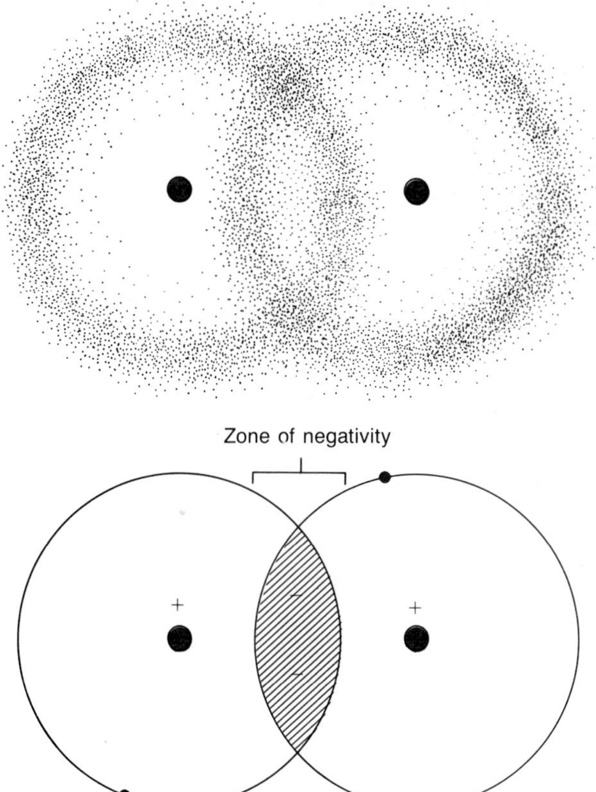

Figure 2.7 The hydrogen molecule, showing the negative zone between the atoms that provides the attractive force for the positive nuclei. The attraction is less powerful than ionic bonds but is nevertheless quite strong.

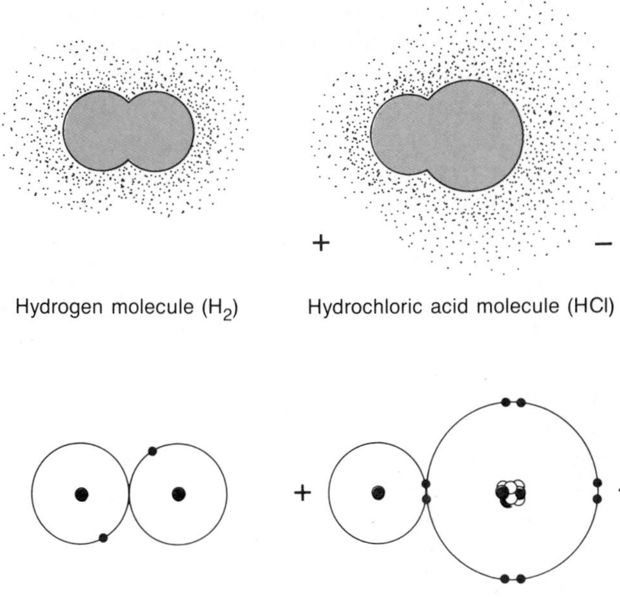

Figure 2.8 Because the two atoms that comprise the H_2 molecule are identical, the electrons circling them are equally shared. The chlorine atom, however, with seven protons in the nucleus and thus a greater charge, tends to attract more electrons than the hydrogen can; hence the hydrochloric acid molecule has a negative zone and a positive zone.

molecules together? The answer is still electromagnetism, but the charge distribution is quite different, and the attractive forces are generally not as strong as in ionic interactions. Because the atomic nuclei are close together, the electron clouds (see second box on page 22) overlap in the region between them, forming a negatively charged cloud to which the positive elements of the nuclei are attracted (figure 2.7).

This attractive force is known as a **covalent bond.** Covalent bonds lack the strength of ionic bonds, but they are more versatile. For example, if nitrogen and hydrogen were able to form only ionic bonds, nitrogen (valence −3) should always combine with hydrogen (+1) in a 1:3 ratio, thus forming NH_3 (ammonia). But because nitrogen and hydrogen tend to share electrons instead of transferring them, this is only one of three possible combining ratios available. The ammonium ion is NH_4^+ while the amine group, a prime constituent of proteins, is NH_2.

A 100 percent covalent bond can exist only when electron sharing takes place between two identical atoms like chlorine or oxygen, because the attraction of one nucleus cannot be greater than that of the other. Compounds composed of different elements do not have 100 percent covalent bonds, because inevitably one nucleus will have a greater positive charge than the other and the electrons, being negative, will tend to cluster near the most positive part of the molecule. Such is the case with compounds like hydrochloric acid or water. The electrons are unequally shared, and this unequal distribution produces a molecule that features a positive zone and a negative zone. (See figure 2.8.) Because such molecules have a positive pole and a negative pole, they are said to be **polarized,** and the bonds that hold them together are termed **polar covalent bonds.**

Organic Chemistry

The terms *organic* and *inorganic,* which are routinely used to define the two separate branches of chemistry, originated years ago when the lights were just beginning to shine on some of the mysteries of chemistry. Intellectuals of the early nineteenth century had managed to work out the fundamentals of atomic assembly. They were beginning to understand how simple salts, bases, and acids were put together and how they interacted with each other. When it came to untangling the molecules in living systems, however, it was quite different. Products of living systems were enormously complicated—much more so than the rocks and nonliving minerals scattered around the world. Rocks and minerals were not alive and never had been. They were part of the *in*organic world.

Compounds that made up animals and plants, however, were different. Many workers of the time, unable to unravel the enormous numbers of atoms and tremendous complexity of living residues, became convinced that the compounds of life were destined never to be deciphered. They belonged to the *organic* world, and that was a province that only God could enter and understand. To the chemists of the time, organic mysteries were not just unknown but essentially *unknowable.* Most believed that the compounds of life contained more than merely atoms. They contained also some mysterious, probably divine, force, and no human could ever expect to decode or synthesize organic molecules.

This theory was blown into a cocked hat early in the nineteenth century when urea, an organic compound if there ever was one, was synthesized in a laboratory in Germany. Since that time literally thousands of organic compounds have been analyzed, and their once-unknowable mysteries have been probed and solved. Plastics, synthetic clothing, synthetic furs, synthetic rubber, and a multitude of other things are products of organic chemical synthesis—it is the hottest research area in modern chemistry. And chemists don't just *make* such items . . . they understand their atomic structure and know the shape of the molecules they are working with. Humanity has, in the last fifty years, learned a tremendous amount about a chemistry the knowledge of which was once thought to be restricted to the gods.

Carbon

Today, although the term *organic* is still with us, this branch of chemistry would be more accurately termed *the chemistry of the carbon compounds.* Carbon is the central element, and the study of carbon and the structures it forms is the essence of modern organic chemistry. Carbon is an unusual element. It possesses four valence electrons, and because of this, it would be unable to form the stable octet without either losing or gaining four electrons. Either would require so much energy that neither ever happens, and as a result, carbon cannot form ionic bonds. Instead, it links to other atoms—including other carbon atoms—through the *sharing of electrons.* Like so many other elements, carbon achieves chemical stability by acquiring eight electrons in its valence shell. In order to form stable compounds, therefore, carbon must share all four of its valence electrons, and the atoms it is linking to must also produce four such electrons. *Carbon,* therefore, *always has four bonds.*

The most amazing thing about carbon's bonding capabilities is its knack for forming long, stable chains of nothing but carbon atoms. There are literally thousands of compounds, all with different physical and chemical properties, established on streams of carbon atoms. Sometimes such chains link to each other, forming sheets or sprays of carbon atoms all bonded into a single structure. Such structures needn't be comprised solely of carbon atoms. When hydrogen atoms link to carbon's available bonds, **hydrocarbons** are produced, and science today knows the structure and chemistry of more than thirty-five hundred hydrocarbons. Hydrogen is not the only foreign element that can become part of these carbon edifices. Sometimes they link to oxygen, sometimes sulfur, or phosphorus, or nitrogen, or some other element. When you consider the incredible variation that can result from such atomic manipulations and the number of different compounds that could be formed, you begin to realize that the total number of unique carbon compounds may well be uncountable. Recent writings indicate that science has identified and described nearly four million such compounds, and new ones are being added to the list at the rate of about one hundred thousand a year.

Carbon Chemistry: Some Unique Characteristics

Organic compounds are usually so big that when a pair of them come together to react, only small parts of them are actually affected. On the other hand, *inorganic* reactions change everything involved, and they do it very quickly. When an ionic (or inorganic) reaction is about to take place, you don't want to blink or you'll miss it, because such reactions often are complete in less than a second. The reaction between lye (NaOH) and hydrochloric acid (HCl), for example, goes like a flash, producing sodium chloride (NaCl) and water almost instantaneously. By contrast, even the simplest organic reactions are slow and often will not occur at all unless something is added to speed them up. Chemical agents that speed up reactions are called *catalytic agents* or **catalysts.** In living systems, these catalytic agents are called **enzymes,** and we require and possess them in the millions.

Identifying Organic Compounds

Structural formulas

Organic compounds usually consist of only a few elements, but each molecule may contain hundreds of atoms of each element. What is more, there are often dozens of compounds that have identical formulas in terms of the total number and variety of atoms present, yet each has different properties because the atoms are arranged in different ways. For this reason, **molecular formulas,** which are so common in inorganic chemistry (for example, H_2SO_4, HNO_3, $CaCl_2$), are inadequate to describe organic compounds. To illustrate, utilizing a molecular formula, we indicate the

Figure 2.9 A comparison of the simple sugars glucose, fructose, and galactose. All three have the same molecular formula yet are quite different structurally. Galactose and glucose vary in the highlighted areas, while fructose is a five-membered ring (a pentagon as opposed to a hexagon). Their physical characteristics are different, too. Fructose is more than twice as sweet as either of the other two.

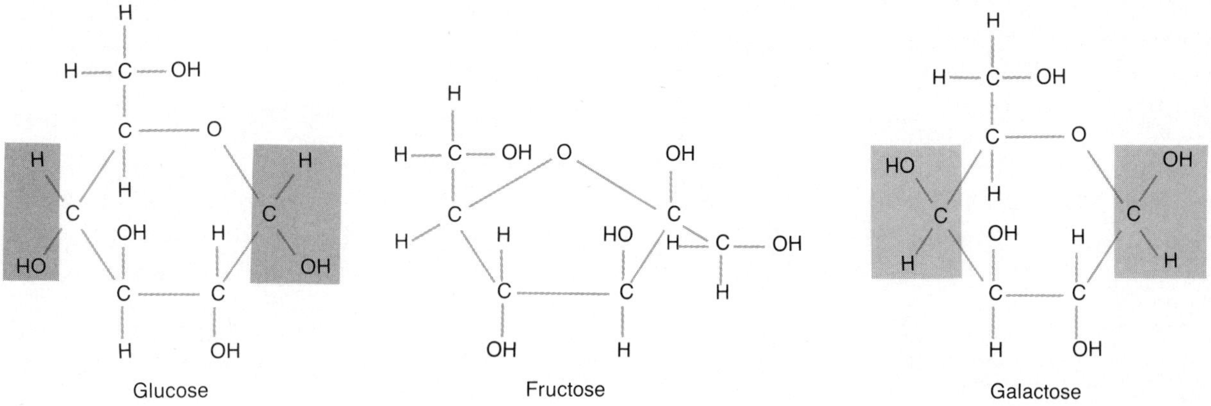

Glucose Fructose Galactose

Figure 2.10 The molecular formula gives minimal information. It tells only the ratio of involved elements and does not identify the compound. The formulas as they appear in line 2 identify the compound but don't show structure or bonds. Lines 3 and 4 show how the bonds are arranged and the angles of the radical groups, while line 5 shows bonding angles and electron arrangement around each atom. When discussing compounds this small, most chemists would use the formulas on line 2 for communication.

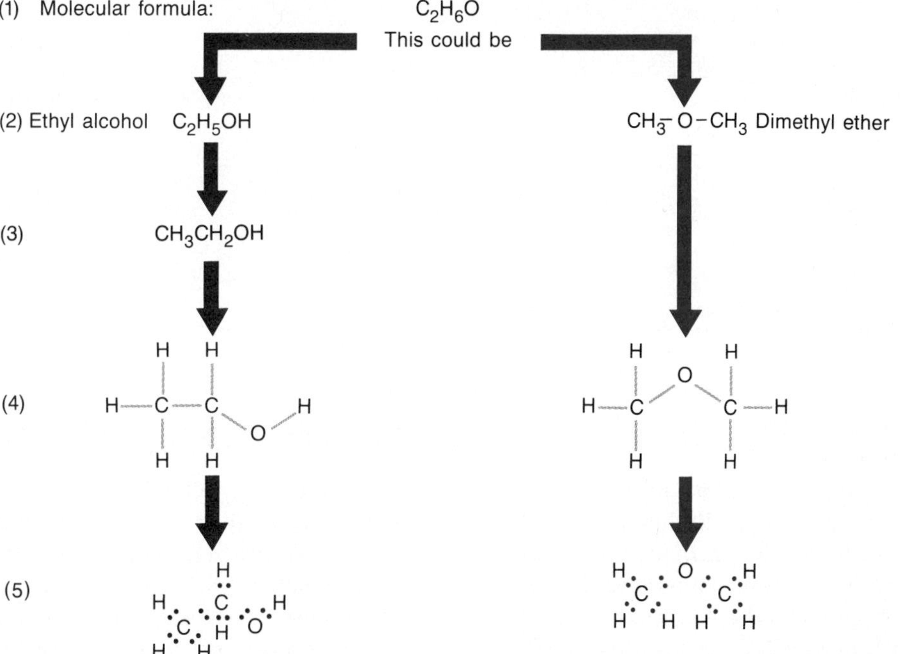

presence of three elements in the following ratio: $C_6H_{12}O_6$. Several common organic compounds have this formula, and all are simple sugars. They all possess the same atoms, but the compounds are not the same. They are all white crystals, but they don't taste the same and their molecular structures are different (see figure 2.9). Compounds like these that are structurally different but have the same molecular formula are known as **isomers.**

When communicating with one another, scientists use the simplest means of clearly identifying a given compound. Consider, for instance, the formula C_2H_6O. The molecular formula tells us that the compound has two carbon atoms, six hydrogen atoms, and one oxygen atom. This is undoubtedly the *simplest* way to describe the compound, but it is unsatisfactory from a chemist's point of view; more detail of its structure is needed. However, one need not draw the most complex structure in order to convey the necessary information. Figure 2.10 illustrates several ways of describing the compound C_2H_6O.

Table 2.3 Functional Groups

Name of Group	Structure[1]	Found In	Biological Significance
Hydroxyl or alcohol	—OH	Carbohydrates, especially simple sugars	Energy source
Carbonyl			
(a) Aldehyde	H | R—C=O	Carbohydrates	Intermediate metabolic products
(b) Ketone	R | R—C=O	Proteins, lipids	Intermediate metabolic products
Carboxyl	—COOH	Organic acids	Amino acids, fatty acids, etc.
Amine	$R-NH_2$	Proteins	Building blocks of protein
Sulfhydryl	S—H	Proteins	Maintain secondary and tertiary structure of proteins
Disulfide	S—S	Proteins	Same as sulfhydryl
Phosphate			
(a) Monoester	O ‖ O⁻—P—OH | OH		
(b) Pyrophosphate	O O ‖ ‖ O⁻—P—O—P—O⁻ | | O⁻ O⁻	All energy-source compounds	Stored chemical energy for quick release and use
Benzene (aromatic) ring	HC(H) ring: H–C, HC, CH, HC, CH, C–H or (hexagon with circle)[2]	Core of aromatic compounds	Nucleus of cholesterol and all steroid hormones

1. The letter *R* in a chemical formula indicates any hydrocarbon "residue."
2. The circle indicates the presence of three alternating double bonds within the ring.

Organic Functional Groups

The number and variety of carbon compounds sometimes appear limitless. No one really has any idea how many there might be. As has already been noted, nearly four million have been named and described, and there are probably at least that many more left. Yet despite this abundance of compounds, there are certain specific combinations of small elements that show up repeatedly everywhere. These small organic clusters are known as **functional groups** or **organic radicals,** and they impart certain significant chemical characteristics to the compounds they are linked to. They also provide a convenient way to identify and categorize some pretty complicated organic compounds. They are listed in table 2.3.

The Major Biological Compounds

As I indicated in chapter 1, life, for the most part, is composed of very average chemical elements. Magnesium, sodium, chlorine, and potassium are on hand in respectable amounts, but none are incorporated to any extent in the big organic molecules. The huge, unique, and incredibly elaborate biological molecules are made of even more modest atoms. As noted previously, biochemicals are mainly composed of hydrogen, carbon, oxygen, sulfur, nitrogen, and phosphorus, organized into structures as rudimentary as urea and as involved as petroleum. All of the organic compounds are, as we have seen, compounds of carbon, usually joining carbon to hydrogen or carbon to carbon-hydrogen units. To be considered organic, a compound must have carbon-hydrogen links somewhere. Thus, methane (CH_4), propane (C_3H_8), and ethane (C_2H_6) are organic, while compounds like CO_2, water, and sodium carbonates (Na_2CO_3) are not.

The arrangement of the organic compounds is orderly, and when a prosperous arrangement evolves, living systems tend to stick with it as much as possible, producing huge numbers of variations around successful central themes. So despite the fact that life is probably the most complex thing in the universe and that there are millions of biological compounds involved, nearly all of them belong to one of just four main categories. These categories are **carbohydrates, lipids, proteins,** and **nucleic acids.**

Figure 2.11 (*a*) A monosaccharide, consisting of six carbon atoms and six water molecules arranged carefully together. (*b*) A disaccharide (maltose). There are twelve carbon atoms present, but only eleven water molecules. One water molecule was lost forming the bond that links the two monosaccharides together (see text).

(a) Simple sugar **(b)** Double sugar

Carbohydrates

Carbohydrates more often than not consist of just three elements—carbon, hydrogen, and oxygen. They are arranged in such a way that for every carbon atom that is present, there is a water molecule—hence the name "hydrated" (watered) carbon. The general formula for carbohydrates is $C_x(H_2O)_x$ (x representing any small, whole number), which means that x number of carbon atoms is attached to the same number (x) of water molecules. Carbohydrates, for the most part, are sugars, and there are hundreds of them.

Monosaccharides

Many carbohydrates found naturally are simple, single-molecule sugars and fit nicely into the general carbohydrate formula, which demands an equal number of water molecules and carbon atoms. Because they fit this general concept, and because they can't be broken down to smaller sugars, these sugars, like fructose and glucose, are termed **monosaccharides.** There are more than two hundred natural monosaccharides, and for most of them, their physical properties—including the taste—seem to be pretty much alike. The major variation among the rest seems to involve flavor. Some have no taste at all, some are not sweet, some are supersweet, and there are a few that are so scarce that no one has ever found enough of them to taste. Fructose is the sweetest of the common sugars and so is often used as a low-calorie sweetener (the "low calorie" idea is based on the observation that because it is so sweet, you will use less). Except for glucose, galactose and fructose are the most common monosaccharides ingested by humans, and both are quickly converted to glucose in the liver. Glucose (blood sugar) is the primary energy source for most living cells, except during cases of extreme starvation, when special homeostatic adjustments can be made.

Monosaccharide sugars are categorized according to the number of carbon atoms they possess. Fructose and glucose contain six carbon atoms and so are **hexoses**—the prefix (hex-) referring to the number of carbons present, and the suffix (-ose) describing the presence of a sugar. A monosaccharide with three carbon atoms would be known as a *triose*.

Generally speaking, monosaccharides are not found solo in nature, but instead are the building blocks of larger saccharides, some of which are quite large indeed. Many carbohydrates are composed of several simple sugars linked together. Categorizing molecules like those according to the number of carbon atoms they contained would not be much of an abbreviation, nor would it be very descriptive. For that reason, complex sugars are categorized according to the number of monosaccharide molecules they contain.

Disaccharides

Disaccharides, as the name indicates, are formed by the union of two monosaccharides. The most common of these is simple table sugar—**sucrose**—which is a union of fructose and glucose. **Lactose**—a combination of galactose and glucose—is abundant in the milk of all mammals and is an important nutrient for infants. The simplest disaccharide is grape sugar or **maltose,** a disaccharide formed of two identical glucose molecules (figure 2.11). Almost all known disaccharides are formed of linked hexose sugars.

For reasons that are not quite clear, refined sugar has an unsavory reputation among health-food advocates and a small number of health care people. This is not new. Sugar has been blamed at one time or another for practically every disease that has perplexed mankind. As recently as forty years ago, physicians were warning patients that a diet too high in sugar could result in diabetes (the disease is still referred to as *sugar* diabetes). For the first fifty years of this century, diets high in sugar were often blamed for macroparasite infections like tapeworms, liver flukes, or intestinal roundworms, and children were often cautioned to shun candy for fear of such infestations.

Figure 2.12 Two complex carbohydrates, starch and cellulose. Cellulose, the most abundant organic compound on earth, cannot be digested by humans.

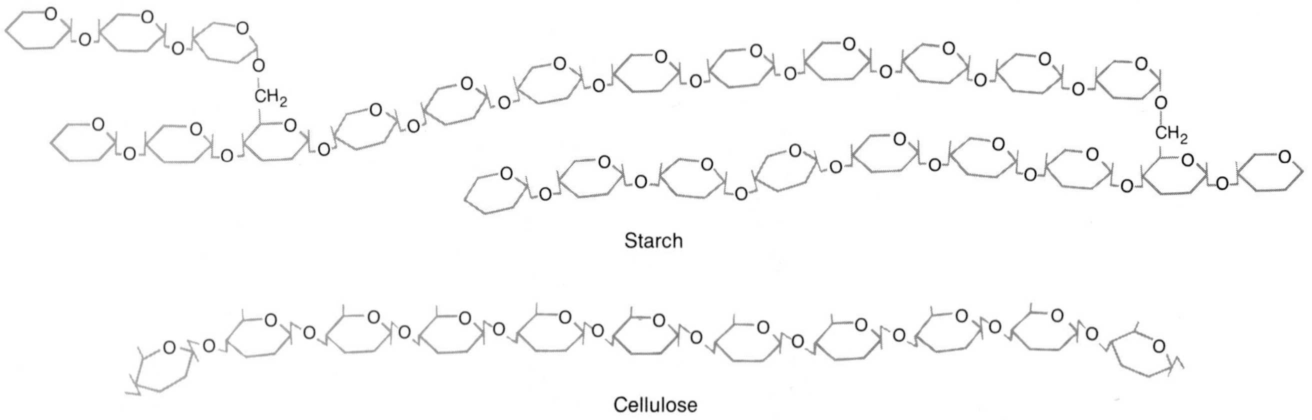

Starch

Cellulose

Polysaccharides

Much of the sugar found in nature is present in caches of large storage molecules. The two most abundant polysaccharides in nature are **starch** and **cellulose,** both composed exclusively of glucose (figure 2.12). In humans, most sugar is in the form of **glycogen,** a polysaccharide synthesized by, and stored in, the liver (figure 2.13). In a polysaccharide, the component molecule that repeats itself over and over is known as the **monomer** of the larger molecule, which is, in its turn, the **polymer** of the small one. Glucose, therefore, is the monomer of glycogen, and glycogen is a polymer of glucose.

Of all organic compounds occurring on earth, cellulose is the most abundant. Often there are as many as two thousand glucose monomers in a single cellulose molecule, and glucose is edible. Despite this, cellulose is not a human nutrient. The bonds that hold the glucose molecules together in cellulose can't be broken apart by human enzymes, so the glucose cannot be used. This does not mean that cellulose has no value in the human diet, however. Humans take in lots of cellulose in lettuce, cabbage, and many other fruits and vegetables. Since we cannot break it up and digest it, it must pass through the gastrointestinal tract unchanged. This indigestible material is called **fiber** or roughage and is currently finding much favor as a dietary item.

Starch is not as big as cellulose, nor is it as abundant, but as a food it is considerably more important. It usually consists of two or three dozen chains of glucose molecules strung together like a long, rather narrow fishing net (see figure 2.12). It is one of the most common carbohydrates in plants and is particularly important to humans and many other animals, because it is a major nutrient source. Unlike those of cellulose, the bonds that hold the glucose molecules together in starch *can* be broken by human digestive juices, and the energy-containing glucose molecules can be separated and absorbed.

Biological Synthesis

Creating a polymer from any of the monosaccharides involves catalyzed reactions that link the small building blocks together to produce larger molecules. In biological systems the linking often involves the removal of water molecules; this is known as **dehydration synthesis.** For instance, the combining of glucose and fructose into common table sugar, sucrose, requires that a water molecule be removed. The molecular formula of sucrose is $C_{12}H_{22}O_{11}$, and as can be easily seen, there are twelve carbon atoms, but only eleven water molecules. Disaccharides, therefore, do not conform to the general carbohydrate formula. And the more monosaccharides used to form the polymer, the further from the fundamental carbohydrate formula the result will be, because every new glucose molecule that links to the chain requires the removal of another water molecule. The synthesis of maltose is shown in figure 2.14.

Dehydration synthesis is, naturally, not the only method by which polymers or large molecules can be formed, but it requires only a little energy to accomplish and it has the advantage of being easy to reverse. The reverse process is called **hydrolysis.** In hydrolysis, a water molecule is catalytically added to a complex polymer and the polymer is split. This is the means by which polymers of all kinds are broken down when food is digested.

Figure 2.13 (*a*) The branching, bush-like structure of glycogen. Each circle represents a glucose molecule. (*b*) A more detailed view of the arrangement of glucose molecules in a glycogen complex.

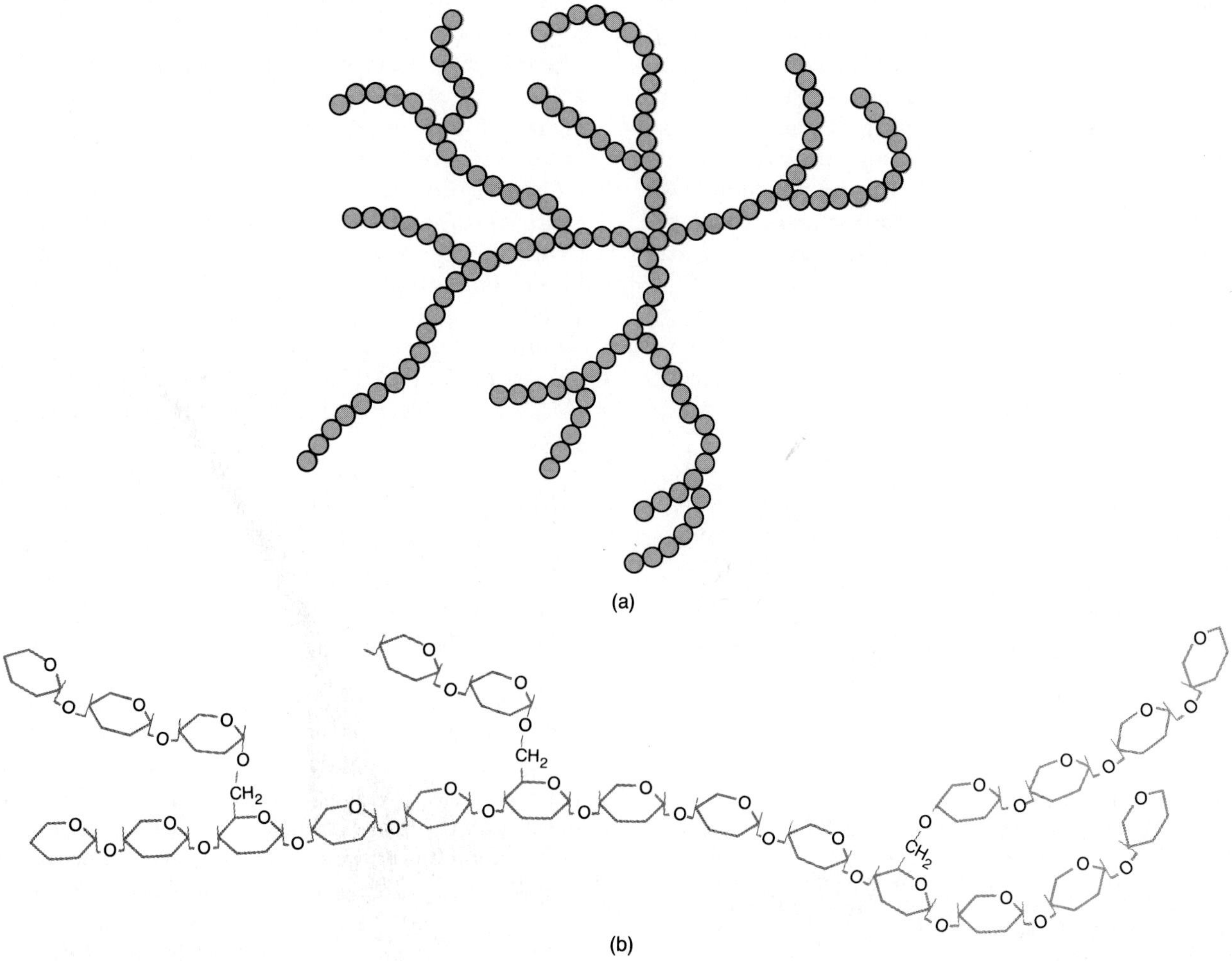

(a)

(b)

Figure 2.14 The process of dehydration synthesis. A water molecule (broken line rectangle, left) is removed from the reacting glucose molecules, and a bond forms across the oxygen atom that remains.

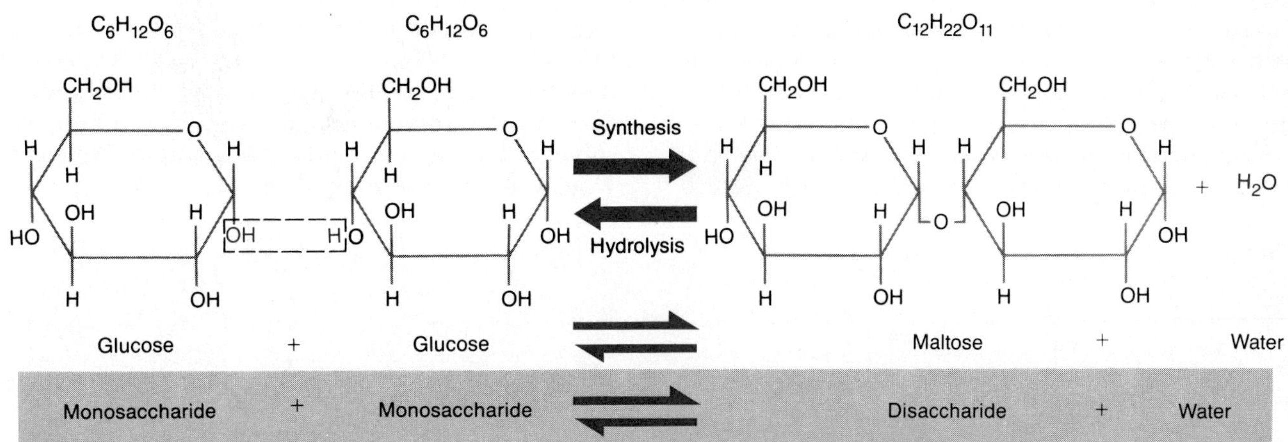

Carbohydrate Function

Carbohydrates are not utilized much as structural components in animals. Less than 1 percent of a human body is built of carbohydrate, although there is much more than 1 percent actually present in living systems. Carbohydrates, obtained mainly from fruits and vegetables, provide most of the fuel that is needed to produce free energy for living systems. Glucose rides the central energy-producing pathway and represents the initial energy resource of our blood. As we have seen, in animals most body glucose has been polymerized and is stored as glycogen or animal starch.

Less than half of the food consumed in the United States is carbohydrate, which makes it a little less important as a nutrient here than it is in other parts of the world. Statistics from the World Health Organization indicate that the percentage is much higher elsewhere, and in some areas it represents more than 90 percent of the diet. In spite of the fact that the most plentiful carbohydrate is inedible, there are lots of carbohydrates that humans *can* eat, and they exist in staggering quantities. Carbohydrates are the most abundant human nutrient on earth. As a source of energy, they are unsurpassed. Not only do they provide energy for the machinery of life, but they also provide it for the machinery that warms and cools our houses, provides us with electricity, and takes us around the world. Much of the energy in oil and all of the energy in coal comes from sunshine that lit the earth millions of years ago and was stored in carbohydrate by plants that no longer grow on this planet. The amount of radiant energy that has been converted to carbohydrate and stored by plants staggers the imagination. Even today, with much of the world's forest land turned over to developers, experts estimate that the plants that remain form nearly 300,000,000 tons of carbohydrate every 24-hour period.

Current evidence seems to suggest that carbohydrates are not indispensable to the human diet. If they were completely absent, there is no reason to believe that health would suffer—provided the necessary calories were made up by protein and lipids. But that would be difficult. You might like the idea of subsisting only on steak, fish, roasts, and other foods of animal origin, but you would not for long. It would be quite a job, day after day, to cram enough protein and fat into our mouths to satisfy nutritional requirements, and there is a chance that the diet would be less than optimal—not for lack of nutrient carbohydrates, but for the lack of an indigestible one, cellulose. As I mentioned before, cellulose is the dietary "fiber" that evidence indicates is so important. Probably we would also be eating far too much fat. There is an awful lot of fat in meat, and while we may like to think of ourselves as essentially predators, we really are not fashioned to consume flesh. Both our anatomical blueprint and our physiological processes seem to favor a vegetable diet. Also, without carbohydrates in our diets, all glycogen stores would have to be created by converting other foodstuffs to glucose, which would be a pretty inefficient method of acquiring an energy backlog. All things considered, it is probably a very good thing that we do not have to do without carbohydrates.

Lipids

Fat in all forms, including all fatty derivatives, is collectively designated **lipid.** The term includes items commonly known as oils and waxes as well as that flavorless, rather mushy substance we trim from our meat.

Like the carbohydrates, lipids are composed of carbon, hydrogen, and oxygen, but unlike the carbon in sugars, the carbon in lipids is not hydrated. There are many more carbons and hydrogens per lipid molecule than there are oxygens—in fact, lipids are generally considered to be hydrocarbons, molecules that consist of just hydrogen and carbon atoms. Lipids are not a distinctive group except for their long chains of hydrocarbons, and their nature is so varied that they can't be classified according to any particular chemical characteristic. So how are lipids distinguished from other organic groups? It's very simple. When homogenized plant or animal tissue is exposed to a nonpolar solvent like alcohol or benzene, part of it dissolves and part of it does not. According to chemical rules established decades ago, everything that dissolves is lipid, and what does not is nonlipid. So if an organic compound will dissolve in a nonpolar solvent, that organic compound is a lipid. Lipids obviously are insoluble in water.

Figure 2.15 The synthesis of a neutral fat. Glycerol and three fatty acid chains are linked together via dehydration synthesis to form a neutral fat. Water molecules are removed at the zones highlighted. To hydrolyze (digest) the neutral fat, water is catalytically added, again at the highlighted zones, splitting it into glycerol and three fatty acids.

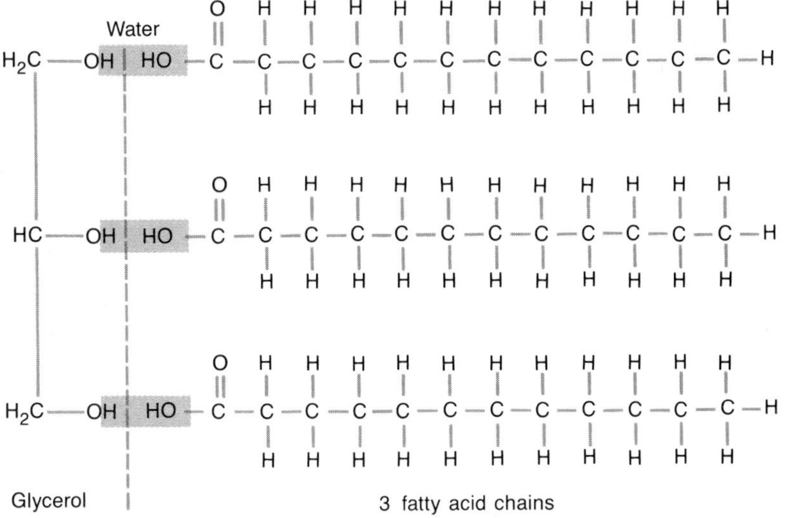

Table 2.4 Common Acids Derived from Fats

Name	Molecular Formula	Structural Formula
Lauric acid	$C_{11}H_{23}COOH$	$CH_3(CH_2)_{10}COOH$
Myristic acid	$C_{13}H_{27}COOH$	$CH_3(CH_2)_{12}COOH$
Palmitic acid	$C_{15}H_{31}COOH$	$CH_3(CH_2)_{14}COOH$
Stearic acid	$C_{17}H_{35}COOH$	$CH_3(CH_2)_{16}COOH$
Oleic acid	$C_{17}H_{33}COOH$	$CH_3(CH_2)_7CH=CH(CH_2)_7COOH$
Linoleic acid	$C_{17}H_{31}COOH$	$CH_3(CH_2)_4CH=CHCH_2CH=CH(CH_2)_7COOH$
Linolenic acid	$C_{17}H_{29}COOH$	$CH_3CH_2(CH=CHCH_2)_3(CH_2)_6COOH$

Water rejects lipids with such vigor that, even if tiny oil droplets are widely dispersed in a water matrix, they will find a way to come together into a single, large oil sphere. This happens because water molecules have a strong attraction for each other but none at all for the dispersed lipid molecules. The polar water molecules therefore keep thrusting the nonpolar lipids aside in order to link up to nearby water molecules, and as the oil droplets move through the water matrix, sooner or later they will encounter one another. When they do, they coalesce, thus exposing a smaller surface area to the surrounding water. As this process continues, the individual droplets get fewer and larger until finally there is only one large one left. The water still rejects any association with the oil and forces it into the shape of a sphere, because the sphere is the geometric shape with the smallest possible surface area. This, plus the reduction in number of particles, insures that the water molecules will have to contend with the smallest possible surface area of lipid. The tendency has led to the designation of lipids as being **hydrophobic** (*hydro* water, *phobic* fear of).

In animals, most fats are **neutral fats.** They are made up of three spines of fatty acids attached to a head consisting of a three-carbon compound known as *glycerol* (figure 2.15). The fatty acids are attached to the glycerol molecule via dehydration synthesis, just as carbohydrates are polymerized. The fatty acids in figure 2.15 are known as lauric acid and individually have the molecular formula $C_{11}H_{23}COOH$.

The fatty acids in common lipid molecules can vary across a broad spectrum. This variation occurs in one of two main areas: in the length of the hydrocarbon chains or in the ratio of hydrogen to carbon atoms (table 2.4). A variation of the first kind merely increases the *size* of the lipid, but the second variation may be physiologically important. Fatty acids are long chains of carbon atoms with hydrogen atoms connected to their free bonds (figure 2.16). When each carbon atom in the chain with the exception of the last one is holding all the hydrogen atoms it can hold,

Figure 2.16 Two fatty acids: (*a*) A saturated fatty acid. Note that, except for the terminal atoms, each carbon atom is holding two hydrogens—a full load. (*b*) An unsaturated fatty acid. Six of the carbons in this chain are holding only one hydrogen atom each. These carbons have formed double bonds between each other, thus taking care of carbon's four bonds.

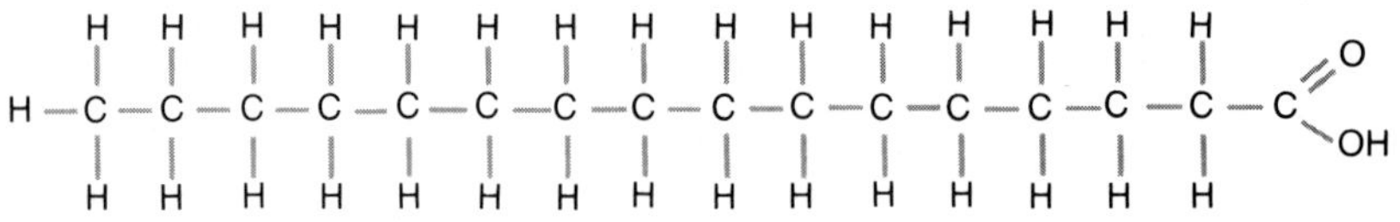

$CH_3(CH_2)_{14}COOH$

(a)

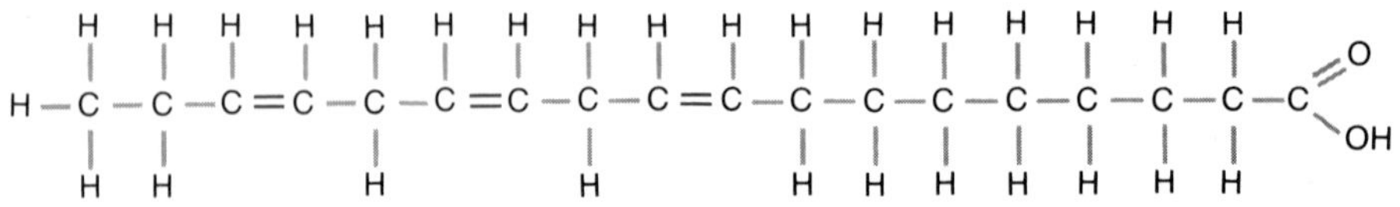

$CH_3\ CH_2(CH = CHCH_2)_3(CH_2)_6COOH$

(b)

it is considered to be **saturated** with hydrogen atoms. (Remember, each carbon atom has four bonds.) If, however, some of these carbon atoms were to form double or triple bonds with some of their carbon neighbors (and they often do), the fatty acid would not be holding the maximum number of hydrogen atoms and hence would be considered **unsaturated** (see figure 2.16*b*).

Lipids are stored in the human body as neutral fats, and despite advertising claims to the contrary, most such fatty acids are unsaturated, having at least one double or triple bond somewhere. In fact, nearly all naturally occurring fatty acids are unsaturated, including animal fats. Nevertheless, there are more of the saturated fatty acids in animal fats than there are in plant fats, and since saturated fatty acids have an unpleasant reputation as nutrients, lipids from vegetable sources are usually considered better for humans.

Phospholipids

The phospholipid is one of the most important types of lipid that exists in biological systems. As the name implies, these fats contain a phosphate group similar to those illustrated in table 2.3 and generalized here:

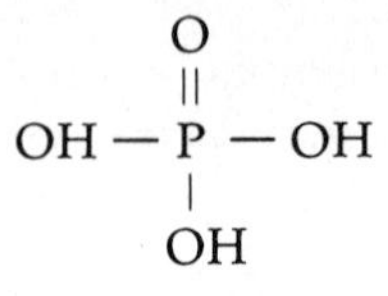

$$\begin{array}{c} O \\ \| \\ OH - P - OH \\ | \\ OH \end{array}$$

Phospholipids are essentially neutral fats that have been altered a little to accommodate the phosphate group, usually linking this group onto either the top or bottom of the glycerol molecule in place of the fatty acid (figure 2.17). What makes this arrangement so important is that, unlike the fatty acids, which are homogeneous (hence nonpolar) chains of hydrocarbon, the phosphate molecules can and usually do have a polar or charged configuration. The charge means that the phosphate part of the molecule can slip in between water molecules and form an association with them—a relationship not possible with nonpolar molecules. Phosphate groupings on fatty acids are said, therefore, to be **miscible** with water. As we will see, this permits the formation of some interesting and highly important structures in living systems.

Lipid Function

Fat appears to be an indispensable nutrient for humans, although only a very little bit is needed to provide the minimum daily requirement. Fats of one kind or another are present almost everywhere, and so little is required that it is very difficult to produce a fat deficiency in experimental animals. It is hard to believe that a dearth of dietary fat would ever be a health problem for humans. As storage molecules, however, fats are unsurpassed.

Storage occurs when an animal ingests more food than is used during a given time period. Ingested foods are easily converted into lipid molecules, so

Figure 2.17 (*a*) A schematic diagram of a neutral fat. When only one or two fatty acids are linked to a glycerol molecule, the compound is called a glyceride. (*b*) A phospholipid. Note that there is a phosphate group linked to the glycerol molecule instead of a third fatty acid.

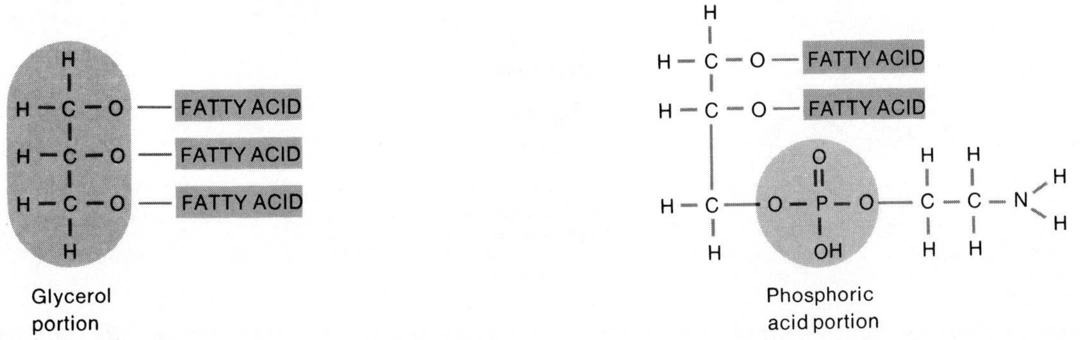

Glycerol portion

(a) A fat molecule (triglyceride)

Phosphoric acid portion

(b) A phospholipid molecule (cephalin)

when blood glucose is at its proper level and glycogen stores are bulging, fat is synthesized and deposited rapidly. It is the ideal storage molecule because per unit mass, fats contain more energy than any other organic molecule; more than twice as much as either protein or carbohydrate. Just imagine, if nature had chosen protein to store excess energy, overweight people could be twice as big as they are now . . . a sobering thought, particularly if you are overweight.

Energy storage is important, but it is not the only function of lipids. Unlike carbohydrates, lipids play vital roles in the body's structure. The membranes surrounding body cells are composed mainly of phospholipids. All of the sex hormones as well as hormones of the adrenal cortex belong to a group of compounds known as **steroids,** and steroids are made from the lipid called cholesterol. Cholesterol, which has perhaps the worst reputation of all the lipids as a dietary ingredient, is also an important structural component of body cells.

Proteins

The third class of physiologically important compounds is the **proteins,** and they constitute the major bulk of organic compounds in animals.

Like the others, proteins contain hydrogen, carbon, and oxygen, but unlike the others, they possess an indispensable fourth element, *nitrogen.* Nitrogen is not found in sugars or fats, but it is a fundamental fraction of proteins. Its presence is so consistent that it is a universal practice to determine the percentage of protein in meat products by measuring the amount of nitrogen present.

Figure 2.18 The same amino acid depicted two different ways. The *R* in the molecule may be a single atom or a complex molecule, depending on the amino acid. If the *R* is simply a hydrogen atom, the amino acid is alanine.

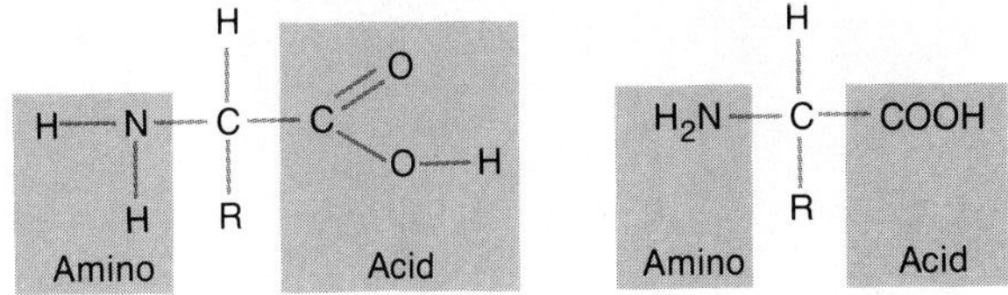

Proteins are easily the most variable of all the carbon compounds. Their sizes span an enormously broad range, and the complexity of their organization is staggering. Proteins are polymers of organic compounds called **amino acids** (figure 2.18) arranged in long, twisted, and branching chains. Amino acids are so called because they have two of the functional groups listed in table 2.3 from which the compound name is derived: the amine group (*amino*) and the carboxyl group (*acid*).

Organic chemists have so far identified nearly two hundred amino acids, but only twenty are ever found in proteins, each linked to its neighbor through the formation of a **peptide bond** produced through dehydration synthesis (figure 2.19).

The letter *R,* when used in organic chemical formulas, means literally any hydrocarbon *residue.* It has a function much like that of an algebraic *x,* meaning it represents a definite thing, but its precise value isn't known. When used as in figure 2.18, it could represent just a hydrogen atom, in which case the amino acid is *alanine,* or it could represent a very complex grouping of many carbon, hydrogen, and oxygen atoms (see figure 2.20).

Figure 2.19 Dehydration synthesis linking two amino acids into a dipeptide.

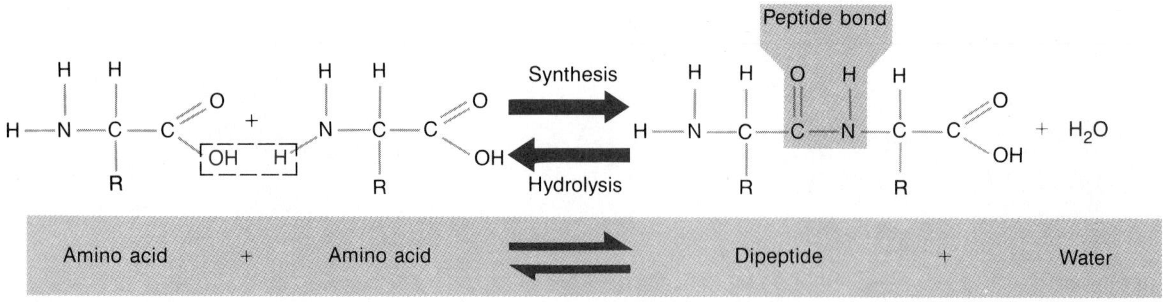

Peptide bond

Synthesis

Hydrolysis

Amino acid + Amino acid ⇌ Dipeptide + Water

$+ H_2O$

Figure 2.20 Some representative amino acids and their structural formulas. Each has a particular shape due to its parts. The portion common to all amino acids is in black. The portion represented by the letter *R* in the general formula is in color.

Amino acid	Structural formulas
Alanine	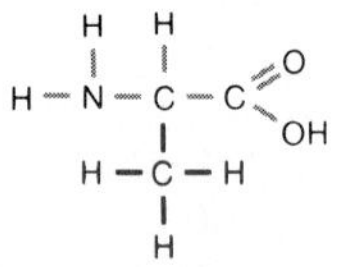
Valine	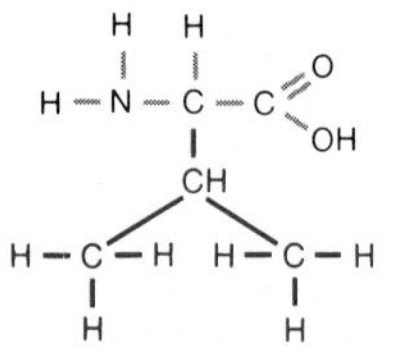
Cysteine	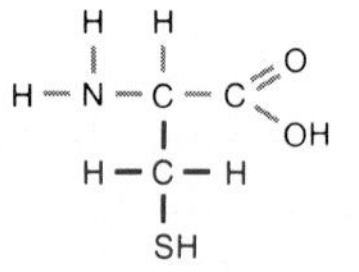
Phenylalanine	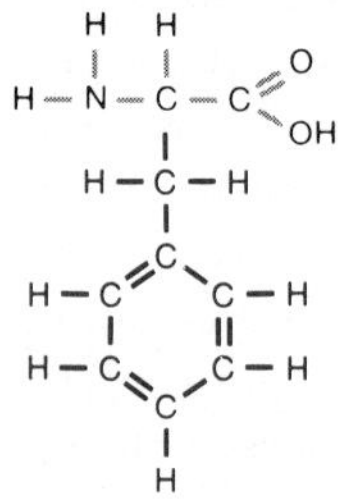
Tyrosine	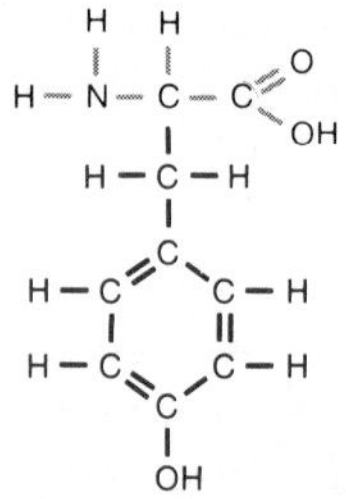
Histidine	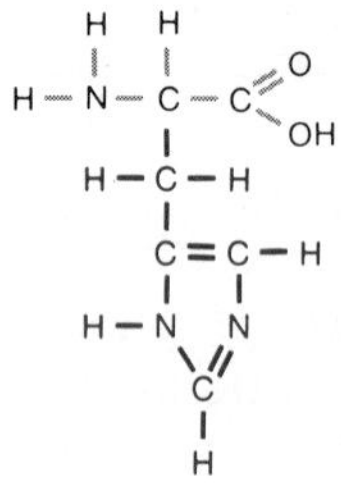

Figure 2.21 A chain of seven linked amino acids. Note that these are not seven *different* amino acids. Chains of hundreds of amino acids, linked in this manner, represent the primary structure of protein molecules.

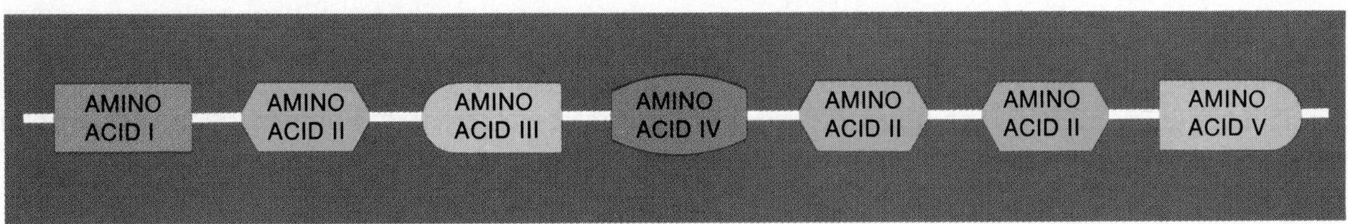

Figure 2.22 The four structural levels possessed by proteins. The secondary and tertiary structures determine the shape of the protein molecule, and the molecule's shape determines its function. Secondary and tertiary structures are easily disrupted. Quaternary structures consist of two or more protein chains linked together.

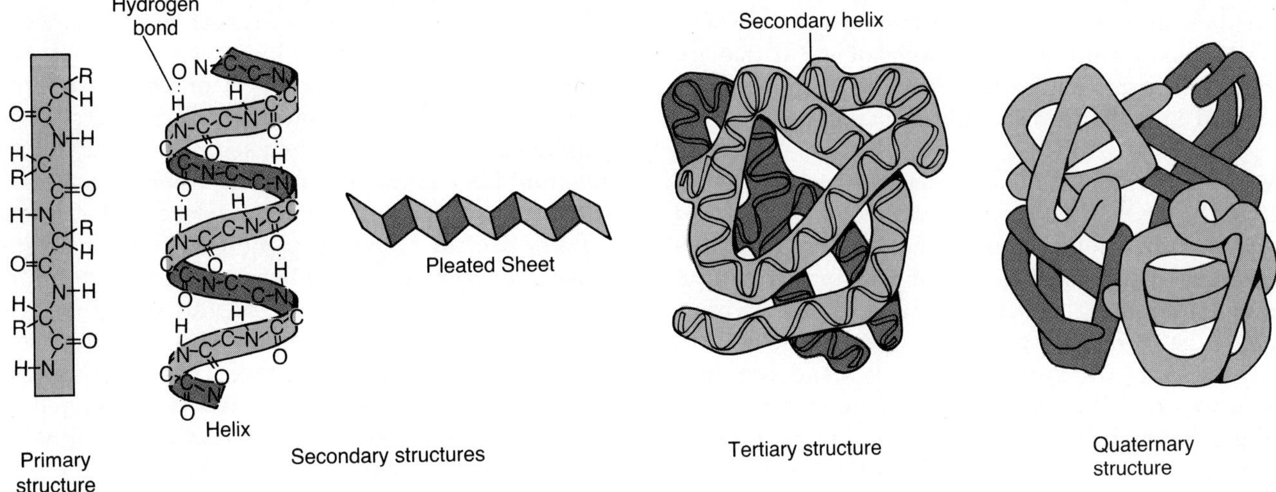

The utilization of only twenty amino acids may appear to restrict protein complexity, but if it does, it's the difference between the number of grains of sand in the world and the number of stars in the universe. None of us will ever be able to detect it. A protein may contain one or all of these twenty amino acids arranged in any order and present in any quantities or ratios. Even without considering any other type of variability, this gives proteins an almost limitless diversity (figure 2.21).

Primary Structure

In one respect, assembling a protein is much like assembling a word or a sentence from a collection of letters. There are twenty-six letters in our alphabet, and think of the variety of combinations we can make to create words, paragraphs, and books. With them we can render virtually every thought or dream ever experienced or contemplated. The twenty "letters" available to proteins may have similar plasticity. The sequence of amino acid succession in a given protein constitutes that protein's **primary structure** (figure 2.22).

Subordinate Structures

All by itself, the primary structure provides proteins with a variety that we would have to consider endless. Yet there are three other structural variations that are common in proteins, and they serve as determinants of how a protein will function in a living body. Chains of carefully arranged amino acids don't just wave around in the body fluids like fishing lines in a trout stream. Each protein has a definite three-dimensional architecture, and this **topography,** as it is called, is very carefully shaped, artfully arranged, and functionally critical.

Secondary Structure The **secondary structure** is more restricted than the primary, since it has only two variations. Sometimes it consists of a twisted or folded configuration known as the **pleated sheet.** In this arrangement, two side-by-side chains of amino acids link together in such a way as to resemble a narrow, folded sheet (figure. 2.22). Other times a chain of amino acids is twisted into a corkscrew-like pattern called a **helix** (plural *helices*). Sometimes these helices exist alone, sometimes one is linked to a second, similarly twisted chain to form what is known as a double helix, and occasionally a third chain is added, thus forming a triple helix. Both the sheets and the double and triple corkscrews are held in position against each other by **dipolar bonds**—bonds that are not covalent but electromagnetic, very like those that hold atoms and ionic molecules together, but much weaker. These bonds usually form between atoms of sulfur that are present in certain amino acids, and the bonds are then referred to as **disulfide bonds** (see table 2.3).

Tertiary Structure The tertiary structure forms when the double helix or pleated sheet is twisted into a three-dimensional figure. These often look like tinkertoys that have been assembled into structural snarls resembling a ball of churning earthworms (figure 2.22). Such tangles may appear senseless, but they are not. The complicated twists and convolutions are carefully blueprinted and are critical to the proper function of the protein. They are maintained primarily by relatively weak dipolar forces interspersed with an occasional covalent bond.

Quaternary Structure The variability of proteins does not end with the tertiary structure. Often two or more chains of similar proteins, each with its own primary, secondary, and tertiary framework, are locked into a pliable relationship with one another. Once linked together, they form still another three-dimensional structural pattern in space, a quaternary structure, where familiar shapes are about as easily discernible as they are in a cluster of fighting cats (figure 2.22).

The Delicate Protein

When we combine letters to make words, we need only be concerned with the sequence of the letters. But in the combination of amino acids in a protein, the three-dimensional patterns they form are also essential to proper function. The curling corkscrew shape twisting back and forth across itself and the linkages to other folded corkscrews are as much a part of a protein's message as the sequence of the amino acid "letters." These observations lead to two disquieting conclusions. First, whatever can disrupt any of these shapes can impair or destroy the protein's function; second, such complicated messages must be relatively easy to addle, since every curl and switchback is crucial. The fragility of proteins is further emphasized by the observation that much of the three-dimensional geometry is held in place by dipolar forces, which are on the flimsy side and break pretty easily.

Such misgivings are well-founded. Proteins are among the most easily damaged compounds in living systems. The peptide bonds are tough, and splitting them requires considerable energy, so the primary structure is seldom disrupted. But the amino acid sequence does not have to be altered to render the protein useless. If the chains or sheets don't wrap around each other the way they are supposed to, if the tangled shapes aren't exactly right, nothing works. Small changes in temperature or hydrogen ion concentration—things that have no effect on covalent bonds and so do not damage carbohydrates or fats—will rupture dipolar bonds. When secondary and tertiary relationhips change, the protein becomes useless to the organism, except maybe as a source of raw materials. Useless or not, the protein, as such, is still intact. The topographical alterations that have ruined its function seldom affect the peptide linkages of the primary structure. All the amino acids are still present and are still in the same sequence. That being the case, it is hard to consider the protein as having been chemically destroyed. Nevertheless, a name must be given to such proteins to indicate that their biological value and their chemical *nature* have been ruined; hence such proteins are said to have been **denatured.**

Most people have denatured a good many proteins. For instance, when an egg is fried, consider what happens to the egg white. The white of an egg, when uncooked, is nearly transparent, definitely liquid, and has a slippery, mucoid consistency. But apply only a little heat, and almost immediately this translucent material will change into an opaque white mass, totally unlike its raw state. By contrast, the yolk, which has been exposed to the same temperatures, will remain soft and runny, just as it was in its raw state. Why? Because the solid material in egg white is pure protein, hence is easily damaged, while the yolk contains a high percentage of less vulnerable fats.

Proteins, clearly, are the sensitive chemicals in biological systems. Sometimes, if an alteration in the protein's environment is not very drastic or if it only lasts for a short time, the protein may denature only slightly. Then when the disturbing influence is removed, if the amino acid "words" are still in the right place, they can reach across to each other and replace temporarily dislocated bonds, returning the protein to its original state. This suggests that the amino acid sequence determines the secondary, tertiary, and quaternary arrangement, and the secondary, tertiary, and quaternary contours determine what the protein will do and how it will operate in the human body.

Personal Proteins

Some proteins are common to everyone—hemoglobin, for instance, is the same in all humans—but most proteins are peculiar to an individual. Everybody has his or her own personal set of proteins. People share carbohydrate and lipid types, and mineral content in humans is pretty much the same from person to person, but most of the proteins are unique to an individual. In fact, this is what makes transplantation of body organs or tissues so difficult. Unless the donor is an identical twin, the recipient's immune systems—which are conditioned to detect anything that does not belong to the recipient—will spot immediately that the proteins in the donated tissue are not theirs, and they will attack and destroy them. And as it turns out, the antibodies often used to destroy foreign proteins are themselves proteins.

Protein Function

Proteins have a tremendous variety of uses in biological systems. As energy sources, they are excellent. They are easily converted to glucose (a process called **gluconeogenesis**) and can be oxidized immediately or converted to fats and stored. But the use of proteins for energy is rare unless a person is half-starved, because it is an extravagance—like burning antique furniture to keep the house warm.

Proteins have critical structurai roles. They line every channel in cell membranes and function as receptor areas on the outside of these membranes. When large, water-soluble molecules can't get into a cell, they can leave a message with these protein receptors telling mechanisms inside the cell what to do. Proteins move materials back and forth inside the cell, and they are mainly responsible for preventing the cell from collapsing in on itself like a punctured balloon. They provide muscle with its contractile ability. As part of our chromosomal material, they are involved somehow in cellular management and in the passing of hereditary information through generations.

Enzymes

Possibly the most important function of protein is that of a catalytic agent. Protein catalysts make *all* biological reactions possible—not just synthetic reactions, but those that break things up as well. Such catalysts are known as **enzymes,** and every enzyme is a protein. There are literally millions of them, and each one is specifically designed to catalyze a single reaction or type of reaction. The process of building a large molecule from smaller ones may seem relatively simple, but it is not like putting a building together with mortar and bricks—it is much more complicated. Aspirin, for instance, is a simple molecule, yet its assembly requires fifteen steps and results in the formation of more than thirty intermediate compounds. Think, then, of the number of steps required to build a muscle protein that is one thousand times the size of an aspirin molecule, and remember that each step must be catalyzed or it won't occur. We must also consider the fact that the raw materials used in such a construction project are brought into the body as food, and food mostly consists of complex polymers formed by other organisms. Few of these can be used as they are; they must be broken down to their monomers. Destructive reactions, like constructive ones, must be catalyzed, and all the catalysts are specialized proteins.

Nucleic Acids

We have now examined three of the organic chemical groups in living systems. What more *can* there be? They are all impressive—in some cases, downright overwhelming. Yet even with carbohydrates, lipids, and proteins all present in the correct amounts, and with the inorganic elements dispersed throughout our internal water matrix, we still have not seen anything to unite them all. There is nothing that we could consider an administration center—no activity hub to shepherd this scattered array of elements, compounds, and dispersions into a harmonious, cooperating team. The chemicals we have discussed give us the potential of utilizing fuels, the potential of having an organized structure, and the potential of catalyzing biosynthetic or catabolic reactions, but we have identified nothing that is able to orchestrate all these potentials into a functioning essence. Nothing we have seen so far can supervise and make them all work. That is the job of the **nucleic acids.**

Like the proteins, nucleic acids are made up of repeating units, and the sequence of these units in the nucleic acid chain is actually a code. This code provides instructions for the daily operations of the organism it governs. In addition, it represents the genetic blueprint that passes information from one generation to the next. Each repeating unit is an individual nucleotide and is composed of three dissimilar subunits, each of which belongs to a different organic group. One of these is a **phosphate group** (see table 2.3), which is an inorganic acid (phosphoric) when it is on its own; the second is a carbohydrate, and the third is a **nitrogen-containing organic base** that is organized into a single- or double-ring structure.

Figure 2.23 The biological "battery molecule" ATP. The sigmoid lines between the outermost phosphates represent high-energy bonds, and it is in these bonds that the molecule's energy is stored.

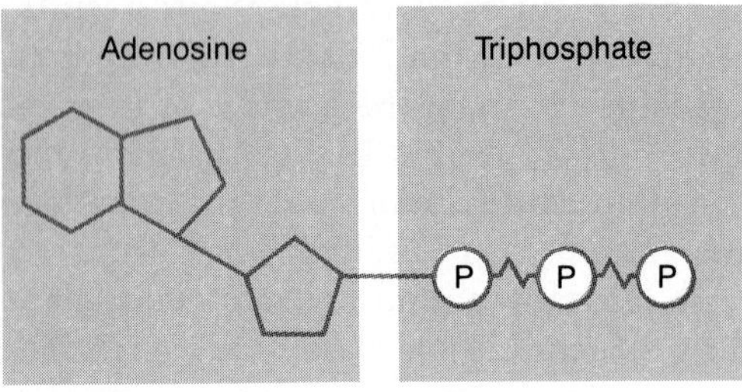

Figure 2.24 The pentose sugars found in nucleic acids. Ribose is the sugar found in RNA, while deoxyribose is the carbohydrate in DNA. The difference between the two molecules is highlighted. As you can see, only a single oxygen atom is involved.

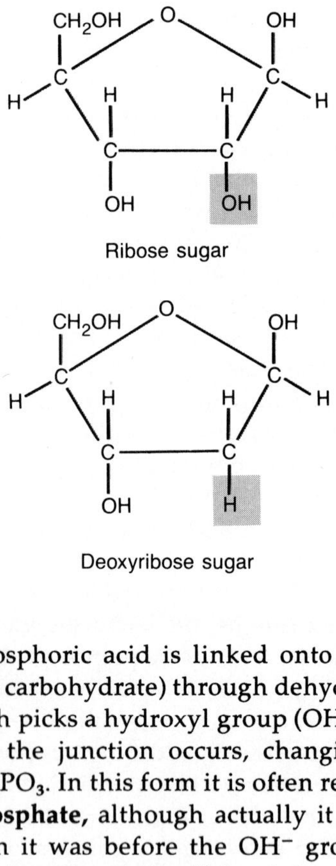

Ribose sugar

Deoxyribose sugar

The phosphoric acid is linked onto the second subunit (the carbohydrate) through dehydration synthesis, which picks a hydroxyl group (OH^-) from the acid before the junction occurs, changing it from H_3PO_4 to H_2PO_3. In this form it is often referred to as **organic phosphate,** although actually it is no more organic than it was before the OH^- group was removed. For the sake of simplicity, it is customary to utilize the symbol **P** to represent the 'organic' phosphate or **~P** to indicate what is called a **high-energy phosphate** (figure 2.23).

The carbohydrate involved in nucleic acid chains is a **pentose sugar** and it is, in fact, the sugar that determines the compound name. If the sugar is ribose, the nucleic acid is **ribonucleic acid (RNA);** if the sugar is deoxyribose, it is **deoxyribonucleic acid (DNA)** (see figure 2.24).

Figure 2.25 The nitrogen-containing nucleotide bases. All nucleotide bases contain nitrogen, and all are ring structures. Purines and pyrimidines differ in the *number* of rings they contain.

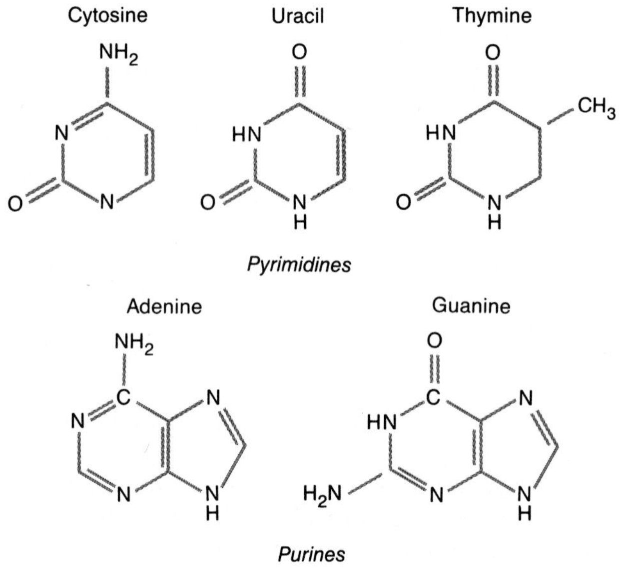

Cytosine Uracil Thymine

Pyrimidines

Adenine Guanine

Purines

Because the remaining subunit of nucleic acids forms a ring structure, it is known as a **heterocyclic compound** (*hetero* because not all of the inner ring elements are carbon atoms, and *cyclic* because of the circular ring). It is an organic compound, and it does contain nitrogen, but it is *not* a protein residue. For one thing, only a small quantity of the nitrogen is in the form of amines, and furthermore, there is no carboxyl group (remember?) so characteristic of amino acids. Anyhow, they are not acids but are instead considered bases, because if they are dissolved in pure water, the acid/alkaline nature of the resulting solution is in the alkaline range. There are several types of heterocyclic compounds, but all of the nucleotide bases are derivatives of just two—either **pyrimidines** or **purines.** Pyrimidines have only a single ring, while the purines are made of two rings, one of which is a pyrimidine hooked to a second, different type of ring (figure 2.25).

Actually, the pentose sugar is not the only place where we see a difference between RNA and DNA. There's a difference in the bases, too. **Adenine** and **guanine,** the purine bases, are the same in both types, but the pyrimidines are not. If the compound is RNA, the two pyrimidines are **cytosine** and **uracil,** whereas in DNA, **thymine** replaces the uracil (see figure 2.25).

These three groups of compounds—the nucleotide bases, the pentose sugars, and the phosphate groups—link together in a 1:1:1 ratio to form the molecules of nucleic acid. As we have noted, the phosphates are hooked onto the ribose sugars via dehydration synthesis (figure 2.26), and the two groups

Figure 2.26 (*a*) The phosphorylation of ribose is, like so many organic synthetic reactions, a process of dehydration. The atoms that make up the water molecule created in the process are highlighted. (*b*) Phosphorylate ribose linked to (*left*) a pyrimidine and (*right*) a purine.

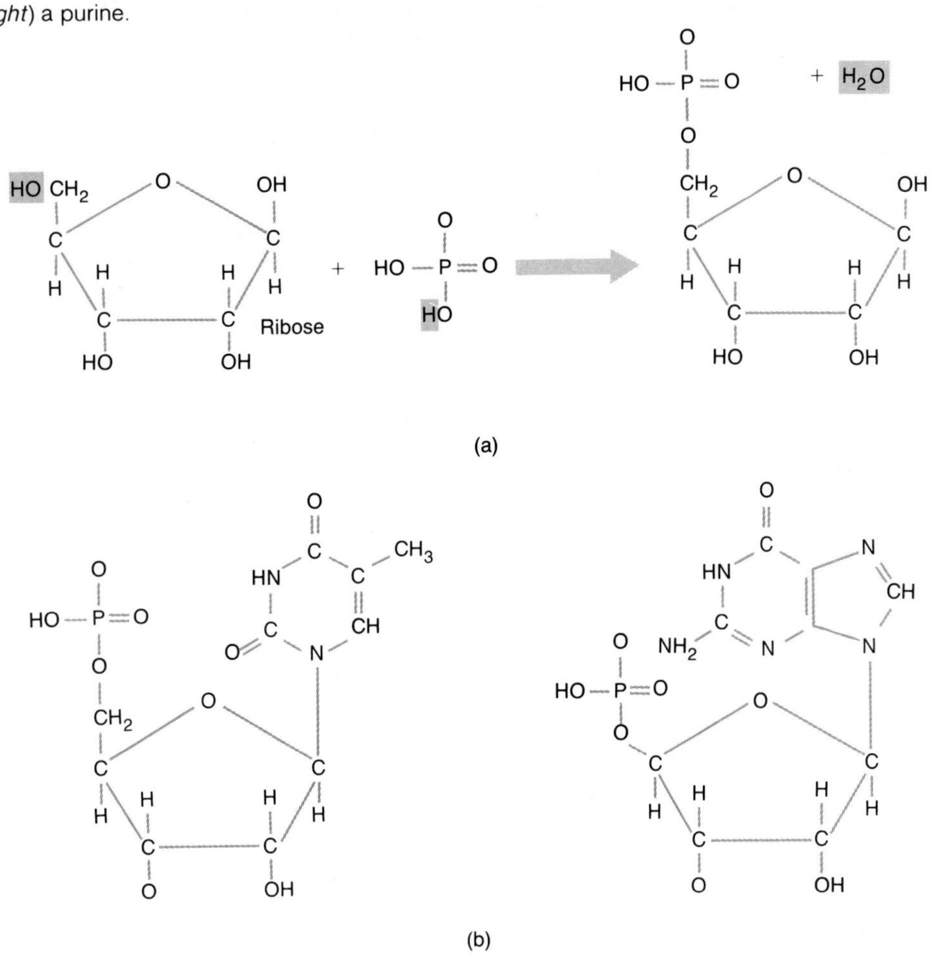

(a)

(b)

form the backbone of the nucleic acid chain (figure 2.27). The bases—both single- and double-ringed—hook onto the opposite end of the molecule and serve as the link between the two chains that make up the DNA molecule in living systems.

A Double Helix

Early research into the chemistry of the nucleic acids was fraught with frustration as workers concocted structures of every conceivable shape in the hope of fulfilling the chemical and physical requirements that they knew nucleic acids would have to possess. For years all efforts failed. The constituents of the nucleotides were fairly well worked out, but the shape and arrangement of the molecules was a real mystery. The problem arose from one simple fact: Reams of research had made it clear that whatever information was on the nuclear DNA could be passed from one generation to the next. Obviously, the nucleic acids could duplicate the information that they contained; hence whatever topography was suggested would have to explain how this was possible. The breakthrough came when it was noted that two strands of

Figure 2.27 Schematic of a nucleic acid strip. The nucleic acid is a polymer of units, each unit made up of a base, a five-carbon sugar, and a phosphate group. There are four such units in the diagram.

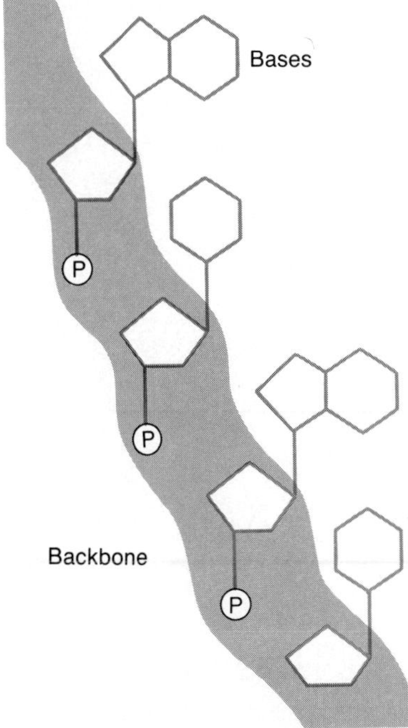

Figure 2.28 The uneven, bulging DNA strand that would form if the nucleotide bases were to pair up with one another in a random fashion. The fact that the helices are always the same distance apart means that purines always link to pyrimidines.

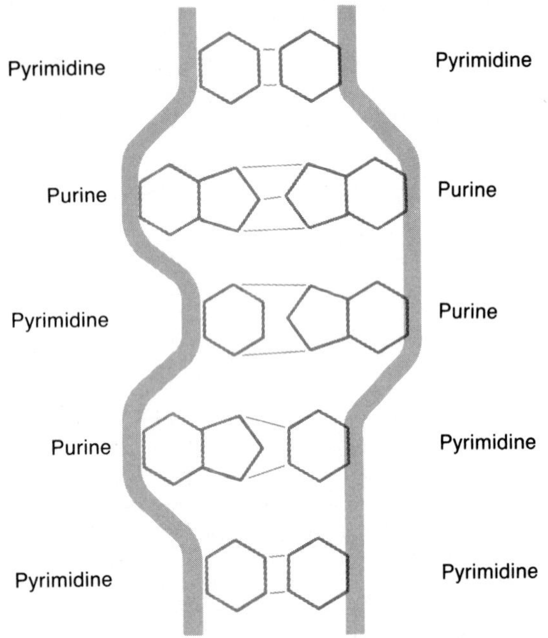

DNA faced each other, linking together, and that the distance between the two strands was always the same. That almost demanded that pyrimidines link to purines, for if that were not the case—if, for example, purines could link to purines and pyrimidines to pyrimidines—there would be bulges and dips in the helices (figure 2.28). Further investigation of the chemical nature of the purines and pyrimidines that were present in DNA suggested an even more specific relationship. When the two strands are linked together, facing each other, they are held in place by a type of electromagnetic bond called a **hydrogen bond,** so called because it always involves a hydrogen atom. As it turns out, guanine and cytosine can form three such bonds, while thymine and adenine can form only two each. That means that adenine must always link to thymine, while guanine and cytosine must pair with each other (figure 2.29). If the arrangement of bases represented a code that our physiological mechanisms could interpret, it was suddenly obvious how information could pass from one generation to the next.

The presence of hydrogen bonds to hold the two strands of nucleic acid together helped explain some other abilities of DNA. Individual hydrogen bonds

Figure 2.29 A link in the deoxyribonucleic acid chain. The nucleotide bases may form two or three sets of hydrogen bonds, and the number determines which bases will link to each other. The links are always purine to pyrimidine, and since adenine and thymine each are able to form two hydrogen bonds, they always link to each other. Similarly, cytosine and quanine, both able to form three hydrogen bonds, are always paired together. A hydrogen bond is a weak type of electromagnetic attractive force that always involves a hydrogen atom.

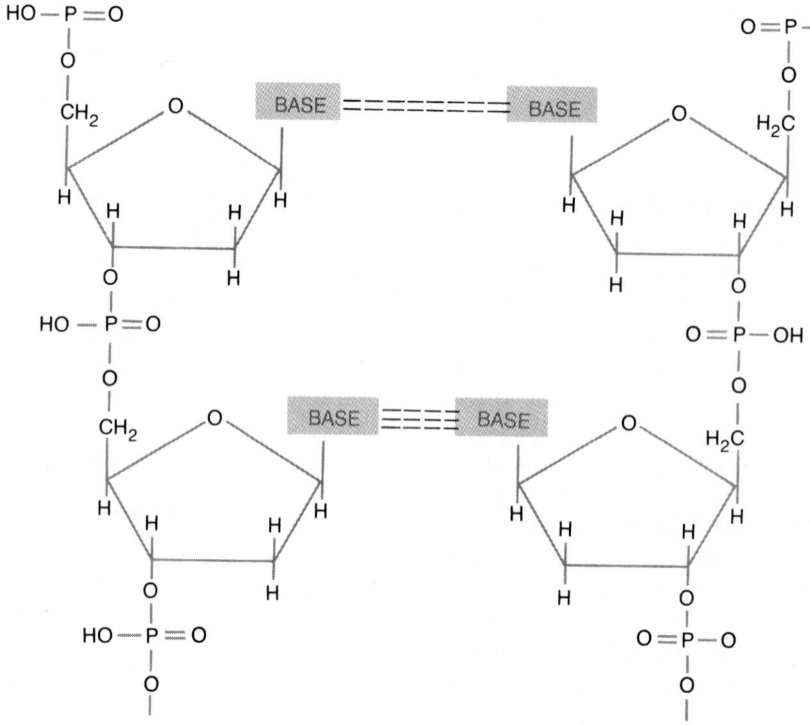

are very weak—thus the DNA strands could smoothly unzip when cells divided—yet collectively they are strong enough to maintain the DNA molecule in a firm, predetermined shape up to the moment when that splitting takes place.

Nucleic Acid Function

As is obvious from this discussion, one of the primary functions of nucleic acids is to pass genetic information from one generation to the next. All of the information that is necessary to produce a living, breathing human being is on our DNA. Hence, if we pass that along to the next generation, we will be able to produce more living human beings. The rather specialized means of transmitting such information is discussed in detail in chapter 18.

Transmitting genetic information is, however, only one of the things the nucleic acids do. As I mentioned earlier, something is necessary to organize all the complex organic molecules into an arrangement that makes sense and permits a type of chemical cooperation that results, somehow, in something alive. Orchestrating all these molecules is the job of the DNA. We will see how it performs this job in the next chapter.

Summary

Atoms: The Indivisible Units

I. Matter consists of "indivisible" particles called atoms.
II. Atoms consist of:
  Protons: particles with a positive charge of +1
  Electrons: particles with a charge of −1
  Neutrons: particles with no charge
III. Protons and neutrons are the same size. Electrons are much smaller.
IV. A Tiny Solar System. Atoms are like small planetary systems. Protons and neutrons form the central mass (a solar center). Electrons circle the central mass (as do planets).

Categories of Matter

I. Elements. Are composed of atoms that all have the same number of protons.
II. Chemical Symbols.
  A. Each element has its own chemical symbol.
  B. Each element has combinations of properties that make it unique.

Properties of Matter

I. Physical Properties. Color, texture, freezing and boiling points, etc. Each element is able to assume three different physical states:
  A. Gas phase—the high-energy phase
  B. Liquid phase
  C. Solid phase—the low-energy phase
II. Chemical Properties. These deal with combining abilities—how easily will one interact with another? This involves electrons—their number and atomic arrangement determines chemical properties.
  A. Electron Orbits. Electrons form "clouds" around the atomic nucleus. Statistically, each electron cloud occupies a zone a specific distance from the nucleus. Each such zone (called a *shell*) has room for a specific number of electrons. It will take fewer, but never more than, that specific number. The outermost zone is known as the valence shell. The valence shell determines the element's chemical properties.
  B. The Stable Octet. An element is stable when it refuses to react with other elements or compounds. Stability is greatest when there are eight electrons in the valence shell.
III. Ions—the Charged Particles. Charged particles (ions) form when elements strive to achieve a stable octet. Ions can be either positive or negative, and since unlike charges attract, such ions can be attracted to each other, forming linkages called ionic bonds.
  A. Sodium
  B. Chlorine

Compounds

A compound is one or more elements linked together by means of chemical bonds.

I. Compounds have characteristics totally different from their component elements.
II. Compounds release energy when they form. They require energy in order to be broken apart.
III. Compounds consist of units called molecules. Molecules are not indivisible, but if they are broken apart, the characteristics of the compound disappear.

Chemical Bonds

I. Ionic Bonding. Ionic bonds are the result of positive and negative ions attracting each other.
  A. Ionic bonds are the strongest of the chemical bonds.
  B. Ionic bonds normally form between metallic and nonmetallic ions.
  C. Every positive charge must be matched by a negative charge. One atom of an element with two positive charges requires two atoms of an element with one negative charge to make a stable compound.
II. Covalent Bonding. Covalent bonds are produced as a result of electron sharing by two or more elements.
  A. They are not as strong as ionic bonds, but are nevertheless quite powerful.
  B. Covalent bonds are not formed between ions.
  C. Covalent bonds can be formed between atoms of the same element.
  D. Covalent bonds are the only bonds ever formed by carbon atoms.
  E. Covalent bonds are central to organic chemistry.

Organic Chemistry

I. Carbon. Carbon is the fundamental element of all organic compounds.

II. Carbon Chemistry. Carbon chemistry *is* organic chemistry. Organic compounds must contain carbon and hydrogen linked together.

III. Identifying Organic Compounds

- A. Organic chemistry uses structural, not molecular, formulas to describe its compounds.
- B. Carbon compounds number in the millions.
- C. Organic compounds are much more complex than inorganic compounds.
- D. Organic compounds often contain dozens—sometimes hundreds—of atoms.
- E. There are usually only a few elements in organic compounds.

IV. Organic Functional Groups. Elements making up organic compounds often form simple yet consistent molecular structures. These common, small structures are known as functional groups. Functional groups can confer specific characteristics on any larger organic molecules they may be a part of.

The Major Biological Compounds

Organic compounds fall into categories partly because of the chemical characteristics of their functional groups. Most organic compounds fall into one of four major groups: carbohydrates, lipids, proteins, and nucleic acids.

I. Carbohydrates. Small carbohydrates contain carbon, hydrogen, and oxygen in a 1:2:1 ratio. Nearly all small carbohydrates are sugars, and there are hundreds of them.

- A. Monosaccharides. Single-molecule sugars are called monosaccharides. There is a water molecule for each carbon in a monosaccharide. Most monosaccharides are sweet, white crystals.
- B. Disaccharides. Two monosaccharides can be linked together to form a disaccharide.
- C. Polysaccharides. Many monosaccharides can be linked together to form still larger compounds. Such compounds are known as polysaccharides.
  1. The most abundant organic compound on earth is the polysaccharide cellulose.
  2. The second most abundant is the polysaccharide starch.
  3. Starch is digestible, cellulose is not.
- D. Biological Synthesis. Monosaccharides are linked together to form larger saccharides by a process called dehydration synthesis.
- E. Carbohydrate Function. Carbohydrates are mainly used as fuel by animals, including humans.

II. Lipids. Lipids are mainly carbon and hydrogen. There is also a little oxygen. Neutral fats consist of a glycerol molecule linked to three fatty acids. Fatty acids may be saturated or unsaturated. Generally speaking, they are insoluble in water.

- A. Phospholipids. Phospholipids form when fats contain a charged phosphate group. They are partially soluble in water, partially soluble in fats.
- B. Lipid Function. Lipids serve as structural materials, nutrients, and energy-storage molecules. One group of lipids, known as steroids, serve as message-carrying hormones.

III. Proteins. Proteins contain hydrogen, carbon, oxygen, and nitrogen. They are formed of many smaller compounds called amino acids. Only twenty amino acids are ever found in proteins.

- A. Primary Structure. The amino acids in proteins are arranged in a specific sequence. The amino acid sequence in proteins is known as its primary structure.
- B. Subordinate Structures
  1. Secondary Structure. The secondary structure forms when the chains of amino acids are twisted into corkscrews called helices or laid out side-by-side into pleated sheets. Much of the secondary structure is maintained by a weak chemical bond known as a disulfide bond. The secondary structure of proteins is often further twisted into a spatial arrangement known as a tertiary structure.
  2. Tertiary Structure. The tertiary structure forms a specific three-dimensional shape that is critical to the protein's function in living systems. Like the secondary structure, its configuration is maintained by relatively weak bonds.
  3. Quaternary Structure. Sometimes two proteins, each with a primary, secondary, and tertiary structure, will link together to form a quaternary structure. Quaternary structures are held together mainly by weak bonds.
- C. The Delicate Protein. The quaternary, tertiary, and secondary structures of proteins can easily be disrupted. The disruption process is called denaturing the protein. The primary structure of the protein determines the subordinate structures. The subordinate structures determine how the protein will function.
- D. Personal Proteins. Everyone's proteins are unique. No one else has a set of proteins identical to yours.
- E. Protein Function. Proteins can serve as energy sources in living systems. Proteins also have a structural function.
- F. Enzymes. Enzymes are catalytic agents, meaning they change the rate of biological reactions. All enzymes are proteins.

IV. Nucleic Acids. Nucleic acids contain carbon, hydrogen, oxygen, and a "nonprotein" type of nitrogen. Nucleic acids are formed of repeating groups of organic compounds.

- A. Each individual group is known as a nucleotide.

B. Each nucleotide consists of three different types of organic compounds—a phosphate group, a five-carbon sugar, and a nitrogen-containing base.
C. The sugar may be ribose or a deoxygenated form of ribose called deoxyribose.
D. The sugar and phosphate are hooked together, forming the "backbone" of the nucleic acid.
E. One base is hooked to each ribose molecule and projects into space away from the molecule's backbone.
F. A Double Helix. The repeating groups that form the molecular backbone of DNA hook together to form long, twisted chains. Each nucleic acid chain is able to link to its "complementary image" by means of weak chemical bonds known as hydrogen bonds. Hydrogen bonds form between nucleotide bases on different nucleic acid chains. The hydrogen bonds always form between two specific bases. Each base is able to link to only one complementary base. By linking only to a specific complementary base, the long chains of nucleic acid can form perfect complementary images of themselves and thus are able to build personal replicas.
G. Nucleic Acid Function. Nucleic acids transmit genetic information from one generation to the next. They also manage all day-to-day activities of the body, including unforeseen emergencies. They are the cellular organizers.

Review Questions

1. What is matter? How does it relate to the science of chemistry?
2. Why was the elaboration of the atomic theory so important to all the physical sciences?
3. Name and describe the three subatomic particles and their arrangement in a typical atom.
4. What are the three categories of matter?
5. Define an element. How many are found in living systems?
6. Name some physical properties of an element.
7. Identify and describe the three phases matter can assume.
8. What are the chemical properties of an element? What subatomic particles determine these properties?
9. What is an isotope?
10. Describe the orbital arrangement of electrons in an atom. Which of the orbitals is most important to a chemist?
11. Discuss the stable octet and the formation of ions.
12. How does the formation of ions contribute to the formation of compounds?
13. How would you describe the valence of a given element?
14. What are covalent bonds and under what circumstances do they develop?
15. What are some characteristics of the element carbon that make it so important to the chemist?
16. Discuss the formation of organic compounds and the significance of structural formulas.
17. Name the major functional groups of organic chemistry. Be sure to mention:
    a. their chemical characteristics.
    b. their structure.
    c. in which organic compounds each is usually found.
18. What are the four major categories of organic compounds?
19. Of what elements are carbohydrates formed?
20. Describe each of the following in as much detail as you can:
    a. monosaccharides
    b. disaccharides
    c. polysaccharides
21. What are the main functions of carbohydrates in human beings?
22. Describe the process of dehydration synthesis.
23. Of what elements are lipids composed?
24. Of what are neutral fats formed?
25. How does a saturated fat differ from an unsaturated fat?
26. What is a phospholipid and what is its significance in biological systems?
27. What are the main functions of lipids in human beings?
28. What is the diagnostic element found in proteins that clearly distinguishes it from carbohydrates and lipids?
29. Name the building blocks of which proteins are formed and draw a typical one. Be sure to indicate the important functional groups that are present and be able to name them.
30. Describe the primary, secondary, tertiary, and quaternary structure of proteins. Which ones are most easily disrupted?
31. What are the primary functions of proteins in human beings?
32. What are the three basic units of nucleic acids? Be sure you know the structure of each.
33. How many major types of nucleic acids are there? How do they differ from each other?
34. Discuss the importance of the nucleotide bases in the formation of the double helices of which DNA is made.
35. What are the functions of the nucleic acids in humans?

Chapter 3 Water Systems and Molecular Movement

Study Hints

This chapter deals with some fundamental physical and chemical facts, knowledge of which is essential for proper understanding of the workings of biological engines. While reading:

1. Pay particular attention to the characteristics of water that enable it to disperse and control heat. Humans can function wonderfully in high temperatures as long as water is available.
2. Note that whenever a molecule possesses a charge anywhere on its surface, it is miscible with water, even if the majority of the molecule is nonpolar.
3. Note that all of the methods of determining the acidity or alkalinity of biological systems are predicated on the solutions involved being aqueous.
4. Remember that pH is a representation of a *negative* number; hence when hydrogen ion concentrations go up, pH goes down.
5. Read the section on buffers carefully.
6. Be sure you understand where the energy comes from to drive both diffusion and osmosis.
7. Pay particular attention to the fact that it is particle number and not particle size that plays the more important role in osmosis.
8. Active transport uses tremendous amounts of energy in living systems and is as important as any single operation in maintaining life. Be sure you understand it completely.

Objectives

When you have finished reading this chapter, you should:

1. be able to describe the characteristics of water that make it so important as a matrix for living systems.
2. know the difference between mass number, atomic number, and gram atomic weight.
3. be able to work out the gram molecular weight of a given compound.
4. understand the meaning of the word *mole* and be able to define it precisely.
5. know two ways to define an acid and be able to distinguish it from a base.
6. be able to define a strong acid as opposed to a weak acid.
7. know the function of a buffer.
8. know the difference between diffusion and osmosis and be able to describe both.
9. be able to describe facilitated diffusion and active transport and explain the differences between the two processes.
10. know where the energy comes from that drives active transport, diffusion, facilitated diffusion, filtration, and osmosis.

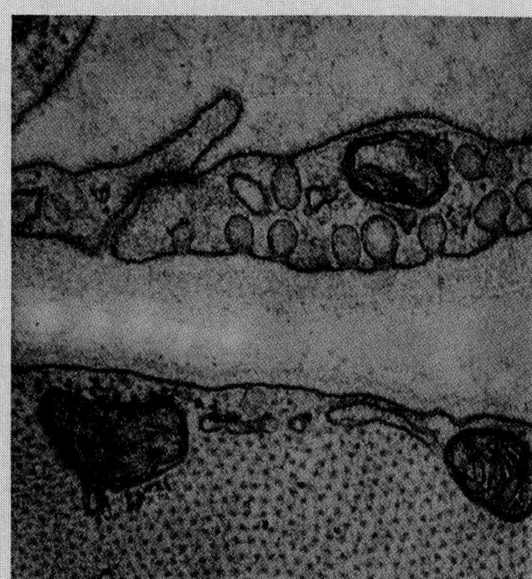

Micyopinocytosis vesicles in capillary wall.

Introduction

One of the reasons that our bodies can attain homeostasis is the presence of that universal solvent and cradle of life, water. Water is more than just the most abundant compound in living systems. Its characteristics make it chemically and physically fascinating and definitely unique. Because of water's distinctive and essential properties, George Wald, one of the greatest scientific educators of this century, has stated:

> Indeed, I am convinced that there can be no way of composing and constructing living organisms which is fundamentally different from the one we know.

This means that if we ever reach other worlds in our galaxy where life exists, he thinks we will find that life there is essentially like life here, which is to say carbon-based and cultivated in water.

What is it about this tiny molecule that makes it so remarkable? Why is it so critical? What are the characteristics that are so important?

The chemical formula is simple enough—H_2O. This means in chemical shorthand that the molecule consists of two atoms of hydrogen and one of oxygen. Small and simple! Yet within that molecule is a panorama of remarkable properties upon which all living organisms on this earth depend. Life originated in water, it developed in water, and is linked inexorably to water. We tend to forget this, sometimes . . . after all, we walk on land, take oxygen directly from the atmosphere, and no longer lay eggs in water. We go for a swim once in a while, but we don't have to, and we certainly can't spend much time submerged. Yet despite all this, are we honestly free of water?

Definitely not. The dependence of all living things on water is universal and ubiquitous. We carry our oceans around inside of us, and these oceans are carefully supervised. The various salts and chemicals dispersed in them are present in precise concentrations, movement is controlled, volume is monitored—everything is maintained by special homeostatic mechanisms designed to resist change. Nearly all physiological reactions occur in aqueous solutions, and many of the properties of living matter are actually the physical characteristics of water. Before oxygen is picked up by the blood, it must first dissolve in water. To fertilize a human egg cell, the sperm must swim to it through water. It seems reasonable, then, to assume that if we can gain an understanding of water, we will have gained some important fundamental insights into the chemistry of life.

The Chemistry of Water

Water is composed of hydrogen and oxygen, both nonmetallic elements. Hence valence electrons are shared, each hydrogen atom sharing its lone electron with oxygen, which in turn shares one of its two valence electrons with each hydrogen. The bonds that hold the compound together are thus *covalent.*

Since the atoms that form water are dissimilar, the bonds between them are slightly distorted. The valence electrons are shared, of course, but the eight positive charges of the oxygen nucleus have a powerful attraction for the others. (The unshared ones are called **lone pairs,** and they take up a position as far away from the bonding pairs as possible.) This results in pear-shaped electron clouds and produces a **zone of negativity** on the oxygen side of the molecule and a **zone of positivity** between the two hydrogen nuclei, so that when the molecule is viewed as a whole, one end has a positive charge and the other a negative one (figure 3.1). Therefore, despite the fact that the bonds that hold it together are nonionic, the water molecule has two oppositely charged poles and is therefore considered a **polar molecule.**

Figure 3.1 The distribution of subatomic particles is such that the water molecule actually has a positive and a negative zone, and they are at opposite ends of the molecule. Thus, despite being held together by covalent bonds, the water molecule is polarized.

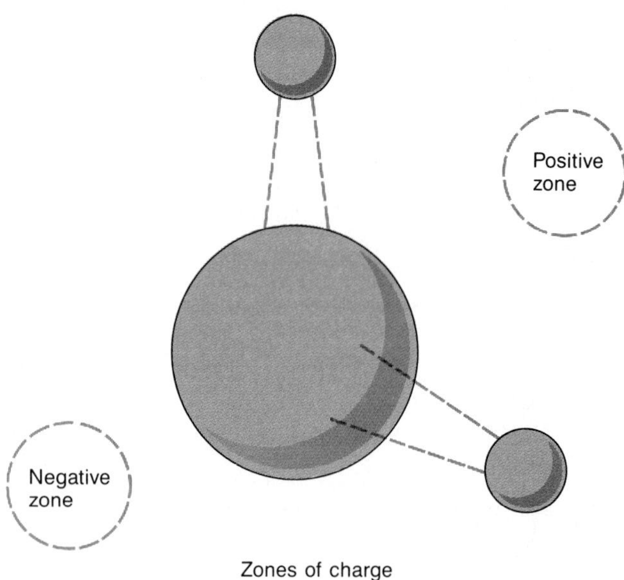

Hydrogen Bonds

Molecules in the gaseous state tend to be pretty widely spaced. As we have seen, their energy content is high enough to keep them moving past each other so fast that there is no time for one molecule to attract another. Even if they collide, their velocity is such that they bounce apart rather than stick together. As long as their energy content is high, they will remain in the gaseous state. Remove enough energy, however, cool them down, and their velocity decreases to the point where it is not enough to overcome the attractive forces between them, and the rapid, independent zooming around is abruptly arrested. Throughout the whole mass they begin to line up against one another, and electromagnetic forces take hold. These electromagnetic forces are *hydrogen bonds,* and they are powerful enough to hold together the entire liquid mass of the world's oceans. The water molecules still pull on the bonds, each trying to move independently, and in liquid water the bonds are more like rubber bands than steel cables. But although the bonds can flex a little, they won't break. Molecular movement is no longer independent. Each molecule's vibration is transmitted to its adjacent neighbors, and individual movement is harmonized with the water mass as a whole, becoming controlled and regular as it is in the ocean.

Hydrogen bonds are of particular interest because they are responsible for many of the characteristics that water exhibits. First of all, although they are dipolar forces like those involved with proteins, they possess unusual strength—quite possibly they are the strongest of all dipolar forces. They extend from the hydrogen atom of one water molecule to the oxygen of its neighbor, so each molecule can project hydrogen bonds out to two other water molecules and simultaneously provide a negative oxygen "anchor" for a third. As part of any liquid mass, therefore, a water molecule is held in place by bonds between itself and three other water molecules (figure 3.2).

Physical Properties of Water

Unusually stable. The collective strength of the hydrogen bonds provides water with an assortment of remarkable properties which, taken together, make it an unusually stable environment. The fact that the oceans can have such a tremendous effect on the temperature of the air, and therefore on the planet as a whole, emphasizes the importance of this stability. Water's physical phases shift only after being exposed to rather extreme conditions. It is even harder to affect chemically. It is almost as persistent in resisting change as living systems, which is another reason why it is so ideal.

Figure 3.2 Hydrogen bonding between water molecules. Hydrogen bonds are the strongest of all the dipolar forces, yet individually they are very weak compared to covalent or ionic bonds.

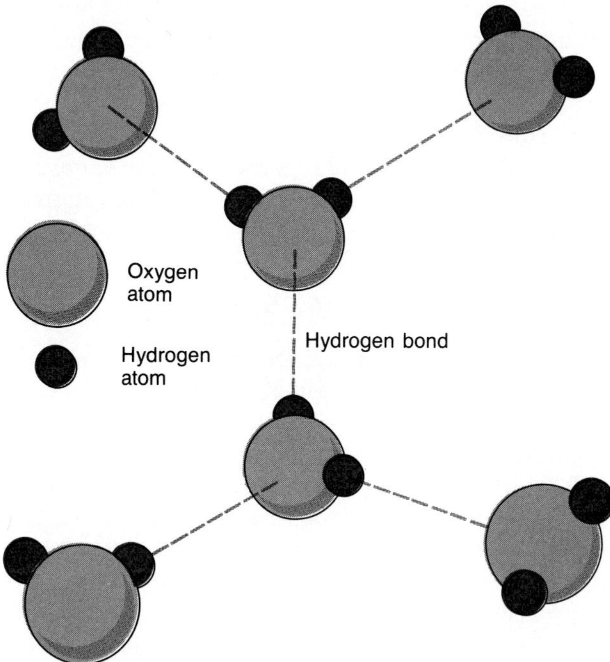

Water is an extremely good conductor of energy. A person standing in the shade of a tree on a lake bank can be 20° to 25° F cooler than someone standing in the sun a dozen feet away. A fish in the same shade in the lake near the bank is not any cooler than a fish in the water that is in direct sunlight—not because the water does not accept the heat, but because it spreads it so rapidly throughout its entire mass. Heat tends not to concentrate in any given location when water is involved.

This is very important to the homeostatic process of temperature regulation. Warm-blooded animals generate large quantities of heat, especially when they are in motion. Because of water's great thermal conductivity, heat produced in any localized area of the body never has a chance to concentrate and thus do any damage. The energy is rapidly distributed throughout the mass of water around the busy tissues, then is just as quickly shared with the water in the blood as it rushes by.

High heat capacity. Water's ability to absorb energy is phenomenal. It takes a whole calorie of energy to increase the temperature of a gram of water from 4° to 5° C, and few liquids can absorb so much energy with so little change.

This aids the thermal homeostatic mechanisms by rendering the blood capable of absorbing large quantities of heat without its own temperature increasing significantly. Active body tissues can run at full capacity with impunity despite the huge quantities of heat they are generating. The blood, being mostly water, can absorb large quantities of energy without significant temperature changes; it further minimizes the heat buildup by circulating localized heat throughout the entire mass of the body.

But even the tremendous heat-carrying capacity of water has its limitations. If heat were to continue pouring into the blood, sooner or later it would overheat. Ultimately, therefore, there must be a means of discarding the excess. This is accomplished by moving the blood through body regions near the skin surface, where its excess heat can be released. As long as the skin surfaces are cooler than the blood, this is no problem. But when the weather is hot, the skin may be warmer than the blood, and this is where another of water's wonderful features comes into play.

High heat of vaporization. Water has an unusually high heat of vaporization, which means it takes a huge input of energy to make it shift from a liquid to a gas. It takes 100 calories of energy to change the temperature of a gram of water from freezing (0° C) to boiling point (100° C). But once it has reached a temperature of 100°, liquid water does not automatically change to a gas. Before it can change to a gas even at that temperature, that gram of water must absorb 540 more calories—more than five times as much energy as it took to get from 0° to 100°.

The physiological significance of this feature is tremendous and is exploited by our homeostatic machinery. When body surfaces get warmer than the blood, heat receptors in the skin are activated, nerves carry the information to the brain, and the brain in turn sends instructions to activate the sweat glands. This activation covers our body surfaces with water, some of which will evaporate. Every gram of water that evaporates from the skin surface carries away 540 calories of body heat, permitting the blood to cool even when the ambient temperature is unusually high. The ability of humans to regulate their body temperature by sweating is not equalled by any other species.

High boiling point. There is a difference of 100° C between the freezing and boiling points of water; hence water remains a liquid through a broad range of temperatures. This makes for a stable environment, internally or externally. A lot of compounds boil within a couple of degrees of their freezing point, and living things couldn't exist in a medium that changed from a solid to a liquid and then rapidly to a gas simply because the sun came up and the day began.

Water expands when it freezes. In water's solid form (ice), the clusters of water molecules lock into a stiff tetrahedral structure in which the hydrogen bonds are much more rigid than they are in the liquid. As a result, the water molecules cannot crowd as closely together, so the solid is less dense, which means that liquid water at 0° C is heavier than ice at the same temperature. Because of this, ice floats instead of sinking.

The importance of this to living systems cannot be overestimated. If ice were heavier than water, it would sink the instant it solidified, which means that during cold weather, the water at the oceans' surfaces would be continually producing thin sheets of ice that would sink immediately. These sheets wouldn't sink very far at first. The warmer water beneath would melt them very quickly. But gradually the whole mass of water in the oceans would become cooler as a result of constantly having to melt the fine ice sheets, and each time one appeared, it would sink a little farther before it melted. Before very many years had passed, these sheets of ice would be sinking to the oceans' bottoms, and as the centuries passed, there would be a gradual thickening of this submarine ice. The effect would spread rapidly, cooling the liquid water in the oceans, which would, in turn, reduce the temperature of the air. In a few millenia, the mean temperature of the water and the air would hover very close to freezing, even at the equator, and the oceans would be solid masses of ice where no life, as we know life, could exist. Obviously there would have been no possibility for life to develop or evolve, and our planet would, today, be a sterile globe.

Powerful surface tension. The power of the hydrogen bonds is responsible for water's surface tension. Most of us know a little about this phenomenon. Small insects seem to be able to walk on water. Water striders actually run across the surface of a pond *bending* the water under their feet, instead of falling through. The more bonds that must be broken, the harder it is to get beneath the surface. This is why a razor blade placed flat on the water's surface will float, while if it is slipped in edgewise, it will flip immediately to the bottom. The mass is the same in both cases. What changes is the number of hydrogen bonds that must be broken to penetrate the surface. When enough are present, they will float a sheet of steel, if it is not too thick.

Electrical Conductivity: Electrolytes

There is another physical property of water and water mixtures that is very important. Pure water, while it will conduct electricity a little bit, is not a good conductor—in fact, it is probably a reasonably good insulator. However, when a little common table salt is mixed with water, its conductivity increases enormously. This is true of many salts, and the name **electrolyte** has been given to substances that, when added to water, make it a better conductor. It is characteristic of electrolytes that they separate into ions when introduced into water, and the more they ionize, the better the solution conducts. Generally speaking, minerals and salts ionize pretty well, so these are usually considered electrolytes. Large, complex compounds that are not held together by ionic bonds tend to release very few ions and are considered **nonelectrolytes.**

Chemical Properties of Water

Chemical stability. Water's chemical properties are every bit as substantial as its physical ones. Thanks to the power of the covalent bonds holding the molecules together, a tremendous input of energy (up to 2700° C) is necessary before water shows any signs of breaking into its component elements. No temperatures we will ever encounter on the earth, with the possible exception of volcanic activity, would ever approach that value.

Chemically labile. That which is labile is able to adapt readily and easily to change, and water certainly fits into that category. Chemically, it is extremely flexible. It can donate or accept electrons, so it is neither a natural acid nor a natural base. Instead, water is **amphoteric,** which means it can assume the acid/base characteristics of whatever enters it, and it is able to adjust itself throughout the entire acid/base range. In living systems, all kinds of polluting materials continually pour into the watery matrix of the interior, so this versatility is fortunate indeed. In humans it tends to assume acid/base characteristics very close to neutrality, and because of its amphoteric properties it is able to stay that way.

A remarkable solvent. The fact that individual water molecules are polarized permits them to be held in place, in liquid form, by hydrogen bonds (see figure 3.2), and compounds that ionize or possess a charge will dissolve. Water dissolves a tremendous number of things, and if there isn't a universal solvent on earth, water is nevertheless close to it. Ionic compounds like NaCl rapidly break up into their component ions and insert themselves between the water molecules. As was noted in chapter 2, in the case of table salt, the negative Cl^- ions are attracted to the positive zone at the hydrogen end, while the sodium ions (Na^+) line up against the oxygen (figure 3.3). Many organic compounds with imperfect covalent bonding have charges on their surfaces and so can develop hydrogen bonds with water molecules. Most sugars and a good many proteins can do this.

Figure 3.3 The negatively charged oxygen ends of water molecules are attracted to the positively charged Na^+, whereas the positively charged hydrogen ends of water molecules are attracted to the negatively charged Cl^-. Other water molecules are attracted to this first concentric layer of water, forming hydration spheres around the sodium and chloride ions.

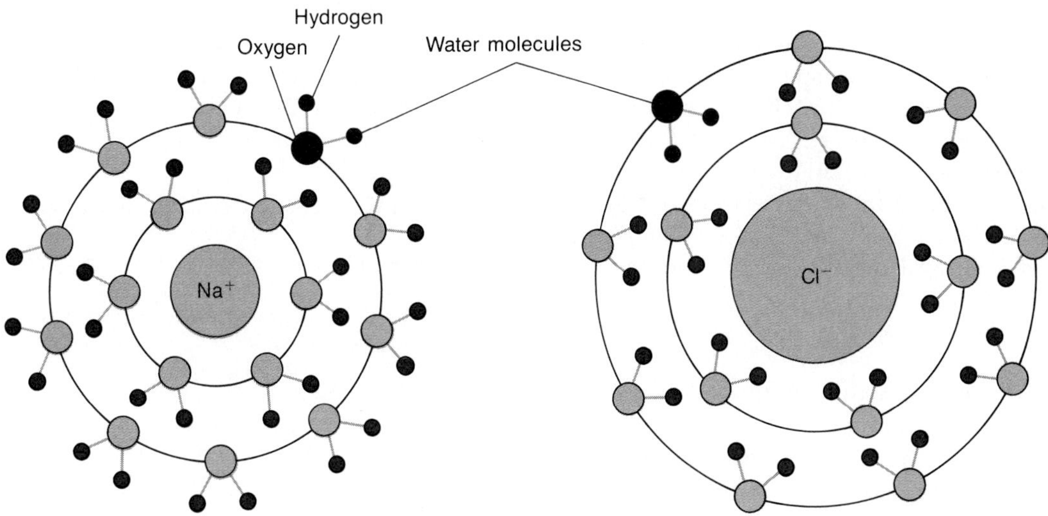

In living systems, water tends to concentrate in the areas where the most metabolic activity is taking place, so it would seem that tissues with the highest metabolic rates would contain the highest percentage of water, and they do. Both of these facts are related to the observation that biological activity occurs mainly in aqueous solution.

Dispersions, Mixtures, Solutions, and Colloids

Dispersions and Mixtures

The term **dispersion** refers to a huge array of conditions. Whenever particles of one kind are spread through particles of another, a dispersion system is created, and such systems embrace all the states of matter. Dust spreading through the atmosphere is a dispersion of a solid in a gas. Carbon dioxide dissolved in water (soda water) is an example of gas dispersed in a liquid. Perfume or ammonia vapor dispersed in the air is a gas-in-gas mixture, and fog or aerosol spray blown into the air represents a liquid-in-gas mixture. There are many more. One important characteristic of dispersions is that the particles may be interspersed, but they are not joined to each other by chemical bonds, so they can be separated by purely physical means. For our purposes, the terms *dispersion* and *mixture* are synonymous.

Most of the material inside the skins of living animals is a vast dispersion. More than 75 percent of an animal is water, and what is not is dispersed in the water or bathed by it. Many of the dispersed materials are tiny ions of inorganic salts. Others are enormous, twisted proteins almost large enough to see with a light microscope. Still others are the large formed units of living matter. Whatever they may be, they are all parts of an aqueous dispersion.

Suspensions

A **suspension** is a particular kind of dispersion. It is therefore a bit more restrictive in its meaning, but it is still a broad term. In general use, it tends to refer only to dispersions in which the interspersed particles remain suspended and never settle out. Water and sugar stirred together represent a suspension. So does salt dissolved in water. As is the case with all dispersion systems, in suspensions the individuality of the atoms or molecules involved is not lost. Their properties—both physical and chemical—remain unchanged and the suspension can be *un*mixed quite easily. When salt is dissolved in water, it may look like it has changed, but it hasn't. Despite the fact that it ionizes, it is still there and it is still salt, an observation that can be easily confirmed by simply tasting the suspension.

Water and sand stirred together represent a dispersion system also, but it is definitely not the same as salt and water stirred together. Water and sand can be strained through a cloth and separated, but you cannot do that with brine—the salt particles are too fine for a simple filtration procedure to work. Salt must be separated from water by the more energy-consuming process of boiling or evaporating the water away. Since it is necessary to resort to different methods of separation, it is logical to assume that the water-and-sand dispersion is different in some way from the water-and-salt dispersion, but what could these differences be? Since a dispersion involves only physical interaction, there has been no chemical change in the particles involved. This means that any observed differences between the two dispersions must be due to the physical characteristics of the solvent and/or the particles. One very obvious difference between the sand-in-water dispersion and the salt dispersion is *particle size.*

Solutions

When sodium chloride dissolves in water, the ionic bonds holding the sodium and chloride ions together are interrupted, and the two ions insert themselves between the water molecules. They are atom-size, so obviously they can't be seen, and since they are so light, they certainly won't ever settle out. Since the particles don't settle out, such a dispersion is also a suspension . . . a particular kind of suspension. A salt-and-water dispersion is known as a true **solution.** In such dispersions the size of the particles never exceeds 10 Angstroms (see appendix). Often they are smaller. Molecules of tiny organic compounds like table sugar and single amino acids range from 5 to 7 Angstroms (Å) in size, so when dispersed in water they would form true solutions, too. Making a filter with holes large enough to let water molecules through but small enough to capture sodium ions or sugar molecules would be essentially impossible. Hence filtration is impractical for separating solutions.

Colloids

Living systems utilize billions of organic molecules. Most of these range in size from 10 to 1,000 Angstrom units, with the majority of them in the 30 Å to 80 Å range. Such particles are larger than salt or sugar particles that form true solutions, yet they are still too small to be separated by simple filtration. They belong to a separate category known as **colloids** that covers particle sizes that range between 10 Å and 1,000 Å.

Although most large organic molecules are colloids, the colloidal state is not unique to any particular substance or group of substances. Colloids often form when complex molecules are attracted to each other or are thrust aside by the dispersing substance in which they are immersed. When this happens, they cluster into groups of a few hundred or a couple of thousand. Almost any substance can become a colloid under the right conditions; about the only circumstance in which a colloid cannot exist is in a dispersion of two gases (see box). The formation of colloids in water is very common (figure 3.4).

Most of the particles in living systems fall into the colloid category. See panel 3.1 on page 60 for more about colloids.

Working with colloids has become very important—not just in chemical laboratories, but almost everywhere. The humus (decaying organic matter) in soil is a colloid, as are many of today's chemical and natural fertilizers. Hence, those who work with soils—including farmers—would help themselves if they knew a little colloid chemistry. Manufacturers of gelatin desserts or the fillings for cream-style pies, whether they know it or not, work with colloids too, since these luscious pastes are all colloids. Fog and clouds are liquid colloidal particles dispersed in a gaseous medium; smoke and dust particles are solid colloidal particles dispersed in a gas, and glues are generally composed of liquid colloidal particles dispersed in a solid. Colloids can form from solids dispersed in solids, liquids in liquids—even solids in a gas. In fact, about the only type of arrangement that will *not* produce a colloidal dispersion is gas in a gas. Remember from chapter 2 that gas is the high-energy state of matter. Gases always exist as single molecules because they never stay put long enough to link onto anything. Thus they will never form complex molecules, and even the largest atom—all alone—would not be big enough to constitute a colloidal particle.

Temporary Suspensions

Naturally, living systems contain a good many particles that are larger than colloidal size. Such dispersions are known simply as suspensions if they are solids dispersed in liquids, or **emulsions** if a liquid is dispersed in another liquid. As long as the particles do not settle out, these terms apply, but sooner or later particle size increases to the point where they are too heavy or too dense to remain in a suspended state within the system. Given time, they will settle out. Such mixtures are usually referred to as **temporary suspensions.**

Temporary suspensions have characteristics that permit a highly efficient method of analyzing solutions in which they are dispersed. Since they contain large, heavy particles, they will separate by themselves if they are left undisturbed for enough time, but that is impractical for laboratory analyses. Fortunately, we can expedite the process of separation by applying several times the acceleration of normal earth gravity (1 G) through the use of a **centrifuge.**

Figure 3.4 Colloidal particles in a polar dispersion medium. Colloidal particles form when complex molecules are dispersed in dispersion media. In this case, the molecules have a polar end formed by phosphate groups and a long chain of nonpolar fatty acids. Dispersed in a substance like water, the nonpolar ends would be forced together by the tendency of water to exclude them, while the polar ends could mingle with the water. These colloidal particles quite naturally repel each other.

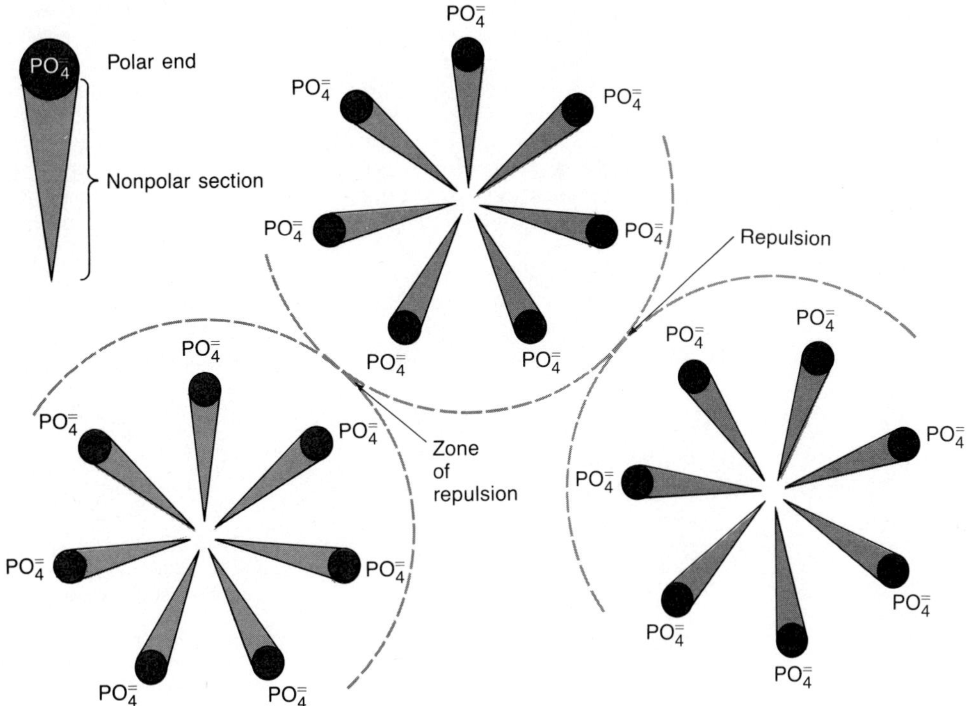

Centrifuges are machines that apply increased "G forces" by spinning at several thousand revolutions per minute. Through selective alteration of these G forces, we can segregate assorted particles from a single temporary suspension. Inevitably, some particles will be heavier than others, and in general, particles settle out rapidly or slowly according to their weight. Applying a force of, say, sixty times normal gravity (60 G) for two minutes might cause the heaviest particles to settle to the bottom of their container while leaving all the smaller ones still suspended. The heavy particles can be left where they are at the bottom of the centrifuge tube, while the mixture on top is poured off. Now this **supernatant,** as it is called, can be subjected to further centrifugation—this time, say, 120 G. The greater centrifugal force will drive a second group of particles out of suspension, effectively isolating *them,* and the process can be continued until all the particles in a given suspension have been segregated. The procedure is called **differential centrifugation** and is extremely useful in biological or chemical research laboratories. (Differential centrifugation procedures won't work on true solutions or colloidal dispersions, because such particles are in true suspension, hence won't settle out no matter how great the G forces.)

In biological systems, temporary suspensions are generally whole entities like red blood cells or *intracellular organelles,* both of which will be discussed in detail in a later chapter.

Measuring Atoms

Atomic Mass Units

One thing that was needed from the beginning was a universally accepted method of identifying elements so they could be studied and quantitative calculations made. In 1961, at a worldwide convention of scientists, the element carbon was agreed upon as the standard for atomic weights. Because its most common isotope contains six protons and six neutrons, carbon was given an **atomic mass unit** value of exactly 12. As a result, 1 *atomic mass unit* is now defined by the International Bureau of Standards as exactly one-twelfth of the mass of a carbon atom, or just about the mass of one nuclear particle. With carbon being the standard element, every other element is referred to it for description or chemical definition.

Panel 3.1
Colloids

Many of the unusual features of colloids have been exploited in today's cultures. Cooking, radiography, generation of solar energy—even the modern tobacco industry—all are indebted to the colloid chemist. For example, most filters in today's cigarettes contain what is called **activated charcoal.** Most people know this, but what you may not know is that activated charcoal is a product of research into colloidal phenomena. Chemically, activated charcoal is no different from ordinary charcoal; both are pure carbon. Charcoal is "activated" by being baked in hot, airless ovens or blasted in "live" steam baths until it is much like a sponge, displaying thousands of tiny caverns and passages winding back and forth throughout its mass. These myriad passageways, coupled with the charcoal's highly reactive surface, permit a phenomenon known as **adsorption** to occur on an enormous scale, and this degree of adsorption is usually restricted to colloids.

Adsorption

*Ad*sorption is not the same as *ab*sorption. Absorption in the physical sense refers to the ability of a substance to swallow energy in one form and then convert it to some other form the way plants do when they absorb sunlight—they convert the radiant energy of the sun to the chemical energy of foodstuffs.

Despite the similarity in the two words, adsorption is very different. It refers to the ability of surface particles of a substance to grasp anything that rubs across them or bumps into them, and to hang on. Adsorbed particles are usually only a couple of molecules thick, so the volume of substance that can be adsorbed on the surface of a large object is not very great, and this is why the charcoal is "activated" for use in cigarette filters. Activation increases adsorptive capacity by exposing extra surfaces in the thousands of new tunnels and grottos, and it does so to such an extent that a chunk of charcoal only a cubic inch in volume may have a surface area of several hundred square feet. If every carbon atom on the surface of the charcoal snags a particle of tar or nicotine as the cigarette smoke passes through it, an awful lot of tar is going to be filtered out before it can get to the mouth and lungs. Activated charcoal is not actually a colloid, but its surface is ordered in such a way that it resembles colloidal particles in its effectiveness . . . it is all a matter of surface area. This business of increasing the surface area of a substance without altering its total volume brings us, of necessity, to discussion of the concept of what is called **surface-area-to-volume ratio.**

Surface-Area-to-Volume Ratio

Whenever any structure is reduced to a smaller size without altering its shape, the surface area increases with respect to the volume. Let us examine a sample of charcoal having a volume of one cubic foot. If this lump of charcoal is in the shape of a cube, then its six surface squares will expose a total area of six square feet or 864 square inches. If we break up that cubic foot into eight equal cubes, the edge of each will now measure ½ foot or 6 inches, and the surface area will measure ½ foot × ½ foot × 6 sides × 8 cubes = 12 square feet or 1,728 square inches (figure 3.A). If we were to divide that cubic foot into 1,728 little one-inch

Atomic Number

Actually, several methods are used to identify elements. One of the earliest was known as the **atomic number** method. The atomic number represents the number of positive charges (protons) in a given atom's nucleus, and since the number of protons determines what the element *is,* this makes a good deal of sense.

Mass Number

It is also possible to utilize the *nuclear mass* of the atom as a basis for indentification, and this is also relatively common. The figure is called the **mass number** of the element and represents the sum of the protons and neutrons (collectively called **nucleons**), ignoring, as usual, the mass of the infinitesimal electrons.

cubes, the surface exposed would be 1 inch × 1 inch × 6 surfaces × 1,728 cubes = 10,368 square inches. The total volume in all three cases never changes. In this last case, it is still only one cubic foot . . . but the surface area has increased from 6 square feet to 72 square feet.

Making the cubes still smaller would increase the surface-area-to-volume ratio even more. If a cube one millimeter square (about the size of a very small particle of kitty litter) were divided into cubes that are 100 Angstrom units long per side, we would have roughly ten quintillion particles. Each particle would have six sides and that would, all together, expose a combined surface area of more than 5,400 square feet. Convert that to floor space and we would be talking about a structure that could comfortably house a family of six—all that surface area from a single particle with a volume of just one cubic millimeter.

The countless tiny particles in most colloidal dispersions have a combined surface area that can stagger the imagination. It is not unusual for the particles in a single pint of colloid to have a surface area as large as Manhattan Island's.

Naturally, when billions of tiny particles are fused together into a larger mass, the surface-area-to-volume ratio decreases accordingly. Single-celled organisms the size of a horse or even a mouse do not exist in nature, because their surface area is too small to absorb enough material to nourish the large interior volume. The concept of a terror like *The Blob*—an oversized ameba-like organism that absorbs cats, dogs, people, cars, and small buildings—while an entertaining movie, is scientifically ludicrous.

Figure 3.A An example of how surface area changes when particle size is altered.

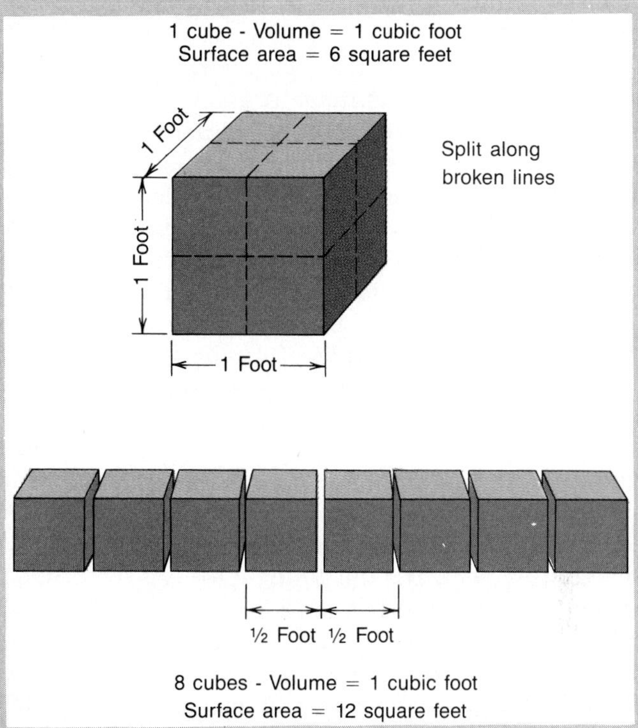

Carbon, with six protons and six neutrons, would have an atomic number of 6 and a mass number of 12 (written $^{12}_{6}C$). Oxygen, with eight protons and eight neutrons, has an atomic number of 8 and a mass number of 16 ($^{16}_{8}O$); helium has an atomic number of 2 and a mass number of 4 ($^{4}_{2}He$), and so on.

These identification methods had their uses, but something more was needed—some practical method of referring elements to one another *quantitatively*, so scientists could apply their knowledge of elemental activity. This led to the development of the concept of atomic weight, which requires some explanation.

Atomic Weight

Common sense tells us that nobody can weigh single atoms. Even if we could separate out a single atom and put it on a balance and weigh it, its absolute weight would have very little meaning, because weight is a measure of the earth's gravitational attraction, and that varies with altitude. A given element's weight in Miami would be slightly different from its weight in Denver, and that is not accurate enough for scientific measurements. What was needed was some way of relating the *mass* of an individual atom to measurable amounts of the element, and this was done by equating each atomic mass unit to the gram. Since the carbon atom consists of twelve atomic mass units, the **gram atomic weight** of carbon was settled on as 12, and now chemistry had its measureable units.

The Mole

The next step was to provide some designation whereby workers could recognize *comparable numbers* of atoms in every element, and this brought into existence the concept of the **mole.** A mole is very precisely defined entity and is of considerable importance to physiologists. Since carbon was the standard element, and since it was established that the gram atomic weight of carbon was 12, it was decreed that thenceforth 12 grams of carbon would constitute one mole of carbon. Over the years, the exact number of atoms in 12 grams of carbon was determined, and with that in mind as the standard, it was further ordained that when a quantity of any substance contains exactly the same number of basic particles as there are atoms in 12 grams of carbon, there is exactly one mole of that substance present. What that translates to is as follows: *one gram atomic weight of a given element is one mole of that element.*

Since elements vary in size, obviously a mole will vary in weight, depending on the element. Some will be heavier than carbon and some will be lighter. A mole of hydrogen, for instance, has a gram atomic weight of just over 1, while a mole of lead has a gram atomic weight of 207.2. But whether light or heavy, a mole always has the same number of basic particles. Using the concept of the mole and the scale of relative atomic weights, researchers can obtain equal numbers of lead and hyrogen atoms through the use of a simple analytical balance. And the system is really quite flexible.

Gram Molecular Weights

Consider, for instance, the elements carbon and oxygen. Since the gram atomic weights of both elements are known, obviously one mole of carbon will be 12/16 the weight of one mole of oxygen, and if we wish to manufacture the compound carbon monoxide without wasting either carbon or oxygen, we would have to assemble both elements in that ratio—twelve carbon atoms for every sixteen oxygen atoms. It wouldn't matter whether we have twelve grams or twelve tons of carbon as long as we had sixteen similar units of oxygen. To produce carbon *di*oxide (CO_2) without wasting any raw materials, we would double the number of oxygen units before combining the elements, meaning that for every carbon atom present, we would now have *two* oxygen atoms to link up with it. So, if we had twelve grams of carbon, we would have to add thirty-two grams of oxygen (2×16), and so on. The unit weight of the resulting compound would then be the sum of the gram atomic weights of all the elements it was composed of. This is, therefore, the compound's **gram molecular weight.**

Calculating the gram molecular weight of NaCl, for example, is simply a matter of adding together the gram atomic weights of its two elements. Sodium's gram atomic weight is almost 23. Chlorine's is about 35.5, so the gram molecular weight of NaCl is $23 + 35.5 = 58.5$. This is true of all compounds, so if a scale of atomic weights is available, calculating the gram molecular weight of a compound is pretty simple. One has merely to look up the gram atomic weights of all the elements involved, make sure the correct number of atoms of each is taken into account, and then add them all up.

Students are sometimes confused when they see that the atomic weights assigned to elements often do not represent the sum of protons and neutrons given in the **periodic table of elements.** This is because the modern definition of atomic weight of an element is "the average, by weight, *of all the naturally occurring isotopes* of that element." This value is seldom the same as the atomic mass unit-value of the most abundant form of the element. We know from rigid analysis that in a sample of iron, for instance, nearly 92 percent of the atoms have a value of 55.94 g; about 6 percent consist of an isotope with a value of 53.94 g; just a little over 2 percent has a mass unit value of 56.94 g; and there is one very rare isotope (0.31 percent) with a value of 57.93 g. All these added together and then averaged out give us the "official" gram atomic weight of iron—55.85 g.

Acids and Bases

When considering chemical activity in biological systems, there are many effects we must take into account. Among the most crucial is the correct balancing of acids and bases so as not to damage complex organic compounds. Most people have only a vague idea of what constitutes an acid, and they seldom think of bases in the same context. The word *acid* conjures up the picture of a liquid that sears away skin, flesh, and muscle, leaving behind a frothing skeleton. Some powerful acids—only a few—will actually do this, and obviously they are quite dangerous. Some, however, are useful as foods or food flavorings, and several are even considered essential to health.

The earliest descriptions of acids and their basic counterparts dealt with physical properties. Acids were usually described as sour in taste and able to turn litmus indicators red, while bases were bitter, felt slippery, and turned litmus blue. Chemically, there is a much more precise way of describing acids and bases, and it's all a function of the ions present in water. A surprising number of things ionize in water. Even water itself breaks into small numbers of ions, one atomic and the other molecular. The reaction looks like this:

$$H_2O \rightarrow H^+ + OH^-$$

OH^- is called the **hydroxyl ion,** while the other ion (H^+) is called the **hydrogen ion.** Acids and bases are usually defined in terms of these two water ions.

Actually, the ionization of water looks like this: $H_2O \rightarrow H^+_{(aq)} + OH^-$, the $H^+_{(aq)}$ being known as the **hydronium ion** and often designated as H_3O^+. However, for readers of this text, the designation *hydrogen ion* (H^+) will be used exclusively and will refer simply to a proton.

When pure water ionizes, obviously there will be equal amounts of hydrogen and hydroxyl ions, since there are no other ions possible, and by convention pure water is considered **neutral**—neither acid nor basic. When either of the water ions outnumbers the other, neutrality can be converted into an acid or a base, and the earliest accurate definition of acids and bases emphasized this: *An acid is an aqueous solution in which the hydrogen ions outnumber the hydroxyl ions. In a base, the hydroxyl ions outnumber the hydrogens.* This definition is still considered accurate.

Early in this century, a broader definition of acids and bases was proposed, and we will mention it here because it aids somewhat in the understanding of acid and base activity in organic chemistry. It is known as the **Bronsted definition,** and according to this, *any substance that can donate protons to an aqueous solution is an acid, whereas any substance that accepts protons is a base.* Since hydrogen ions are protons, we could reword the above definition and state *anything that donates hydrogen ions to an aqueous solution is an acid. . . .* This clearly relates the Bronsted definition to the earlier water definition and for our purposes, the water definition is more appropriate.

Obviously then, any substance that delivers hydrogen ions to pure water will produce an acid. The more hydrogen ions it delivers, the more acidic it will make the water, so if a compound contains hydrogen, the more it ionizes, the greater its acid strength. The strength of an acid is not reflected in how badly it burns a person, but rather its tendency to produce hydrogen ions, so the ability to ionize in water distinguishes between a strong acid and a weak one.

Strong acids ionize completely in water. Examples of strong acids are hydrochloric acid (HCl), nitric acid (HNO_3), and sulfuric acid (H_2SO_4).

Weak acids are not necessarily harmless—in fact, some can produce much worse burns than acids classified as strong. The major difference between these weak acids and those we consider strong is clear: weak acids don't tend to ionize very much in solution, while strong acids do. Examples of weak acids are acetic acid (CH_3COOH) and carbonic acid (H_2CO_3).

The same definition applies to weak and strong bases . . . it is all a matter of ionization. Sodium hydroxide ($NaOH$) and calcium hydroxide ($Ca[OH]_2$) are examples of strong bases; ammonium hydroxide (NH_4OH) is a weak one.

Acid/Base Balance and pH

The balance between acids and bases in body fluids is vitally important, because it can affect the physical and chemical properties of so many biological compounds. The *relative* concentration of the two ions is the most important thing in physiological systems, but it's the concentration of the hydrogen ion that is usually monitored. Before any of this could have real meaning, however, the degree of acidity and alkalinity had to be standardized so that scientists who routinely work with small acid/base concentrations could communicate precisely with each other.

pH

The term **pH** (small *p*, capital *H*) is used to express the relative concentration of hydrogen ions in a given aqueous solution. Mathematically, its relationship to the hydrogen ion concentration is as follows:

$$pH = -\log_{10}[H^+]$$

We know from previous research that the pH of pure water is 7, and since pure water is considered by international agreement to be our standard of neutrality, any solution that has a pH of 7 is neither acid nor basic, but neutral.

When students first begin to work with pH, things often seem to be running backwards. At first glance it seems logical to assume that since pH relates to hydrogen ion concentration, when the latter goes up, the pH should go up, too . . . but it doesn't work that way. Look at the formula. The pH is *minus* the hydrogen ion concentration, and that negative sign changes things. It means that when the hydrogen ion concentration goes up, the pH will go *down*. We already know that the more hydrogen ions a solution has, the more acid it will be, hence the lower the pH, the more acid the solution is. When the hydrogen ion concentration in a water solution goes down, the relative hydroxyl ion concentration goes up and vice versa, so by monitoring only pH, we can ascertain how alkaline the solution might be as well. Therefore, identifying the pH stipulates acid/base characteristics of any aqueous solution, and its designations are universally understood.

Aside from its physiological relationships, knowledge of exactly what pH means has some everyday applications as well. Surely the term pH is no stranger to any of you, since it is currently all the rage in television advertising for various kinds of detergents. Advertisers fondly believe that it increases the appeal of their product to be "scientific," so certain shampoos are ballyhooed as having "perfect pH balance" or being "non-alkaline." It sounds learned and deeply technological so is bound to be impressive, yet the chances are that neither the advertisers, the salespeople, nor the prospective buyers know what "pH balance" is. But *we* should. Does this kind of advertising really *mean* anything? Is there any merit to a non-alkaline shampoo?

As a matter of fact, there is. Hair shafts viewed microscopically resemble long strings of scales that lay on top of each other like stacks of paper coffee filters. When hair gets dirty or is washed in alkaline water, these scales flatten out and their edges stick out perpendicular to the hair shaft, making the hair frizzy and uncontrollable. Using a shampoo that is neutral or even slightly acid leaves these scales flat and smooth and the hair remarkably manageable. Beer has a pH of about 4.0 and this is why, years ago, people used to rinse their hair in beer to make it easier to style. So for once what appears to be merely another advertising gimmick actually makes sense. It is worth contemplating, however, just how much shampoo would be sold if it were advertised as being "slightly acid."

Table 3.1 Hydrogen Ion Concentration and pH

pH	Hydrogen Ion Concentration	Hydroxyl Ion Concentration
0	10^0	10^{-14}
1	10^{-1}	10^{-13}
2	10^{-2}	10^{-12}
3	10^{-3}	10^{-11}
4	10^{-4}	10^{-10}
5	10^{-5}	10^{-9}
6	10^{-6}	10^{-8}
7 (neutrality)	10^{-7}	10^{-7}
8	10^{-8}	10^{-6}
9	10^{-9}	10^{-5}
10	10^{-10}	10^{-4}
11	10^{-11}	10^{-3}
12	10^{-12}	10^{-2}
13	10^{-13}	10^{-1}
14	10^{-14}	10^0

Acid/base balance of body fluids is of vital importance to living systems, because it can affect the physical and chemical properties of so many biological compounds. Blood pH is never more than half a pH unit away from neutrality, varying normally from 7.35 to 7.45, and the narrow pH range through which it varies reflects the extreme care that is taken to maintain it. Acids and bases are continuously entering the blood from a variety of sources like food, liquids, respiration, and metabolism, and yet its most acid pH is only a tenth of a unit lower than its most alkaline pH.

Buffers

The kind of pH changes that can be induced by only a small quantity of hydrogen ions is striking. One hundredth of a mole of hydrogen ions (the amount available in 5 ml of stomach acid) added to a liter of plain water could reduce the pH from 7 to just a bit over 2. In the human body, that kind of pH change would be instantly fatal. But if you add that volume of stomach acid to a liter of blood plasma, the pH goes down by only a tenth of a pH unit instead of five whole units. Why? What is there about blood plasma that makes it different in this way from pure water?

The pH of blood is maintained very precisely by a system of chemicals known as **buffers.** Buffers are designed to resist changes in pH, and blood plasma is a buffered solution. The acid/base balance of the blood is monitored conscientiously and when necessary is adjusted with extreme precision.

Ordinarily, in living organisms, buffer systems contain two related compounds—a weak acid and the salt of that acid, or a weak base and the salt of that base. Such combinations are known as **buffer pairs.**

Table 3.2 Buffer Pairs in Body Fluids		
Bicarbonate pairs	$NaHCO_3$ / H_2CO_3	(Sodium bicarbonate) / (Carbonic acid)
Phosphate pairs	Na_2HPO_4 / NaH_2PO_4	(Basic phosphate) / (Acid phosphate)
Plasma protein pairs	Na proteinates / Dissolved proteins	(Protein salts) / (Weak acids)
Hemoglobin pairs	KHb or $KHbO_2$ / Hb or HbO_2	(KHb and $KHbO_2$ are salts) / (Hb and HbO_2 are weak acids)

In such a system, one member of the buffer pair will react with the hydrogen and by doing so will remove it from solution and prevent the pH from significantly changing. The principal buffer pairs in body fluids are outlined in table 3.2.

In general, buffers act in the following way: Consider, for example, acetic acid (a weak acid) and sodium acetate (a salt of acetic acid). If equal amounts of acetic acid and sodium acetate were dissolved in water, the resulting equilibrium would have significant concentrations of both the weak acid (CH_3COOH) and the acetate ion (CH_3COO^-) from the sodium acetate molecule. Both compounds contribute to a small reserve of acetate ions in solution in the water:

$$CH_3COONa \longrightarrow CH_3COO^- \longleftarrow CH_3COOH$$
$$Na^+ \qquad\qquad H^+$$

When an equilibrium is achieved, the pH of the solution will be slightly acidic due to the presence of the extra H^+ ions, but once the pH is established, it will be hard to change it. For example, if a small amount of hydrochloric acid were added to such a solution, the acetate ion would take up the extra hydrogen ions and become acetic acid.

$$HCl \rightarrow Cl^- + H^+$$
$$Cl^- \qquad H^+ + CH_3COO^- \longrightarrow CH_3COOH$$

That would increase the total amount of acetic acid in the solution, but because the extra hydrogen ions were removed, it would not alter the pH. To lower the pH, the hydrogen ions have to be free in the water, and since they aren't, the pH stays the same. So as long as the sodium acetate holds out, hydrogen ions added to the solution will continue to be picked up, and the pH will hardly change at all.

Addition of a strong base like NaOH to a similar buffer solution results in the hydroxide ions combining with acetic acid to form acetate and water. Essentially, the reaction is running in the opposite direction:

$$Na^+ + OH^- + CH_3COOH \rightarrow CH_3COO^- + H_2O + Na^+ \rightarrow CH_3COONa + H_2O$$

As long as there are intact molecules of acetic acid in solution, the excess hydroxyl ions will continue to be converted to the weak acid salt and pH change will be negligible.

In human blood, the optimal ratio of bicarbonate to carbonic acid is 20:1, and as long as that ratio is retained, all is well. Acids or bases entering the blood, however, can change that ratio, and should they succeed in overwhelming this buffer pair and lower the pH enough, the result could be disastrous. A different, although equally dangerous condition, might ensue if the pH were to increase above tolerance limits. The pH deviations don't have to be very great to be fatal. If the pH of blood should slip lower than 6.8 or range higher than 7.8, it would be pooling in a motionless corpse, which is a pretty good indication of how momentous correct acid/base balance is to living systems and how smoothly and powerfully the chemical mechanisms of the blood maintain it.

Molecular Movement in Living Systems

The status of the fluids within a living organism, like that of the entire body, can best be described as one of **dynamic equilibrium.** In order to keep things the same, the body must keep changing and adjusting to new conditions, and these changes involve the movement of molecules and ions from place to place within the body. Sometimes the body must spend a bit of its hard-earned energy to accomplish these movements, and sometimes it needn't. It all depends on how the molecules are distributed in the water within the body.

The principal mechanisms that move molecules from place to place are known as *diffusion, osmosis, filtration, active transport,* and *facilitated diffusion.*

The basic consideration is avoiding disorganization, and there is a tendency in existence for disorganization to overtake everything. Here, in our little chunk of the universe, organization exists. Matter is grouped in organized clusters everywhere, and that of living systems is tremendously complex. Maintaining this organization is no minor achievement. The environment animals live in is not organized the way their bodies are. The body fluid of fishes is different from the water they live in, yet they don't turn into water. Similarly, mammals, lizards, birds, and the other land-dwellers stay pretty much the same inside, despite the fact that the air we all live in is not much like our body organization.

How is this accomplished? Well, if some random flow toward disorganization is occasionally permitted, and if energy is specifically expended to reverse or stop this flow at other times, life can retain its organization. It is all a matter of taking the energy that is available and directing it toward a specific goal.

As long as the temperature is above that known as **absolute zero** (−273° C), energy will exist in everything, living or nonliving. It is present in the form of molecular motion, and the higher the temperature, the more motion there will be. When molecules or atoms move, they pick their directions at random, and since they possess **inertia,** they move in straight lines until something gets in their way and they bang into it. When such collisions occur, the molecules bounce apart and dash off in different directions, moving as before in straight lines. Out in space where there are cubic miles of emptiness, particles can travel a long way before they bump into anything, but on earth matter is more tightly organized. Even in forms as tenuous as gases, molecules do not travel far before they hit something. They move and collide, move and collide, again and again in both liquids and gases, and much of the time the movement is random. Even in solids, where molecules are locked firmly in place, they are constantly in motion—vibrating, trying to break free. Molecular motion exists everywhere on earth, and living systems take advantage of this movement and its energy to serve their purposes when it is possible.

There are two basic methods of producing movement in living systems. One method uses only the energy that is available in the molecules that are involved in the movement, and no energy is contributed by the organism. Such movement is known as **passive.** Needless to say, when passive movement is possible, it behooves living systems to utilize it to its fullest extent. Frequently, however, it is simply not possible—circumstances are such that the energy available in the molecules is either inadequate to do the job or is flowing in the wrong direction. In such cases, the energy must be provided by the organism, and the movement is therefore said to be **active.**

Diffusion

If we had a one-liter jar filled with a colored gas and we were to transfer that gas into a second jar with a capacity of two liters, we would notice almost immediately that the gas had distributed itself equally throughout the entire two liters. The gas expanded to fill up all of the increased space. What the gas did was run "downhill," down a **concentration gradient,** from a zone where particle concentration was high to a place where it was lower. What is more, this downhill flow continued until there was no longer any such gradient—no high or low anywhere. It stopped when the concentration everywhere in the two jars was the same. Once such equality was achieved, *net* movement ceased. With everything the same everywhere, there was no hill to run down anymore. Each particle continues to zip around and ricochet back and forth, but overall movement in a given direction ends once the concentration gradient disappears and equality throughout is achieved. This simple, downhill flow of molecules to that equilibrium is known as **diffusion.**

Figure 3.5 Diffusion. (*a*) A perfume bottle is opened and the scent fills a room because the molecules have moved away from the bottle. Note that the windows in the room are closed and the curtains are still; there are no convection currents to help disperse the perfume. (*b*) A tablet of dye is placed in a beaker, and water becomes colored because the molecules have moved away from the original area of the tablet.

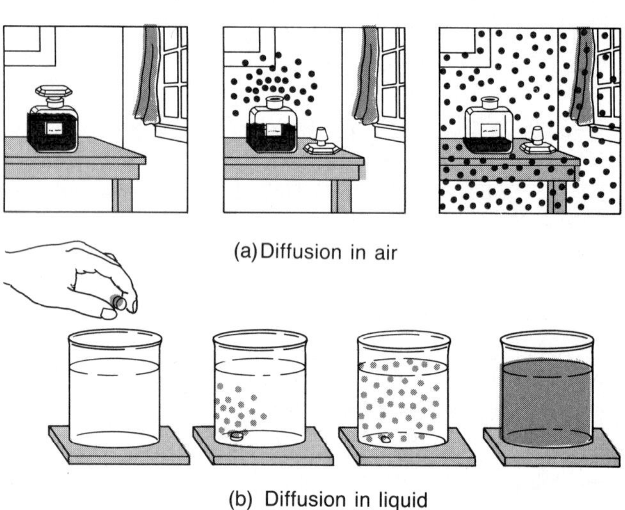

Anyone who has ever been in a room where someone is using ammonia has experienced the effects of diffusion. No fan is necessary to spread the odor throughout the room—diffusion does not require convection currents to occur. All that is necessary is a "hill" that particles can run down, a concentration gradient. Diffusion can spread dispersed substances throughout virtually any kind of medium, liquid, solid, or gas. It happens when sugar is spooned into coffee. Stirring the coffee with a spoon speeds up the process and assists in the uniform rearrangement of the various molecules, but it isn't essential (figure 3.5). Diffusion is a passive method of moving materials. No energy input is necessary because the molecules are already moving. A scientist would say "the energy is in the *system.*"

Living organisms take advantage of this tendency to run downhill. By using diffusion to transfer materials from place to place within their bodies, they can move particles around without having to spend any energy. Solid particles moving through a liquid medium are the most common in physiological studies, but diffusion affects all particles, no matter what their physical state. Diffusion in living systems often involves gases and is particularly important during ventilation. In the lungs, molecules of oxygen diffuse from the air spaces into the blood because their concentration is higher in the air than it is in the blood. Carbon dioxide molecules, in a similar way, move in the opposite direction, because they are more concentrated in the blood than in the air. No matter where they are encountered, the forces of diffusion operate effectively, and if the distances are not too great, they work with surprising speed.

Osmosis

Living systems utilize a rather specialized type of diffusion to move the water in their body fluids from place to place. On a molecular level, there are no known physiological mechanisms that can take a water molecule and push it from one location to another, so to get it where it is needed, it is necessary to take advantage of the diffusion phenomenon, plus some rather unique properties of certain membranes within the body.

Membranes within the body rarely offer any restriction to the movement of water, but water-soluble particles seldom pass through easily, and when it is necessary to move water from place to place, these living membranes adjust themselves to present a near-total barrier to solutes. Such membranes are known as **semipermeable,** or more accurately, **selectively permeable,** with respect to water-soluble particles. Water, moving freely through such membranes while the solute particles must stay behind, can produce a very powerful energy gradient with no expenditure of the organism's energy reserves.

In most modern cities, water for general consumption is pumped into large tanks that sit on pedestals high above the ground. These tanks tend to cluster in the immediate vicinity of housing or industrial developments and they provide a downhill gradient or *hydraulic pressure* to supply the homes or factories beneath them. Since the energy is supplied by gravity, the higher the tower is, the greater this hydraulic pressure will be.

The energy gradients developed by two solutions separated by a selectively permeable membrane can provide water pressures, too, and there is no expenditure of the organism's energy reserves. For example, assume a beaker is divided into two sections by inserting a selectively permeable membrane right down the middle and sealing the edges against the glass. Assume also that the membrane separates a 20 percent sugar solution from an equal volume of pure water (figure 3.6). If this beaker were left undisturbed for an hour or so, the volume of fluid on the side containing the sugar solution would increase, while the volume of pure water would diminish. An analysis of

Figure 3.6 A beaker containing two different liquids separated by a semipermeable membrane. The fluid on the left of the membrane is a sugar/water solution; that on the right is pure water. The particles depicted represent water and sugar—oversized, of course. Part *b* shows a schematic representation of a highly magnified membrane area. As you can see, the solvent particles can pass freely through the pores, while solute particles cannot. In time, the tendency will be for the water to move into the left side of the beaker.

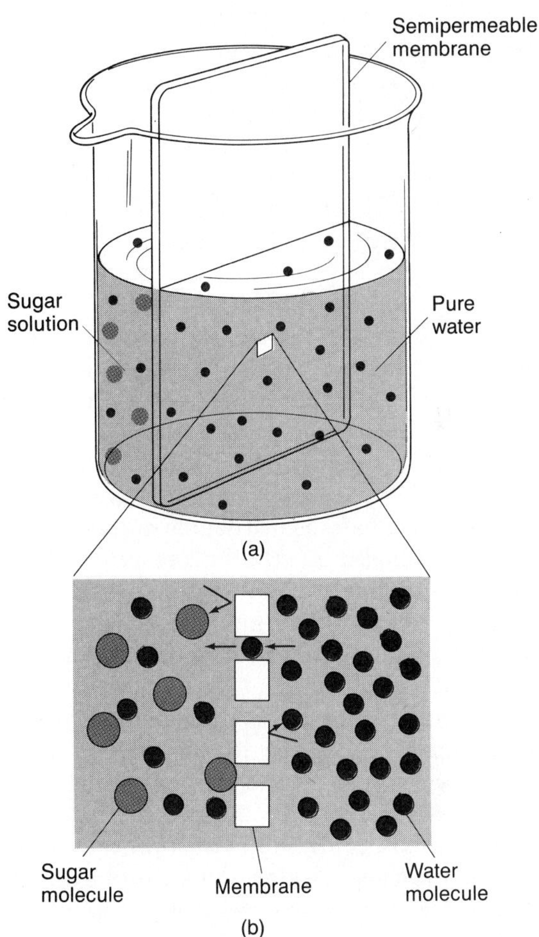

Figure 3.7 The beaker shown in figure 3.6 after an hour has passed.

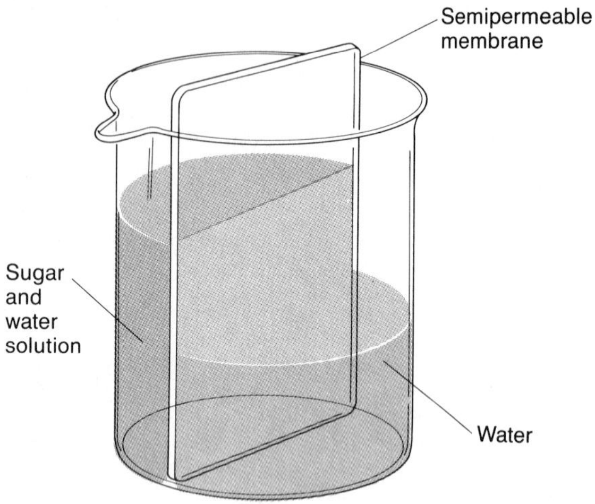

Figure 3.8 Schematic diagram showing how osmotic pressure is defined. The amount of pressure that must be applied to the piston to prevent any net water movement through the membrane is said to be the *osmotic pressure* of the sugar and water solution.

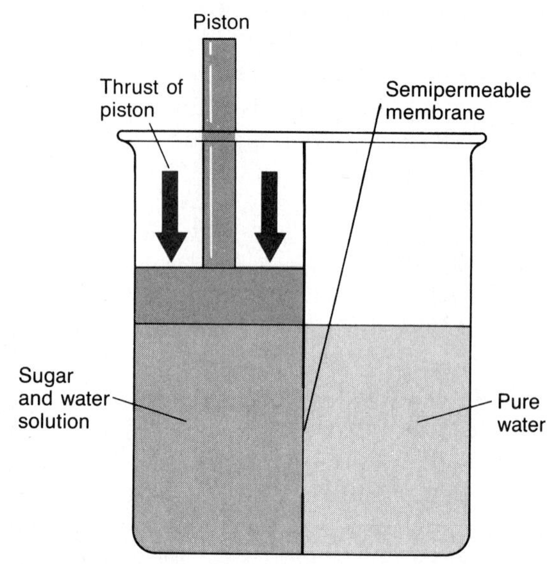

both sides would indicate that the sugar solution was slightly less concentrated than it was originally, while the water would still be pure (figure 3.7).

Here is what happened. If the membrane had not been present, simple diffusion would have taken place and there would have been a double movement. Sugar would have diffused into the mass of water, and water would have diffused in the opposite direction, both running down their concentration gradients. But with the membrane in place the solute couldn't move. The water could, and it did.

Osmotic pressure is every bit as real as hydraulic pressure and is just as easy to measure. Figure 3.8 illustrates the concept behind the determination of osmotic pressure in a solution. If a piston is inserted into the side containing the higher concentration of solutes, and pressure applied until the movement of water stops, the pressure necessary to stop this movement—but not reverse it—is the **osmotic pressure** of the sugar solution.

Osmotic pressures are always quoted in comparison to pure water, and they are expressed in terms of the height of a water column that that amount of pressure will support. The amount of force that can be present during osmotic disequilibria can be pretty hard to believe. For instance, to stop pure water from moving into a 20 percent sugar solution, the amount of pressure that must be applied to a piston like the one in figure 3.8 would support a column of water 250 meters high—that's more than 800 feet—an incredible pressure. Concentration differences of this magnitude are never encountered in biological systems, but clearly, osmotic pressure is respectable and is capable of moving water any place it has to go.

For purely practical reasons, measuring water columns hundreds of feet high would be rather silly, particularly in a student laboratory, so we try to avoid such problems. To conform to international agreement, we convert our water columns into columns of mercury, a liquid metal that is much heavier than water and so has shorter columns. The average blood pressure in the arteries of the human kidney would support a column of water a little over 30 inches high. That 30 inches converts to just 70 mm of mercury (not quite 3 inches), a much handier size to work with. Both osmotic and hydrostatic pressures are expressed in millimeters of mercury for the sake of easy calculation and convenience in the laboratory.

There are other terms that are frequently used to describe osmotic relationships between solutions. A solution with a higher osmotic pressure than another is said to be **hypertonic** to the weaker solution. The weaker solution is **hypotonic** to the stronger, and if the two solutions have equal osmotic strength, they are said to be ***iso*tonic** to each other.

It is important to understand the relationship between the terms *tonicity, osmolarity,* and *concentration.* As referred to in the text, *tonicity* is intended to equate to *osmolarity;* hence two solutions that are *isotonic* to each other must, by definition, also be *isosmotic.* However, *tonicity* and *osmolarity* are not synonyms. The term *tonicity* can be used when osmotic phenomena are not involved in any way. For example, when two solutions of different concentrations are exposed to each other directly, without involving a membrane of any kind, it would be correct to refer to the more concentrated solution as being hypertonic to the other. Thus in this context, *tonicity* is correctly equated to *concentration.*

Figure 3.9 Effect of tonicity on an animal cell. In an isotonic solution, there is no net movement of water, and the appearance of a red blood cell remains the same. In a hypertonic solution, there is a net movement of water (*arrow*) to the outside of the cell and the cell shrinks. In a hypotonic solution, there is a net movement of water (*arrow*) to inside the cell and the cell swells to bursting. (Circles = solute; stipples = solvent.)

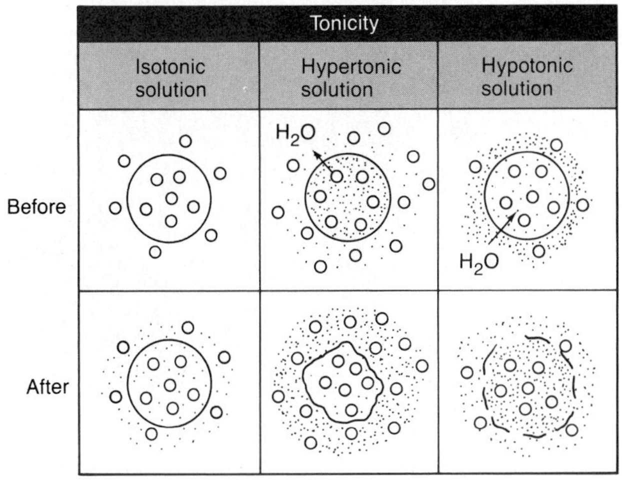

	Tonicity		
	Isotonic solution	Hypertonic solution	Hypotonic solution
Before		H_2O	H_2O
After			

Any time there is a difference in the water concentration between two compartments separated by a semipermeable membrane, water will move. Volume changes in various body zones reflect osmotic changes in the blood and extracellular fluids. This is the reason for using **physiological** (isotonic) **saline** to replace body fluids lost during illness. The saline solution is intended to maintain equilibrium throughout the system. Control systems that regulate water balance are ultimately geared toward maintaining osmotic equilibria among the body compartments that contain water—the interstitial fluid, the blood plasma, and the body cells (see figure 3.9).

There is a rather unusual concept that probably should be elucidated now. I stated in the discussion on diffusion that the passive movement of materials was always from a high concentration to a lower one, and we have seen that osmosis is a passive method of translocating water. Yet when water moves in obedience to an osmotic gradient, it flows from solutions of low solute concentration to those where the concentration is relatively high and that may seem, on the surface, to be a contradiction.

It isn't, really. It is difficult to think of a container as having a higher concentration of water than some other beaker, but in a sense that is what obtains during osmotic movement. In a beaker containing only water, a given volume might contain, say, 1,000 molecules of water. In a beaker containing sugar and water, the same volume of fluid might contain 800 molecules of water and 200 molecules of sugar. Thus, in a given volume of pure water, there will be more water molecules than there will be in any fluid that contains dissolved particles. When osmotic movement occurs, therefore, water is actually flowing from a high concentration *of water* to a lower concentration *of water.*

Filtration

Living systems use a lot of techniques to translocate materials from place to place, but occasionally it becomes necessary to select solute particles of a specific size and restrict their movement while permitting relatively free movement of others present in the same dispersion. This involves a principle with which all of us are familiar and have almost certainly used at one time or another—the principle of **filtration,** the segregation of particles according to their linear dimensions.

Energy from "Outside the System"

Filtration differs from osmosis and diffusion in one very important and basic way: it requires external energy to effect the separation—the energy is not "in the system." Pouring crushed pineapple into a sieve will separate the juice and tiny pulp particles from the larger chunks of fruit, and gravity supplies the energy to draw the fluid through. When we expand our chest cavities to draw air into our lungs, we filter dust particles from the entering air by means of a network of hairs inside our nasal passages. The energy for this filtration process is supplied by atmospheric pressure and is a result of the "suction" we provide through use of our muscles. On a finer level, the pumping action of the heart furnishes the energy for blood filtration in the capillaries of our circulatory systems, which act as sieves. In all cases, the materials that pass through the filter are separated from those that don't on the basis of size: only the smaller ones pass through.

Active Transport

When diffusion or osmosis occurs, the movement of involved particles is always downhill—from a high concentration to a lower one. Yet in the human body, there are instances when movement has obviously occurred in the opposite direction. Our body cells contain high concentrations of potassium, excluding most of it from the fluids outside. The thyroid gland accumulates large concentrations of iodine while the fluids all around it have only a trace, and sodium is kept out of body cells despite its tendency to diffuse into the interior. Such imbalances indicate the presence of a system that can move particles in a direction opposite to the way they want to diffuse, and that kind of movement requires a carefully directed expenditure of energy. The process is known as **active transport,** and it requires the active participation of a living system.

Over the years, the mechanisms involved in active transport have been the subject of much speculation and considerable research. The most favored model offered today suggests that a group of proteins extending completely across the cell membrane can recognize the required materials and trap them. Then, by using energy to change conformation slightly, these proteins—which are actually enzymes—tip on a central fulcrum like a pair of teeter-totters facing each other, closing off the original opening and releasing the transported material into the interior of the cell (see figure 3.10).

The energy spent in these operations is prodigious. Recent calculations indicate that living systems spend more energy in active transport operations than for any other purpose. Movement of materials from inside the gut . . . across the intestinal walls into the blood . . . movement of waste products from the blood into waste-disposal structures . . . concentration of *any* products anywhere in the body must be an active process.

Facilitated (Carrier-Mediated) Diffusion

Facilitated diffusion is a poorly understood process that may represent a modification of carrier-protein movement similar to, yet subtley different from, those hypothesized for active transport. Just as some materials must be made to move uphill, *against* concentration gradients, there are a few that need help to move despite the fact that they want to coast downhill. Glucose, for example, is required constantly by all body tissues. Inside body cells, it is broken up as a source of energy. Since it is being used up inside the cells, its concentration outside will nearly always be greater than it is inside; hence the diffusion gradient should carry it in easily . . . but it doesn't. The problem is that cell membranes are made mostly of lipids, so only lipid-soluble materials can go *through* the membrane. Glucose molecules are polar, hence are *water*-soluble. Characteristically, water-soluble molecules like glucose enter cells by passing through protein-lined pores in the membranes, but glucose molecules are, more often than not, too big to slip through the pores in cell membranes. Yet in spite of this they manage to get into the cell easily.

Figure 3.10 Active transport is apparent when a molecule crosses the cell membrane toward the area of greater concentration. An expenditure of ATP is required, presumably to allow a protein carrier to transport molecules across the cell membrane.

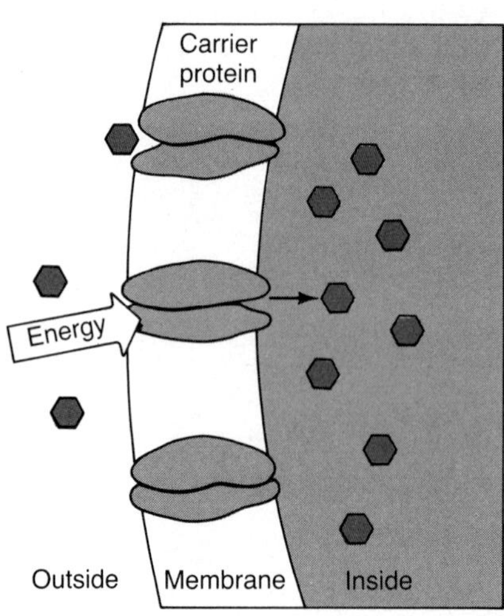

Nobody is sure exactly how they do it, but there are several hypotheses. One model suggests the existence of special kinds of enzymes called **carrier enzymes.** These are special proteins designed and built for the sole purpose of attaching to certain molecules and literally "carrying" them from one place to another. They operate in the following manner: A molecule (molecule *A*) is required on the inside of a cell, and it is more highly concentrated outside than it is inside, but membrane pores are not big enough to let it move freely through them. To move additional quantities of molecule *A* into the cell, a carrier enzyme (*X*) moves from the inside of the cell membrane to the outside. It can use the energy of diffusion to do so because the concentration of enzyme *X* is greater at the inside surface of the membrane than it is at the outer surface. At the outside surface of the membrane, a portion of the enzyme sticks out into the fluid around the cell, and when molecule *A* chances to brush against it, it sticks to enzyme X. Molecule *A* and its carrier are now linked together into a complex (*AX*), and in that form, they can diffuse across the membrane to the inner surface, because the concentration of *AX* particles is greatest at the outside of the membrane. Once on the inside surface of the membrane, the enzyme disconnects from molecule *A*, and *A* is released into the interior of the cell.

Figure 3.11 One proposed model of facilitated diffusion. Only by following concentration gradients could movement occur through a cell membrane with no systemic expenditure of energy. This figure suggests one way this might happen. (*a*) The enzyme concentration is equal on both sides of the membrane—no net movement. (*b*) When complex AX forms, concentrations change. AX is more concentrated on the left side of the membrane. Enzyme X is concentrated on the right. (*c*) Following concentration gradients, enzymes X migrate across to the left. The AX complexes move to the right. (*d*) Once it reaches the inner surface of the membrane, complex AX breaks apart, releasing molecule A into the interior of the cell. Enzymes X, meanwhile, are forming new complexes on the other side.

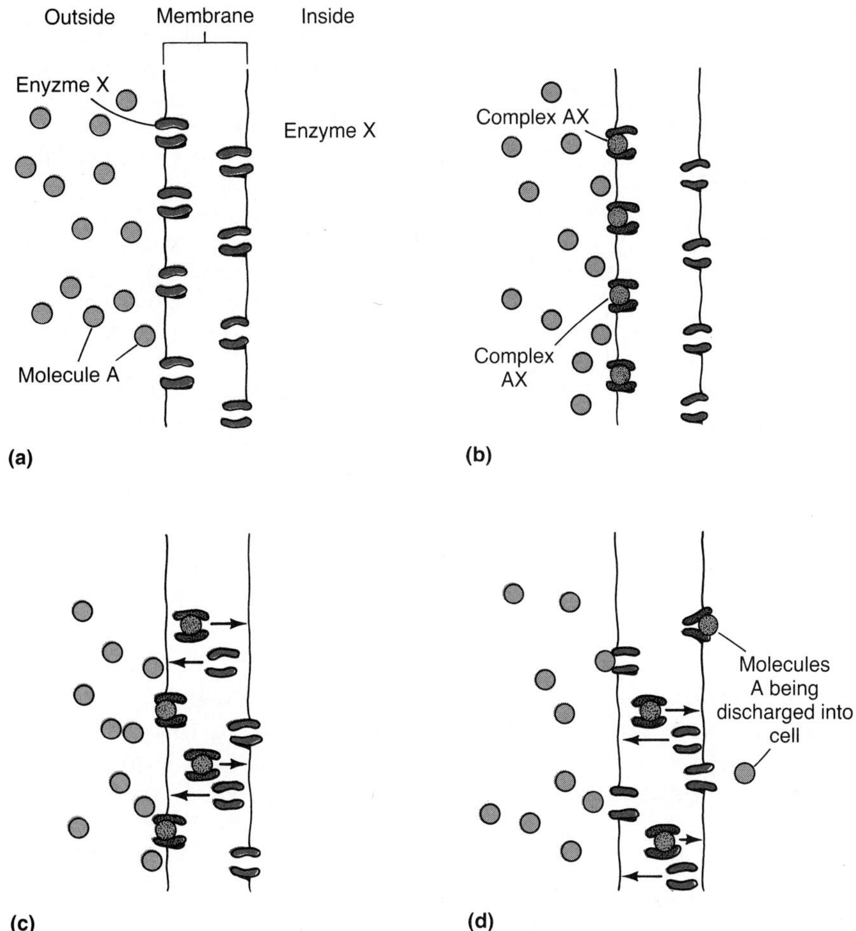

In the thyroid gland, molecule *A* could be iodide. In a muscle or nerve cell, it might be potassium. Or, as mentioned in a preceding paragraph, molecule *A* might be a glucose molecule. Figure 3.11 illustrates this model.

This latter hypothesis is particularly appealing for several reasons. Possibly the most important is the fact that it could move the glucose without using any cellular energy to do it, and that is apparently how the system works. It also has some circumstantial support. Facilitated diffusion shows all the properties that are consistent with what we already know of carrier enzymes. First of all, we know that carrier enzymes are *specific,* which means they will carry only one type of molecule and no other. Secondly, they can be *saturated,* and the facilitated diffusion of certain molecules like glucose and amino acids displays these same properties.

Summary

The Chemistry of Water

Water is held together by covalent bonds. It is composed of hydrogen and oxygen in a 2:1 ratio. The spatial arrangement of the atoms is such that it is a charged molecule.

Hydrogen bonds. Hydrogen bonds are the strongest of the weak polar attractive forces. They are responsible for holding liquid or solid water molecules together in a mass. They are also responsible for many of the physical properties of liquid water.

Physical Properties of Water

I. Water is unusually stable. It requires large energy inputs to force changes in temperature.
II. A good conductor of energy. Temperature equilibrates throughout its mass very quickly.
III. High heat capacity. A large input of energy is required to increase the temperature of water.
IV. High heat of vaporization. A large input of energy is necessary to change water from a liquid to a gas.
V. High boiling point.
VI. Water expands when it freezes. This means that solid water (ice) will not sink in liquid water. This has prevented our oceans from becoming solid ice.
VII. Powerful surface tension. This is related to hydrogen bonding.
VIII. Electrical conductivity. Water's conductivity increases enormously when electrolytes are added.

Chemical Properties of Water

I. Water is stable chemically. It can operate as an acid, as a base, or as a neutral solution.
II. Water is chemically labile. Its pH is adjustable throughout a wide range.
III. Water is a remarkable solvent.

Dispersions, Mixtures, Solutions, and Colloids

I. Dispersions and Mixtures
  A. Whenever particles of one kind are spread through particles of another kind, a dispersion is created. There are many kinds of dispersions.
  B. A mixture is a dispersion in which two or more pure substances are involved.
II. Suspensions. The word *suspension* refers to a dispersion in which the interspersed particles never settle to the bottom of the container.
  A. Solutions are suspensions in which the particles are all less than 10 Å in size.
  B. Colloids are suspensions in which the particles are between 10 Å and 1000 Å in size. Most of the particles in living sytems are colloidal.
  C. Temporary suspensions are dispersions in which the particles are sufficiently heavy to eventually settle to the bottom of the container.

Measuring Atoms

I. Atomic Mass Units. An atomic mass unit is one-twelfth the mass of a carbon atom.
II. Atomic Number. The atomic number of an element represents the number of positive charges on the element's nucleus.
III. Mass Number. The mass number of an element represents the total number of protons plus neutrons (collectively called nucleons) in the nucleus.
IV. Atomic Weight. The term *atomic weight* is a misnomer. It refers not to weight but to the mass of the element involved. One gram atomic weight is exactly one-twelfth the mass of a carbon atom. Whenever the number of atoms in a quantity of any element equals the number of carbon atoms in 12 grams of pure carbon, there is one gram atomic weight of that element present.
  A. The Mole. Whenever the quantity of any substance contains the same number of basic particles as there are atoms in 12 grams of carbon, there is one mole of that substance present. The particles can be atoms or molecules.
  B. Gram Molecular Weights. Whenever the number of molecules in a quantity of any compound equals the number of carbon atoms that are present in 12 grams of pure carbon, there is one gram molecular weight of that compound present.

Acids and Bases

I. Pure water is neither acid nor basic. It is neutral.
  A. Water consists of H_2O molecules. Some of these will ionize, producing hydrogen (H^+) and hydroxyl (OH^-) ions.
  B. In pure water, the concentration of hydrogen ions is equal to the concentration of hydroxyl ions, or $[H^+] = [OH^-]$.
II. Acids. Whenever the number of hydrogen ions in a water solution is greater than the number of hydroxyl ions, the solution is an acid. The more the hydroxyl ions are outnumbered, the more acidic the solution is.
III. Bases (alkalines). Whenever the number of hydroxyl ions in an aqueous solution is greater than the number of hydrogen ions, the solution is basic. The more the hydrogen ions are outnumbered, the more basic the solution is.

Acid/Base Balance and pH

I. pH. The term *pH* is a mathematical designation that refers to the hydrogen ion concentration in an aqueous solution.
  A. The pH of pure water is 7. Any aqueous solution that is neutral, therefore, has a pH of 7.

   B. Since pH represents a negative hydrogen ion concentration, any pH reading that is less than 7 is acid. Any pH reading greater than 7 is considered alkaline.
II. Buffers. Buffers are weak acids (or bases) and the salts of those acids (or bases).
   A. Their function is to resist a change in pH.
   B. Living systems use armies of buffers to maintain homeostasis in their body fluids, which are all aqueous.

Molecular Movement in Living Systems

I. Passive Movement. Whenever the movement of materials in a living system is accomplished without using any of the organism's energy, the movement is considered passive. The energy for passive movement is in the molecules of which the substance is composed.
II. Diffusion is a passive means of translocating materials.
   A. Diffusion occurs whenever a substance is more concentrated in one area than in another and there are no obstacles between.
   B. For diffusion to take place, all that is necessary is a concentration gradient for the materials to "coast" down.
III. Osmosis is a passive means of translocating water. It occurs whenever two liquids of unequal density are separated by a membrane that permits movement of the solvent but not the solute. Such membranes are called semipermeable. Water moves from where its density is greatest to where it is less dense.
IV. Filtration
   A. An external energy input is needed.
   B. Filtration occurs whenever an outside force is used to force a dispersion through a sieve. Particles are separated from one another on the basis of size.
V. Active Transport. Whenever the movement of materials within a living system requires an input of energy from the organism, the movement is said to be active.
   A. Active transport occurs whenever an outside force is used to force particles to move against a concentration gradient.
   B. Living systems use more energy in performing active transport than they use for any other purpose.
VI. Facilitated diffusion is an unusual form of passive translocation.
   A. No external energy is required, but movement of materials is faster and easier than it would be without the intercession of facilitating agents.
   B. Movement is always from high concentration to a lower one.

Review Questions

1. Describe the water molecule. Be sure to mention:
   a. the type of chemical bond that holds it together.
   b. the reason for the electrical charges that render it a polar molecule.
2. Discuss hydrogen bonding and the location of these bonds in a mass of water.
3. Identify and describe the seven physical properties of water that make it an ideal matrix for life. Be sure that you're able to relate each of these properties to some important aspect of living systems.
4. Identify and describe the three chemical properties so important to life.
5. Outline the characteristics of the following:
   a. dispersions
   b. mixtures
   c. suspensions
   d. solutions
   e. colloids
   f. temporary suspensions

   Be sure that you are able to distinguish between each of these and can describe them in a manner that is satisfactory to someone who has no knowledge of what each might be.
6. Define the following:
   a. atomic mass unit
   b. atomic number
   c. mass number
   d. atomic weight
   e. mole
   f. gram molecular weight
7. What is the gram molecular weight of H_2SO_4? HNO_3? NH_4OH? C_2H_5OH?
8. Define an acid. How does it differ from a base?
9. What is the difference between a strong acid and a weak one?
10. What does the following expression identify: $-\log_{10}[H^+] = ?$
11. What table is used to describe the acid/base balance in biological systems?
12. Why is acid/base balance important to living systems?
13. What is the function of a buffer?
14. Diffusion takes place whenever a concentration gradient exists in a mixture of substances. Where does the energy come from that makes diffusion possible?
15. How does osmosis differ from diffusion? Of what significance to living systems are these two phenomena?
16. Define the terms *hypotonic, isotonic,* and *hypertonic.*
17. In what fundamental way does the process of filtration differ from diffusion and osmosis?
18. Is it possible for active transport to occur outside of a living system? Explain.
19. Describe the process of facilitated diffusion to the best of your ability.

Chapter 4 The Cell

Study Hints

When reading this chapter, try to understand that every living thing—including you—is built of individual units that are too tiny to see with the naked eye. We are the sum of individual units; hence we work according to the way *they* work.

1. Note that each individual cell contains still smaller structures that function as organs do in whole organisms.
2. Note that these little chemical systems are the very foundation of life. They are composed of the biochemicals that we discussed in chapter 3, and somehow, when they are assembled into the structures we will investigate, they produce life.
3. It may be beneficial to view the fluid contents of the cell as an infinitesimal ocean in which the materials that comprise life are suspended.
4. Try to appreciate the fact that it is the job of this tiny ocean to provide these living particles with a completely benevolent medium in which to live and that its activities are essentially aimed at maintaining homeostasis.
5. It is important to be aware that the cell is not a drop of living materials tucked away inside an inert bag. The membrane that surrounds each body cell is as alive as anything else within the body and is definitely *not* inert.
6. Try to view the cell as a factory in which all necessary manufacturing and food production for the entire body takes place. The nucleus represents the executive offices from which all instructions come, and control of all operations resides therein.

Objectives

When you have finished reading this chapter, you should:

1. be able to relate the importance of the cell theory to modern physiology.
2. understand the nature of phospholipids and be able to explain how they arrange themselves in a watery matrix.
3. know the fundamental chemical structure of the cell membrane and be able to explain in part how it controls the movement of fats and water-soluble chemicals across itself.
4. be able to describe the function of the cytosol.
5. know the structure and function of the cellular organelles.
6. be able to describe the cellular framework.
7. know how cells are able to obtain and get rid of particles too large to pass through the cell membrane.
8. be able to discuss protein synthesis.

SEM scan of Golgi apparatus.

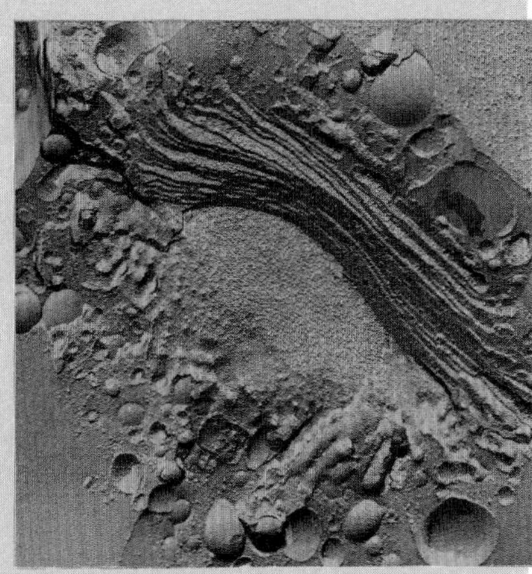

Introduction

The invention of the microscope in the mid-seventeenth century made humanity suddenly aware of the existence of a new, miniscule universe. Even with low magnification and primitive single lenses, there was a whole new world opening up. Exploration, which had been thought of mainly as enlarging the world, suddenly found a new, smaller one, and interest that had been directed outward turned inward as well. With perceptions expanded by the new instruments, a flurry of microscopic investigation began. Scholars and curiosity seekers began buying or grinding lenses of greater and greater precision in the hope of seeing something wonderful in dust or flower pollen.

The most successful of the early microscopists was a Dutchman named Antonie van Leeuwenhoek, who is recorded historically as the first person to see microorganisms.

From the standpoint of social status, the most distinguished of the earliest microscopists was an Englishman named Robert Hooke (1635–1703). Hooke's interest in microscopes was essentially casual, but it was nevertheless he who gave the name **cell** to the indivisible units that serve as the component modules of the human body (see figure 4.1).

A couple of centuries passed before Hooke's observations became a revered part of biological history. Partly because of technological limitations, microscopial observations drifted into a scientific limbo, but with the nineteenth century came advances in optics and an efficient, practical compound microscope was at last developed (figure 4.2). With a new research plateau suddenly appearing a few meters higher than the old one, a covey of researchers promptly leaped up onto it.

To really appeciate the significance of the cell theory, we must consider the problems that confronted nineteenth-century physicians and biomedical scientists. The foundation of all physiological postulates at that time was that the whole person was the indivisible living unit, a position that was not difficult to justify. Persons are indivisible in the sense that if you divide them in half, the characteristics of life disappear. And certainly no one would argue against the presumption that each individual is a unique entity. No two people are exactly alike—not even identical twins. One person wants to be a farmer, another a clerk. One person dies of plague, while a sibling, repeatedly exposed to the same disease, might never contract it. This, to the nineteenth-century biologist, was more than enough evidence that the living unit was the entire individual. It was logical, but it left physiologists with a hopeless task. To learn how people worked, they were confronted with the prospect of experimenting on people as separate and unrelated units, and discoveries applied only to one person. Facts uncovered about one person told nothing about how some *other* person might work, because everybody is unique.

As long as the science of physiology was theoretically constricted by this outlook, any attempt to figure out how living systems worked was futile. Corked up in a philosophical bottle, the science of physiology sat helplessly fettered until two German researchers walked in and changed the rules.

The complete hypothesis known as the *cell theory* was published in 1839 by M. J. Schleiden, a botanist, and Johannes Schwann, a zoologist. They had been working separately for years with their respective materials, and it was not until they met and talked together that they realized they were both investigating the same things. The union of their ideas gave birth to the new theory. Whether or not they appreciated the tremendous potential of their mutual discovery is not known . . . possibly they did, probably they did not. Its impact was so sweeping—so universal—that it is hard to believe even the most egotistical person would expect it.

The circumstances that led to Leeuwenhoek's discovery of microorganisms make an interesting story. He had always been curious about the unusual effect that pepper had inside of the human mouth, and now he believed he was in possession of a tool that might solve his problem. His first hypothesis was that pepper, when placed in water, released a series of tiny spears. These spears, he reasoned, punctured the tongue, gums, and cheeks, producing the painful "hot" sensation. Having decided on a theory, he set out with true scientific fervor to see if he was right. His first test consisted of examining some pepper placed in a droplet of water, but the results of this test were negative. Undaunted, Leeuwenhoek decided that water alone didn't release the tiny spears . . . it took *more* than just water. He decided that the little spears were only released under the influence of something that was in the human mouth, so he placed some of his own saliva on a watch glass, added a couple of grains of pepper, and took a look. The results were utterly unexpected. He saw no tiny spears, but he did see something wriggling—something alive! His drawings indicate that he saw several different kinds of protozoans and some bacteria. If the microscopic livestock inhabiting his mouth is any indication of the general public's attitude toward oral hygiene, Hollanders of the seventeenth century must have had mouths like compost heaps.

The Cell Theory

Simply stated, the **cell theory** holds that *all life is cellular in nature,* and that *all life emerges from preexisting cells.* Profound statements indeed, and as it turned out, their implications were even more profound. The cell theory presented biological science with a unifying force at least as important as Darwin's evolutionary theory and a good deal less controversial. Some, particularly those working in the field of microscopy, had suspected for years that large organisms were actually a huge collection of tiny cells, but for reasons of their own they had kept their ideas to themselves. When Schleiden and Schwann published their hypothesis, therefore, they already had a considerable number of supporters.

A New Scientific Plateau

Schleiden and Schwann's theory provided biological scientists with the common denominator they had been looking for. Just as the discovery of the atom provided physicists with a means of understanding how matter was arranged and how it worked, the cell theory provided biologists with a means of determining how life was assembled and how it worked.

Figure 4.1 (*a*) A primitive microscope similar to the type used by Hooke when he coined the word *cell* to describe the compartments he saw in a piece of cork. (*b*) A drawing of the empty cells of a cork particle.

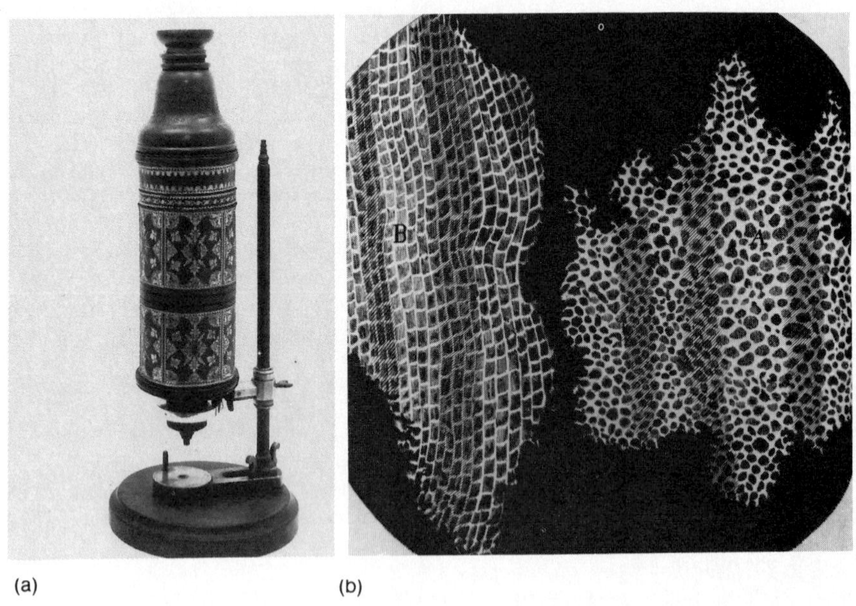

(a) (b)

Every human being might look different, but now researchers could assume that the diversity was only in the arrangement of the cells, and what was true for one cell might be true for all of them. Physiological efforts could be focused on discovering how *cells* functioned. When a scientist figured out how a cell worked, it might be possible to predict how cells would interact to form tissues, then how tissues might interact to form organs, and finally how individuals worked, because individuals were the sum of their parts, and their parts were all cells.

Even more importantly, animals were formed of cells just as humans were, and what worked for a rat or a guinea pig might work the same way for a human. It might be possible to find out how people worked without experimenting on humans. The task facing physiological scientists was no longer impossible. It was a door to a brand-new scientific plateau, and it suddenly opened like a flower in the sun.

The cell theory provided the foundation for all of the medical and biological advances of this century. Without it, chances are that we would never have advanced beyond a primitive, almost mystical, view of living organisms. With it as a basis, we cannot begin to see the end of what we can learn. We have merely seen the end of the beginning.

The "Generalized" Cell

The first "composite cell" was collated and diagramed by the American cytologist Edmund B. Wilson (1856–1939). Using all the cytological techniques available at the time, he prepared, stained, viewed, and sketched hundreds of different cells and cell types. He peered at drawings and photomicrographs of hundreds of others produced by various workers around the world. Finally, in 1926, he published a drawing of what he called a "generalized" cell containing all the things he felt were present, more or less, in all cells. His efforts were accepted as definitive until the late 1950s. Diagrams made in the 1920s and 1930s were repeatedly used *in toto* or slightly modified in both high school and college textbooks (figure 4.3), and the reason was, quite simply, that the light microscope had shown us all it was capable of showing. It took the electron microscope to significantly alter our perception of the cell.

The Electron Microscope

Although it is called a microscope, it is not very much like the instrument most people think of when they hear the word. For one thing, you cannot look at things through an electron microscope the way you can with an ordinary one. The electron microscope

Figure 4.2 A modern compound microscope.

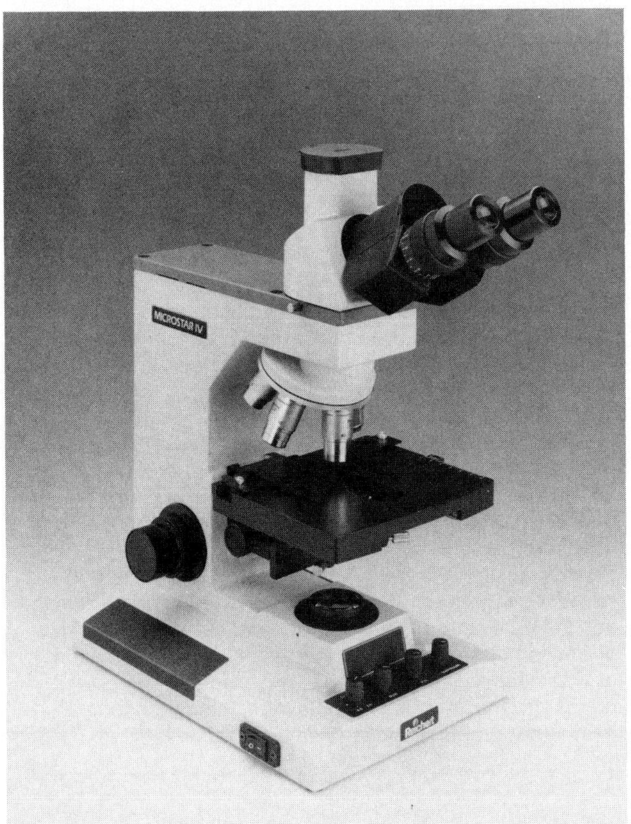

Figure 4.3 A generalized cell typical of those appearing in textbooks from 1930 to 1960. This was about as good a morphological representation of a cell as light microscopy was capable of providing. Compare it with our current view of the cell (figure 4.5).

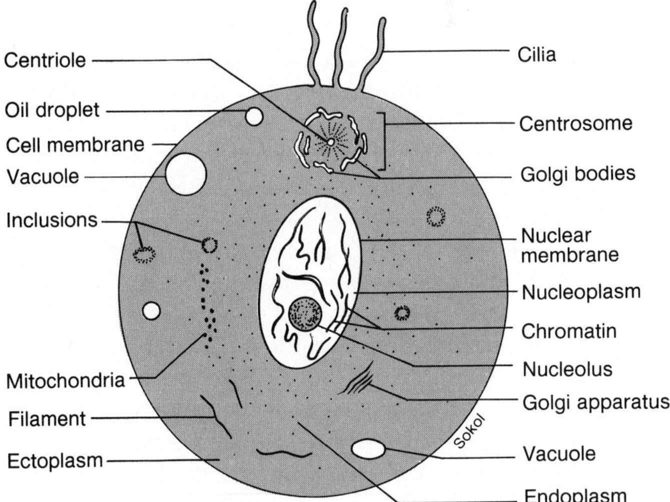

does not illuminate an object so it can be seen directly. Instead, it draws a picture of what it "sees," and we must wait until it is finished before we can examine what it has drawn. Its pencil is a stream of electrons, and its drawing board a sheet of photographic film that we develop when the sketch is done. Modern electron microscopes can project a picture of what is "visible" under its scanner, but one cannot view the object directly.

Furthermore, one can never view a sample in its living state. Merely the preparation of a sample for electron microscopy renders it quite dead. The sample must first be completely dried and imbedded in some solid matrix, usually a soft plastic. Then it is sliced. The slicing is done with special knives made from plate glass, and the slices they cut may be thinner than any living unit that exists. Even if the material could survive the imbedding and the slicing, it could never survive the vacuum of the electron microscope. The microscope draws pictures with electrons, and electrons are smaller than air molecules. If there is any air present when the beam is making its sketch, the picture will not be perfect, because the electrons will bump into air molecules. The drawings must be made, therefore, in as total a vacuum as technology can produce.

Artifacts

Of course, new problems arrived with the new instrument. Sometimes the things that must be done to prepare a specimen for electron microscopy, which are known collectively as **fixation,** produce weird figures or wrinkles that are not present in living cells, and these are faithfully reproduced by the electron beam. They are known in the discipline as **fixation artifacts,** and they're hard to cull out of new research. Every new electron microscopial discovery is therefore subjected to critical scrutiny by many workers using various kinds of fixation techniques before they are accepted as genuine by the scientific world.

The electron microscope has opened incredible vistas. We can actually view pictures of sugar molecules and the chemicals comprising the cell wall of a germ. We have photographed DNA molecules and the proteins that make up a viral coat. The electron microscope has told us beyond a shadow of a doubt that life is not just a drop of slime amorphously packed in an inert bag, as the early microscopists believed.

Maybe the single most important thing that the electron microscope has given us is a feeling of how infinitesimal the essence of life must be. As we inspect ever more closely the tiny shapes inside these diminutive living units, we are increasingly aware of an aura of something alive. This is perplexing, because as we unravel the cellular ultrastructure we find nothing but chemicals—mostly organic, but just chemicals, nevertheless. They are complex arrangements of carbon, hydrogen, oxygen—sometimes nitrogen and maybe one or two other elements twisted and rearranged. Many of them would probably look and behave the way they do if they were just dumped into a jar of buffered saline. Yet for some reason, when all these separate chemicals are organized into cellular structures—the cell membrane, the cytoskeleton, and the various organelles—and they, in their turn, are combined into the cellular organizational plan, the result is life! There may even be life in the watery fluid inside the cell. It certainly is active enough.

Maybe this is why it's so hard to precisely define life. There is so much to it . . . and simultaneously so little. The individual biochemicals that we investigate cannot possibly be *alive,* can they? They seem to be inert . . . they obey the physical laws that lumps of clay obey . . . and yet if they are not alive, then what is? There is nothing else.

The electron microscope has shown us the most incredible things. Items that were mere black spots under a light microscope have taken on a definite structure and meaning when seen by electron microscopy. Things appear whose presence wasn't even suspected, while others expand into complexities no one would think possible in entities so infinitesimal (see figure 4.4).

Actually there are two basic types of electron microscopes, and each has its disadvantages and advantages. The **transmission electron microscope** (TEM) is capable of tremendous magnification. Theoretically it is capable of separating images that are a mere half an Angstrom unit apart, which means its resolving power is nearly 2,000,000× that of the human eye. Unsolved technical problems have so far prevented magnifications on that scale, although images of 5 Angstrom units have been resolved. The biggest problem is that electron beams cannot penetrate very much. Anything prepared for viewing must be sliced *very* thin indeed—so thin that the samples sometimes fall apart before they can be photographed. And to get an idea of the three-dimensional aspects of any structure, dozens and dozens of slices have to be photographed and arranged, one on top of the other. The **scanning electron microscope** (SEM) is arranged so that instead of the electron beam penetrating the object being viewed, it rebounds from the outer surfaces, scattering and emitting secondary electrons. Thus it often draws an external view of the sample, providing a beautiful three-dimensional scan of whatever is prepared for viewing. Its resolving power is not as great as the TEM's, but since it usually scans an item's topography, it doesn't have to be.

Figure 4.4 (*a*) Under this type of light microscope, the mitochondria in a mouse liver cell (*b*) appear as dark spots. (*c*) Under this type of transmission electron microscope, the details of a single mitochondrion (*d*) are clear.

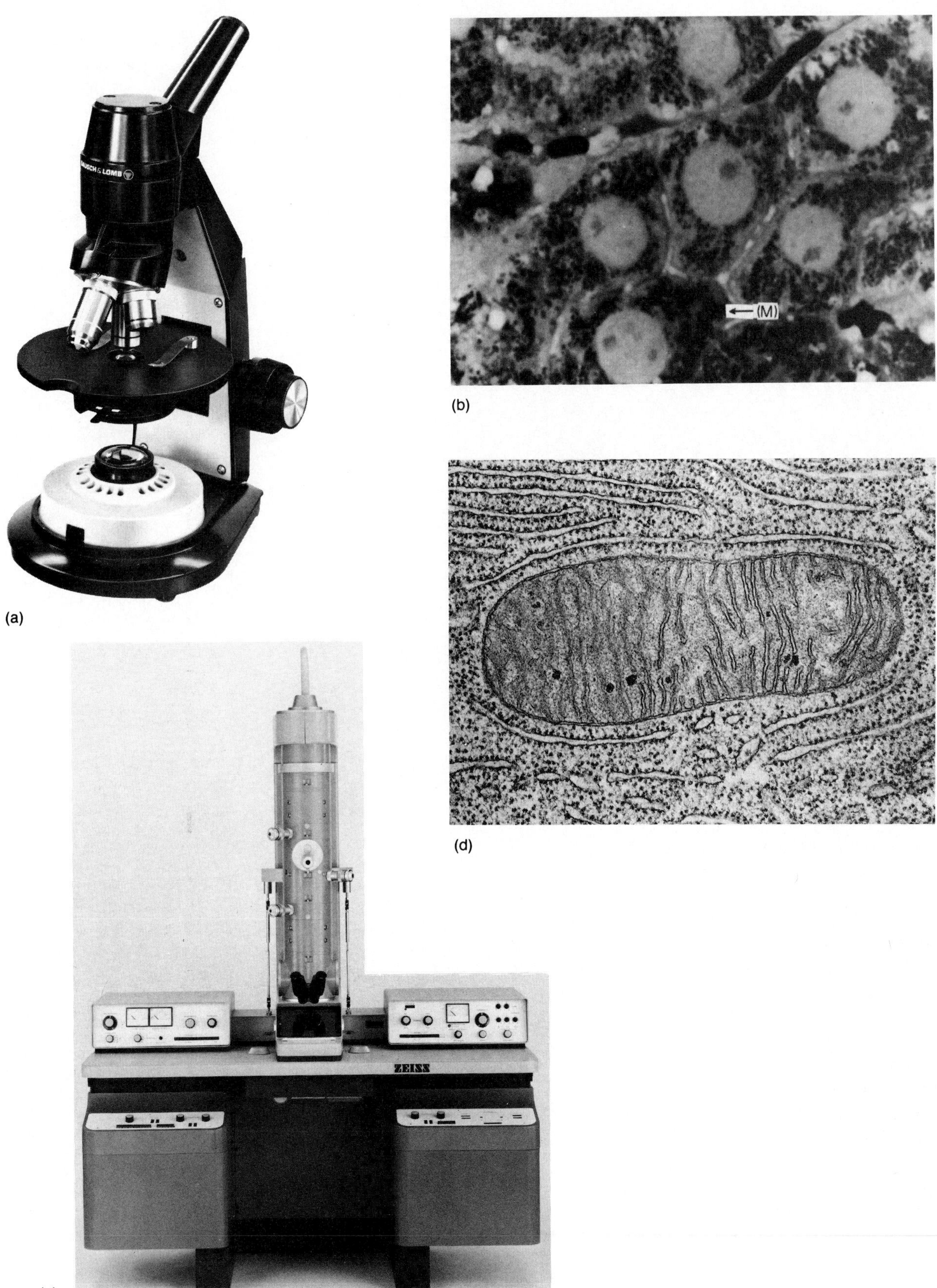

Figure 4.5 Compare this modern view of the cell with that perceived only thirty-five years ago (figure 4.3). The electron microscope has completely altered that earlier view of the cell.

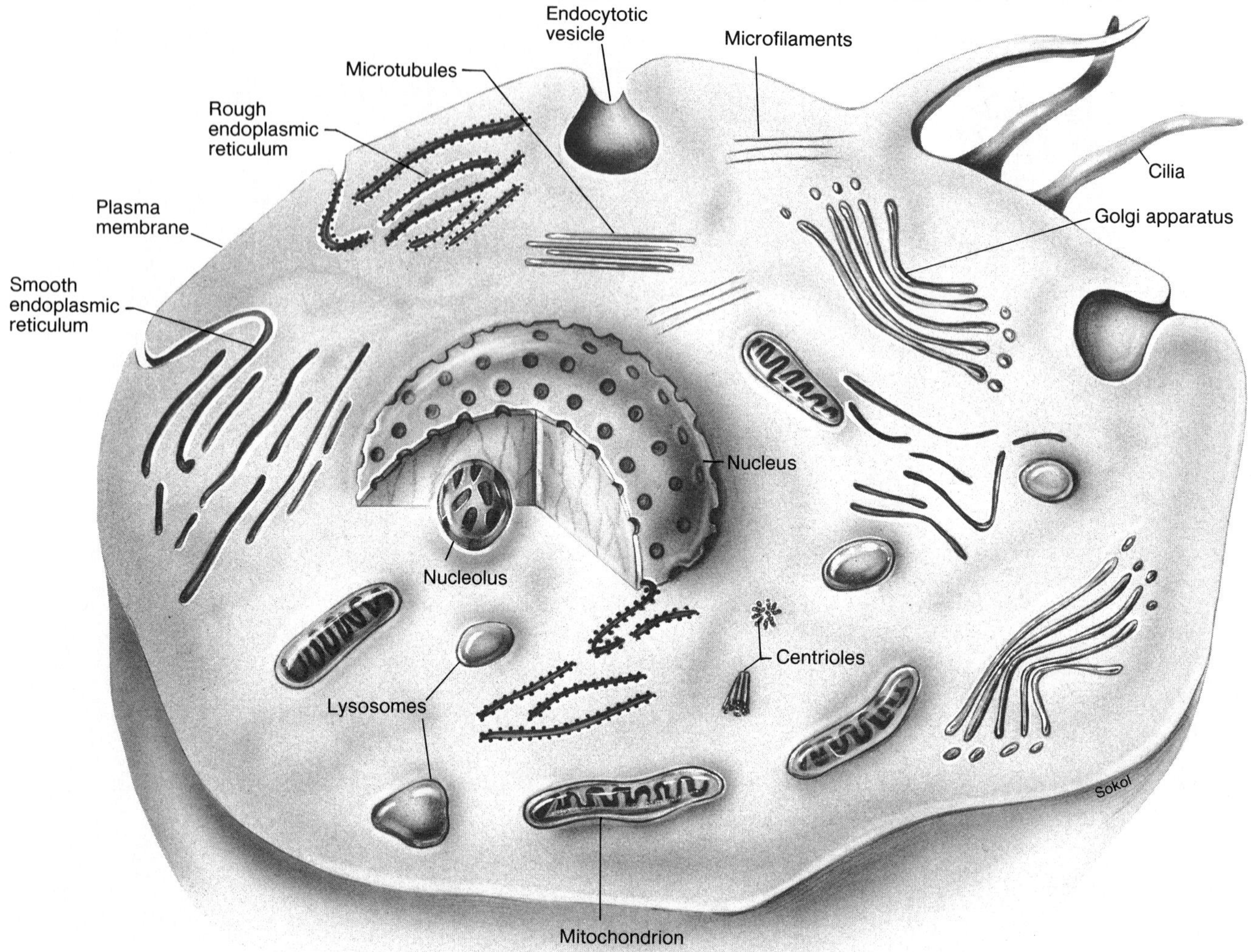

Cellular Ultrastructure

The incredible complexity of the cell with which modern biologists are familiar would stun cytologists of the 1930s and 1940s. A relatively gross view of today's cell shows many more structures and internal arrays than anyone of those years would have believed possible (figure 4.5).

Despite the disarray that appears to exist in the cellular interior, there is no lack of organization. Everything is where it is supposed to be, and there is just enough of everything to do what needs to be done. The components and substructures are carefully placed, and each is the size and shape best suited to its location and the job it does. Each performs its own special job, and all the separate operations are orchestrated like notes in a Beethoven symphony, each logically following its predecessor and leading smoothly to its successor. In this way, not only does the whole unit run in polished integration, but the operation of individual units is subordinated to the proper function of the cell as a whole.

Table 4.1 The Organelles

Name	Structure	Function
Cell membrane	Bilayer of phospholipid and globular proteins	Passage of molecules into and out of cell
Nucleus	Nuclear envelope surrounding chromosomes (DNA) and nucleoli	Cellular reproduction and control of protein synthesis
Nucleolus	Concentrated area of RNA in the nucleus	Ribosome formation
Endoplasmic reticulum	Folds of membranes forming flattened channels and tubular canals	Transport by means of vesicles
Rough	Studded with ribosomes	Protein synthesis
Smooth	Having no ribosomes	Lipid synthesis
Ribosome	Protein and RNA in two subunits	Protein synthesis
Golgi body	Stack of membranous saccules	Packaging and secretion
Vacuole and vesicle	Membranous sacs	Containers of material
Lysosome	Membranous container of hydrolytic enzymes	Intracellular digestion
Mitochondrion	Inner membrane (cristae) within outer membrane	Cellular respiration
Microfilament	Actin or myosin proteins	Movement and shape of cell
Microtubule	Tubulin protein	
Centriole	9 + 0 pattern of microtubules	Organization of microtubules
Cilium and flagellum	9 + 2 pattern of microtubules	Movement of cell

In a sense, the cell is a world unto itself. It has a definite structure, substances move into and out of it according to its requirements, and it can manufacture molecules of astonishing complexity. There is even a tiny skeleton to provide definite size and, when necessary, rigidity. The fluid inside, although it has no structure and seems to flow randomly, conforms to movements and needs of the cell and has very definite chores to do. As it flows through the cellular interior, it percolates around the various internal structures, slips through spaces between the girders and crosswalks of the cytoskeleton, washes debris out of even the sharpest corners, and carries with it everything the cell might require at any given time. Much of the work done by the cell is accomplished by the large and impressive family of subcellular particles that operate in the cellular interior. Collectively they are known as **organelles,** and the name hints at where they fit in cellular design. These tiny structures, although functionally organs, are *sub*cellular in size and *intra*cellular in placement, hence the name organelle—"little organ." See table 4.1.

The Plasma (Cell) Membrane

The outermost boundary of the living unit is the plasma membrane. Since it represents the outer boundary of the cell, one surface will face the cytosol while the other will be surrounded by the extracellular body fluids. The appearance of the outer surface depends on where the cell is in the body and what kind of job it must do. Some membranes are smooth—even glossy—while others are as rough as sandpaper or filled with craters like the bays of the moon. Some are covered with tiny cylindrical projections like the **microvilli** (*villus*—"shaggy hair") of the small intestine that increase absorptive surface area or the **cilia** (*cili*—"eyelash" or "small hair") of the trachea that move mucus or debris across the cell surfaces.

Each of these surface permutations has a function; hence each represents a specialization for a specific role it must play in the overall scheme of things. The membranes are remarkably adaptable, their variability seemingly endless, but all have one function in common. Whether they enclose a nerve cell or a lump of muscle, a kidney cell or a cell in the eyeball, they set their cell apart from all other cells. The membrane is therefore responsible for the internal privacy of the cell, and it is the membrane that makes the cell an individual unit.

The membrane is not merely an inert bag. It is a highly complex structure that is, above all, constantly changing. It regulates all relationships between what is inside the cell and the external fluids, including interaction with other cells. Its ability to interact with both lipid-soluble materials and water is unusual and essential.

Figure 4.6 Phosphatidyl choline: A typical membrane phospholipid.

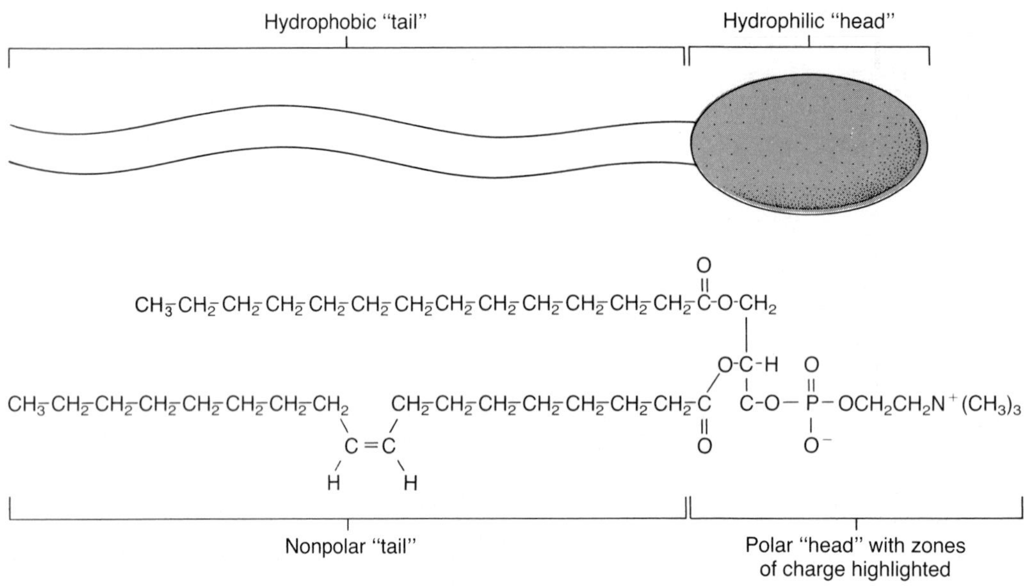

The Schizophrenic Lipid

The secret lies in the dual nature of the lipid that makes up the membrane. The molecules are **amphipathic** (*amphi*—"double"; *pathos*—"passion" or "experience"), meaning that they "experience" two things simultaneously, which is exactly how this lipid behaves. Physically, each individual molecule looks like a tadpole with a heavy, forked tail (figure 4.6). It is called a **phospholipid** because the ovoid "head" of the little tadpole contains a negatively charged phosphate and because it is there that the tadpole's head is water soluble. This is the part of the molecule that is said to be **hydrophilic** (*hydro*—"water"; *philo*—"loving"). The "tail" end is composed of two long, twisted fatty-acid chains—chains that are typically lipid. Being strictly hydrocarbons, they have no exposed charges, so they won't react with water—in fact, they want nothing to do with it, and this is the **hydrophobic** (*phobia*—"fearing") end of the molecule.

Using the term "water fearing" to describe the fatty-acid end of the phospholipid molecules isn't exactly correct. It is not so much that uncharged fatty acids are afraid of water as it is that water is snubbing the fatty acids. Water molecules are attracted to anything that is charged and don't like things that are not. Since water molecules themselves have a charge, they are drawn to each other, and when uncharged molecules appear, they brush them aside. The linking of hydrogen bonds between molecules of liquid water cordons off the oil molecules and effectively quarantines them. The spurned lipid molecules are pushed together into compact masses where they huddle in oily globes that expose the smallest surface area possible. We have all seen these phenomena. Oil and water won't mix.

Phospholipids are mainly fatty, but when they are placed in water they do not behave the way most lipids do. Because one end is charged, not only do they not roll themselves into globs like ordinary oil, but they will actually interact with water. The polar heads are strongly attracted to water, and the water is attracted to them. If it were not for the presence of their hydrophobic tails, they would dissolve, like sugar, but those tails are there—they will not go away and they won't associate with water. The phospholipid molecules solve the whole problem by forming what is known as a **micelle** (*micell*—"little crumb").

As you can see in figure 4.7, amphipathic molecules form these micelles by arranging themselves into little globe-shaped spheres with all the hydrophobic tails isolated inside, facing each other, while the polar heads stick out into the water. This way, the charged part of the molecule can interact with the water that surrounds it without exposing any of the nonpolar hydrocarbons. Each individual micelle is extremely small and tends to stay that way, so amphipathic molecules do not usually form the familiar large, oily globs when mixed with water. Micelles are also the low-energy arrangement of such molecules in a water matrix, so they form spontaneously. The micelle, however, is restricted in size to a diameter just over twice the length of the hydrophobic tail. That makes their upper size limit about 200 Å, and that is too small to enclose a living cell.

Figure 4.7 (*a*) A schematic diagram of a phospholipid micelle as it forms in water. Water is excluded from the inner zone of the micelle, which is occupied instead by the long, nonpolar tails of the phospholipid molecule. (*b*) Schematic representation of micelle globules in a water matrix. Each micelle is a unit, completely miscible with water and with no tendency to coalesce into larger spheres. Although *b* shows the micelle globules as they would be in a watery matrix, they are much too small to be seen, even with a microscope.

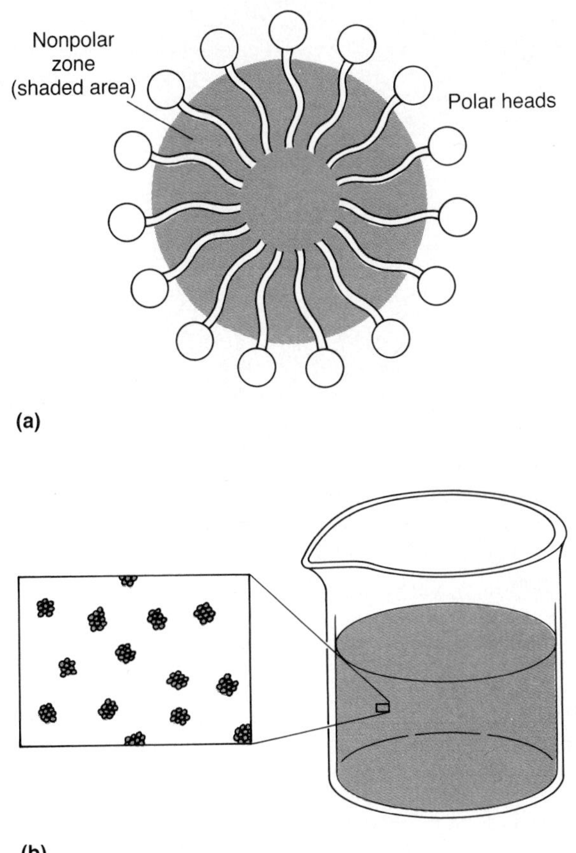

Figure 4.8 Shorthand representation of a lipid bilayer in a water matrix.

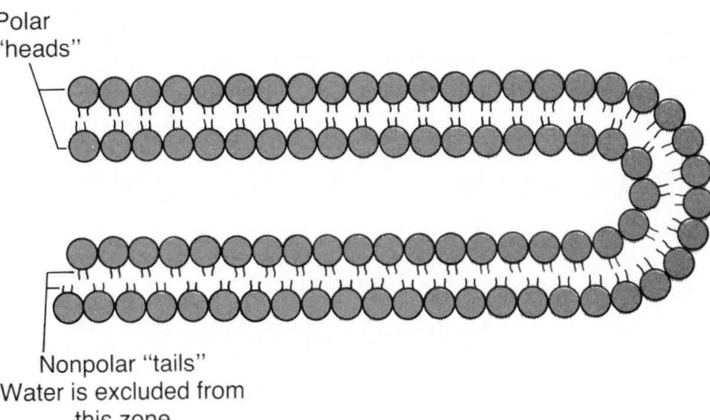

Knowledge of such bilayer phenomena is at least a half-century old. Manufacturers of detergents and soaps have produced such amphipathic molecules for decades, for that is what their products are. Detergents are known among chemists as **surface active agents.** They can disperse oil droplets in water because they are able to form amphipathic molecules that can mix with both water and oil droplets simultaneously. By doing so, they keep the oil droplets from coalescing and forming oily films, and they make it easy to rinse away oil (figure 4.9*a*). In fact, the bubbles of detergents that make homemakers so happy when they're thick on the surface of their wash water are actually very similar to cell membranes in some physical and chemical characteristics. Bubbles are really sheets of water held in place by two layers of amphipathic molecules. The sheet of water makes up the core of the bubble, and the detergent encloses it, with its hydrophilic, polarized ends facing each other in the thin film of water. The hydrophobic tails project into the air both inside and outside of the bubble (figure 4.9*b*).

The Lipid Bilayer

When large quantities of phospholipids are introduced into water, they form, instead of micelles, a figure called a bimolecular sheet or **lipid bilayer** (figure 4.8). Like the formation of micelles, the genesis of such a bilayer is spontaneous. It does not require energy input from a living system. If there are enough molecules to do it, a bimolecular sheet will form in preference to a large number of micelles, because the energy requirement is lower. This is a happy eventuality from a biological point of view, because such a sheet will be *big* . . . big enough to enclose all the organelles and supporting materials in a live cell. The molecular arrangement is similar in at least one way to that of the micelle. The molecular heads are all immersed in water, while the fatty acid tails huddle together, avoiding the water.

One very important capacity that such bilayers have is an ability to seal, instantly, holes that are poked in them. It is a phenomenon that you can observe yourselves, first hand, with only a sharp knife or large pin and a pan of soapy water. Stir the water to establish a population of large bubbles on the surface and wet a sharp knife thoroughly with detergent and water. Now stick the knife into a bubble or two. You'll see at once that *puncturing* such a bubble is simple, but *bursting* it is not. The bubble will, more often than not, seal around the gash made by the knife and will remain filled with air. If the bubble does not dry out too much before you try it, you may even be able to remove the knife without breaking it.

Since cell membranes are composed mainly of similar polar-lipid bilayers, body cells can survive in the same way when they are damaged. Actually,

Figure 4.9 (*a*) Schematic of a detergent micelle surrounding an oil or fat droplet. Detergent micelles are larger than phospholipid micelles because they are not limited to twice their "tail" length. They form around oil droplets, keeping them miscible with water and preventing them from coalescing into a thick oil scum or film. (*b*) Soap or detergent bilayers can form in air, and when they do, they imprison a sheet of water between their hydrophilic heads. The result is a bubble.

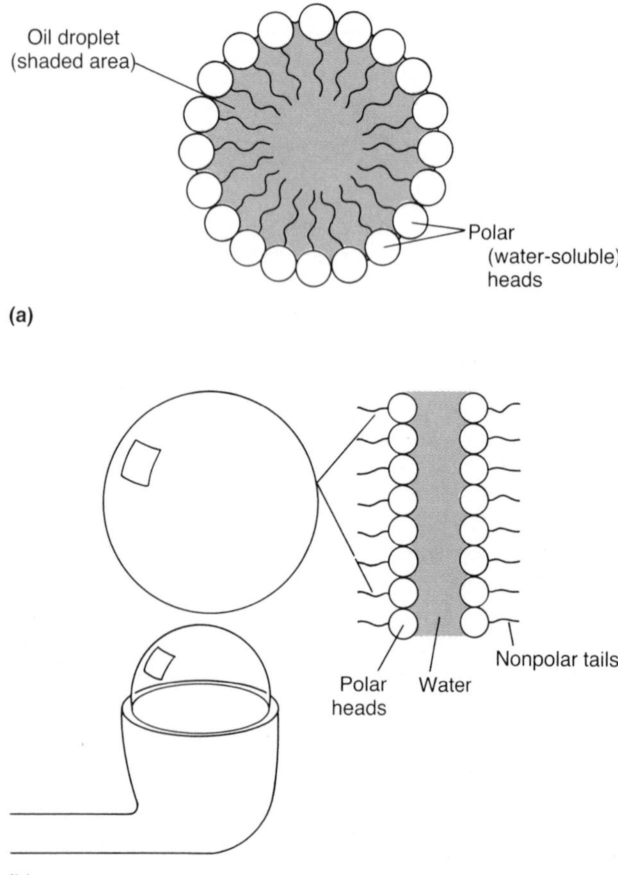

Figure 4.10 An electron micrograph of cell membranes. There is a circle (lower left) around one complete unit membrane. The three-layered nature of the membrane is clearly visible, two dense layers (the phosphate ends of the phospholipid) sandwiching the less dense fatty acid layer.

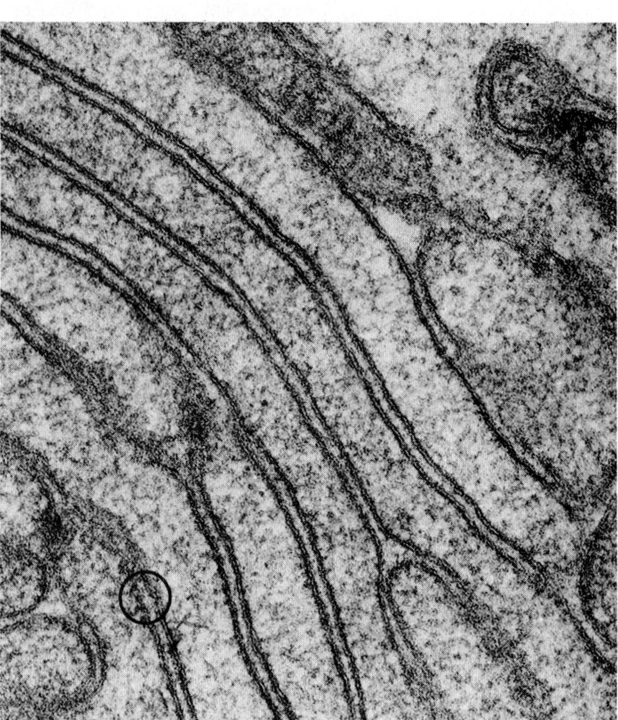

Modern technology uses bilayer phenomena in some products of industry. Commercial and military aircraft all have such layers in fuel tanks that are designed to seal holes immediately without requiring further repair. Most top-of-the-line automobile tires will also seal small puncture holes without patches being required. Rest assured, however, that cutting a tire in half will not produce two smaller tires.

plasma cell membranes are better at doing this than soap bubbles, because plasma membranes are more pliable and do not dry out. When a cell is cut into, the knife penetrates easily and the membrane promptly collapses on the knife, pressing firmly against the metal to seal the opening. As the knife is withdrawn, each molecule in the membrane drops into position, fusing with its neighbor as the knife edge narrows. When the sharp edge is withdrawn, the gash it made is sealed behind it. If the cell gets cut completely in half, the two halves will often seal up at the ends, forming two smaller cells. See figure 4.10.

Limitations of a Lipid Bilayer

Despite all these parallels, however, the plasma membrane is more than just a simple lipid bilayer. A lipid bilayer would keep *all* water-soluble particles from crossing it, because lipid bilayers are inert barriers like dams, and like a concrete and steel dam, their obstructive nature is not variable. Water-soluble materials, therefore, should not be able to get into or out of a cell. Yet while they don't cross without some effort, they *can cross*—and water itself penetrates the membrane with ease. Also, the membrane of a living cell is too pliable to be only lipid. Obviously, then, the plasma membrane is more than just lipid. The extra ingredients are protein.

Figure 4.11 The Singer/Nicholson model of the cell membrane. Protein "chunks" float in and on the phospholipid bilayer.

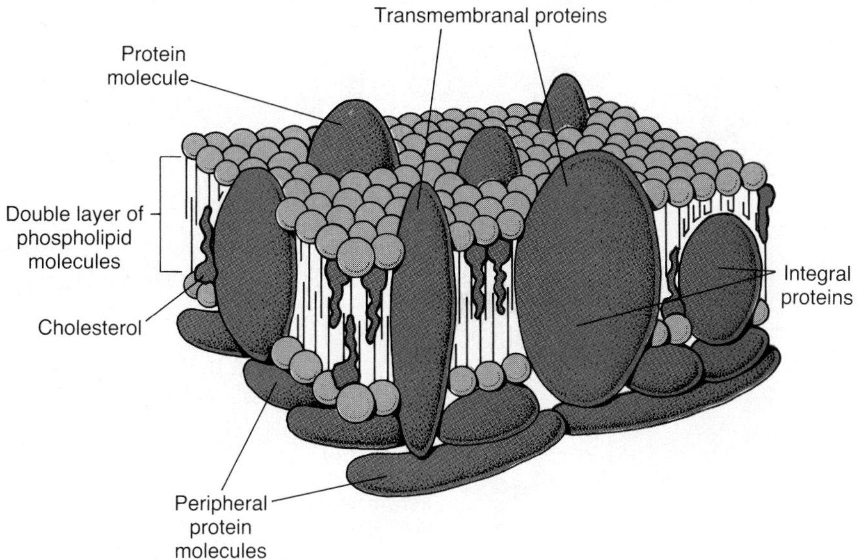

The Fluid-Mosaic Membrane

There is still some debate over the precise nature of the plasma membrane—not its chemical components, but rather the way they are arranged. It is generally agreed that the membrane is composed mainly of lipid with some associated protein. The discussions have arisen over exactly how the protein is arranged in the lipid bilayer. The most widely accepted model was suggested early in the 1970s by S. J. Singer and G. L. Nicholson.

Their offering is known as the **fluid-mosaic model,** and the modern version is essentially that (figure 4.11). It smooths out many of the problems encountered by earlier models. For instance, it

1. explains how protein content of the membrane can vary over a wide range from cell to cell.
2. is inherently adjustable. Short-term changes in membrane permeability can be explained with relative ease.

Some features are common to all of the proposed models—the idea of the lipid bilayer, for example. Lipid is definitely present in plasma membranes, and the lipid bilayer concept fits with what can actually be seen. Also, everyone agrees that the membrane is a *selective* barrier between the interstitial fluid and the fluid within the cell, because we can observe that things needed inside the cell can usually get in, and waste products, water-soluble or otherwise, are ejected. Furthermore, the differences between the fluid inside the cell and the fluid outside must be due to the membrane, because there is nothing else around that could do it. Not only does it establish differences initially, it must also be able to maintain them, because there they are.

The Membrane's Proteins

The proteins in the membrane help sustain the picture of a vital, bustling fabric. They ornament the lipid like cloves and toothpicks stuck into a ham, and like such cloves, they vary in their surface arrangement and their depth of penetration. Usually they cluster in discrete little bundles, but sometimes they are scattered, apparently at random, all across the lipid sheet. It is hard to decide whether or not they favor any particular kind of arrangement in a given cell type, because their patterns can change so quickly. Many of them can move freely along the membrane surfaces, and this ability probably accounts, at least partially, for some of the permeability changes that are so common and occur so rapidly.

There are two basic arrangements of these proteins within the lipid bilayer of the membrane, and they permit classification according to this arrangement. Some proteins merely float on the surface of the lipid bilayer, drifting among the polar heads but not penetrating into the lipid core. These are known as **extrinsic** or **peripheral proteins,** because they never

Figure 4.12 A schematic drawing of the complete cell membrane. Proteins, fibrous and globular, are imbedded in a phospholipid core. Hooked onto the outer surface of certain proteins are the glycolipid and glycoprotein calices. Interspersing within the fatty acid chains are cholesterol molecules.

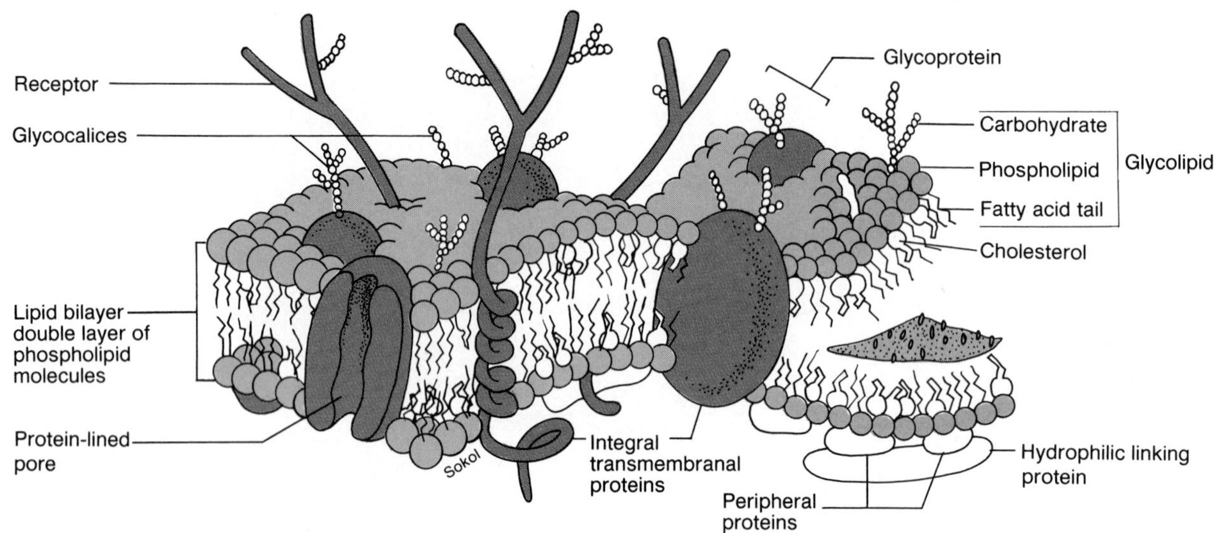

associate with the fatty acids of the bilayer and because there is a suspicion that they are not permanent residents—that they can drift away from the membrane when necessary. The other group of proteins penetrates the lipid bilayer, and these are the **integral** or **intrinsic proteins** (figure 4.12).

The intrinsic proteins vary in the depth to which they probe the membrane's lipid core. Some of them extend all the way through, from one side to the other, both ends projecting into the aqueous surroundings. These are the **transmembranal proteins,** and at least one of their functions is to line the tiny channels through the lipid interior of the membrane through which water-soluble materials are able to pass. Transmembranal proteins frequently are linked to chains of carbohydrate that project into the interstitial fluid in which body cells are immersed. No such chains extend into the cellular matrix; hence such proteins are asymmetrical (figure 4.12). As you can see from figure 4.12, not all integral proteins are transmembranal. There is a second group of integral proteins that extends into the core of the lipid bilayer, but not completely across it. Since they don't go all the way across, they can't function as channels, but they may perform other jobs involved in transmembranal movement of water-soluble materials. They intermingle with the fatty acid core of the bilayer, so they are permanent parts of the membrane. As is the case with all integral proteins, they cannot move out of the membrane because their fat-soluble parts cannot leave the lipid core and mix with water, while at the same time, the water-soluble zone has to stay away from the hydrophobic "marrow."

Peripheral proteins differ from the integral proteins in that the former are entirely water-soluble, and that means no part of them ever enters the fatty-acid core of the membrane. They avoid that deep zone and remain floating along the water-soluble surface, often with much of their substance projecting away from the membrane into the interstitial fluid. Whether or not they are transient members of the membrane is not known, but because of their solubility characteristics, it is certainly possible. Such proteins are often referred to as **adsorbed proteins,** because they never penetrate far beneath the membrane surface.

Studies of different types of tissues have shown that varying cell types often have the same phospholipid molecules in their cell membranes, while the proteins are similar only in *identical* cells. For example, nerve cells all have the same kinds of proteins, but their proteins differ from those found in muscle cell membranes or membranes of the cells lining the intestinal tract. Each has its own special proteins, and no other cell type has exactly the same kind or number.

Structure

Some of the proteins present in every cell membrane represent part of the membrane's permanent structure. Structural proteins may be present in almost any form. They may be amphipathic or hydrophilic; they may be adsorbed on the membrane surface, partially imbedded within the membrane, or they may extend completely across from one side to the other.

Surface Receptors

Some of the membrane proteins function as receptors for other molecules, and many of the important interactions between a cell and its environment are due to them. There are many kinds of receptor proteins on the surface of any given cell. Some of them are glycoproteins, proteins that have a carbohydrate-containing component. Many substances that are "caught" by the receptor proteins are hormones, and the specifics of the hormone-receptor interaction will be discussed more fully in chapter 10. Substances that are trapped in this manner are known as **ligands,** a word referring to any substance—ion or compound—that attaches to another, usually larger, molecule by means of weak, easily broken bonds.

Carrier Proteins

Other proteins in the cell membrane act as transporting, or "carrier" proteins. In this respect, they determine to some extent which water-soluble materials will enter the cell and which will not. The transmembranal proteins can simply open and permit free movement of substances along diffusion gradients, or they can operate as active-transport mechanisms (see chapter 3). In either case, the membrane seems able to determine which molecules will be accepted and which will not.

Enzymes

Many of the proteins imbedded in or on the cell membranes have catalytic functions; hence they are enzymes. Transmembranal proteins often operate as carrier enzymes, actively transporting necessary materials into or out of their cell against concentration gradients (see chapter 3). Other proteins catalyze reactions that result in the synthesis of critical intracellular polymers, while still others are involved in the degradation of fuels or waste materials. Often, enzymes that subserve the same function are linked in clusters so that they can move and work collectively. They are held together by rodlike hydrophilic proteins that are present on the inner membranal surface (figure 4.12).

Markers

Some of the protein and glycoprotein material on the cell membranes provides the cells with a means of identification; hence they are known as **markers.** They represent a chemical I.D. that, to the various mechanisms within our bodies, is evidently as reliable a means of recognition as medical and dental records are to a pathologist. These markers are constantly checked by elements of our body's immune systems, and woe betide the cells that are unable to produce the correct I.D. Any such are treated as invaders and are promptly killed, starved, or isolated.

Some Ancillary Molecules

Several other chemicals are present in or on cell membranes. **Glycolipids** (lipids that contain sugar) are present on the outer membranal surface, often forming many-branched bushes of carbohydrate that project out into the interstitial fluid. **Cholesterol,** a rather unusual and much-publicized lipid, is present within the hydrophobic core in considerable abundance (figure 4.12).

Glycolipids

Apparently the glycolipid bushes that wave back and forth on the outer surface of the membrane are the mechanisms that function as both food detectors and receptor sites for materials the cell occasionally uses. Passing particles that brush up against them are carefully screened by these tiny branches, and if the particle is something that the cell can use, the tiny receptor sites can grip and hold on. No other function has been suggested for these glycolipids and glycoproteins. The reason is, quite simply, that every single saccharide bush that has ever been seen on a membrane has always been on the *outer* surface. These **glycocalices,** as they are called, are particularly abundant in absorptive areas like the GI tract.

Cholesterol

Cholesterol's function is less clear than is that of the glycolipid bushes, but it is hard to believe it would be as copious as it is were it not important. Cholesterol is a rather unusual form of fat found mainly in animals, and it has developed an unsavory reputation in recent years. We have been so vigorously warned against ingesting it that it may come as a shock to many to learn that our bodies are loaded with it. Although its precise function has never been elucidated, it is clearly an integral part of every cell membrane, and its very abundance suggests that it is important.

Selective Permeability

The term *semipermeable* (*semi*—"half"; *permea*—"passes through") was used by early workers to describe the physical nature of the cell membranes, and like many original scientific names, it's only semi-appropriate. A collander or a screen door is semipermeable. These things control a restricted continuity between two compartments, because they are capable of separating particles of different sizes. But they are inert, and their control is completely passive. This is only partly true of the plasma membrane.

The lipid bilayer goes all the way around the cell, so it represents the main barrier. Fat-soluble materials can dissolve in the lipid and pass into the cell fairly easily. But water-soluble molecules cannot dissolve in fat, hence can't pass through the membrane. In a way, the bilayer is like a rock wall around a city. Like a city wall, the membrane has passageways through it—passageways made of protein—hence lipid solubility is not the only key to the interior of the cell. Water-soluble particles can pass into the cytoplasm through the protein gateways, but unlike passage through tunnels in a city wall, admission to cellular passageways is not a random thing—the membrane is not witlessly selective. It seems aware of the ever-changing demands of the cellular machinery and is able to quickly alter certain of its own properties to conform. No passive sieve can do that. If there is something outside that the cell needs or can find a use for, it is permitted to enter. If the cell does not need it, or if it could be harmful, the membrane sends it on its way. Apparently it all depends on what is needed and what is available, which suggests that the membrane monitors the fluids on both sides of it. Membrane mechanisms can even correct minor errors. Should an undesirable alien manage to slip inside the cell (which occasionally happens), the interloper is grabbed by energy-consuming machinery in the membrane and promptly kicked out. The membrane is not *semi*permeable as the old concept would have it, but *selectively* permeable, meaning it can choose its level of permeability and alter it if necessary. It operates like a highly selective purchaser for a business, carefully segregating only those things that its cell or organelle needs while refusing delivery of all frivolities and nonessentials.

Some General Comments

The conviction of earlier workers that the membrane around living cells is similar to a plastic bag or a sack with holes in it has been hard to dispell, yet nothing could be further from the truth. The membranes of living cells are as dynamic as the constantly bubbling fluids within. The lipid fraction of the membrane does retain much of its structure and composition, but it does so because to stay that way requires no energy. It would, in fact, require energy to change. The individual molecules that make up the membrane are not firmly anchored in place. Each phospholipid molecule in the membrane is, like an individual soldier in a company of soldiers, free to function as a separate entity within the limits imposed by the group.

Those limitations are pretty clear. Each hydrophilic head must avoid the fatty heart of the membrane. The fatty acids in the core must, in their turn, remain isolated from water and water-soluble parts. So the phospholipid molecules keep their heads dipped in the water while their hydrocarbon tails remain steadfastly pointing toward each other, avoiding the wet.

In this respect, the unit arrangement is rigid, but within that restricted envelope, each molecule is free to move around a great deal. In fact, thermal stimulation keeps them moving back and forth so much that the properties of the bilayer are more like a liquid than a solid. In fact, in its behavior, it seems only slightly more viscous than the water surrounding it. The phospholipid molecules flow *along* the aqueous interface in pretty much the same way the water flows against it; two liquids moving independently across each other's surface. So long as each part of the phospholipid molecule stays with its own kind, each unit is free to move anywhere it wants to go, and it can move very quickly indeed. Phospholipid molecules have been recorded moving from one end of a bacterium to the other—a distance of about 0.5 micrometers—in a single second. Expand that lipid molecule to the size of the family car and the little traveller would be zipping along at more than 68,000 miles per hour. The space shuttle doesn't go that fast! Under the circumstances, to say that the membrane is dynamic is something of an understatement. What is more, its capacity for variability is rendered even greater by the ability of the phospholipid molecules to flip over from one side of the membrane to the other. They do not do it often, and they cannot do it nearly as quickly as they can rush along the membrane, but they *can* do it.

The membrane's vivacity is not limited to the lipid molecules. Most of the proteins in the membrane are able to flow with nearly as much freedom. They are restricted by the same mechanisms as are the phospholipids . . . free to move, yet with the movement limited by the nature of the lipid bilayer. The integral proteins are evidently a permanent part of the membrane structure. Only the peripheral proteins are free to leave whenever they are required to, but even they cannot cross the membrane—not without help.

Figure 4.13 A schematic of the proposed lattice-like framework within a living cell. Since it supports and shapes the cell, it has been called the "cytoskeleton." (From "The Ground Substance of the Living Cell," by Keith Porter and Jonathon Tucker.)

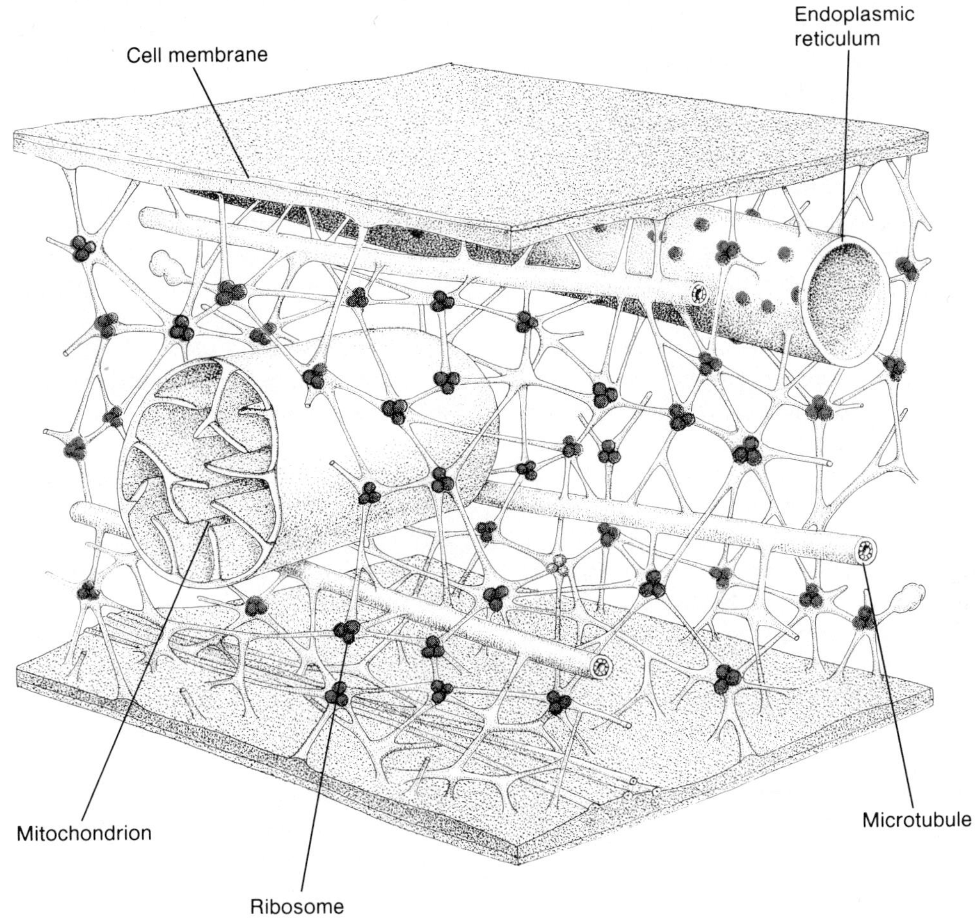

The Cytoplasm

The Cytosol

The fluid portion of the cell's interior is called the **cytosol.** Although some workers still feel that it is the living part of the cell, it has no obvious structure and seems to flow randomly. It represents about a third of the total mass of the cell and appears to be nothing more than a water matrix containing dissolved minerals and organic compounds, all thoroughly mixed together. The only order that is discernible in this matrix is its internal homogeneity. But it apparently has definite jobs to do. If we are to believe the latest hypotheses regarding the interior of the cell, we must conclude that there is a snarl of internal supports and communication elements that somewhat resembles the tangle of ropes and sailing gear of an old-time wooden sailing ship. There are sheets, cables, and supporting girders everywhere, criss-crossing back and forth, running stiffly along the interior of the cell membrane, forming lattices and scaffolding throughout (figure 4.13). Through all of these obstacles, the cytosol flows. Even considering the infinitesimal nature of the cellular interior, its watery matrix manages to sneak through the tiniest cracks and to slosh into the sharpest corners.

Cytosol Function

There is seldom a buildup of any kind of particle anywhere, because the diffusive energy present in the warm water keeps everything moving back and forth. Thanks to the conductive nature of water, no part of the cell stays warmer than any other part for very long. The heat fans out, spreading rapidly and uniformly throughout the watery cytosol. The concentration of dissolved solids and gases is likewise equal throughout. Like a glass of milk with all its suspended particles, it is amorphous (without form) but possesses internal homogeneity.

There are plenty of homeostatic mechanisms at work to see that it stays that way. Its chemistry is carefully regulated to maintain pH, osmolarity, and food concentrations at optimal levels. It carries the nutrients and raw materials for all the cellular organelles, making it, among other things, a completely benevolent medium. Also, a lot of things go on in this fluid matrix. Dissolved in it are the enzymes that catalyze the cell's biosynthetic and energy-producing efforts, and nearly all those reactions occur in solution. Because certain portions of the cell are metabolically more active than other parts, there is constant movement of heat away from these active zones, and that serves to stir the fluid, to keep it in motion. Vigorous biosynthesis produces a constant rush of newly synthesized materials away from where they were made to where they are needed. As raw materials are used up in these zones, replacement substrates flow in from other parts of the cell, eliminating concentration gradients before they can become established for more than brief instants.

Living or not, the cytosol is a hotbed of furious movement and chemical activity. Throughout its mass there is turbulence—a raging storm of unmitigated industry. Frantic construction of all kinds of organic materials runs side-by-side with an equally feverish breakdown of fuel molecules to provide the energy the cell must have to sustain its biosynthetic exertions. The cytosol may be mostly water, but it is certainly not inert.

The Endoplasmic Reticulum

The cell membrane insures that each cell is an individual entity with a life of its own. Yet to fully appreciate cellular operations, we must never forget that the cell is part of a whole organism and must function as a tiny, integrated part of a much larger plan. Every cell in the body is expected to contribute its share to the general welfare, and to do this, it must be more than self-sufficient . . . it must also be able to manufacture goods for "export." To accomplish this, there must be mechanisms in each cell that "know" what its export product is and can synthesize it, segregate it, store it, and finally move it to the exterior of the cell where it will be used.

The **endoplasmic reticulum** (*reticulum*—"network") does most of these things. It is a system of tubules that wriggle and squirm rather tortuously back and forth in the cytoplasm like extraordinary long, living hairs (refer back to figure 4.5).

Generally speaking, the components of the endoplasmic reticulum are similar to those of the cell membrane. The most significant differences are that the endoplasmic reticulum (ER) is more compressed than the cell membrane, and the ER contains no cholesterol. Sometimes the tubules of the reticulum contact the cell membrane and fuse with it the way two soap bubbles being pushed together will often fuse into one. When such a fusion takes place, it creates a pore that opens into a diving and zooming circular tunnel that meanders all through the cellular interior. Activity within the endoplasmic reticulum can be frenzied when materials are being stored or moved from one place to another, and the interior of these tunnels is often completely blocked on one end or another and will remain so until the time comes to move its contents out of the cell.

Function of the Endoplasmic Reticulum

Our cells are cities of industry where there are seldom any recessions, everyone works overtime, and most of the products are for export. All kinds of things are manufactured by the cell that are released into the endoplasmic reticulum for refining or storage. They might be digestive enzymes for use in the GI tract, lipid-based hormones destined to be carried by the blood, or protective secretions like **mucin,** the mucopolysaccharide that coats the interior of the stomach. All these things are manufactured within individual cells, stored within the ER, and secreted when they are needed. Sometimes the secretions are directed into channels or ducts that take them to where they are going to be used, and sometimes the cells simply dump them into the interstitial fluids, where they can be picked up by the blood.

Some cells specialize in one or two products, while others manufacture and secrete many. We have cells in our skin that produce sweat for thermal regulation, cells by our eyes that produce tears to keep the eye surfaces wet, cells in the reproductive tracts that produce lubricating oils to facilitate copulation and acids that destroy wandering bacteria. Digestive enzymes are stored in ER tubules and, not having any penchant for suicide, the ER stores them in harmless form. They are not activated until after delivery, when the cellular machinery is sure it is perfectly safe. Not all of the products stored in the ER are intended for export. Sometimes the cell will break up raw materials for use as spare parts in the synthesis of some structural component, and the enzymes for this purpose are stored in the ER. There are two kinds of endoplasmic reticulum inside living cells.

Figure 4.14 (*a*) An electron micrograph of rough endoplasmic reticulum. (*b*) A line drawing showing the three-dimensional orientation of this organelle as it exists in living cells. The particles that cover its surface are ribosomes and are involved in protein synthesis.

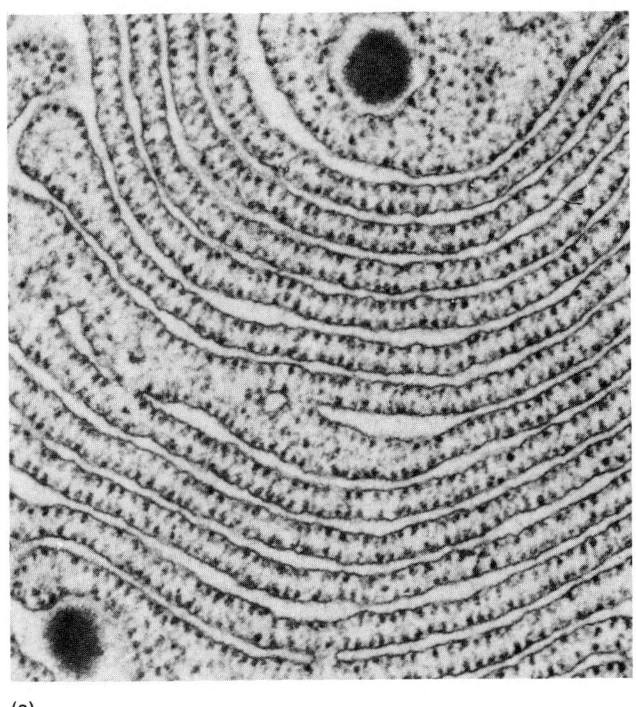

(a)

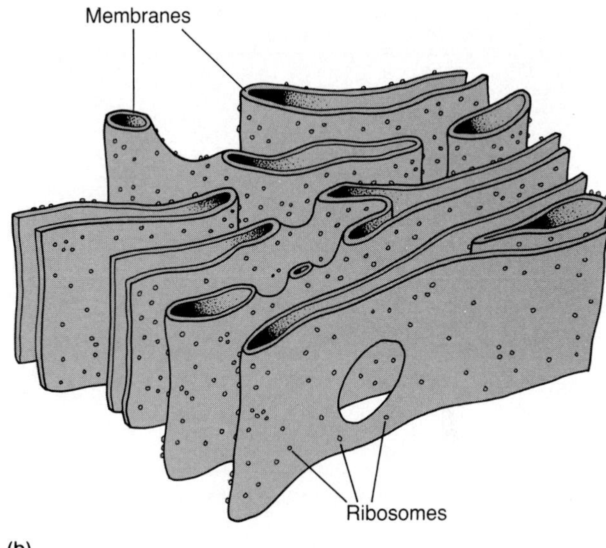

(b)

Rough Endoplasmic Reticulum

The **rough endoplasmic reticulum** is so called because it is studded with granules all along the cytoplasmic surface—granules that gave early electron microscopists the feeling they were looking at sandpaper. These tiny, seemingly insignificant particles turned out to be another type of organelle called *ribosomes.* They are the sites of protein synthesis within the cell (see figure 4.14).

Smooth Endoplasmic Reticulum

Not all endoplasmic reticulum is studded with ribosomes. Cells that do not synthesize proteins for export have an endoplasmic reticulum with a polished surface that has given rise to the name **smooth endoplasmic reticulum** (see figure 4.15). It is particularly abundant in cells of the adrenal cortex and the gonads, which are sites of synthesis and secretion of lipid-based hormones. The liver cells that are responsible for the synthesis and secretion of cholesterol also have a lot of smooth ER. In addition, the so-called **sarcoplasmic reticulum** of muscle cells is really nothing but a highly specialized smooth ER. In cells that have both rough and smooth endoplasmic reticulum, the two are continuous, and there is a gradual transition from one to the other.

Golgi Apparatus

Some time around the turn of the century, the great Italian microscopist Camillo Golgi published drawings of a new structure he had found near the nucleus of certain cells. It was given the name **Golgi apparatus,** and its structure is very similar to that of the endoplasmic reticulum except for the fact that the membrane layers composing it are slightly flatter and broader. It resembles a stack of hollow saucers piled one on top of the other with the concave faces all pointing in the same direction (figure 4.16).

On the inner face (called the *endoplasmic face*), the membrane is highly compressed and lacks cholesterol, just like the membrane of the endoplasmic reticulum. As we progress through the Golgi complex toward the plasma membrane, the membrane thickens

Figure 4.15 (*a*) An electron micrograph of smooth endoplasmic reticulum. Note the absence of ribosomes. (*b*) A three-dimensional drawing of the same organelle. Smooth ER often tends to be less regular in shape and arrangement than is the rough ER.

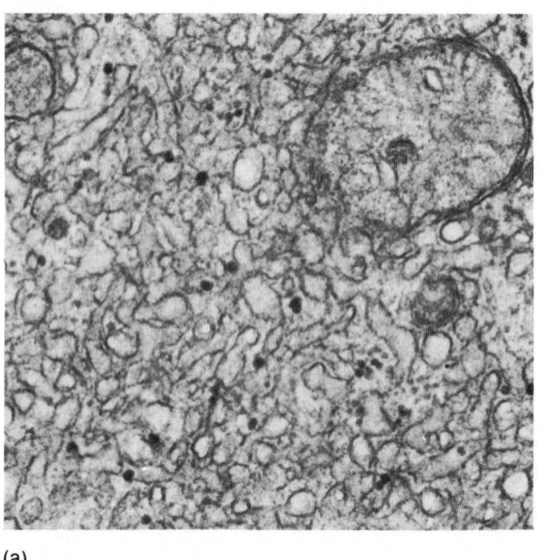

(a)

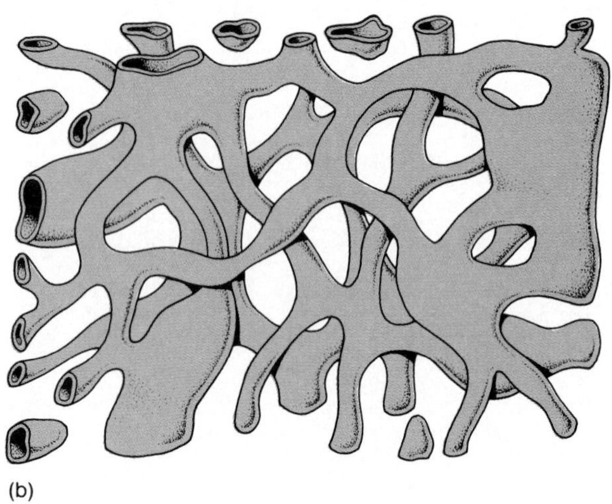

(b)

Figure 4.16 The Golgi apparatus. Its topographic arrangement suggests the regularity of rough ER, although it totally lacks ribosomes.

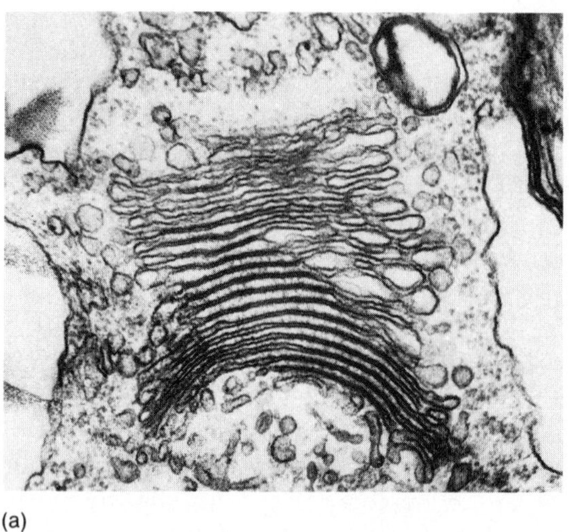

(a)

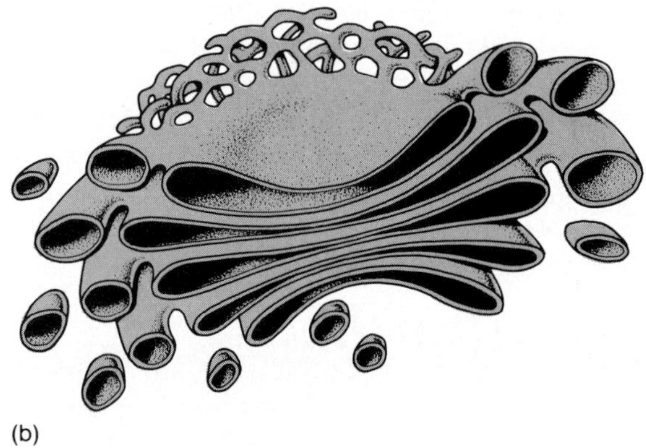

(b)

and cholesterol molecules start to appear. Finally, on the center of the outermost concave surface (the *exoplasmic face*), its components are identical to those of the plasma membrane, although there is a functional difference. Unlike those of the plasma membrane, the phospholipids of the Golgi membrane do not seem able to move around very much. As a result, the two faces retain their differences in structure permanently.

There is both a morphological and a functional continuity between the Golgi apparatus and the endoplasmic reticulum, particularly the rough ER. Proteins synthesized on the rough ER can be passed right into the Golgi apparatus without having to cross a membrane, probably in little vacuoles that move constantly between the two structures.

Figure 4.17 The compartments of the Golgi apparatus processing newly synthesized proteins.

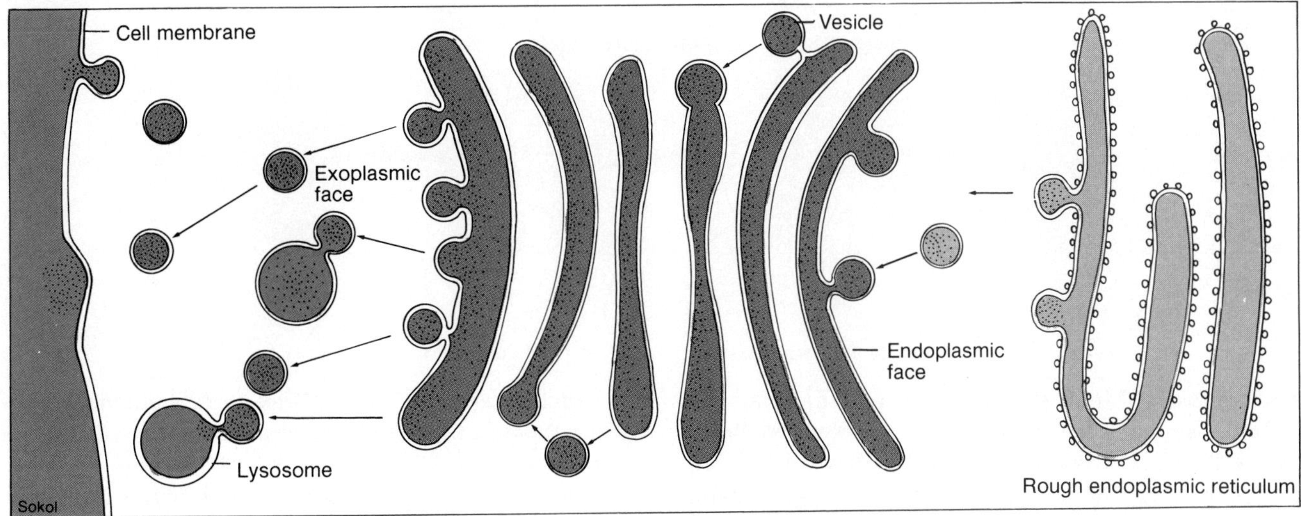

Golgi Function

After they enter the Golgi apparatus, proteins can undergo a variety of changes. Newly synthesized proteins are sorted and segregated. Some are used within the cell and some are packed for transport out of it. Sometimes the apparatus adds saccharides or fats to assemble glycoproteins or lipoproteins (like, for example, mucus). Sometimes the Golgi apparatus activates various enzymes that are moving through. Generally speaking, however, when newly synthesized proteins arrive at the endoplasmic surface of the Golgi apparatus, the vesicle that carries them fuses with the Golgi membrane and releases them into the interior. Each "saucer" of the apparatus then processes the proteins and transports them via another vesicle to the next "saucer" in line. Each protein is graded and segregated according to where it is going and what it has to do, and finally each is carefully packaged and sent to its proper destination. When processing is complete, vacuoles containing the specialized particles are separated from the exoplasmic face and carried to wherever they are supposed to go. Those containing digestive enzymes fuse with nearby *lysosomes,* while those leaving the cell head for the plasma membrane, where a fusion occurs and the contents are released into the interstitial fluids (figure 4.17).

Not all the vesicles that pinch off from the Golgi apparatus are destined for export. There are vesicles that remain within the cell. Those that do are often loaded with special enzymes, most of which are digestive. Such vesicles are known as **lysosomes** (*lys*—"to loosen or dissolve"; *soma*—"a body"; hence, "dissolving body").

The Lysosome

Lysosomes are abundant. There are hundreds of them in most living cells, and their morphological variability is so endless that in size and shape each one could be unique. Their contents can vary, too, although not as much, apparently, as their structure. Lysosomes are membranous in origin, and like all membranes in the cell, the border is a lipid bilayer studded with proteins. The organelles tend to be **polymorphous** (*poly*—"many"; *morph*—"forms"), meaning they assume various shapes and states. When they first break off from the Golgi apparatus, they are known as **primary lysosomes.** Primary lysosomes are usually relatively small, and their contents are usually densely packed within.

Lysosomal Function

Broadly speaking, lysosomes function as the cell's "stomach," and there can be enormous variation in the contents of these stomachs. It all depends on what the cell needs and what is available. Lysosomes contain high concentrations of powerful enzymes designed to break organic molecules apart. Normally these enzymes break up molecules that have been brought into the cell in a very special way, a process known as **endocytosis.**

Figure 4.18 Solid particles too large to penetrate the cell membrane can be surrounded by the cell through endocytosis.

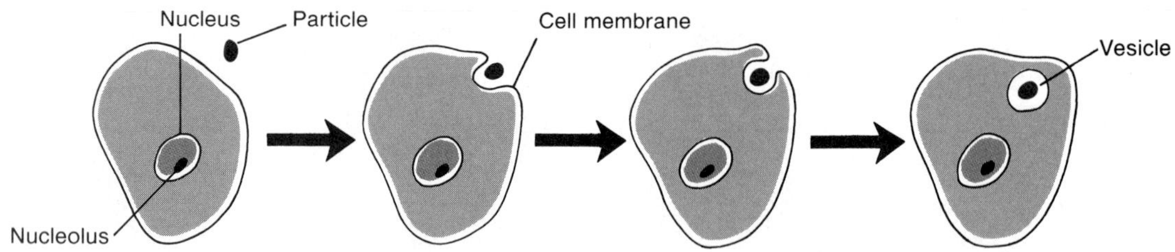

Endocytosis Molecules of important materials repeatedly appear outside the plasma membrane. Often, the cell can use these materials, but they are too big to get through the membrane, even with enzymatic help. Since there is no way to get the particle *through* the membrane, nature has devised a devious method of getting it within the confines of the plasma membrane, where it can be handled when convenient. First of all, the particle is wrapped in a little membranous bag and then it is drawn, bag and all, into the cytoplasm. It is a three-step process:

1. The particle is adsorbed on the surface of the membrane, possibly trapped by one of the glycoprotein calyces.
2. The cell membrane invaginates to form a cup around the particle and begins to poke into the cytosol.
3. A little "diving bell" forms around the particle and is pinched off from the membrane (see figure 4.18).

This membranous bubble is surrounded on all sides by cytosol and is free to float anywhere within the intracellular matrix. However, the purpose of forming the vacuole was to obtain its contents, and to do that, the cell must break the particle down into bits small enough to be drawn across the membrane into the cytosol itself. This breakup is called **digestion,** and on a molecular level it is the opposite of dehydration synthesis (chapter 2). It consists of breaking chemical bonds between monomers by adding water, an operation known as **hydrolysis** (*hydro*—"water"), and as we will see in chapter 15, it is the method our digestive tracts use to split our chewed food into smaller materials.

Intracellular Digestion Once the vacuole is within the cytosol, a primary lysosome is drawn to it, and the two vesicles fuse, at which point the lysosome becomes a **secondary lysosome.** The enzymes are activated inside the sack and the process of digestion begins. When all the worthwhile material in the particle has been digested, the cytosol absorbs all that it needs, and the lysosome breaks free and migrates away.

Exocytosis All that was not absorbed by the cytoplasm is considered waste and is dumped outside the cell by means of **exocytosis,** a process that is essentially the reverse of endocytosis. It is a method of getting large granules *out* of the cell and into the extracellular fluid. The vacuole now contains only debris. It moves to the interior of the cell membrane, where its membrane aligns with the flowing molecules of the plasma membrane, and the two fuse at the point of contact. Again, like a soap bubble being pushed into another, the vacuole loses its identity and blends in with the other membranous material, actually becoming part of it. Its erstwhile contents, meanwhile, are summarily dumped into the surrounding interstitial fluid.

Exocytosis does not serve merely to rid the cell of waste products. It is also the mechanism that is used when the cell wishes to secrete proteins or any water-soluble molecules it has synthesized that are too large to get through membranous pores. The entire process is outlined in stepwise fashion in figure 4.19.

This, then, is what lysosomes do—it is their job. But they are more than merely intracellular "stomachs." Couple their digestive ability with a little "intracellular judgment" and we find that lysosomes also play a very important role in salvage and reconstruction within the cell.

Figure 4.19 Large particles engulfed by a cell must be broken down before they can cross a membrane. Lysosomal particles accomplish this by fusing with the endocytic vacuole and releasing digestive enzymes within. Leftover debris is expelled by exocytosis.

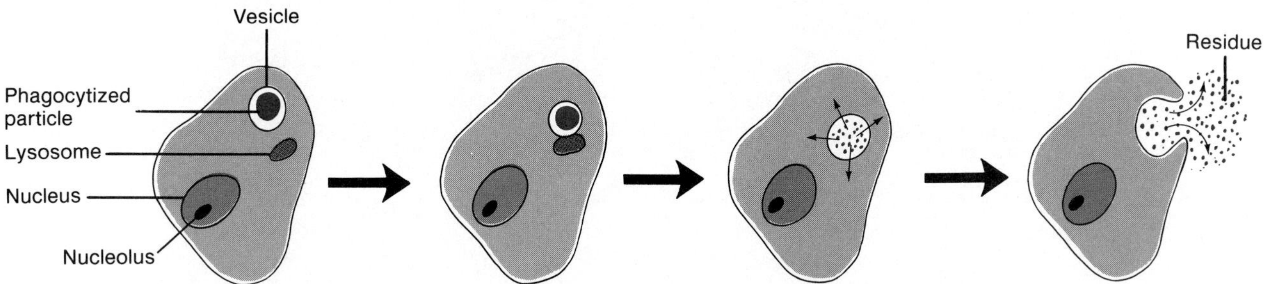

The Constructive Lysosome

As organisms mature, functioning body parts are constantly wearing out and needing replacement. When this occurs, far more often than not, the materials of which these parts are made are not discarded but are selectively salvaged. Internally, we "learned" long ago that recycling is usually much less expensive than building anew. When body cells wear out—and they do, by the millions every second—they are not discarded. The worn-out areas are very carefully broken up. Large molecules like proteins and portions of the membrane are carefully taken apart and the useful components added to the cell's stockpile of raw materials. Those parts that cannot be used, known as **residual bodies,** are disposed of via exocytosis. This is a continual process as most body cells are refurbished continually, although it may not be obvious. It has been calculated that the average liver cell is completely torn down and rebuilt every week. The necessary operations are done so quickly and smoothly that when it is all finished the cells look exactly the same as they did when it began. They function the same way and they produce and require the same materials, but they are different cells than they were a week ago. It is like the automobile fanatic who constantly fusses with his vehicle. Two years after he purchases his new car it looks like it just left the showroom floor, but only the body and seats are still the same; the anxious mechanic has replaced everything inside.

The Destructive Lysosome

Despite their obvious importance as cellular renovators, lysosomes carry potential disaster around with them. Anything that will break up an organic food particle or carefully dismantle a damaged chunk of membrane has the potential to break up structural components of the cell as well. If a lysosome ever burst while floating around inside the cytoplasm, the result could be about the same as if someone walked into a fireworks factory smoking a large black cigar. The destruction might be a bit less spectacular and might take a little longer, but it would be just as complete, and the cell would be dead.

No one knows why this doesn't happen to living cells. As far as researchers have been able to determine, the lysosomal membrane is constructed of the same materials as the cell membrane, and the cell membrane shatters when exposed to lysosomal enzymes. The lysosomal membrane should shatter too, and researchers cannot explain why it does not. Even after the lysosome has joined up with an endocytic vesicle and the enzymes are clearly active, while everything inside—lipids, proteins, and sugars—are being ripped and torn asunder, the membrane enclosing all this activity remains unscathed.

We do not know why.

Mitochondria

The **mitochondrion** is the intracellular organelle responsible for providing the major portion of free energy that the cell uses. As is the case with lysosomes, mitochondria are quite variable in both size and shape. Some are long and skinny, others resemble a fat knockwurst, and still others are egg-shaped or spherical. There are even cells in which the mitochondria are strung together like frankfurters or clustered together in clumps that form other unusual designs.

Regardless of shape or size, the basic structural plan is standard. They are composed of two separate membranes, one packed inside the other. The outer membrane is firm and smooth; it actually has a polished appearance in some electron micrographs. The

Figure 4.20 (*a*) An electron micrograph of a longitudinally sectioned mitochondrion. (*b*) A three-dimensional drawing of a mitochondrion with a section peeled away to show the internal topography.

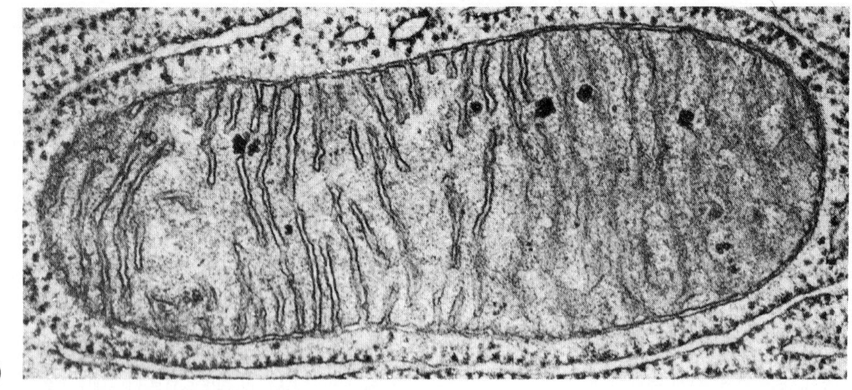

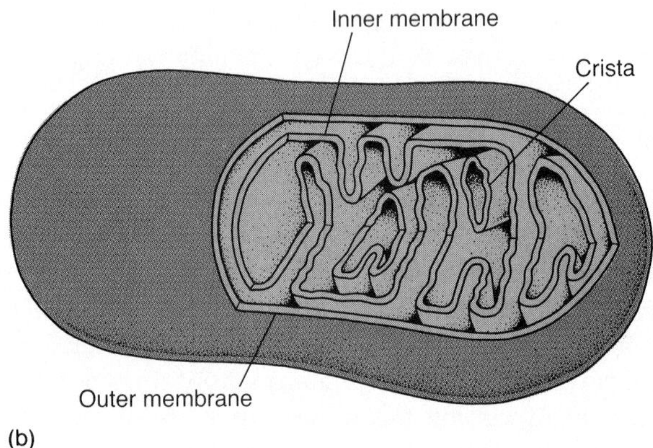

inner membrane, however, is flaccid like a deflated balloon and is more complex than the outer one. Electron microscopy indicates that it is quite limp and has numerous convolutions and invaginations all across it. These invaginations form clefts in the membrane called **cristae,** clefts that push deep into the interior. Inside the inner membrane is the fluid interior of the mitochondrion—the **matrix**—and the partitions formed by the cristae break up the single room of the mitochondrial interior, giving it the appearance of a rather simple maze (figure 4.20).

They also provide a huge surface area within the mitochondria on which is laid an array of enzymes, coenzymes, and carrier molecules that interact cooperatively to produce high-energy particles for use by the cell. Within the depths of the matrix itself are enzymes that are designed to break up residues of fatty acids and carbohydrates in an orderly and controlled manner, pinching off energy-containing electrons and protons, thus producing a steady flow of electrons through other enzyme-containing particles on the inner surface of the inner membrane. These latter particles are regularly spaced along the membrane interior. They are exactly 10 nanometers apart and are known as **F_1 particles.** They contain all the elements of what is known as the **respiratory chain** or **cytochrome system,** which is responsible for extracting energy from this flow of electrons and transducing it into the chemical bonds of ATP molecules.

Mitochondrial Function

The most efficient energy-yielding reactions of cell respiration take place in the mitochondria, and so these organelles are often described as the "cellular power plants." Their complete role in intermediary metabolism is discussed in the next chapter.

Ribosomes

The only reason that organic reactions can proceed at all is because of the existence of enzymes, the organic catalytic agents peculiar to life (see chapter 2). However, all enzymes are proteins, and proteins are large and very complex molecules. The process of building proteins is a long, sequential procedure in which each step builds upon the preceding one. To assemble a single protein would therefore require several dozen—possibly several hundred—synthetic steps, each requiring an enzyme catalyst. Many of these catalysts are built on organelles like those that cover the entire cytoplasmic surface of rough endoplasmic reticulum—the **ribosomes.**

Ribosomes are scattered throughout the cellular cytoplasm, but in most cells they tend to concentrate on the cytosol surface of the endoplasmic reticulum. They are tiny—about 200 Å in diameter on an average—and they are composed of two subunits called, for the sake of simplicity, the **large subunit** and the **small subunit.** These subunits are fitted together in such a way that they resemble a bacterium-sized, ultramodern telephone (figure 4.21).

Research with these organelles has shown that if a ribosome is broken up and its particles scattered,

Figure 4.21 A three-dimensional model of a ribosome showing its two-part structure. This is the way it is usually seen in electron micrographs.

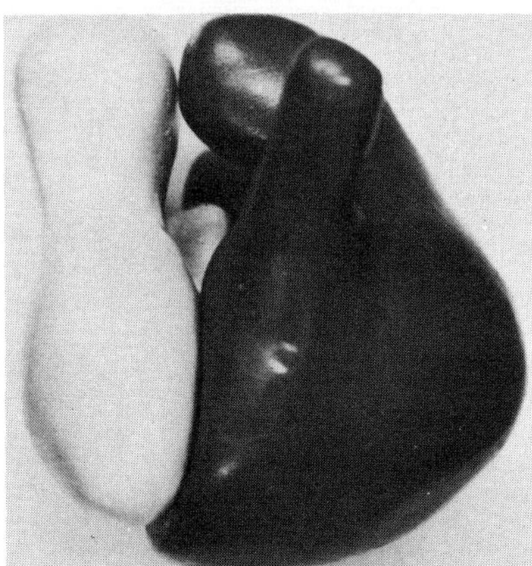

those particles, if mixed in a solution similar to cytosol, will spontaneously rearrange themselves to form an intact ribosome once more. Why this happens is not clear, nor is it known precisely where the energy for the reassembly comes from, but it seems certain that this is the method that the cell uses to assemble its ribosomes. Apparently all the cell has to do to obtain a ribosome is to direct the construction of the necessary parts, and they'll go together all by themselves.

Ribosomal Function

The ribosomes, directed and assisted by assorted nucleic acids, produce the original proteins for each cell. This process will be discussed in detail.

The Framework of the Cell

The cellular membrane is, as we have seen, a flowing, dynamic border between the interstitial fluid and the cytosol inside the cell. In addition, it is used as the basic structural element of the Golgi apparatus, lysosomes, mitochondria, and the endoplasmic reticulum. Obviously it is a versatile and capable arrangement, but despite its numerous features, it is not very strong. Without some support, some sort of framework, the plasma membrane would not be able to maintain its shape and integrity and would collapse in on the cytosol like an oversized, water-filled balloon. To avoid this, there is an assortment of microtubules and microfilaments within the cell that function as a sort of cellular skeleton. These structures are all formed of protein and are generally quite similar to the proteins that are responsible for the contractile ability of vertebrate muscle tissue (see figures 4.22 and 4.23).

Figure 4.22 The internal framework of the cell. (*a*) An electron micrograph of the tubules and filaments involved. (*b*) A three-dimensional drawing of the framework, showing the arrangement of some other organelles within this framework.

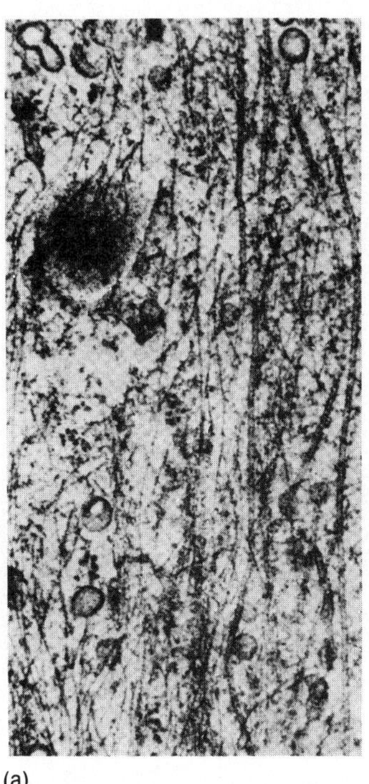

(a)

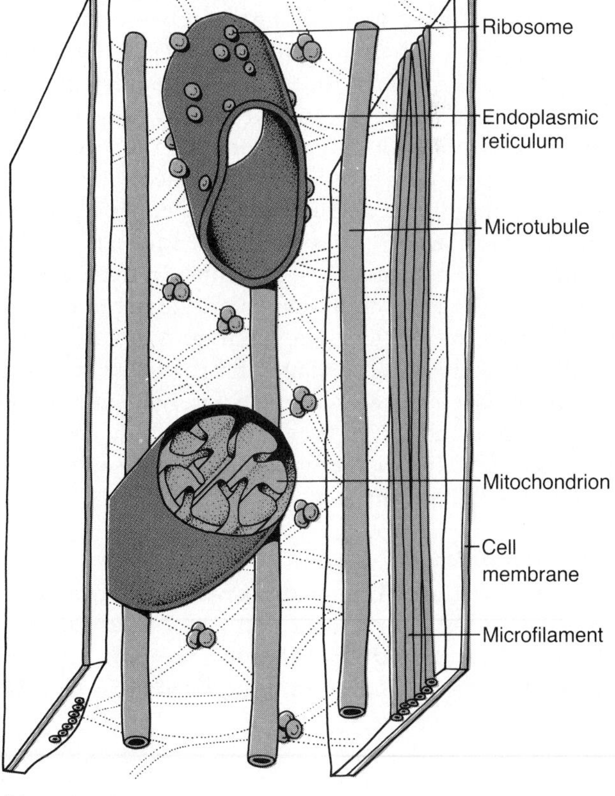

(b)

Figure 4.23 An electron micrograph of the microtubules that form the cytoskeleton. Note the concentration in the vicinity of the nucleus, which may suggest added protection for this vital center.

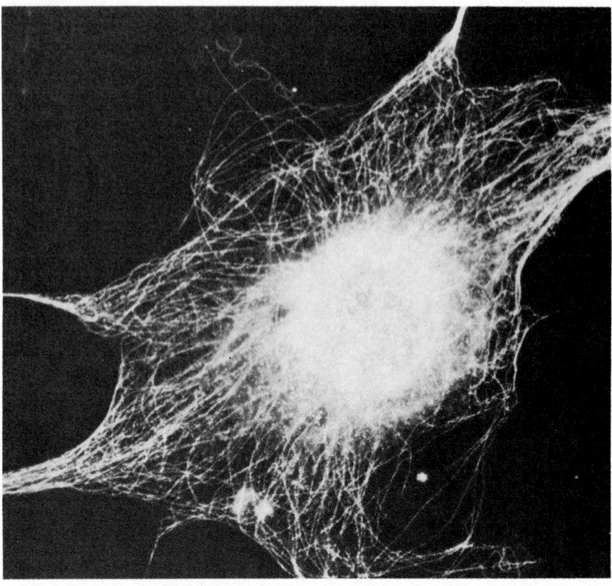

Figure 4.24 (*a*) Detail of a microfilament. (*b*) Detailed drawing of a microtubule. Note the arrangement of the globular proteins of which it is made.

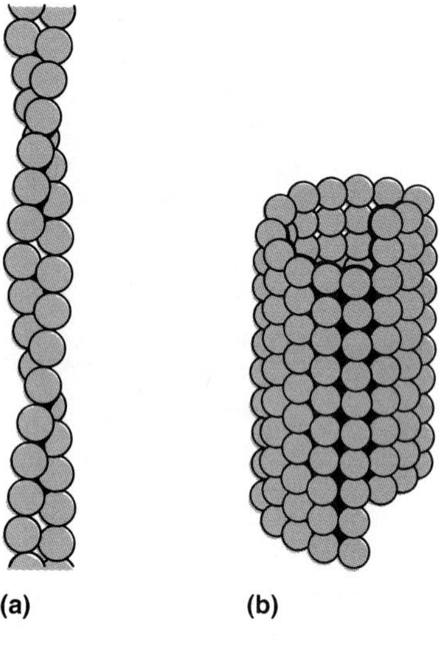

Microfilaments

Microfilaments (figure 4.24*a*) are extremely fine, threadlike structures, usually involved in some kind of movement. They are particularly abundant in areas that are changing shape as the cell moves or pulsates. For instance, when a white blood cell begins to wander about within the interstitial spaces of large organisms, observers can tell which way the cell plans to move by looking for the area where microfilaments are most heavily concentrated. Once in position, microfilaments pull opposing edges of the cell membrane toward each other and "squeeze" the cytoplasm, like toothpaste from a tube, in the direction the cell wishes to go. Other microfilaments provide rigidity to the parts of the membrane that are being pulled together. These filaments are buried in a layer of proteinaceous material immediately inside the cell membrane, and when they are rigid, they can function as stiffening elements as well as anchors for any elements that might want to contract.

Microtubules

Also within the cellular matrix are literally thousands of long, tubular structures that are also, apparently, involved in providing cells with support and motility. These are the **microtubules,** structures about 240 Å in diameter with a 150 Å hollow bore (figures 4.24*b*, 4.25). The diameter is apparently pretty much a constant, but the length can vary enormously. Some microtubules are just a little longer than they are wide, while others—like those present in transmission fibers of nerve cells—can be as much as 250,000 Å (25 μm) in length.

Figure 4.25 An electron micrograph of an array of microtubules within a cell.

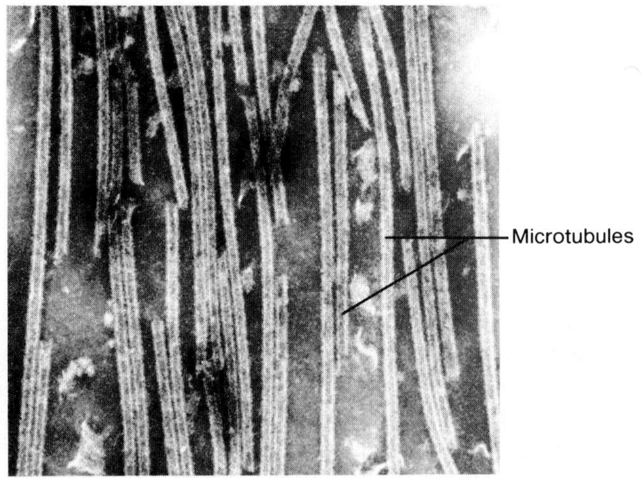

Figure 4.26 Microtubules appear, disappear, and move about in a cell by assembling and disassembling. By assembling at one end while simultaneously disassembling at the other, the tubule appears to migrate through the cell.

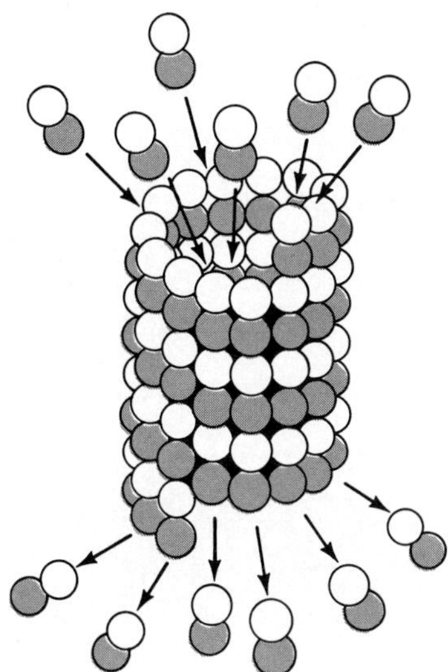

Microtubule Function

Microtubules form the *spindle apparatus* that is present in animal cells during cell division (mitosis). They are clearly visible in dividing cells, apparently clamped onto the centrioles at one end and the chromosomes at the other. When the right moment comes, they appeared to shorten and pull the chromosomes apart. Their presence in nerve cells (which never divide) made it clear very early in cellular research, however, that they did not restrict their activity to cellular division. They have subsequently been located in all kinds of cells, usually functioning as contractile elements. They are particularly abundant in cells featuring surface extensions like cilia or the longer, whiplike appendages called **flagella** that provide many tiny organisms like protozoa and bacteria with the ability to move. The tails of spermatozoons are flagella, and the lashing movements of this appendage are responsible for propelling the cell toward the egg. There is also abundant evidence that microtubules are the organelles responsible for moving lysosomes back and forth within the cellular matrix, and their association with endocytic vesicles is well documented.

It has been suggested by some workers that the microtubules are responsible for providing cells with skeletal support in much the same way as the microfilaments do. This is possible, but microtubules are so unstable by nature that it does not seem very likely. They are constantly being taken apart and rebuilt into different structures at some point or other within the cell . . . not a very permanent way for skeletal structures to behave (see figure 4.26). It is far more likely that the microtubules provide movement rather than support.

As figure 4.22 shows clearly, the microfilaments and microtubules interlace with each other to form a lattice-like framework throughout the interior of the cell. This framework serves many functions, some of which we have already seen. Other possible functions have been suggested by workers recently. It may be that the regular nature of the internal structure serves to organize many of the cell's enzymes. There is evidence that the enzymes responsible for initiating the breakdown of food molecules inside living cells are organized along the lattices of the microfilamentous framework instead of being left to float at random through the liquid phase within the cell. It is also possible that ribosomes not anchored to the cell membrane can still have their activities coordinated by being carefully oriented within the lattice of the cytoskeleton.

Cilia

Most body cells that line hollow tubes or surround the interior of a goblet-shaped gland have the tiny, hair-like projections on their surfaces called *cilia.* In cross-section, these tiny projections resemble shortened sperm tails, and like the sperm tails they contain microtubules in a circular arrangement with a hub composed of two microtubules (figure 4.27). When present on the surface of an associated group of cells, these cilia beat in rhythm, forming movement patterns like long swells on the ocean's surface, and like waves on the ocean, cilia can move things. In the respiratory system, when dirt and dust particles are able to escape the hairy filters of our nostrils, they are almost always trapped by the thick mucus that is secreted by cells lining our breathing tubes. This mucus, along with all the air-borne debris it has managed to encompass, is moved by rapidly beating cilia to the external nostrils to be expelled or to the pharynx to be coughed up and swallowed (figure 4.28). Cilia are also abundant in the female reproductive tract, and when a female mammal's egg is released by the ovarian follicle, it is the rapid beating of cilia lining the fallopian tubes that moves the egg down to the uterus for implanation after fertilization.

Figure 4.27 The microtubular arrangement within a cilium and flagellum. (*a*) This drawing shows the 9 + 2 pattern of microtubules within. (*b*) A cross-section of *a*. (*c*) An electron micrograph of a flagellar cross-section.

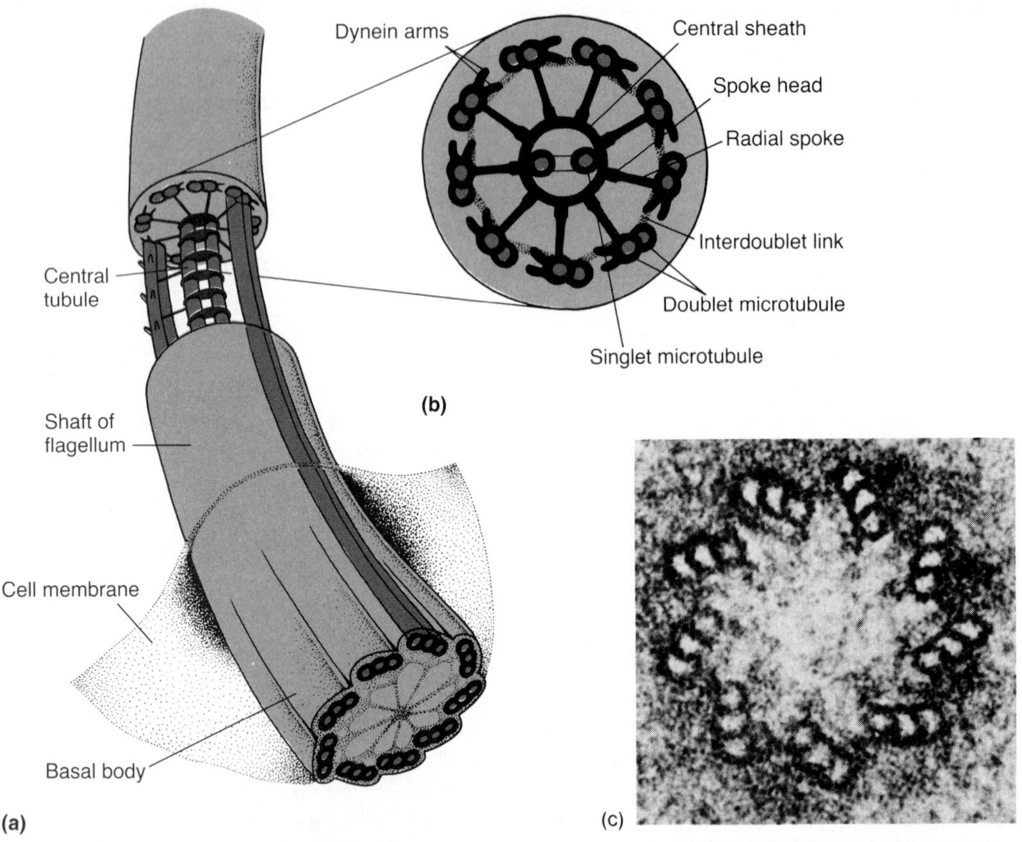

Figure 4.28 An electron micrograph of a ciliated surface of a cell. Cells like these line the inner surface of respiratory tubes. (Magnification about 10,000×.)

The Centrosome

In the depths of the cytosol, near the Golgi apparatus and often at the midline of the cell, is the **centrosome.** Usually located within a few Angstroms of the nuclear envelope, this organelle is composed of two hollow cylinders, each of which is known as a **centriole.** Centrioles are composed of microtubules that are arranged in triplets (figures 4.29 and 4.30) around a hollow core, and they are usually at right angles to each other. During cellular division, the centrioles move away from each other and migrate to opposite ends of their cell, where they are involved in the process of mitosis (see chapter 5).

The Nucleus

Of all the organelles, the largest is certainly the nucleus. It was the first one that was seen and identified as a permanent resident and the first one to receive an official name. It is usually ovoid or circular in shape and is separated from the rest of the cell by a double membrane known as the **nuclear envelope** (figure 4.31).

Figure 4.29 (*a*) An electron micrograph of a centriole seen in cross-section. (*b*) A drawing showing the 9 + 0 microtubule arrangement in centrioles. Note how it differs from those of cilia and flagella.

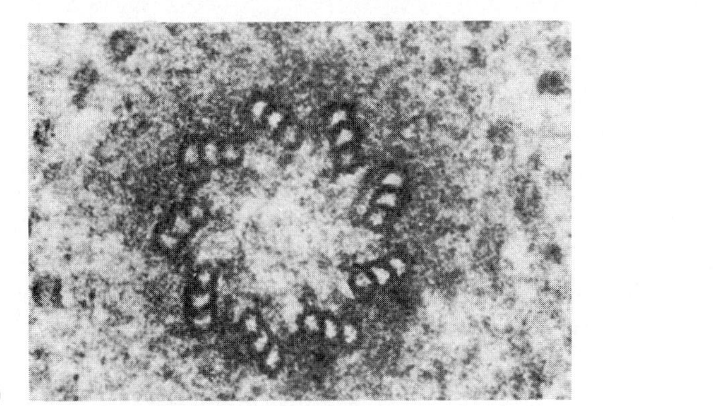
(a)

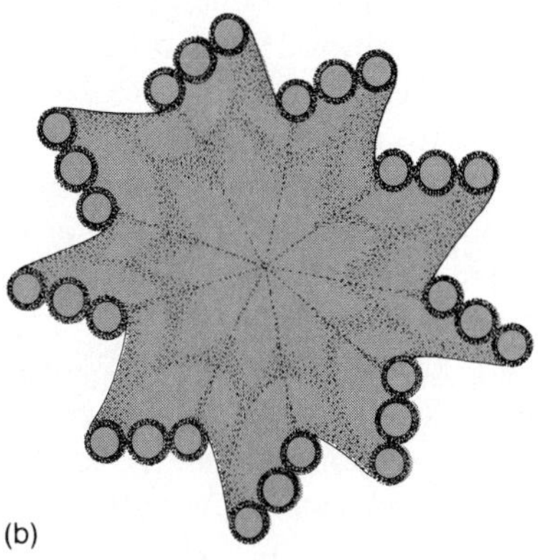
(b)

Figure 4.30 (*a*) An electron micrograph of two centrioles, one in cross-section, the other longitudinal. (*b*) The orientation of the centrioles to one another in three dimensions.

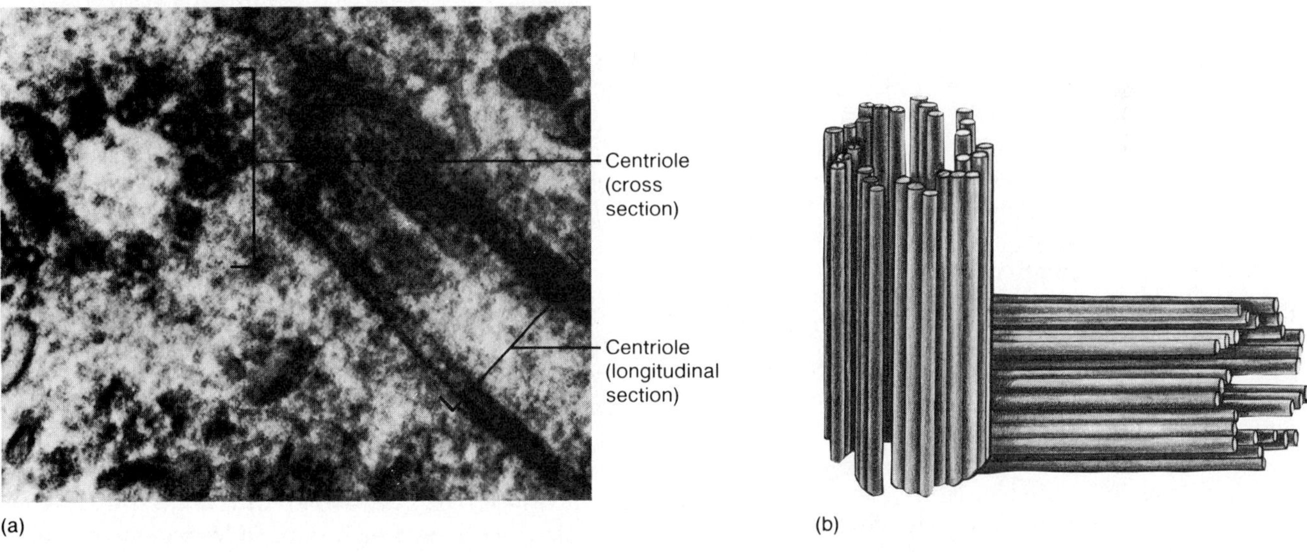

Figure 4.31 (*a*) An electron micrograph of a cell nucleus. Note the presence of the nucleolus and the obvious pores in the nuclear envelope. (*b*) The pores in three dimensions, showing arrangement and abundance.

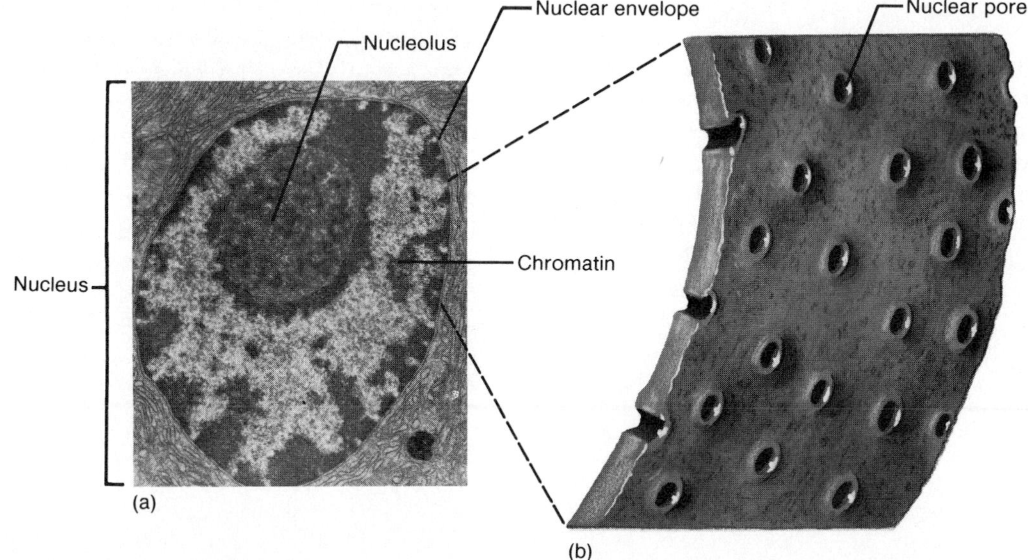

This "border" between the nuclear material and the cellular cytoplasm is composed of membranous material that appears to be slightly modified rough endoplasmic reticulum. It is as if the normally round or slightly ovoid endoplasmic reticular tube has been flattened out into a sheet, then shaped into a globe around the nuclear material. Its cytoplasmic surface is studded with ribosomes, but there are none on the internal surface, because there is no protein synthesis inside the nucleus (figure 4.31).

There are holes going right through both membrane bilayers of the nuclear envelope, which means the cytoplasm can communicate directly with the nucleus. These openings were given the name *pores* years ago. At that time, they appeared to be nothing but simple holes going through the envelope from one side to the other, but workers have since discovered they are much more than mere holes. Each is lined with, hence completely guarded by, special proteins and can be opened or closed by movement of valve-like protein "flaps." Communication is obviously strictly censored because nothing moves between cytoplasm and nucleoplasm except through these pores, and movement there is carefully monitored.

Even materials that are highly fat-soluble and can move easily through the cell membrane are stopped by the nuclear envelope, their movement blocked by a thick layer of proteinaceous material known as **lamina.** The lamina covers the entire inner surface of the nuclear envelope and is broken only by the protein-lined pores. Regardless of its chemical properties, nothing moves into the nucleoplasm without approval of these proteins.

Inside the nuclear envelope, protected by every means in the cell's arsenal, is the functioning heart of the cell, the chromosomes. The chromosomes are the cellular memory bank as well as the control center. All the blueprints, all the detailed formulas, all the information on how and what to build when the cell is functioning are in the chromosome's DNA.

The Nucleolus

Also within the nuclear envelope is the **nucleolus.** The literal meaning of nucleolus is "tiny kernel," but literality was not what its discoverers had in mind when it was named. They were looking on it as the "nucleus within the nucleus," and that is as good a way as any to approach it. When it was first analyzed chemically, it turned out to be primarily RNA and protein, and for quite a while it was uncertain what this meant. Recently it was discovered that the chromosomal DNA passes its instructions to the other nucleotide—the RNA—a process known as **transcription.** Once synthesized, these newly made strips of RNA are transported into the nucleolus, where they are combined with protein, forming brand-new ribosomes. As the ribosomes attain final form, they are released from the nucleolus and migrate through the pores of the nuclear envelope into the cytosol.

The process of transferring information from an audio tape to typewritten notes is known as *transcribing,* and the notes are therefore *transcriptions.* Transcriptions are reproductions of information from one medium to another, but the language always remains the same. This is exactly what happens when the instructions present on the long strands of DNA are transferred to shorter strips of RNA. When RNA takes these written instructions into the cytosol and uses them as a guideline for building proteins (see chapter 5), the information is changed to a chain of amino acids, which is an entirely different language. Since the DNA code has been changed, the operation is no longer a simple transcription. Now the process is known as *translation,* and using the audio tape/typewritten notes analogy, this would be like utilizing the newly transcribed English-language notes to make another written copy of the information in French.

With the exception of a few isolated viruses, all the RNA in the world is single-stranded. Also, RNA generally carries only enough information to manufacture a single protein or polypeptide, so RNA strands tend to be extremely short. There are several kinds of RNA, and each type is designed for a specific job. The length of RNA strands, regardless of the type, is measured in Angstrom units, and there is no possibility of ever seeing an RNA strand in a light microscope.

DNA, on the other hand, is always composed of two strands, precise complements of each other, wound around a single axis to form a double helix. These strands can be as much as 10 cm long in humans, and if they were about a hundred times thicker than they actually are, they could easily be seen with the naked eye. They are never actually stretched out to this length, simply because there isn't enough room anywhere in the nucleus of a cell to do it. The DNA is as relaxed as it is ever going to get during the long intervals between the cell's dividing activities, the period known as *interphase.* Throughout this time the partially unravelled strands fan out and pack the whole interior of the nucleus. Because they are so fine, no one using just a light microscope was ever able to find them. In any form, however, chromosomal material tends to complex readily with basic dyes. It is this tendency that imparted the dark color to the whole nucleus in stained cell preparations and rendered it so identifiable by early light microscopists.

When the cell is preparing to divide, this tendency disappears, because the chromosomal material begins to concentrate. DNA compresses itself into an incredibly complicated series of windings-within-windings in which it tends to flip-flop back and forth on itself like a switchback path leading to the top of a mountain. And just as the switchback path wraps around the mountain, DNA wraps around a central core of protein, a core that compresses its length while increasing its thickness enormously. The DNA is doubled around itself and redoubled and redoubled again, and the whole is wrapped around a collection of nuclear proteins called **histones** ("webs" or "tissues"). The resulting tangle is so intricate and involved that it would make a fisherman's backlash look as simple as a cat's cradle (figure 4.32). It is these matted snarls that stain so darkly and are so clearly visible when the cells are undergoing division, and it is the configuration in which chromosomes were studied with such verve for nearly a century in the hope of learning the secrets of heredity.

DNA strands are so fine that their actual length is often obscured, especially when they are all tangled up in the chromosomal mats during division. To give some idea of the capacity of cellular DNA in humans, it has been calculated that if all the DNA present in the cells of a single human were to be unravelled, it would stretch out to a length of more than 20 billion miles. That figure, like so many figures in science, doesn't have any meaning to most of us, but it does if we translate it into movement that we can understand. The DNA in a single human being would stretch from the earth to the orbit of Pluto and back again, twice. If the space shuttle in which the U.S. takes such pride were to head toward a rendezvous with Pluto, it would take it more than twenty years to get there and just a little less than fifteen to get back—a total of thirty-five years—half a lifetime. And that's just one trip! Our DNA, unravelled, could go out there and back—twice!

Figure 4.32 (*a*) A chromatid compressed preparatory to cell division. (*b*) A supercoil in the chromatid. (*c*) The chromosomal tangle within the supercoil. (*d*) A single chromosome strand coiled around a histone protein backbone. (*e*) Within the strand: DNA wound around histone protein "cushions." (*f*) The double helix of DNA.

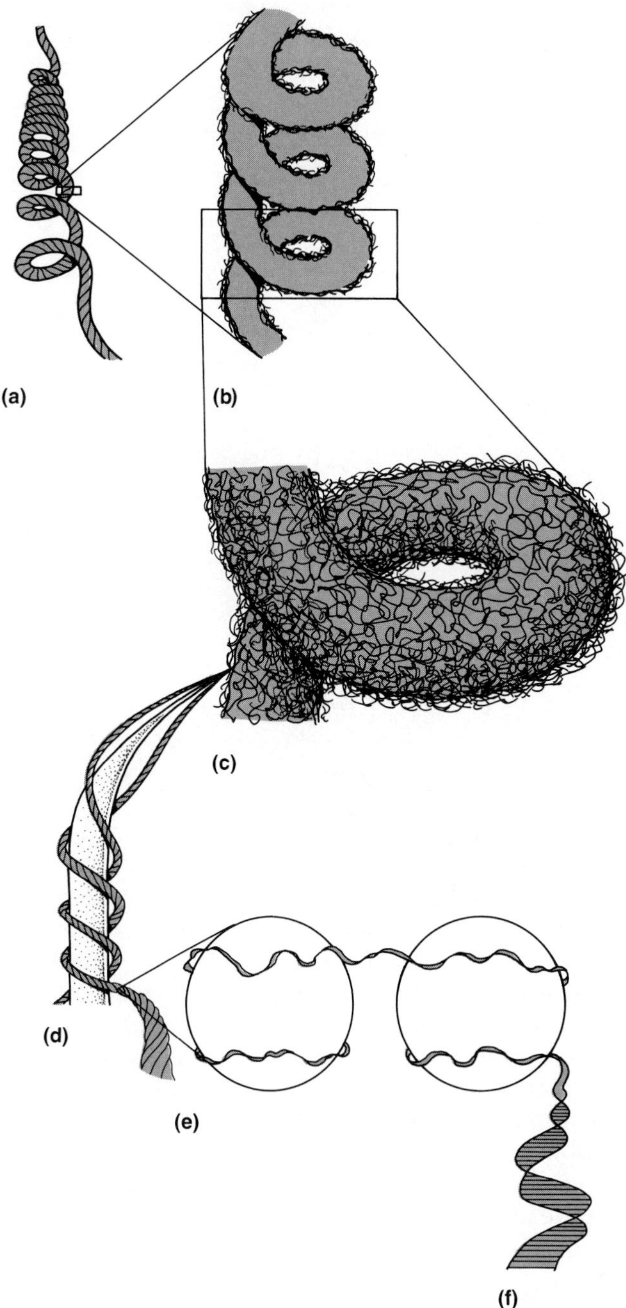

Protein Synthesis

Within the nucleus are the chromosomes. All the information for continued growth and development of the organism is encoded on the DNA in these organelles. Any description of how the cells synthesize their unique proteins must therefore relate the processes by which the DNA-contained information is translated into protein structure.

Figure 4.33 The double helix of DNA. (*a*) The two strands are linked together by hydrogen bonds that form between complementary bases. (*b*) The specific pairings of the four DNA bases. Note that purines always link to pyrimidines, thus keeping the helices straight and orderly.

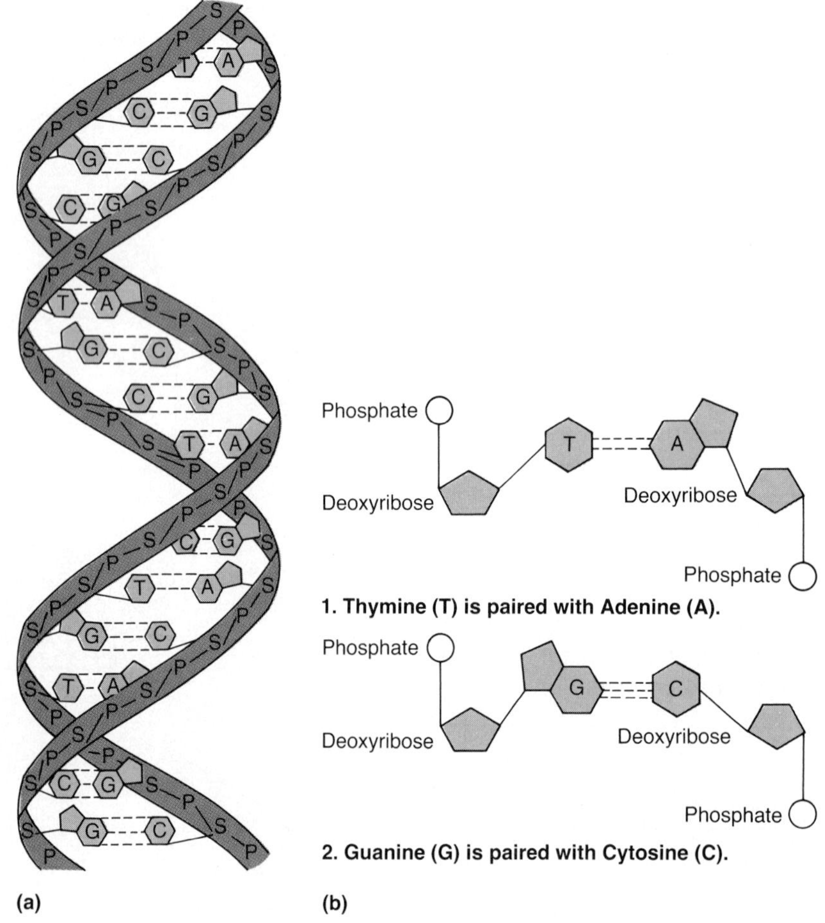

Figure 4.32 illustrates the relationship between the circumstances and DNA. In figure 4.33, the double helix has been magnified to show its chemical and topographical configuration. As you can see, the arrangement resembles a ladder that has been twisted into a corkscrew shape so that the sides wrap around each other while the steps between them hold them apart a constant distance. The sides of the ladder are made up of the phosphoric acid and deoxyribose, while the rungs are formed of the base pairs. The figure identifies these bases with the abbreviations **A (adenine), T (thymine), G (guanine),** and **C (cytosine).** As indicated in chapter 2, purines always link to pyrimidines—adenine always with thymine and cytosine always with guanine.

The initial step in DNA replication is the breaking of the hydrogen bonds that hold the two helices together. When hydrogen bonds are present in large numbers, as they are in a mass of water, they are very strong, but individually they are really rather weak and easily separated. The hydrogen bonds are therefore broken one at a time and the DNA molecule is "unzipped." Since the cell must replicate the entire chromosome, each of the DNA helices must act as a template on which a complementary strand can be synthesized. As each hydrogen bond breaks, the DNA strand unwinds from that link, and the two bases that were once attached to each other are exposed for the placing of a new, matching nucleotide (see figure 4.34). The units are placed opposite their complementary bases, thus forming two new strips of DNA, each growing on the surface of an "old" one. As the original helix slowly rotates, two new strands of completed DNA, each a double helix, curl out into the nucleoplasm from beneath. Each of these new double helices contains a brand-new strip of DNA and an original "old" strand.

Figure 4.34 The method by which DNA is able to replicate. This model is called "semi-conservative" because each newly formed strand is paired with an original "old" one.

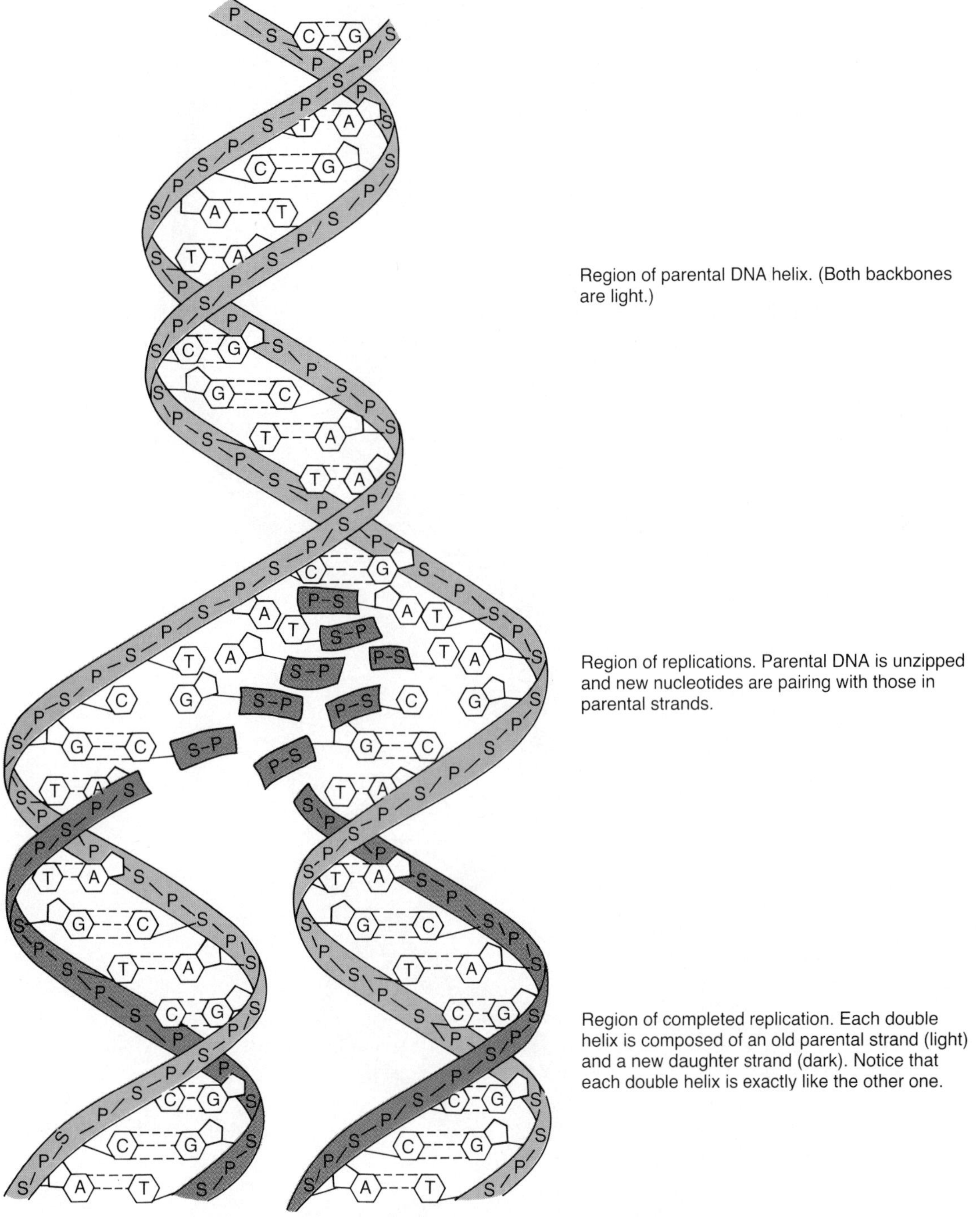

Figure 4.35 The process by which an RNA strip is built according to instructions from DNA. The operation is known as *transcription* because both RNA and DNA use the same code "language."

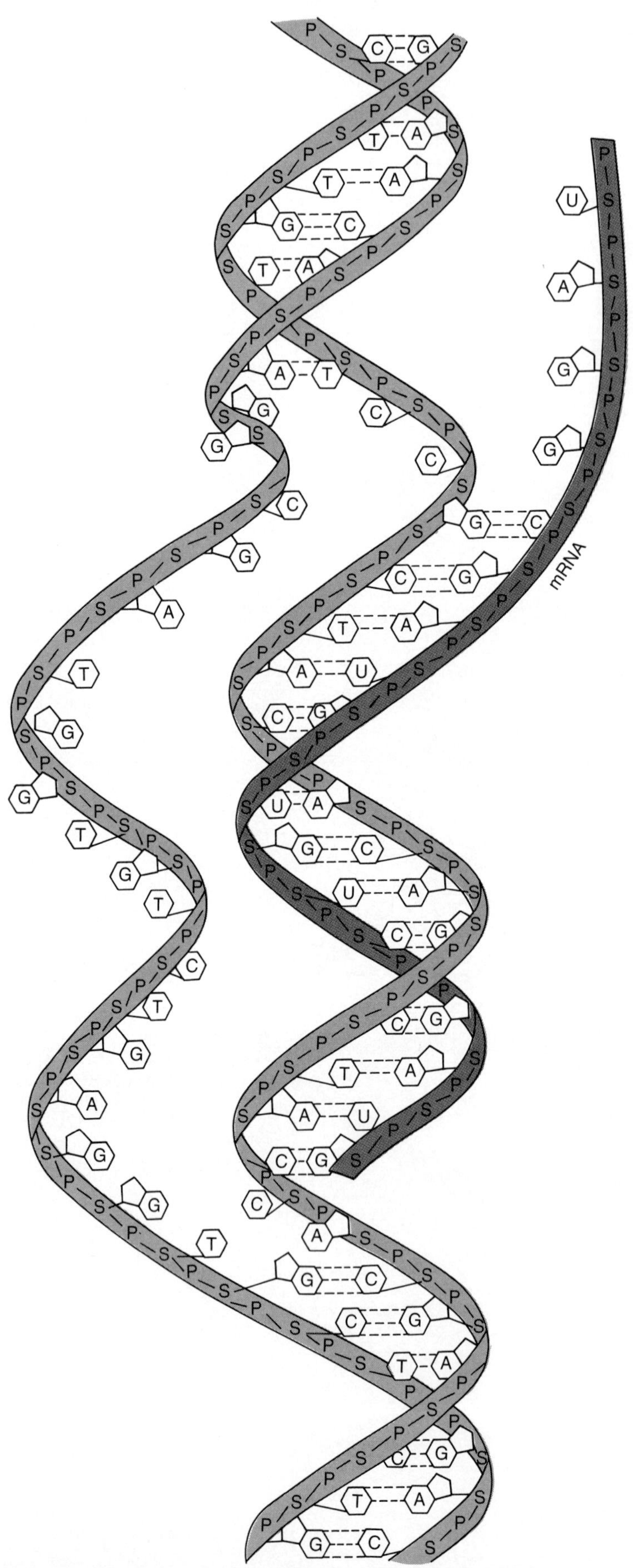

When DNA decides it is time to begin synthesis of a new protein, a special group of enzymes swings into action. These enzymes catalyze the process of copying the information contained in the DNA onto a strip of RNA (figure 4.35). Remember, RNA is structurally different from DNA in one nucleotide base (it features uracil instead of thymine), its pentose sugar, and its size. It also differs in function.

DNA is a permanent resident of the nucleus—it cannot leave. Yet all protein synthetic activities take place in the cytosol of the cell, so there must be a means of getting information provided by DNA into the cytosol. That job is handled by RNA. After picking up the necessary information, this RNA slips through the pores in the nuclear envelope and enters the cytosol, where it serves as a template for protein synthesis. The RNA that carries this message from the DNA into the cytosol is known, appropriately enough, as **messenger RNA (mRNA).** The coding method used by DNA and RNA is one of the most active research areas in biology today.

When Samuel Morse first became obsessed with the idea of transmitting messages instantaneously along electrical wires, he was confronted with a really big problem—how to transmit 26 different letters and 10 different figures without using 36 different wires. He solved his problem, as is well known, by devising the Morse Code, a system of dots and dashes to describe the letters he was sending. Each letter had its own special combination of dots and dashes, and when he wanted to switch to numbers, he merely stuck in a code meaning "shift to figures." With just three variables in his code—long, short, and pause—he was able to designate every letter in the alphabet without difficulty. There was even enough flexibility left to toss in a couple of codes meaning things like "end of communication" and "finished with this message, stand by for another." DNA is able to do the same thing with its "dots and dashes." The bases adenine, guanine, cytosine, and thymine (uracil in RNA), when arranged in groups of three, code one "letter." DNA sends the messages by transcribing each of these "triplets" into the messenger RNA, and the mRNA takes this information out to the ribosome and lays out complete instructions for the assembly of a protein.

Messenger RNA is not the only RNA that is present in the cytosol. There are two others. Once in the cytosol, mRNA heads for the ribosomes and presents its instructions to the **ribosomal RNA (rRNA)** that is part of the ribosome structure. As it slides along between the two halves of the ribosomes, the mRNA strip is read, and amino acids necessary for assembly of the protein are placed on its template by still another type of RNA, **transfer RNA (tRNA).** The growing protein projects out at right angles to the mRNA strand (figure 4.36).

Transfer RNA is arranged in a very specific configuration (see figure 4.37). It looks like a slightly irregular Maltese cross, the base of which contains the nucleotide triplet for a specific amino acid. Normally, tRNA consists of about eighty nucleotides, and since there are twenty different amino acids used in the building of protein, there must be twenty different types of tRNA. Each tRNA molecule has a special zone on its surface that contains three nucleotides arranged in a special sequence. These are known as **nucleotide triplets,** and each triplet has a particular meaning. Each one refers to a specific amino acid—the one that the tRNA molecule is carrying—and the triplets will fit only into complementary triplets on the mRNA molecule that is directing the synthesis of the protein.

Possibly the easiest way to visualize the process of protein synthesis as well as the specific roles of the various nucleic acids is to consider the cell a large, money-making conglomerate.

The nucleus of the cell functions like the corporate offices, and within the nucleus is the chromosomal DNA. This is the chief executive—the chairman of the board or the company president—and like many chief executives, the DNA never leaves its nuclear office to venture into the factories where the everyday labor is done. There is one glaring difference between DNA and a company president, however. Most company presidents only *think* they know everything, whereas DNA really does.

Nuclear DNA is doubly valuable, actually, because it not only knows all the right things to do, but it's the only thing in the cell that does. It never does any of the actual labor, of course, but it knows exactly what to do and when. It limits its dealings with the lower echelons to conversations with its chief aide, in this case, the general manager—a certain high-class type of RNA (mRNA). Naturally, the chief executive never tells everything he knows to his subordinate manager, so the mRNA gets only enough information to complete the next job. The boss keeps the rest of it to himself until it is needed. As a result, the RNA carrying the message to the factory supervisors is only a fraction of the length of the DNA molecule.

Figure 4.36 The process of translating. The language of the nucleic acids is changed to that of proteins on the cellular ribosomes. Transfer RNA particles add their amino acids onto the messenger RNA template according to the latter's instructions. As each tRNA molecule drops into place, the amino acid it carries is locked into the growing polypeptide chain. As the mRNA template glides through the ribosomes, the protein chain projects out from it.

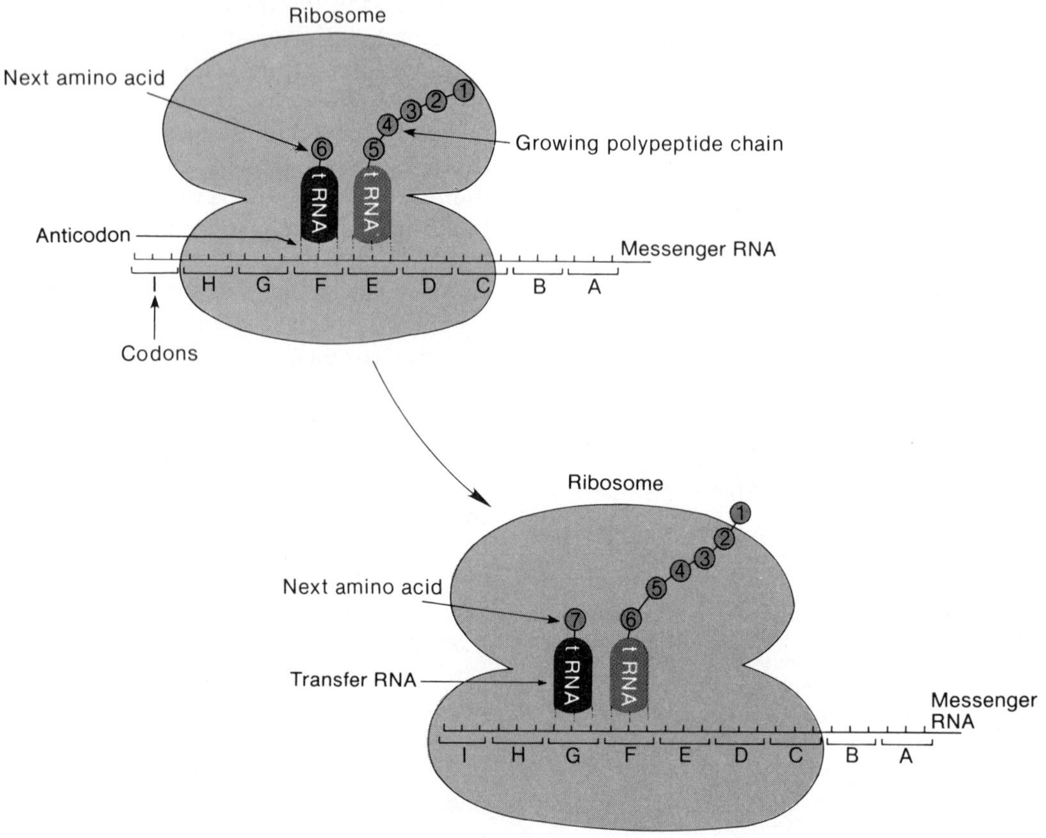

Figure 4.37 A molecule of transfer RNA (tRNA).

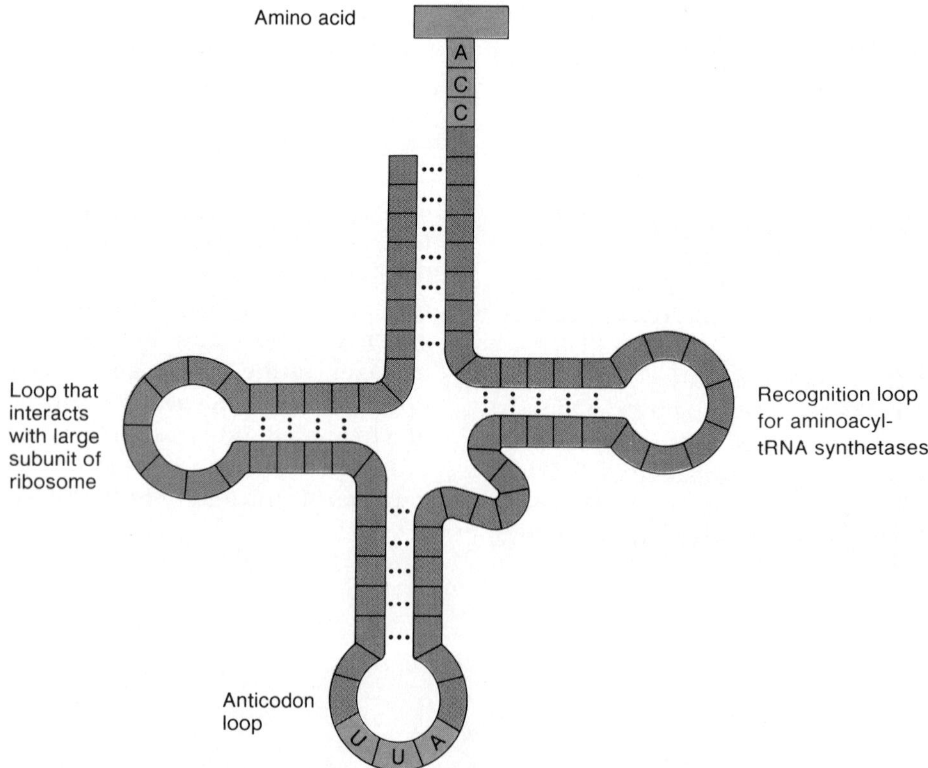

Once the instructions are outside the executive offices (the cellular nucleus) and in the factory (the interior of the cell), the supervisors and skilled laborers in the cell can be given the bits of information that they need to know in order to complete the job ordered by the DNA. All kinds of specialized workers are involved in these operations, and mRNA has instructions for them all. First of all, it displays its blueprint (or template) to the plant manager (rRNA), and the template is laid out on the assembly line (the ribosome). Now the work can begin. There are tiny fragments of RNA that put the proteins together, one piece at a time (tRNA). These particles rush about, picking up the various protein modules in the free amino acid pool and transferring them to the assembly line in the cell. Once beside the assembly line, the tRNA molecules, each with its special load, wait attentively as the personal codes show up on the mRNA blueprint. Each time one comes up, a tRNA molecule with the matching code rushes in and places its amino acid on the template at which time the foreman—an enzyme known as **peptidal transferase**—clamps them in place in the growing protein chain. The tRNA, still hooked to the amino acid, then shifts along the assembly line to the next position, where it releases the amino acid, and off it goes into the cytosol to pick up another molecule of the same amino acid so it can repeat the procedure if necessary.

As the protein chain grows, the strip of mRNA slides through the ribosome like a strip of ticker tape, exposing a new triplet with each move. All the while, clusters of tRNA molecules, each carrying their amino acid, wait in line, looking for the code that means their amino acid goes on next. The process is repeated again and again until the protein is complete and a code appears on the mRNA meaning "stop." At this point, the protein chain is broken free of the ribosome and heads off to do its job.

If the newly synthesized protein is earmarked for export, it is pushed through the membrane of the endoplasmic reticulum as it grows. This is why so many ribosomes cluster on the cytoplasmic surface of the ER. Many proteins are manufactured for use outside the cell, and most are stored inside the ER until they're shipped. Putting the factories right "on the river," in a sense, simplifies transportation problems, particularly if the products are to be modified further within an adjacent Golgi apparatus.

Proteins that are used within the cell are released and used where they are assembled, and in such cases there is no particular reason to synthesize them on the ER. They are assembled and released by the ribosomes that drift around in the cytoplasm or are anchored to the lattice framework. Once assembled, the proteins usually go right to work. If they are structural, they are anchored where they are needed. If they are intended for catalysis, they are moved to where they can be used. They may be needed to repair a tear in the cell membrane, or to digest some new fuel source, or maybe even arrange some special proteins near the cell surface so that the cell can contract and pull the edges of a cut together. All emergencies, as well as all routine operations, are handled according to instructions emanating from the nuclear DNA. What to do is all written down somewhere . . . everything we need to keep us running properly throughout our lifetimes. Each chemical compound and element that we need will show up in precisely the proper concentration and at exactly the right place and the proper time—as long as the nucleic acid mechanisms are not interfered with in some way.

Clinical Considerations

Diseases that can be attributed specifically to a breakdown of some intracellular organelle are not well known; hence there is not much I can add to this section. However, something should probably be said at this point about the lysosome, because it has the potential to be so destructive. For all its power to resist digestive enzymes, the lysosomal membrane is not immune to problems. Like every piece of machinery—organic or inorganic—there are times when it fails, and on occasion the breakdown can be disastrous. Incorrect osmotic situations or an unfortunate chemical distribution in the cytosol can sometimes physically disrupt the membrane, and when the membrane of the lysosome breaks up, its contents are turned loose on the interior of the cell. It takes only a few moments for the protein-splitters and fat-splitters to hydrolyze membranes and organelles alike, and within moments the cell suffers irreparable damage. Fractured lysosome membranes may be the end result of many painful and essentially incurable metabolic diseases like *gout* and *arthritis.*

Also, there are times when the lysosomes do not work right, and when they malfunction, the whole cell suffers . . . sometimes the whole organism suffers. Some really deadly afflictions are associated with lysosomal malfunction.

Every once in a while, a child will be born with an inherited deficiency in a digestive enzyme that is supposed to be present in the lysosomes. This sort of thing occurs several times each year in this country, and pediatricians usually recognize the signs immediately. *Tay-Sachs disease,* which seems to strike children of Semitic parents particularly hard, *Gierke's Disease, Hand-Schuller-Christian's Disease, Stokes-Adam's syndrome,* and a whole host of cardiovascular diseases may be due to enzyme-deficient lysosomes. In all of these afflictions we find cells jam-packed with lysosomes, each one of which contains materials that it cannot digest because certain necessary enzymes—enzymes that should be present—just are not there. Yet the lysosome can't throw these indigestible materials away like waste, because the cell will not let it. The cellular machinery needs parts of it and refuses to permit the disposal of any of it. Before long, the cells are swollen with bloated lysosomes. With their membranes bursting at the seams, the cells strangle to death. Irreversible mental damage, mangled motor control, and often-deadly kidney disorders are frequent sequels in the case history of these genetic lysosomal disorders.

Summary

The Cell Theory

States that all life is cellular and that it emerges from preexisting cells.

- I. A New Scientific Plateau. Made physiological experimentation possible.
  - A. Resulted in the development of the discipline known as cellular physiology.
  - B. Stimulated intensive interest in microscopial investigations.
  - C. May have been the prime motivator for development of the electron microscope.
- II. The "Generalized" Cell. A cell containing all organelles and structures found in most cells; an "average" cell.
  - A. The Electron Microscope. Permitted much more detailed inspection of the cell.
  - B. Artifacts. Artifacts are false structures or effects that are produced during the preparation of specimens for inspection. The more drastic the preparations, the more artifacts there will be.

Cellular Ultrastructure

Cells are composed of cytosol and intracellular organelles.

The Plasma Membrane

The plasma membrane is composed mostly of lipid with proteins of various shapes and sizes imbedded within or "floating" on it.

- I. The Schizophrenic Lipid
  - A. Membrane lipids have a polar end and a nonpolar end and form a bilayer, the outside of which is miscible with water.
  - B. The interior of this bilayer is nonpolar fatty acids and is not miscible with water.
- II. The Lipid Bilayer. Fat-soluble materials can dissolve in the membrane and easily penetrate into the cell.
  - A. Limitations of a Lipid Bilayer. Water-soluble materials must either stay outside or enter through protein lined pores.
  - B. The Fluid-Mosaic Membrane. The morphology of the plasma membrane must be able to explain its abilities and limitations. The fluid-mosaic model does this.
- III. The Membrane's Proteins
  - A. Structure. Some of the membrane proteins are structural in nature.
  - B. Surface Receptors. Some of the membrane proteins serve as receptors for various water-soluble materials in the body fluids.
  - C. Carrier Proteins. Some serve as membrane-transport mechanisms.
  - D. Enzymes. Many of the proteins in the plasma membrane are catalytic in nature, hence are enzymes.
  - E. Markers. Some membrane proteins serve as I.D. for their cell.
- IV. Some Ancillary Molecules. The plasma membrane also contains glycolipids, glycoproteins, and cholesterol.
  - A. Glycolipids. The glycolipids and glycoproteins are apparently part of the external receptor process.
  - B. Cholesterol. The function of cholesterol is uncertain.
- V. Selective Permeability. The plasma membrane can govern what will cross it and what will not.

The Cytoplasm

- I. The Cytosol. Cytosol is a nutrient saline solution whose pH and osmolarity are rigidly controlled. Most of the intracellular chemical reactions take place in the cytosol.
- II. The Endoplasmic Reticulum. The endoplasmic reticulum consists of membranous tubules that wind back and forth in the cellular interior.
  - A. Function of the Endoplasmic Reticulum. The endoplasmic reticulum serves to segregate, store, and process materials synthesized by the cell for use elsewhere. There are two types of ER—rough and smooth.
  - B. The Rough Endoplasmic Reticulum. The rough ER is studded with organelles known as ribosomes. Much protein synthesis takes place on the rough ER.
  - C. The Smooth Endoplasmic Reticulum. The smooth ER has no ribosomes.
- III. Golgi Apparatus. The Golgi apparatus is a membranous organelle. It serves to segregate, sort, and process certain proteins made by the rough endoplasmic reticulum.

IV. The Lysosome. These organelles serve to break up materials present in the cytosol.
   A. Lysosomal Function. Lysosomes can function as a cellular "stomach," digesting materials needed by the cell.
      1. Endocytosis. Endocytosis is a method of getting large, water-soluble materials into the cytosol of the cell.
      2. Intracellular Digestion. This is accomplished in the endocytotic vesicle when the lysosome fuses with it.
      3. Exocytosis. This process removes large, water-soluble wastes from the cytosol.
   B. The Constructive Lysosome. Lysosomes can selectively destroy damaged cell parts and salvage the raw materials. They can also aid in "preventive maintenance."
   C. The Destructive Lysosome. Lysosomes can destroy the cell if they rupture or release their enzymes when they are not supposed to.

V. Mitochondria. The mitochondrion is a membranous organelle. It is the site of the most efficient energy-providing reactions in the cell.

VI. Ribosomes. Ribosomes are not of membranous origin. All protein synthesis that takes place within the cell occurs on the ribosomes.

The Framework of the Cell

I. Microfilaments. Microfilaments are not of membranous origin. They provide the cell with rigidity and an interior framework.

II. Microtubules
   A. Microtubules are not of membranous origin. They are composed of microfilaments arranged in a cylindrical shape.
   B. Microtubules are involved mainly in movement of materials within the cytosol. They provide movement for cilia and flagella.

III. Cilia and Flagella. Cilia and flagella are hair-like protrusions on the outer surface of cells that are able to beat in rhythmic waves. This beating enables tissues to move materials across their surfaces.

IV. Centrosomes. Centrosomes are composed of two cylinders called centrioles. Centrioles are composed of microtubules arranged in triplets. They are involved in mitosis.

Nucleus

The nucleus is surrounded by a double membrane for extra protection. It encloses the cellular DNA, which controls chemical synthesis and contains all our genetic information.

The Nucleolus. The nucleolus contains ribosomal RNA and ribosomal proteins.

Protein Synthesis

Protein synthesis originates with a set of instructions on nuclear DNA. These instructions are passed on carefully to a smaller strip of RNA. There are several kinds of RNA: ribosomal RNA, which is enclosed within the ribosome; messenger RNA, which carries the instructions from DNA to the ribosomes; and transfer RNA, which carries amino acids to the ribosomes.

Review Questions

1. What was the theory proposed to the scientific community by Schleiden and Schwann? What was its significance?
2. What is a "generalized" cell?
3. How are artifacts formed when samples are prepared for microscopic viewing?
4. Compare the microstructure of a cell as revealed by a light microscope with the ultrastructure as revealed by an electron microscope. Draw a generalized example of both.
5. Name the various intracellular organelles that have been revealed to us by electron microscopy.
6. Describe the chemical makeup of the plasma membrane. Of what organic chemical type is it chiefly composed?
7. Outline some of the important structural characteristics of the plasma membrane.
8. Describe the fluid-mosaic model of the plasma membrane.
9. What are adsorbed proteins? integral proteins?
10. Name at least three functions of the membrane proteins.
11. Discuss the functions of the plasma membrane and how its structure enables it to fulfill those jobs.
12. How does the cytosol differ from the cytoplasm?
13. Describe the cytosol. What is its function?
14. Of what is the endoplasmic reticulum composed? In what ways is it similar to plasma membrane? How is it different?
15. Describe the structure and function of the two types of endoplasmic reticulum.
16. Describe the structure and function of the Golgi apparatus.
17. What is a lysosome? What is its relationship to the processes of endocytosis and exocytosis? Describe these two processes.
18. Of what value to a cell are lysosomes?
19. Describe the structure of a mitochondrion.
20. What are ribosomes? Where are they usually located within a cell and what is their function?
21. Identify and describe the two types of organelles that are involved in forming the skeletal support of a living cell.
22. Of what is the nuclear envelope made? How does it differ, structurally and functionally, from a plasma membrane?
23. What forms the nucleolus?
24. What nuclear factor provides the information necessary to protein synthesis?
25. Where in the cell does protein synthesis take place?
26. Describe the types of RNA involved in protein synthesis and outline their roles in this process.

Chapter 5 Growth and Energy Production

Study Hints

Strictly speaking, the word *reproduction* doesn't refer to the production of a new human being, but rather to the production of a duplicate of the original. Hence it refers more accurately to the process of cell division than to procreation. Cell division is known to biologists as *mitosis*, and, along with a discussion of the methods by which cells accumulate free energy, it will be dealt with in this chapter.

1. Pay particular attention to the fact that the operations of mitosis are thoroughly orchestrated; each step has an established antecedent, a set progression, and a predictable succession.
2. The reactions that produce energy for the cell are as important as breathing. You should learn them to the point where you can discuss them easily with your colleagues.
3. Learn the reactions of intermediary metabolism in three groups:
   a. The anaerobic group (glycolysis)
   b. The Krebs cycle
   c. The process of oxidative phosphorylation (respiratory chain)

Objectives

When you have finished reading this chapter, you should:

1. understand what true reproduction is.
2. be able to outline the process of mitosis, step by step.
3. know what oxidation is and be able to describe it.
4. know what redox reactions are.
5. be able to describe the various steps in the anaerobic breakdown of glucose.
6. understand what is happening when lactic acid builds up as a result of lack of oxygen.
7. be able to relate the steps in the aerobic reactions of the Krebs cycle and know where electrons and CO_2 molecules are lost from the substrates.
8. be able to describe the respiratory chain in terms of its capabilities.
9. understand the function of oxygen in living systems.
10. be able to knowledgeably compare the efficiency of the aerobic reactions with those of anaerobic metabolism.

"Hybridoma" cells dividing.

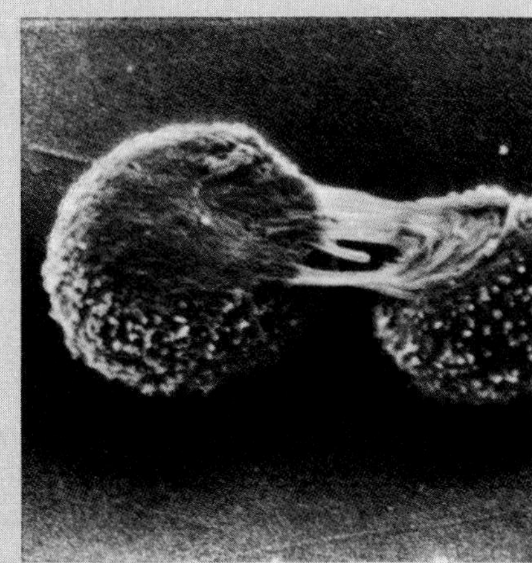

Introduction

When we note that a seldom-seen nephew, niece, or cousin has "grown considerably" since we last saw them, it is natural for us to think in terms of their having increased their total body mass. The general attitude is that the person has simply gotten bigger, and few of us ever wonder how this happened.

Growth in a multicellular organism does indeed consist of an increase in total body mass, but it doesn't reflect an increase in the size of any individual parts. Body cells seldom increase very much in size, because it would reduce their efficiency. As we have seen, when something increases in size without changing its shape, its surface-area-to-volume ratio decreases to a point where it is unable to get enough materials into the cell to maintain the increased volume. At the same time, the deep interior cannot get rid of waste products it generates, because the surface is too small and too far away. In a competitive world, there is no room for inefficiency.

Yet there are definite advantages for the organism as a whole to become large, and most of them are self-evident. The larger the organism is, the less likely it is to fall victim to some flesh-eating killer, the fewer the number of creatures that can threaten it, the greater its food-seeking range, and so on. Anything that helps the whole organism to survive is bound to be advantageous to its cells. Consequently, it's reasonable to say that anything that is good for the organism is good for the cell. If it's good for the organism to grow to large size, then it's good for the cell to see to it that such growth is possible.

The Cell Cycle

But if the cell cannot increase its size and remain efficient, how does it provide the organism with this advantageous growth? Well, if cells cannot make the organism bigger by growing in size themselves, there is only one way left, and that is for them to *grow in number.* This is what growth really is in a multicellular organism, an increase in the total number of body cells. In the fertilized ovum, in the fetus, and in the adolescent child, cell division is rapid in nearly all body tissues. In adults the process is a little less frantic, and fewer tissues are involved.

Of course, body growth is not the only reason for cell proliferation. Injuries require repair, and when a large bite is taken from some portion of an animal's hide, or when some tissues get damaged in a fall, the cells must be replaced. It is all handled by cell proliferation. Already-existing cells split in half, so that where there was originally just one cell, there are now two. However, it is much more complicated than merely dividing. The information contained in the chromosomes is absolutely vital and so comprehensive that a most precise series of control mechanisms must ensure that it will be passed, intact and unchanged, to all the cells in the body. So when cell division does occur, the various steps or *stages* follow each other with rigorous precision. The process is known as **mitosis,** and it is part of the **cell cycle.** It is a system of sequential events that is easily separated into several different phases (figure 5.1).

Interphase

When not actually involved in the process of division, our cells exist in a state known as the **interphase.** Interphase is divided into three subordinate activity phases, the first of which is known as the **gap one (G_1) phase.** Gap one phase begins at the end of mitosis. Cells that have just divided are small and have only single copies of their DNA strands within their nuclei. They need time to grow to maturity, and a lot of work is necessary to do the job. So during G_1 phase the cells are busy handling their day-to-day affairs and accumulating materials that will be needed to produce extra proteins, membrane lipid, and other spare parts—a *very* full-time job. Yet when the time arrives, they can shift to the process of division very rapidly.

The G_1 phase, therefore, is the period of time following mitosis and preceding the initiation of DNA synthesis.

Figure 5.1 The cell cycle.

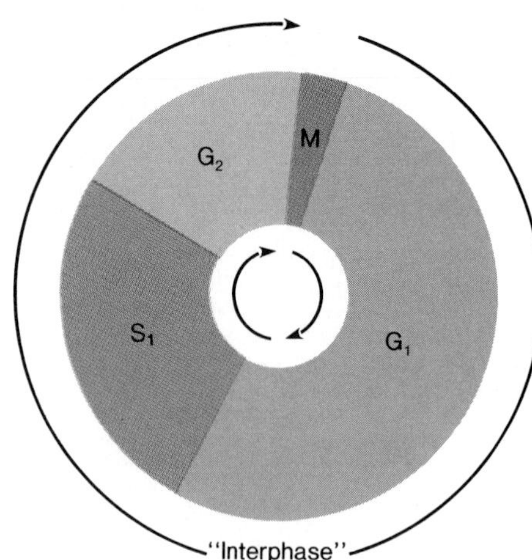

Should a signal to divide inspire the cell, the G_1 phase abruptly ends, and the cell quickly shifts from its "daily activity" phase into what is called the **synthetic** or **S_1 phase.**

S_1 is the phase of the cell cycle during which replication of DNA occurs.

Once this phase begins, routine activities slow down or cease altogether while the cell gathers its resources and begins the process of duplicating all its nuclear DNA. This involves a lot of synthetic activity as both strands of DNA are feverishly copied by the machinery of the cell. So vigorously is this goal pursued that every last strip of DNA is completely copied in only about four hours' time.

Now another gap period occurs. This one, known as the **gap two** or **G_2 phase,** represents *the period between the end of DNA synthesis and the beginning of mitosis.*

During the whole of interphase, the chromosomal material is dispersed throughout the nucleus. As the duplication process grinds to a halt, however, the long, fine strands of DNA begin to twist and compress themselves into the kind of switchback snarl that earthworms somehow manage to twist themselves into when left in a can with only a little dirt.

Mitosis

Mitosis has begun. This takes place in four distinct phases: *prophase, metaphase, anaphase,* and *telophase.* They are most easily distinguished from one another by the position of the chromosomes.

Figure 5.2 (*a*) The chromosomes of a human male. Note the fact that each chromosome is paired and that the sex chromosomes (*x* and *y* at bottom right) are the only pair that are dissimilar. (*b*) The line drawing shows how the DNA strand is arranged within. (*c*) Electron micrograph of a chromosome in prophase.

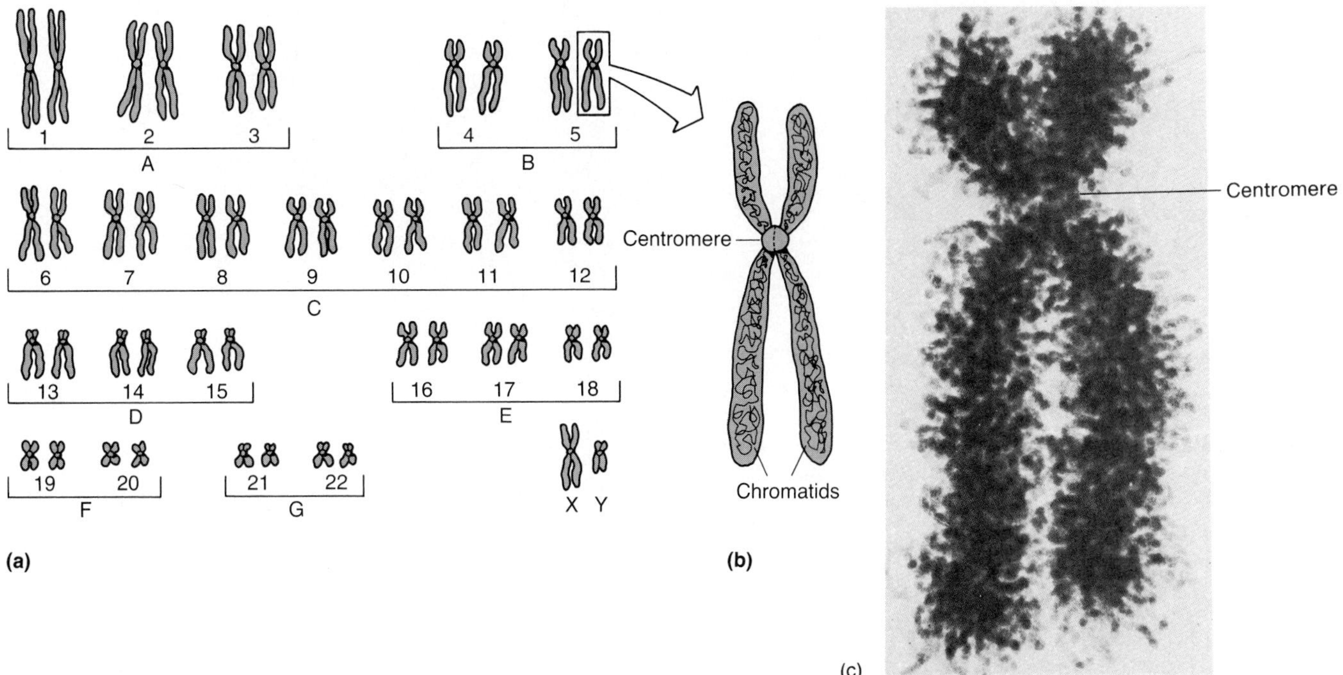

Prophase

During **prophase,** the strands of DNA that were spread throughout the nucleus and were so fine dive and zoom back and forth, forming enormous tangles of meandering matting that ultimately produce the compacted whorls of DNA and protein that are clearly visible to light microscopes and which early scientists named "chromosomes." When the process is finally finished, the nucleus of the cell features a whole battery of DNA jungles looped in an incredible labyrinth around special protein spindles. How these meshes form and what plan is followed while they do is a complete mystery. The wrappings and convolutions of the visible chromosome are so numerous and complex that even the electron microscope has not been able to unsnarl them (see figure 4.31).

In addition to compacting their DNA into a tightly coiled mass, each chromosome has separated into two clumps called **chromatids,** each the precise complement of the other and each joined to its reflection by a solid bridge known as the **centromere** (see figure 5.2).

While the chromosomes are slowly winding into these convoluted lumps, the nuclear envelope is disappearing into the mass of materials and organelles in the cellular interior, and the membranous boundary line between nucleoplasm and cytoplasm ceases to exist. Simultaneously, the two microtubule complexes known as the centrioles move apart, taking up positions on opposite sides of the chromosomal mass. From each a spray of tiny, individual microtubules flares out in all directions.

By the end of prophase, the nuclear envelope has completely disappeared, and a zone within the cellular interior that includes the section that was once the nucleus has been swallowed up by a palisade of microtubules. These gradually form a shape resembling a whirring spindle on an old-time spinning wheel, with the centrioles at the hubs (figure 5.3). With surprising informality, this structure has been given an intelligible name in English—the **mitotic spindle.**

Figure 5.3 The spindle apparatus in an animal cell. The spindle fibers are formed of bundles of microtubules.

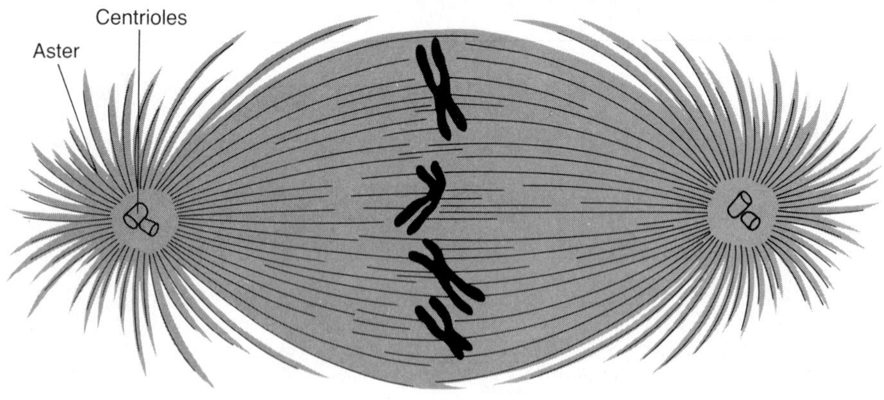

Figure 5.4 A metaphase spindle. Note the disappearance of the spindle fibers as they approach the centrioles.

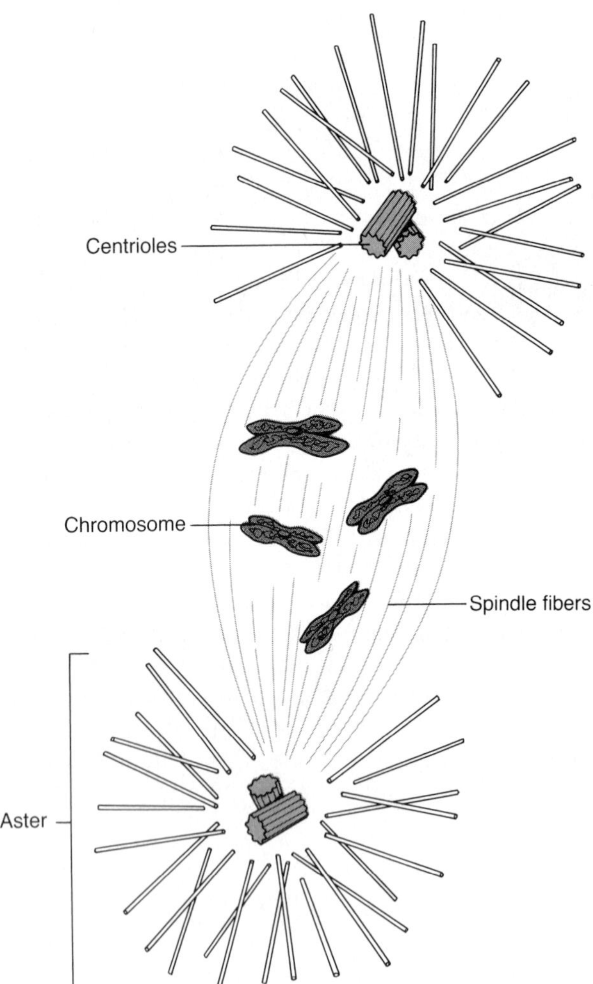

Metaphase

The lining up of the chromosomes on the metaphase plate is the definitive characteristic of **metaphase,** and it is accomplished as follows: As metaphase begins, sprays of microtubles begin to emerge from individual chromosomes, right at the centromere. As they snake outward, something inspires them to head toward the nearest centriole, and as a result, each chromatid is connected to a group of tubules growing away from it.

The tubules grow parallel to the spindle fibers, and they must, in some way, form a junction with these fibers, because something appears to provide them with an anchor and there is really nothing else that can. Once anchored to the spindle fibers, they elongate and press the chromosomes they are attached to into a more or less uniform arrangement on a single plane. This plane is near the middle of the cell, runs approximately perpendicular to the spindle fibers, and is known as the **equatorial** or **metaphase plate** (figure 5.4).

The centrioles are the hubs of the spindle, and from them a scattering of microtubule fibers stretches out toward the plasma membrane as if to form some kind of anchorage. Yet they dissolve into the cytoplasm, disappearing from view before any contact is visible. Nevertheless, reason insists that they must grab hold and form a mooring of some sort, because by the end of metaphase, all the fibers are beginning to apply firm and increasing tension on each chromatid. This wouldn't be possible if they weren't firmly rooted to some sort of solid foundation.

Anaphase

No one is really sure how long this tugging goes on, but it produces a surprisingly sudden and uniform result. **Anaphase** begins when the individual chromosomes suddenly yield—all at about the same time—to the relentless traction of the microtubules. Each chromosome has two chromatids. These chromatids are attached to centrioles at opposite ends of the cell, so as the tubules begin to contract, there is great pressure for the chromosomes to tear apart. Finally, when the tension reaches a certain critical point, that's exactly what happens. The centromere is torn asunder, and the individual chromatids begin to drift, like spaceships suddenly released from the bonds of gravity, away from the metaphase plate. Why do all the centrosomes split at about the same time? We don't know, but several suggestions have been made. Maybe the contracting process is centrally controlled, and the centromeres break simultaneously because all the fibers produce critical traction at the same instant. Another idea propounds the thought that there is an enzyme that is designed to attack the centrosomes, and it is released on a specific biological signal. Both are reasonable possibilities.

Anaphase draws to a conclusion as the individual chromatids begin to form new chromosomal clusters at opposite ends of their cell.

Telophase

As the chromosomes take up their new positions, the microtubules that were so firmly attached to the individual chromatids fall away and the spindle collapses. Microtubules begin now to arrange themselves in a line of parallel filaments running across the middle of the cell from one centriole to the other. These clusters are known as **stem bodies,** and as the last mitotic phase—the **telophase**—runs its course, they are pressed into a smaller and smaller space by the constricting membrane until they are finally nipped in two.

Before that can happen, however, the membrane must compress in the middle to form a boundary for the two new cells. To accomplish this, the membrane of the cell begins to **furrow,** and as the furrow increases in depth a constriction forms, like a drawstring tied around a tube—a constriction that is ultimately destined to pinch the single cell in half. While the plasma membrane has been relentlessly pursuing this final mitotic duty, shards of endoplasmic reticulum cluster around the chromosome clumps at each end of the cell and begin to deploy in small, orderly formations like platoons of soldiers. Gradually they fall into line and fuse, thus taking the first step in the genesis of a new nuclear envelope around the chromosomes. The centrioles, still fussing with the microtubule fibers, remain outside in the cytoplasm, excluded from the newly forming nucleus.

Figure 5.5 A summary of the cell cycle. Interphase includes the G_1, S_1, and G_2 phases of the cycle. Mitosis begins with prophase and ends with telophase.

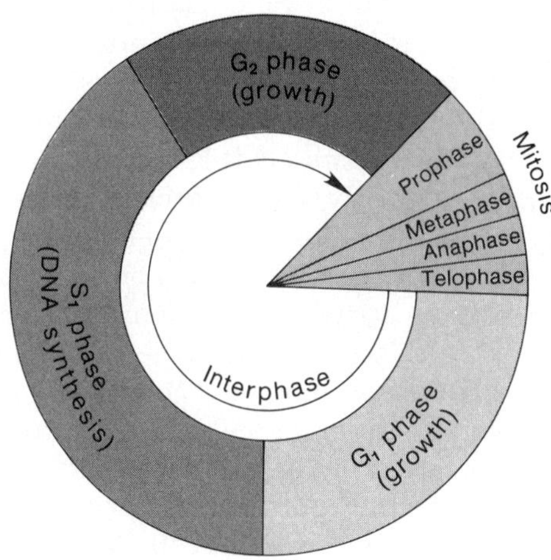

Interphase Again

Telophase and mitosis both end as the membrane crimps, severing the stem bodies, and then fuses in place, effectively splitting what was once a single cell into two smaller cells . . . smaller, but with exactly the same content of genetic information as the original and capable of doing the same things. Eventually, both will grow to the size of the original mother cell.

The whole process, from the beginning of prophase to the end of telophase, has consumed about an hour. See figure 5.5.

Energy

Living systems are organized hundreds of different ways, and their requirements are as broad as the earth itself. There is one inflexible requirement that all of them have in common, however, and that is energy. Energy is a very abstract concept to most people. The term is used a great deal in everyday conversation. The observation is often made that some people seem to have a lot of energy, while others seem to need an "energy transfusion" just to get them to the point of apathy. We will discuss energy in considerable detail in chapter 6, but some cursory mention is necessary at this point to help us understand what it is and why our bodies require so much of it.

Energy is necessary for anything to perform work. When things are moving around, **kinetic energy** is involved. Active transport, for instance, constitutes a release of kinetic energy by the cell. **Potential energy** is *stored* energy. It can be stored in **adipose tissue** (fat) or as glycogen in liver or muscle tissue. These stores represent an energy "stash," but the energy is not immediately available to the cell. Before the cell can convert the potential of glycogen into action, the glycogen first must be processed and biochemically changed to special high-energy molecules that are able to release their energy to the cell on demand.

What is the energy used for? Most is used to maintain the proper arrangement of materials within each organism. The internal organization of living systems is not like the media through which they move. The concentration of salts and organic compounds within the cytoplasm of single-celled organisms is not the same as it is in the water in which they live, whether it is seawater or fresh. The arrangement and distribution of materials within our bodies is certainly nothing like the atmosphere that surrounds us. As a result, there is a natural tendency for materials to diffuse into, and out of, our bodies. Remember that the natural flow of energy in the universe is toward homogeniety everywhere, and so there is a tendency for living systems to break apart and flow outward into a universal equilibrium. For the most part, this kind of diffusion would not be desirable, and to counter it requires an expenditure of free energy—"free" in the sense that it is available for use.

In addition, our bodies contain all kinds of organic molecules—proteins, nucleic acids, carbohydrates, fats, amino acids, peptides, and so on—by the millions. These compounds are tremendously complex and are synthesized from simpler building blocks obtained outside the body. Organic synthesis requires a tremendous input of free energy. Moving from place to place requires energy. Gathering food requires energy, breathing requires energy—*living* requires energy. Without a supply of energy that can be used whenever it is needed, life is not possible. The fact that life exists in such profusion tells us that the problem of accumulating free energy was solved long ago and that the solutions were enormously successful.

The similarity between our processing of digested foods and the burning of organic fuels in stoves was spotted quite early in physiological research. The French scientist Lavoisier noticed it in the 19th century, and in 1824 he told the world about it. Chemical energy is released in both processes, and they produce the same byproducts—CO_2 and water. The one thing neither Lavoisier nor his colleages could understand was how people could "burn" fuel without some portion of their bodies getting super-hot.

Today, the expression "burning up food" is part of our everyday vocabulary, and some aspects do resemble combustion, but the concept is not really correct. Biological systems do not really *burn* foodstuffs. They *oxidize* them, and the two processes are not the same. First of all, as Lavoisier realized 150 years ago, nowhere in our bodies do temperatures even begin to approach the ignition point of carbohydrates. Even if they did, the carbohydrates would not burn for two very good reasons. First of all, there is no gaseous oxygen present to support combustion, and secondly, our bodies are filled with water.

Enzymes

Living systems can circumvent the high temperature requirement by using chemicals that Lavoisier suspected might exist but was never sure of—chemicals whose job it is to speed up organic reactions without themselves becoming involved. As we know, the general term for such chemicals is **catalysts,** and cells of the human body are filled with such catalysts. In living systems, the catalysts are protein in nature and are known as **enzymes.** Enzymes are involved in virtually every reaction that occurs in living systems. They are an indispensable tool in building up the body's chemicals as well as in the reactions that break fuel molecules down. Each reaction has its own enzyme catalyst, and for the layperson this is the fact that is most difficult to comprehend. *Every single one of these catalysts is specific!* That means that every reaction has a special enzyme that is made for it and often for it alone. If one thousand reactions are required to synthesize a chunk of cell membrane, then before the chunk can be made, the cell would probably have to synthesize close to one thousand enzymes to serve as catalysts in the building process. Each reaction requires a specific enzyme to make it go. Some enzymes are versatile enough to be able to handle other substrates or even to catalyze slightly different reactions, but many catalyze only one of those one thousand reactions . . . just one . . . no other. If fifteen reactions are required to take apart a tiny molecule of glucose and produce free energy for the cell, there will be fifteen specific proteins available to catalyze each of the reactions involved. When you consider the number of chemical reactions that must be going on in a body cell at any given time, the enzyme requirement is enough to boggle the mind. No wonder Lavoisier wasn't able to comprehend, let alone explain, how living systems could "burn" carbohydrates without high ignition temperatures.

The existence of enzymes was demonstrated in 1892, and it was thirty-four years before the first one was isolated and crystallized. Then, like a snowball rolling downhill, research in enzyme chemistry accelerated, slowly at first, then faster and faster, getting bigger as it rolled. As each discovery was made, it opened the door for more discoveries, each new observation leading more quickly to the next one. Ten years after the first enzyme was isolated, three others were successfully isolated. The snowball was bigger and moving faster. Five years later several dozen had been discovered, and today there is a huge snowball moving at tremendous velocity. More than a thousand protein enzymes are known, and more than 150 have been isolated, purified, and crystallized.

Oxidation

The processing of food molecules to remove the energy they contain is a process known as **biological oxidation.** The word *oxidation* has been equated in common jargon with burning, and perhaps it should not be. When a piece of paper is lit in a fireplace, the carbohydrates of which it is composed are certainly oxidized, and all of the energy they contain is released, but it is released so rapidly that it is all lost in the form of heat. The oxidations that occur in the human body are much slower and more carefully controlled; hence not nearly as much of the energy is lost as heat. The critical chemical changes that occur involve *electron movement,* and these movements take place during cellular respiration.

Chemists or biologists do not necessarily think of oxidation as being associated with combustion. To them, oxidation involves electron movement of a very specific kind. The designation *oxidation* is derived from an archaic concept. Originally it was intended—very logically—to refer to a process by which a substance combined with oxygen. But that is not true any more. Our modern view of oxidation actually has very little to do with the element oxygen. Oxidation is *a loss of electrons* to a modern scientist, and whatever substance loses the electrons is oxidized.

Such electron losses occur during rapid burning (wood in a fireplace) or in the slower process of rusting. In the burning of wood, for example, the carbohydrate cellulose is oxidized, and the electrons that are lost are linked to atmospheric oxygen to produce water. When iron rusts, the iron atom loses a trio of electrons, which results in the formation of Fe^{3+}, or the *iron three* ion. These reactions do involve oxygen, but there are lots of reactions in which compounds or elements will give up electrons, and despite the fact that oxygen is not involved, such reactions are considered "oxidations."

Reduction

The essence of oxidation, biological or otherwise, is the movement of electrons from place to place. The word *movement* is preferable to *lost,* because electrons cannot be taken from a given substance and simply discarded. They are *material*—they cannot just disappear. They *always* have to go somewhere. In the case of rusting iron, the electrons that are lost by the iron atoms are moved to atmospheric oxygen, and a new ionic compound (Fe_2O_3) forms:

$$2Fe \longrightarrow 2Fe^{3+} \text{ (loss of six electrons)}$$
$$3O \longrightarrow 3O^{2-} \text{ (gain of six electrons)}$$

Since the iron atoms lost electrons, they are considered to have been *oxidized.* The loss of three electrons from each iron atom means that there is now a surplus of positive charge on those iron atoms, and they have become, as noted above, the iron three or "ferric" ions (Fe^{3+}). Those six electrons moved over to the three oxygen atoms, sorting themselves out in such a way that each oxygen atom received two of them. Each oxygen atom now possesses a surplus of negative charge, and ionic oxygen (O^{2-}) has formed. The oxygens thus *gained* six electrons, and there is a special term for what happened to them. The term is **reduction.**

Redox Reactions

Whenever anything is oxidized, something must simultaneously be reduced. One phenomenon simply cannot occur without the other taking place. The electrons removed by oxidation are matter; they cannot be destroyed. An acceptor must receive them, and that receiver is reduced as soon as it does. The two reactions are so inseparable that even their names have been collapsed into a single term—**redox.**

Figure 5.6 The ATP molecule. You can see the five-carbon sugar (ribose) and the purine base adenine. The last two phosphates are connected to the central molecule by high-energy bonds, which are indicated by the wavy lines.

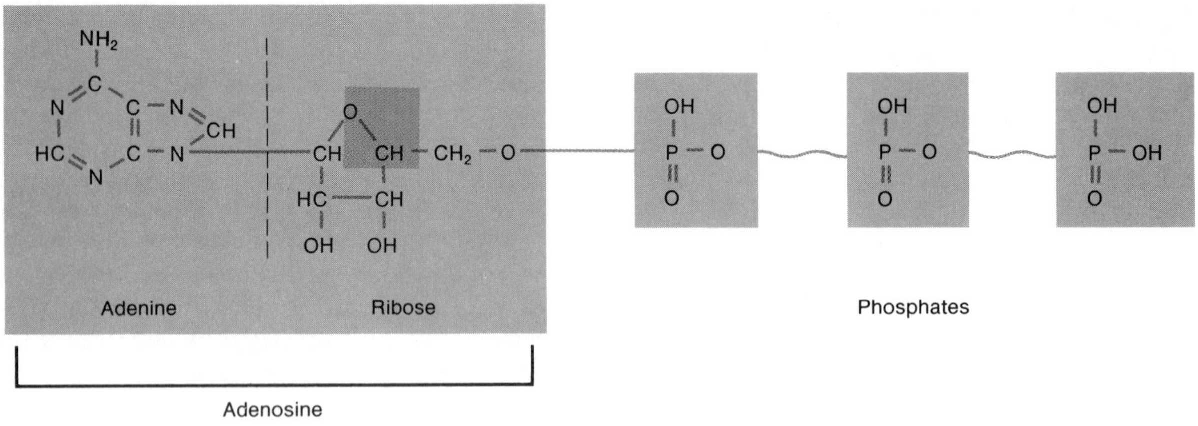

As you can probably imagine, it is not difficult to become confused as to which half of a redox reaction—oxidation or reduction—constitutes the loss of electrons and which constitutes an electron gain. For those who might have such a problem, let us suggest a mnemonic that worked for us. The mnemonic is the word **LEO.** Leo is the astrological sign for people born at the wrong time of year and in this context is an acronym for **L**ose **E**lectrons, **O**xidation. Obviously, if you can ascertain which of the two alternatives represents oxidation, there should be no difficulty determining what happens during reduction.

In the metabolic reactions that take place in biological systems, we often find protons accompanying the moving electrons. When this happens, the redox reaction is obviously more than a movement of electrons. If a proton accompanies each electron, then the redox process consists of a loss of hydrogen atoms by one compound and the acceptance of these atoms by another. Please note, however, that the strict definition of redox is not being violated. There is still a transfer of electrons. It is merely a situation in which electrons and some other subatomic particles are moving together.

ATP—the Biological Battery

Obviously there's abundant chemical energy in almost every organic compound—even toxic ones. Yet despite the fact that dieticians refer to sugar, for example, as a "quick energy" source, living organisms cannot utilize even the simplest sugar without considerable processing. Before it can be considered *instant* energy, the chemical energy in sugar must be transferred to a chemical that living systems can tap *immediately*. The chemical must be inert enough to be storable, yet must be able to release its energy instantly. There are only a few compounds that fulfill these conditions. The most ubiquitous one is **adenosine triphosphate (ATP).** (See figure 5.6.)

ATP makes chemical energy instantly available for conversion into muscle movement, electricity, heat production, biosynthetic reactions—whatever the body needs at any given time. The energy is released by catalytically converting the ATP molecule into **ADP** (adenosine **di**phosphate) and orthophosphoric acid.

The high-energy phosphates are actually derived from the compound orthophosphoric acid. This is a moderately strong inorganic acid with the chemical formula H_3PO_4, but it is usually designated by biologists and biochemists as P_i for the sake of convenience. It is present in the aqueous matrix of biological systems in considerable abundance, usually linked to esters, amides, or anhydrides. As $HPO_4^{=}$, it is incorporated into ATP as the first, second, and third phosphate groups. When the last phosphate group is enzymatically broken free, the energy released can be utilized immediately for whatever the body may need.

ATP is like a cocked pistol. All that is needed is the correct enzyme to pull the trigger and release the energy "bullet." As you might have guessed, the human body is abundantly supplied with the proper enzyme. In biology, the terms *ATP* and *energy* are synonymous. See figure 5.7.

The hydrolysis of ATP is a near-instantaneous operation requiring only that ATP and the proper enzyme be brought together. When it takes place, a

Figure 5.7 The building and discharge of ATP molecules. The process of building ATP from ADP and P_i and its subsequent breakdown into ADP and P_i are both part of a cyclical process that somewhat resembles cocking and firing a gun. Energy to recharge the molecules comes from the fuels we consume.

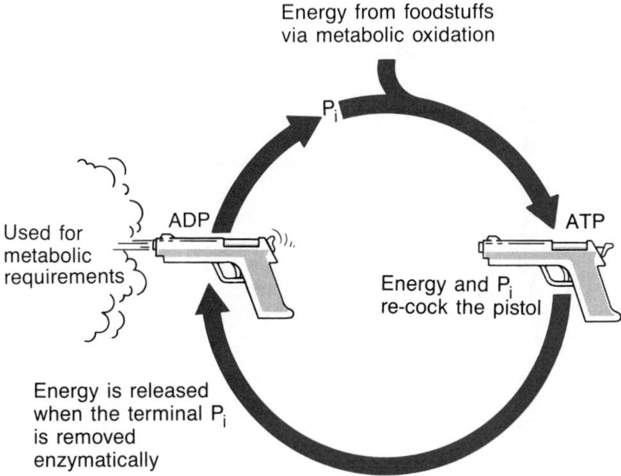

considerable quantity of raw energy is suddenly available for whatever the body wants. The importance of ATP to living systems is paramount—nothing is more vital—and many of our intracellular operations emphasize this. For one thing, none of the reactions designed to break down fuel molecules can proceed unless ADP and P_i are present in sufficient quantities. The breakdown of fuel molecules and the production of ATP are linked reactions, meaning one cannot proceed without the other.

Cellular respiration has one primary goal: the production of energy that the cell can use. The CO_2 and water produced during these reactions have their uses, as we will see, but they are essentially byproducts, not end products.

The water produced by the metabolic breakdown of foodstuffs is genuine water and as such can be used by living systems just as any other water would be used. In humans it is of little significance, but in many of our permanent desert dwellers it is the only source of water they have. We tend to think of the camel as being the mammal best adapted to the desert, but there are many smaller animals—mainly rodents—that are much better at living where water is scarce. These small animals never drink water, and the food on which they live yields little, if any, since most of these animals subsist on dry seeds. Their only water comes from the metabolic breakdown of foods in their body cells, and thanks to some remarkable physiological water-conservation mechanisms, it is all they ever need.

Anaerobic Metabolism: The Glycolytic Pathway

With all of the activity going on in living cells, fuel molecules must constantly undergo systematic dismantling to produce the energy the cell has to have to sustain its biosynthetic exertions. In the relatively large volume of the cytosol, these fuel breakdowns happen rapidly. Whenever the proper catabolic enzyme encounters an appropriate fuel molecule, there is an immediate burst of activity, and the substrate is broken apart, offering new substrate for the next step in the energy-producing sequence. These reactions never stop, because without them, living systems would cease to function very quickly indeed.

The process whereby glucose is fermented in the cytoplasm of living cells was methodically investigated for the first time in the early 1930s, and considerable time passed before the puzzle began to unravel. Eventually, facts that had been available in bits and pieces came slowly together through the efforts of people from all over the world. Today the process is pretty well mapped. A sequence of chemical reactions that required nearly forty years to work out and consumed the efforts of some of the finest biochemists in the world is now considered fundamental information in the most elementary of physiology courses. We will cover it all in a few pages.

The word **metabolism** is one we are all familar with, but its meaning is not always as clear as it should be. Few people have ever heard of **anabolism** and **catabolism** as subordinates of metabolism, so a word of explanation is included here.

Catabolism literally means to "tear down," and to a biologist it refers to the processes by which biological systems break down foodstuffs to produce energy (ATP).

Anabolism is the opposite. It means literally that something is "built up"—a process requiring an input of energy and which, to a biologist, refers to biosynthetic operations.

Metabolism is the sum total of all of these reactions.

The initial catabolic reactions that begin the breakdown of energy-rich food molecules take place in the total absence of molecular oxygen. Chemically, during glycolysis the six-carbon sugar *glucose* is converted first into two three-carbon sugars and, ultimately, into the organic acid **pyruvate.** In order to begin, the process must remove some ATP from the cell's stored energy banks. Removal of cellular energy is certainly not what fuel breakdown is supposed to accomplish, but it gives it all back with interest a little later on. The chemical

Table 5.1 ATP Gain per Mole of Glucose as the Result of the Glycolytic Process.

Reaction	NADH	ATP
1		−1 ATP
2		−1 ATP
3		
4	2 NADH	
5		+2 ATP
6		
7		+2 ATP
Net gain	2 NADH	+2 ATP

energy in glucose is converted to ATP, and the net gain from all of this anaerobic activity is *two moles of ATP* (see table 5.1). Since each mole of ATP contains somewhere on the order of 10,000 calories of energy, this represents a free energy gain of 20,000 calories, energy that is now instantly available for utilization by the body.

The glycolytic pathway is schematically outlined in figure 5.8.

The figure of 10,000 calories per mole of ATP is an average value. It requires about 14,000 calories of free energy to form one mole of ATP from a mole of ADP and P_i, yet when the mole of ATP is split, the free energy actually captured is on the order of 7,500 calories. No transduction of energy is ever accomplished without some losses, so this is nothing extraordinary. However, to say that the energy content of a mole of ATP is 14,000 calories would be grossly inaccurate, because it is not possible to get that much energy from its hydrolysis. On the other hand, to say it contains only 7,500 calories isn't right either, because of the calories expended in its formation and the fact that there must be more than 7,500 actually present in the molecules. The figure 10,000 is not an exact average, but it is pretty close, and in a decimal system like ours, using a figure with a base of ten presents us with at least one factor in any calculation that is easy to work with.

There is a very important oxidation-reduction (redox) reaction that occurs during glycolysis, and we need to pay particular attention to it. It takes place just after the six-carbon sugar fructose diphosphate splits into the two 3-carbon sugars (figure 5.8), and it involves a compound known as a **cofactor.** This cofactor is known as **nicotinamide adenine dinucleotide (NAD^+),** and its most important characteristic is its ability to carry electrons back and forth. It can accept free electrons (and be reduced) without fuss, cart them around awhile, and then release them (and be oxidized) when conditions are right. In biological systems, that is its job.

Figure 5.8 Glycolysis (also known as fermentation or anaerobic metabolism) takes place in the cytosol of our body cells. It produces a net gain of two ATPs for every glucose molecule that enters the pathway.

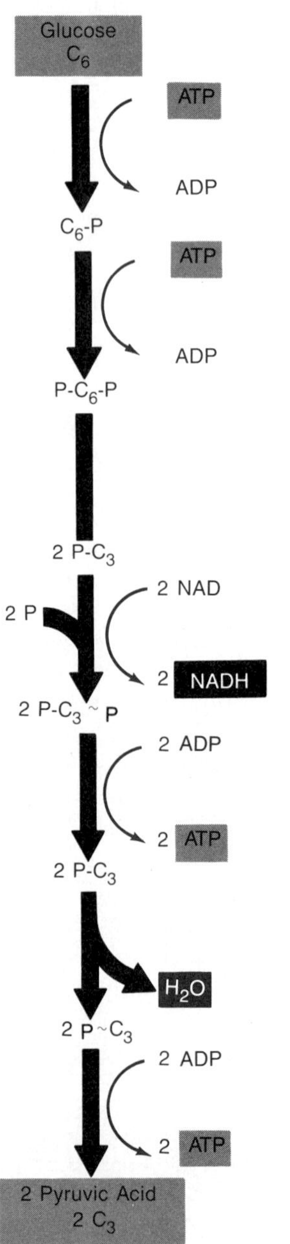

1. Phosphorylation of glucose by ATP gives glucose—1 phosphate, an activated molecule.

2. Rearrangement, followed by a second ATP phosphorylation, gives fructose diphosphate.

3. The six-carbon molecule is split into 2 three-carbon phosphoglyceraldehyde molecules (PGAL).

4. Oxidation followed by phosphorylation produces 2 NADH molecules and gives 2 diphosphoglyceric acid molecules (PGAP) each with one high energy phosphate bond.

5. Removal of high energy phosphate by 2 ADP molecules produces 2 ATP molecules and gives 2 phosphoglyceric acid molecules (PGA).

6. Removal of water gives 2 phosphoenolpyruvic acid molecules each with a high energy phosphate bond.

7. Removal of high energy phosphate by 2 ADP molecules produces 2 ATP molecules and gives 2 pyruvic acid molecules.

Rapid Energy Consumption and Fatigue

Since the cytoplasm of the cell is so voluminous when compared to the various organelles, there is a rather huge space available for glycolytic reactions to occur. Hence there are a great many glycolytic reactions taking place at any given time. The oxygen-requiring reactions that follow glycolysis take longer, and, because they take place in the tiny volume of the mitochondria, they are limited in number. When lots of

Figure 5.9 The lactic acid "siding" onto which pyruvate is shunted by NADH.

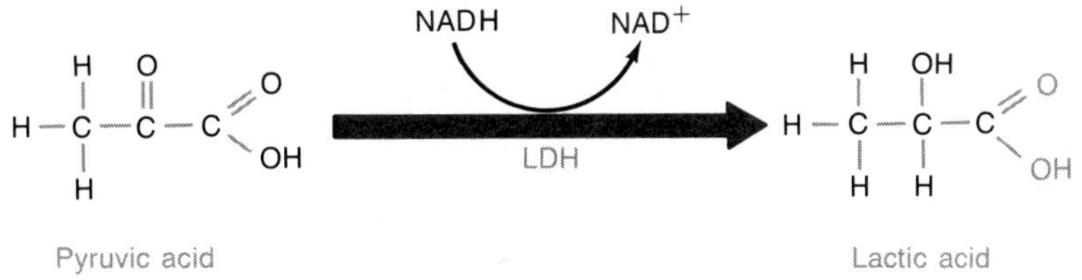

NADH NAD$^+$

LDH

Pyruvic acid

Lactic acid

energy is needed quickly, there isn't time to wait for the dribbles of ATP that emerge from these miniscule organelles. We must tap the large cauldrons of the cytoplasm, where we can draw upon many millions of reacting sugar molecules, and this is where we run into difficulty.

When we are dealing with a series of sequential reactions, logistical problems can crop up when the final product is not being used right away. It is like assembling a line of boxcars on a long, straight railway track. As each new boxcar is added, the train is pushed on down the line, and new cars are added as soon as they are put together. If there is a dead end down the line, and there is not some means of removing some of the cars, before long the tracks will be full, and there will be no way to add more cars. Some provisions must be made to get those farther down the line out of the way. In railroad operations, as the "mainline tracks" begin to fill up, a "shunt" locomotive is used to push the cars that are in the way off onto a siding to make room for more.

It has to be comforting to know that nature is at least as smart as the people who run railroads. As pyruvate begins to build up in cells, nature has provided a siding that the pyruvate "cars" can be pushed onto to get them out of the way. This biological "siding" is known as **lactic acid,** and the shunt locomotive that is used to push the pyruvate over there is the reduced cofactor, NADH. As figure 5.8 shows, the cofactor is reduced during the glycolytic process. If glycolysis is to continue, NAD$^+$ (oxidized cofactor) must be available so it can pick up electrons (and be reduced). When there is adequate oxygen available, the reduced cofactor (NADH) is taken into the mitochondria, where it will be able to drop its load of electrons (be oxidized). When oxygen is not available, or when glycolysis is producing pyruvate too fast for the oxidative machinery to keep up with it, the only way NADH can be oxidized is for it to release its electrons someplace else.

Lactic Acid

As it turns out, NADH can kill two birds with one stone by dropping off its load of electrons at pyruvate. That gets the pyruvate "cars" off the mainline and out of the way by converting them to lactic acid and shunting them onto a siding (figure 5.9). Simultaneously, this process oxidizes the cofactor so it can go back to work in the glycolytic pathway. This is not a permanent solution. Lactic acid gradually builds up to problem levels inside the cell, but glycolysis can run a lot longer this way than it could without that siding available. Eventually, however, the siding gets full, and when it does, glycolysis must stop.

Full lactic acid "sidings" are common, particularly in active people. The condition is known as **muscle fatigue,** and when it sets in, activity must cease, or at least slow down. Once heavy muscular activity is no longer taking place and glycolysis is not outstripping the oxidative processes, the aerobic fraction of metabolism has a chance to catch up. Chemically this begins by changing the lactic acid back to pyruvate. The oxidative reactions then consume one pyruvate molecule at a time until all the lactic acid "boxcars" that have accumulated on the sidings have been converted to pyruvate and processed. For conversion to pyruvate, the lactic acid molecules must surrender their electrons to the cofactor NAD$^+$.

With plenty of oxygen available, the pyruvate boxcars on the mainline are moving along nicely, and the reduced cofactor no longer needs to pass its electrons to pyruvate. It now has a different destiny. It is shunted into the mitochondria to be oxidized by other mechanisms. We will deal with this shortly.

Of course, not all the accumulated lactic acid is completely oxidized—the system doesn't need that much energy. Usually about 20 percent is converted to CO_2 and water. The remainder is resynthesized to glucose and is taken to the liver, where the glucose can be converted into the polysaccharide glycogen and stashed away for the future.

Oxygen Debt

All of us are familiar with fatigue. It occurs because we burn energy at a high rate and pile up lactic acid more rapidly than the body's oxidative reactions can deal with it. The medical profession calls this problem an **oxygen debt,** because when it occurs, the quickest way to get rid of the lactic acid is to increase systemic oxygen by breathing faster. And so, after heavy exercise like a 100-meter sprint or a vigorous game of basketball, we have to stand around and pant for a while. Recovery rate gives some indication of how relatively slow the oxidative reactions are. It takes about an hour and a half for a person in reasonably good condition to repay the oxygen debt accumulated by a 100-meter sprint. Clearly there are sharp limitations on the capacity of the oxidative appliances in our cells, but ultimately they catch up.

Oxidative (Aerobic) Metabolism

Glycolysis is a high-speed means of providing small units of energy on a very large scale, but in the overall scheme of energy production, it is essentially nothing more than a preliminary step that leads us to an involved series of substrate breakdown and redox reactions that ultimately wrings all the energy out of the pyruvate molecules and hangs onto most of it. There is more to energy production than just adding oxygen to pyruvate, however. For one thing, it required the development of a highly specialized organelle, an organelle that is unique and *very* necessary. Without it, it would be impossible for living systems to generate energy through utilization of molecular oxygen, and so much of the energy contained in food molecules would be wasted that it is highly unlikely that intelligent, warm-blooded life would be possible. There might be a few lethargic marine or fresh water organisms loafing about the world, but no active, adventurous mammals, fishes, or birds. There would simply not be enough food for them.

Mitochondria

Fuel oxidation actually takes place in the mitochondrion. We were introduced to this organelle in chapter 4, but its function was not discussed because it is so unusual.

The major portion of oxidative activity takes place inside the inner membrane of the mitochondrion, many of the reactions occurring on the inner surface of the cristae. As we have seen, the cristae form clefts that push deeply into the interior, becoming walls that

Figure 5.10 (*a*) Three-dimensional sketch of a typical mitochondrion, cut away to show the interior. (*b*) Schematic drawing of a generalized mitochondrion. The fluid "mitochondriaplasm" within the organelle is known as the matrix, and all the enzymes necessary to Krebs cycle reactions are in the matrix.

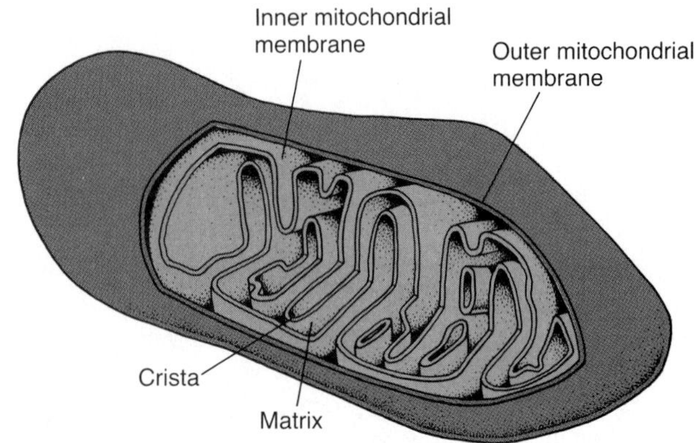

(a)

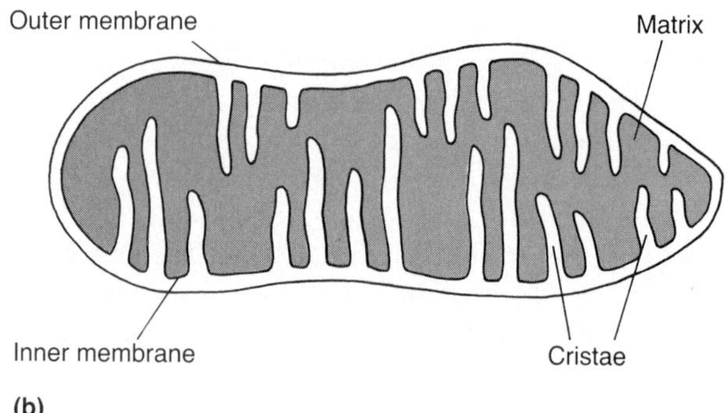

(b)

form partitions that break up the single room of the mitochondrial interior. As figure 5.10 shows, they don't go all the way across, so the inside of the mitochondrion is not separated into a bunch of little rooms, but rather into a kind of three-dimensional maze.

Inside this maze-like interior are the oxidative enzymes, all dissolved in the "mitochondrioplasm" known as the mitochondrial matrix. These are the enzymes that finish the fuel breakdown that began in the cellular cytoplasm. Here, in the protein-laden succulence of the mitochondrial matrix, a cycle of reactions gradually strips fuel molecules of their energy-rich electrons and generates ATP in sufficient quantities to satisfy even the highly competitive machinery of life.

Figure 5.11 The first of the oxidative reactions within the mitochondria. Pyruvate is converted to acetyl coenzyme A.

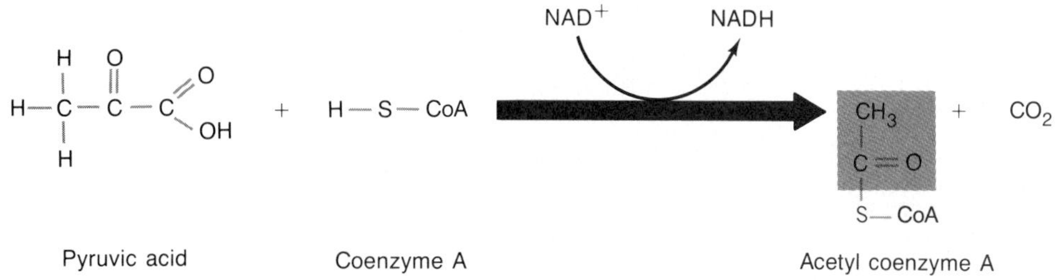

$$\mathrm{H{-}\overset{H}{\underset{H}{C}}{-}\overset{O}{\overset{\|}{C}}{-}C{\overset{\displaystyle O}{\underset{\displaystyle OH}{}}}} \;+\; \mathrm{H{-}S{-}CoA} \xrightarrow{NAD^+ \;\to\; NADH} \mathrm{CH_3{-}C{=}O{-}S{-}CoA} \;+\; CO_2$$

Pyruvic acid — Coenzyme A — Acetyl coenzyme A

The Krebs (Citric Acid) Cycle

Sir Hans Krebs worked for years to uncover the secrets of oxidative metabolism. In 1937 he outlined the mechanics of the reactions that he believed followed the process of fermentation, reactions that subsequent research has confirmed. In his honor, the reaction sequence that he worked so hard to elucidate has been given the name the **Krebs cycle.** Fats, proteins, and carbohydrates are all introduced into the Krebs cycle in the mitochondrial matrix. We will restrict ourselves to the processing of pyruvate.

Pyruvate is the final product of the glycolytic reactions, but only a little energy has been removed by the glycolytic reactions; most of the energy present in the original carbohydrate molecule is still locked up inside. To remove it, the pyruvate must be transported into the interior of the mitochondrion.

Combustion of a sort occurs in the interior of these flyspeck furnaces, but it is a flameless and heatless combustion that releases energy a tiny bit at a time and does not involve combining fuel with oxygen until nearly all the fuel's energy has been drawn off. The final oxidation that takes place involves electrons that have so little energy they are close to inert. Even more unusual is that before "burning" the substrate molecules, living systems force them into combination with water. Who ever heard of burning something by first combining it with water? Strange as it may seem, that's what happens. The end product—energy—and the by-products—CO_2 and water—are exactly what we would get if we set the carbohydrate on fire and let it combine with free oxygen in the air.

Within the mitochondrial matrix, the various enzymes swirl back and forth until they encounter their specific substrates. They split the substances by combining them with water molecules, and each time a substrate molecule is split, it releases a pair of electrons, often in the company of a proton. The energy in the food is passed to the electrons, and when they break free from the food molecules, the system has

Figure 5.12 The transition reaction. This reaction oxidizes pyruvate, removes a CO_2 molecule, and attaches the resulting acetyl group to coenzyme A.

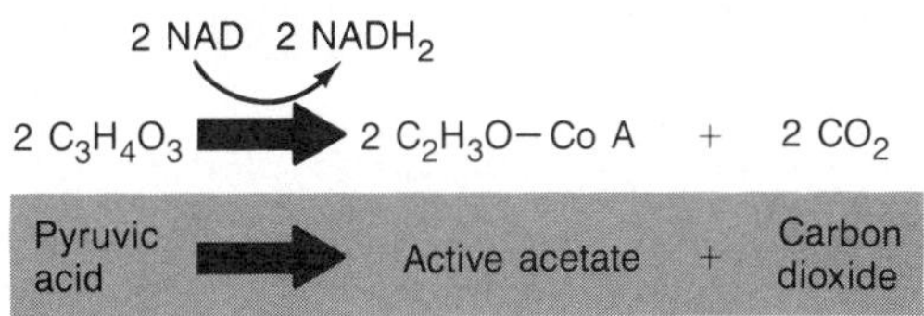

what it has been after all along—tiny energy-laden particles that can be bled of their energy a little at a time.

As we will see, it is not called a cycle without good reason. The process as a whole *is* circular, each reaction building on its predecessor until the process is complete, at which point it's back where it started, ready to begin again. We will begin with the assumption that an oxygen debt has accumulated and there is a substantial quantity of lactic acid that has to be removed.

1. Once oxygen is available in sufficient quantities, the particles that reduced pyruvate to lactic acid are returned to the cofactor NAD^+. This reaction accomplishes two goals:
   a. it reduces the NAD^+ to NADH, and
   b. it oxidizes lactic acid to pyruvate.
2. Once the pyruvate is inside the mitochondrion, it is promptly assaulted by an enzyme that removes a CO_2 molecule and simultaneously oxidizes it (figure 5.11).
   a. The electrons taken from the pyruvate are handed to another NAD^+ molecule, thereby reducing it to NADH, an operation known as the **transition reaction** (figure 5.12).
   b. The CO_2, meanwhile, diffuses away, carrying off one carbon atom and leaving behind a molecule that is no longer pyruvate but a two-carbon compound—**acetate.**

Figure 5.13 The major steps of the Krebs cycle.

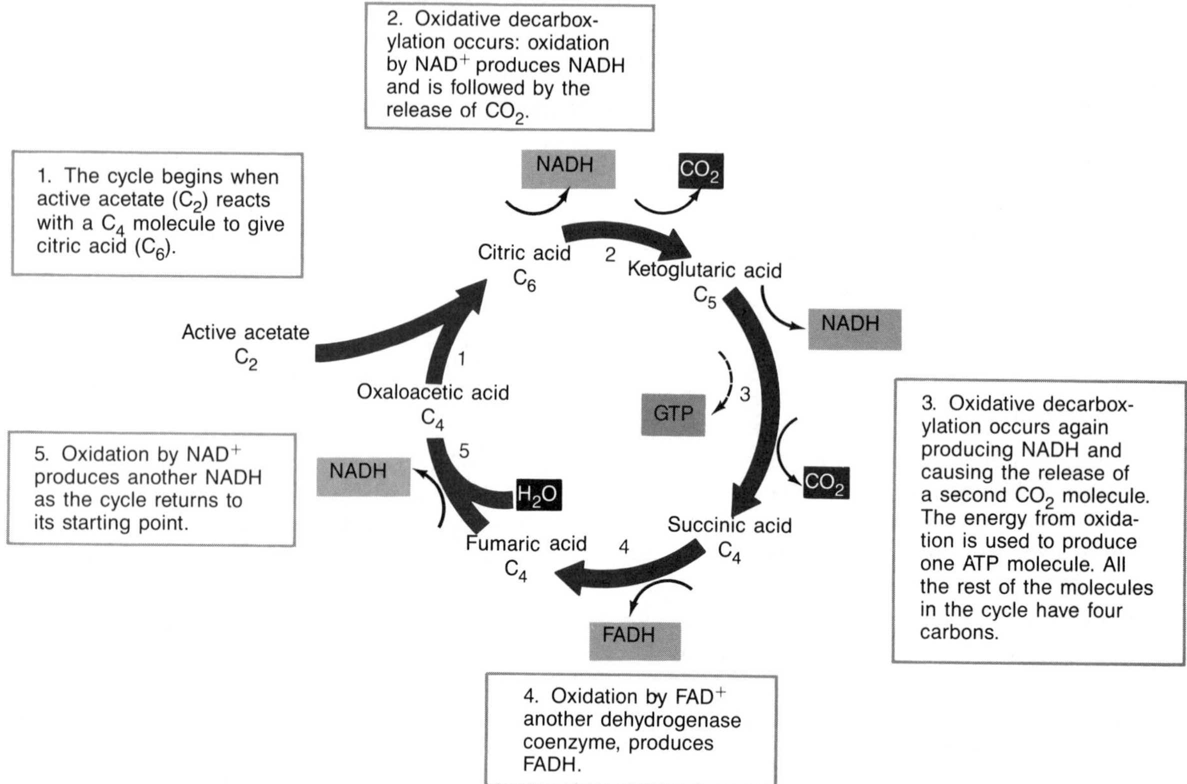

3. The acetate is promptly linked onto a special enzyme known as **coenzyme A.** Coenzyme A has a central role in metabolism. It is a carrier of acetyl groups, and in intermediary metabolism, it carries them into the catabolic reactions that occur in the mitochondrial matrix. By so doing, it serves as the key that unlocks the closed Krebs cycle. Once within this cycle, another enzyme releases the acetyl molecule from the enzyme carrier and links it to a four-carbon compound called **oxaloacetate.** This reaction produces the six-carbon compound **citric acid** and constitutes regeneration of the worn-out Krebs cycle substrate. This is generally considered to be the point at which the cycle begins.

The reactions now proceed following the sequence illustrated in figure 5.13, carefully monitored and governed by mitochondrial enzymes. Periodically, vitalized electrons are removed from the substrates and clamped onto the cofactors NAD^+ or FAD^+, then are carried, loaded with energy, into the granules that cover the interior of the inner mitochondrial membrane. The process is reminiscent of a Fourth of July pinwheel, spinning madly in a circle, throwing off energized electrons, protons, and CO_2 particles as it whizzes around. Caught as they leave, the electrons and protons are carried away, while the food compounds that produce them pursue their destiny in a never-ending pirouette. Each time a substrate molecule encounters the correct enzyme, one of the cycle's reactions occurs, removing a CO_2 molecule or oxidizing the molecule and pushing a pair of electrons and a proton out of the cycle.

Not all of the energy-freeing reactions are the same. As figure 5.13 indicates, there are four separate sites in the cycle where oxidative dehydrogenation takes place, and a cofactor picks up the wayward particles. Three of these involve the cofactor NAD^+, while the fourth results in the reduction of a different cofactor, the flavoprotein **FAD^+**. Its job is the same as that of NADH's—take the electrons where they are supposed to go. In addition, there is a substrate phosphorylation at the point where alpha ketoglutarate is converted to succinate. A single molecule of guanosine diphosphate (GDP) is phosphorylated to guanosine triphosphate (GTP), which then transfers its terminal phosphate to a molecule of ADP.

The oxidations that reduce the cofactor NAD^+ don't involve only electrons. Electrons do move, of course, but each pair that does so is accompanied by a proton; hence, in actuality, each redox reaction consists in the movement of one hydrogen atom (proton and electron) plus one other electron. This is why the process is diagramed:

$$NAD^+ \rightarrow NADH$$

The hydrogen atom links onto the NAD^+ molecule, forming $NADH^+$, and the extra electron neutralizes the + charge. The process is known as *oxidation by dehydrogenation* and is typical of those that take place throughout the Krebs cycle's fuel breakdown.

Each successive reaction occurs inexorably on the heels of its predecessor, and with each, the fuel molecule gets smaller and its accumulation of high-energy electrons decreases. Finally there is nothing more that can be taken from it. As oxaloacetate, it has reached the low-energy point—the "end" of the cycle. The end is also the beginning, for now another energy-filled acetyl coA molecule is brought in to revitalize the worn-out fuel molecule and start the cycle again.

Essential Molecules

As with glycolysis, none of the reactions could continue were there not a steady stream of oxidized cofactors available to grab the excited electrons as they emerged from the cycle. In glycolysis, these cofactors are oxidized through the reduction of pyruvate to lactic acid. Inside the mitochondria the cofactor oxidation takes place at the start of the **respiratory chain.**

The Respiratory Chain (Cytochrome System)

Some of the energy that was in the food molecules is now present in the electron pairs that have been handed over to the cofactors. In this form, it is more readily available than when it was locked in the sugar molecule, but that kind of energy is like a sinking depth charge: If the electrons were to encounter molecular oxygen at this time, their stored energy would be released in a single, uncontrollable flash that would dissipate as heat, and we would gain none of it. Our cells are more frugal than that. The energy they want is obtainable, but it must be carefully nurtured and released a tiny bit at a time.

Therefore, instead of permitting the invigorated electrons to combine with oxygen immediately, they are introduced onto a chain of enzymes—the cytochromes.

The Cytochromes

As each cofactor encounters the respiratory chain on the inner mitochondrial membrane, it unloads one pair of electrons and a single proton and, as figure 5.13 shows, segregation quickly occurs. The protons are diverted from the chain and are run through a shunt that bypasses most of the cytochromes. The electrons, meanwhile, flow through the cytochrome's enzymes like balls bouncing down a short flight of stairs, from one energy level to another . . . always over a cliff, but never much of a fall. The enzymes and cofactors of which the cytochrome chain is composed are each designed to be easily oxidized and just as easily reduced. When it accepts electrons, an enzyme is reduced . . . then it is oxidized as it passes them on to the next link in the chain. Just as buckets of water are removed from one person and passed to the next in a bucket brigade, the electrons are passed from one cytochrome to the next, and within the cytochromes they are not casually moved from place to place or carelessly pushed over their staircases. Each movement is carefully monitored, and at precisely the right moment, as the electron pairs drop down to a lower step, some of the potential energy they contain is released—but only a little. Just enough for the system to grab and quickly lock into the chemical bonds of ATP before it can be lost.

The ADP molecules are phosphorylated by the energy released as the electron pairs bounce "hand-in-hand" down their tiny energy staircases. Each ADP molecule has with it an inorganic phosphate molecule in the form of orthophosphoric acid, and some of the energy within the flowing electrons is transferred to these two molecules. A high-energy bond is formed between them, and thus an ATP molecule is born. The phosphorylation is an oxidative one, and the process that produces them is therefore known as **oxidative phosphorylation.** It occurs in only one place—on the inner surface of the cristae. There, sticking out into the mitochondrial sap, are the tiny

Figure 5.14 (*a*) The mitochondrion in a three-dimensional representation. Note the tiny particles (called F_1 particles) on the inner membrane's inner surface. (*b*) An electron micrograph of the inner membrane showing the F_1 particles clearly. (*c*) A schematic representation of the F_1 particles.

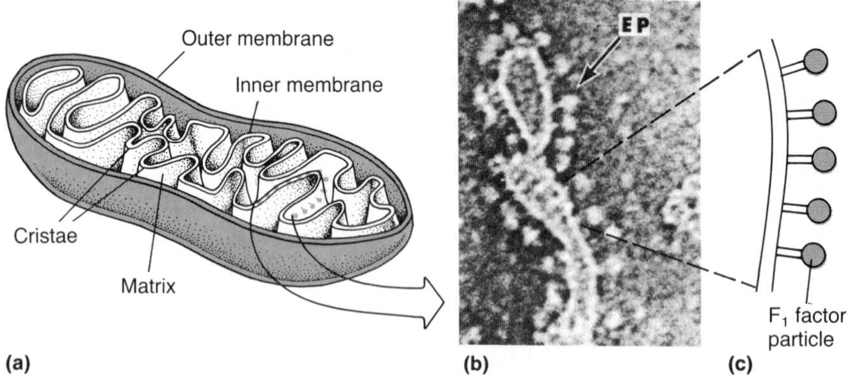

Figure 5.15 Particle movement through the respiratory chain. Electrons flow down an electrochemical gradient from one cytochrome enzyme to the next, reducing each as they enter and oxidizing each as they leave. At select points as they descend, a molecule of ADP is linked to a P_i, and an ATP is generated. As you see, NADH enters the flow sooner than FADH. As a result, electrons carried by NAD^+ are able to generate one more ATP than those brought in by FADH.

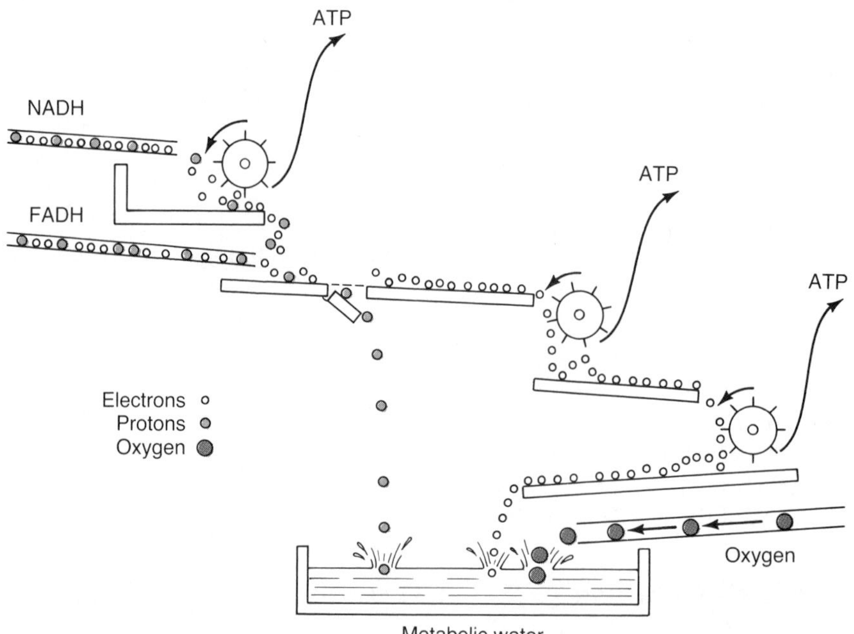

granules where the ATP is generated—the F_1 granules of the respiratory chain (figure 5.14). Once the ATP molecule forms there, it promptly leaves the mitochondrion and goes where it can do some good.

Depending on which cofactor brought them to the chain, there may be two or three energy steps to descend. If NADH carries the electrons, each pair will drop three steps and will therefore yield three ATP molecules before it is bled dry. If FADH provides the transport, the ATP yield is only two. Why the difference? Simply put, FADH drops its electrons off at a different entrance; one where there are only two steps to the end of the chain (figure 5.15).

Oxygen, the Final Acceptor

Once they have dropped off the last step, the electrons are nearly devoid of energy and can be discarded. It is important for us to recall once again that these electrons are material things . . . they will not simply disappear. If they were left to clutter up the interior of the mitochondrion, in a very short time the entire organelle would be filled with vibrating electron pairs and would be useless for any further production of energy. Therefore, when the last cytochrome is oxidized, something must be available to pick up the electrons that are pouring out of the respiratory chain—an electron acceptor must be present.

Figure 5.16 The metabolism of fats.

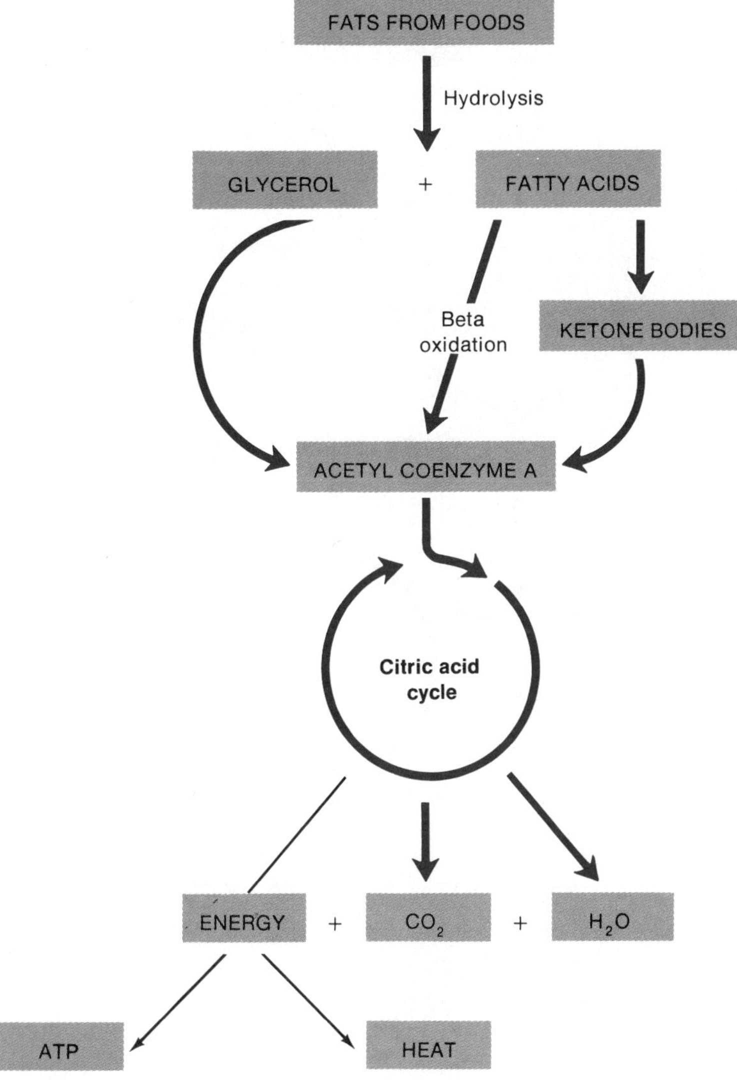

In nearly every living thing this electron acceptor is oxygen, and this is the reason that nearly every living thing breathes. It certainly is why *we* do. The reason our lungs, our red blood cells, and all other respiratory mechanisms exist is to get the oxygen into the interior of the mitochondria, where it can pick up the "empty" electrons and the excess protons that are dumped out of the respiratory chain. The matrix of the mitochondrion represents the bottom of the hill to electrons, protons, and oxygen. This is the valley into which all these particles flow . . . and it is where oxygen is used up and disappears. It combines with the electron pairs and whatever spare protons are lying around and forms what is known as **metabolic water.** Living systems can always use a little extra water, of course, but since we cannot subsist on metabolic water, its significance to humans is limited.

Lipids

In living systems, fats can be just as important a source of energy as carbohydrates, sometimes even more important. Gram for gram, fats contain nearly twice as much energy as either carbohydrates or proteins, so in a fasting state they can represent an extremely important fuel source. Most fatty materials are catabolized in the liver. The neutral fats (chapter 2) are first hydrolyzed to separate the glycerol and fatty acids, and then the fatty acids undergo a process known as **beta oxidation.** β-oxidation then breaks the fatty acids into acetyl coenzyme A and runs them into the Krebs cycle. Glycerol, being a three-carbon carbohydrate, can enter the Krebs cycle in the same manner as pyruvate. See figure 5.16.

Figure 5.17 Amino acid breakdown. Note the fact that not all amino acid particles enter the Krebs cycle at the same place.

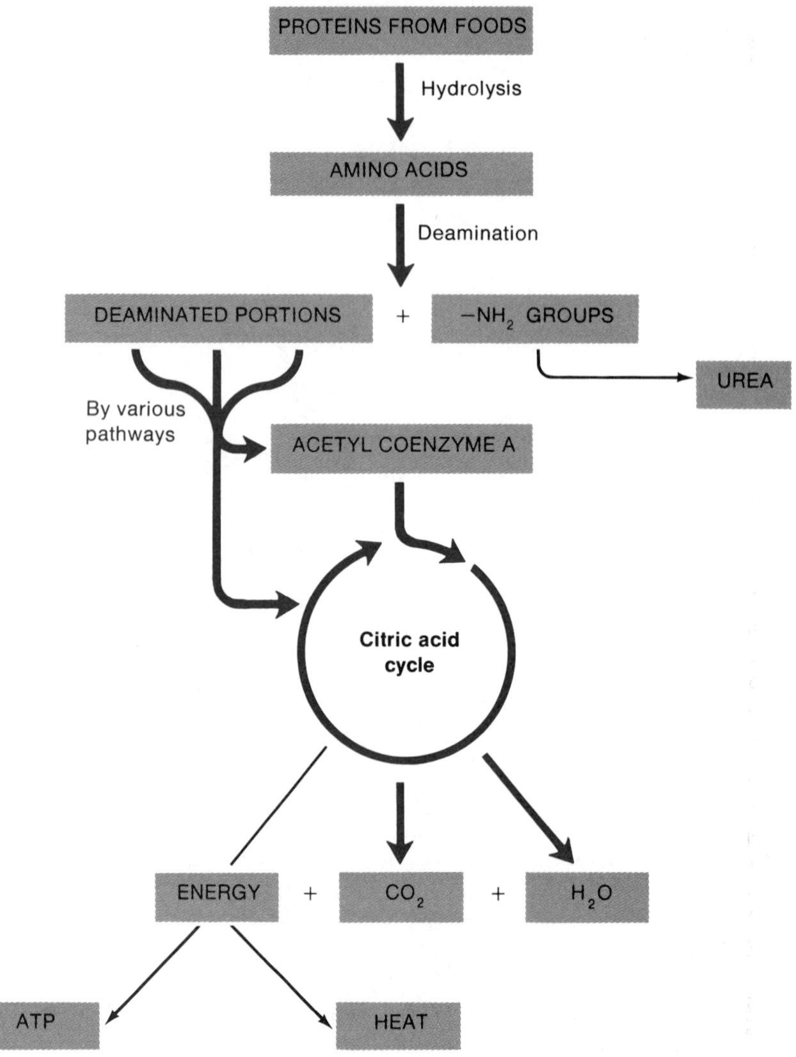

Amino Acids

Protein molecules are usually too important to utilize as fuel molecules, but when glucose levels get low and glycerol runs out, amino acids can be utilized to provide energy to keep the cell alive.

Amino acids contain amine groups, and since these have no value as a fuel, they are stripped from the molecules as a first step—a process known as **deamination.** These free amine groups will ultimately form **urea,** the main waste product in urine. The remaining portions of the molecule can be converted to acetyl coenzyme A and enter the Krebs cycle (figure 5.17).

There is another route that amino acids can follow if the need for *glucose,* rather than energy, is urgent. When glucose is being utilized by the body cells with no glycogen store to replenish the cell's supplies, blood glucose levels can fall. If they are permitted to tumble too low, the organism could go into shock—a highly undesirable result. If protein is available, shock can be avoided. Amino acids can be converted directly to glucose—a process known as **gluconeogenesis.**

The Importance of Oxygen

Oxygen is the final electron acceptor. It serves to pick up all the subatomic debris that spins out of the mitochondrial reactions. To people first learning of this, it somehow doesn't seem very important. "After all," one might argue, "how much oxygen can a tiny, almost invisible, organelle inside of a body cell use in a minute or an hour—or even a day? If the oxygen that we breathe isn't used for anything else—and it's not—we shouldn't need very much."

We can get a pretty good idea of its importance by just considering the number of specialized internal mechanisms that are devoted to the transport of oxygen. Our respiratory system—the lungs and all the involved tubes—are present mainly to trap oxygen and present it to our blood. Almost all the cells in the blood are red cells, and their function is to transport oxygen. Behavioral responses to a temporary lack of oxygen are extremely powerful and often amount to panic in living organisms. Further measure of oxygen's importance can be gleaned from asking the simple question: How long can we last without it? Four minutes? Five? Not any longer than five—not if we are to avoid irreversible damage to our nervous system. Think of the teeming billions of mitochondria that must be present inside our body cells to use up the huge supplies of oxygen we keep rushing to them in a perpetual flow. Oxygen pours into our bodies, and every molecule collects two electron pairs that have just finished a trip down the respiratory chain. The demand for ATP staggers the imagination! If energy can disappear that quickly, our body cells must be insatiable!

Realizing our dependence on oxygen leads to contemplation of some unpleasant facts. The quickest and easiest way to induce death in an animal is to cut off the oxygen supply. Lots of things do this. Animals can drown. Predators smother their prey by crushing their windpipes or bleeding them to death—bleeding ultimately causes death by depriving cells of oxygen—and these are the slow ways.

Metabolic Poisons

There are things that can interfere directly with oxygen transport, and their appalling toxicity is a tribute to the essential nature of that simple gas. **Cyanide,** for instance, prevents oxygen from accepting electrons and thereby prevents electrons from leaving the respiratory chains. This has the effect of damming up the entire respiratory pathway, and as each cytochrome system plugs with electrons, the Krebs cycle operations grind to a halt. Within seconds, the lactic acid shunts fill and glycolysis stops. Intermediary metabolism is jammed up throughout the body. Unable to produce any energy, body cells cannot prevent disorganization, and their individual integrity rapidly disappears. The breakup is quick and final. Cyanide is thus able to kill a human in just over a minute.

There are other metabolic poisons that can block electron flow along the respiratory chain—poisons like **rotenone** and **antimycin A.** Like cyanide, they interfere with electron movement in the respiratory chain. They break into the chain a little sooner than cyanide does, and in that respect they are different, but they all share the malignant ability to kill living things with startling speed.

The tremendous virulence of these poisons is rendered more thought-provoking when we realize that in most respects, they are not really *damaging* chemicals. They don't dissolve tissues as acids do, they don't break them apart the way an enzyme might—they don't even denature a few proteins as sunlight often does. Testimony that no harm is done is available in the observation that if a single cell is exposed to cyanide and promptly presented with plenty of free ATP, it will not die. Cyanide does no physical damage. None of the mechanisms important to smooth biochemical function are harmed in any way; the only problem is the inability of the mitochondria to produce ATP. This is the kind of observation that makes one sit and contemplate just how delicate life is and how terribly close to disruption one wanders every day.

Efficiency of Metabolic Reactions

Glycolysis

Glycolysis produces an awful lot of energy in a big hurry, but as we have seen, it is not a particularly efficient process . . . not when you consider the total energy content of a mole of glucose molecules. You will recall from table 5.1 that there is a net profit of two ATP molecules during glycolysis, and that constitutes an energy gain of only about 20,000 calories per mole of glucose. When we consider that a mole of glucose actually contains 686,000 calories, recovering only 20,000 is not really very good. It is actually less than 3 percent.

It looks a little better from an efficiency standpoint when we realize that breaking a mole of glucose into two moles of pyruvate does not release all 686,000 calories. It releases only about 47,000 calories of energy. This means that even if glycolysis were 100 percent efficient, it could only recover 47,000 calories. The rest is still locked up inside the pyruvate molecules. Twenty thousand calories out of a possible 47,000 means the efficiency rate is just over 40 percent, and while that *seems* better than 3 percent, it would really not be better if all the energy remaining were lost. Twenty thousand calories is just not very much energy, and if biological systems had no way of oxidizing pyruvate, we would have to ingest so much food we'd be eating all of our waking hours, and we still might not be able to consume enough food to keep us alive. Since we are not required to do this, obviously there must be a way of extracting that energy, and as we have already seen, there is. The oxidative reactions of the Krebs cycle—the ones that take place inside our mitochondria—are the means of obtaining the maximum energy possible from each mouthful of food.

The Aerobic Reactions

As to the efficiency of our oxidative (aerobic) operations, figure 5.13 shows that there are three sites in the Krebs cycle where NAD^+ is reduced and one site for FAD^+. Each NADH molecule ultimately provides us with three ATP, while each FADH gives us two. That means for each turn of the Krebs cycle, we obtain eleven molecules of ATP from the efforts of these coenzymes (see table 5.2). In addition, as you can see, there is the reduced cofactor (NADH) from the transition reaction and a single molecule of **GTP** produced by *substrate phosphorylation* within the mill of the Krebs cycle itself. That provides four more high-energy phosphates for a total of fifteen. Each pyruvate molecule that enters the mitochondrion enables the Krebs cycle to turn once, and since there are two pyruvates produced by every glucose molecule, the cycle turns twice every time a glucose molecule is processed (figure 5.18).

Table 5.2 ATP Gain per Mole of Glucose Resulting from Aerobic Reactions*

Step	CO_2	NADH	FADH	GTP	ATP
1 transition reaction	1	1			3
2	1	1			3
3	1	1			3
4				1	1
5			1		2
6		1			3
Totals	3 CO_2	4 NADH	1 FADH	1 GTP	15 ATP

*Per turn. Cycle turns twice per glucose molecule.

Intermediary Metabolism as a Whole

Every time a glucose molecule passes along the glycolytic pathway, there is a gain of two ATP molecules, and the oxidative operations account for thirty more. If that were all we were able to glean from one glucose molecule, we would have gained a total of thirty-two molecules of ATP. That's 47 percent efficiency, and it's not bad, but there is more . . . a reaction that has not been mentioned yet, because it is really an independent one. It doesn't really belong to the Krebs cycle or to glycolysis.

Figure 5.18 A simplified summary of intermediary metabolism of glucose. (*1*) Note that during glycolysis, each glucose molecule splits in two. (*2*) Each of the two pyruvate molecules now proceeds through a single turn of the Krebs cycle. In each case, one FAD^+ molecule and three NAD^+ molecules are reduced. (*3*) The reduced coenzymes deposit their electrons on the respiratory chain. Here ATP is produced by oxidative phosphorylation.

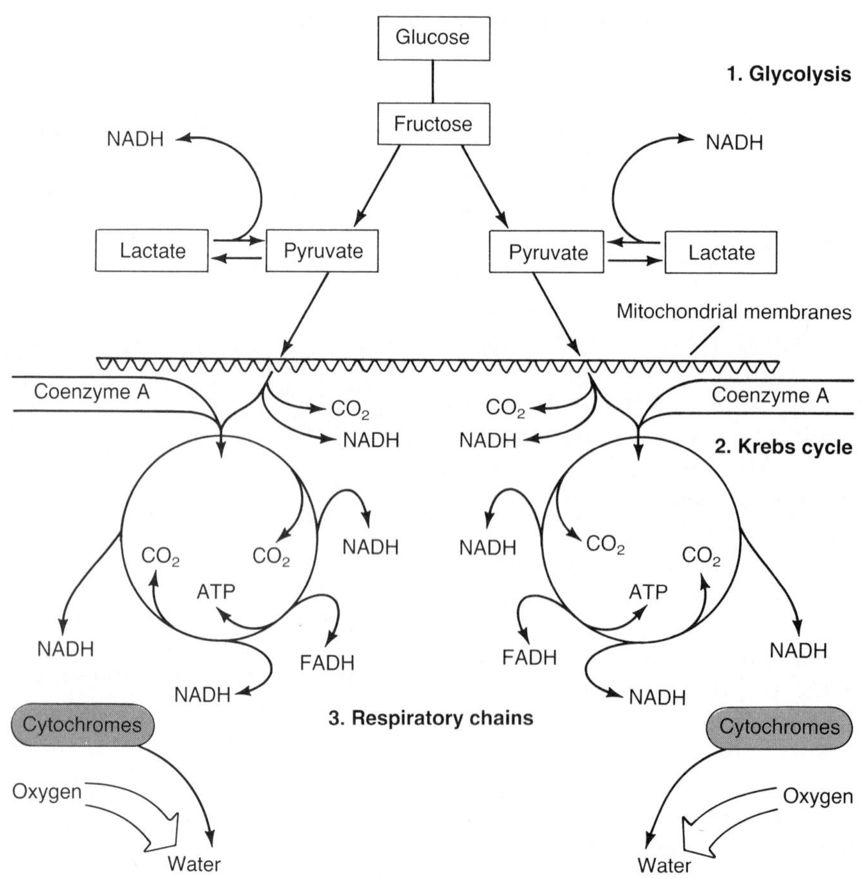

The Adjunct NADH

Let us return to the NAD^+ molecule that is involved in the substrate phosphorylation in glycolysis, the one that reduces pyruvate to lactic acid when oxygen is not present. When oxygen *is* available, that NADH molecule is no longer needed to reduce pyruvate to lactic acid, so it is transported straight into the mitochondria, where it provides the respiratory chain with another pair of electrons for oxidative phosphorylation. In this particular case, however, we do not get three ATP. Since this particular cofactor is reduced *outside* the mitochondria, and since it must get *inside* to deliver its cargo, it must ride a shuttle into the mitochondrial matrix, and it cannot ride for nothing; it costs one ATP. We are therefore able to realize only two ATP from its cargo, and that brings our total energy capture for one mole of glucose to thirty-six moles of ATP (see table 5.3). That is more than 360,000 calories of usable energy that have been captured from each mole of glucose that is completely oxidized. It is an impressive achievement.

Calculations based on these figures show our mechanisms are functioning at about 55 percent efficiency. When you consider that our civilization—which we generally think of as possessing tremendous engineering talent—has not built any machine of significant capacity that can do better than about 38 percent, we must concede that this is quite remarkable. However there is considerable argument on this subject. The figures I have cited indicate 55 percent efficiency, but if we were to use 7,500 calories as the amount of energy available from each mole of ATP, this rating would drop to about 40 percent efficiency. It becomes a matter of debate as to which is the actual case, and I have explained why I use the figures I do (see the box on page 122). Regardless of which is accepted, there is another datum that must be considered. The electron pairs have to be moved from place to place by carrier enzymes. They also have to be transferred *through* the various enzymes of the "electron bucket brigade" in the respiratory chain, and all this moving about requires energy. The energy does not come from our stores of ATP, so it must come from the electrons being moved around in the chain. Thus the efficiency of the system may be greater than any of the aforementioned figures, whether they are 40 or 55 percent, and that is *really* remarkable. Biological systems are indeed efficient.

ADP and P_i—Essential Raw Materials

Keep in mind, however, that none of this will happen if there is not a good supply of substrate phosphates. They are indispensable to intermediary metabolism, just as the cofactors NADH and FADH are. Consider their interactions. Obviously, if NAD^+ and FAD^+ cannot be reduced by the fuel molecules, the Krebs cycle will stop. This means there must be a perpetual supply of cofactors in the oxidized state. A steady supply of oxidized cofactors will only exist if the reduced cofactors can unload their electrons when they encounter the cytochromes. We can therefore state a simple condition that must be met if metabolism is to continue:

The acceptors on the respiratory chain have to be in the oxidized state so they can accept the electrons from the cofactors.

That means electrons must be moving along the electron transport system. The electron transport system is designed to produce ATP, and ATP cannot be produced if there is not an ample supply of ADP and P_i to use as substrates. Obviously, then, if ADP and P_i are not present in the mitochondrial matrix,

Table 5.3 Total ATP Gain per Mole of Glucose

Phase of Respiration	High-Energy Products	ATP from Oxidative Phosphorylation	ATP Subtotal
Glycolysis (glucose to pyruvic acid)	2 ATP	——	2 (total if anaerobic)
	2NADH	4	6
Pyruvic acid to acetyl CoA	1 NADH (×2)	6	12
Krebs cycle	1 GTP (×2)	——	14
	3 NADH (×2)	18	32
	1 FADH (×2)	4	36
		Total (aerobic)	36 ATP

Note: Thirty-six moles are produced because the electrons picked up outside the mitochondria by NAD^+ must be transported into the respiratory chain, a process that costs some energy. As a result, these electron pairs produce just two ATP each instead of three.

electron transport along the respiratory chain will stop. If electron transport stops, so does everything else. This dependence on phosphate substrates is reinforced at the mitochondrial membrane. Every time an ATP molecule leaves the mitochondrion, an ADP molecule and inorganic phosphate must enter. If this exchange does not occur, nothing inside the mitochondrion will work. Clearly, if ADP and P_i are not present in the cytoplasm and readily available to the respiratory machinery, it makes no difference how much glucose or oxygen is present or how many of the correct enzymes are around; the glycolytic pathways will remain deserted.

Obviously, a lack of ADP and/or inorganic phosphates can be just as deadly to living systems as a quick dose of cyanide.

Life may be efficient, but it is also fragile.

Summary

The Cell Cycle

I. Interphase. Interphase consists of:
  A. a G_1 phase, which is the period between end of mitosis and the beginning of DNA replication;
  B. an S_1 phase, which is the DNA replication period;
  C. a G_2 phase, which is the period between the end of S_1 and beginning of mitosis.

II. Mitosis
  A. Prophase. During prophase, dispersed DNA strands coil into chromosomes. The centrioles move apart, and the spindle forms.
  B. Metaphase. During metaphase, chromosomes line up on the equatorial plane of the cell. Microtubules extend out toward the cell membrane.
  C. Anaphase. During anaphase, chromosomes separate into individual chromatids and are pulled to opposite ends of the cell.
  D. Telophase. During telophase, a furrow forms in the membrane to divide the cytoplasm into two parts. The spindle collapses, and the furrow deepens until the cytoplasm is pinched apart.
  E. Interphase again. Mitosis ends when interphase characteristics take over again.

Energy

There are different kinds of energy. One kind, *potential,* is stored energy. Another, *kinetic,* is energy of motion.

I. Enzymes
II. Oxidation. Oxidation is a loss of electrons.
III. Reduction. Reduction is a gain of electrons.
IV. Redox Reactions. *Redox* is an abbreviation for *Reduction/Oxidation.*
V. ATP—the Biological Battery. ATP is adenosine triphosphate. It is the primary source of immediate energy in living systems. Living systems go to great physiological pains to accumulate large stores of ATP.

Anaerobic Metabolism—the Glycolytic Pathway

Anaerobic metabolism refers to energy production without using oxygen. It takes place in the cytosol of the cell.

I. Rapid Energy Consumption and Fatigue. Anaerobic production of energy can continue for some time.
  A. Lactic Acid. Lactic acid is evolved in cells when energy is produced without oxygen.
  B. Oxygen Debt. Extra oxygen is required to get rid of any lactic acid produced by anaerobic metabolism; hence accumulation of lactic acid is known as an oxygen debt.

Oxidative (Aerobic) Metabolism

Aerobic metabolism is energy production utilizing oxygen.

I. Mitochondria. Aerobic metabolism takes place in the mitochondria. It begins with the oxidation and decarboxylation of pyruvate. It produces one reduced coenzyme molecule.
II. The Krebs (Citric Acid) Cycle.
  A. Coenzyme A introduces fresh fuel into the "beginning" of the cycle.
  B. The Krebs cycle begins with the six-carbon compound, citric acid.
  C. The cycle concludes with a four-carbon compound, oxaloacetate.
  D. It is replenished each cycle with a fresh two-carbon fuel compound.
  E. It produces four reduced coenzymes and one GTP molecule.
III. Essential Molecules. There are two kinds of cofactors: NADH and FADH. Each is oxidized at a different site.

The Respiratory Chain

The enzymes of the respiratory chain are located on the inner surface of the inner mitochondrial membrane.

I. The Cytochromes. The respiratory chain consists of a line of enzymes called cytochromes. Each reduced coenzyme is oxidized by a cytochrome.
  A. NADH is oxidized at cytochrome #1.
  B. FADH is oxidized at cytochrome #2.
  C. The cytochromes are reduced in the process.
  D. Each cytochrome passes its electrons on to the succeeding one.
  E. Each pair of electrons passed to cytochrome #1 produces three molecules of ATP.
  F. Each pair of electrons passed to cytochrome #2 produces two molecules of ATP.

II. Oxygen, the Final Acceptor. Oxygen removes electrons from the mitochondria after their energy has been tapped. The electrons plus protons combine with oxygen to produce metabolic water.

III. Lipids. Fats can also be oxidized to obtain their energy content.

IV. Amino Acids. Amino acids are also an energy source.

V. The Importance of Oxygen. Without oxygen, a human would die in minutes; body cells would die in seconds. The most rapidly killing poisons block our ability to utilize oxygen.

Efficiency of Metabolic Reactions

I. Glycolysis. The anerobic reactions produce 20,000 calories of energy. That's about 3 percent of the energy content of a mole of glucose.

II. The Aerobic Reactions. The aerobic reactions produce about 300,000 calories of energy per mole of glucose.

III. Intermediary Metabolism as a Whole. Our metabolic operations are between 47 and 55 percent efficient.

ADP and P_i – Essential Raw Materials

ADP and P_i must be constantly available or the metabolic reactions will stop.

Review Questions

1. Two separate subphases make up the portion of the cell cycle known as interphase. Name and describe them.
2. Name the four major phases of mitosis and describe what goes on in each. Be sure you can cite a clearly distinguishing appearance characteristic of each phase.
3. How does biological oxidation of foodstuffs differ from the process of burning the same material? In what way(s) is it similar?
4. What constitutes oxidation?
5. What type of chemical reaction always accompanies a chemical oxidation?
6. Of what value to biological systems is ATP?
7. Outline the reactions of anaerobic metabolism (glycolysis). Pay particular attention to the number of phosphorylations that are involved in the whole process.
8. What is the purpose of the lactic acid "siding" that exists in cellular cytoplasm?
9. Outline the aerobic reactions of intermediary metabolism. Pay particular attention to the points at which a coenzyme is reduced and note the precise number. Where, in the cell, do these reactions take place?
10. Describe the respiratory chain. Where is this chain located?
11. What is the sole function of the oxygen that all living animals must breathe in?
12. Compare the efficiency of anaerobic metabolism with the aerobic reactions. What is the efficiency of intermediary metabolism as a whole?

Section II

The Control Systems

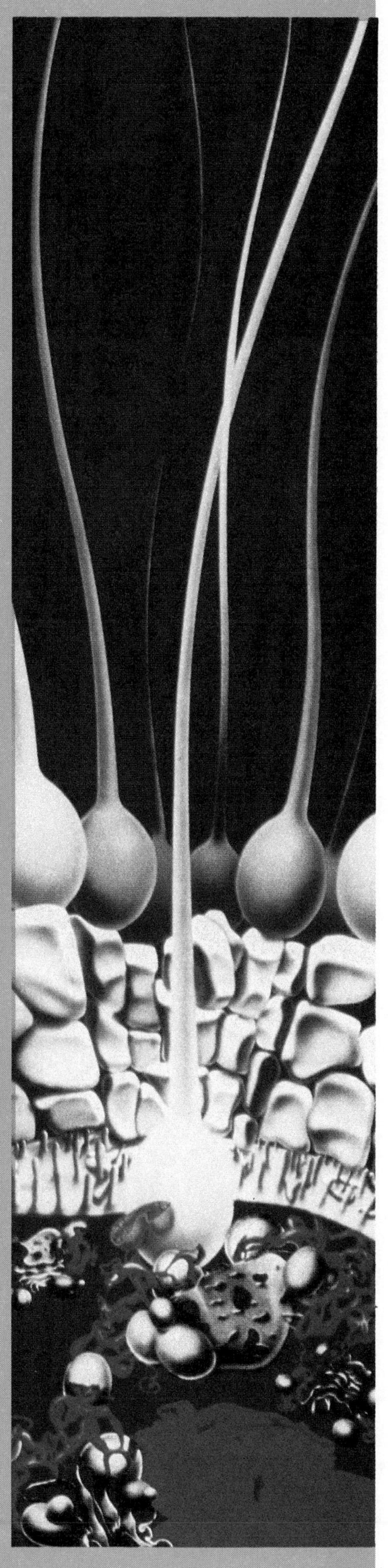

Chapter 6 Bioelectricity

Study Hints

Understanding the fundamentals of bioelectricity is crucial to understanding physiology. Yet one cannot reasonably be expected to understand much about nervous activity or muscle stimulation without knowing a little about energy and the principles of electricity. This chapter offers some fundamentals of electricity to students lacking a background in elementary physics. When reading this chapter, pay particular attention to:

1. **Energy.** Try to distinguish between the different kinds of energy. Try especially hard to grasp the concept of *potential energy* and what it means in electrical theory. This is a must, since voltage *is* potential.
2. **What voltage is.** It's *very* important to be aware that voltage is not electricity. It merely *pushes* electricity.
3. **What current is** and how many different kinds there can be. Pay particular attention to the observation that current in living systems is not the same as the current that flows through the wires in our homes.

Objectives

When you have finished reading this chapter, you should:

1. know what potential energy is and be able to describe how it relates to voltage.
2. be able to describe the difference between volts and electrical current.
3. know how voltage and current are related to each other.
4. know how we can direct current flow and make it work for us.
5. understand why resistances are important in electrical circuitry.
6. understand the relationship between volts, amps, and ohms.

Fiberguide cable used to carry voice, television, and data signals. Fiber optics provide increased capacity to transmit information with greater variety and quality of messages.

Introduction

Most people are vaguely aware that their bodies produce electricity. You have probably heard of polygraphs and know that they can, under the right circumstances, operate as "lie detectors"; you may even realize that they monitor the body's electricity. You may know that electrocardiograph (ECG) records are made when a physician suspects a heart problem or is conducting a routine physical examination. Electrical activity in the brain (EEG) and muscles (EMG) is routinely traced and recorded, yet most of us are surprised to discover that our bodies make and use real electricity . . . not some mysterious, fuzzy force that nobody can figure out, but electricity, just like that which runs our TV sets.

This *personal* electricity is called **bioelectricity,** and it is produced in our bodies through the judicious and meticulous use of chemical energy. Living systems spend this energy with unbelievable precision. It's used to shift atoms and molecules around one at a time, and by carefully manipulating even the tinest particles, every cell in our bodies becomes a tiny "battery." Every cell membrane has a "charge" across it, which means it has the capacity to produce a flow of electricity. This single fact—that electricity is everywhere inside us—hints very strongly that bioelectricity is intimately involved in the process of being alive. It is.

Electricity stimulates our body's muscles to start moving, and the electricity must flow first or our muscles won't work. Bioelectrical impulses tell the secretory glands in our bodies when they must secrete their products and when they must abstain. The digestive glands that abound in our intestinal tract are informed by electricity when their efforts are required, and even our heart, although it can regulate itself and often works unassisted, kindles its contractions electrically.

By far the largest consumer of bioelectricity is the nervous system. Aside from the skin, it is the largest organ system in our bodies, but more significantly, it is the main computer—the one that monitors and controls.

Like all computers, this one is totally dependent on electricity for its proper operation, and it has become so specialized in the utilization of bioelectricity that producing electrical signals has become its *function.* Even animals as immobile as the tapeworm or as simple in body organization as the jellyfish have a means of utilizing electricity for communication inside their bodies. Their simple "nerve nets" carry uncomplicated messages from cell to cell and provide all necessary information about their world so their individual body cells can cooperate with each other.

It is our good fortune that bioelectricity is produced the same way by every animal on earth, because this has permitted us to decipher the fundamentals of bioelectrical phenomena. In addition, during the years that industry has experimented with electricity and electrical appliances, engineers have uncovered a series of important mathematical and physical principles that help in the design of new tools and gadgets. It turns out that most of these principles also apply to bioelectricity, so we are already armed with a lot of thoroughly tested mathematical, physical, and chemical tools to help us understand.

However, it would not make much sense to talk about bioelectricity and how it works in our bodies without being aware of some basic facts. It may seem like a serious detour, moving from a study of the human body into electronics fundamentals, but think about it! It would be senseless to own precision tools of physics and mathematics if we did not know how to use them. For instance, I can tell you that the message running along a nerve fiber is *voltage* and not *current*, and you can memorize that simple fact. You may even remember it (although the chances are that you wouldn't), but the information would probably leave you cold. *Voltage? Current?* What do these words mean? How are they different? Are they not both electricity?

Obviously we need to dissect electricity. We must break it into its various aspects and learn what each one is and how it fits into the collective phenomenon that we refer to in relaxed fashion as "electricity." To do this successfully, we will first have to plumb some basic physical principles.

---

*B*ioelectricity is produced in the same way by every animal on earth! This fact has made a lot of seemingly impossible research relatively easy. Vertebrate nerves are extremely small—most are finer than hairs—and working with them three or four decades ago would have been most unrewarding. The *in*vertebrates, however, have enormous nerve fibers, and one in particular—the squid—has contributed mightily to neurophysiology because of this. The squid has a nerve fiber running the entire length of its body, and even in the little cuttlefish—an animal no more than twelve inches long—this nerve fiber is as big around as the lead in a pencil. It is a tremendous tool for research. Virtually all of the neurophysiological information gleaned throughout the 1930s, 40s, and 50s would have been impossible without the "giant nerve axon" of the squid. Today we have an impressive library of knowledge concerning the function of individual nerve fibers. We know how they produce electricity and how they transmit information, and it is perfectly accurate to state that almost all this information came from research on the giant nerve axon of the squid.

Energy

"Energy" has become a very important commodity in international economics and is a commonly used word in modern vocabularies. Since it is tossed off rather casually on a routine basis, it is probably a good idea to be sure we understand what it is and exactly why it is so important.

Webster calls energy *a capacity for performing work,* and that's pretty accurate. It is not a perfect description, but that is not unusual. Descriptions of energy are terribly elusive, and part of the reason may be that it is so universal—so ubiquitous. Not only is it everywhere, but it lasts forever . . . it can be neither created nor destroyed. We may never know exactly *what* it is, but we can achieve some understanding of its importance by trying to comprehend what it does and how it operates. Often we can predict how it will behave by viewing it in terms of how it relates to other things—things like *work.*

Work

Work is another word people tend to bandy about with perhaps more abandon than they should. Generally it's tossed off to describe all kinds of day-to-day operations, and often it is used when it really should not be. However, it's a little easier to define than energy. *We do work whenever we use force to move something.* There is one key word in that definition that is often ignored in daily usage. That word is *movement,* and if there is no motion, there is no work.

---

*W*hat people commonly think of as "work" may not be so to a scientist. A person might feel that he is working pretty hard when he is asked to hold onto a heavy box until someone can find a table to put under it. After fifteen minutes of holding it up, your muscles would be pretty sore and your body would have expended a lot of energy, but to a scientist, there hasn't been any work done—not if the box didn't move. Only if the force exerted results in *movement* has there actually been any work. A person might look at the ancient Greek Titan Atlas with the whole world on his shoulders, and consider him a very busy person. After all, he braces himself throughout his entire existence holding the heavens and the earth apart, and if he were not there, the heavens would come crashing down onto the earth. By any standards he certainly has not been loafing, yet according to scientific definition, as long as the earth and the heavens remain in their places and don't move around, no work has been done.

Work vs. Energy

How is work related to energy? That's easy. *Any time you do work on a system, you increase its content of energy.* For example, did you know that when you polish a kitchen floor you add energy to it? No one can actually *see* energy, so it is reasonable to ask how anyone can be sure of something like that. The answer is that there are ways of measuring the energy *content* of things. Where the floor is concerned, one way to measure its energy content might be to note how the polishing had changed it. The most obvious change is the glossy smoothness that has appeared. Logically enough, this high polish is therefore a measure of the floor's energy content. You might also check the floor's temperature. It should be warmer when the polishing is finished than it was when it started. Friction increases the temperature, and the additional heat content of the floor is also a measure of its energy content. Observations as variable as these should stimulate a strong suspicion that since energy content can be measured in so many different ways, maybe *there is more than one kind of energy.*

There is.

Potential Energy

We encounter various kinds of energy every day doing simple things—things we do without a second thought. When you carry a package into your house and put it on a table, you use force to move the package, so you have added energy to it. Obviously it is not heat energy or "polish" such as you added to the floor, so what form does it take now? If you lifted it to get it on the table, then the energy that you added is *gravitational* energy. We call it gravitational energy because it is gravity that tries to pull it back to ground level, but it is a special kind of gravitational energy. Until the package actually moves, its energy content is *potential*. And it stays there, in the package, until it is spent . . . and it can only be spent by returning the package to the ground. The energy is therefore *stored* in the package, and that is what **potential energy** is—*stored energy*—energy that has the potential to move something but is not actually moving it. A stretched rubber band contains potential energy—the potential to return to original size. A bullet fired straight up into the air is increasing its content of potential energy with every foot it rises. Once the rubber band starts to snap back to its initial size or the bullet stops rising and starts to fall back to earth, the potential energy changes into something else.

There is a point that should be made clear now. *The potential energy that is in the package* and *the package itself* are two different things. Please keep that in mind. It may seem obvious to the point of being foolish, but there is a good reason for emphasizing this, as you will see presently.

Free Electrons

Electricity is able to do work, and that means motion is involved. It also means that there must be some potential energy available to produce the motion and that there must be some "packages" for this potential to move.

The moving "packages" constitute what we refer to as **current,** and as we visualize it today, these packages of current are atomic or subatomic-sized charged particles. The ones that flow through wires in our homes and businesses are **free electrons,** meaning that they don't "belong" to any particular atom. Free electrons don't orbit any particular nucleus. They tend, rather, to jump around from one to the other. This tends to be characteristic of large elements, because large atoms have the most electrons, and when there are many electrons, sometimes the outer orbits are a long way from the nucleus. The attraction the positive nucleus has for these distant electrons can be pretty weak, and often they don't stay locked in their orbits. Instead, they tend to drift back and forth from atom to atom. Metals have lots of free electrons—in fact, chemists tell us that any element that has "free" electrons is, by convention, considered a metal. That is one of the reasons that metals are used to carry electrical current: they have so many free electrons.

Random Electricity in Metals

In a chunk of copper, for instance, there are free electrons galore drifting around from atom to atom. Their movement is totally random; they just drift back and forth with no particular direction dominating. But they *are* moving, and they *are* charged particles—and *when charged particles are moving around, electricity is flowing.* That means electricity flows constantly in our copper coins, and copper is just one of many metals we use in our culture. If there is electricity flowing in our coins, then maybe it is flowing in our saucepans, our plumbing—even our knives and forks—all the time. And it is—what is more, it always has been. There is nothing new about electricity. People just didn't know what it was or what it could do. To make it work for us, we had to find a way to coerce its flowing electrons out of their random movements and to get them going in a specific direction.

Electricity at Work

Applying a magnetic field across a piece of metal can have an important effect on the free electrons that are present. Electrons, you will recall, are negative particles, so an electromagnetic charge can move them in specific directions, depending on what its polarity is. Since electrons are negative, a negative charge will repel them and a positive one will attract. One way, therefore, to get free electrons where we want them to go would be to expose them to an electromagnetic field.

Another way would be to draw electrons away from a particular zone and concentrate them someplace else. Once there is a surplus of electrons in any given spot, and a dearth of them someplace else, we have established an *energy potential.* Consider what potential energy is, and think about this. At one spot there is a large accumulation of electrons, all of which are negatively charged particles, and they therefore tend to repel each other. They have plenty of energy available to force them to fly apart.

Electrical Potential

We can concentrate electrons in any given spot or structure, but it must be remembered that we did not *create* the electrons. We collected them from other structures—they came from someplace else. Having lost so many electrons, this "someplace else" will not have nearly enough, and as a result, it will have a highly positive charge. Any place with a high positive charge represents a very attractive spot for negative electrons, and they would rush there *en masse* if only they could.

Let us review the situation we have theoretically established. We have two zones in which there is a great deal of potential energy stored. One of them—the negative zone—has the potential to lose electrons. The other—the positive zone—has the potential to attract electrons. Both of these zones represent a store of **potential electrical energy** in much the same way as a package higher than the ground can contain potential gravitational energy. Like *gravitational* potential, *electrical* potential is *stored energy*. It represents the energy that is *capable* of doing work, but is not yet actually *doing* it.

Yet it is energy. Work had to be done to drag the electrons away from one place and concentrate them someplace else. All we have to do is package this concentration difference, and we will have packed potential energy into a container. This is, in a way, what is done when a simple flashlight battery is manufactured. The packaged potential energy is known as **voltage.**

Voltage and Amperes

Most of us are familiar with the term *voltage* because we see it on all kinds of electrical equipment. Signs such as "DANGER: 20,000 volts" are not unusual . . . we sometimes find them even on our television sets. So what is a volt?

Precisely defined, a volt is a unit of electrical potential.

If we were to measure the potential energy content of a battery like the one described earlier, we would measure it in volts—1.5 to be exact. The voltage value tells us how much potential energy the battery has available to push the electrons away from one terminal and into the other (figure 6.1*b*). It is a measure of the charge that exists between the two poles on the battery. It must be emphasized, however, in order to measure that charge, we must measure between the place where electrons are concentrated and where they are not. Electrons will not flow where they are not needed. This is easily demonstrated. If both leads of a voltmeter are placed side-by-side on the battery terminal where the electrons are all concentrated, the voltage reading will be zero (figure 6.1*d*). There is no tendency for the electrons to go from a place where they are concentrated to a second place where they are equally concentrated, and as the voltmeter indicates, there is no potential difference between two such points. That brings up another important point. Potential energy represents a difference in energy content between two or more zones, and that, therefore, makes voltage a difference in stored electrical energy between two zones.

Current Flow

A package sitting on a table well above the floor contains potential energy. If something knocks the package off the table, the potential energy is spent on the way down, but it is the *package* that falls. The voltage in an electrical circuit is the potential energy that is stored there. It is available to move the electrons, but *voltage is not the electrons.* Just as the potential energy in the package drew it to the floor, the potential electrical energy in the battery *pushes* the electrons. Changing terminology into electrical jargon, the voltage *pushes* the current.

Devising a means of concentrating electrons in order to build up electrical potential partially solved the problem of how people could use the energy in electricity . . . but only partially. Piling up an electrical charge can be accomplished just by walking across the right kind of carpeting. A voltage builds up in a person's body and it, too, will cause a flow of electrons when we touch a metal surface. The problem is that it all lets go at once and is gone. You cannot get it back unless you walk across the carpet again. For electricity to be of any practical value there has to be some means of *rebuilding the potential* as fast as it is used up and then keep on doing it so that as the electrons are drawn away from the area of concentration, they are promptly piled up there again. Finding a means of accomplishing this was the key to getting electricity to work for people.

Generating Electricity

To do this, naturally, requires energy, and the energy is obtained from many sources. Power plants burn coal or oil or use the heat from atomic decomposition to "pump up" the electrons. Batteries do it with chemical energy. When the proper chemicals are arranged together, they pull electrons from one zone (called a **terminal**) and thrust them onto another. Once the

Figure 6.1 Measuring potential energy. A measure of potential difference has to be made between two separate points, and their content of energy has to be different. Consider the two packages in (*1*). Both contain the gravitational energy to fall to the floor, so if you measure between a package and the floor, you'll measure a difference. However, if you measure the difference in gravitational potential between the two packages, you'll read a zero (*3*). They each contain exactly the same amount of gravitational energy, so they don't have the potential to fall toward each other. The situation with the charged-up battery is the same. Measuring between two opposite poles of the battery (*2*) produces a potential energy reading (volts.) Measuring between two different points on the same pole (*4*) shows no potential difference at all.

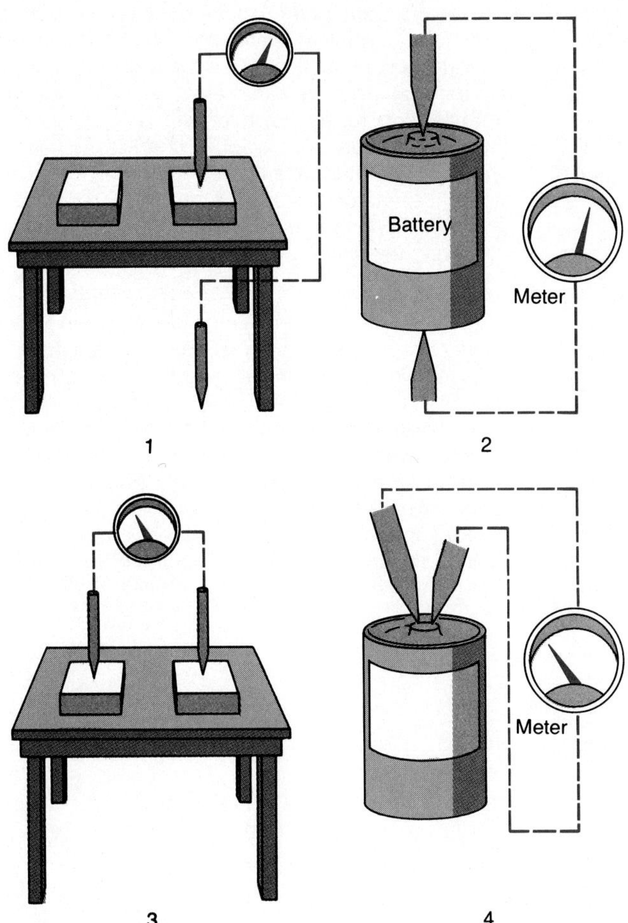

electrons are distributed in this manner, a *potential energy gradient* is established—a gradient that can produce a current flow. This is the **electromotive force (EMF),** or voltage that is present in the battery. Keep in mind that in order for our voltage to accomplish anything, there must not only be a spot where electrons are sparse and a second spot where they are concentrated, there must also be a means of getting them from one place to the other. Without an easy path to follow, electrons will keep piling up in one zone. Eventually, if enough charge builds up, terminals may break down whatever insulator is between them and discharge themselves. This happens routinely in our atmosphere when a particular zone builds up such a tremendous concentration of potential that it can blow apart the insulator (air) between the two terminals. It uses all of its potential energy in the process of breaking down the air's resistance, and the resultant spark that jumps between ground and the clouds produces the spectacular electrical display we call lightning. We *could* do that, but it is not a very rewarding operation. It requires potentials on the order of two or three million volts, and about the only consequence is heated air and a lot of noise.

Panel 6.1

Electricity: How It Works for Us

In many ways, using electricity is like using falling water to do work for us. We could, for example, provide water with extra gravitational potential energy by pumping it from ground level up to a higher reservoir (figure 6.A).

Water tank 1 now contains water with considerable potential energy. It is in the form of gravitational energy, and if we just leave it as it is, the water will retain this energy. We can make that potential work for us, however, with a little manipulation. We can provide the system with a path of least resistance—a *conductor* (2, 3, and 4). By providing such a route we are not just giving the water a *means* of moving, we are also determining the direction it will move. All that is now necessary to get work out of the system is to put something under the falling water that can be moved. Thus we have a working circuit. The pump (5) provides gravitational energy by pushing water up into tank 1. This potential subsequently provides the water with the energy to fall. As it falls, the moving water strikes and turns the wheel, and the resultant motion can be used for anything we choose. As long as we can control the direction the water is going and as long as we can pump it back up into tank 1, it will keep right on working.

Figure 6.A A functioning circuit using falling water as an energy source. The load in this case is a turning wheel. Such wheels have, in the past, been used to perform tasks like grinding grain, while today we often use the energy of falling water to generate electricity. The area bounded by the broken line represents, in this case, a pump, which is run by energy from an external source. It restores the water's potential by pumping it uphill. Since the same water is used over and over again, this represents a *closed circuit,* similar to an electrical circuit that uses the same current over and over again. In practical use, energy provided by falling water is usually captured as the water falls off a cliff or over a dam; hence it cannot be used again. Such arrangements are sometimes referred to as *open circuits.*

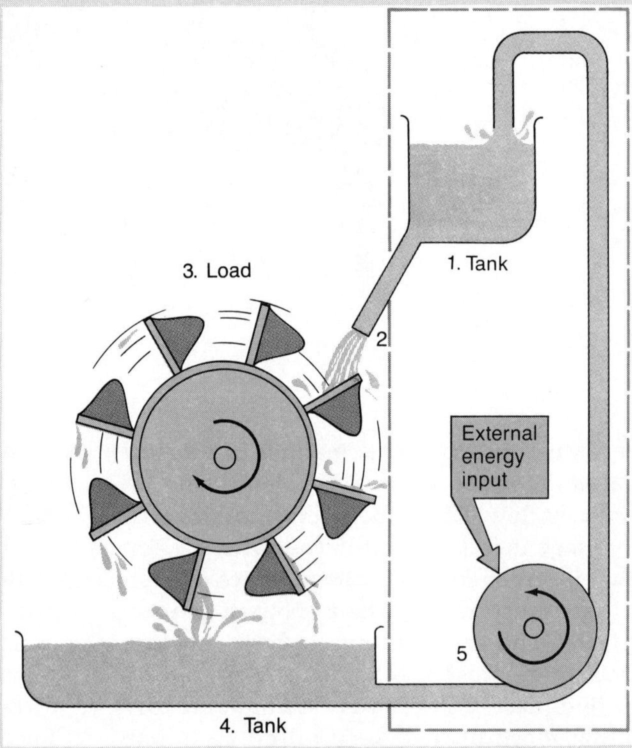

This is pretty much the way a simple electrical circuit operates. The simple dry cell (what is commonly known as a battery) functions in a very similar manner. Using chemical energy, it pumps electrons from one zone *inside* the battery up to a separate zone, providing them with the necessary potential energy to go through the wire again. By convention, the zone that lost the electrons is known as the *positive* terminal, while the one they were all pumped into is the *negative* terminal. A wire conductor (usually copper) serves the same purpose as pipes (2 and 4) working in the pumping system. It serves to take the current in the direction we want it to go. If we consider the lighting of a simple bulb as being the work that we want done, we have our circuit. The battery (figure 6.B) provides the voltage (potential energy), and the voltage then proceeds to push the electrons through the wire, and they light the bulb.

That brings us to the final point.

Resistance

As we have noted, anything that impedes the rush of energy-containing particles represents a resistance. In figure 6.A, the energy-containing particles are water molecules in volume and the resistance is obvious; it is the wheel that the water is required to turn. This represents the part of the circuit where there is work being done and is the reason we constructed the circuit in the first place . . . to turn the wheel.

We build electrical circuits for a similar reason—to perform work for us. We may want to run a lawnmower, or an electric saw, or we may just want to light a bulb. In each case, providing the motion or providing the light is the result of producing resistance to the free movement of current through a circuit.

Resistance in electrical circuits takes many forms. It represents things like the electrical guts of a washing machine, the wave amplifiers of radios or television sets, the compressors of air conditioning units—all of the appliances we pride ourselves on and which make our lives so much easier. When we look at figure 6.A we may have difficulty, in the beginning, understanding why we would go to all the trouble to pump water up such a steep hill just so it could fall back down again. Actually, the answer is pretty simple. There is energy in falling water, but the energy is of no use to us if the water merely spends this energy in making a big splash. We make this energy turn a wheel, which can be converted into a work project that yields something useful. The same is true of the electrical circuit. The energy present in the battery, as simply *electrical potential,* is of no particular value, but if we use it to heat up a *resistor* until it glows white-hot, it will provide us with light.

There is another term that I have not used in conjunction with the text material because it makes things more complicated than they need to be. I will mention it here for the sake of thoroughness. It is **power,** and the definition of power adds time to other considerations. *Power is the rate at which work is done.* In electrical terms it is measured in **watts.** A watt is the amount of power that is dissipated when energy is used at the rate of one **joule** per second. Anyone interested enough in going beyond that definition is referred to any elementary physics textbook for detailed information and probably a few problems to solve. For our purposes, we can simplify the situation a little bit by ignoring the time aspect and viewing the measurement itself. The power rating of electrical motors, for instance, is achieved by running the motor under a full load, measuring the current that the motor is drawing, and multiplying that figure by the voltage that has been applied. The number that results is the power dissipated by the motor and is expressed in watts. Putting it more simply, *the wattage is equal to the current times the voltage.* A 100-watt light bulb working in a household circuit which is rated at 110 volts would thus be drawing 0.9 amps of current ($0.9 \times 110 = 100$).

Figure 6.B A simple electrical circuit. A circuit such as this is all it takes to make a flashlight operate. The area bounded by broken lines (the battery) represents the pumping mechanism that is designed to "pump" electrons uphill and restore their potential. The electrons flow through the wire like water through a pipe, and instead of turning a wheel, they light up a bulb. The electrons run downhill electrically (from 1.5 volts to zero volts), and they lose their potential energy in the light bulb.

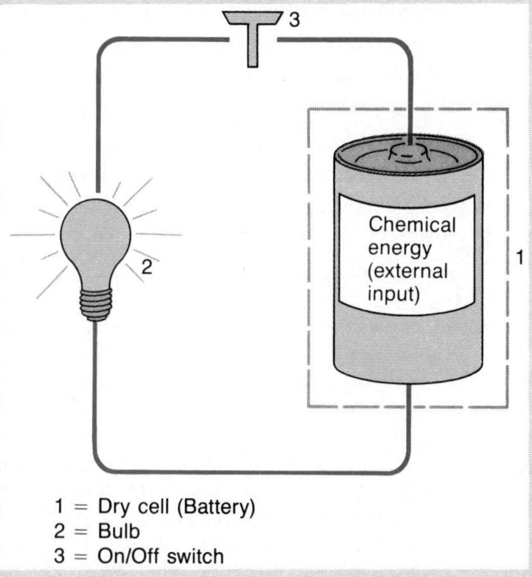

Conductors

The best way to control electron movement is to provide a **conductor** that will give them a nice, easy path that they can follow from the place where there are too many of them to where there are not any. If this "path of least resistance" is constructed with enough care, we can use it to put the electrons to work. With a conductor between the two terminals, the electrons not only have a place to go, they have an easy way to get there. Those that are all piled up on the one terminal can move into the conductor carrying their negative charge with them as they make their mad dash for the other terminal, the one with no electrons around it. If we can control their movement, we can make them work for us as they rush to where they want to go.

Speaking generally, metals tend to be good conductors because of the abundance of free electrons they possess. Some workers feel that in the very best conductors, like silver, gold, copper, aluminum, and calcium, the outer electron shell is never filled—that there is always at least one free electron on every atom. Of all the metals, the best conductor is silver, and it is used freely in precision or research instruments. We don't use it in our homes for obvious reasons . . . nor, for the same reasons, do we use gold, the number two conductor. Copper is generally used for wiring residences and is perfectly adequate. The wire that carries electricity *to* our homes, however, is usually aluminum. Aluminum is not as good a conductor as copper, but it's good enough and is much cheaper for long-distance transmission. It also has a couple of other properties that make it desirable. It is strong and it is light. Copper is a soft metal, easily stretched and easily broken. In addition, it's a dense, heavy element. If copper were used to carry electricity through our cities and countryside, we would need more poles and they would have to be closer together to support the extra weight and to compensate for the weakness of the softer copper. The additional cost of both the copper metal and the poles would be prohibitive.

Resistance

As it turns out, work done by an electrical current really represents nothing more than a **resistance** that the flowing particles have to push aside to get where they are going. By providing a pathway that makes electricity go where we want it to go, we can make it perform work by just giving it a job to do. We do this by placing a "resistance" in the circuit. Resistance is the third fundamental in basic electricity. There are others, of course. Dozens are involved in the way electricity is put to work for humanity, but the three essential fundamentals have now been introduced—voltage, current, and resistance.

Summarizing the electrical concepts covered so far:

1. Flow of electrical current is a movement of charged particles, and in the electricity supplied to our homes, these particles are electrons.
2. Voltage is potential energy. It is the electromotive force that pushes the current.
3. Conductors are materials through which charged particles can flow with very little opposition. The best conductors are metals, elements with lots of free electrons. Conductors are used to transport the "current."
4. Resistances are obstacles placed in conductors that the charged particles (current) have to push out of the way to get where they want to go.

By putting all these bits of information together, it is possible to make current, voltage, and resistance perform work.

Ohms, Volts, and Amperes

These fundamentals can all be expressed in units, of course. The potential energy in a circuit is described in volts, the term **ampere** or **amp** is used to designate units of current, while resistance is expressed in **ohms.** According to convention, one volt will push one ampere of current through a resistance of one ohm. If you fit these values into the equation in the following box, you'll find it works nicely. Naturally there are fractions and multiples of all these units, and we use them frequently. Our household circuits usually carry currents reckoned in thousandths of an ampere—milliamps—and resistances of most appliances into thousands of ohms (kilohms) or millions of ohms (megohms). Normal household voltage is from 110 to 120 volts, depending on where you live, but our appliances can reduce or boost these voltages by impressive factors. The voltage on the picture tube in our TV sets can be as great as 30,000 volts (30 kilovolts).

Current, resistance, and electromotive force (voltage) were related to each other years ago in an extremely simple equation known as **Ohm's law.** This law states that the current (symbol I) is equal to the voltage in the circuit (symbol E or V) divided by the resistance in the circuit (symbol R). Put into purely mathematical terms: **I = E/R.** As you can see, if two of these values are known, the other can be easily calculated. Units like volts, ohms, and amperes are all used to describe electrical phenomena in living systems, and their relationship to each other is the same.

Biological Electricity

Biological electricity obeys the physical and mathematical laws that apply to man-made electricity, but it is subtly different in some ways. Naturally, bioelectrical current must have a voltage gradient to run down, or it won't flow from place to place. The flow of bioelectricity is, like man-made current, a movement of charged particles, but the particles are different. Instead of electron flow, bioelectrical current is a movement of small inorganic ions—sodium or potassium ions, usually. "Potassium current" and "sodium current" are both involved in transmission of information along nerve fibers.

There are other differences as well, and they are also important. Nature doesn't use the more subtle nuances of electrical phenomena in the same way that humans do. Messages are sent in a different fashion, and many things that electrical engineers think are important, nature alters drastically.

In order to get a clear picture of how living systems generate electricity, we must first learn how the involved ions are distributed inside and outside body cells. Not only must we be aware of the differential distribution of these ions, but we must clearly understand both *why* and *how* these differences are maintained.

We should probably begin with a single, empty cell (figure 6.2).

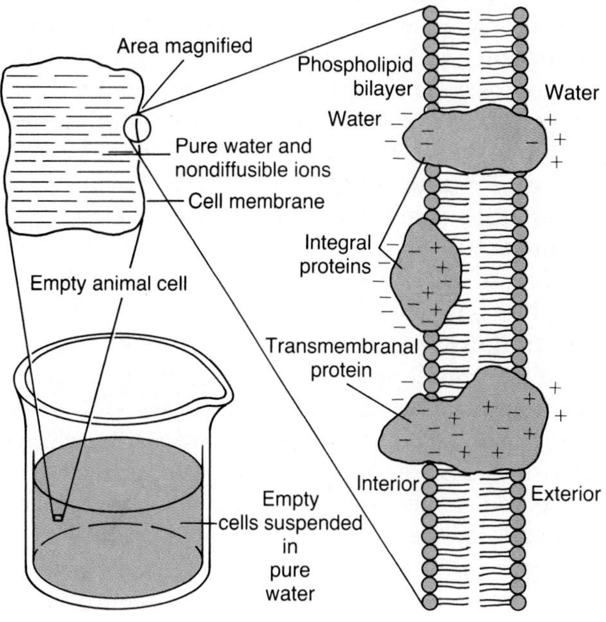

Figure 6.2 A theoretical empty cell consisting of nothing but a standard unit membrane. The medium both outside and inside the cell is pure water, so there is no tendency for movement to occur. The membrane itself is a typical lipid bilayer with both integral and peripheral proteins imbedded within. It is theorized that the negative zones of the proteins project into the interior of the cell, while those layers that are neutral or positive are kept on the outer surface.

The Cell as a Battery

Since this is a hypothetical situation, it is necessary to use a little imagination and see if we cannot establish a set of circumstances that would result in the ionic arrangement that actually exists inside and outside of a living cell. For the sake of simplicity, suppose we start arranging things at the very bottom, beginning with an empty cell. Such a cell would contain only water and would consist of nothing but a completely intact cell membrane separating two compartments filled with water (remember, this is strictly theoretical). There are, however, some beginning conditions that must be presupposed.

Constructing a Biological Battery

The cell membrane must be the standard one, composed of a phospholipid bilayer with islands of proteins bobbing around in it. Like most organic molecules, these proteins incorporate lots of ions, and when you add up all their charges, letting negatives cancel out positives, the charge that remains is usually negative. As it turns out, even those proteins that tend to be neutral (net charge = 0) are often arranged in the membrane in such a way that they all stick their negative zones into the liquid on the inner side of the membrane. In addition, to provide an internal medium that resembles that of living cells, we must add some other negative ions, a few phosphates and some sulfates and so on, none of which can cross the membrane and hence cannot diffuse out of the cell. The result is that the entire interior of the cell is negatively charged with respect to the fluid outside. Unlike a man-made battery, this charge is not typically a concentration of electrons, but rather a concentration of larger negatively charged particles—in this case, fairly large ions. But whether electrons or ions, it is potential electrical energy, and that means it is measureable in volts.

Now suppose we start adding things and we can watch as conditions sort themselves out.

Potassium

It begins with the addition of potassium ions to the medium in which our hypothetical cell is immersed. The charged cell membrane will, naturally, play a role. Obviously, there will be some shuffling around of these newly added ions. There are two forces that will operate to rearrange them.

Force number one is diffusion. (Keep in mind that the only thing necessary for diffusion to occur is a concentration gradient and a clear pathway along which to move.) As is always the case, the energy flow is downhill, so diffusible ions move from high concentration to low. Since there are no K^+ ions at all inside the cell, the diffusion gradient will tend to push them through the membrane into the water inside the cell (figure 6.3*a*).

Force number two is an electromagnetic one. (The membrane is charged, remember?) The inside boasts a collection of organic molecules with all their negative features exposed to the interior of the cell, so the interior of the cell is quite negative with respect to the outside. Potassium is a *cation* (positive charge), and since unlike charges attract, the interior of the cell becomes a powerful lure. This second force therefore *adds* its strength to the diffusive pressure that is trying to push the potassium into the cell. With two such forces operating, the only thing that could prevent the rapid movement of K^+ into the cell would be the membrane. It *could* block off the whole interior. It *could* put a dam there that prevents any potassium ions from penetrating to the inside—but it doesn't. It presents only a slight barrier to potassium movement, and with two forces pushing on it and almost nothing in its way, potassium pours into the cell.

Figure 6.3 (*a*) When potassium ions placed in the external medium encounter the empty cells floating within, two forces immediately try to thrust the ions through the membrane and into the cell. Since the membrane offers no substantial resistance to the movement of potassium, it flows in readily. (*b*) Potassium very quickly fills the cell to a concentration that is greater than that which is outside. Nevertheless, the electrical attraction is still great, and the ions continue to pour into the interior.

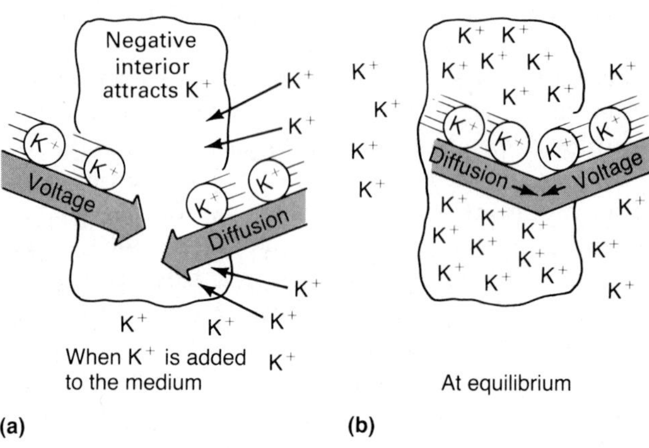

Equilibrium

As potassium ions rush into the interior of the cell using both the energy of diffusion and electromagnetic attraction, their numbers inside gradually increase until the concentration gradient is substantially reduced. Presently, with so many ions crowding in, the concentration on the inside will get to the point where it equals the concentration outside. The diffusive force will therefore disappear, but that will not bring the inward migration to a halt. The forces of diffusion no longer exist because the concentration gradient has vanished, but the electromagnetic attraction is still there. The inside of the cell is still negative and potassium is still a positive ion, so it continues to pour in.

Immediately a new concentration gradient starts to develop in the opposite direction. Now its force tends to thrust potassium *out* of the cell rather than into it. In the beginning it is a weak force, because there are only one or two more potassium ions inside than there are outside, but as the powerful voltage gradient continues to draw more and more potassium ions inside, the diffusion gradient increases in power. The more potassium that enters, the more powerfully diffusion will try to push it back out, adding more and more resistance to their inward flow.

Inevitably, the concentration of potassium inside the cell will increase until the force of diffusion is nearly as strong as the electromagnetic potential, and as the two approach equality, the net movement of potassium ions will finally cease. The final equilibrium that is established involves two equal, opposing forces—an electrical potential that is trying to induce potassium ions to flow into the cell and an exactly equal diffusive force that is trying to thrust the same ions out of the cell.

That does not mean the movement of potassium ions has ceased. When you think about it, you will realize that there is no reason for it to stop. Why should it? The interior of the cell is still negative, so there is still an attractive force drawing the ions into the cell. The concentration gradient is also still there—it is not going to stop pushing potassium ions out. The membrane is still permeable, so there is nothing in the way. The only thing that is different now is that potassium flow in is exactly balanced by potassium flow out . . . the *net* movement (movement in minus movement out) is zero. With the two forces balanced, the voltage developed across the membrane is known as the **equilibrium potential** for potassium.

The Chloride Ion

Now we can introduce a second ion—chloride. As was the case with potassium, we will add these chloride ions to the external medium.

Once again there are two separate forces involved—diffusion and electrical potential. Their overall effect is not the same as it was with potassium ions, because chloride is an *an*ion (negative charge). Instead of supporting each other as they initially did with potassium (see figure 6.4), the two forces are antagonists from the very start.

Since we added the chloride ions to the external medium in the beginning, they will all be outside the cell, so there is going to be a powerful chloride diffusion gradient between the external medium and the fluid in the cell's interior. At the same time, the interior of the cell is negative, so instead of the electromagnetic forces trying to draw the diffusible ion into the cell (as was the case with K^+), there will be an electrical tendency to repel.

Initially, the diffusive forces are able to overwhelm the electrical ones, and chloride ions will flow into the cell. The negative potential inside will try to push them back out, but in the beginning, the diffuse forces are stronger and a few chloride ions will accumulate in the cytosol despite the fact that their presence makes the cell interior even more negative. This situation comlicates things a little bit for the potassium ions. The presence of the chloride in the cytosol adds to the cell's attraction for potassium and results in a minor reshuffling of that equilibrium, but since the membrane permits potassium to move rather freely, a balance can be struck quickly, and the two ions, along with the forces that are at work on them, arrive at a reasonable equilibrium. When a collective calm is finally established, the negative nature of the

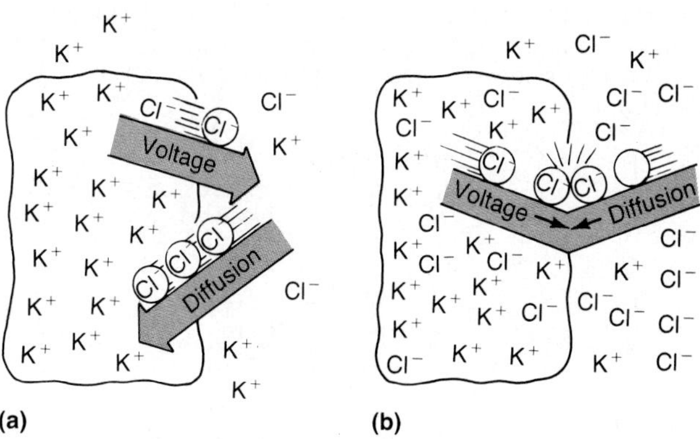

Figure 6.4 (*a*) As with potassium, in the beginning a powerful diffusion gradient exists that tries to rush chloride into the cell. (*b*) As chloride ions accumulate in the interior of the cell, the diffusion gradient decreases and the electrical gradient increases. Equilibrium is reached when the two are equal.

cellular interior is retained, and the potassium is redistributed a little bit. There is a little more potassium inside than there would have been had chloride not appeared, but not much. Also, there is more chloride inside than there would be in the absence of potassium, but again, not much. Both ions are moving back and forth, but as with any other equilibrium, the net movement is zero. The voltage across the membrane would now represent the collective equilibrium potential for chloride and potassium.

The Sodium Ion

Like potassium, sodium is a cation, so when it is added to the external medium, both diffusion and electromagnetic forces are operating to rush it across the membrane into the interior of the cell. There is no ionic sodium inside the cell, so this means a maximum effort by the diffusive force. At the same time, with the cellular interior still negative, there is an electromagnetic potential also trying to attract the positive ions. Two very powerful forces, allied with one another, are trying to get sodium to move into the cytoplasm. The cellular interior should be rapidly filling up, yet sodium remains outside, pounding with futile ionic fists against the membrane. The membrane has erected a barrier against sodium. Cell membranes are normally only slightly permeable to sodium, and the dams they have raised can resist its

Figure 6.5 Ionic distribution at equilibrium. The nondiffusible proteins (A^-) are present in sufficient quantity to maintain a negative potential within the cell, despite the presence of large amounts of potassium. As the arrows indicate, there is a powerful electrical attraction trying to draw potassium into the cell, and it is exactly balanced by the diffusion gradient that is trying to thrust potassium out. Chloride is also in balance. Only sodium is out of balance. There are two forces trying to force it into the cell's interior, yet it is kept out by the impermeable nature of the membrane.

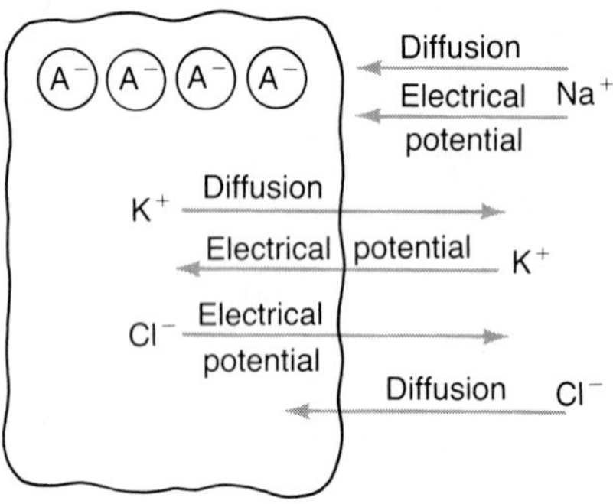

Table 6.1 Concentrations of Critical Ions in Interstitial Fluid

	Na+	K+	Cl−	Nondiffusible Anions
Interstitial Fluid	145	4	120	None
Intracellular Fluid	12	155	4	155

Concentrations are in millimoles per liter.

movement with a power that is astonishing. As a result, almost all of the sodium in body fluids stays outside the cell, in the extracellular fluids, where it represents the most abundant positively charged ion. Inside the cell, potassium is the dominant cation (see figure 6.5).

With all three ions now in place—potassium, chloride, and sodium—the main contributors to biological electricity are present, and their distribution in our hypothetical cell is about what it is in every cell in our bodies. Most of the potassium is inside our cells, most of the sodium is outside (see table 6.1). This differential distribution, coupled with the presence of the nondiffusible anions on the inside of the membrane, has created a voltage across the cell membrane. Chloride and potassium are balanced between the inside and outside of the cell according to their concentration and the voltage gradient that exists across the cell membrane. On the other hand, sodium is nowhere near its equilibrium potential.

Obviously, these three inorganic ions are not the only elements in the extracellular fluids or the cytoplasm; our example is a hypothetical one. In real living systems, the media inside and outside the cell are, as we have seen, packed with minerals and organic compounds, and often their distribution inside and outside of the cell is not in balance. But none of the other compounds or ions appear to affect the electrical gradients in living systems to the extent that sodium and potassium do.

In Living Cells

A Differential Equilibrium

Ionic arrangement in the cells and interstitial fluids of all known animals is substantially as I have outlined. There are many nondiffusible anions fixed within our body cells, and they provide considerable electrical negativity inside the cell. This negative characteristic is bound to have an effect on the small ions that are capable of penetrating the cell membrane and, since the membrane is much more permeable to K^+ than to any of the others, it is natural that K^+ would accumulate within in the greatest concentration. The intracellular fluids have a high concentration of potassium—sometimes thirty times as much as there is outside. Chloride also distributes itself according to the combined electrical and diffusive forces that exist across the membrane and, as is the case with potassium, its movement is relatively unrestricted.

The situation with respect to sodium is quite different. Considering the electrical and diffusive forces that exist across the membrane, sodium should be abundant in the intracellular fluid, yet there is very little there. As was the case with our hypothetical cell, only small amounts actually cross the membrane because the membrane is only slightly permeable to sodium. It is not completely impermeable, however. It yields on a regular basis to the pounding of the electrical and diffusive forces that continually assault it, and there is a relentless movement of sodium ions into the intracellular fluid. As this happens, there are shifts—small, but real—in the electrical and diffusive gradients across the membrane.

Living cells do not have the membrane potentials that they should have. According to the concentration gradients of potassium and chloride, the potential across a nerve membrane should be about −90 mv, and it is not. Actual measurements show that the potential is nearer −70 mv, which means the system is near its equilibrium potential but is not quite there.

Sodium is responsible. Because the membrane is not completely impermeable, sodium keeps leaking in. And every time a positively charged sodium ion leaks in, the interior of the cell becomes one charge less negative; thus the negative nature of the cellular interior can slowly be upset. The diffusive and electrical forces acting on sodium ions are considerable, and despite the membrane's resistance, sodium influx is tenacious. Potassium, on the other hand, being close to its equilibrium potential, does not move out as quickly.

Even so there is considerable exchange of potassium and sodium across the membrane. In one respect, this is good. Losing positive potassium ions from the cellular interior helps retain the internal negativity of the cell despite the invading sodium. But because of the relative power of the forces involved, the sodium influx is greater than the potassium efflux. If it were allowed to continue for any length of time, the inside of the cell would fill with sodium, and much of the intracellular potassium would be lost to the interstitial fluid. If the differential distribution of sodium and potassium were to vanish, the electrical charge across the cell membrane would disappear, too. Yet it doesn't happen. The continued, differential distribution of potassium, chloride, and sodium is one of the great homeostatic achievements of the body. All three of these ions remain in approximately the same concentrations on both sides of the membrane, and the potential across the membrane remains constant for extended periods—sometimes for the entire life of the cell. Obviously there must be some machinery present that can correct leakages and restore original conditions.

The Sodium/Potassium Pump

There is a mechanism present in the cell membranes that is designed to nab sodium and potassium ions and pump them back where they came from. Its effect regarding sodium is coupled to that of potassium, meaning that whenever it takes hold of sodium ions, it must likewise lock onto potassium ions before it can tear through its paces. It is known as the **sodium/potassium pump** (or the *ion pump*), and it represents one of the major *active transport* (energy-consuming) mechanisms present in the cell (figure 6.6).

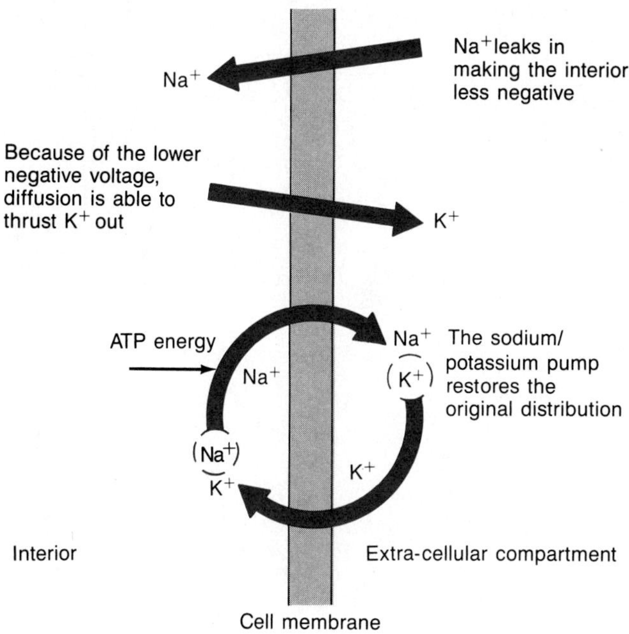

Figure 6.6 The forces involved in maintaining the differential ion distribution that exists across cell membranes. As sodium ions leak in and potassium ions passively move out, mechanisms in the membrane promptly replace them or pump the same ones back where they were. These pumps use considerable energy and are ideal examples of active transport.

Although the sodium-pumping activity is closely linked to the potassium pump, it is not precisely a one-for-one exchange system. The interior of the cell must be kept at a negative value, so considerable energy is expended in insuring that positive sodium ions inside the cell are removed quickly and in large numbers. The mechanism that handles these chores was originally discovered in the large nerve fibers of invertebrates, but it has since been identified in many tissues and in many animals.

It involves two integral membrane proteins in its operations, and the one that does all the work is transmembranal. On the surface that projects out into the interstitial fluid, there is lots of exposed surface,

Figure 6.7 The sodium/potassium pump in action. (*1*) Three sodium ions approach the carrier protein and lock into receptors. (*2*) Sodium/receptor complex activates ATPase. (*3*) ATP energizes protein, and potassium receptors form. (*4*) Binding of potassium stimulates a change of shape in the protein. ADP is released. P_1 is retained. (*5*) Using the energy contributed by ATP, the protein molecule rearranges itself. (*6*) In its new position, the molecule releases three sodium ions into the interstitial fluid, and two potassium ions enter the cytosol. (*7*) The inorganic phosphate is released, and the protein becomes quiescent. (*8*) The cycle begins again.

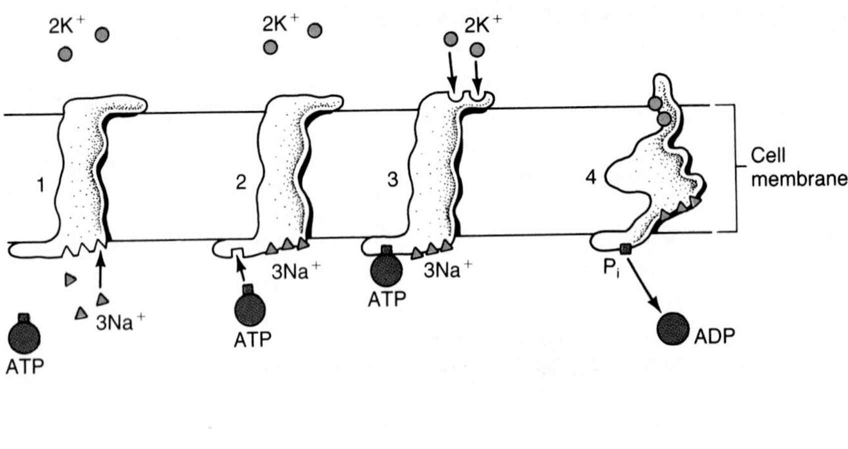

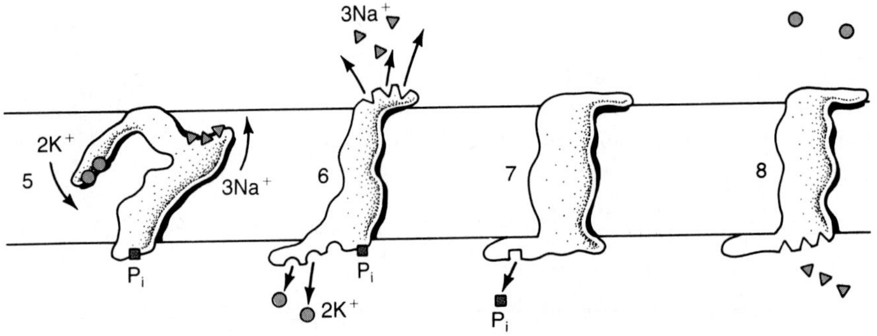

but no specific receptor shapes are evident. On the surface facing the cytosol, there are three sodium receptors and one zone that features ATPase activity (see figure 6.7). The protein's activity is keyed to the sodium receptors on the inner surface. As long as these receptors are empty, it rests quietly, nestled in the depths of the membrane. But when three sodium ions slide onto its receptors and lock into place, it swings into action (figure 6.7).

An ATP molecule is promptly bound and hydrolyzed, yielding its energy to the elements in the protein. Thus energized, the protein surfaces facing the interstitial fluid change shape. They shift to a configuration that will accept a pair of potassium ions, and when two such ions contact the surfaces, they are quickly bound. This triggers the release of the ADP segment of the ATP molecule, while the terminal phosphate group is retained by the protein. Now, utilizing the energy taken from the ATP molecule, the protein writhes into new configurations that move the ions across the membrane—the sodium ions to the exterior and the potassium to the cytosol surface. Three sodium ions are then released into the interstitial fluid, and two potassium ions are added to the interior of the cell. This three-for-two exchange of cations results in a net outward movement of one sodium ion and one positive charge each time the system is activated, thus maintaining the cellular interior in a negative condition with respect to the interstitial fluid.

The Resting Potential

The electrical potential across the membrane of living cells is known as the **resting potential.** It is, as we have seen, due to the differential distribution of sodium, potassium, and chloride ions, together with the nondiffusible anions in the cellular interior, and it is present in every cell that has been investigated. It is maintained with great care. In addition to the sodium/potassium pump, there are several other

Figure 6.8 Schematic rendering of a power supply to a typical American home. The electrons are concentrated at the power source; thus the potential energy (voltage) is applied there. There is little or no loss of potential as the electrons flow through the conductor, and they encounter their first real resistance in the house. This is where they must work to get where they are going, and this is where their potential energy is changed to heat, motion, etc. The electrons now flow back to the power source, where they are "pumped up" again.

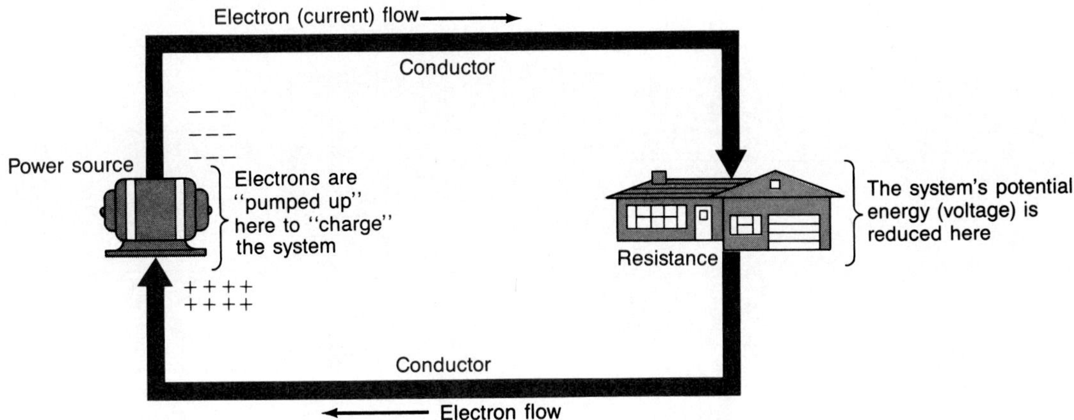

mechanisms that help support the resting potential, and this suggests that its uninterrupted existence must be very important. In some body cells its purpose is not always clear. It is almost certainly involved in the selective movement of materials into and out of the cell, but what other functions it may have are sometimes obscure.

The purpose of the resting potential across nerve membranes, however, is abundantly clear. The nervous system is a communications web, providing information about everything from internal water balance to the existence of food or danger miles away, and it uses electrical impulses to carry this information wherever it needs to go. The messages consist of voltage spurts produced by altering the membrane potential at specific intervals and under specific conditions.

Living organisms use a method of transmitting signals that is unlike anything used in man-made appliances—even computers. No engineer would ever dream up such an arcane method of signal transmission. In fact, if engineers were designing transmission lines to carry information between cities, the method used by our nerves would be extremely slow, extraordinarily cumbersome, certainly impractical—maybe impossible. Nevertheless, for the specific function they have to perform, nerves are as good in most respects as anything humans have designed, and the brain is a model of miniaturized efficiency, as we will see.

Transporting Electricity

In order to appreciate the job that living systems do, perhaps it might be best to compare our body's transmission lines to those that humans build. Not only will it demonstrate the importance of scientific investigation, but it also gives us a chance to use our brand-new knowledge of volts, current, and resistance.

The wires that bring electrical power into our homes carry it from a source that may be miles away, and the current flows through these wires from one end to the other (figure 6.8).

The workings of such a system are a bit more complex because of the presence of so many appliances, but fundamentally, its principle is the same as the circuit depicted in figure 6.B. Instead of using the chemical energy of a battery to provide electrons and to "pump them up," electrons are drawn from the ground and concentrated by generators in our power-producing plants. They move into wires, because the wires are conductors and thus offer the quickest and easiest route for them to follow. Electrons flow through these miles of wire just as they flow through the wire in a flashlight, and when they enter our homes, they encounter resistances that hinder their movement in the same way as the bulb in a flashlight hinders their movement. In overcoming these resistances, they work for us.

Figure 6.9 Where potential energy is lost when work is done. (*a*) Measuring gravitational potentials between points *1*, *2*, and *3* would show negligible differences, and for all practical purposes, their potential is the same. The potential at *4* is considerably lower, however, and measuring between *1* and *4*, *2* and *4*, or *3* and *4* should show a large value. (*b*) A side view of *a*, showing the gravitational gradients. (*c*) An electrical drawing of an electrical gradient equivalent to the gravitational gradients in *a* and *b*. Voltages at *1*, *2*, and *3* are all the same. The voltage at *4* will show the energy change.

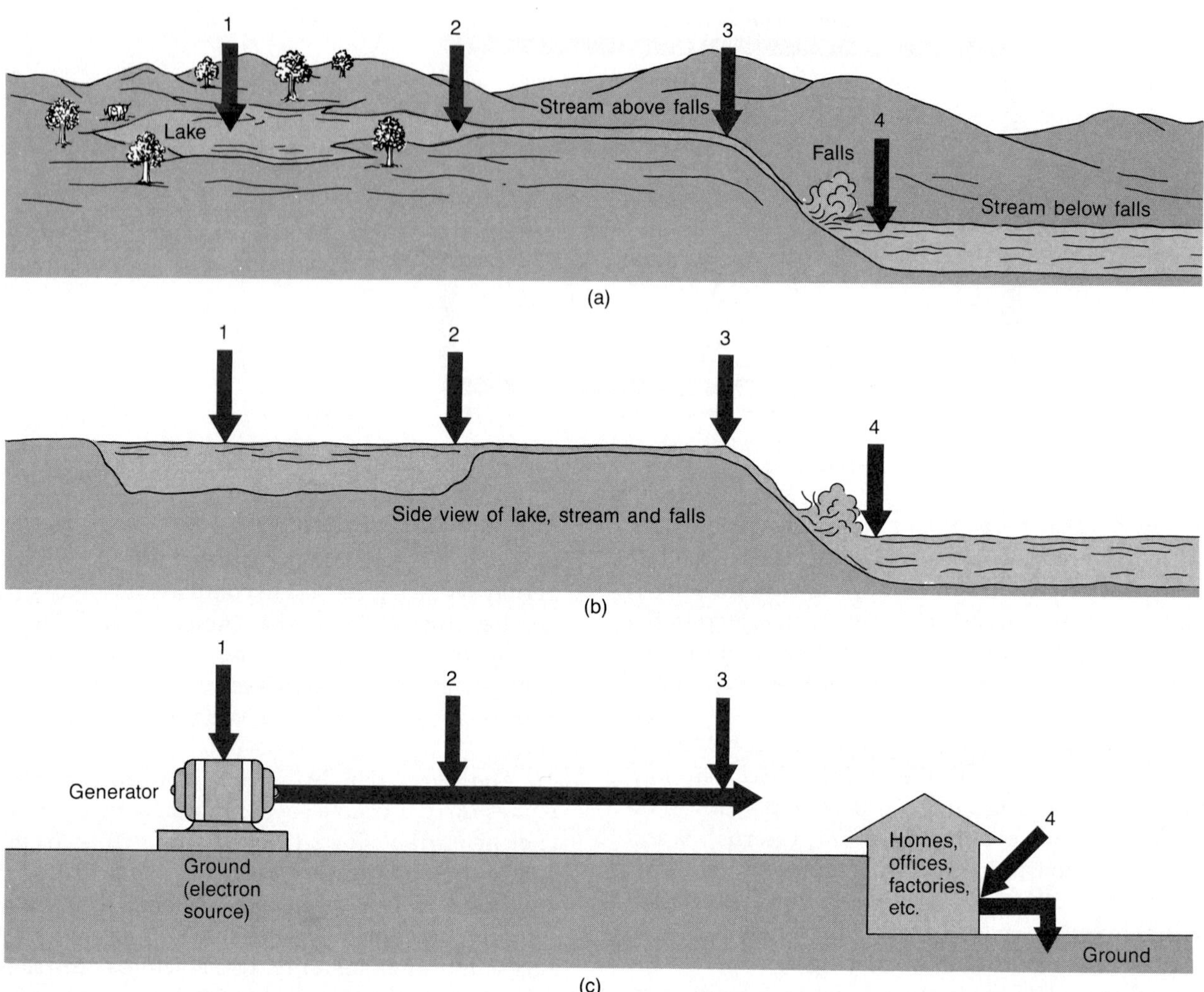

Figure 6.9 shows the circuitry rendered in a slightly more generalized schematic form.

Assuming the wire carrying the current is a good conductor, we can demonstrate where the potential energy is lost by using a voltmeter and placing the leads at various points along the circuit. If we take the two leads of a voltmeter (an instrument designed to read electrical potential differences) and put one of them at point 1 in figure 6.9*c* and the other at point 2, we would read zero. There is no potential difference between those two particular points, because the current has had no resistance to overcome as it flowed from point 1 to point 2. In a way, it is like water in a lake. As long as the water remains in the lake, there is neither loss nor gain of energy, because potential energy is about the same everywhere. When a waterfall is encountered, however, the water immediately loses potential energy as it drops to a new level. As a consequence, there will be a measurable difference in potential energy between the two water levels (points 3 and 4, figure 6.9). Similarly, in an electrical circuit, a difference in potential should appear between points

3 and 4, because the system has encountered resistance, and some energy (voltage) has been lost overcoming that resistance. Because the potential is highest after leaving the generator, and because there is a conductor offering to carry the electrons from a high potential to a lower one, electrons will flow through the wire from end to end.

Information and Current Flow in Telephone Lines

Our cities and countryside are filled with transmission lines that have been manufactured with the intention of using them to carry information from place to place. These lines are designed so that the flow of electricity will be as smooth as possible, resistance minimal, and distortion resisted. To this end, engineers have established a consistent and generally familiar series of criteria to which all transmission lines must adhere.

First of all, the core of the line must be the best conductor that is practical. This is important. The electricity being sent on its way must not waste its potential energy during the journey.

Secondly, the electrical messages must arrive at their destination in good condition. That is not as easy as it may seem. There is electricity everywhere. A functioning city literally sprays it into the atmosphere, adding its low-powered, rampantly scattered oscillations to the broad storage cells of enormous voltage that nature builds up and discharges randomly in shattering lightning bolts. If this so-called electrical noise were allowed to deluge the conductors without restriction, messages would be changed so completely that they would be indecipherable. So engineers block it by interposing a second conductor—a "shield" (see figure 6.10). This second conductor does not carry any information. Its job is to intercept all the electrical noise that might enter the wire and carry it somewhere else before it can get to the internal conductor and interfere with its coded signals. In addition, all transmission lines—copper, silver, or aluminum—are thoroughly wrapped in nonconductors, insulators that prevent the conductors inside them from touching each other and possibly exchanging information or "shorting out." Naturally, the best insulators are used for this purpose. A few years ago, that was rubber, but today our insulators are all man-made. Modern plastics do a remarkably good job, are easily obtained, and are much less expensive than rubber.

As a result, when we send electricity on its way from one place to another, the signals travel first-class. They experience little resistance, moving smoothly through top-notch conductors from one end of the line to the other, protected by special shields and insulators (figure 6.10).

Figure 6.10 A man-made transmission line. Current flows through power lines from end to end. If the transmission line happens also to be a telephone or telegraph line, the flow of information parallels the current flow.

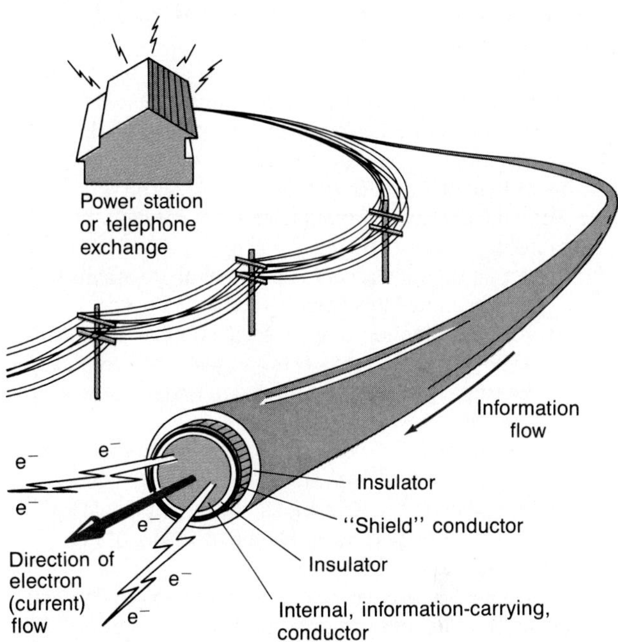

As it turns out, however, even the finest conductors have some resistance to electron flow. Hence over the large distances that we send electrical signals, there is always a small but significant loss of voltage. In addition, the best of shields cannot prevent all signals from entering—there is always some electrical noise that can penetrate and become part of the transmitted signal. The result is that when the information sent through wires finally arrives at its destination, the signal is weaker than it was when it left, and it is always slightly distorted. That really is no big handicap. With compensatory circuits, we can filter out the noise and restore the original shape to the signals. It is even easier to amplify them to where they can drive the speakers in our radios or telephones. These methods work with tremendous efficiency. People can send messages, pictures, music—anything they want to send—around the world almost instantaneously. How can you do better than send current through the finest conductor? How can you improve on the best insulators? It all seems so relentlessly logical it is hard to imagine doing it any other way. How, we might ask, could anybody—including nature—possibly improve on such a system?

We will see how it is done in chapter 7.

Summary

Energy

Energy can be neither created nor destroyed. It is defined as *a capacity for performing work.*

I. Work. Work is done whenever a force is used to move something. If there is no motion, there is no work.

II. Work vs. Energy. Whenever you perform work on something, you increase its energy content. There is more than one kind of energy.

III. Potential Energy. Potential energy is energy that is stored.

- A. A bag on a table contains potential gravitational energy. It has the potential to fall to the floor.
- B. A boat at the top of a waterfall contains potential energy. When it goes over the falls, that potential energy changes to kinetic energy, the energy of motion.

IV. Free Electrons. Free electrons are electrons that don't belong to any particular atomic nucleus. They move from nucleus to nucleus. Since movement is taking place, work is being done. Metals have lots of free electrons.

V. Random Electricity in Metals. Electrons are charged particles. Whenever charged particles are moving, electricity is flowing. Electricity is therefore flowing in all metals, all the time.

VI. Electricity at Work. Making electricity work for us means coercing electrons to flow in a given direction. Concentrating electrons in a given place means they will flow from that zone to a zone where they are not as concentrated.

VII. Electrical Potential

- A. If a zone of concentration is established, there must be a zone where there is a dearth of electrons.
- B. The zone of concentration will be highly negative. The other zone will be highly positive.
- C. As long as these two zones exist, there will be a tendency for movement. That tendency represents potential energy and is known as voltage.
- D. Voltage is stored electrical energy; therefore voltage is electrical potential.

Voltage and Amperes

A volt is a unit of electrical potential. A volt represents a difference in energy content between two points or zones.

Current Flow

Voltage is required to produce a current flow. If current flow is to continue, there must be a means of maintaining or rebuilding electrical potential.

I. Generating Electricity. Energy is used to maintain the electrical potential. Now something is needed to take the electrical current where we want it to go.

II. Conductors. Electrical energy is utilized to do work. To do work, it must be directed toward a definite goal. This means a pathway must be provided for current to flow along. The pathway is a *conductor.*

- A. In order to provide a path of very little resistance, a conductor must have lots of free electrons.
- B. Materials that have lots of free electrons are metals. Metals are the best conductors.

III. Resistance

- A. When electricity is involved, work represents a resistance that the flowing particles must push aside to get where they are going.
- B. By providing a pathway to take electrical current where we want it to go, we can make it work if we place something in the pathway that is not a conductor.
- C. Placing a high resistance in the pathway may result in the generation of frictional heat as the electrons rush through. This could make a glow that would light a room.

V. Ohms, Volts, and Amperes

- A. Ohms are units of electrical resistance. In most home circuitry, resistances are measured in thousands of ohms (kilohms) or millions of ohms (megohms).
- B. Volts are units of electrical potential. In home circuitry, voltages are on the order of 110 to 115 volts.
- C. Amperes (amps) are units of electrical current flow. In home circuitry, current flow is usually measured in thousandths of an ampere (milliamps).

Biological Electricity

Biological electricity is similar to man-made electricity in many ways. It differs mainly in the charged particles that make up current flow.

The Cell as a Battery

I. Constructing a Biological Battery. By arranging the ions inside and outside of a living cell, a battery can be produced.
II. Potassium. Potassium is highly concentrated inside cell membranes. Its concentration is maintained by several forces, including active transport.
III. The Chloride Ion. Chloride distributes itself according to the forces that are present.
IV. The Sodium Ion. Sodium does not distribute itself according to the forces that are present, because the plasma membrane resists its movement. Sodium is highly concentrated outside the cell. It is not abundant inside.

In Living Cells

I. A Differential Equilibrium. The differential distribution of diffusible ions results in an electrical potential gradient across the cell membrane. This potential gradient is maintained, at least in part, by active transport.
II. The Sodium/Potassium Pump. The active mechanism that maintains the potential moves K^+ and Na^+.

The Resting Potential

The voltage across the membrane is known as the resting potential.

I. Transporting Electricity. Man-made electricity (flowing electrons) moves through metal wires. Such current flow can carry messages or force a resistance aside (do work). It flows through metallic conductors because it is running "downhill," from a zone where there are lots of electrons to a zone where there is a shortage of electrons.
II. Information and Current Flow in Telephone Lines
   A. The best conductors practically available are used to transport the current. Even the best conductors dissipate some of the potential energy as the current moves through them.
   B. The best insulators available are used to wrap the conductors to prevent power loss and to avoid picking up atmospheric electrical "noise." Even the best insulators permit loss of some power and cannot block out all the electrical noise in the atmosphere.

Review Questions

1. Define the following words:
   a. energy
   b. work
2. How is work related to energy?
3. What is potential energy?
4. Describe what is meant by a "free" electron?
5. How is it possible to concentrate an electrical charge in one place in a piece of metal?
6. Describe voltage in terms of energy.
7. What is current flow in ordinary electrical wires? What keeps it flowing?
8. What is a conductor?
9. What is a resistance? How is it related to current flow and voltage?
10. Describe the development of the electrical charge that exists across the membrane of our cells. Be sure to mention:
    a. the primary ions involved.
    b. the forces that help keep them in place.
    c. the amount of resistance to movement that the cell membrane represents.
11. What is the approximate value of the potential gradient that is developed across the membrane of human body cells?
12. Describe the resting potential to the best of your ability.
13. Aside from the cell membrane, what is the primary mechanism responsible for maintaining the resting potential at a constant level? Describe its function.
14. How are man-made electrical transmission lines usually constructed? What are the advantages and disadvantages of the various components that are used?

Chapter 7 Nerves and the Nervous System

Study Hints

The similarity between nerves and telephone lines has long been recognized. Yet as we know from the previous chapter, telephone lines, despite all our efforts and precautions, cannot carry messages great distances without some revitalizing of the messages when they reach their destination.

We already are aware that man-made current and biological current do not feature the same charged particles in motion. This chapter will compare the techniques humankind uses to transmit a message with the methods that nature has devised to transmit messages within a living body.

When reading this chapter, pay particular attention to:

1. the relationship between membrane permeability and the electrical potential that exists across it. This is extremely important. It represents a fundamental relationship that must be clear in order for you to understand how electricity is manipulated in the nervous system.
2. where the voltage gradients exist in neurons.
3. which direction the current *must* flow.

Objectives

When you have finished reading this chapter, you should:

1. know the direction of current flow in neurons and be able to explain why it flows the way it does.
2. understand how information moves along neurons from one end to the other without any alteration or diminution of the signal.
3. be able to explain the relationship between membrane permeability to sodium and membrane potential.
4. be able to explain how that relationship is involved in the development of an action potential.
5. know which type of current is responsible for the various events that take place during development of, and recovery from, an action potential.
6. know how Schwann cells contribute to an increase in neuronal conduction velocity.

Nerve cell bodies in the central nervous system.

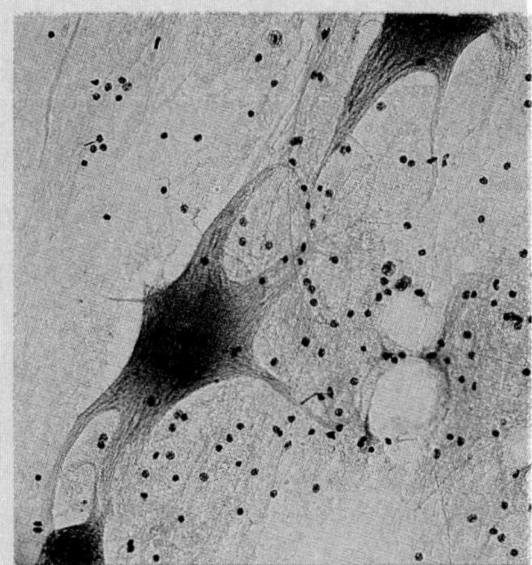

Introduction

The nervous system is one of the two primary controlling systems in human beings, the endocrine system being the other. Like any decent control system, it can receive information concerning the parameters that it controls and can send instructions to maintain or to modify each parameter. Information is acquired from countless neural sentinels that are posted at strategic points throughout the body, and communication is effected by means of coded electrical signals. Masses of neurons collate all input and integrate it with stored information. Then instructions are sent to the effector organs that control these parameters. As with the input signals, the outgoing instructions are relayed in the form of coded electrical messages.

We are not always aware of these operations. When we are, we can control the integration of all information, and we can "write" the instructions that are sent to the various effector organs that will be used to make corrections or to retain homeostasis. Most adjustments that are required in our day-to-day living processes, however, are made without our realizing it. An enormous number of nervous operations take place every second beneath our level of consciousness. Usually, we are unaware that problems exist or that steps have been taken to correct them. When our blood pressure drops a bit too low or gets a trifle higher than it should, corrections are made automatically. When our oxygen intake becomes slightly less than optimal, our respiration rate increases without any conscious effort, and when our body water becomes a bit more abundant than necessary, mechanisms handle the excess without our realizing it. We become aware of the accomplishment only when we are informed that the operations are complete and our bladders are full.

Neural adjustments throughout our body take place constantly, which means there is a steady flow of electricity, and electrical codes are flashing back and forth within us at a mind-boggling rate. The overall operations are unbelievably complex and are not only beyond the scope of this book, they are beyond our current knowledge. Maybe not beyond our ability to learn, however. In attempting to understand how the nervous system works, scientists have started at the bottom, and they are currently working their way to the top. We will start at the bottom also, with the parts of the nervous system that form the functional units—the **neurons.**

The Functional Unit—The Neuron

Morphology

There are many kinds of neurons in the vertebrate nervous system, especially in the mammalian one. Outside the central nervous system, in the body's periphery, there are two basic types, sensory and motor, and nearly all can be fitted into one category or the other (figure 7.1). The central system's neurons are more diverse. A simple examination of the brain's gray matter can show a startling array of shapes and sizes. It would appear, however, that these variations, despite their apparent magnitude, are not fundamental in nature. They seem, rather, to relate to the location of the cell anatomically and to the job it has to do within the body. Nerve cells everywhere, despite the different shapes they have assumed, all seem to be variations on a central functional and morphological theme. The major anatomical features of large, peripheral nerve cells (figure 7.2) seem to be common to all, and they all seem to relate to similar aspects of neuronal function.

A typical peripheral motor neuron is illustrated in figure 7.3. Such neurons are often used by physiologists to illustrate neuronal form and function, because features common to all are present and clearly visible. It is easy, for instance, to separate it into the four major zones common to all neurons.

The Cell Body (Soma; Perikaryon)

The **cell body** or **soma** is the focal point of the cell. This is where the greatest cellular mass is located, and this is where all the controls are centered. It is also the part of the neuron that features the most astonishing variations. In the brain and spinal cord, neuronal cell bodies often exhibit shapes that resemble everything from exploding fireworks and daffodils to jellyfish and gift boxes. Outside the great mass of the brain and spinal cord, in the area known as the **neural periphery,** neuronal morphology tends to be less variable, and the variations that do exist are less garish and a good deal more conservative. This is partly because the environment tends to be more uniform in the periphery and partly because neuronal function varies less.

Figure 7.1 The three neural types found in peripheral areas of the human body. They are shown in relation to the spinal cord. Two of these are motor neurons. Arrows indicate the direction in which nerve impulses travel. (CNS = central nervous system; PNS = peripheral nervous system.)

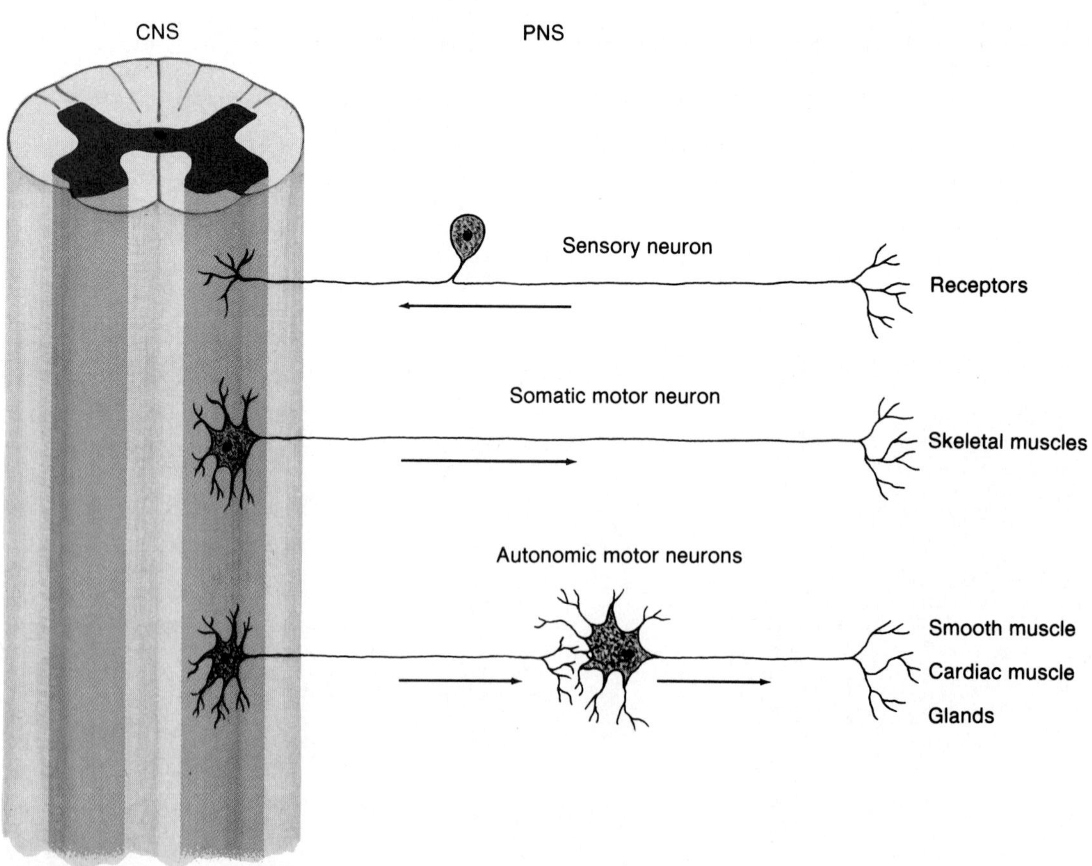

The soma of peripheral nerves is often a rough spindle shape with numerous projections poking out into the surrounding medium (figure 7.3). All the intracellular organelles are present—mitochondria, Golgi apparatus, microtubules, lysosomes, and so on. All of them—including the nucleus—are in the cell body, and only a few are found elsewhere. The cell body, therefore, is where the operations of the cell are programmed and orchestrated, and it is also where most of them are carried out. The rough endoplasmic reticulum and its associated ribosomes are clearly visible under light microscopes; hence it was located early in neurophysiological research. Although its function was unknown, it was given the name **Nissl** or **tigroid substance** (the latter because of the stripy appearance it often gave the soma). As is the case with the rough ER in other body cells, the Nissl substance is where amino acids are linked together to synthesize the neuronal proteins.

Since the cell body contains all of the neuronal DNA, it is critical to the continued existence of the entire neuron. If the cell body should be destroyed, the entire neuron withers and dies. On the other hand, as long as the soma remains intact, the neuron can usually survive damage to other cell parts.

Figure 7.2 Peripheral neuron types, classified according to function: A peripheral motor neuron (*left*) and a peripheral sensory neuron (*right*).

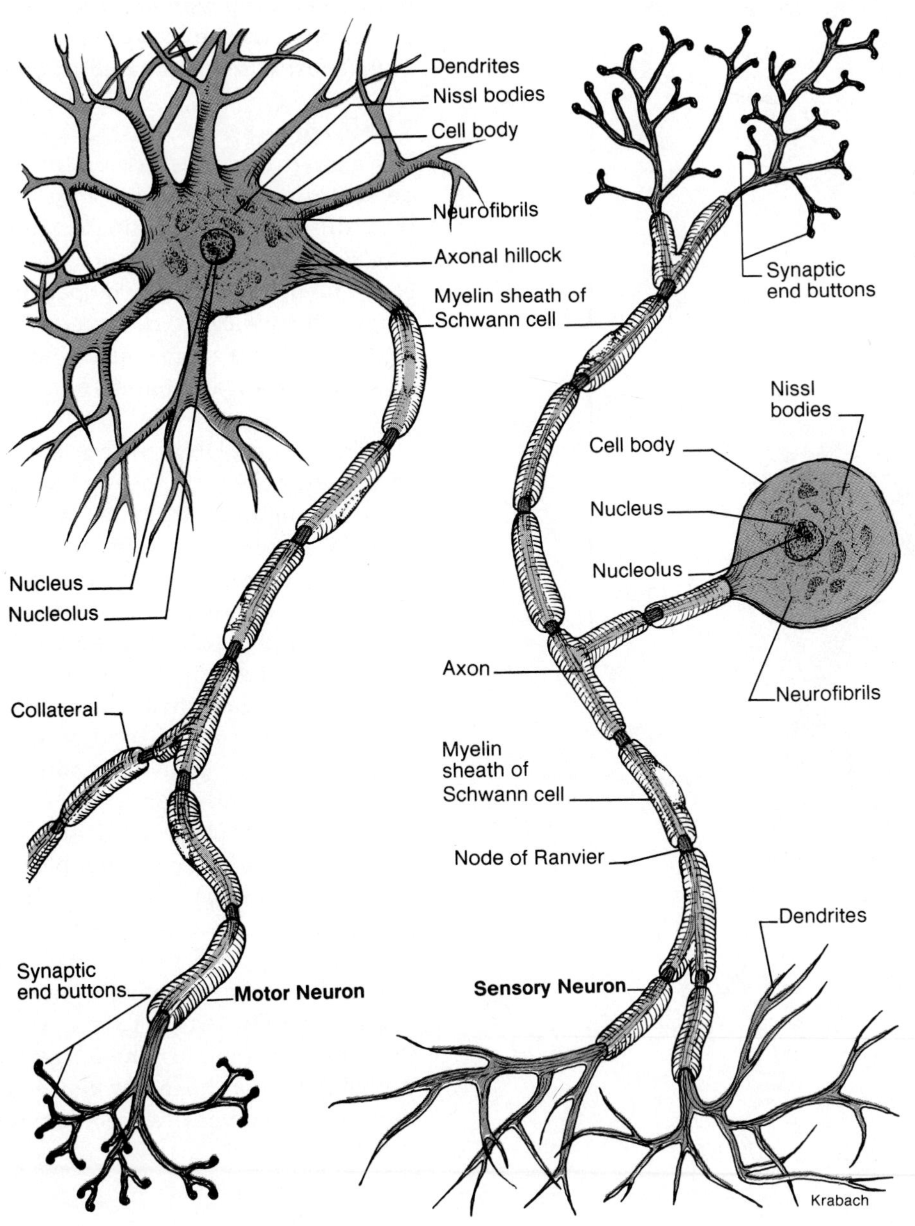

Figure 7.3 The parts and major zones of a peripheral motor neuron.

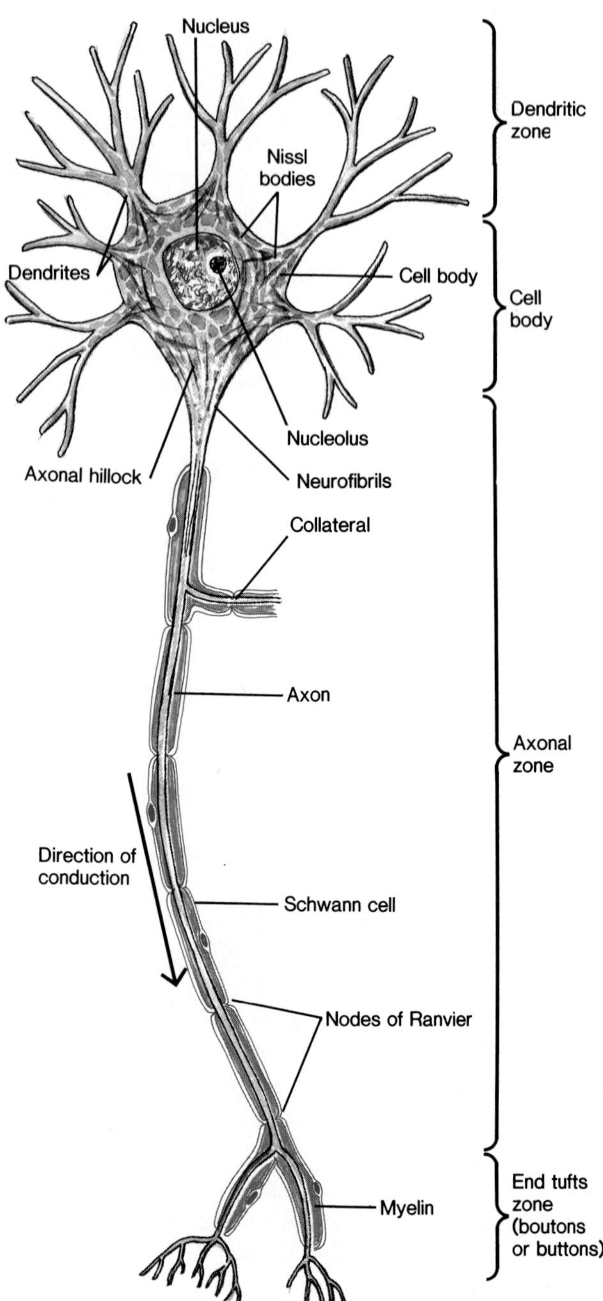

Dendrites

The **dendrites** are cytosol-containing fibers that project outward from the cell body. They vary in number from cell to cell. Some neurons have only one or two, while in others they may cover the somal surface (figure 7.3). Their surface consists of a typical lipid and protein membrane, and within, the cytosol contains a few organelles—mainly mitochondria. Nissl substance is sometimes present, usually at the broadened base of the dendrite, which is essentially just a protoplasmic bulging of the cell body. Broad bases are typical of dendrites, and the diameter tends to decrease the further it gets from the main mass of the cell.

Dendrites are responsible for accepting information from outside the cell—usually from other neurons—and passing it into the neuron for further processing. In the periphery, dendrites tend to be quite short when compared to the axons.

The Axon

The **axon** is the transmission line of the neuron. Like dendrites, axons are extensions of the cell body, but they differ both functionally and morphologically. Their most obvious morphological difference is their constant diameter and, in peripheral nerves, their length. Not all axons, however, are long—some axons in the brain are mere nubs—but short or long, they all share certain anatomical and functional characteristics.

There is no DNA in the axon, and there is some controversy over whether or not it contains any RNA. Current literature seems to suggest that there is ribosomal material present, and if that is correct, then obviously there is RNA in the axon. In any case, the thoroughly organized Nissl substance so common in the soma and dendrites is absent.

The axon emerges from a zone on the cell body known as the **axon hillock,** so called because there is usually a tiny, cone-shaped bulge in the cell body at that point. The axon originates at the summit of this tiny hill and shoots out toward its target from there. In motor neurons of the somatic system, the axon can extend for considerable distances. There can be tremendous variation in both the length and diameter of nerve axons. Depending on the cell it emerges from, an axon can range from less than a half-micrometer to more than 20 micrometers in diameter and can vary in length from a couple of micrometers to more than a meter. The longest axon in humans is probably that of the motor neuron that innervates the muscle that moves the great toe. It emerges from the base of the spinal cord and runs down the leg and into the foot. In a tall man, such axons might be four feet long.

The fact that axons contain neither DNA nor Nissl substance means that if an axon is damaged, it must look to other cell parts for help. The cell body contains the organelles necessary for repair, and should any part of the axon be completely separated from the cell body, there is no way it can sustain itself. Axonal damage often does occur, and when it does, it is not uncommon for great chunks of axon to die and be absorbed. It does not, however, necessarily mean that the neuron is permanently out of action. Overhaul can often take place, although it is usually a pretty slow and involved process. The mechanism of regeneration will be discussed later in this chapter.

Buttons (End Tufts, Brushes, Boutons)

The buttons represent the terminus of the axon. They are designed to translate the information carried along the axon into a message that can be transmitted to the next axon in line or to the effector organ in the circuit. They are as variable in morphology and abilities as in their names.

Neuronal Types

Morphological Classification

Neurons can be classified according to their morphological variations: specifically, the number of projections that emerge from the cell body and which way they go (see figure 7.4).

An **intermediate** or **connecting neuron** with a spherical soma, no dendrites, and a single, short axon would be considered **unipolar** (not shown).

Some neurons have a single dendrite extending away from the cell body and an axon extending out in the opposite direction (figure 7.4). Such neurons, common in the retina of the vertebrate eye, are **bipolar neurons.**

Primary sensory neurons are considered to be **pseudounipolar,** because while there is only a single extension running from the cell body, it splits in two immediately after it leaves, forming a T, with the new extensions running perpendicular to the original.

A typical motor neuron is best termed **multipolar,** because it has many projections, all but one of them dendrites, which cover about half of the surface. The single axon projects away from the cell body, usually in a direction opposite that favored by the dendrites. Most neurons in the central nervous system are multipolar.

Figure 7.4 Three different types of neurons, classified according to their morphological variations.

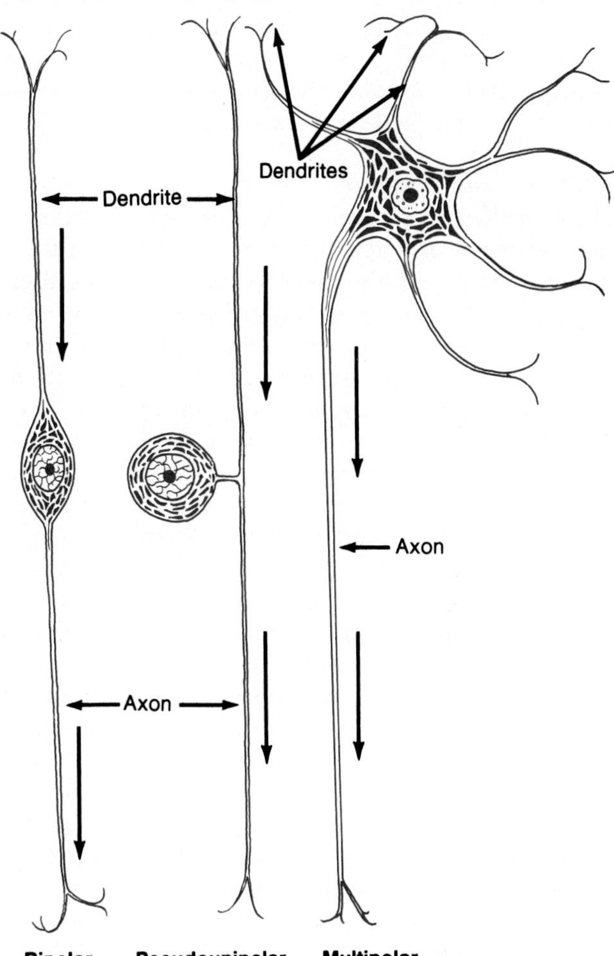

Functional Classification

Functional classification of nerves is usually accomplished by determining where they fit into the electronic circuitry of the body, where their impulses go, and what effects they have when they arrive at their destination.

Primary sensory neurons receive stimuli from the internal or external environment and carry information regarding these stimuli into the central nervous system. In the overall scheme of things, such neurons would invariably be at the beginning of the circuitry, and they would always carry impulses *into* the central nervous system. As a result, they are often referred to as **afferent** neurons (*afferent,* "carrying toward").

Motor neurons are the nerves that innervate muscle cells, carrying instructions from the central nervous system to activate the muscle tissue. Such neurons are usually the last ones in the neural circuit. Because they always carry impulses *away* from the central nervous system, they are also referred to as **efferent** neurons (*efferent,* "carrying away").

Afferent and Efferent

The terms *sensory* and *motor* are quite specific in their connotation. Motor neurons are so called because their impulses cause motion; sensory nerves derive their name from the fact that they deliver sensory messages. The terms *afferent* and *efferent* are more general in their meaning and more fluid in their application. In any given neural circuit, a person can pick a reference point. Any neurons carrying impulses toward that reference point can then be termed afferent with respect to that point, while those carrying impulses away would be called efferent. When discussing animal physiology, however, it is usually understood that the reference point is the brain and the spinal cord, and the terms afferent and efferent are used to describe peripheral neurons.

Not all efferent nerves are motor nerves. Many final neurons in peripheral areas of the body don't innervate muscles, and hence they cannot be termed motor neurons. Yet they are the last elements in their circuits, carrying impulses away from all reference points, and that makes them efferent neurons. An example of these would be those neurons that innervate body areas involved in the synthesis and secretion of hormones, digestive enzymes, or other needed chemicals. In keeping with this general terminology, it should probably be noted that the organs controlled by efferent neurons are, quite logically, known as **effector organs** (see figure 7.5). Similarly, not all afferent neurons are sensory in nature. Sensory nerves are certainly afferent, since they bring in sensory impulses toward all reference points. But they often pass their information to connecting neurons, any one of which would be afferent to the final nerve in the circuit.

Nerves

In body zones outside the central nervous system, axons very seldom travel alone. Groups of axons, running in the same general direction, are usually collected into bundles to form a **nerve.** These fiber bundles travel like super highways running cross-country, giving off collateral bundles periodically just as branch highways leave the main freeway. Nerves vary in size, naturally, according to the number of fibers they contain. They may be as small as a single micrometer in diameter or as thick as 30 micrometers.

Figure 7.5 A typical peripheral neural reflex circuit. The receptor organ converts a stimulus into nerve impulses that are carried into the spinal cord by an afferent fiber. In the spinal cord, the impulses are transferred to interneurons. Some interneurons carry the impulses into the brain for evaluation. Others transfer the signals to an efferent nerve, which carries them to a muscle fiber.

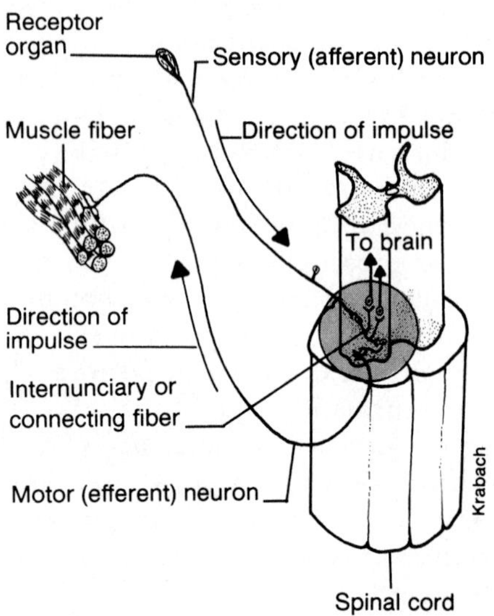

Within the nerve, individual neuronal fibers are rolled into bundles called **fasciculi,** which are, in turn, bundled together inside the nerve and surrounded by heavy layers of connective tissues known as **epineurium.** Each fasciculus is, in its turn, surrounded by insulating connective cells known as **perineurium,** and its delicate contents are thus protected just as glassware is often protected by being packed in popcorn or styrofoam chunks. Although bunched tightly together in nerves, the individual fibers can retain their internal privacy because of protective coats of a lipid-rich connective tissue called **endoneurium** (figure 7.6).

Spinal and Cranial Nerves

The brain and the spinal cord constitute the central nervous system (CNS), and the largest nerves in the peripheral areas of the body originate deep within the CNS. Those originating in the so-called higher centers—in the brain or brain stem—are known as **cranial nerves.** There are twelve pairs of cranial nerves, and they include the **olfactory nerve,** which is actually part of the brain itself. The **optic nerve** and the **auditory nerve,** both of which remain in the head, and the **vagus nerve,** which travels down the throat into the chest and abdomen, throwing off collaterals all the way to its end in the depths of the large intestine, are also cranial nerves. Nerves that originate within the spinal cord are, quite logically, known as **spinal nerves,** and there are thirty-one pairs of them.

Figure 7.6 A typical peripheral nerve with its branching collaterals.

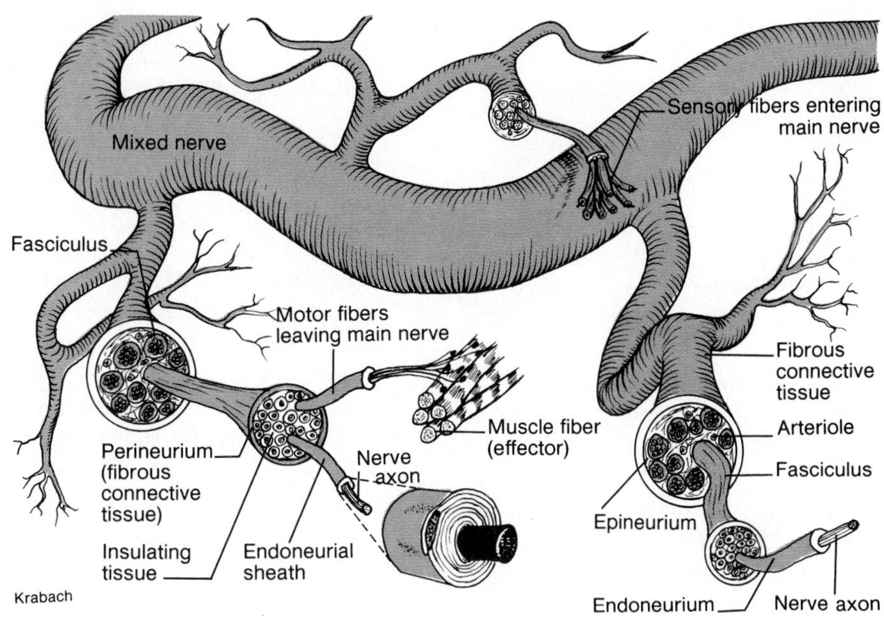

They spray out from the central areas and penetrate into every nook and cranny in the body. Both the cranial and the spinal nerves can contain sensory fibers, motor fibers, or both. Those that have both sensory and motor fibers are considered **mixed nerves.**

Neuronal Function (Neurophysiology)

Neurons are the cells that have been designed to carry messages from one part of the body to another. As the illustrations have shown, neurons are morphologically modified to handle the jobs they must do. Those needed to carry messages significant distances feature axons that have been stretched out until, in many cases, they superficially resemble the wires that carry electricity into our homes. These natural "wires" extend from the main body of the cell as if a glass filled with water were softened at one point and then drawn out into an elongated, thin tube (figure 7.7). Such a tube may be thin, but it is still hollow and still contains fluid.

Except for this fact—that their interior is filled with fluid—the axons that carry the electrical messages in our bodies are quite similar, structurally, to man-made transmission lines, and so there is room for a reasonable analogy. The cytoplasm that fills the interior of the elongated cell is a salt solution, and hence should be a reasonably good conductor—certainly a better one than the lipid membrane that surrounds it. (The lipid bilayer, like any fatty material, tends to insulate.) So the nerve axon is a biological "telephone line." It has a conductor for a core and is wrapped by an insulator, and that is essentially the structure of manufactured telephone wires.

Figure 7.7 Stretching a soft container to produce an "axon." Note that even though the tube may be stretched until very thin, it will still be hollow and will still contain the fluid that is in the main mass of the container.

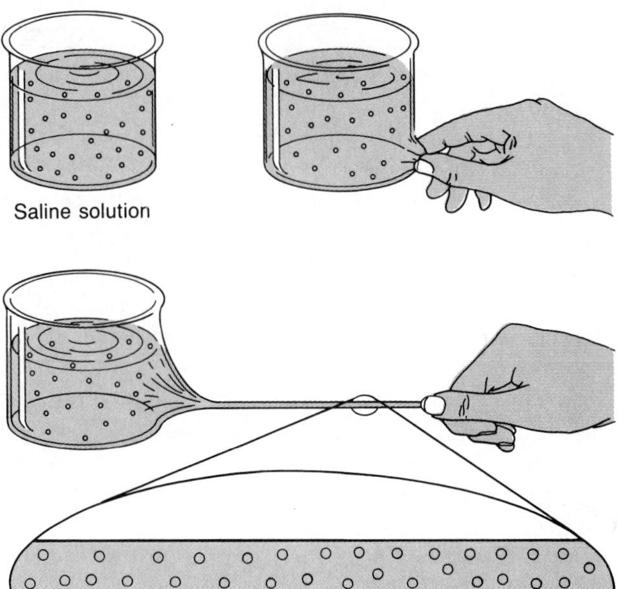

But nerve axons do not work like a telephone line at all! In fact, from a functional point of view, it is hard to imagine anything being more different.

Figure 7.8 A simplifed representation of a neuronal axon.

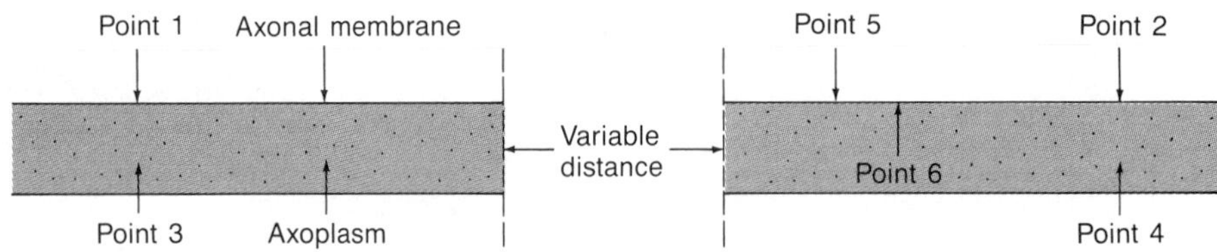

The Axon as a "Telephone Line"

The core of the neuron is a better conductor than the membrane, but as far as conductance is concerned, that is the best that can be said about it. Per unit length, its resistance is roughly ten million times greater than that of copper wire. As to the cell membrane—well, it is a better insulator than the salt solution that is inside it, but not much. Not only does it present about 1/10,000th of the resistance that an equal thickness of rubber would present, but it has holes in it . . . in other words, it leaks! One would assume, therefore, that any message sent along such a line would probably never arrive intact. It would either lose all its voltage to the high resistance of the fluid core or would suffer power losses through the insulator before going more than a couple of millimeters. Even if it should, by some miracle, manage to transmit a tiny fraction of its current from one end to the other, the message would certainly be distorted.

That is what trained engineers would think if one of their students put together a transmission line designed the way a neuron is designed. They would be right, too! If they planned to transmit signals through the nerve fiber from one end to the other in the way it is transmitted through manufactured lines, they could make no other prediction.

Neuronal Transmission

Yet the signals coming out of nerve fibers are not distorted. What is more, there is no loss of voltage as the information is carried from end to end along that awful transmission line. The signal that emerges from the end of a nerve axon is exactly the same as the signal that went in: the same voltage, the same wave shape—everything the same.

Considering the properties of a nerve fiber, this kind of result is not possible if the neuron carries the signal in the same manner as a man-made transmission line does. Obviously, then, neurons do not work the same way. Just how do they work? What properties do they have that permit them to faithfully transmit signals from end to end when they cannot conduct very well and insulation from outside interference is negligible?

Suppose we magnify the elongated "transmission line" of the nerve cell a little bit and examine some of the electrical properties it possesses (figure 7.8). Since information moves along the nerves from end to end, it seems logical to assume that this is the way the charged particles (current) will flow, too.

It is not hard to check that conclusion. Remember, current is pushed by voltage. It will not go anywhere unless it *is* pushed, and it goes *where* it is pushed. The logical thing, then, would be to check and see where the potential differences (voltages) exist in the axon. If the current is going to flow through the nerve as it does through a telephone wire, there must be a voltage difference between points 3 and 4 in figure 7.8, inside the fiber. A check, however, will find no voltage measurable there. There is no potential difference between points 3 and 4, because the charged particles inside the cell are not concentrated in any particular place. Their distribution throughout the interior of the cell is pretty much equal everywhere. This is true of potassium, of chloride, and also of sodium, and it means that *electrical current does not flow through the nerve fiber from one end to the other.*

Continuing the search for a potential difference in the nerve axon, we place the voltmeter's leads at points 1 and 3—from outside the fiber to inside.

And now, we can see the potential difference we have been looking for!

Common sense vs. science: This is a prime example of how important experimentation is. We have had spectacular success with our manipulations of electricity. We have made electrical appliances that will wash our clothes, cook our meals in seconds, provide us with home movies, and balance our checkbooks—we even have electrical machines that can *think.* It seems reasonable for us to be proud of our knowledge and to assume we know what we are doing. There are therefore many solid reasons to believe that nature's methods of transmitting information along wires are the same as the ones we have discovered or invented. Even the design of nature's transmission lines is superficially similar to our own. There is, therefore, every reason to assume that our nerves conduct signals just like electrical wires. Common sense and professional experience tell us so. Without the experiment, logic would leave us there . . . and we would be totally wrong!

Figure 7.9 A neural "transmission line." Information carried by a neuron does move along the axon from end to end, but the flow of current does not parallel it. Instead, current flows *through* the membrane of the axon on a path that is *perpendicular* to information flow. It is unusual, and certainly different from anything humankind has designed, but as the text points out, it may be the only way to transmit information without distortion or power loss.

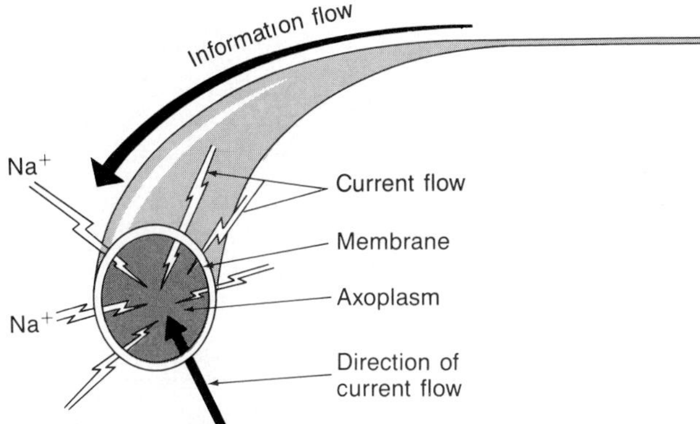

There is also a measurable voltage difference between point 2 and point 4—or points 1 and 3—in fact, anywhere *across* the axon membrane. As you might expect when you consider the characteristics of the elongated piece of beaker depicted in figure 7.7, the stretched-out, elongated axon of a nerve cell has the same properties as a cell. There is a *membrane potential* present—the axon interior is negative with respect to the outside.

Membrane Potential in Volts

The membrane potential has tremendous variability in living systems. Its strength depends on the organism, the cell involved, the cell's function, its location—all kinds of things. Two things, however, are constant from cell to cell and from organism to organism:

1. The interstitial fluid is our reference, and we define our reference as zero.
2. Regardless of the voltage value, the resting cell's interior is always negative when compared to the interstitial fluid.

For the sake of convenience, we will assign it a value of seventy-thousandths of a volt or 70 millivolts (mv). That is the average value that researchers obtained when working with the giant axon of the squid, and it is as good as any. The interior of the cell, therefore, is −70 mv with respect to the interstitial fluid, and thus −70 mv is the resting potential of the cell.

The location of the voltage indicates the only direction that current can flow in the nerve axon. Voltage exists only across the elongated transmission line of the resting nerve cell, so *if current flows at all, it must flow across the membrane* (see figure 7.9).

Current Flow vs. Information Flow

This discovery certainly made things difficult early in neurophysiological research, especially since there was no doubt that messages were carried *along* our nerve fibers from one end to the other. And it posed an interesting question: How could a flow of current across the membrane carry messages from end to end? And what kind of current was it that flowed across the membrane in response to the only voltage present? The reason silver and copper are such good conductors is that they have lots of free electrons. There are no free electrons to speak of in biological fluids, so whatever it is that might flow through the membrane, it would not be electrons.

Bioelectric "Current"

Current flow is a movement of charged particles—any charged particles—and across the membrane of a nerve axon, there are several such particles immediately available that would qualify. The nondiffusible anions, along with K^+, Cl^-, and Na^+, are all involved in maintaining the charge across the membrane, and theoretically, the flowing particles could be any or all of them.

Proteins: Proteins are part of the membrane's structure. They are anchored in such a way that their movement across the membrane is tremendously restricted and in any case, they are much too big to be efficient. Whatever else they may do in the axonal membrane, they will not be moving across it in response to changing electrical fields.

Sulfates and phosphates: Neither of these ions is able to diffuse out of the cell.

Potassium: The membrane permits potassium to move through it with relative freedom, but the gradients involved suggest that there will be no profound movement of this ion. The gradients are working against one another. The interior of the membrane is negative, and that should pull potassium inside, but there are so many potassium ions already there that diffusion pressure constantly forces some to leave. Potassium is flowing out of the cell because of the inward leakage of sodium, but it is so near its equilibrium potential that its tendency to flow is not very great. There is little potential for movement of potassium in a cell so close to equilibrium. Nevertheless, if the equilibrium changed, potassium certainly could move across the membrane.

Chloride: Of all the ions involved in establishing the membrane potential, chloride is closest to its equilibrium potential. As a result, there is almost no tendency at all for this ion to move, despite its being able to move through the membrane rather freely.

Sodium: Where sodium is concerned, the situation is very different indeed. Both the diffusion pressure and the electromagnetic potential want to push sodium ions into the cell, and the sodium ions would respond *if they could.* Under normal circumstances, they cannot—not in any significant numbers, at any rate. Their movement is restricted by the relatively impenetrable nature of the membrane and is opposed by the sodium/potassium pump.

Summarizing

There are many charged particles involved in maintaining the membrane potential, and several of them cannot be involved in bioelectric current flow. Proteins are out, as are the phosphates and sulfates that are present in the cytosol. They simply cannot diffuse through the cell membrane to the outside of the cell. Potassium and chloride could move, and should something happen to alter the membrane potential, they certainly would. But with the membrane potential as it is, their incentive to do is limited.

Sodium, on the other hand, has plenty of incentive. The necessary potentials are all present, and sodium is figuratively "champing at the bit," but there is a barricade preventing it from going anywhere except in small amounts.

That seems to eliminate everything, doesn't it? None of the charged particles appears to be going anywhere, and there are no free electrons available, yet there is no doubt that current *does* flow in the nervous system, so there is only one possible conclusion: some characteristics of the so-called resting membrane must change. Equilibria must alter or permeabilities modulate, or both.

Irritable Membranes

As it turns out, when nerve axons are preparing to send their messages, *everything* changes. It is all made possible by one enormously important feature of irritable membranes: The membrane's permeability to sodium is dependent on the membrane potential, and vice-versa!

An *irritable* membrane produces responses that are out of proportion to stimuli. If you stuck a pin into a cushion, you would get a proportional response. The surface might indent a bit, then the pin would penetrate. No additional energy would appear. If, however, you stuck that same pin into your cat or your sister, you would get an out-of-proportion response, along with lots of additional energy expended. That is what is meant by *irritable*.

At equilibrium, when the membrane potential is at its "normal" value, it is also relatively impermeable, and sodium leaks through at a very slow rate. If the membrane potential is increased, the membrane becomes *less* permeable to sodium. So if the potential were to increase from −70 mv to −80 mv, the membrane's permeability would decline, and the number of sodium ions leaking across the membrane would dwindle.

On the other hand, if the membrane potential were *reduced,* its permeability to sodium would be augmented. So if the membrane potential were to drop from −70 mv to −60 mv, permeability would increase, and there would be more sodium ions squirting into the cytosol. *The relationship between membrane permeability and membrane potential is the key to understanding how a signal develops on irritable tissue and how it is transmitted.*

Once again it is necessary to introduce some terminology. When a membrane is charged up to its normal "resting" potential, it is said to be **polarized.** Recalling the prefix "hyper," we can apply it descriptively to one alteration of membrane potential. When the charge across the membrane is greater than "normal," it is said to be **hyper**polarized. When the potential is at the normal, resting value, it is simply referred to as normal, and when it drops below normal, it is said to be **de**polarized. (The prefixes *iso* and *hypo* would be appropriate to describe normal potentials or below-normal potentials, but for some reason they are seldom, if ever, used.)

The Action Potential

There are a lot of things that can alter the membrane potential of body cells. Chemical changes around the membrane, osmotic changes, injury—all these could shift the established ionic equilibrium and produce a change in potential. However, when the membrane of a nerve axon is preparing to develop a signal and transmit it, nothing unnatural occurs. The sequence of events is pretty standardized, and everything is tied in to the relationship between membrane permeability to sodium and the voltage that exists across the membrane. The easiest way to describe what happens is to assume an artificial situation in which a microelectrode has been inserted into the axoplasm of a neuron (figure 7.10).

Microelectrodes are fairly common in biological research. They are made in several ways; one of the easiest is to obtain a stainless steel insect pin and electrically sharpen the tip until its point is about a half-micrometer across (see the following box). A pin that

Figure 7.10 A microelectrode in place within a neuron and generating a small electrical "field."

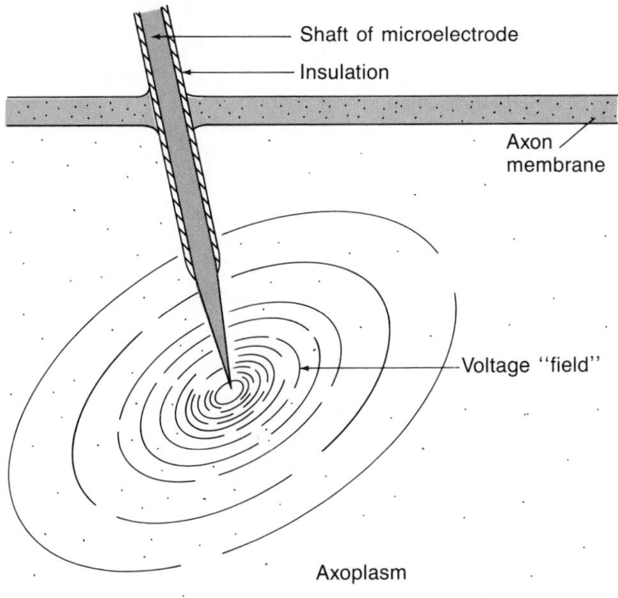

sharp can penetrate the skin of your hand without your even being aware it has happened, and it can easily slip through the membrane of a cell without doing any damage. Just as a wet needle can be thrust through a soap bubble without bursting it, microelectrodes penetrate cell membranes; instead of producing a hole that lets the cytoplasm leak out, the membrane seals itself around the pin, so no injury occurs. Such microelectrodes are insulated along their entire length except for the last micrometer or so; hence a voltage can be applied to the end sticking out of the cell and it will be felt at the electrode tip inside the cell. By applying different voltages to it, we can change the potential in the vicinity of the electrode and observe the effects of these changes on the axon.

The process of electrically sharpening stainless steel pins is actually quite simple. A step-down transformer, some alligator clamps, a carbon rod of the type used in old 35 mm motion-picture projectors, and a beaker filled with KCl solution are all that is needed. The transformer draws its current from an ordinary wall socket, and the alligator clamps are plugged into the transformer. One clamp is then attached to the carbon rod and the rod is immersed in the beaker. The second clamp is affixed to the upper tip of the insect pin and the transformer is turned to deliver about 25 volts. The tip of the pin is then inserted into the salt solution in the breaker and sharpened as the electrical current separates infinitesimal bits of steel from the pin each time its end becomes positive—sixty times a second.

Figure 7.11 Applying a positive voltage to the axoplasm.

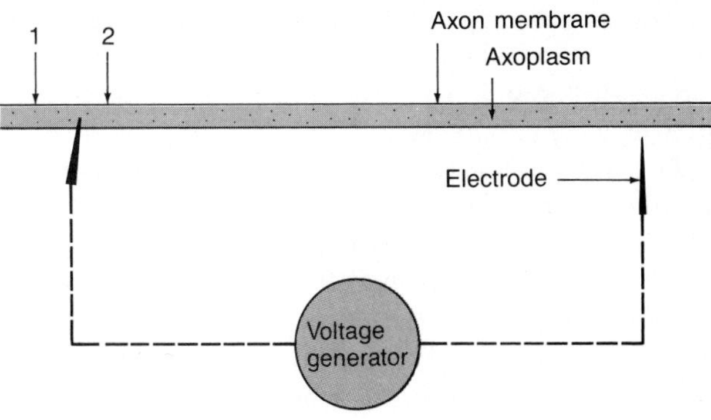

The first voltage applied to the electrode is a small positive one, and it reduces the membrane potential from −70 mv to −68 mv. Immediately the membrane adjacent to the electrode becomes more permeable to sodium, and sodium ions begin to flow through the membrane in greater numbers. This influx of cations naturally has a tendency to reduce the membrane potential even more, and it would, except for two things—the membrane's permeability to potassium, and the sodium/potassium pump. Membrane permeability is the major consideration. Because of the low-level activity of the sodium/potassium pump, its role when considering rapid voltage changes across the membrane is negligible.

As each sodium ion moves in, the negative charge inside the membrane is reduced by one. This reduces the attraction for potassium ions, and this reduced attraction permits diffusion pressure to thrust a potassium ion out into the interstitial fluid. This is usually what happens. The result is an exchange—sodium ions for potassium ions—and since the positive ions moving in are quickly balanced by positive ions moving out, the membrane potential stays under control. If a microvoltmeter probe were placed at point 2 on figure 7.11, it might be possible to detect a slight voltage change in membrane potential, but it would never be picked up at point 1. In this respect, the axon behaves as an electrical engineer would predict: on such a terrible transmission line, the signal is able to travel only a very small distance before losing all power.

The next step is to apply a little more positive voltage to the microelectrode and reduce the membrane potential to −65 mv. Naturally, this will increase the permeability of the membrane even more, and "sodium current" will start to flow through with even greater vigor. However, aside from being able to detect its effects a little further away, this increase wouldn't change things any more than the first voltage change had. Potassium's ability to scoot through the membrane is still greater than sodium's and so is able to keep things under control. As long as potassium can move out as fast as sodium can trickle in, the sodium/potassium pump can keep things under control, and the membrane potential will not change (figure 7.12*a*).

This situation continues as the positive voltage on the electrode is slowly increased. The interior can be exposed to an ever-increasing positive voltage, yet the homeostatic mechanisms working to maintain the membrane potential never seem to lose their grip on the reins. As the electrode's positive voltage slowly increases, a point is suddenly reached where this careful control abruptly vanishes. The membrane potential that seemed so unassailable simply disappears. As if the dam controlling the sodium floodwaters suddenly vanished, positive ions pour through the membrane into the axoplasm, and the negative membrane interior is inundated in a deluge of sodium current. The membrane potential drops until it disappears completely, but that doesn't stop the influx of sodium, and it continues to flood into the axoplasm, surging through in such quantities that it actually reverses the original membrane potential, driving the voltage up until the interior of the axon is +40 mv compared to the interstitial fluid (figure 7.12*b*).

What happened? The loss of control was like an explosion. Why should the membrane lose it so suddenly, and why was the loss so complete?

The Threshold Phenomenon

To understand what took place, we must examine membrane permeability again and note how the voltage changes affected it (figure 7.13). Keep in mind that the axon's membrane potential is tied tightly to the sodium permeability of that membrane. Applying a positive voltage to the electrode tip reduces the membrane potential, and as the graph shows, when the voltage across the membrane decreases, membrane permeability to sodium goes up. This means, naturally, that more positively charged sodium ions will be able to cross the membrane and enter the cell. As we noted above, the membrane can control this, within limits. There are countering forces available. Potassium can diffuse out, thus removing positive ions from the cell interior. These diffusive forces, coupled with the activities of the sodium/potassium pump, are able to maintain the negativity of the interior of the cell.

Figure 7.12 Ion flow when subthreshold and threshold voltages are applied to the axoplasm of a neuron.
(*a*) Subthreshold stimulus. The outflow of K^+ is equal to the inflow of Na^+. The ion pump works slowly but surely to restore normal ion distribution, and when the stimulus is removed, normal resting potential is quickly restored.
(*b*) Threshold. The influx of Na^+ is greater than the efflux of K^+, and K^+ movement cannot keep up with the inpouring of Na^+. As the positive potential inside the membrane goes up, the ion pump shuts down.

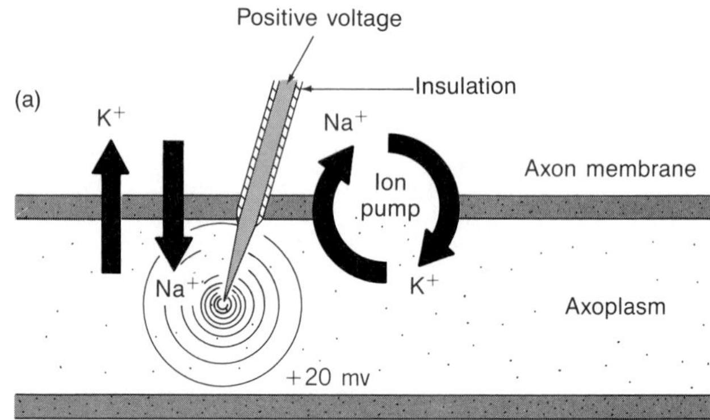

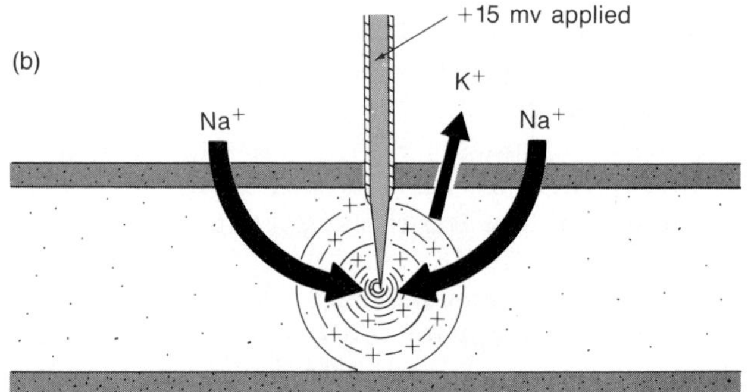

Sodium "Gating"

Ultimately, however, if the voltage applied to the electrode is steadily increased, a point is reached (arrow, figure 7.13) when the membrane becomes more permeable to sodium than to potassium. The membrane's characteristics change abuptly. Its resistance to sodium all but vanishes, and sodium suddenly is able to pour into the cell. This rapid increase in membrane permeability is referred to as the *opening of sodium gates* in the axon membrane. The analogy is an apt one, because the channels through which sodium can move are changeable. Sometimes they are closed, and sometimes, just like the gates in a fence, they swing open. During the period when the membrane is maintaining a steady potential, permeability of the membrane to sodium is small; hence the sodium "gates" are deemed to be closed, or nearly so. They open just a little when the resting potential is reduced slightly, and they open wide when threshold is reached (figure 7.14).

Figure 7.13 Voltage and permeability changes in a nerve axon prompted by a microelectrode inserted in the axoplasm.

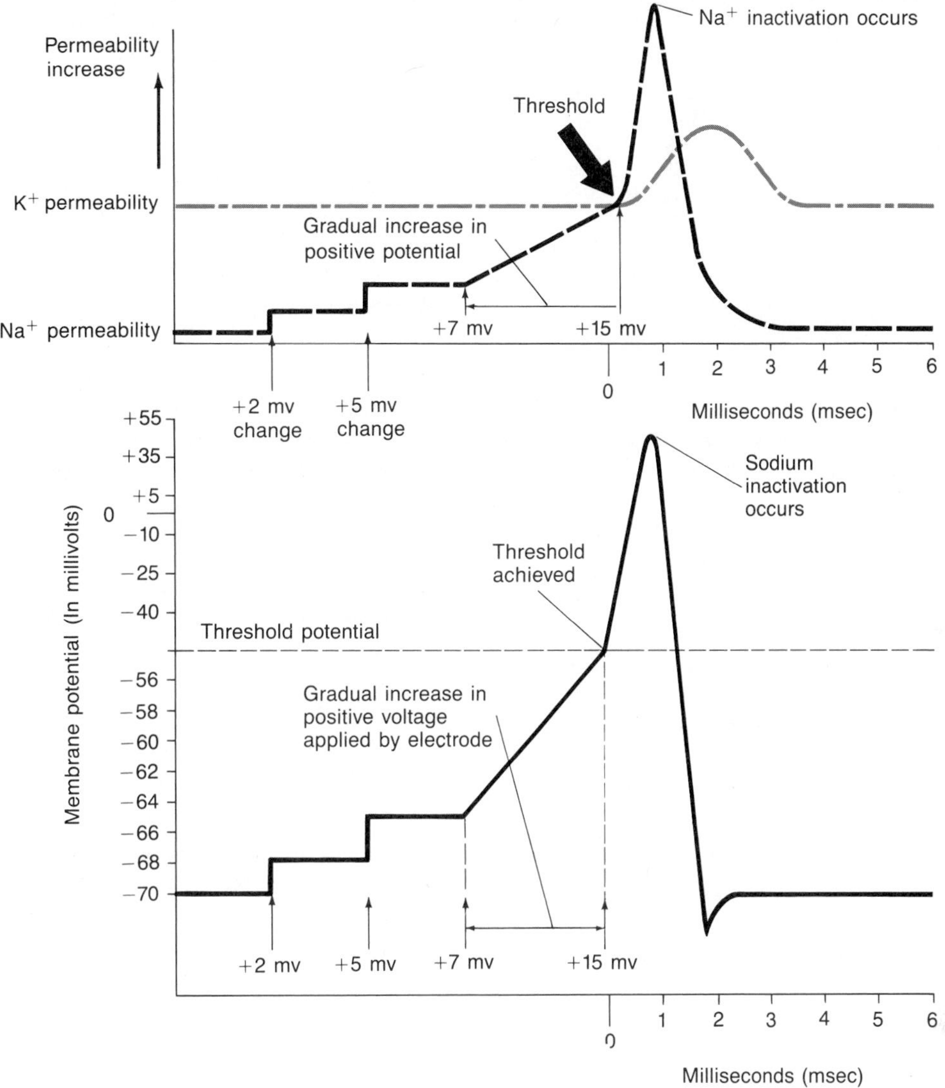

Figure 7.14 A pair of protein-lined channels in the axon membrane. The open channel is a permanent one. The gated channel is capable of considerable variation from completely closed to wide open. The membrane's sodium channels are thought to be "gated."

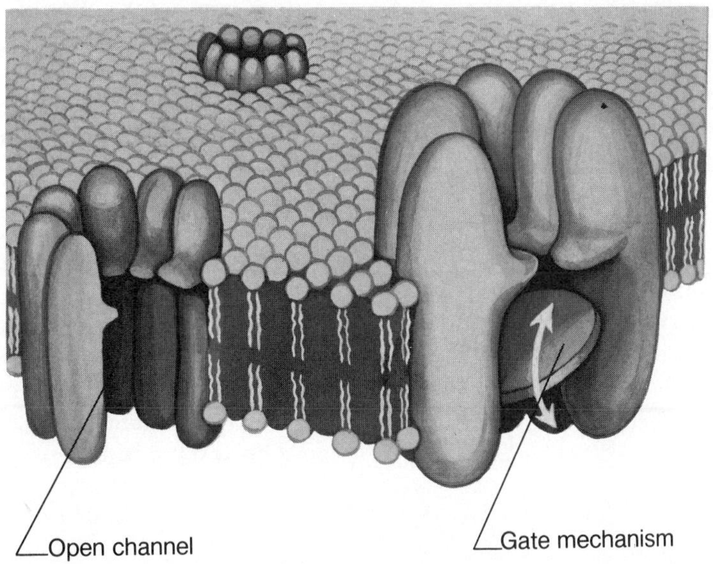

Figure 7.15 The positive feedback cycle that occurs in an axonal membrane during development of an action potential.

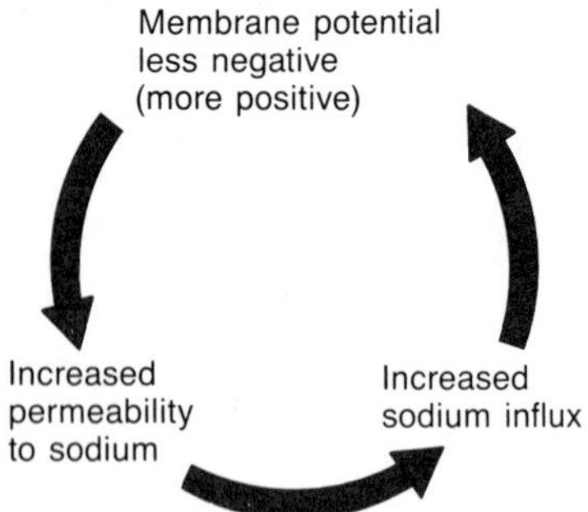

Positive Feedback

With sodium flowing in faster than potassium current can flow out, a process begins that is known as **cyclic positive feedback** (figure 7.15). Each event, as it occurs, strengthens the event that follows. Sodium ions pour in and increase the positive charge on the membrane's interior. This makes the membrane more permeable to sodium ions, so more sodium ions pour into the cell, making the interior of the membrane even more positive. That makes it still more permeable, and we have turned our full circle. To increase the effectiveness of the positive feedback process, the membrane's sodium/potassium pumps stop operating. Researchers are not sure what stimulates the shutdown of these pumps or how the pumps are stopped, but stop they do.

The Membrane Recovers

Sodium Inactivation

Since each event supports a succeeding one, an observer would be justified in asking why the feedback process doesn't either run amok or continue forever. After all, there is nothing in the cycle that suggests a means by which it could be stopped. There is a partial answer to that question. We know *what* happens, but we do not as yet know how or why. It is known, for instance, that when the interior surface of the membrane achieves a certain positive voltage, the membrane's sudden increase in permeability to sodium vanishes as fast as it appeared, a phenomenon known as **sodium inactivation** (figure 7.13).

The Role of Calcium

Researchers are not aware of all the things involved in this increased resistance to sodium flow, but ionic calcium apparently plays a significant role—at least in motor nerves. There is considerable evidence to indicate that calcium blocks the sodium gates in the membrane of motor nerves, effectively damming them up and preventing the ion from moving in either direction. But while it seems that calcium is probably involved, almost nothing more is known about the inactivation mechanism. Perhaps we would be justified in stating that the membrane is programed to shut off sodium current when the potential across it reaches a specific value. After all, the membrane is involved in life (if it's not, what is?), and surely there are receptors that are capable of determining when a critical value has been reached.

Repolarization

In any case and whatever the cause, the sodium influx suddenly drops almost to zero as membrane resistance increases. Just as suddenly, and at the same time, there is an increase in the already-substantial permeability to potassium. All these things have their effect.

1. Sodium stops moving in, so the interior of the cell stops becoming more positive.
2. Positive potassium ions are pouring out, making the interior more and more negative and speeding the return of the resting potential.
3. As the axon's interior becomes negative again, the ion pump switches back on to aid in restoration of the proper ionic distribution across the membrane.

The whole process, from the moment the membrane loses control over sodium until the resting potential is restored, occupies a time span amounting to less than 2/1,000 of a second (2 msec). The phenomenon has been given the name **action potential, spike,** or **nerve impulse.**

How Often Can a Nerve Fire?

Considering all the changes that occur during development of an action potential, it is reasonable to assume that the return of normal membrane potential to the membrane would not restore all conditions that existed before the action potential occurred. There is, after all, considerable shifting around of both potassium and sodium, and there is bound to be movement of other ions as the voltages change and the various equilibria subsequently alter. As a result, it is perfectly logical to expect that considerable time would be required to restore the lost K^+ to the neural interior and to pump out the excess Na^+.

It does require a little time to handle all these things, that is true, but an average neuron can fire many times before such changes become important. The electrical and diffusion events taking place during a single action potential involve such a tiny stretch of the axonal membrane, and the ionic movement is so infinitesimal, that the solutions inside and outside the axonal membrane are hardly affected at all. In fact, the actual number of involved ions is so small it is sometimes hard to believe. Experiments indicate that the presence inside the membrane of one sodium ion every tenth of a micrometer is enough to produce membrane depolarization and an action potential. An average-sized mammalian motor axon would have to fire about one thousand rapid action potentials with no rest in between just to double the number of sodium ions inside . . . and keep in mind, the sodium concentration inside a "resting" axon is *very* low to begin with.

In very small nerve fibers, sodium entering during action potentials can be a limiting factor. Axons running from pain receptors, for instance, are usually very fine, and if a pain fiber were to fire one or two dozen times in rapid succession, it would probably have to rest for a few minutes before it could fire again, even if the ion pumps were operating at top speed. This may partly account for certain subjective observations—that pain, for example, often seems to come in waves.

The Nerve Impulse

It is now time to examine the significance of the action potential. What is the point of such a phenomenon? What is it for?

If it were an isolated thing and occurred in just one place on the nerve axon, it wouldn't be much good for anything, but that is not what it does. Suppose we take another look at the nerve axon where the action potential took place and try to deduce what might happen to the rest of the axon as a result of its appearance at one point. What, for instance, would an action potential appearing in zone A of figure 7.16 do to the membrane at zone B?

Consider what has been discussed of action potentials and the ionic distribution that takes place around a membrane that has suddenly become "active." The threshold of our axonal membrane is −55 mv. That means that to get the membrane anywhere along the axon to fire an action potential of its own, all that is required is to lower its membrane potential from −70 mv to about −55 mv. That is a total change of +15 mv, and it is all you have to apply to the inside of the cell membrane—anywhere on the nerve axon—to get it to flare up. With an action potential present on the membrane at zone A, the membrane immediately adjacent, at zone B, is being exposed to an internal voltage of +40 mv. That means the interior of the membrane at zone B is being exposed to a voltage change of +95 mv, and that's more than six times what it needs to make it fire, so it fires.

Figure 7.16 Propagation of an action potential.

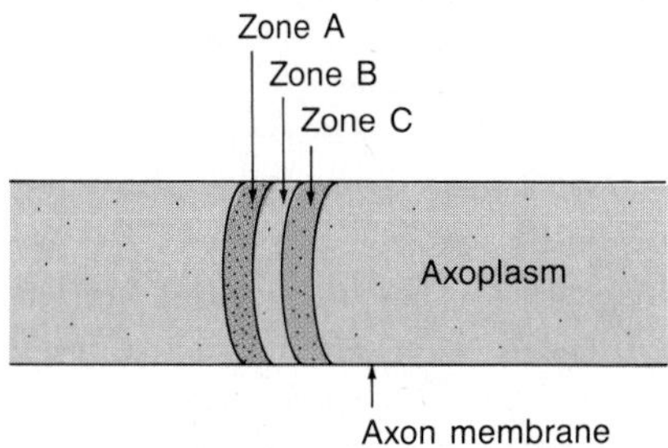

Once it fires its own action potential, the large positive potential inside the membrane at zone B is all that is required to set off zone C—and so on, all the way along the nerve fiber. Like a firecracker fuse with the flame moving down its entire length, each section catches fire as the hot flame touches it.

This is actually an easily predicted phenomenon. Just think about what happens when a piece of paper is set afire. Everyone has done this, and everyone knows what happens, but the reasons are not often considered. When a flame is applied to a piece of paper, the paper begins to burn. It burns because a temperature of 451° F will set paper on fire. Four hundred fifty-one degrees Farenheit, therefore, is known as paper's *ignition temperature,* and as soon as the match flame makes things that hot, the paper will start to burn. If the match flame is removed from the paper, the paper does not go out. As we all know, it continues to burn. What everyone doesn't know is that it does so because paper burns at a temperature that is higher than 451° F.

Above-Threshold Phenomena

To put it into scientific jargon, the paper's combustion temperature is higher than its ignition temperature or combustion threshold. Paper burns at more than 1,000° F, and as it burns, it exposes the unignited paper right next to the flame to a temperature of 1,000° F. That is well above the combustion threshold of paper. All that unignited bit of paper needs to begin burning itself is a temperature of 451° F, and here it is, exposed to a temperature more than twice as high. Naturally, it is going to catch fire. Once it begins to burn, it exposes the paper next to it to a temperature of 1,000° F, so the next piece will begin to burn, and so on.

That is exactly what is happening when a nerve fiber produces an action potential, with voltage taking the place of degrees Farenheit. As each part of the membrane produces an action potential, it exposes the membrane adjacent to it to an internal voltage of +40 mv. All the membrane needs to fire itself is an internal voltage of −55 mv, and here it is, exposed to a voltage that is six times as high. Naturally, it is going to flare up into an action potential. When it does, it exposes the membrane next to it to an internal voltage of +40 mv, and so on.

As a result of these sequential activations, the action potential moves all the way along the axon, from end to end, producing the information-carrying phenomenon called the nerve impulse.

Refractory Periods

Absolute Refraction

In the meantime, what happens in the section of the nerve that has just produced the action potential? Look back at figure 7.16; what happens at zone A after zone B has begun to fire? Keep in mind that normal membrane potential is restored because of two rapid-sequence membrane phenomena—sodium inactivation and increased potassium permeability. The action potential, you will recall, occurs because of a surge of sodium ions across the membrane into the axoplasm. This produces a positive feedback cycle that could destroy the membrane integrity if permitted to run. Hence it is stopped by an outside source. That outside source is ionic calcium, and it inserts itself into the sodium channels in the membrane, plugging them and preventing any further movement through them. The positive feedback cycle thus ends with the sodium gates dammed by ionic calcium. This is the process of sodium inactivation, and if sodium is thus inactivated, it cannot penetrate the membrane at all. Obviously, if sodium cannot cross the membrane at all, there can be no action potential. So for a short time (less than half a millisecond) immediately following an action potential, *nothing* can induce that part of the membrane to fire a second time, simply because sodium cannot penetrate it. This half-millisecond time span is known as the **absolute refractory period,** and throughout its duration nothing short of physical damage to the membrane will permit sodium ions to penetrate.

Relative Refraction

During the absolute refractory period and for some time following, the membrane's permeability to potassium is much higher than normal (see the top graph, figure 7.13). Potassium, taking advantage of this state, is gushing out of the cell in its haste to reduce the internal positivity and restore the normal membrane potential. This increased permeability to potassium lasts a lot longer than sodium inactivation does, producing an interval following absolute refraction when the membrane is said to be **relatively refractory.** It is possible, during the relative refractory period, to overwhelm the increased potassium permeability and make the nerve produce a second action potential, but it's hard to do. During relative refraction, the threshold voltage is a good deal higher than normal, so an unusually high stimulus is necessary (see the following box).

Relative refraction clearly has an effect on the frequency at which any given axon wil be able to fire. Often the intensity of a stimulus is indicated by the frequency at which the neuron is firing, and when the stimulus intensity is extremely high, it can sometimes overcome relative refraction and cause the neuron to fire at unusually high frequencies. Stimuli of extreme intensity often indicate emergency situations, and bursts of exceptionally high frequency would thus inform the integrating areas of a possible emergency and permit a more effective response.

Both the absolute and the relative refractory periods have solid physiological reasons for existing. Consider figure 7.16. The action potential shows up at zone A and stimulates a subsequent discharge in zone B. When the action potential is peaking in zone B, it has died down at zone A, and you could legitimately wonder why the high voltage now in zone B does not stimulate zone A to start up again. After all, the discharge at zone B is going to cause zone C to fire, and if the voltage is high enough to stimulate such a potential at zone C, why not at A as well?

This is a very sound question—so sound that it didn't escape nature, and it is one of the reasons for the existence of the absolute refractory period. During the time that the action potential exists in zone B, zone A is refractory . . . the impulse *can't* be reflected backward. By the time zone A has recovered and sodium inactivation is shut off, the impulse has passed from zone B, and zone B is itself refractory.

Action Potential—Voltage, Not Current

By now, it should be obvious why we spent so much time and effort discussing current, voltage, potential energy, and all the other physical phenomena. The flow of information along a nerve axon is not like water flowing through a pipe or electricity rushing through a wire from end to end carrying a telephone message. Instead, what seems to travel along the nerve axon is a wave of voltage change. The information is carried from end to end, but current flow is into and out of the axon, not along it.

Figure 7.17 Transmission of an action potential. (*a*) The flow of explosions as each firecracker on a single fuse "discharges." This is not a *movement* of a single discharge, but rather a series of successive discharges. (*b*) Apparent movement of an action potential along a nerve axon as each zone on the nerve axon "discharges." As with the firecrackers, there is no movement of a single discharge, but rather a series of sequential discharges.

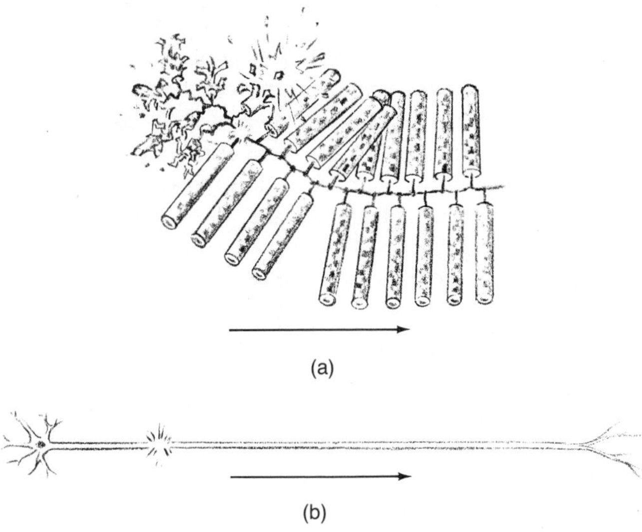

The reason the signal is able to move the whole length of the nerve fiber and emerge at the end without distortion or loss of power is that the signal being transmitted *propagates itself* at each point on the membrane. It is like a string of firecrackers hung on a single fuse (figure 7.17). Each part of the membrane fires the zone adjacent to it, which in its turn goes off like a firecracker, causing the next membrane zone to discharge. The "bang" made by the last firecracker is the same as the "bang" the first one made, because each explosion is an individual event. What is more, if you will think about it a little, you will realize that the explosions are not really moving at all. Each one occurs, then is gone, and a succeeding one takes over. The same is true of action potentials. They are not moving along the fiber, either. They merely *seem* to be moving. Each action potential is an individual discharge, just as each firecracker explosion is an individual discharge. Therefore, there is no reason at all why the last "bang" should be any weaker than the first. The analogy, in fact, is really quite appropriate except for the obvious fact that the axonal membrane is not permanently destroyed by the discharges the way firecrackers are.

The All-Or-None Law

The analogy to a series of firecrackers going off is appropriate for another very good reason. When an irritable membrane is exposed to a potential-reducing voltage, it may fire or it may not, but if it does, it fires just as hard as it can. As we all know, you cannot explode a firecracker quietly, simply because there is no such thing as half of an explosion. The firecracker either goes "bang" just as hard as it can or it remains quiet. The same restrictions apply to irritable membranes. There is no such thing as half an impulse or three-quarters of an impulse. The membrane either fires as hard as it can or it does not fire at all, a phenomenon known as the **all-or-none law.**

The Slow-Moving Impulse

Understanding the nature of the nerve impulse and its apparent movement also helps us understand why a nerve impulse seems to move so slowly along the nerve axon. The electrical current still travels at an extremely high velocity, but it is not the current that is moving down the axon. The current flows only 200 to 300 Å from one side of the axon membrane to the other. What appears to travel the length of the axon is a series of voltage discharges, and each one has to reach a certain value before it can set off the next one. That is what slows the process down.

The transmission of electrical impulses through man-made transmission lines approaches the speed of light—that's 300,000 kilometers per second. Obviously, when dealing with movement from place to place on earth, that kind of speed means transmission is virtually instantaneous. Transmission of impulses along nerve axons is a good deal slower. The fastest-conducting nerves in the human body transmit impulses at about 100 meters per second, and relatively speaking, that's really crawling. A bullet from a high-powered rifle goes seven times as fast. We have jet airliners that can carry us from coast to coast almost three times as fast, and a good many racing cars can hit speeds that are greater.

Sometimes it is slowed too much, so nature has stepped in with a few methods to speed the transmission of neural impulses. One way to do it is to decrease the internal resistance of the nerve axon by increasing fiber diameter. This works nicely, and all animals, including humans, have utilized this method

Table 7.1 Examples of conduction velocities and functions of mammalian nerves of different diameters.

Diameter (μm)	Conduction Velocity (m/sec)	Examples of Functions Served
12–22	70–120	Sensory: muscle position
5–13	30–90	Somatic motor fibers
3–8	15–40	Sensory: touch, pressure
1–5	12–30	Sensory: pain, temperature
1–3	3–15	Autonomic fibers to ganglia
0.3–1.3	0.7–2.2	Autonomic fibers to muscles

From Stuart Ira Fox, *Human Physiology*, 2d ed.

to some extent. Everyone has tiny fibers that conduct impulses rather slowly (one meter per second) and larger ones that conduct more rapidly (see table 7.1). In the invertebrates, enlarging the individual fibers is evidently the primary technique used. In fact, in the higher invertebrates, nerve fiber diameters have become remarkably large, culminating in the giant axon of the squid. But effective as this method is, it detracts from what appears to be a highly desirable goal of all neural systems—miniaturization.

Increasing Conduction Speed

Simply stated, the problem faced by our vertebrate ancestors was how to increase the brain's ability to store and process information without reducing speed of transmission. The invertebrates may have forever capped their neurological development by resorting mainly to an increase in fiber diameter to boost the velocity of information transfer. The vertebrates, on the other hand, possess no giant fibers, but way back in our evolutionary past, our ancestors apparently followed a developmental pathway that concentrated on a different plan—an idea that may turn out to have been the greatest wrinkle yet observed in nature. Vertebrates focused on boosting the speed of neural transmission without increasing fiber diameter to cumbersome size.

Glial Cells

The job was accomplished by accessory cells—cells that are not neuronal but apparently exist to support the neuronal cells. Collectively, such accessory cells are known as **glial cells** (*glia* = "glue"), and there is a tremendous number of them—more, in fact, than there are nerve cells, even in the central nervous system. This suggests that they have important roles, although no one is sure exactly what it is they are supposed to do. Researchers are aware of some of their functions, however. We know, for example, that there are glial cells wrapped around a huge percentage of the body's neurons and that they are probably involved to some extent in transferring nutrients between the interstitial fluid and the neurons. They apparently provide structural support as well. It's hard to imagine thin, flimsy axons going as far as they do without some means of support, and this support is almost certainly provided by the glial cells that butt up against them. Glial cells are also capable of altering electrical characteristics of some of the neurons they are involved with, although nobody is too sure just what that may signify.

The Schwann Cell

One type of glial cell, the **Schwann cell,** is extremely important. It is found in conjunction with every peripheral nerve axon, and one of the primary functions of Schwann cells involves regeneration of peripheral axons that have been damaged by disease or injury.

Neural Regeneration

Unlike most body cells, neurons have very limited regenerative capabilities. In the ninth month of fetal life, nerve cells apparently lose the ability to undergo mitosis, so humans are born with all the nerve cells that they are ever going to have. There is no way to get more, so if a cell body is destroyed, that neuron is gone forever. However, that is not necessarily true when other parts of the neuron are damaged or destroyed.

In the central nervous system, it is very rare for any part of the neuron to regenerate, although it does, on occasion, happen. However, when the axons of peripheral neurons are damaged, regeneration is not unusual at all. As long as the damage is restricted to the axon, the chances are good that some recovery will take place. Normally, the portion of the axon distal to the damaged zone is completely reabsorbed by phagocytic cells. While this is going on, DNA in the cell body is regrouping and organizing RNA to begin the process of restoring axonal material to the nerve.

Figure 7.18 If successful—and it is not always—the regeneration process can consume from one month to one year, depending on how long the nerve searches for the old sheath and how far it has to grow. If regeneration is unsuccessful, a mat of collateral neurons called an *amputation neuroma* forms. This is often what forms at the stump of an amputated limb, hence the name.

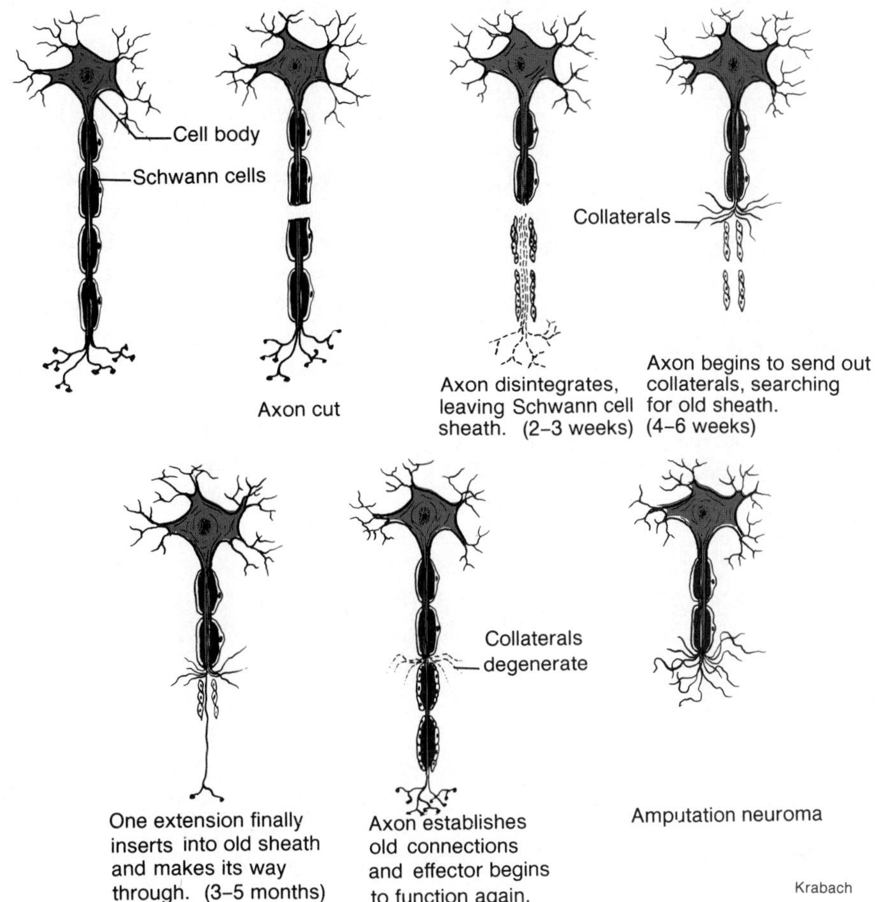

Within three to four weeks, neural axons will thrust out from the tip of the damaged axon, probing for the Schwann cell sheath that the old axon ran through (see figure 7.18).

Regeneration of the fiber often requires a great deal of time, sometimes as much as a year. All materials that will be used for repair have to be assembled in the soma before being shipped out to the damaged area, and all information about progress has to be processed in the nucleus. At normal diffusion rates, this would be an enormous hassle, and restoration would probably require several years. Fortunately, the movement of many materials down into the axon is an active process and takes place at rates up to two hundred times that of simple diffusion, so it doesn't take as long as one might think. Actually, once regeneration in the old sheath has begun, the new axon can grow as rapidly as 3.5 to 4 mm per day (table 7.2).

If the regenerating axons should be unable to find the old sheath—and that occasionally happens—the tips of the neuron often twist themselves into a tangle of fibers all pointing toward each other. This is the kind of neural tangle that occurs in motor nerves at the end of an amputated limb; hence it is known as an **amputation neuroma.** The effector—muscle or gland—will never operate again, should such a structure form.

Directing axonal regeneration is not the only service that Schwann cells perform in peripheral areas of the body. Schwann cells also form protective sheaths around virtually all the nerve axons, wrapping them in non-neuronal coats of varying thicknesses. Sometimes they simply wrap once around the axon, forming a single layer. But often they loop around it again and again, forming thick, bulging wrappings at specific intervals along the axon. When such sheathing forms, the nerve fiber resembles a bunch of juice cans strung along a thin rope (figure 7.19).

The Myelin Sheath

The heavy wrappings that result when the Schwann cells form these laminations around nerve axons are known as **myelin sheaths,** because much of their bulk consists of a lipid-like compound known as *myelin.* These sheaths form during embryological development when individual Schwann cells envelop the nerve axon at specific intervals and then proceed to wind around it, forming layer after layer, until finally the desired thickness is attained (figures 7.20 and 7.21).

Being lipid, the cylinders serve as insulators—good ones! Hence, the zones of the nerve axon that are wrapped up in myelin cannot be penetrated by sodium, potassium, or any other ions. On the surface, that would seem to preclude any possibility that such axons could serve as transmission lines, but that is not the way it works out. These myelinated nerves not only transmit signals, but thanks to the intermittent nature of their insulation, they do so at a surprisingly high rate of speed.

Table 7.2 Axoplasmic Flow Compared with Axonal Transport

Axoplasmic Flow	Axonal Transport
Transport rate comparatively slow (1–2 mm/day)	Transport rate comparatively fast (200–400 mm/day)
Molecules transported only from cell body	Molecules transported from cell body to axon endings and in reverse direction
Bulk movement of proteins in axoplasm, including microfilaments and tubules	Transport of specific proteins, mainly of membrane proteins and acetylcholinesterase
Transport accompanied by peristaltic waves of axon membrane	Transport dependent on cagelike microtubule structure within axon and on actin and Ca^{++}

Figure 7.19 Myelinated and unmyelinated neurons.

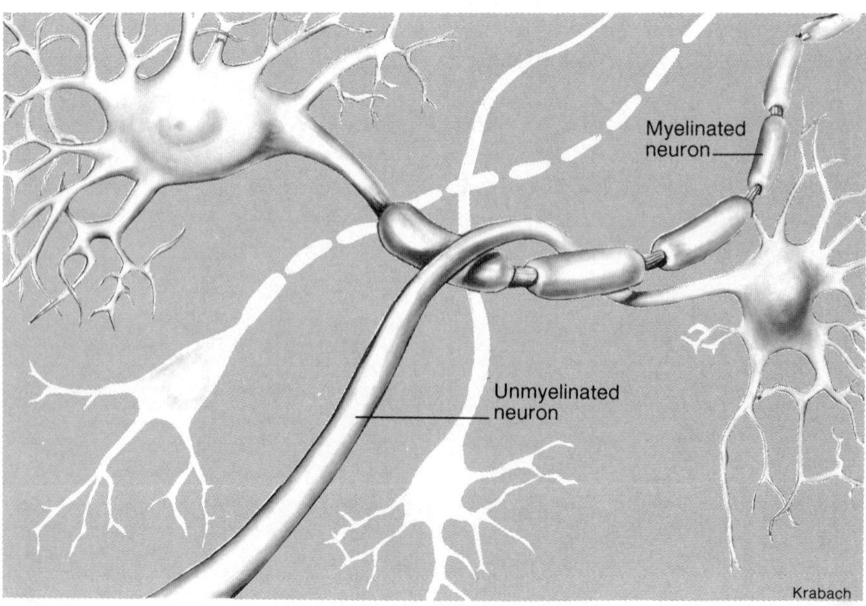

Figure 7.20 The formation of a myelin sheath. The Schwann cell wraps around the axon, forming tight folds that provide effective insulation against random ion flow.

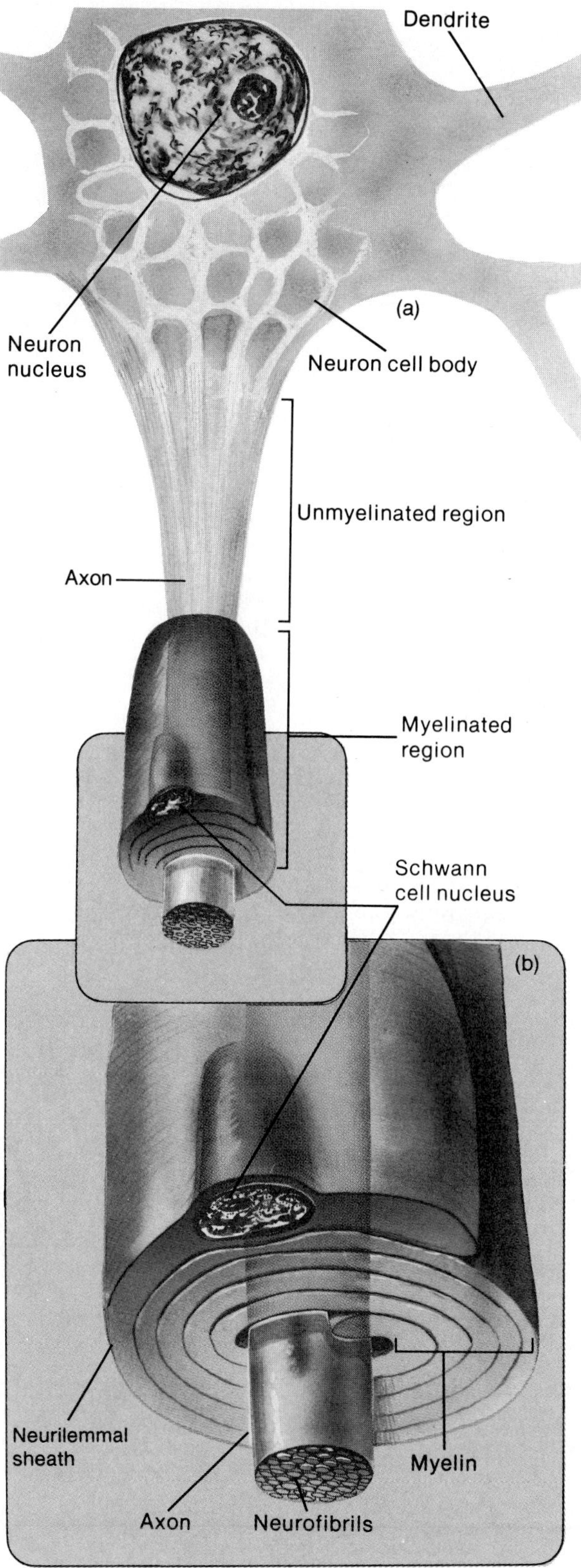

Here is how they do it. As you can see from figure 7.22, the individual myelin cylinders are separated by tiny patches of bare axonal membrane. These naked surfaces are called **nodes of Ranvier,** and they are the only sites on the axon where current can flow across the membrane. Therefore, when action potentials are propagated on such neurons, the nodes are where they occur. Since they cannot develop in areas surrounded by the myelin sheathing, if they are going to travel along the axon, they must "jump" from node to node, and that is what they appear to do. The process is known as **saltatory** ("jumping") **conduction,** and not only does it accelerate the transmission of information, but it's unusual to the point of being fascinating. Impulses can be detected as they appear at each node of Ranvier, and they give the appearance of bouncing along the axon at a high rate of speed (figure 7.22), hence the name. As far as movement is concerned, it is like taking steps with seven-league boots. Instead of one step travelling only a couple of Angstrom units, as is the case in unmyelinated nerves, the "strides" along myelinated axons are vastly elongated. Discharges leap hundreds of Angstroms at a time, bouncing from node to node, bypassing the segments of axon that are blanketed by fatty insulation, hurdling each myelin chunk like a gazelle bounding across a field.

Figure 7.21 An electron micrograph taken through a myelinated axon. The insert (upper left) shows the laminated nature of the myelin wrapping.

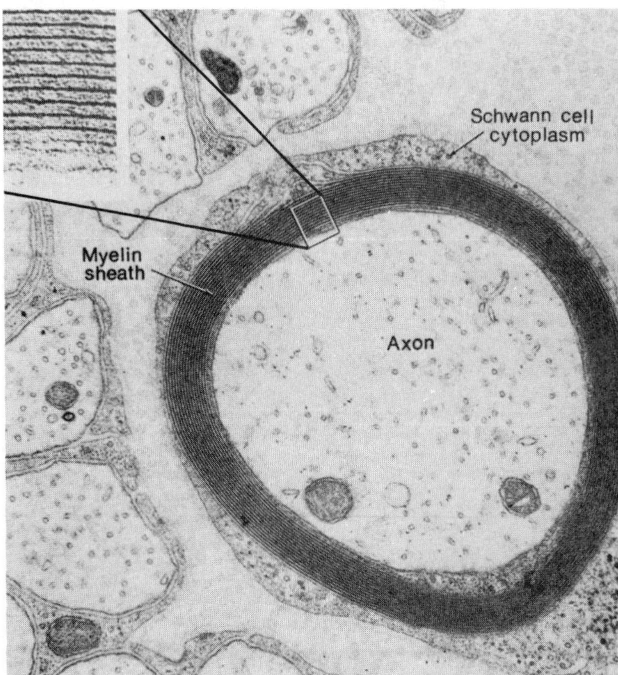

Figure 7.22 The saltatory progress of an impulse along a myelinated axon.

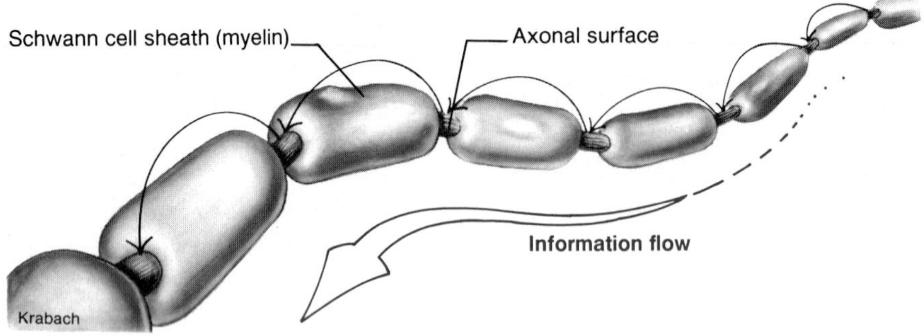

Figure 7.23 Current flow patterns in unmyelinated and myelinated axons.

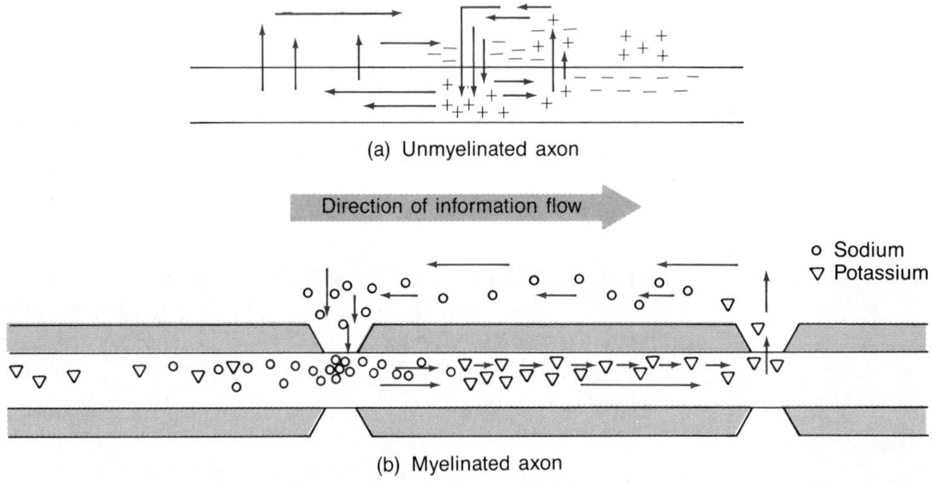

This is the primary advantage to the myelin sheathing . . . it makes the individual action potentials go farther with each "bounce" than is possible on unmyelinated fibers. Figure 7.23*a* shows the propagation of the action potential along an unmyelinated axon. As threshold is achieved and the sodium rushes into the interior of the axon, the positive field it generates repels potassium ions both ahead of and behind it, and the clustering of potassium ions up ahead increases the positive nature of the membrane interior at that point. Potassium flows out through the membrane, trying to counter this effect, until threshold is reached and the membrane at that location flares up in its turn.

On a myelinated fiber, the process is essentially the same. But when the repelling sodium ions enter a node of Ranvier, the potassium that is pushed away cannot flow out of the fiber immediately. It must flow along the axon until it reaches the next node of Ranvier. The subsequent piling up of positive charges in this area facilitates the development of a threshold voltage, which promptly produces an action potential at the node next to the one already firing.

As you can see, the impulse must "jump" along both types of nerve in order to get from point to point, but the distance it travels with each "jump" is much shorter on an unmyelinated fiber.

Like the movement of an action potential along unmyelinated fibers, the saltatory movement that takes place on myelinated fibers is only an illusion. If voltmeter leads are placed as indicated in figure 7.24, the illusion of motion is promptly disrupted by an incredible observation: The action potential is clearly detectable at point 1 and a finite time later at point 3. However, between the nodes at point 2 no action potential appears.

Thus, if the impulse were actually *moving*, it would have to go from point 1 to point 3 *without passing through the space in between*. We may find someday that such a thing can actually be done, but at the moment it is without precedent, and it may be impossible. It emphasizes, however, the observation that the "movement" of the action potential along the axon is not really what it appears to be. As we have already seen in our investigation of action potentials, when a string of firecrackers is lit, the sound appears to be moving from one end to the other, but it is not really.

Figure 7.24 Voltage patterns in a myelinated fiber.

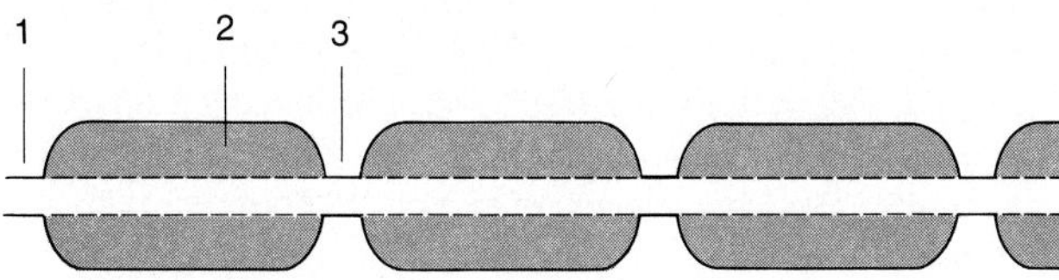

Each explosion is an individual event occurring at one place and then disappearing. In the same way, the bouncing neuronal discharges occurring on myelinated fibers give the *illusion* of motion, but like the explosions of firecrackers, the individual action potentials themselves do not go anywhere. They simply appear, then disappear.

An Emergency Plan

Workers investigating such phenomena recognized immediately that there was some danger in this method of neural transmission. There was no doubt that it speeded up transmission of neural impulses nicely, and it did so without significantly increasing axon diameter, but what if something happened that damaged one of the nodes? Not something really bad, just some slight incapacitation affecting only a tiny area of membrane like the amount exposed at a node. If that kind of injury should afflict an unmyelinated neuron, a propagated impulse would simply jump across the tiny injured zone and the nerve could continue to function. But what if such an injury knocked out a node of Ranvier—would the nerve cease to function?

As it turns out, this possibility was evidently anticipated by whatever forces are responsible for designing our organ systems, and the solution is built in. Should injury render a given node incapable of producing an action potential, the nerve does not become useless until the damage is repaired. The neural message can jump such a node and continue along the axon to its destination. All myelinated nerves that have been tested to date apparently can provide similar detours so impulses can bypass injured nodes until repairs have been affected. However, there are limits to such abilities. One node is apparently all that a travelling impulse can hurdle. Two non-functioning nodes, side-by-side will put a neuron out of action. Apparently, trial and error has shown that the likelihood of two adjacent nodes being incapacitated at the same time is stretching probability.

In any case, this process of accelerating neuronal conduction velocity by "leaping" from node to node has provided vertebrate neurons with the ability to transmit information very rapidly, and it has done so without significantly increasing neuron size.

Invertebrates and Vertebrates Compared: Some Free Thinking

Invertebrates have used myelination to increase neural conduction velocity only partially, and this may be one reason why they lag far behind vertebrates in expansion of the nervous system. To illustrate just how important this can be, compare some attributes of the giant nerve axon of the squid with a motor nerve axon in the leg of a frog.

The sheath around the squid axon constitutes about 2 percent of the total diameter of the axon, whereas in the sciatic nerve of the frog the sheath represents more than 25 percent. Both fibers can conduct at about the same velocity (20 meters per second), but the disparity in size is remarkable. The giant axon of the squid is often more than half a millimeter in diameter (about 1/10 inch), whereas the frog axon is usually less than 10 micrometers (2/1,000ths of an inch).

What Does All This Mean?

In terms of survival capability, this probably means a lot. Vertebrates generally use myelination instead of larger fibers to increase conduction velocity along nerve axons. This means that vertebrates can process much greater amounts of information than any invertebrate can, and the vertebrates can deal with these larger amounts just as fast as, or faster than, the invertebrates deal with theirs. For instance, the frog can transmit a lot of visual information at an extremely high speed—much more than any invertebrate the same size could obtain in as short a period of time. The optic nerve of a big bullfrog is roughly 1.2 mm in diameter. In order to dispatch as much information from the eye to the brain in the same length of time, an invertebrate would need an optic nerve nearly 78 mm in diameter. That's more than three inches, and it is obviously out of the question for an animal the size of a bullfrog.

In terms of survival, neural myelination has given vertebrates a fantastic advantage. It has permitted processing of huge quantities of information at tremendous speed while retaining the advantages of miniature neural circuitry. In modern industry, this *kind* of discovery has made possible some tremendous forward strides in electronics. Today's digital wristwatches have internal circuitry that would have jam-packed a trunk in the 1960s and filled a two-story house in the 1940s. Ten years ago, business computers often occupied most of an office-building floor, yet today we have home computers no bigger than typewriters that can do as much. Speculation is that maybe a similar, sudden, evolutionary step forward occurred in living thought patterns when vertebrates developed myelin sheathing.

Summary

The Functional Unit — the Neuron

Morphology

The neuron is the functional unit of the nervous system. It is formed of four major zones:

I. The Cell Body or Soma. The cell body contains the organelles, including the nucleus.

II. The Dendrites. The dendrites carry information into the neuron. They are tapering extensions of the cell body.

III. The Axon. The axon is the part of the neuron that carries the action potential. It is an extension of the cell body. Unlike the dendrites, it carries information away from the neuron.

IV. The End Tufts or Buttons. The end tufts or buttons are instrumental in transmitting information from one neuron to another or to an effector organ.

Neuronal Types

I. Morphological Classification. This method classifies neurons according to their structure.

II. Functional Classification. Neurons are also classified according to the job they have to perform.

A. Primary Sensory Neurons receive sensory information from the environment and carry that information into the nervous system.

B. Motor Neurons carry impulses into muscles. The information is always carried away from the central nervous system.

C. Afferent and Efferent

1. Afferent neurons carry impulses toward a reference point; efferent neurons carry impulses away from a reference point.
2. Sensory neurons are always afferent; motor neurons are always efferent.

Nerves

Groups of axons bundled together form nerves.

I. Spinal nerves originate in the spinal cord. They can be sensory, motor, or both.

II. Cranial nerves originate in the brain. They can be sensory, motor or both.

Neuronal Function (Neurophysiology)

I. The Axon as a "Telephone Line." Nerve axons would make poor telephone lines because of their high resistance and poor insulation.

II. Neuronal Transmission. Neurons carry information in the form of coded signals. These coded signals are in the form of bursts of voltage. The voltage bursts are generated by the neurons themselves. They emerge from the terminal of an axon exactly the same as they were when they entered the axon.

III. Membrane Potential in Volts. Membrane potential in an average nerve fiber is on the order of 70 millivolts, with the inside of the axon negative with respect to the fluid outside.

IV. Current flow vs. Information Flow. Current flow is perpendicular to the neuron's long axis. Information flow is parallel to the same axis. This is unlike any man-made transmission line and is unique to living systems. It permits the transmission of signals without distortion or loss of power.

V. Bioelectric Current. The membrane potential is maintained by a differential distribution of diffusible and nondiffusible ions plus carefully controlled active transport.

VI. Irritable Membranes. Where irritable membranes are concerned, the membrane's permeability to sodium depends on the membrane potential, and vice versa.

The Action Potential

The membrane permeability varies according to the voltage developed across it by the ionic distribution.

I. The Threshold Phenomenon

A. Sodium "Gating"

1. When the membrane potential decreases, the membrane's permeability to sodium increases.
2. When the membrane potential reaches a certain value, permeability to sodium increases greatly and sodium rushes into the axon. The membrane potential disappears and a new voltage appears.
3. The new voltage is the signal carried by the neuron.

B. Positive Feedback. The mechanisms that drive the voltage change support each other.

II. The Membrane Recovers

A. Sodium Inactivation. When the action potential reaches a certain value, the sodium gates close.

B. The Role of Calcium. It is thought that the sodium gates are blocked by ionic calcium.

III. Repolarization. Sodium can no longer move across the membrane, but potassium can. The increased outflow of potassium current decreases positivity inside the axon. This reduction in positive charge, combined with active transport, restores the membrane potential. A nerve can fire many times without needing to rest.

The Nerve Impulse

The purpose of a nerve impulse is to carry information.

I. Above-Threshold Phenomena. Nerve threshold potentials are lower than action potentials. Because of this, the nerve impulse is propagated all along the axon.

II. Refractory Periods

A. Absolute Refraction. During the period that sodium is deactivated, the neuron will not fire regardless of the stimulus intensity.

B. Relative Refraction. During the period that the membrane's permeability to K^+ is higher than normal, a greater than normal stimulus is required to fire the neuron.

III. Action Potential—Voltage, Not Current. The action potential, which seems to be moving along the neuronal axon, is not a flow of current, but rather a series of voltage changes.
IV. The All-Or-None Law. Nerve axons either fire maximally or they don't fire at all. There are no impulses smaller than maximum.

The Slow-Moving Impulse

Nerve impulses are propagated along axons rather slowly.

Increasing Conduction Speed

Conduction speed can be increased by making axons bigger. One of the amazing things about human nervous systems is their incredible miniaturization. Obviously, a way had to be found to increase conduction speed without increasing axon diameter significantly.

I. Glial Cells. Glial cells are non-neuronal cells present in the central nervous system.
II. The Schwann Cell. Schwann cells are glial-like cells that are present outside the CNS.
III. Neural Regeneration. Schwann cells can aid in the regeneration of neuronal axons as long as the cell body is intact.

The Myelin Sheath

I. Schwann cells wrap nerve axons at specific intervals. The wrapping is composed mainly of a fat called myelin and is an excellent insulator.
II. Each Schwann cell wrapping is separated from its neighbors by regions of bare axon. These regions are known as nodes of Ranvier.
III. Axonal conduction velocity is increased by making impulses jump from node to node. Conduction can be accelerated.
IV. An Emergency Plan. If a node is damaged or injured, impulses can skip it and go to the next node in line. An impulse cannot skip two nodes in a row.

Invertebrates and Vertebrates Compared: Some Free Thinking

Conduction velocity in vertebrate neurons is usually increased through myelination. Invertebrates use this technique also, but not to the extent that vertebrates do. More often, invertebrate nerve conduction is increased by making the axons larger. This has reduced the miniaturization capabilities of the invertebrate CNS.

Review Questions

1. Identify and describe a generalized functional unit of the nervous system.
2. Identify and describe each of the four major parts of this functional unit.
3. How many ways are neurons normally classified? Describe each, and explain the reasons for its classification in its category.
4. Define the terms *afferent* and *efferent*.
5. Describe the morphology of a typical nerve, as opposed to a neuron.
6. What is the difference between a cranial nerve and a spinal nerve?
7. Describe the nerve axon. In what ways is it specialized to perform its function?
8. How does the current flow in a neuron differ from current flow in a man-made electrical wire?
9. Summarize the distribution of the major ions inside and outside a nerve axon.
10. Describe the development of an action potential. Be sure to mention:
    a. the significance of threshold voltage
    b. sodium gating
    c. the positive feedback phenomenon that characterizes the action potential and how it is controlled
11. Describe the process of axon recovery from an action potential. Be sure to mention:
    a. the sodium inactivation phenomenon
    b. calcium's possible role
    c. the role of potassium
12. What is the function of a nerve impulse?
13. Describe the progress of an action potential along a nerve axon.
14. What is refraction?
15. How does the movement of an action potential along a nerve axon differ from the transmission of a signal through a telephone line?
16. What is the all-or-none law?
17. What are glial cells?
18. What is the role of Schwann cells in acceleration of nerve impulses?
19. Identify and describe two major functions of the myelin sheath.

Chapter 8 Neural Integration

Study Hints

When reading this chapter, make every effort to understand. As with the two preceding chapters, there is simply too much information here to grasp by memorizing individual facts.

1. Associate the electrical phenomena with the movement of the various ions, and be sure you understand how this movement will affect voltage (charge).
2. Pay careful attention to the fact that we deal in this chapter with slowly-developing potential changes. These are completely different phenomena from action potentials, which develop explosively.
3. Keep in mind that the slow voltage changes are the predecessors of action potentials. (Action potentials are "set off" by slow potential changes.)
4. Pay particular attention to the structure and function of the nerve-to-nerve junctions (the synapses).
5. Be sure you understand the function of neurotransmitters: what they do, how they do it, and their fate once they have done their job.

Objectives

When you have finished reading this chapter, you should:

1. be able to describe the appearance of a typical synapse, including the pre- and postsynaptic elements and their contents.
2. be able to identify the structures that protect the central nervous system.
3. be able to list the twelve cranial nerves and their functions.
4. understand the classification schemes that apply to central and peripheral neurons.
5. understand the fundamental principles of transmission from nerve to nerve, including the difference between electrical and chemical neurotransmission.
6. understand the alterations in membrane and ion distribution that precede slow potential changes and be able to contrast them with those that occur when action potentials develop.
7. be able to describe, step-by-step, the transmission of neural information from pre- to postsynaptic fiber.
8. be able to name and locate the major zones in the human brain.
9. be able to compare the major structural and functional differences between the autonomic nervous system and the somatic nervous system.

Perineurium body nerve cells in the CNS.

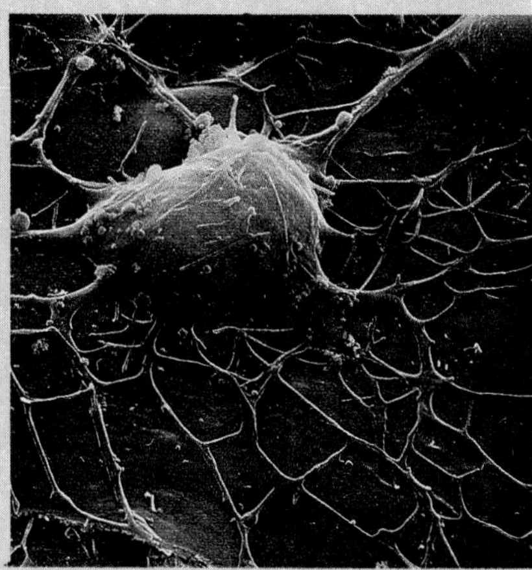

Introduction

Learning how action potentials develop and carry messages along nerve axons is just an introduction to neural phenomena. The action potential as described in chapter 7 was propagated by theoretically inserting a microelectrode into the axoplasm and manipulating the internal voltage artificially. This method is practical and has been accomplished in experimental laboratories, but obviously it is not the way action potentials are produced in living animals. Biological systems have their own ways of producing action potentials, and they involve the utilization of intermediate mechanisms such as special chemicals or highly specialized receptor tissues. Some of the processes feature the intricate interaction of electrical elements and chemicals; they maintain submicroscopic separations with such precision that expert computer engineers have not even *tried* to duplicate them.

Probably the easiest way to explain the instigation of an action potential by a biological engine would be to outline the development of what are called **receptor potentials.** Such potentials are produced by the specialized receptors of primary sensory nerves, and they are the same in all animals so far investigated.

As with many things, the best place to start is at the beginning, which means we have to discuss once again the neuronal membrane.

Slow Potential Changes

Neuronal Membranes

Neural membranes are considered *irritable* or *electrically excitable* because the membrane permeability to sodium is solidly tied to the voltage that exists across it and to the condition of the sodium gates (see chapter 7). It is an indispensable characteristic, because it is what permits membranes to achieve the so-called **active state**—the condition that exists when the membrane suddenly discharges and produces the action potential. You should keep in mind, however, that only nerve membranes or muscle cell membranes exhibit this characteristic; hence, *only neuronal, or muscle-fiber, membranes can produce action potentials.* Non-excitable membranes, lacking the characteristics necessary to produce action potentials, can respond to stimuli, but like man-made telephone lines, their electrical response is passive.

In order for us to be aware of all the stimuli that our bodies receive daily, each stimulus must be transmitted to our brains in the form of electrical signals. Yet the stimuli themselves are seldom, if ever, electrical. Heat, light, the cut of a knife, or the pressure of a sudden blow—even vibrations in the air around us—all these things will stimulate neural receptors, and normally we are aware of all of them. Yet none of them are electrical in nature when we first encounter them. Obviously then, when a stimulus impinges on one of the body's receptor organs, something must change the energy it contains into an electrical message that our nerves can transmit. Otherwise the message would never reach our brain.

It would certainly be nice if there were just one kind of mechanism to handle this operation. How much easier neurophysiology would be if all receptors converted external stimuli into electrical signals in the same way. As you can probably guess, it is not that simple. Different kinds of stimuli offer different forms of energy to the body's receptors. Our eyes, for instance, receive their stimuli in the form of radiant energy in a specific frequency range, and this energy cannot even be detected by other body receptors. The eyes, on the other hand, cannot pick up the waves of energy that are accepted by our ears, and so on. Each type of receptor, therefore, must be designed to accept energy in a certain specific form and then, using its own special methods, must **transduce** the stimulus energy into electrical signals. (Transduction is the conversion of one form of energy into another form of energy.) In this respect then, each type of neural receptor is unique.

But the main differences we find among the body's receptors are concentrated in the ways that they are designed to accept and transduce stimuli. Once this transduction has been accomplished, receptors appear to have many things in common. The receptor that receives the stimulus obviously must be able to convert it into electrical activity, and—if the stimulus is strong enough or lasts long enough—into an action potential. Therefore, the stimulus, no matter what it is, must somehow affect the receptor's membrane potential. If it affects the voltage across the receptor membrane, it must in some manner adjust membrane permeability to permit unusual movement of specific ions. Keep in mind that at normal membrane potential, the ion that is going to move most readily is sodium. Potassium is diffusing a little but is very close to its equilibrium potentials; hence its penchant for movement is considerably less than that of sodium. As we know from chapter 6, there is a delicate and carefully maintained balance between the electrical charge on the membrane and the internal and external concentrations of chloride and potassium. Chloride is at equilibrium, and potassium is very close. But that is not true of sodium. Because of the additive electrical and chemical concentration forces, if given any opportunity at all, sodium will rush into the cell.

This opportunity is provided when a stimulus alters the receptor membrane.

Pressure Stimuli

Probably the easiest process to visualize involves pressure stimuli, so let us consider the changes that might occur in a specialized pressure receptor when the correct stimulus is encountered. No one knows for certain just how pressure causes membrane permeability to change, but it is not unreasonable to suggest that when something starts to push on the receptor, it might produce a mechanical distortion like the distortion you would see if you pushed in a soft rubber ball with your finger (figure 8.1). Pushing into such a soft surface stretches things and produces a distortion that could easily elongate or enlarge some of the pores, disrupting the membrane's integrity and decreasing its resistance to sodium flow.

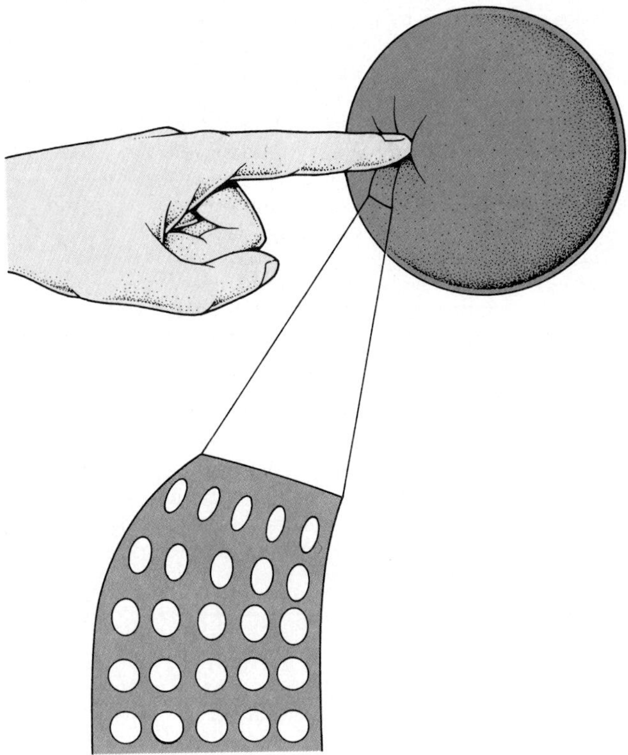

Figure 8.1 Distortion of a membrane (in this case the surface of a rubber ball) due to physical displacement.

Before the Stimulus

An instant before the stimulus arrives, the ionic situation around the receptor membrane is the same as it would be around any cell membrane during its "resting" state (chapter 6). Sodium ions are poised in great numbers in the interstitial fluid, under considerable pressure to get into the cytosol. They are being tugged at by electromagnetic forces inside the membrane and pushed from behind by diffusion. Only the resistance of the membrane keeps them from rushing into the interior. Change that resistance, weaken it only a little, and sodium will flow into the cytosol.

The Receptor Potential

If our hypothesis is correct, when pressure is applied to the proper receptor, the characteristics of its membrane change sufficiently to open the sodium gates a little way, and sodium then slides down its gradients into the cytosol of the cell. Potassium flow increases also, but since it is much closer to its equilibrium potential than sodium is, potassium flows out much more slowly. In some respects, it is like the initial phases of an action potential, but there are some important differences. For one thing, permeability changes are not profound; hence the potential change on the membrane is not very large. As a result, the influx of sodium current never becomes the seemingly uncontrolled surge that one sees when an action potential begins—it is neither that rapid nor that massive—and in any case, the outward movement of potassium tends to keep it under control. Instead of the "bursting dam" of the action potential, the movement is slower, and there is really no hint that the membrane may be showing the profound changes one sees in an action potential.

In terms of voltage, the result is a depolarization that is maximal at the site of the stimulus and is directly proportional to the intensity of the stimulus. This means that as the stimulus increases, so does the depolarization. The more pressure that is applied, the more the surface is distorted, and the more distortion that occurs, the less resistance there is to ion movement. As the ion movement increases, the interior of the membrane gets less and less negative. This depolarization spreads across the receptor like the ripples in the smooth surface of a pond after a pebble is dropped in. Voltage waves fan out from the point of origin, spreading wider and getting weaker and weaker as they move. This slowly weakening potential spread is one of the most important differences between action potentials and these slow receptor potentials.

The unmyelinated parts of the receptor membrane have a high threshold, but the first myelinated segment's threshold is quite low. If the receptor potential can spread as far as the first segment, its chances of stimulating an action potential are good. Once the first segment fires, of course, the self-regenerating action potential is on its way.

Decremental Transmission

The voltage changes on receptors are smaller in magnitude than any action potential, they occur much more slowly, and as they spread away from their point of origin they gain no additional support from membrane phenomena. All the energy they possess was given to them by the initial stimulus. Since the neuron is not a particularly good conductor, these signals must overcome considerable resistance as they move.

Hence the farther they get from the source, the weaker they get. The spread of these slow depolarizations is known, therefore, as a **decremental** one, meaning as it spreads farther and farther away from the origin of the stimulus, the potential decreases exponentially in intensity.

Unlike the self-regenerating action potential, which exists at any given point on a neuron for only about a millisecond, these slow changes can last a relatively long time. Exactly how long depends to some extent on the duration of the stimulus, but even if the receptor is only stimulated for a half-second or so, membrane depolarization can last for several seconds. If a stimulus is applied for a long enough period of time, the change can persist even longer.

Other Characteristics

Some other characteristics of slow potentials and the membranes where they occur:

High threshold: The parts of the receptors where these slow depolarizations are taking place have a very high threshold potential, and an unusually powerful stimulus would be necessary to cause this part of the nerve to fire. It is almost never reached. However, receptor membranes will produce the slow potential changes in response to very tiny stimuli, and the response is detectable for equally tiny distances.

Graded response: Since such stimuli can vary almost without limit, so can the receptor potential. Since it is the direct result of the stimulus, the receptor potential changes as the stimulus does. When the stimulus increases in duration, so does the receptor potential. When the intensity of the stimulus increases, so does the magnitude of the slow potential change. Unlike the action potential, this slow potential is not an all-or-none response.

Duration of perception is a function of stimulus: The duration of the receptor potential is a fairly accurate reflection of the duration of the stimulus. Some receptors are designed to indicate absolute values **(static receptors),** and some are intended to detect only changes in state **(phasic receptors).** Phasic receptors produce slow potential signals only when the stimulus is actually changing, while static receptors continue to produce such potentials as long as the stimulus is present. Nevertheless, in both cases, the most profound slow potential signals occur while the stimulus is actually *changing* in value. The electrical changes that occur in the membrane as a result of the stimulus begin to dwindle rapidly as soon as the stimulus stops changing, and in the case of phasic receptors, it vanishes completely.

This particular phenomenon is a little harder to understand than most, and sometimes it doesn't seem to make much sense. Nevertheless, it appears to be almost universally true. Even where pain receptors are stimulated, it seems that unless the stimulus is consistently changing, it tends to lose receptor potential strength. A good example of this is familiar to all of us: the initial plunge into a swimming pool on a hot summer day. Very few people bother to ease themselves into the cool water of a swimming pool, ocean, or lake, simply because it serves only to prolong the agony of entry. Most of us leap into the water, experiencing a brief shock that rapidly dwindles away as we become used to the water. Few of us stop to wonder what has happened, although we probably should. After all, the water has not suddenly gotten any warmer. What *has* happened is that the receptors on our skin surfaces have *accommodated* to the new temperature. They shocked us with a barrage of neural information during the period of actual temperature change—that is, when we jumped into the pool—but the changing condition has disappeared. The receptors still let us know that the new medium we are immersed in is cooler than the air we just left, but they no longer bombard us with shocking information, because *change* has ceased.

Some Neuroanatomy

Functionally, as was noted in chapter 7, there are three basic nerve types. Those that receive stimuli from the external or internal environment are *primary sensory* or *afferent* neurons. Fibers that stimulate muscles to move or glands to secrete are *motor* or *efferent* neurons, while the fibers that accept information from the sensory nerves or pass instructions to motor fibers are *connecting neurons* or *interneurons.*

In terms of numbers, connecting or interneurons far outnumber all the other kinds. Primary sensory and motor neurons represent only a tiny fraction of the neurons in our bodies, yet without them, the brain would be an ineffectual lump, capable of much profound thought, but nothing else. Sensory and motor neurons are almost all in peripheral body areas, but they are crucial to the function of the entire organism. Sensory neurons provide our central computer with the only informaton it gets about what is happening around us or inside of us. Without sensory input, we would perceive nothing, good or bad; without motor neurons, the brain would have no way to respond to environmental changes, even if it could detect them. Clearly, numbers do not necessarily indicate the importance of a given nerve type.

As regards the nervous system as a whole, there is an obvious anatomical separation in all vertebrates. The portion known as the *central nervous system* consists of the spinal cord and the brain, and everything neural that is outside this system is considered part of the *peripheral nervous system.*

The Central Nervous System

The spinal cord runs right down the middle of the organism, dividing it into two symmetrical halves. The cord itself is a hollow tube, the sides of which are composed of masses of neurons and glial cells. The rostral (*rostra*—"beak" or "snout," hence the front) end of this tube is swollen in all vertebrates, and the size of the swelling depends on the animal. In the most primitive vertebrates it is small, and the spinal cord resembles an elongated medicine dropper. But as animals become more complex, the brain enlarges with respect to the spinal cord, and the rostral swellings get larger and larger until finally, in the mammals, they have reached the point where in terms of sheer volume, the cerebral hemispheres have swollen to enormous size and dominate the entire neural mass. In primates the epitome has been achieved. The primate brain is so huge that the spinal cord seems insignificant, dangling from it like a thin pigtail on a person's head. Yet even in primates, it is clear that the brain and spinal cord are anatomically one continuous organ.

The Spinal Cord

For the sake of order, however, it has been decided that the spinal cord separates from the brain at the point where the nerve tissue actually leaves the braincase. It courses from the skull all the way down the back and ends as a single tube at the last thoracic element (figure 8.2). Below that point, it separates into a mass of nerve fibers carrying motor and sensory information back and forth between the CNS and the lower extremities.

Figure 8.2 The vertebral column and the spinal cord within. The elements are numbered from top to bottom in each segment. The last thoracic segment is T12, and that is where the cord ends.

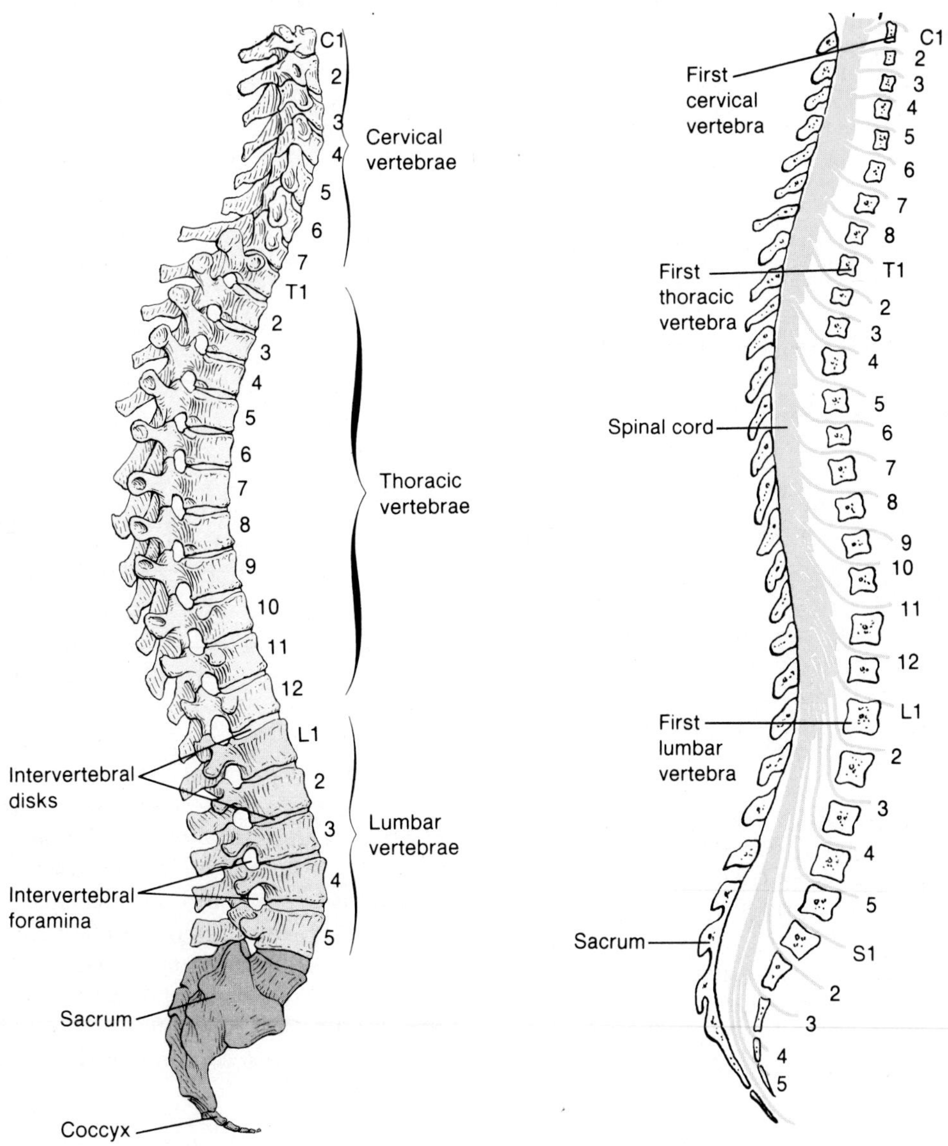

Figure 8.3 The spinal nerves in humans.

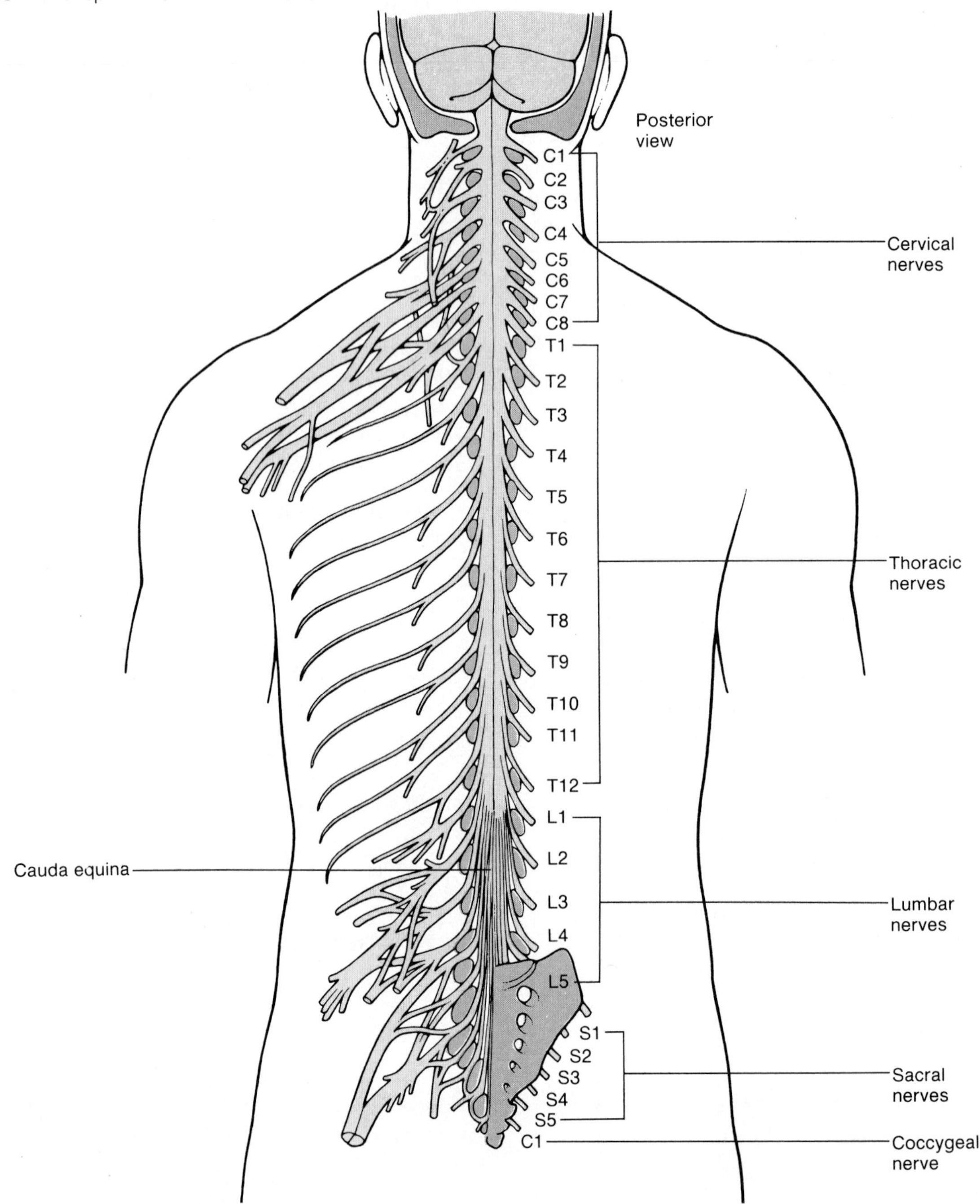

Spinal Nerves

There are thirty-one separate vertebral elements in the spinal column, and from between each of these a pair of **spinal nerves** emerges and sprays sensory and motor fibers out to various parts of the body (see figure 8.3).

Individual spinal neurons are attached to the CNS by two nerve "roots" that emerge from the vertebral column laterally. The **anterior** or **ventral root** carries mainly motor nerves, while the **posterior** or **dorsal root** handles primarily sensory traffic. As figure 8.4 shows, there is a swelling near the posterior horn—the **spinal ganglion** or **dorsal root ganglion,** which consists of the cell bodies of all the primary sensory neurons travelling through that spinal nerve. The cell bodies of the motor neurons are inside the spinal cord in the anterior columns of gray matter (figure 8.4). Spinal neurons leave the cord in huge bundles and usually unravel shortly thereafter, forming neural **plexuses** at various points in the body.

Figure 8.4 The spinal cord in cross-section.

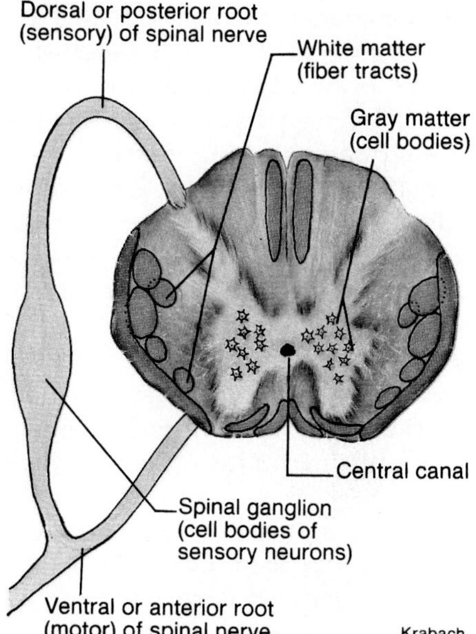

A plexus is an interlaced mat of motor axons. Plexuses are found throughout the body's periphery, with the exception of the thoracic region. There is a **cervical plexus,** a **brachial plexus,** a **sacral plexus,** and a **lumbar plexus,** and from these plexuses motor nerves branch out to supply information to effector organs. Upon leaving these various plexuses, the bundles cease to be spinal nerves and become **peripheral nerves.**

In general, the spinal cord functions as a brain accessory and relay station between peripheral nerves and the higher centers. All sensory input accepted from receptors below the head region must enter the CNS via the spinal cord. The spinal cord is, therefore, the initial integrating center for most of the body's sensory input, and reflex activity for all parts of the body except the head are routed through the spinal cord.

The Cranial Nerves

Cranial nerves emerge from the brain rather than from the spinal cord. With one notable exception, they tend to concentrate all their informative efforts on the upper reaches of the body. The exception is the tenth cranial nerve, the vagus. Fibers from the vagus are abundant in the thorax, where they can exert considerable control over respiratory and heart activities. There is also a large number of vagal fibers that pass through the thorax and dive down into the abdomen, where they innervate the entire gastrointestinal tract and its accessory organs. Vagal influence on visceral activity is widespread, and there is substantial evidence to suggest that it can modify some endocrine functions. There are twelve pairs of cranial nerves, and they are designated either by Roman numerals I through XII or by specific names. They are listed in table 8.1.

Table 8.1 The Cranial Nerves in Humans

Number and Name	Type	Mission
I Olfactory	Sensory	Detect odors
II Optic	Sensory	Vision
III Oculomotor	Motor	Moves eyelid Constricts pupils Moves eyeball
IV Trochlear	Motor	Moves eyeball
V Trigeminal	Mixed Sensory Motor	Tongue, teeth Facial skin Inside of mouth Chewing
VI Abducens	Motor	Eye movement
VII Facial	Mixed Sensory Motor	 Taste buds Makes facial expressions Crying Salivation
VIII Vestibulocochlear (Auditory)	Sensory	Hearing Equilibrium
IX Glossopharyngeal	Mixed Sensory Motor	 Taste buds Swallowing Gagging Salivation
X Vagus	Mixed Sensory Motor	Throat, thoracic cavity, and abdominal viscera Swallowing, throat musculature, speech Visceral organs
XI Accessory	Motor	Shoulder movement Head movement Shrugging
XII Hypoglossal	Motor	Movement of tongue

There is an old mnemonic that has been used for years to help students remember the cranial nerves and to associate them with their proper numbers. It goes as follows:

"*On Old Olympus's Towering Top, A Fin And German Viewed A Hop.*"

Clearly, the line itself makes no sense at all, but the first letter of each word (including the article and the conjunction) refers to one of the cranial nerves, and the order is correct if you use the term *auditory* for the eighth cranial nerve.

The Meninges

The neural tube expands to enormous size at the rostral end, thus forming the brain, but most of its basic design is retained, with some modification. For instance, the hollow middle-portion of the tube is still present inside the brain, but it has swollen and been sculptured to match the tissues around it, forming a series of enlarged caves called **ventricles.** The hollow interior means that there is an inner surface in the CNS as well as an outer one, and covering the entire central nervous mass, inside and out, is a series of membranes (figure 8.5).

Figure 8.5 (*a*) The outer surface of a human brain, showing the meninges and an arachnoid villus. The latter is the site of reabsorption of cerebrospinal fluid. (*b*) A choroid plexus (where cerebrospinal fluid originates) enlarged.

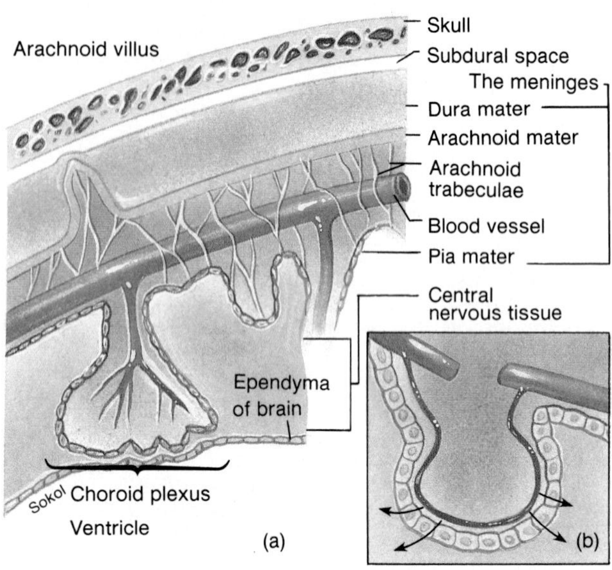

These tissue cowlings are called the **meninges** (singular, *meninx*), and there is little doubt that they serve a protective function. The innermost one is named the **pia mater** (*pia*, "tender"; *mater*, "mother"). The pia is an extremely fine membrane, seldom more than a single cell in thickness, and it enfolds the entire brain, inside and out, actually touching neuronal surfaces in many places. The pia enjoys such intimate contact with brain cells that many workers feel it may not be a meninx at all, but non-nervous brain tissue. The meninx that encloses both the pia mater and its contents is the slightly tougher but still rather delicate **arachnoid mater** (*arachna*, "web"). The cerebrospinal fluid runs through the space between the arachnoid and pia maters, forming a liquid interface between the two membranes. Outside the arachnoid mater, covering the entire central nervous system and forming an interface between it and the bone of the skull and vertebral column, is the tough, fibrous **dura mater** (*dura*, "hard").

Between the pia and the arachnoid mater there is a rather large space. And as I said, in this space is a slow-moving river of serous fluid, flowing over the outer surfaces of the brain and spinal cord and filling the spinal tube and ventricular lakes with liquid. This is the **cerebrospinal fluid (CSF),** an ultrafiltrate of the blood, and it completely encloses the central nervous tissue like a sheet of liquid armor. It is filtered from the blood within the ventricles of the brain, and then, forced to move by the same pressure that filtered it, it pushes slowly through to the back of the brain and glides down the hollow of the spinal cord. At the bottom it moves out of the tube and spreads over the outer surfaces of the cord. Relentless, gentle pressure forces it back up the outer surfaces of the spine and over the outer brain surfaces, where it is reabsorbed and returned to the blood (figure 8.6).

About half of the CSF is secreted by capillaries in **choroid plexuses** of the brain (see figure 8.5), with the remainder being filtered out of cerebral vessels in the pia mater. Although the basic pattern of flow is as I have described, there is a fairly constant exchange between the blood and CSF everywhere there is capillary contact between them. Most CSF is filtered from the blood into the brain ventricles, and considerable pressure builds up within these chambers, forcing the CSF to follow the flow plan described. Having completed its circuit of the CNS, the CSF is mostly reabsorbed in structures known as **arachnoid villi** (figures 8.5 and 8.6), where it enters the venous circulation of the brain (see the following box). The whole process, from secretion to absorption, takes about three hours.

Most people, if they are aware of the cerebrospinal fluid at all, probably don't expect it to be involved in a health problem. Yet when the systems that produce it and reabsorb it are malfunctioning, it can be disastrous. In normal humans there is a wide band of tolerance in the secretory rate, which ranges between 200 and 500 ml per day. The reabsorption rate normally keeps up with production, but on occasion there can be a desynchronization that may produce real problems.

Regardless of the pressure inside the ventricles, the secretory rate remains fairly constant, and CSF production is steady. That, however, is not true of reabsorption. The rate of CSF reabsorption depends on the pressure that is present inside the brain ventricles. As long as the pressure remains where it should be, reabsorption proceeds apace with secretion, but if for any reason intraventricular pressure should fall below 70 mm Hg, reabsorption stops. Production, however, continues relentlessly, steadily producing more CSF and permitting fluid to accumulate. Ultimately, this increases pressure and starts the reabsorption process up again. The whole thing is a perfectly normal, self-regulating feedback loop that is designed to insure a correct volume of CSF at all times. Sometimes, however, the arachnoid villi stops working properly and fluid is not reabsorbed or is reabsorbed too slowly. This, of course, does not affect secretory rate, which continues as usual, producing more and more fluid inside the brain. As fluid accumulates, intraventricular pressure climbs steadily, crowding nervous and non-neuronal tissue within the skull to a point where damage can occur. This is known is **external hydrocephalus** (or *water-on-the-brain* as it was once called). If not corrected, it can result in irreversible neuronal damage.

Figure 8.6 The brain and spinal cord in sagittal section. The flow of CSF is indicated by the arrows.

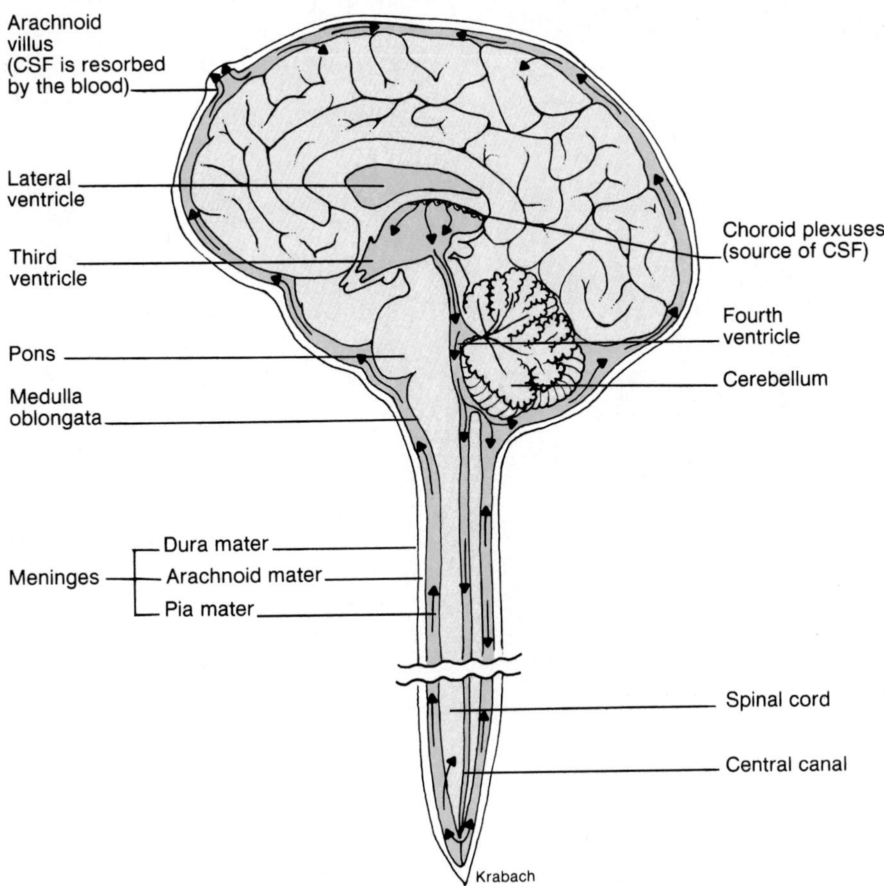

The exact function of the cerebrospinal fluid has been and still is a subject of some debate. Many functions have been suggested for it, but none of them is totally satisfactory. At one time it was thought to act as an intermediate between the blood and the brain tissue, and it was hypothesized that both nutrients and wastes had to go through the CSF in order to get from one to the other. This seems unlikely. Depriving the brain of its blood supply for as little as four minutes can result in irreversible tissue damage, yet a person can be completely drained of CSF for as long as several hours without any noticeable problems beyond a temporary, severe headache. Another theory suggests that the CSF is an electrical shield intended to prevent unwanted electrical signals that might be crackling around in the atmosphere from entering the brain and interfering with normal thought patterns. This is possible—the CSF is a pretty good conductor—but if it actually does this, it is something of a mystery as to where it might direct the oscillations it has intercepted. About the only contacts it has are with two of the meninges, and it doesn't seem very likely that it would permit them to be interrupted by such signals.

The Brain's Shock Absorber

The most widely accepted view is that the cerebrospinal fluid is a mechanical shock absorber. Certainly a mass of tissue as delicate and as irreplaceable as the brain needs something of the sort to protect it. This theory suggests that the CSF is a liquid "damping" mechanism, designed to protect the delicate neurons and supporting cells of the brain from touching the solid bony mass of the braincase. Because it is a liquid, it is incompressible; hence it can partially absorb even such destructive jolts as might result from blows to the head or sudden, violent movements. If this hypothesis is correct, then the thin, watery fluid that encloses the central nervous system is very important indeed. It augments the protective function of the skull bones and surrounds the entire mass of the brain with a hydraulic cushion.

Figure 8.7 A nerve fiber bundle typical of those outside the central nervous system. Nerve fibers bundle together in a somewhat similar fashion in the brain and spinal cord. Called *tracts* in the CNS, such bundles course back and forth throughout, picking up and sending out branches.

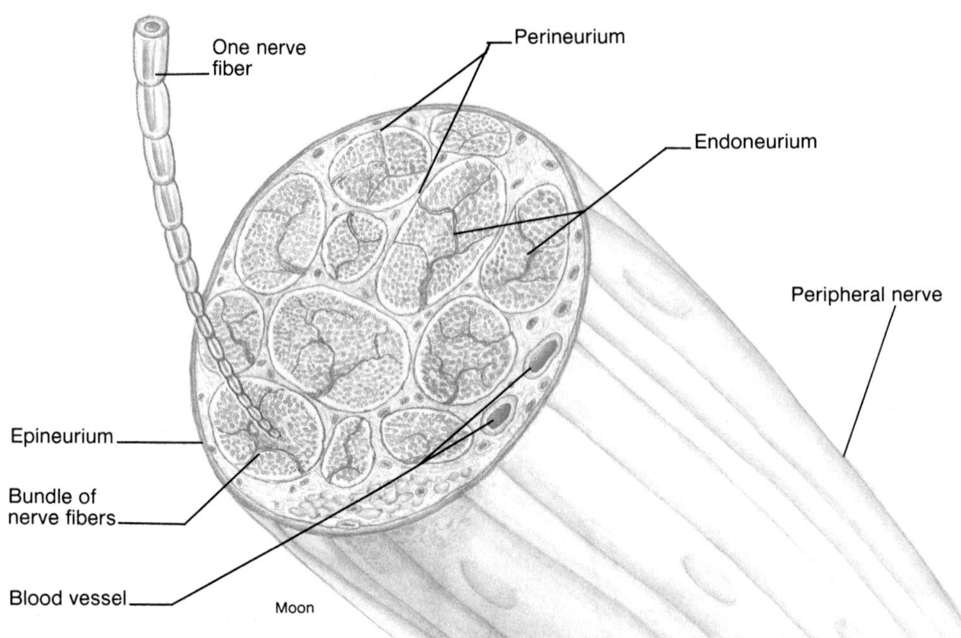

In all vertebrates, including humans, the skull provides reasonable protection from blows to the head, but the mass of the human brain is much greater than that of any other animal's. Because of this unusual size, the cerebrospinal fluid may be an even more important protection than the skull, especially when it comes to "damping out" the shock of sudden movements. Notice how rapidly a dog, a cat, or even a horse is able to shake its head without any ill effects. Have you ever tried to move your head that quickly? It can be done, but it hurts, suggesting that it is not too good an idea. Without the cushioning effect of the CSF, a movement as innocent as a sudden 90-degree turn might render us unconscious.

Central Nervous Circuitry

The great mass of tissue in the CNS is an immense snarl of cells, fibers, and supporting vessels, collectively forming a matted labyrinth that resembles in miniature the rear of a huge computer console with its arrays of wires all gathered here and there into bundles that travel *en masse* through the central processor (see figure 8.7). Great axonal rivers course up and down the spinal cord in more or less ordered assemblages, with tributary bundles entering and leaving the various mainstreams on a regular basis. As the packages of fibers enter the hindbrain, nerve cell bodies begin to increase in number, sometimes appearing singly, more often in clusters, busily communicating with fibers entering or leaving the streams of axons gliding past. When these fiber streams plunge into the central mass of brain tissue, they suddenly seem to lose much of their directional unity. Tributaries spray from them in incredible profusion, entering and becoming part of the teeming jungle of cell bodies, fibers, non-neuronal supporting cells, and blood vessels that make up the brain.

Passing Information from Nerve to Nerve

The tangle of wires and the galaxy of flashing lights that make up a computer console may appear random—even nonsensical—but it is all very ordered. Each wire has a specific destination, each light a specific function, and the individual circuits all talk to one another in special ways. So it is with the central nervous system. Despite its garbled, seemingly incomprehensible architecture, every neuron has a specific job to do, and each fiber has a specific source and destination (see figures 8.8 and 8.9). Neural signals travel in a logical pattern, the route of transmitted information is variable but deliberate, and perception is rational. Like a modern computer, the human brain is composed of literally billions of individual units that are orchestrated into complex patterns and designs that we are just beginning to comprehend. We know the unbelievable snarls of fibers and cell bodies form sensible, functional patterns, because the human brain works. But science really has only the vaguest idea as to what the tangled meanderings of our neural circuitry might mean.

Figure 8.8 Specific pathways from peripheral receptor areas into the brain and spinal cord.

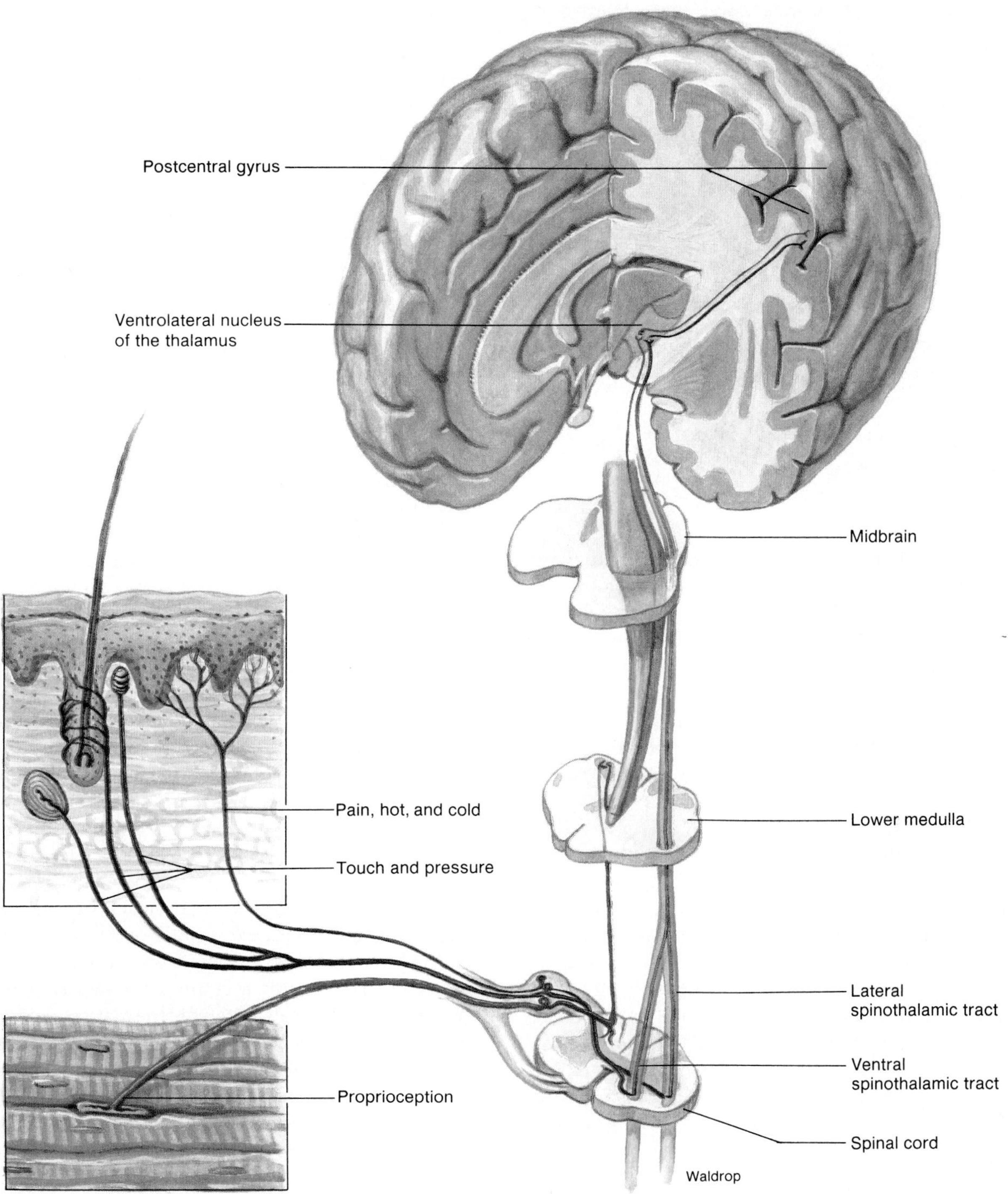

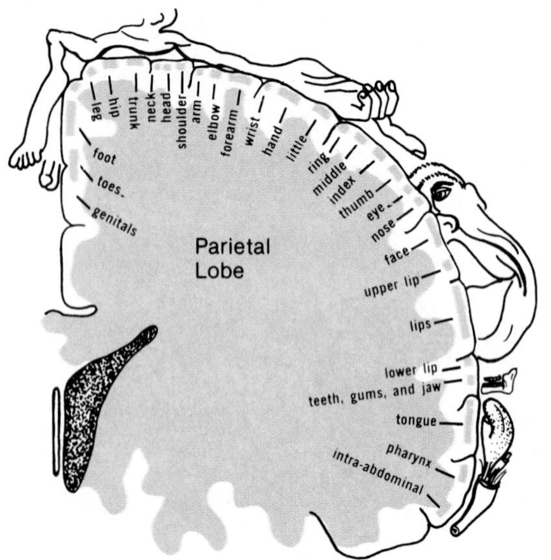

Figure 8.9 Parts of the cerebrum that receive input from peripheral sensory receptors. Areas that are disproportionately large receive a heavier concentration of input than those that are smaller.

We are helped somewhat by similarities between the brain and computers. For one thing, each mature nerve cell is functionally and anatomically an independent unit, just as are the individual components in a computer. In addition, the codes carried by the units in both are digital codes. As we saw in chapter 7, a neuron either fires or it does not. There is no halfway firing or low-voltage action potential. Some of the brain's circuitry even seems to be understandable, but that is strictly the superficial circuitry. The detailed circuitry deep in the brain is, for the time being, incomprehensible. Careful, patient study is gradually producing results, and most workers are confident that someday we will unravel some of the major secrets of thought transference and memory storage. Right now, however, we are struggling to understand the tiny, everyday operations that the brain undertakes and how these small but detailed processes fit into whole major circuits. One of the biggest stumbling blocks lies in the way information is transferred between the units. We have a gross comprehension of what goes on at nerve junctions, and much work is currently being done to try and figure out what it all means. One thing is sure—it is not much like our computer contacts. In computers, all contiguity between elements is electrical. As we will see shortly, in vertebrate nervous systems, most nerve-to-nerve continuity is chemical.

The Synapse

Once a fiber gets where it is going, it has to be able to transfer the information that it is carrying to the next element in line. If the information is being carried by a motor nerve, the next element will be a muscle or a secretory gland, but only a tiny fraction of the neurons in our bodies are motor neurons. More than 99 percent of all neurons are interneurons—in fact, the central system consists almost completely of interneuronal fibers—so most of the cross talk takes place between nerves, and nerves talk to each other across interneural encounter zones known as **synapses.**

When neurophysiology was in its infancy, it was assumed that nerve impulses were simply passed from one neuron to the next at a point of physical contact, and our light microscopes seemed to confirm this. Careful electrical measurements, however, showed that there was a short delay (about 0.5 msec) before an impulse crossed from one neuron to another. This meant there had to be a gap between the terminus of one neuron and the dendrites of the next. The distance involved, however, was minuscule—undetectable even with a microscope—and could be easily jumped by electrical impulses in the same way that electricity jumps across the gap of an automobile spark plug. The time delay could be explained by assuming that when the impulse arrived at the end brushes, the presynaptic membrane had to charge up before the spark could jump across, and that took about half a millisecond. It all seemed to make sense.

Some perplexing facts cropped up, nonetheless. Workers using microelectrodes had probed the synaptic junctions and noticed that the electrical impulse, when it arrived at the end brushes of a nerve, simply stopped right there. About half a millisecond later, an apparently new impulse suddenly flared up on the postsynaptic fiber. There was no electrical spark between the two, nor was there any evidence of current flow in the cleft between the nerves (see figure 8.10). Also, it had been observed on more than one occasion that certain chemicals could cause a postsynaptic neuron to fire when there was *no* presynaptic impulse present—all you had to do was put the chemical into the synapse.

In 1921, a scientist named Otto Loewi published experimental evidence indicating that a major nerve (the vagus) entering the heart used a chemical of some sort to transfer its commands to the heart muscle. He did not know what kind of compound it was, but he

Figure 8.10 When an action potential travels down the presynaptic fiber, it is easily detected by microelectrode 1. Microelectrode 3 shows an action potential about 0.5 msecs later, but no voltage changes of any kind appear at microelectrode 2. If the electrical impulse were indeed continuous, it would have to go from 1 to 3 without going through the space between.

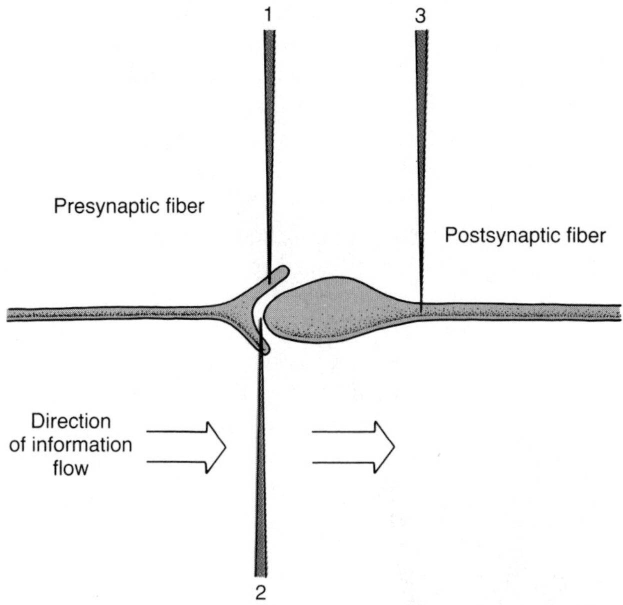

had succeeded in trapping this chemical in physiological saline solution, and he repeatedly demonstrated its ability to slow and even stop beating hearts, without any neural intervention at all (figure 8.11). The idea that chemicals might be the means of transmitting impulses from neuron to neuron suddenly leapt into prominence. Chemical synapses became all the rage in neurophysiology, and the earlier concept of electrical contact between neurons lost most of its adherents. The idea that vertebrate neurons might exchange information by means of purely electrical cross talk all but vanished for a while.

It could not vanish completely, however. Electrical synapses were well known in invertebrates and in fact were fairly common. Because of their abundance in these animals, many physiologists were confident they would find them in vertebrates sooner or later, and they continued to search. Finally, in the late 1950s, a cluster of such synapses was found in goldfish. Since then, they have been found in every vertebrate investigated, and presumably, therefore, they are present in humans.

The "spark-gap" idea has vanished, however. The potential energy that builds up in a nerve ending as a result of an action potential is nowhere near great

Figure 8.11 A simplified rendering of Loewi's heart/heart preparation. Using excised frog hearts, Loewi set them up as shown. The perfusion fluid passed through the heart on the left (the donor heart), then through the heart on the right (recipient heart). Stimulation of the vagus nerve slowed the donor heart, and after a short pause, the recipient heart also slowed. Since the only communication between the two hearts was via the perfusion fluid, Loewi concluded that the inhibition of the recipient heart had to be due to a chemical that entered the perfusion fluid when the vagus nerve was stimulated.

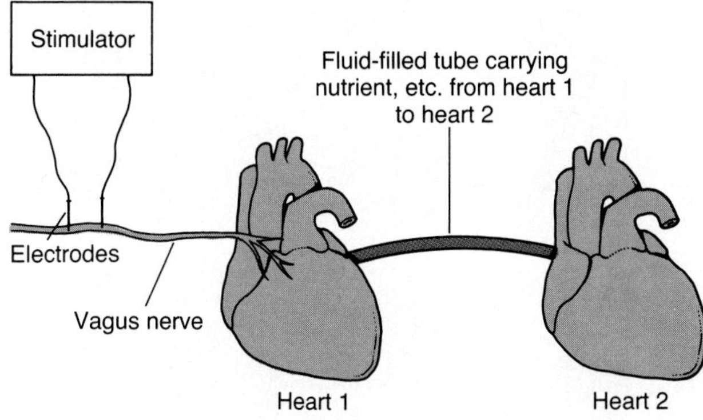

enough to permit it to actually leap across even the tiny gap between nerve cells. In any case, it is not necessary. Thanks to an ingenious design, electrical transmission is actually much simpler and requires considerably less power than a spark gap would, and impulses travel from one cell to the next as if there were only a single membrane between the two cells.

Gap Junctions: Electrical Synapses

Electrical communication between nerves takes place at structures known as **gap junctions.** These junctions represent points of physical contact between membranes of adjacent cells, and if electron-microscopial observations are correct, they can answer a lot of questions concerning electrical transmission of neural messages.

There are two membranes present, as figure 8.12 shows, but as far as flow of charged particles is concerned, there may as well be only one. The phospholipid portions of the membranes do not actually touch each other, but the proteins do, and it has been suggested that these adjacent membranes share protein channels (see figure 8.12*c*) that permit cell-to-cell movement of ionic particles. If prevailing theory is right, transmitting depolarizing impulses from one cell to its neighbor would certainly appear to be uncomplicated. Ions could flow through the superimposed protein channels in the two membranes as they

Figure 8.12 A gap junction between two cells. These junctions are common in the vertebrate brain and are abundant in muscle tissue in the heart and the viscera. (*a*) The photograph shows that cell membranes of two cells are fused together in the gap junction; (*b*) a surface view of a gap junction is seen. (*c*) The information presented in these and other electron micrographs is interpreted by the illustration.

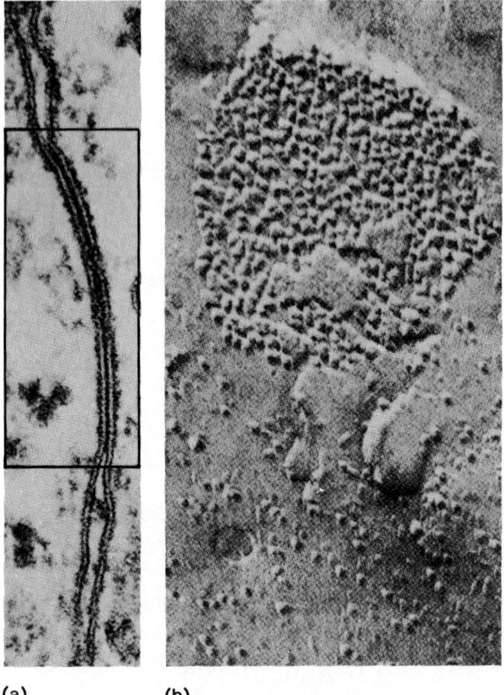

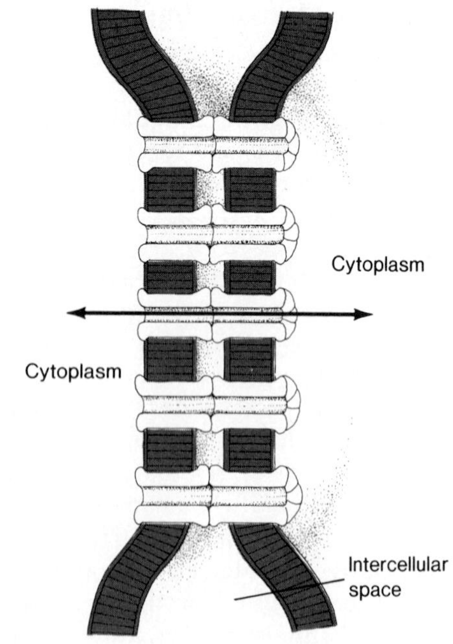

would through a single membrane. An action potential on either cell membrane would automatically depolarize its neighbor, transferring the action potential quickly and easily to the other cell.

Gap junctions may not, however, be as simple as they appear. For one thing, if they represented nothing more than superimposed protein conduits between adjacent cells, current would be able to flow freely from one neuron to the next, and action potentials could cross, unrestricted, in either direction. Sometimes they can, but not always. Some gap junctions are unidirectional, and this suggests hitherto unsuspected complexity.

Cytologists are currently hinting that these apparently simple contact points may represent a whole new family of intracellular organelles. So far there is not much known about them beyond the synaptic abilities mentioned. But they have been implicated in cellular operations that have nothing to do with the spreading of electrical information, and for some unknown reason, they vanish whenever their cells are about to divide. They may turn out to be capable of widely divergent processes yet to be uncovered (see the following box).

Whatever their other functions, they can definitely serve as points of electrical continuity between adjacent neurons. Just what it is that they are able to do that chemical synapses cannot has not yet been uncovered; hence the precise reason for their existence has never been satisfactorily explained. In any case, their numbers in mammalian brains are extremely small in proportion to the total number of neurons.

The idea of pure electrical communication between cells is not restricted to interneural communication. Investigation into primate physiology has shown that individual muscle cells in the atria of the heart apparently pass electrical signals to one another directly, without using chemicals as intermediates and without the intervention of any neural tissue. We will discuss this more completely in chapter 10.

Chemical Synapses

By far the majority of synapses in vertebrate nervous systems use chemicals to carry their messages from nerve to nerve and from nerve to muscle. There are many different kinds of neurotransmitters, and their activity varies through a wide range because of the manner in which they are packaged by the nerve endings. Their operations are basically the same, however, which makes things a lot easier for physiology students.

Figure 8.13 Different types of chemical synapses: (*a*) axodendritic, (*b*) axoaxonic, (*c*) dendrodendritic, and (*d*) axosomatic. Dendrodendritic synapses, unlike the other chemical synapses, are apparently able to conduct in either direction.

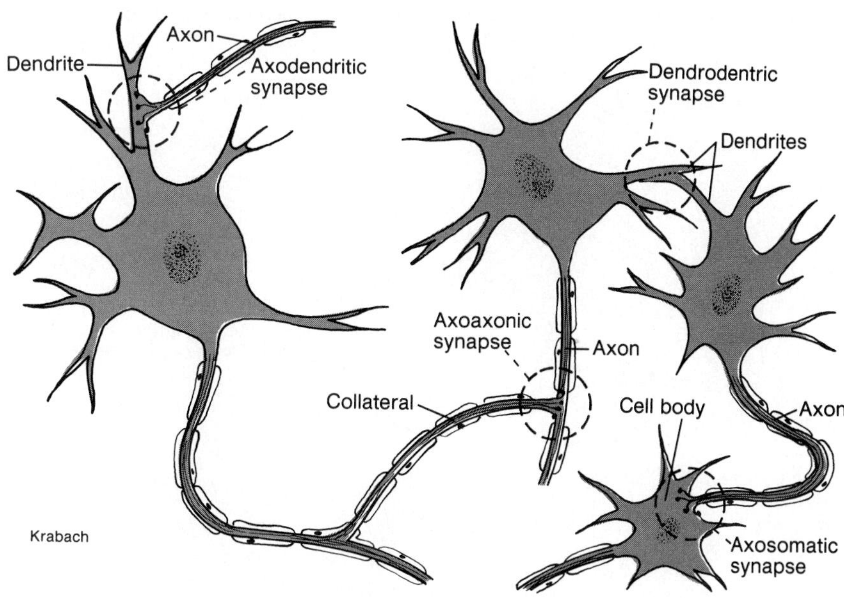

One thing they certainly provide is **rectification.** Rectification permits free passage of electrical signals in one direction but places an insurmountable barrier to movement the other way. Axons, as we know, can carry action potentials in either direction, yet neural circuitry obviously has unidirectional overtones. If signals could reflect back and forth at every junction, action potentials would be bouncing back and forth through the brain circuits, producing nothing but confusion. Neuronal axons can transmit signals in either direction with equal alacrity, so rectification certainly cannot take place there. Since there is no other place where it *could* happen, rectification in signal transfer must take place in the synapses.

For the most part, electrical circuitry terms are part of a jargon that you, as an elementary physiology student, need not be concerned with. The term *rectification,* however, is used with such abandon in neurophysiology, that I think the reader should know what it means. Rectifiers are electrical entities that restrict current flow to a single direction in any given circuit. Rectifiers are important elements in circuits that convert alternating current to direct current, and if you have purchased a gadget designed to protect your expensive computer or color television from voltage surges, that, too, contains a rectifier circuit. They can be transformers, capacitors, transistors—even vacuum tubes—as long as the current that flows through them does so in only one direction. Neural synapses, therefore, qualify as rectifiers, since nearly *all* the chemical ones and some electrical ones permit information flow to proceed in only one direction.

Chemical synapses are generally viewed as points of contiguity between neurons, although unlike electrical synapses, they provide no actual physical contact. There are several kinds of chemical synapses. The most common contiguity, for instance, is between axons and a dendrite. Another, also fairly common, is between the terminus of an axon and a cell body. In the periphery there are even instances—rare ones—of continguity between axons (see figure 8.13).

Also, the relationship between neurons at their synapses is not necessarily one-to-one, which is to say, a neuron may get its information or instructions from more than one other neuron. Outside the CNS, it may not; peripheral neurons often feature a 1:1 or 1:2 relationship across a synapse. But in the CNS, synaptic connections are seldom that simple. Depending on the circuitry and the neurons involved, there could be anywhere from half a dozen to a quarter million neurons synapsing on a single large neuron. Motor neurons in the spinal cord often have between 2,000 and 5,000 end buttons from connecting fibers forming synaptic contact with them, and large brain cells can have as many as 200,000 synapses on a single dendrite (figures 8.14, 8.15).

The tremendous number of contacts that are possible at any given synapse should heavily underscore the importance of rectification. If the synapse could pass information freely in both directions, a single input intended for a large brain cell could enter the cell at one synapse, then jump backward across all the

Figure 8.14 A typical reflex loop detailing the interneuron/motor neuron synapse. (*a*) A schematic drawing of a spinal reflex. The sensory fiber carries information from the receptor into the dorsal (posterior) root of the spinal cord, where it passes its message to an interneuron. The connecting neuron transfers the information to a motor neuron, which can then fire a muscle. (*b*) The soma (cell body) of such a motor neuron may have dozens or even hundreds of interneurons contacting its dendritic surface. (*c*) A motor dendrite enlarged, showing the myriad interneuron contacts. (*d*) One such contact.

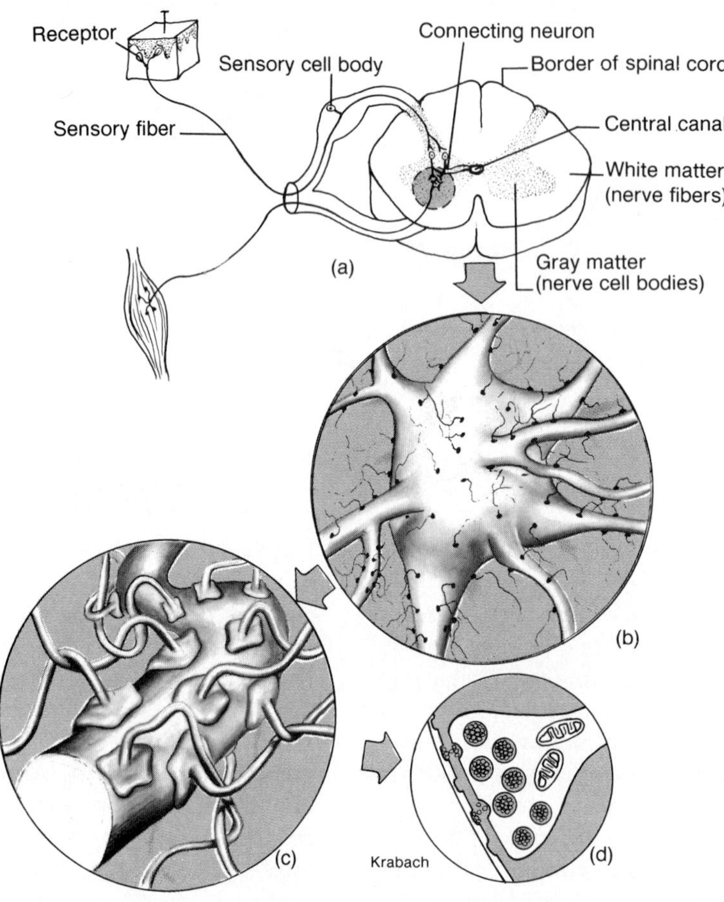

Figure 8.15 An electron micrograph of synaptic contact in an invertebrate, showing a large number of nerve endings on a postsynaptic cell body (×6,000).

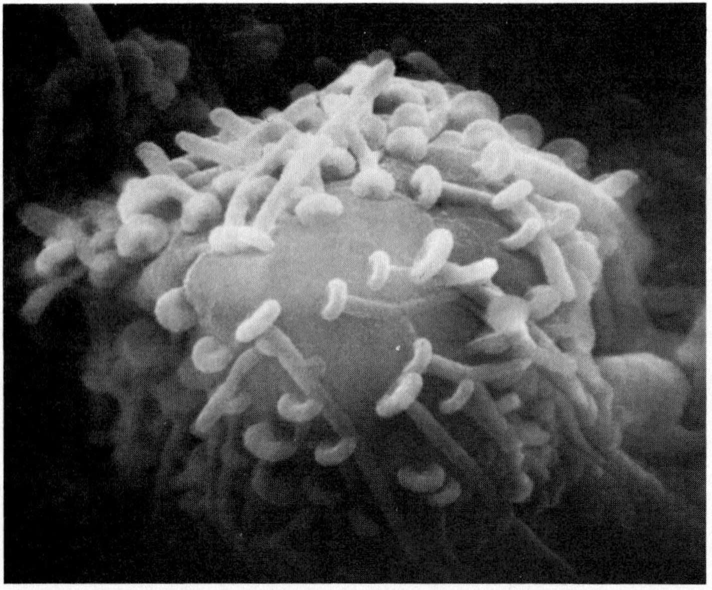

other synapses and spray off in 200,000 different directions. The confusion that could result from that sort of randomness boggles the mind—and that's just from one cell.

Morphology of the Synapse

The structure of the chemical synapse precludes forever just this sort of malfunction; it simply *cannot* happen, as you will see when we investigate the synapse more closely. It begins at the terminal of almost any neuron.

The end of a neural axon is actually a tiny knoblike structure called an **end button, bouton, synaptic knob,** or **presynaptic membrane,** and it is this button that synapses with the succeeding dendrite or soma. Electron micrographs taken of fibers synapsing on motor nerves in spinal reflex loops such as the one shown in figure 8.15 indicate that the buttons of presynaptic fibers are usually separated from the postsynaptic membrane by a space of 200 Å or less. This discontinuity between the two nerves is known as the **synaptic cleft** and is the point in the loop where the electrical impulses both end and begin.

As figure 8.16*a* shows, there are three main elements in the synapse:

1. The presynaptic element
2. The synaptic cleft
3. The postsynaptic element

Chemical Neurotransmission

The presynaptic element is the button or terminal knob of the presynaptic fiber. Within its cytoplasm are numerous mitochondria, and some small, irregularly shaped vacuoles filled with darkly staining chemical granules. These are the **vesicles** of the presynaptic element, and the dark-staining granules within are small packages (called *quanta*) of the neurotransmitter, which, in the periphery, is usually **acetylcholine (Ach).** There are similar dark-staining granules outside the vesicles in the cytoplasm; in fact, they are distributed equally between the interior of the vesicles and the cytoplasm outside the vesicles.

Early research produced several theories to suggest what might happen when an impulse arrives at the end button of the presynaptic fiber, but science finally singled out one as the consensus favorite. For decades, this theory prevailed. It was generally agreed that Ach was synthesized into small packets of neurotransmitter, which were stored in small, membrane-enclosed vesicles in the cytoplasm. When an impulse arrived at the terminus of the axon, these vesicles migrated to the terminal membrane, fused with it as an exocytotic vesicle does, and released the Ach packages into the synaptic cleft. Recent work done at the University of Geneva, however, suggests that this concept must be modified; it has produced the following model:

When the terminal knob depolarizes, the presynaptic membrane, which has been impermeable to calcium, increases its permeability to these ions, and they are permitted to enter (figure 8.16*b*). The calcium stimulates certain proteins in the membrane to open a series of acetylcholine "gates," and the acetycholine quanta within the cytoplasm stream from the terminal ending into the synaptic cleft (figure 8.16*c*). As the quanta leave the cytoplasm, the equilibrium with the quanta inside the vesicles is upset, and some quanta leave the vesicles to reestablish the proper balance.

If firing in the presynaptic neuron continues for a prolonged period, the acetylcholine quanta stored within the vesicles flow freely into the cytoplasm, and thus more quanta are made available for further transmission. As the quanta leave the vesicles, they are replaced by ionic calcium, which streams into the vesicles from the cytoplasm. This has two effects: (1) it permits the presynaptic element to regulate its response to action potentials by removing the calcium from the cytoplasm, and (2) the vesicles provide handy vehicles for isolating the calcium that has entered and storing it for future disposal.

Meanwhile, the transmitter quanta released from the presynaptic membrane move across the cleft to the postsynaptic membrane. No one is really sure what is involved in this movement. It may be that there are enzyme carriers present, although current evidence suggests that this is unlikely. It is felt that once they are released into the cleft, the quanta move to receptors on the surface of the postsynaptic element as a result of simple diffusion.

Figure 8.16 (*a*) A chemical synapse at rest. (*b*) The synapse as an impulse arrives. (*c*) The transmitter diffuses across the cleft to the postsynaptic receptors. Protein gates begin to close as Ca^{2+} migrates into vesicles. (*d*) All receptors are occupied. The localized depolarizations summate. Protein gates in the presynaptic membrane close up. (*e*) The transmitter is completely hydrolyzed, ending generator potential. Acetate and choline fragments are reabsorbed by the presynaptic membrane. (*f*) Hydrolyzed fragments of neurotransmitter leave the vicinity of the postsynaptic element and diffuse back to the presynaptic element for reassembly into neurotransmitter.

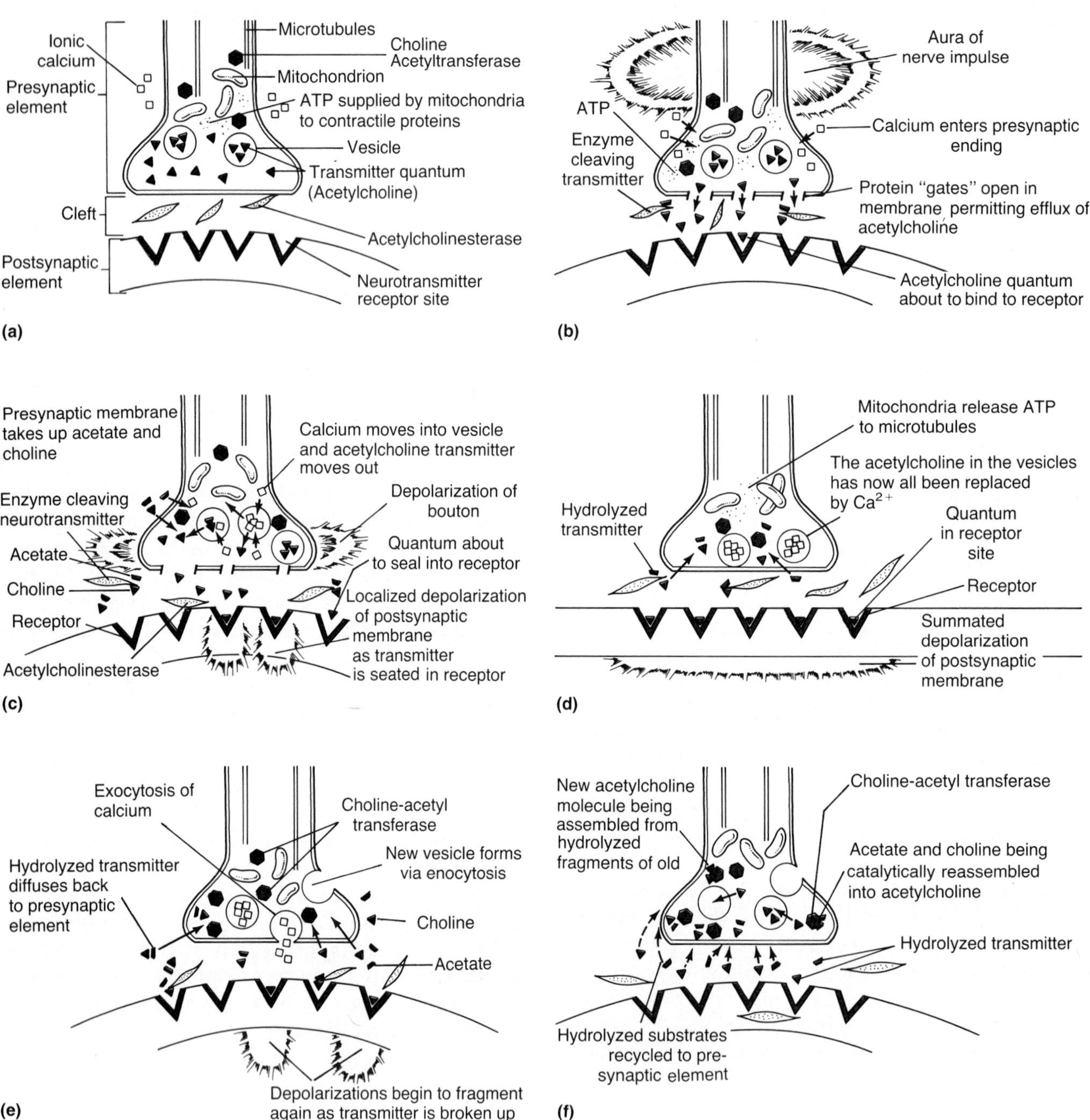

Once they get across the synaptic cleft, these neurotransmitters fit themselves into receptors, which are believed to be specialized proteins, on the postsynaptic membrane. Once there, they seat into place, causing depolarization—called a **postsynaptic potential (PSP)**—on the postsynaptic membrane adjacent to and beneath them (figure 8.16*d*). Precisely what causes this localized depolarization is uncertain, but we know that the resulting phenomena are very similar to a receptor potential. Resistance to both sodium and potassium is slightly reduced, permitting movement of both ions down their respective gradients. Obviously, the transmitter/receptor complex must somehow produce a change in permeability of nearby elements of the postsynaptic membrane. As with receptor potentials, the increased permeability is not great, and the subsequent depolarization is also relatively small—often only a millivolt or two. Since the threshold of the unmyelinated parts of the postsynaptic neurons is quite high, these tiny depolarizations cannot fire the membrane at their point of origin. Instead, the localized depolarizations begin to spread. The spread is slow and, as is the case with receptor potentials, decremental.

The amount of postsynaptic membrane each individual quantum is able to influence is usually very small. Nevertheless, each exerts its influence over its own little section of membrane, and when a large number of adjacent sites is occupied, the localized, mini-depolarizations can coalesce into larger zones of depolarization, which combine in a phenomenon known as **spatial summation.** Now, the PSP takes on all the ionic and electrical characteristics of the receptor potentials described earlier. If it reaches the first segment of the axon, it will probably fire the neuron; if it doesn't, then it simply dies out.

Recovery

Once it has produced its depolarization, the transmitter/receptor complex must be broken apart, and the neurotransmitter must be removed. Otherwise the PSPs will continue endlessly, and the flow of additional information along that pathway will be impossible. If the neurotransmitter is acetylcholine, and it usually is in peripheral nerves, the breakdown is accomplished by an enzyme that is present on the outer surfaces of the synaptic membranes and in the synaptic cleft (see figures 8.16*d* and *e*). This enzyme—**acetylcholinesterase**—catalyzes hydrolysis of the neurotransmitter, a reaction that is essentially the reverse of dehydration synthesis, by which most large biological molecules are assembled (see chapter 2). As a result of its activity, the transmitter splits into acetate and choline.

This hydrolysis serves a dual purpose. First of all, it limits the activity of the transmitter, an important aspect of neural integration. And, in addition, it recycles the breakdown products, providing raw materials for the synthesis of more neurotransmitter in the presynaptic button. The transmitter molecules are hydrolyzed on or near the postsynaptic membrane, and that produces a high concentration of breakdown products in that vicinity. The result is a concentration gradient that permits diffusion back across the synaptic cleft, where these products are picked up by the presynaptic membrane. Once on the membrane, they are drawn into the interior of the button by specialized carrier-protein systems. Once back in the presynaptic cytoplasm, under the catalytic influence of choline acetyltransferase, they are reassembled into neurotransmitter. New vesicles, meanwhile, are formed by endocytosis (figure 8.16*e*) and promptly fill with new transmitter quanta as the reassembly of the recycled substrates proceeds. Eventually these processes will reestablish the original distribution of neurotransmitter quanta between the terminal axoplasm and the interior of the vesicles.

Each action potential that arrives at the end button produces a response, and if impulses arrive in long trains, a lot of transmitter has to be assembled and ready to go. This effectively underlines the importance of having a ready store of neurotransmitter present inside the vesicles and already-synthesized molecules of acetate and choline available as substrate material for new transmitter. As these transmitter fragments cycle back into the presynaptic membrane, their assembly into new molecules of acetylcholine is a one-step linking process that can be accomplished quickly and with little energy. Without an abundance of such raw material, many nerves would suffer from an inability to do their jobs after a few bursts of activity.

Figure 8.17 The calcium disposal mechanism in presynaptic elements. (*a*) Vesicles crowd in the button, moving randomly, occasionally colliding with the membrane. Often the stenin and neurin slip together (*b*), but in the absence of Ca^{2+}, they bounce apart (*c*). (*d*) When Ca^{2+} displaces the neurotransmitter, stenin is activated. Now when neurin and stenin touch, they complex (*e*), forming neurostenin, locking onto the membrane and contracting, causing a permeability change in the membranes (*f*), and releasing the calcium. (*g*) When Ca^{2+} is released, the complex breaks and the vesicle drifts free of the membrane.

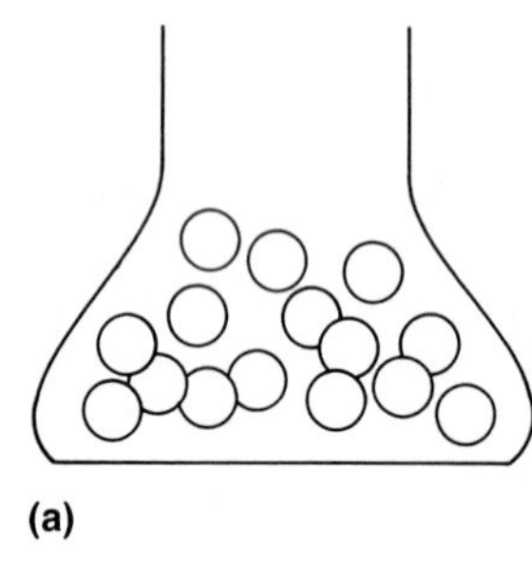

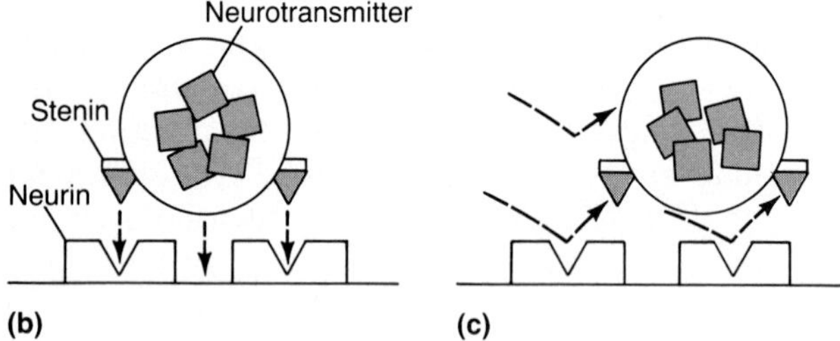

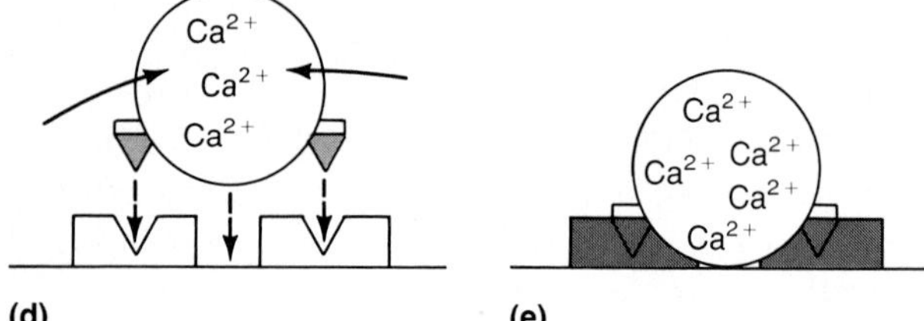

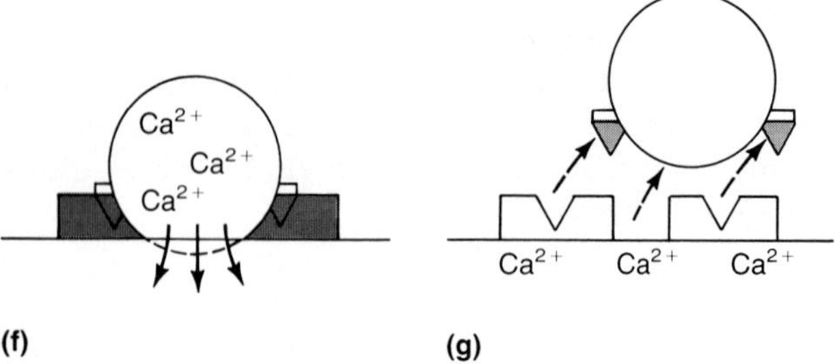

Removal of Calcium As figure 8.16 shows, the calcium that is permitted to enter the presynaptic terminal is carried back to the membrane and released outside the cell. The vesicles that accomplish this were, until the arrival of action potentials in the nerve terminal, filled with neurotransmitter, and they showed no tendency to adhere to the membrane and perform exocytosis. Theorizing how vesicles might get up against the membrane is not difficult. There are a lot of them in the cytoplasm of the presynaptic button, and they are in constant, probably undirected, motion. Sooner or later, each is bound to touch the membrane. The problem that has bothered researchers is why the membrane permits the vesicle to just slide away when it is filled with neurotransmitter, yet grips it when it contains calcium. That problem may finally be solved! Workers have recently identified a pair of contractile proteins that are almost certainly involved and may be solely responsible. One, called **stenin,** is present on the vesicular membrane, while the other, **neurin,** is evidently linked to the membrane of the presynaptic button. These proteins are almost identical in chemistry and function to the contractile proteins of muscle tissue (see chapter 10). Like muscle tissue, they require ionic calcium (Ca^{2+}) and ATP to function properly. Events apparently adhere to the following sequence:

During the periods when there is no electrical activity along the presynaptic axon, the transmitter-filled vesicles are abundant in the presynaptic button. Movement of these vesicles is probably random, and several are probably against or near the membrane at any given instant. Should the two contractile proteins neurin and stenin contact each other while the vesicles are filled with neurotransmitter, nothing happens. Both proteins are inactive. But the infusion of calcium into the vesicle changes things. Calcium is present in the presynaptic cytoplasm and, as noted above, during prolonged activity it replaces the acetylcholine within the vesicles. In a manner that is not yet clear, the ionic calcium within these vesicles activates the stenin, so that when it contacts the neurin on the membrane, it is as if two pieces of gluey paper suddenly touched. The two proteins adhere to one another, forming in the process a new compound, which is known, reasonably enough, as **neurostenin.** This newly formed neurostenin begins to contract just like a muscle fiber, and the shortening proteins clamp the transmitter-containing vesicles tightly against the terminal membrane (see figure 8.17). The vesicles are now pressed firmly against the membrane. Continued contraction of neurostenin cannot move them any closer, but contraction continues, nonetheless. This continued activity produces a rapidly mounting tension, which is believed to open channels that permit the calcium to diffuse out of the vesicles and reenter the interstitial fluids. Once the calcium is gone, the glue-like attraction that neurin and stenin had for each other vanishes, the neurostenin breaks apart, and the captured vesicle leaves the membrane.

The Postsynaptic Membrane and the PSP

There is considerable mystery surrounding the postsynaptic membrane and the activity involving the specialized receptor zones there. It is not known, for instance, just what happens when the receptor/transmitter complex forms. There seems to be little doubt that it somehow produces permeability changes in the postsynaptic membrane, but the method by which this is accomplished is largely unknown. There is a simultaneous increase in membrane permeability to both sodium and potassium. This has the net effect of quickly reducing the membrane potential in the vicinity of the receptor/transmitter complex.

There is an important difference between the development of these PSPs and the propagation of action potentials. You will recall that the action potential's initial rise to a high positive value is due primarily to a huge influx of sodium into the cytosol. Increased permeability to potassium ions follows this influx and initiates recovery from the active state. Apparently, in postsynaptic membranes, this sequential flow of sodium and potassium ions does not occur. There is a sudden, simultaneous change in membrane permeability toward *both* of these cations. The result is not as overwhelming as the action potential, however. Whereas the latter actually reverses membrane polarity, the PSP equilibrium is about −10 mV.

Typically, synapses within the central nervous system are axodendritic, and there are often many presynaptic terminals ending on single dendrites. As previously described, simultaneous potentials produced by many terminal buttons can summate when the terminals involved are close to one another. When they do, they produce the large, slowly spreading PSPs that fan out toward the axon hillock, and they can, if they are great enough and last long enough, produce action potentials in the postsynaptic axon (figure 8.18).

Figure 8.18 A "typical" neuron in the CNS, showing synapses capable of spatial summation and the functional zones of the neuron. Should two or more of the contacting interneurons fire simultaneously, the postsynaptic potentials thus produced could summate, thus increasing the likelihood of producing an impulse in the large neuron shown.

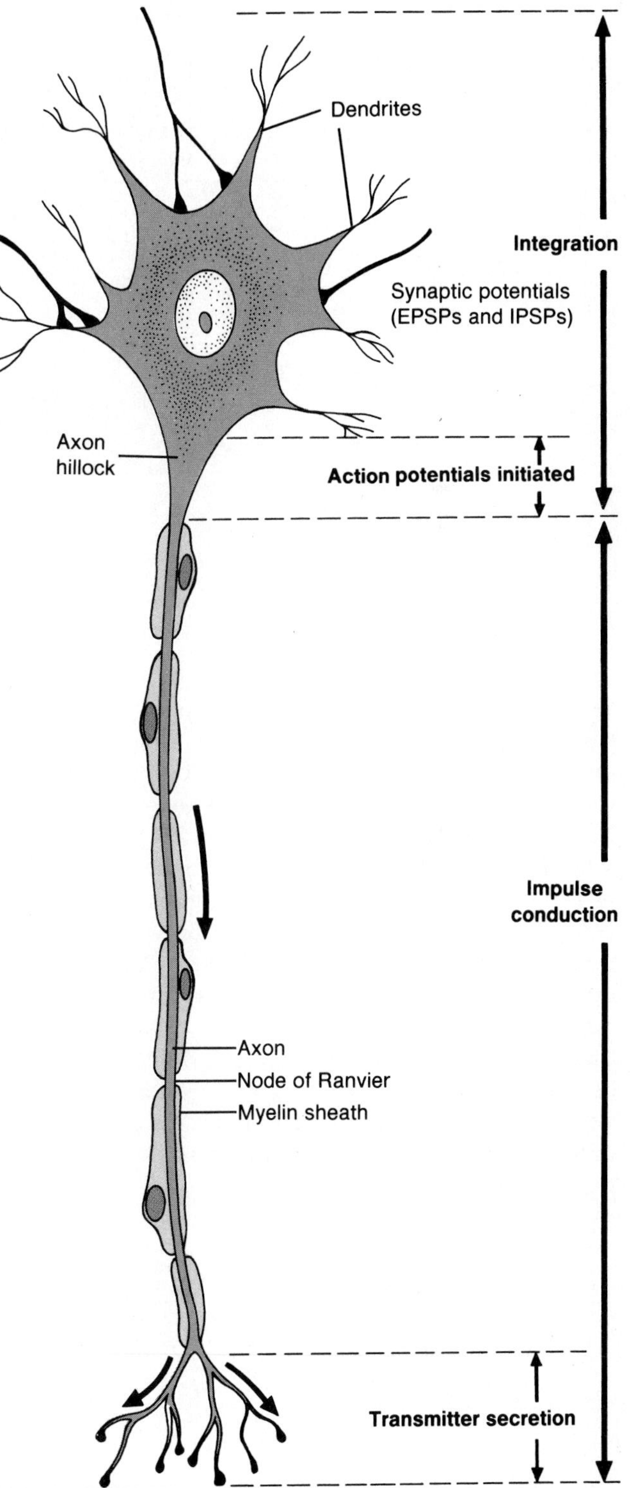

Figure 8.19 A graph illustrating temporal summation.

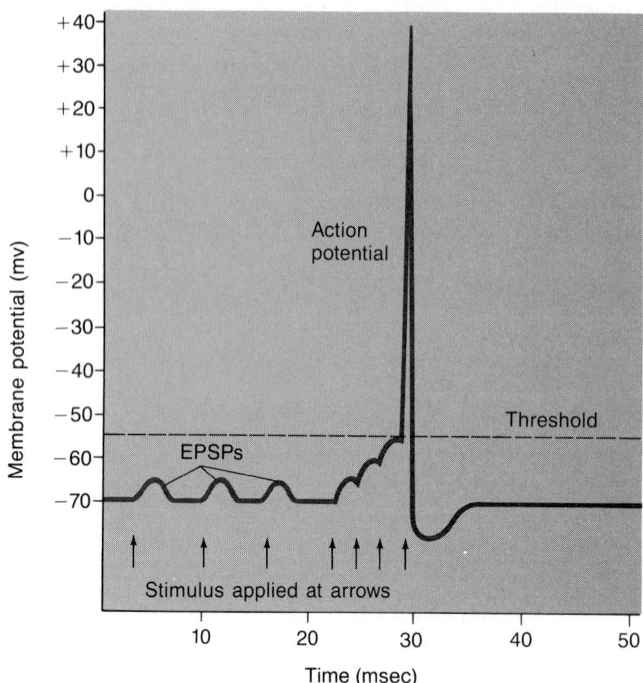

Spatial Summation Like receptor potentials, slow-spreading PSPs are not regenerative. Their spread is decremental, and power is rapidly lost. In addition, the area of the postsynaptic membrane that is affected by a single PSP is very small. Single PSPs, therefore, seldom produce significant electrical alterations in the whole postsynaptic membrane, particularly on a large cell with many synaptic contacts. But if such PSPs occur in clusters of synapses that are very close to each other, the summated depolarizations can usually produce an action potential in the axon. As noted earlier, this is *spatial summation.* Obviously, then, there must be many action potentials simultaneously rushing down a lot of presynaptic fibers to produce a response in large postsynaptic fibers, particularly spinal motor neurons.

Temporal Summation Occasionally, one or two terminals will receive a series of action potentials in rapid succession, thus producing an almost continuous release of neurotransmitter onto the postsynaptic membrane. The rapid bursts of transmitter produce a near-continuous flow of PSPs that overlap one another in time, thus producing another kind of summation known as **temporal summation** (figure 8.19).

Whether or not an action potential will fire in a postsynaptic nerve can also depend on the nature of the PSP. As we have seen, most neurotransmitters open channels in the postsynaptic membrane that permit a relatively free movement of both potassium and sodium. The potential across the membrane is thus reduced and tends to produce an active response

Figure 8.20 Inhibitory and excitatory fibers often synapse on the same neuron. Part of the process of integrating nerve signals involves the postsynaptic cell's accepting and evaluating different kinds of input.

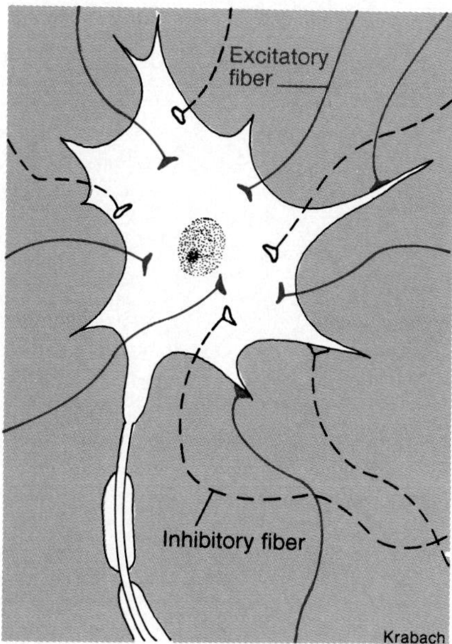

in the axon. This type of postsynaptic response is known specifically as an **excitatory postsynaptic potential (EPSP),** and it is similar to a receptor potential in many ways. Both vary in amplitude, both produce depolarizations that spread slowly and decrementally from their point of origin, and in both cases, the potential changes can summate.

However, not all neurotransmitters excite the postsynaptic membrane. Different kinds of fibers often synapse with a single cell, and not all release neurotransmitters that produce EPSPs . . . indeed, some have an opposite effect (figure 8.20). Some presynaptic membranes release chemicals that do not open channels in the postsynaptic membrane to both sodium and potassium. Instead, they increase their permeability only to potassium and/or chloride, and they ignore sodium. With passage made easier, the highly mobile potassium ions flow out in greater numbers than normal, thus making the interior of the dendrite *more* negative instead of less. Such *hyper*-polarizing potentials are known as **inhibitory postsynaptic potentials (IPSPs).** These inhibitory potentials, like EPSPs, can algebraically summate with EPSPs. Thus they can inhibit neurons from firing, or they can require a greater stimulus input than normal (figure 8.21).

Figure 8.21 Because of the presence of an IPSP on the postsynaptic membrane, a neuron that normally requires only four EPSPs in rapid succession to produce an action potential (see fig. 8.19) now requires six EPSPs. Inhibitory potentials summate, too. It is all a part of neural integration.

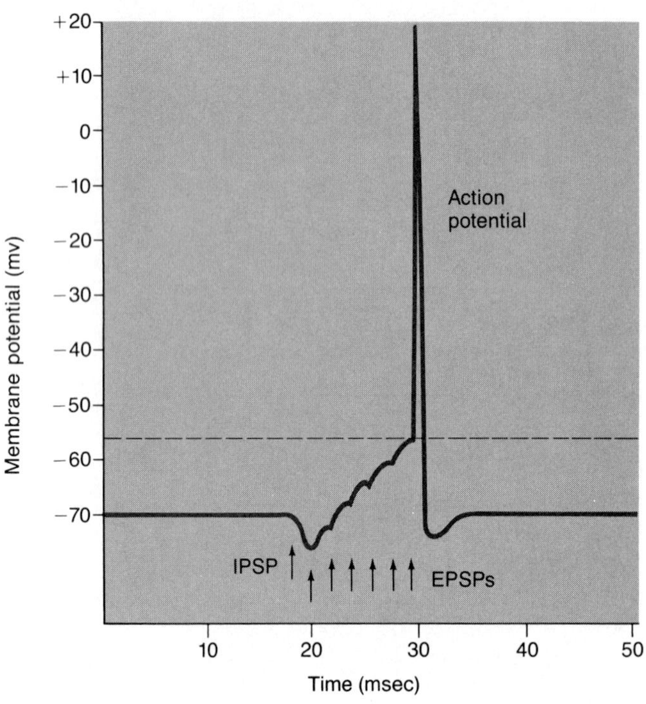

Table 8.2 Neurotransmitters
Known Peripheral Transmitters
Acetylcholine (Ach)
Norepinephrine
Epinephrine
Known Central Nervous System Transmitters
Acetylcholine
Norepinephrine
Epinephrine
Dopamine
Gamma-aminobutyric acid (GABA)*
Serotonin (5-hydroxytryptamine)
Suspected Central Nervous System Transmitters
Adenosine triphosphate (ATP)
Histamine
Glycine
Aspartic acid
Glutamic acid
Taurine

*Is often inhibitory

PSPs last much longer than action potentials do, but it is important to proper neural function that each one end as quickly as possible so that successive instructions or information can flow through the circuit. The catalyzed breakdowns of transmitter probably begin before the PSP shows up, and they continue as long as neurotransmitter is present. Neurons in the periphery that transmit with acetylcholine break it up as I have described, utilizing enzymes present on the membranes and in the synaptic cleft. Other neurotransmitters are handled in different ways. Norepinephrine, for instance, is broken up by an enzyme called **monoamine oxidase (MAO)** that is located in neural mitochondria. There are almost certainly other enzymes that perform the same function for different neurotransmitters. And there a lot of neurotransmitters. Table 8.2 lists some of those that researchers are most familiar with.

Table 8.3 compares the characteristics of slow potential changes to those of action potentials.

Table 8.3 Slow Potential Alterations vs. the Action Potential

Slow Potentials	Action Potentials
Initiated by opening gates for sodium and/or potassium.	Initiated by opening of sodium gates.
Depolarization occurs slowly.	Depolarization is explosive.
Spread is decremental.	Spread is nondecremental. Impulse is self-propagating.
No threshold voltage.	Has a threshold that must be reached before action potential will occur.
No refractory period.	Has two kinds of refraction—absolute and relative. Both limit frequency of firing,
Amplitude variable, depending on stimulus strength.	Impulse is always the same amplitude.
Summation possible with other similar potential changes.	No summation possible. Each impulse is unique.
No feedback support for potential changes.	Positive feedback supports development of impulse.
Maximum voltage change approximately 60 mv (−70 mv to −10 mv).	Maximum voltage value approximately 95 mv (−55 mv to +40 mv).

The Significance of the Chemical Synapse

Neural circuitry provides humans with logic. Hence it is logical to expect the brain to be able to supervise and manipulate the flow of information that moves through it. If each neuron merely served to pass on every electrical signal as it showed up, like a person in a bucket brigade, very little integration would be possible. There must be a point, somewhere within the CNS, where decisions about information processing are made; otherwise action potentials would randomly bound back and forth through the various brain circuits, producing nothing but confusion. It seems obvious that the axons serve merely as transmission lines; they play no role in the processing of integration, so we must look elsewhere. Sooner or later, all the information must enter other parts of the neuron—the dendrites, the end brushes, and the cell bodies. Information *might* be integrated or processed within these structures, although very little has been accomplished researching this aspect of neurophysiology.

Synaptic elements could also play an important role in the integration of neural information. What a postsynaptic neuron will do at a given moment is probably determined, at least in part, by the torrent of impulses streaming onto its membrane through a variety of neuronal contacts. Each of the synapsing fibers could affect the postsynaptic membrane in a different way.

As we have seen, not all neurotransmitters are designed to stimulate. Some are intended to inhibit. Keep in mind that neurotransmitter chemicals are not released into the synaptic cleft as chemical molecules, but are packaged in tiny parcels (quanta). Because of this, the transmitter units can vary in size, shape, or electrical charge distribution, and each variation could represent a different bit of information to the postsynaptic receptors. And the transmitter quanta are not the only things in a synapse that can vary. The cleft itself can vary—in width, certainly, and possibly also in the amount of transmitter breakdown that occurs after the quanta are released. It must also be remembered that the postsynaptic membrane is not a static structure with a battery of single-minded receptor sites, but rather a dynamic entity capable of shifting its sensitivities. This may be the most critical portion of the synapse, because it is here that the neurotransmitters exert their effects, and obviously the effects are *most* important. What stimulated the postsynaptic membrane very powerfully a millisecond ago may excite it only very slightly now, and the degree of stimulation and/or inhibition may depend on the location of the synapse as well as the condition of the postsynaptic membrane. Obviously, the transmission of information across a synapse can vary considerably. Chemical synapses could well be of tremendous integrative importance.

Neurotransmitters

In the last few years, neurotransmitters have become the focus of the most vigorous research efforts in behavioral sciences and neurophysiology. Physiologists have long known how neurotransmitters can affect muscles and glands. They have at least partially defined their functions in carrying information across synapses between neurons. Now other evidence is accumulating, evidence that suggests that these same neurotransmitters may also play a prominent role in the mediation of behavior patterns. It is common knowledge that epinephrine makes the heart beat faster and increases breathing rate, but we are only now beginning to realize that it may also change the state of the conscious mind. Research psychologists say it boosts overall attentiveness and makes people more aware of movement occurring close by. A close relative of epinephrine—norepinephrine—may be involved in dreaming and experiencing pleasure.

Psychiatrists and clinical psychologists are also showing more interest in transmitter chemicals, because evidence indicates that many of the so-called mind-altering drugs accomplish their task by interfering with normal synaptic transmission. Further, there is evidence to suggest that spontaneous changes in neurotransmitter concentrations in certain brain areas can produce abnormal behavior. This latter theory is supported by the observation that drugs designed to return neurotransmitter concentrations to the normal range can turn aberrant behavior patterns toward normal as well. Plainly, there is good reason to believe that some types of mental illness may be caused by unusual secretions of certain transmitters.

For decades it was assumed that an individual neuron could release only a single neurotransmitter. This principle, known as **Dale's Law,** has since been refuted. It is now clear that individual neurons can release more than one kind of neurotransmitter as well as certain neuromodulators. Nevertheless, acceptance of the "law" gave us a new series of terms that are still used and still have meaning. Nerves that respond to or use acetylcholine are known as **cholinergic nerves,** those using epinephrine (adrenalin) are called **adrenergic,** those that secrete and/or respond to dopamine are **dopaminergic,** and so on.

The Postsynaptic Membrane

It is important to remember that neurotransmitters do not determine all by themselves how their effector organs will respond. Transmitters, all by themselves, can't do anything. There has to be a receptor on the postsynaptic membrane, and it must be the right kind of receptor if the synapse is to perform its job properly. It is the formation of the transmitter/receptor complex that produces the response, and responses can vary considerably.

Postsynaptic receptors are categorized according to the kinds of chemicals that they respond to, and they are said, therefore, to be **pharmacologically defined.** We know, for instance, of two distinct types of cholinergic receptors. Acetylcholine binds with and activates both, yet as it turns out, the responses produced are distinctly different. There are obviously some fundamental differences among the receptors on these postsynaptic membranes. One type can be activated with *nicotinic acid* as well as Ach, and hence is called a **nicotinic receptor.** The other cholinergic receptor cannot be stimulated with nicotinic acid, but will respond to the compound *muscarine.* Hence it is called a **muscarinic receptor.** Stimulation of the nicotinic receptors by the neurotransmitter produces an almost instantaneous response; consequently we find nicotinic receptors abundant in muscles where speed of response is paramount. Activation of the muscarinic receptors, on the other hand, produces a slower but more prolonged response. Muscarinic receptors are found most commonly in effectors like visceral muscles, where slow but consistent activity is the keynote. See figure 8.22.

There are also two different types of adrenergic receptors. They are known as **alpha** (α) and **beta** (β) **receptors,** and these are further divided into two subtypes, α_1 and α_2 and β_1 and β_2 receptors. These subtypes are not equally sensitive to their two neurotransmitters (epinephrine and norepinephrine), and effector response varies depending on which complex forms. According to recent research, epinephrine can complex with both α and β receptors, producing good, general responses. Norepinephrine, on the other hand, while it can combine with all four subtypes, produces more selective and generally less pronounced responses when it combines with β receptors than it does when it combines with α receptors. (figure 8.23).

Activation of α receptor sites results in things like reduction in blood-vessel diameter, dilation of the eye pupils, relaxation of the visceral musculature, and heavy sweating. Activation of β sites, on the other hand, produces an *increase* in the diameter of selected blood vessels, such as the coronary arteries and the arterioles in voluntary muscles, and an increase in

Figure 8.22 Cholinergic receptor types: *a* and *b* are muscarinic receptors typically present on the membranes of effector cells that show smooth, prolonged responses to stimuli, such as (*a*) a smooth muscle cell typically found in the viscera or (*b*) a secretory cell. (*c*) The nicotinic receptor typically features a short, explosive response to stimuli. Nicotinic receptors are abundant in skeletal muscles.

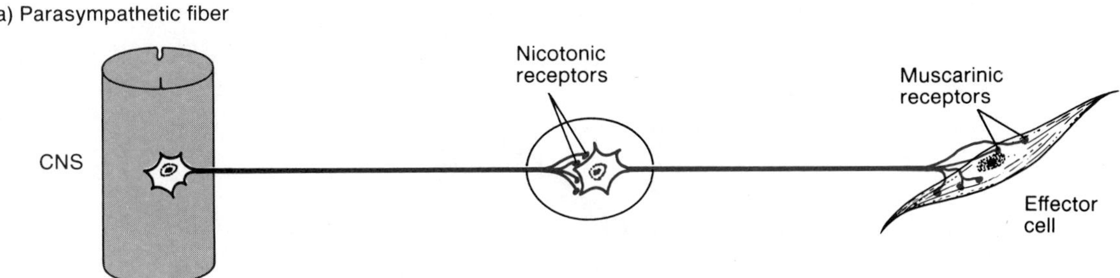

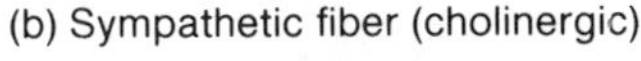

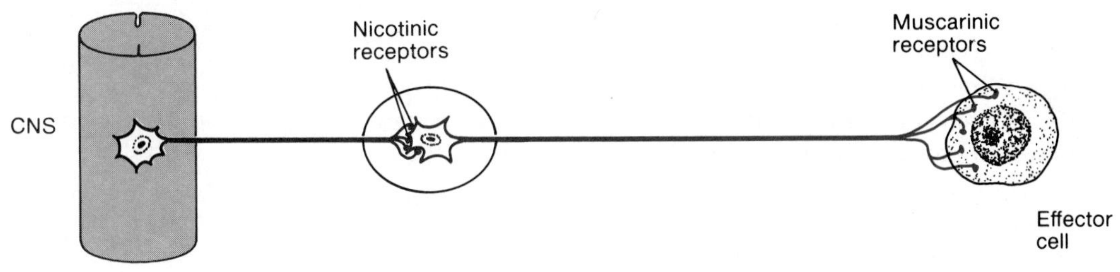

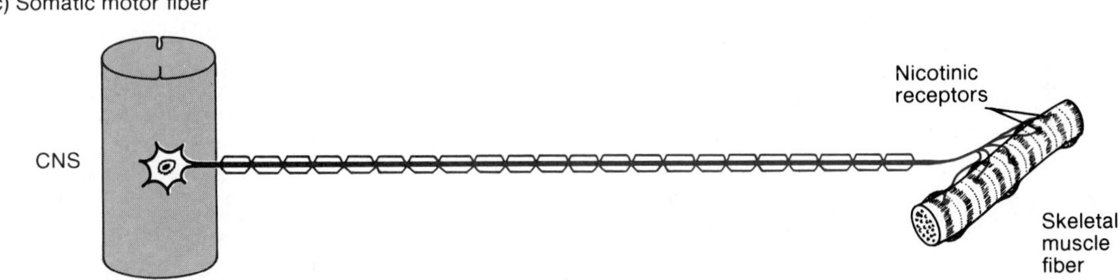

heart rate, while relaxing smooth musculature in the reproductive tract. Modern medical practice takes advantage of these diverse tendencies, and use of specific α- or β-blocking agents is common.

Anesthetics

No one looks forward to surgery under the best of circumstances, but one thing few people are concerned about is how much it will hurt *during* the operation. Everyone knows that during the surgery, they will be "asleep" or otherwise rendered insensitive to pain, thanks to the presence of a multitude of chemicals known as **anesthetics.** We have dozens of different kinds of anesthetics today, but essentially they all boil down to two basic types: **local anesthetics** and **general anesthetics.**

Local anesthetics are used when only a small part of the body is involved and the duration of the operation is short. Usually, except for the occasional hypersensitive patient, few complications occur with

Figure 8.23 Adrenergic receptor surfaces—a schematic. Epinephrine can combine with both α and β receptors, producing a similar response in both. Norepinephrine can combine with both, but responses in β receptors are weak. It is mainly an α stimulator.

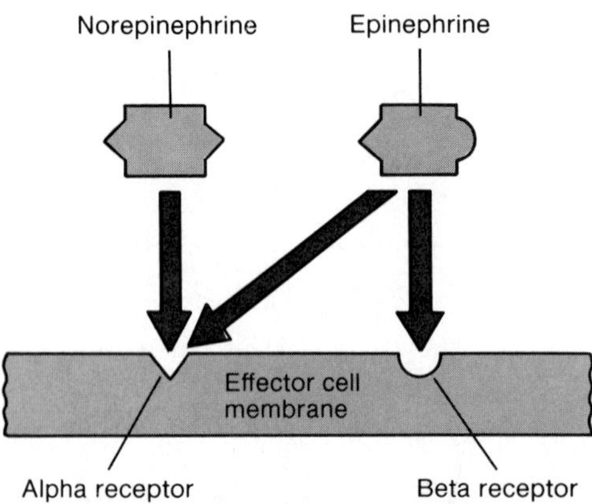

local anesthetics. When local anesthetics are used, the patient is fully awake. The brain is fully functional, and the patient often holds conversations with the attending dentist or physician. What is more, the pain has not been eliminated—not really. Receptors in the surgical area are picking up their stimuli with normal efficiency and transducing them into action potentials for transmission along their axons. The perception or *awareness* of pain is eliminated by the anesthetic, which places an obstacle in the way, one that alters the permeability characteristics of the axons. By blocking the sodium gates in the axons of pain-sensitive neurons, the anesthetic prevents the action potentials produced by pain receptors from travelling to connecting fibers and thence to pain centers in the brain (figure 8.24). The pain is there and is being detected, but the patient never perceives it.

Procaine and its derivative drugs (Xylocaine, Novocaine, etc.) operate by uncoupling the link between membrane permeability and transmembranal voltage so that sodium permeability does not increase when the membrane potential at the axon is reduced to threshold value. The result is, the sodium gates never open, and the axon will not fire. Everything else is working nicely. However, with no action potentials taking the pain messages to the brain, patients are never aware that they are being hurt. These local anesthetics are most commonly used in the practice of dentistry.

Despite their reputation for safety, local anesthetics cannot be used with abandon. Even the best have their problems. Like anything else injected into the body, local anesthetics are ultimately dispersed by the blood, and the blood, of course, carries them everywhere, including into the brain. If the levels of anesthetic in the brain get too high, things like restlessness and central nervous system depression can occur, and (rarely) convulsions and respiratory paralysis may follow. The dosage has to be monitored with considerable care, and practitioners take great pains to inject only enough to do the job. Dentists in particular, because teeth are sensitive and so close to the brain, are very careful with their placement of anesthetics so they will get maximum results with as little chemical as possible.

General anesthetics are the choice when the surgical procedure is complicated and of considerable duration. When general anesthesia is required, there are, as a rule, two objectives: to reduce or remove sensitivity to pain and to render the patient unconscious. At the same time, it is desirable to produce minimal interference with homeostatic control centers, particularly those involved in respiratory, thermal, or circulatory regulation. Often the varying requirements necessitate a thorough knowledge of anesthetics and the special characteristics of each. Barbiturates, for instance, can render a person unconscious quickly, but they do not relieve pain at all. Conversely, morphine can sometimes abolish pain completely without putting the patient to sleep.

Figure 8.24 The action of local anesthetics. (*a*) A typical "resting" neuronal membrane. The sodium gate is closed. (*b*) The arrival of an action potential opens the gates, and sodium pours through. (*c*) Local anesthetics like novocaine change the electrical characteristics of the membrane in such a way that arrival of an action potential does not open the sodium gates. With the gates closed, the action potential cannot continue along the axon.

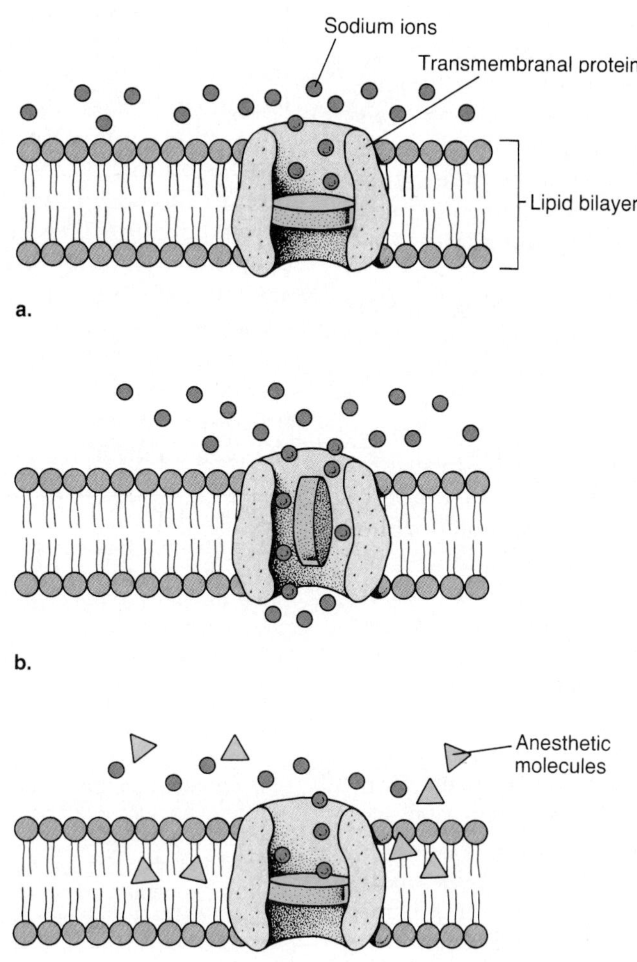

The opiates are the quintessential pain-relieving drugs. Medicine knows of nothing, synthetic or natural, that can equal the ability of certain opiates—particularly heroin—to eliminate the perception of pain. Characteristically, the best pain-relieving opiates have multiple target areas. Some of the pain relief undoubtedly begins in the spinal cord, where the sensory nerves have their initial contacts with elements of the central nervous system. Pain reception is dulled in these areas through the raising, by the opiates, of the neural thresholds at the synaptic contact points. In the brain itself, these drugs modify synaptic transmission in areas where pain information is integrated. Volatile anesthetics such as ether, halothane, and nitrous oxide evidently produce a general inhibition of synaptic conduction throughout the brain areas where they operate. Other painkilling anesthetics may work in still different brain areas, but the objectives appear to be basically the same: to interfere with transmission across specific synapses, thus producing **narcosis** (a state of stupor or numbness) in parts of the brain where sensory input is subconsciously integrated. By numbing these integrating brain areas, anesthetics can wall off the conscious brain from sensory input. When general anesthesia is successful, patients are in a deep sleep, are insensitive to pain, and are completely unaware of their surroundings.

Neuropeptides

In the last dozen years or so, a new group of neurotransmitters has burst into the spotlight and is receiving considerable research time and money. The newly discovered class of chemical transmitters is the **neuropeptides.** Their presence had been suspected in a vague sort of way for a good many years, but specific research and definitive biochemical analysis never really began until the late 1970s. It is speculated that the total number of neuropeptide transmitters may be in the thousands, but the most fascinating so far identified are the **enkephalins** (*endogenous morphines*—**endorphins**).

Scientists began to suspect that something like the endorphins must exist when they noticed that opium and opium derivates such as morphine tended to concentrate in certain areas of the brain—areas associated with pain. At first, this observation didn't raise any eyebrows. Morphine's painkilling abilities were well known, and it was certainly logical to expect a painkiller to concentrate in areas responsible for the perception of pain. More serious thinking, however, forced researchers to ask, "Why should it? What mechanism would be available to direct these chemicals to concentrate in one area any more than anyplace else?" The only answer that made sense was that the brain was familiar with the chemical, that it recognized it when it appeared and sent it where it could best be used. A little more thought led to speculation that there had to be receptors in the brain that are specific for morphine or for some very similar compound. Ultimately, workers concluded that some part of the brain must synthesize morphine or a compound very much like morphine. Subsequent research has confirmed this. Two such compounds were discovered initially and were named enkephalins by their discoverers. Technically, the term *enkephalin* now refers to any compound produced in the brain that has an opiate-like ability to deaden pain, and today we are aware of several.

It turns out that a good many of the body's peptides have a neurotransmitter or neuromodulator function. Researchers have isolated and identified more than fifty-five such, and there are probably more remaining to be found. These neuropeptides are found in specific neuronal pathways within the brain, and the functions of the neurons with which they are associated are well known. Many of them are concentrated in the same brain area where the enkephalins are also found, brain areas that are deeply involved in producing the emotions that are so characteristically human. This suggests that the neuropeptides may have a role in regulating emotional behavior.

It's All In Your Head

The discovery of the enkephalins has explained a good many phenomena that researchers and medical practitioners were aware of for years but had either misunderstood or misinterpreted. One such phenomenon has to do with pain deemed by someone else to be imaginary. Often, when sufferers are given sugar tablets and told that they are painkillers, they experience relief from pain. In the past, this led to the conclusion that the pain was imaginary and the sufferer had hypochondriacal tendencies. The discovery of enkephalins has ruined that argument. When people complaining of aches and pains are told they are being given painkillers, a genuine belief that they are about to experience relief evidently results in the secretion of β-endorphins. These endorphins are then carried to the pain-sensitive areas in the brain and proceed to reduce or eliminate pain perception. Both the pain and the painkillers are obviously genuine.

The concept that some affliction is "all in your head" is common enough, but few people using that phrase really think about what they have suggested. As most scientists view it, pain is a central nervous experience; hence a person must be consciously aware of it, or it is not pain. If a person's chest or abdomen is cut open, it should hurt a great deal, and of course, it does. At the same time, everyone knows that a person undergoing abdominal surgery does not scream or thrash about. They reconcile this apparent contradiction by noting that a person undergoing surgery does not suffer because his conscious centers are not aware that pain exists. Although they would probably not use these terms, what they are saying is that the painful stimuli certainly exist, but the patient never experiences pain because the stimuli never reach the conscious centers. It seems that no one argues with this concept. It is perfectly reasonable to assume that cutting open the patient's chest doesn't hurt because the person is not aware of the pain. Why then do people sometimes state that pain which is *perceived* is imaginary? Inadvertently, people who contend that pain is "all in one's head" are suggesting that individuals are not experiencing pain at all, but are practicing a deception—that they are lying to themselves about feeling pain. It is not likely very many people actually have that in mind when they make such an accusation, but it is worth remembering.

Acupuncture

The existence of enkephalins may also explain the effectiveness of **acupuncture,** the old Chinese method of applying anesthesia. Acupuncture has been practiced in China for hundreds of years, but Western science was, until very recently, skeptical of its efficacy. Established physicians who watched acupunctured patients undergo successful, painless surgery were convinced that what they had seen had been falsified somehow or that the patient had been mysteriously "brainwashed" into not feeling pain. Like the rest of us, they were advocates of "all-in-your-head" pain and "all-in-your-head" relief from pain. They never stopped to consider what that *really* meant.

Recent research indicates that there is nothing imaginary about the effectiveness of acupuncture. When acupuncture anesthesia is used, sterile needles are inserted in select portions of the body and vibrated or spun until the anesthesia is induced. Just where the needle has to be inserted to deaden pain in any given area was carefully researched by the Chinese centuries ago, and there is now an impressive library of locations. To deaden pain in the jaw, the needle is sunk into the hand between the first finger and the thumb. For an appendectomy, a needle would be inserted in the thigh and vibrated.

Once anesthesia is induced, it can last as long as six hours, and its effects are impressive. No one is certain why it works as it does, but the discovery of the enkephalins has provided one or two reasonable theories. One such theory suggests that puncturing the body in specific places stimulates, in some unknown way, the production of β-endorphins by the brain, and within minutes of the insertion of an acupuncture needle, patients receive a central nervous dose of anesthetic. Another theory states that the needles produce their blocking effect in the spinal cord, not in the brain. This latter theory suggests that each pain-receiving sensory neuron synapses in the spinal cord with several interneurons and that there is an enkephalin-producing neuron also at the synapse. Insertion of the acupuncture needle somehow stimulates this latter neuron, and the release of enkephalin into the synapses blocks pain transmission through that synapse (see figure 8.25). Somehow the Chinese made this astonishing discovery and were performing successful operations long before Western science managed to uncover chemical anesthesias.

Figure 8.25 One theory of how acupuncture works. The acupuncture needle is inserted, and it stimulates neuron A. Cutting with a scalpel sends pain impulses down sensory nerve P. The two neurons meet in the spinal cord, where they synapse with each other and an interneuron. In one version of the theory, enkephalins released by neuron A prevent neuron P from releasing its transmitter. Another version of the theory suggests that enkephalins released by *A* take up the receptor sites on the interneuron, and transmitter released by *P* has nowhere to go. The enkephalins inhibit, rather than stimulate, the interneuron.

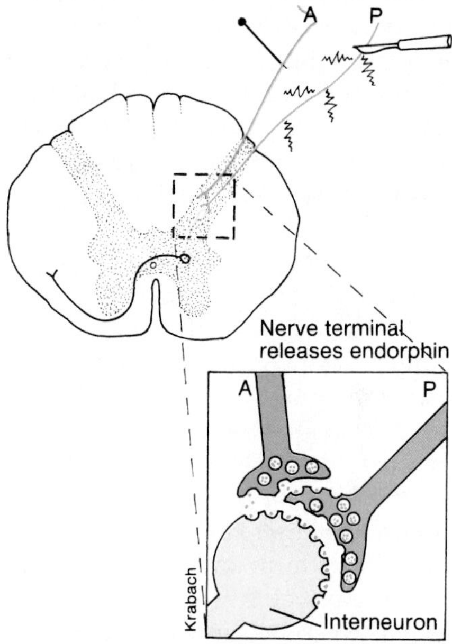

Natural "Highs"

Workers are also reporting that enkephalins can do more than just suppress pain. Physiological psychologist John Liebeskind and his group at UCLA have uncovered evidence that these and many other neuropeptides often aggregate in a part of the brain called the **limbic system**—an area associated more with emotion than pain perception. This suggests that some neuropeptides are involved with perceptions other than pain and may have a role in regulating emotional behavior. Researchers at the Loma Linda Medical Center in Ontario, California, have not only confirmed this idea, but have added to it. They have detected a relationship between exercise and production of β-endorphins by the pituitary gland. During exercise, β-endorphin production increases, and the amount released is proportional to the individual's daily activity. Habitually active people, when they exercise, evidently produce endorphins at a much higher rate than habitually inactive people produce when *they* exercise, and it has been suggested that this might explain the feeling of euphoria—the "high" that is so often experienced by well-conditioned people while they are running, pumping iron, or playing a vigorous game of tennis or basketball.

Other Neuropeptides

Other neuropeptides are demonstrating some remarkable abilities under the prodding of scientists across the country. As is the case with enkephalins, many are involved with neurons in brain areas where the function is well known, and so they are assumed to play a role in that function, whatever it may be. But it is turning out that many of them have other jobs to do as well. The hormone **cholecystokinin (CCK)** is one such peptide. It is known as one of the controlling mechanisms for increasing bile levels in the intestinal tract, and for years it was thought to restrict its activity to this. But now, evidence is increasing that it can also affect the brain. Recent work suggests that CCK and a closely related hormone called **gastrin** can reduce appetite. Clearly, there are many things to be learned from this exciting new branch of neurophysiology.

The Brain

The swollen, rostral end of the neural tube is the brain. It is the largest division of the nervous system and easily the most complex organ in the entire body. Brain complexity is beyond belief. Even the pinhead-sized brain in wasps and houseflies has so far defied circuit analysis. In these tiny concatenations, all efforts to pin down what memories are and how they are implanted have failed.

One reason workers tried to analyze the circuitry in insect nervous systems was that they were hoping for simplicity; the insects' brains are very small. Another reason was that they expected all the circuits to be the same in any given species of insect. The patterns in these tiny brains are almost certainly species specific, meaning, in a way, that all these insects have the same "memories" and instincts. The insect brain is almost entirely preprogramed . . . learning is minimal, and virtually every behavioral process is "instinctive." Not so in vertebrates.

The most primitive vertebrates have well-developed brains, and by examining these brains, we can learn a lot about how certain animals go about doing what they do. Fishes have a fairly large brain, and the distribution of brain cells and relative sizes of the various structures can tell us a great deal about how these animals hunt and which senses they tend to rely on for survival. In sharks and their relatives, for instance, the **cerebellum** and the **olfactory lobes** are dominant (figure 8.26). As you can see from the figure, the cerebellum is a portion of the **hindbrain.** It is involved mainly in nerve/muscle coordination and apparently serves as an integrating center. For example, when voluntary muscles move, sensory nerves pass the information about the movement to the cerebellum, which in turn relays it to higher centers. The higher centers then tell the cerebellum where the muscles *should* be. The cerebellum integrates all this input, then determines what kinds of movement are necessary to get the muscles where they should be. Instructions travel through motor nerves, and the movement is accomplished. Without the cerebellum, complex, rapid body movements would not be possible.

The **cerebral hemispheres** are the parts of the vertebrate brain that provide conscious thought. The fact that the olfactory lobes in sharks are larger than the cerebral hemispheres clearly shows the relative importance of the two organs in this animal. The olfactory lobes are responsible for relaying odors in the water to the integrating centers of the shark's brain, and plainly, sharks rely on their sense of smell a lot more than they do on their ability to think.

Figure 8.26 The shark brain.

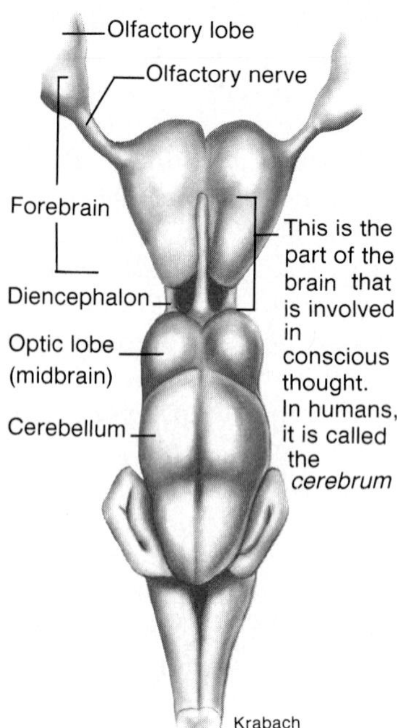

Investigating the brains of amphibians, reptiles, and mammals, we see the cerebral hemispheres gradually increasing in relative size until in the mammals—and particularly the primates—they overwhelm all the other parts (see figure 8.27).

Note how different the thought-oriented human brain is from the instinctively controlled nervous system of sharks. In humans, the cerebrum dominates the entire brain (figure 8.28). Most of it consists of nerve fibers **(white matter)** with an outer surface made up of cell bodies **(gray matter).** Like the cerebellum, the cerebral hemispheres are highly **convoluted,** meaning that the surface is folded back and forth against itself, probably to increase the total volume of gray matter without having to increase the size of the skull. Folding is a great way to do this . . . if you doubt it, try folding a sheet of paper into an accordion-like configuration and note how much more compact a container you can fit it into once it is folded. The cerebral hemispheres represent the part of the brain that is concerned with consciousness—with thought, memory, learning, intellectual ability, conscious control, personality—in short, with everything that makes us unique individuals.

Figure 8.27 The human brain. In humans the cerebrum awarfs all other structures. It consists of two hemispherically shaped neural masses separated by a deep fissure.

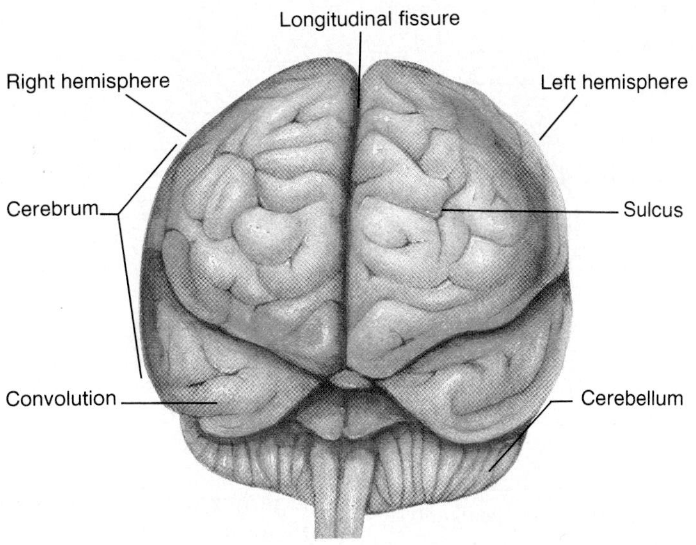

Figure 8.28 A sagittal section of the human brain, showing the major structures.

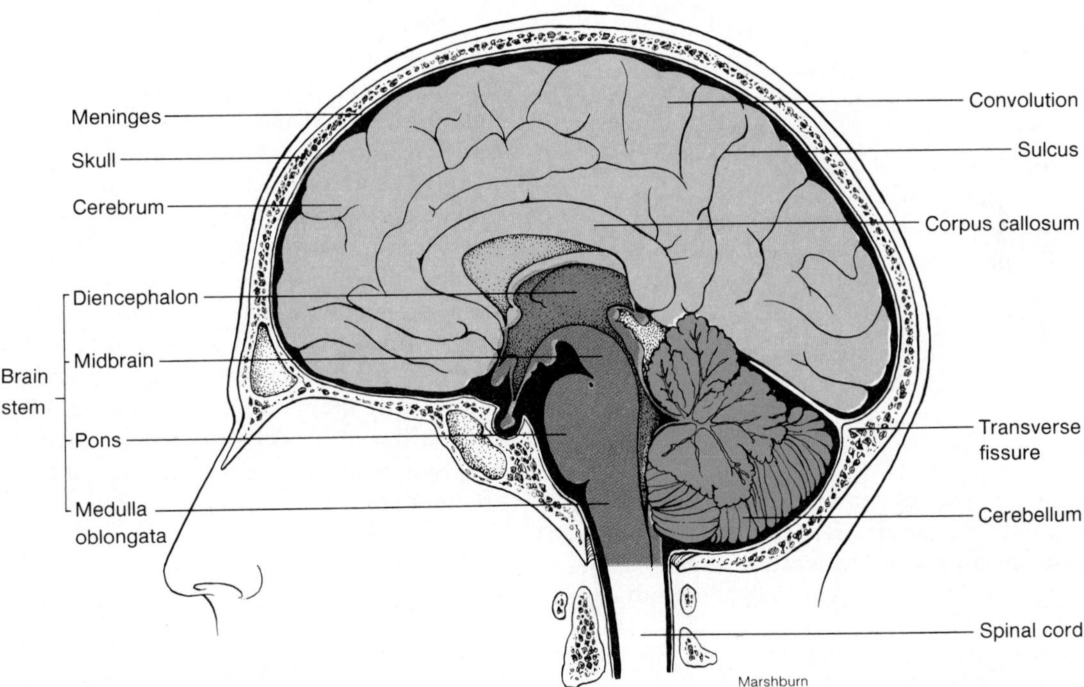

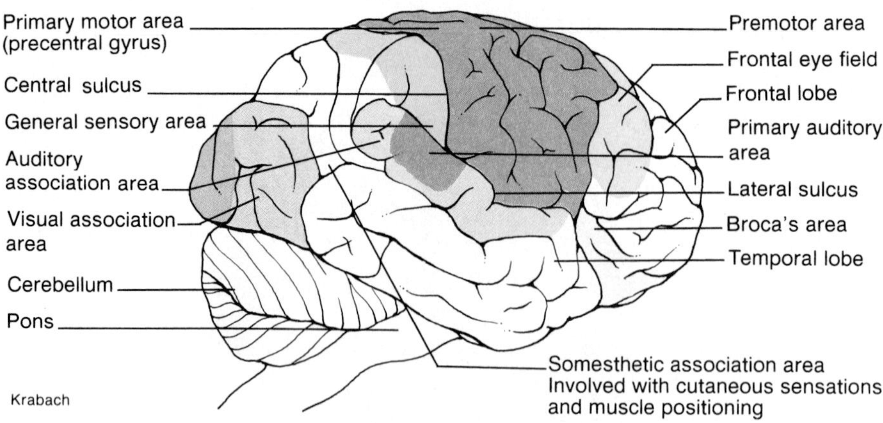

Figure 8.29 The functional zones of the cerebrum.

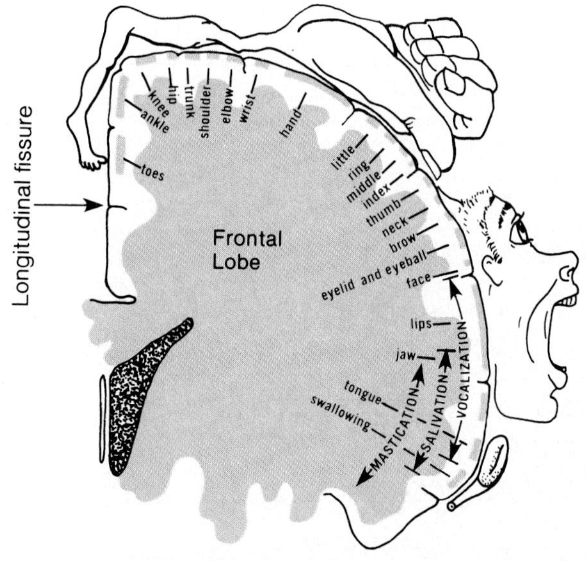

Figure 8.30 Motor controls of the cerebrum indicating by size the relative volume of brain devoted to each.

Three major types of cerebral control zones have been identified: the **motor areas,** the **sensory areas,** and the **association areas.** The location of these is depicted in figure 8.29. Certain zones in the brain control specific functions in humans, and we have learned, often through unfortunate accident, what certain parts of the cerebrum control. For instance, when an accident unfortunately ablated a portion of the left side of a woman's brain near the midline and just slightly aft of the **central sulcus** (see figure 8.29), doctors discovered that she was unable to put words together without help. She could understand everything that was said to her, and she knew exactly what she wanted to reply. She simply was not able to put her thoughts into words and say them—and she could not write them, either. Obviously, the portion of the brain that was damaged in the accident dealt with speech and the use of words.

As a result of similar observations in other patients and a lot of controlled experimentation in more primitive animals, the surface of the cerebrum has been pretty well mapped in a rather gross way (see figure 8.30). And from the amount of cerebral gray matter devoted to various body zones and structures, we can estimate the relative *fineness* of control humans can exert on various parts of the body. For instance, because so much of the cerebrum is involved with the hands, it is obvious that a person's hands and fingers are controlled with more sensitivity and discrimination than are the muscles of the back and thighs, since only a little gray matter is associated with their control. And, for the same reasons, control of lip, cheek, and tongue muscles is more precise than is control of the foot and toes.

Memory

Memory is the heart and soul of intelligence. We often tend to denigrate memorizing things as not being indicative of real intelligence: "Far better," people say, "to be able to reason and make use of facts than to simply memorize things." To some extent this is true, but what everyone seems to forget is that we are able to reason only by comparing current experience with past memories. Making use of facts actually means applying things that we remember to current problems. Without our memories, we are just machines.

But what is memory? This is a question that has plagued researchers for millenia. The first really scientific search began in 1917 when neurophysiologist Karl Lashley began his search for what he called the **engram** — the brain's memory patterns. Lashley really did not know what form these memory patterns might take, although he suggested that they might be sequences of biochemicals that held keys to certain electrical circuitry in the cerebrum. Using the only method that seemed reasonable at the time, he began systematically removing small portions of brains of experimental animals and noting carefully any memory loss. After more than thirty years of painstaking effort, he informed the world that while he had never succeeded in finding the engram, he could at least show where it was *not*. He concluded that memory existed everywhere in the brain, scattered throughout its mass. He called this hypothesis **equipotentiality.**

His theory may be correct, but it is still vigorously debated. The simple truth is that even today, we really do not have much of an idea what happens to our brains when a new memory takes up residence there. Some workers feel that the new engram represents an electrical circuit similar to a memory circuit in a computer—one in which the synapses permit an easy, patterned passage once the beginning has been opened. Others feel that electrical circuitry is the effect, not the cause of memory, and that the real memory patterns are locked in special biochemicals, among them certain types of RNA. Still others are convinced that while RNA may direct the development of memory, the final memory patterns reside in certain small proteins or neuropeptides that show up when a new engram is established in some part of the brain. There is empirical evidence to support all these contentions. There is, for instance, no doubt that computer memory banks are electrical circuits, so it is certainly possible that human memory is electrical. Still, other workers have produced results that suggest chemicals may be responsible for at least part of memory. Their experiments seem to show that after a rat has learned a task, a certain neuropeptide shows up in his brain, and if it is extracted and injected into a naive rat, this second rat will be able to perform the task. Whether or not this latter work is valid has been vigorously debated, and most workers seem to think it is not. But even if it is not, the possibility still exists that the operations of the brain's memory banks depend more on chemicals than electricity.

All these things give us some indication of the tremendous activity that must take place in a brain when a new item or activity is learned, but none of them indicate what form this engram might finally take. There seems to be little doubt that there is more than one kind of memory. For instance, if someone said to you, "my phone number is 813-4611," you might hasten to write down the number before you forget it. The person usually need not repeat the number; we can remember it for a few minutes. But that is all. This is our **short-term memory,** and it is evidently quite different from permanent or **long-term memory.** For those of us who have worked with computers, we might think of the difference in this way: the short-term memory is like the internal memory in a computer, the part that engineers call the random-access memory or RAM. It lasts until we turn the machine off, and then it is gone forever. The long-term memory, on the other hand, is like the disk or tape where these bits of information are stored in the form of magnetic patterns; barring accident, they last forever and can be retrieved by the computer any time they are required.

However, as you can easily imagine, the memory pattern on the disk is not the same thing as retrieving and displaying the pattern on a computer monitor. So it is with the brain. The memory patterns are stored somewhere below the level of consciousness in a form we know very little about. They can be retrieved by inserting the proper code into the "computer," and if the proper code is not used, they cannot be retrieved. Unlike commercial computers, the brain can handle many codes, and the codes can take many different forms. Odors, music, certain tactile patterns, flavors, or visual patterns can all trigger memories, retrieving them from their "storage disks" and displaying them on the conscious monitor of the cerebrum. And sometimes, we just cannot retrieve a memory no matter how hard we try. How often have you had a person's name on the tip of your tongue but were unable to drag it out of storage onto the monitor?

As for our capacity to remember things, once again we are stumbling around in the dark. We know from experiments that most people can hold about seven bits of information in their short-term memory, and these bits are usually retained by taking a mental photograph of the items or making a mental audio recording. If someone tells us their phone number, we have an audio recording; if we got the number from the telephone directory, we retain a photograph of it. Some people can hold these photographs for very long periods of time—the so-called **photographic memory** — but such people are very rare indeed. Short-term memory is usually just as the name implies—viable for only a short time. Once you have used the information, you tend to discard it. How many times have you had your friend or spouse repeat the same directions to a certain destination while you were driving?

Figure 8.31 Peppermint Patty filling her head with facts.

Long-term memory is quite different. These memories are stored permanently in our brains, and no one knows how many items can be stored in our long-term memories because no one has ever filled up their "disks." We might make up jokes about it (see figure 8.31), but fortunately it has never happened. For all we know, our capacities may be virtually unlimited.

Obviously, if we wish to retain a lot of information, we must first accept it in small doses for storage in short-term memory and then transfer it from short- to long-term memory. We don't really know what is taking place in the brain during this process. We do know that it is not easy to transfer engrams from our short-term memory into our long-term banks. How many times have you met someone you really like and managed to get their name and phone number, then have forgotten the number before you can write it down? Often you will repeat the number over and over to yourself as you search the area for a scrap of paper or a pencil with which to write, yet by the time you find the item you need, you realize that you've forgotten the number. There are all kinds of tricks that people use in an attempt to successfully transfer an engram from short- to long-term memory, and all of them work. Some try to associate a familiar object or a common name with what they are trying to remember; others try to mentally reconstruct the setting in which the numbers or names were first mentioned; still others try to store their facts by always attempting to memorize them in the same location . . . there are all kinds of little tricks that can be used. None of them is infallible, yet they all tend to work when used correctly. The transfer of information from short-term to long-term memory, however, is a tricky process and fails more often than it succeeds, as many a struggling student will tell you.

Other Brain Parts

Scientists engaged in brain research have defined the brain zones to a point that is more precise than we have to deal with in this course (see figure 8.32). However, it is necessary to know the location of the major zones and how they exert their control over the body's homeostatic mechanisms.

The Basal Ganglia

The **basal ganglia** are a collection of fairly large nuclei lying in the central zones of each cerebral hemisphere. (*Ganglia* is actually a misnomer for these structures. The word *ganglion* is reserved for a collection of nerve cell bodies clustered together outside the central nervous system, and the basal ganglia are clearly within the CNS. A similar collection within the CNS is termed a *nucleus;* hence the name *basal nuclei* would be more appropriate.) They form a kind of border around the thalamus, and they include four main structures: the **putamen,** the **globus pallidus,** the **caudate nucleus,** and the **corpus striatum.** The function of this brain area is relatively obscure, but there is little doubt that it is involved in the control of muscle movements. The caudate nucleus and the putamen have been associated with unconscious movements of skeletal muscles that are involved in retaining balance. Other regions apparently play a role in regulating muscle tone.

The Thalamus

Partially wrapped by the structures of the basal ganglia is the **thalamus,** a large cluster of nuclei that collectively resemble a pair of rugby balls (egg-shaped balls that are fatter than footballs). It is an extremely complex structure just ahead of the midbrain, and only a little is known about it functionally. It is certainly a major relay station. Its nuclei receive fibers from the

Figure 8.32 A sagittal section of the brain, showing the brain stem and other subcerebral structures.

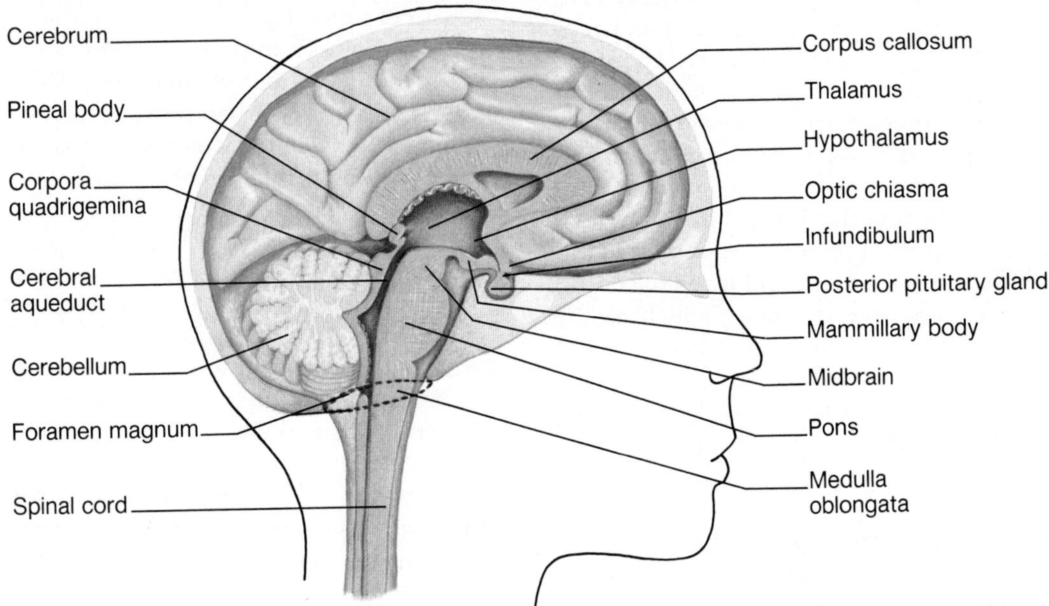

optic tract, auditory centers, and somatic sensory systems, and it relays information carried into the auditory zone of the cerebral cortex, the visual cortex, and the somatic sensory cortex. It is also involved in sleep and wakefulness, but its precise role in these states is not clear.

The Hypothalamus

The **hypothalamus** is a subcortical structure that covers the floor of the braincase in the forward part of the head. It is roughly just above the roof of a person's mouth and runs as far toward the rear as the opening to the throat. In actual size, it is quite insignificant. But in function it is of enormous importance, particularly to those who study autonomic control systems, because it seems to be linked to nearly all of them. The hypothalamus is involved in control of hunger and thirst, thermal regulation, blood pressure, sleeping, and wakefulness, and it is generally viewed as the primary control center for the endocrine system, since so many endocrine feedback loops run through it (chapter 10).

The Limbic System

The name *limbic* has nothing to do with the body's limbs, but is derived from the Latin word *limbus,* which means "an edge" or "circular band." The word was originally applied because this system forms a ring or band around the inner border of the cortical mantle. It is made up of several subordinate structures but for our purposes will be considered a single structure. It is relatively underdeveloped in most of the lower vertebrates, where many behavioral patterns are instinctive, but it shows considerable enlargement in organisms that possess fewer instincts and more learning patterns. For this reason it has been associated with an evolutionary break from instinct toward learning and a concomitant variation in inherited behavior. Parts of the limbic system have been associated with emotions like rage or burning anger, but one portion, the **hippocampus,** is apparently deeply involved with learning and memory, particularly the acquisition of new memory patterns. As is often the case, someone's misfortune provides us with much information. Researchers studying **Alzheimer's disease** have discovered that the brains of Alzheimer's patients show heavy neural deterioration in the hippocampus and in areas leading to and from this structure. The net result of this deterioration is apparently an electrical isolation of the hippocampus from other brain centers—particularly the cerebral cortex. This deterioration coincides with the victim's inability to gain new information and gradual loss of *all* memory as the disease progresses. We will have more to say about this in chapter 19.

The Hindbrain: The Medulla, Pons, and Cerebellum

The **medulla** is at the base of the brain. It sits just above the uppermost segment of the spinal cord and represents the first significant rostral enlargement of the neural tube. It contains a large region consisting of many cell bodies (gray matter) and a few fibers (white matter). This region is known as the **reticular formation,** and it is important to sleep and arousal mechanisms. Also, within this formation are some of the most important control centers in the entire brain. There is a **cardiac center,** which is involved in control of heart activity, a **respiratory center,** which, as the name implies, controls respiratory rate and depth, and a **vasomotor center** that controls circulatory tone throughout the body. From a functional point of view, it is one of the most critical structures in the entire nervous system. Even a tiny bit of damage in this area can cause immediate death.

The **pons** is just above the medulla. It consists mainly of reticular cells and is important in sleep and arousal mechanisms. In addition, it serves as a relay station between the spinal sensory nerves and the higher brain centers, and it has also been associated with the control of respiration. Many motor tracts run through the pons, carrying instructions from conscious centers in the cerebrum to the muscles that move our bodies.

The *cerebellum* resembles, in a way, a second, smaller brain that has been glued onto the back of the pons (see figure 8.32). Its function in sharks has already been discussed, and it seems to subserve a similar function in all known vertebrates. The major difference between the fishes and more advanced vertebrates seems to be less and less reliance on the cerebellum to *initiate* muscle control. In the fishes and some amphibians, the cerebellum controls all muscle movement, whereas in mammals and birds, the orders for skeletal muscle movement (with the exception of spinal reflexes) originate in the cerebral hemispheres. However, even in mammals, damage to the cerebellum results in jerky, uncontrolled motion and loss of ability to exert any fine control over the muscles. It seems clear that the cerebellum is responsible for orchestrating muscle movement and maintaining clear harmony between their operation and the orders descending from the conscious centers in the brain.

The Autonomic Nervous System

The **autonomic** (involuntary) **nervous system** is not a distinct *physical* division of the nervous system; it is interwoven both functionally and anatomically with the **somatic** (voluntary) **nervous system.** Nevertheless, it does have certain morphological features that belong to it alone and serve to distinguish at least some parts of it from somatic nerves. Functionally, although it is *mostly* accurate to say that it subserves the unconscious homeostatic functions of our bodies, it is not *entirely* accurate; people can—through biofeedback techniques—learn to control some of these erstwhile "involuntary" operations.

Anatomically, the autonomic nervous system can be distinguished from the somatic—at least in peripheral neural areas—by the presence of a synapse between the spinal cord and the effector organ. Somatic motor neurons exit the spinal cord and snake their way to their effectors with no synaptic intervention (see figure 8.33).

The autonomic nervous system is designed to function without any conscious effort, a benefit of which most of us are unaware. It is the autonomic nervous system that handles things like the circulatory adjustments that are necessary when food is being absorbed, changes in the eye when moving from dim to bright light, changing respiratory rate and depth when blood gases are abnormal—all the operations that keep an organism healthy and comfortable, but that no one has to concentrate on.

There are two distinct parts to the autonomic nervous system: the sympathetic and the parasympathetic. Nerves from both often run side-by-side into an effector organ, where they almost always produce opposite effects. A muscle that is stimulated into activity by impulses from the parasympathetic system will be inhibited by impulses from the sympathetic. A gland that the sympathetic system stimulates to increase its secretory activity will be turned off by the parasympathetic system. By carefully adjusting the balance between the two systems, the autonomic nervous system can maintain a proper level of function in our body organs during both routine and emergency operations.

Like the rest of the nervous system, autonomic processes respond to sensory input through reflex loops similar to those involving somatic nerves. Receptors in areas like the large blood vessels or visceral musculature pick up information and relay it to the spinal cord. Within the cord, this information may be

Figure 8.33 Somatic efferent pathways compared to autonomic afferents. Note the presence of a synapse in the autonomic pathway.

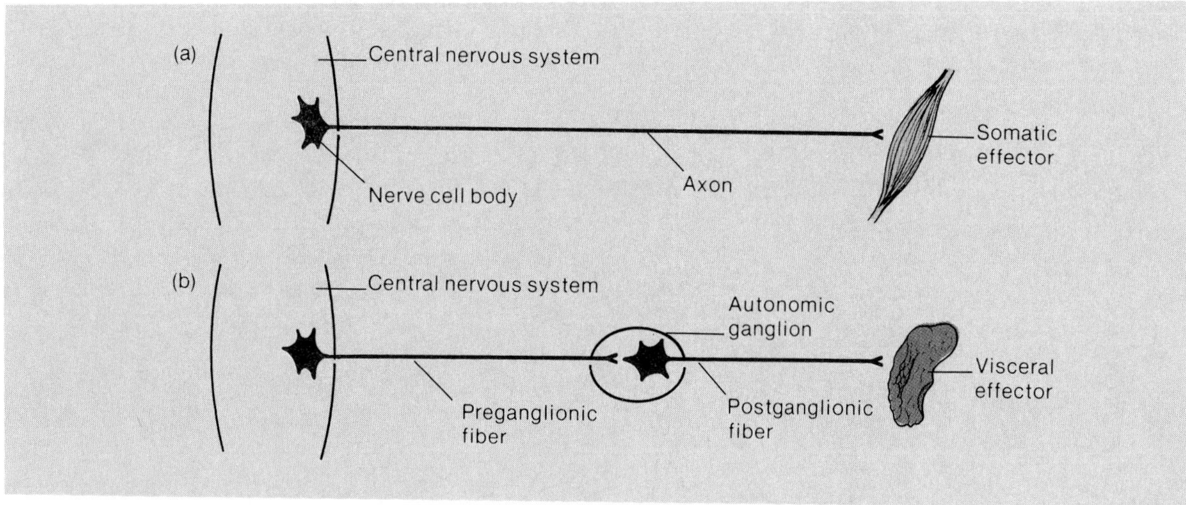

handled by reflex or it may be funneled up to brain centers for more detailed integration before any adjustments are made. When the final neural alignments are accomplished, instructions are sent along efferent neurons to the organs involved, and the system is fine-tuned so that homeostatic harmony is maintained. Neither the sympathetic nor the parasympathetic system can be considered inhibitory or stimulatory, since they do both, depending on the organ system involved (see figure 8.34).

Generally speaking, the sympathetic nervous system prepares the whole organism to handle an external emergency. If you keep this basic goal in mind, the seemingly disconnected details of sympathetic function are more easily learned. If you were hiking along a lonely, narrow trail in high mountains and upon turning a blind corner, were suddenly confronted by a bear that wanted right-of-way, this would be such an emergency. Regardless of the ultimate solution to the problem, you would need every ounce of physical capability at your command. To fulfill this requirement, the sympathetic system fires all its guns at once:

Pupils dilate
Breathing tubes open wide
Respiratory rate increases
Heart rate goes up
Vessels carrying blood to the limb muscles open up wide
Salivary secretions slow to near zero
Blood is diverted from the visceral organs
Visceral muscle activity stops
Secretory activity in the digestive system ceases
The brain becomes focused and alert

Any other adjustments that would help to accelerate physical activity and awareness would all swing into action, bracing you for whatever you must do to survive. This sequence of events is typical of sympathetic activity and has been termed the **3-F** or **"fight, flight, fright" response.**

When you consider the purpose, all these apparently disconnected preparations make perfect sense. The pupils dilate to increase the field of vision. (Constriction of the pupils increases visual acuity, but in a situation like this, you don't need acuity as much as a wide angle of vision . . . if there is a way out, you need to see it *now*.) Breathing tubes open wide, and respiratory rate increases to provide all necessary oxygen as rapidly as possible so you *can* move quickly. The heart rate goes up and peripheral blood vessels dilate for the same reason—to carry nutrients and oxygen to limb muscles that are suddenly going to need all they can get. Under the circumstances, the last thing a person needs to be concerned with is digestion of food; the energy going into that process is needed elsewhere, so those operations shut down.

Figure 8.34 Some of the functions under control of the autonomic nervous system.

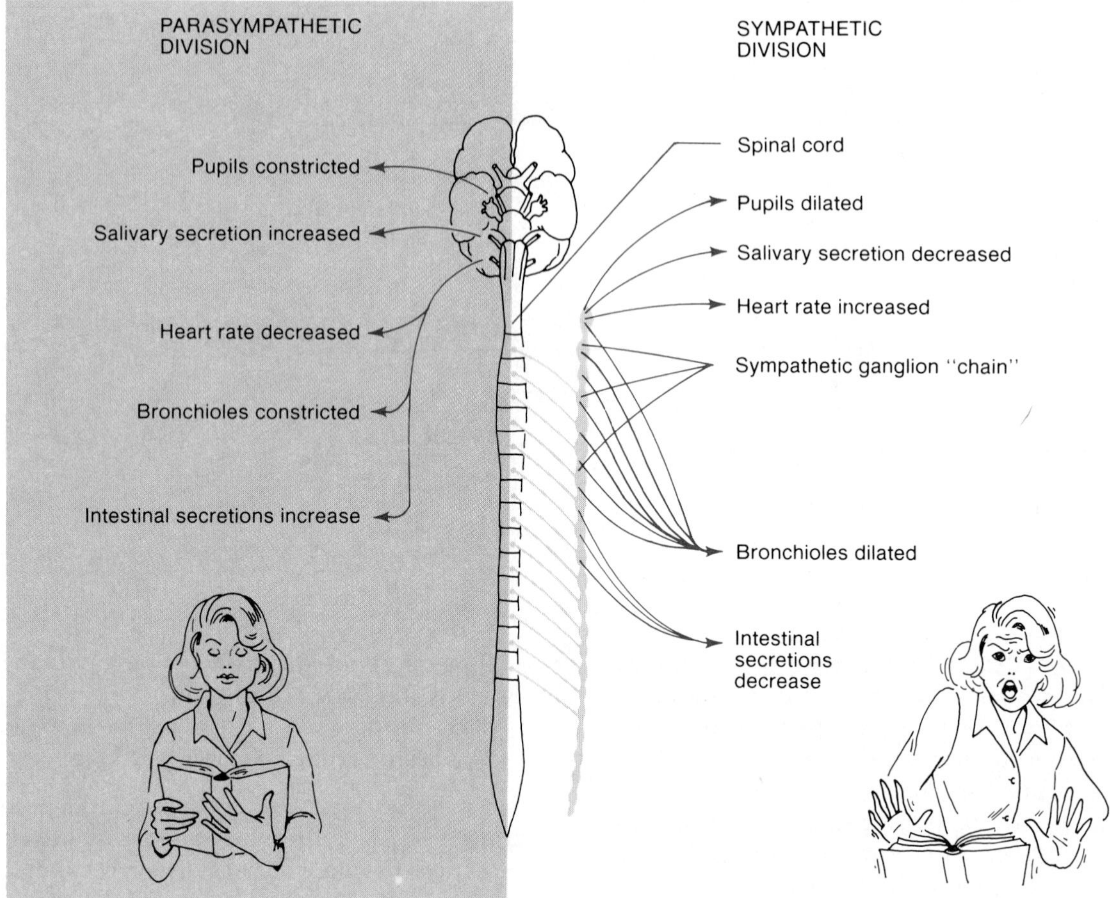

In many cases, particularly if running is the most obvious solution, being encumbered by the weight of food in the gut is a handicap, and the body dumps all it can—rapidly. Humans consider it a disgrace to defecate in fear, but other animals don't. They accept it as a survival mechanism, and humans, whether disgraced or not, often do, too. Ask any G.I. who has been with a troop of men under fire for the first time what the odor was like in the vicinity. Even experienced combat troops have to consciously constrict their anal sphincter muscles when a heavy artillery bombardment starts dropping shells among them or an enemy tank suddenly appears on top of a hill fifty yards away.

The parasympathetic system, on the other hand, deals with everyday problems—no emergencies, just life's little homeostatic adjustments. This system fires its neurons more selectively than the sympathetic does. When the sympathetic lets go, it fires everything at once. Not so the parasympathetic. When eating is imminent, parasympathetic fibers stimulate salivary secretions, then they begin the churning movements of the stomach, and they often initiate some gastric fluid secretion as well. During these periods, the phenomenon known as **borborygmus** (stomach growling) often shows up. When food enters the small intestine, it is the parasympathetic system that increases the flow of blood through the viscera so that digested food can be properly absorbed. Parasympathetic impulses will slow—sometimes even temporarily stop—the heart. They will constrict breathing tubes and reduce blood flow to the peripheral muscles. This may seem undesirable—even detrimental—and often it is, but there are times when it is not. When we are sleeping or relaxing, maximum blood flow to skeletal muscles, heavy breathing, or high heart rates are a terrible waste of energy, and adjusting parasympathetic controls prevents such losses. But even more than that, the parasympathetic system must often undo what the sympathetic has done.

Consider your experience with the bear along the narrow mountain trail. You went through a tremendous nervous upheaval on several fronts. Naturally, the conscious brain is accepting some pretty traumatic neural outbursts. The eyes bring the stimulus of "BEAR!" into the brain, and it is relayed rapidly to the cortex. The cortex has to decide what to do, and whatever it decides to do, it has to be done quickly. But it is no quicker than the sympathetic system. By the time you decide to do something, the 3-F syndrome has already swung into action, and anyone who has experienced a real fright is familiar with the dry mouth, the pounding heart, and the sweat pouring from pores they didn't know they had. But if we assume that the bear turns and grunts his way back along the path, ending the confrontation as soon as it begins, what then? How can you shut down all these emergency procedures that have been called into play?

Like so many aspects of physiology, the shutdown is accomplished by an antagonistic control program—in this case, the parasympathetic nervous system. As calm is restored, it constricts the eye pupils, reroutes much of the blood from the peripheral muscles back into the rest of the system, and slows the heart. Parasympathetic impulses also reduce the size of the breathing tubes and calm jerky, agitated respiratory muscles and cortical impulses, gradually bringing a terrified or anxious person back to normal through simple manipulation of antagonistic controls.

The two autonomic branches are easily distinguished from each other morphologically. To begin with, they emerge from the spinal cord at different levels. Parasympathetic nerves leave the CNS from centers in the brainstem and from the bottom or **sacral region** of the spine (see figure 8.35). The sympathetic

Figure 8.35 The origin of the parasympathetic efferents. Their control is applied less generally than that of the sympathetic nervous system.

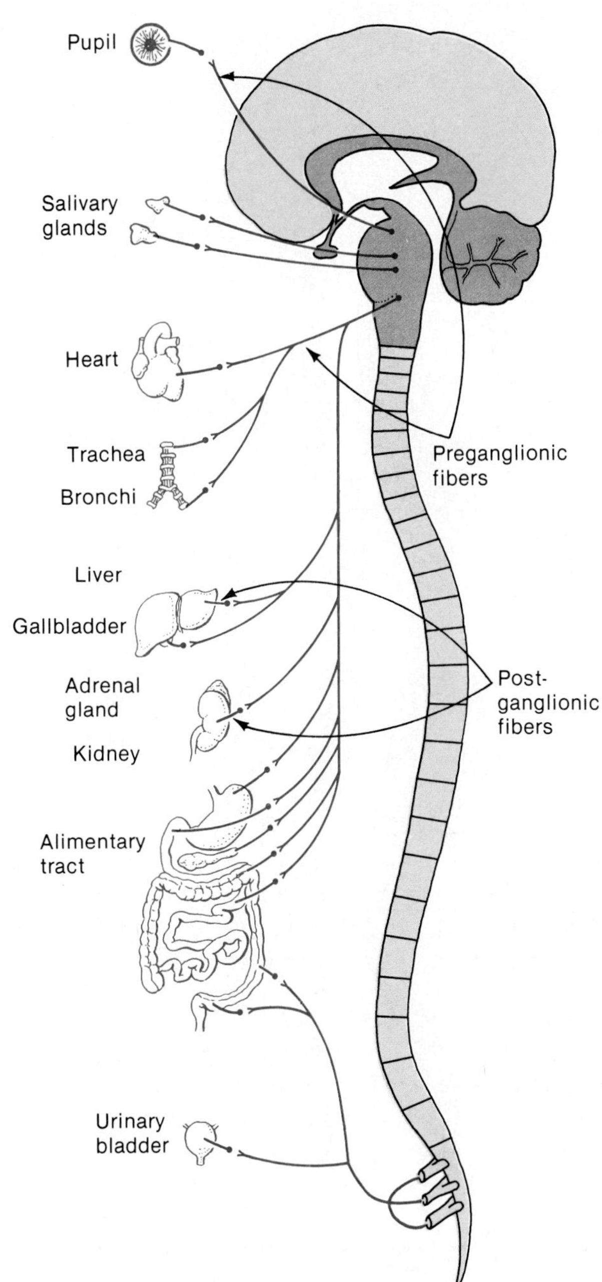

Figure 8.36 The origin of the sympathetic efferents and the organs they control.

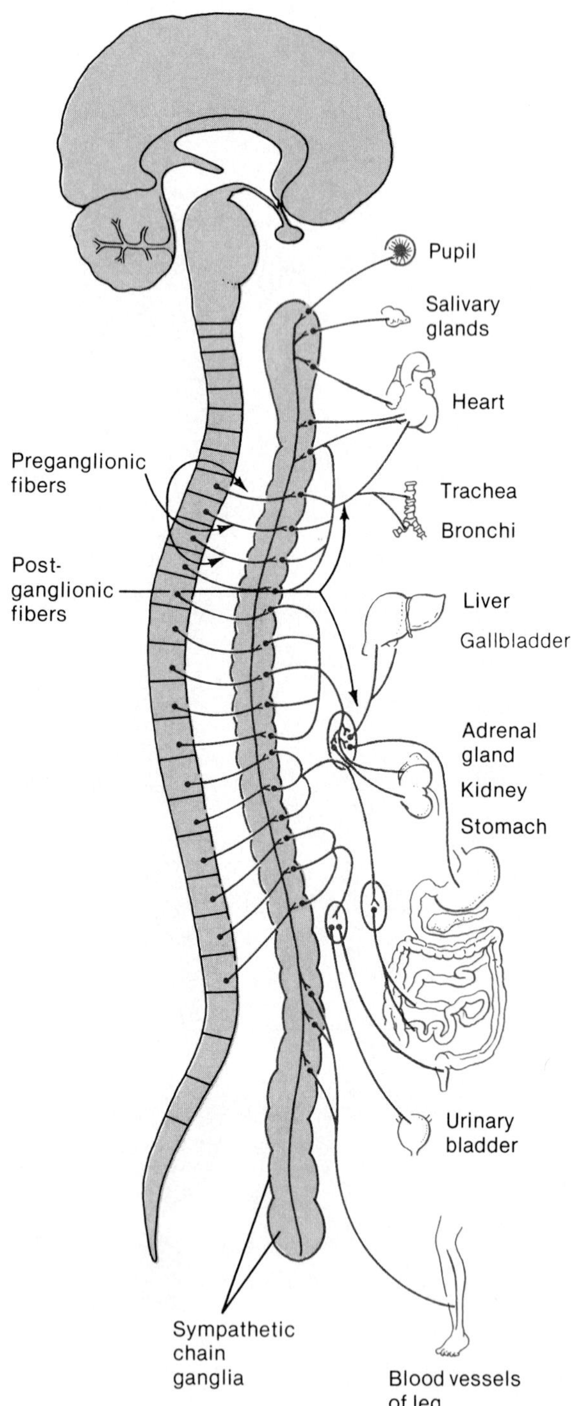

nerves leave the central nervous system in the middle part of the cord—surging forth from between the **thoracic** and **lumbar vertebrae** of the spinal column (figure 8.36). Autonomic nerve fibers emerging from the spinal cord are known as **preganglionic fibers,** and they travel with somatic fibers, leaving the cord in spinal nerve bundles.

Sympathetic neurons go only a very short distance before branching from the spinal nerves and forming a short loop, like a cloverleaf on a freeway. Within the cloverleaf loop, the preganglionic fibers enter a **nerve ganglion,** where most of them synapse with their succeeding nerves. These ganglia are right next to the spinal cord, and they form two processions known as **sympathetic chains** that run down both sides of the spinal column (figure 8.37). After leaving the ganglion, the postganglionic fibers usually loop back into the spinal nerve from the ganglionic "cloverleaf" and travel with it to their effector organs. Although most sympathetic fibers follow this route, not all of them do. Some slide past the sympathetic ganglia, synapse in **collateral ganglia,** and never do rejoin the spinal nerves (figure 8.38).

The parasympathetic system, on the other hand, has very long preganglionic fibers. Most extend from the CNS nearly all the way to the effector organ before they form a synapse with their postganglionic fibers, usually in ganglia near the organs they will influence (figure 8.39).

It is worth mentioning that the relationship between pre- and postganglionic fibers in the parasympathetic nervous system is usually one to one, whereas in the sympathetic system, one preganglionic fiber will often synapse with many postganglionic fibers. This is a reflection of the rather diffuse control exhibited by the sympathetic system when compared to the more precise operations that are orchestrated by the parasympathetic system. When the sympathetic system operates, it usually fires everything it has, all at once. For this reason, a single preganglionic fiber can be permitted to control a dozen or more postganglionic fibers, since the greatest concern is getting them all firing. The parasympathetic system, on the other hand, exerts a much tighter control over its system. When, for instance, food moves through the gastrointestinal tract, for optimum absorption, the digestion of food should be a well-controlled *sequence,* rather than a storm of events.

Figure 8.37 The chain of sympathetic synapses known as the sympathetic ganglia or sympathetic chain.

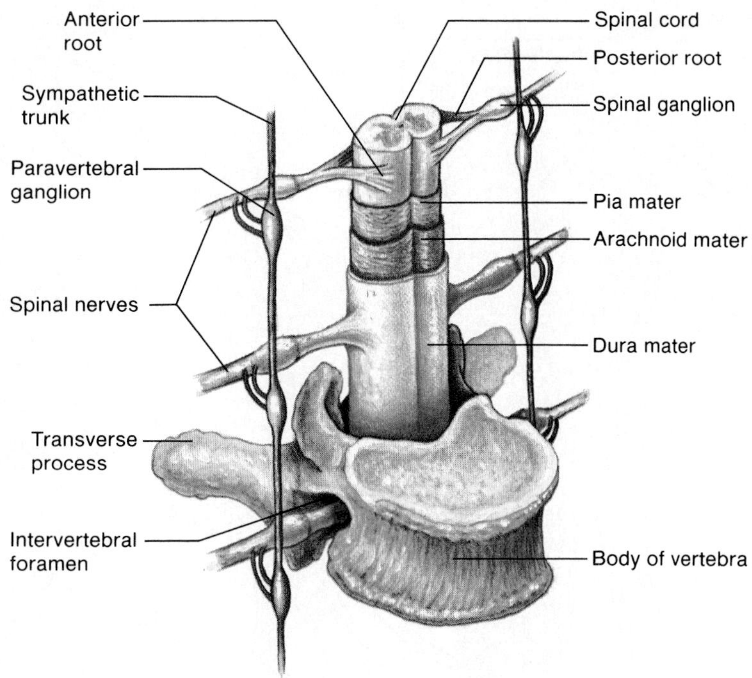

Figure 8.38 Most sympathetic neurons synapse in the sympathetic chain after leaving the spinal cord, but not all do. Some pass through the ganglia and synapse in collateral ganglia.

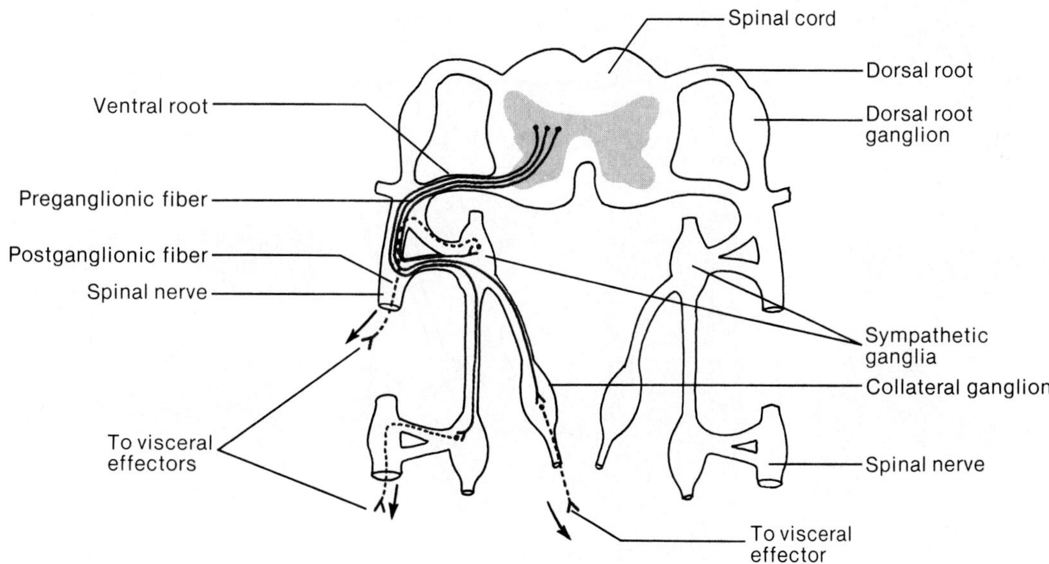

Figure 8.39 The preganglionic fibers of the parasympathetic division arise from the brain and the sacral region of the spinal cord (*left*), while those of the sympathetic division arise from the thoracic and lumbar regions (*right*).

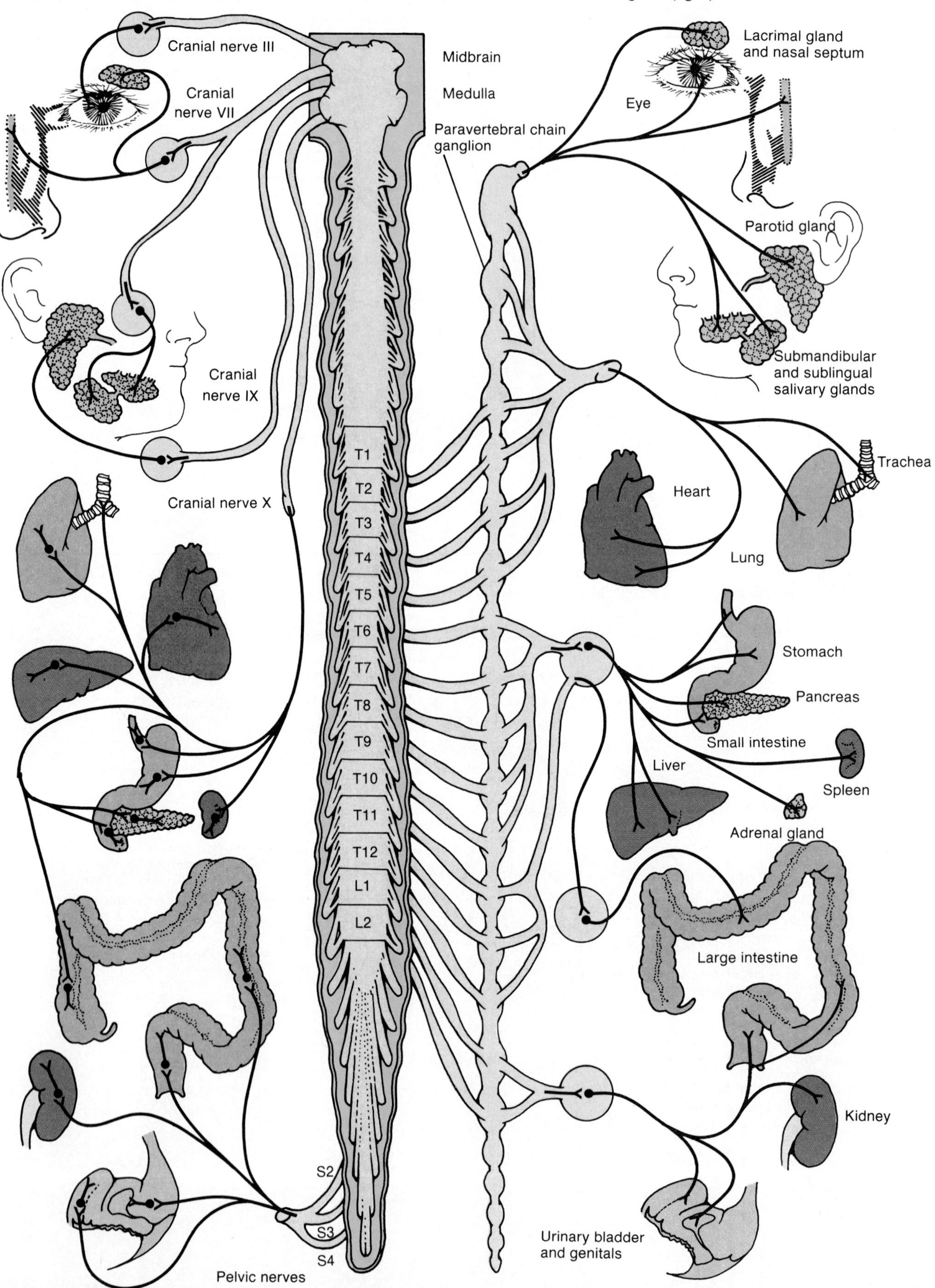

Antagonistic Control Mechanisms

Early researchers often noticed that there were two different neurons entering certain visceral organs, and they frequently stimulated both artificially to note the effects. For years one of the great mysteries of neurophysiology was how such stimuli could have opposing effects. "After all," these workers reasoned, "the nerves are entering the same organs, often at nearly the same location. Both are carrying similar electrical stimuli and should, therefore, have similar effects, but their effects instead are antagonistic." It was the discovery of neurotransmitters that gave research the key to this seemingly unexplainable phenomenon.

Both the sympathetic and the parasympathetic nervous systems secrete the neurotransmitter acetylcholine from their preganglionic nerve endings. Hence all junctions between pre- and postganglionic fibers are cholinergic. But the synapses are just relay stations, transferring information from pre- to postganglionic fibers. It is the postganglionic fiber that gives the instructions to the effector organ, so it is the postganglionic secretion that determines, in part, what the final effect will be.

Like all preganglionic fiber endings, the postganglionic fibers of the parasympathetic system secrete acetylcholine; hence, their synapses are all cholinergic. Sympathetic postganglionic fibers, however, secrete **norephinephrine,** so most of their junctions are adrenergic. There are some exceptions to this latter. For instance, the sympathetic postganglionic fibers that innervate certain sweat glands (eccrine glands) secrete acetylcholine, as do some of the sympathetic fibers controlling blood-vessel dilation.

Clinical Considerations

As we already know, research into the human nervous system today seems to support the contention that a human is born with all the nerve cells he or she is ever going to have. The individual cells can grow, and some can develop new axons and dendritic trees, but no mitosis has ever been seen in human nerve cells. Furthermore, as we have seen, the higher mammals tend to rely less and less on instinctive behavioral patterns and more on conscious control and incorporation of learning into behavioral responses. Anything that might deprive a human of a nerve cell, therefore, cannot be taken lightly, nor can any neural damage be considered minor until it is clearly demonstrated to be so. Since individual cells are so important, obviously large collections of neurons are even more critical, so spinal damage or brain damage can produce disastrous results in the whole organism.

Figure 8.40 Testing the patellar or knee-jerk reflex, an example of a monosynaptic reflex.

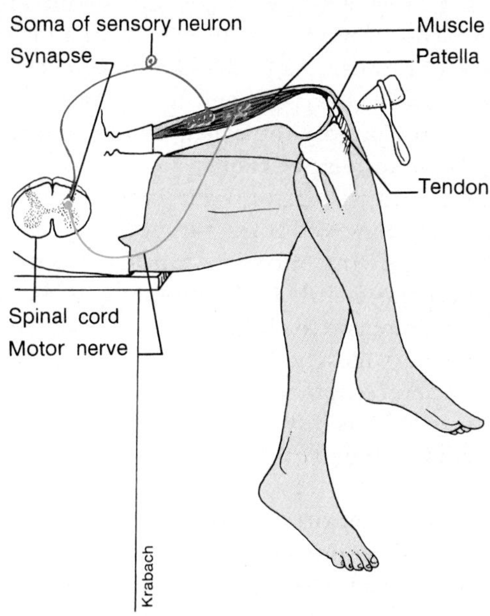

Sometimes the simplest procedures can yield a lot of information. Consider, for instance, the testing of a **patellar reflex** (figure 8.40). Tapping the knee is a routine procedure, and no one pays much attention to the result unless something unusual should happen. When it does, the test becomes an index of considerable importance. Spinal damage could be indicated if tapping the patellar tendon produces no motion at all. Or, should there be some damage to the motor cortex of the brain, tapping the patellar tendon might result in a wildly exaggerated response in which the leg flies up as if the patient were kicking a ball.

Tumors

Probably the most common non-injury that afflicts the CNS is the tumor. Tumors that develop in the spinal cord are usually not considered as deadly as tumors in the higher centers, because about 60 percent of them are benign, but even if the tumor is not malignant, its very presence can produce symptoms ranging all the way from pain to paralysis. The pain and loss of neuronal function is almost always due to compression of the spinal cord as the tumor begins to crowd it against the vertebral column. More often than not, tumors in the spinal cord arise from the nervous tissue itself, and unless they are removed, they can cause permanent damage. Spinal surgery is never minor surgery, but the success rate involving removal of tumors compressing the spinal cord is well above 90 percent. Usually, movement is completely restored, and the back pain vanishes along with the tumor.

The brain is subject to a variety of tumoral growths, some benign, some malignant. The problems that arise when they are malignant are self-evident. The prognosis is always poor, and we will not dwell on those. As to the benign tumors, people can sometimes survive them. It depends on where they are, how rapidly they are growing, and whether it is possible to remove them.

The meninges often produce benign tumors that can be easily removed if they are found soon enough and are not growing into some critical brain area. They cause problems mainly by compressing the brain. The biggest problem with these tumors is that they usually grow very slowly; hence neither the patient nor his physician recognize the insidious onset of central nervous problems until it's too late.

Cerebral blood vessels occasionally produce tumors. One type—called **angiomas** – are congenital and represent malformations of blood vessels that get worse as the patient grows older. They cause problems through compression of nervous tissue, and they are extremely difficult to treat unless they happen to be in vessels right on top of the brain.

Tumors growing within the brain seldom arise from nervous tissue. Usually the growth is a glial cell group running wild, crowding and compressing the nervous tissue surrounding it. The most obvious symptoms of brain tumor are headaches—often producing flashing, blinding pain—and nausea and vomiting. Despite the fact that many brain tumors are benign, they are tremendously dangerous, because they can compress neuronal tissue, possibly damaging it permanently. To make things worse, often they are untreatable because they cannot be excised without endangering critical brain areas. As they increase in size, they give rise to all sorts of neural deficits, sometimes producing wildly aberrant behavior or seizures. Pressure within the cranium sometimes causes compression of critical blood vessels and deprives certain brain zones of necessary nutrients, producing stroke-like signs and symptoms. Behaviorally, the patient often becomes more and more childlike as the tumor increases in size, destroying more and more portions of the brain. No malignancy could kill more surely.

Injuries

Injuries can happen anytime, and anything capable of causing damage to portions of the central nervous system can be extremely dangerous. Spinal cord injuries most often occur in heavy, collision-type sports or automobile accidents. For that reason, spinal cord injuries occur most often in people under the age of 35. The spinal cord is the body's only means of getting sensory information from below the head into the brain, and in addition, it is the integrating center for all the body's rapidly acting neuromotor reflexes. All reflex activity involving voluntary muscles depends on both sensory and motor communication existing between the brain and the spinal cord, and if either aspect is interrupted, there will be motor or sensory malfunction.

Figure 8.41 Any abnormal movement of the bony vertebral elements can pinch the spinal cord. Such pinches or compressions can result in paralysis.

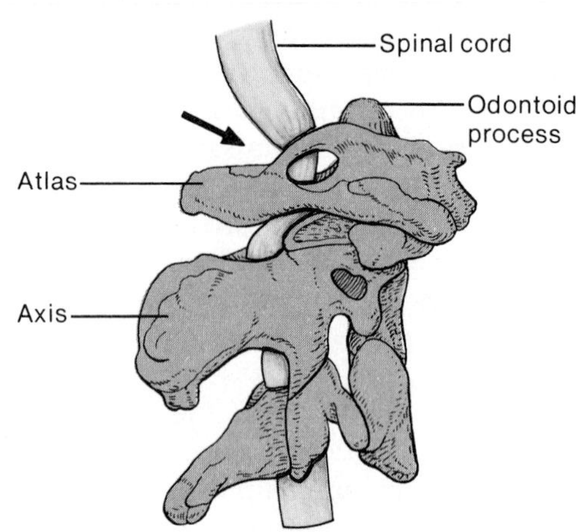

Most spinal damage that occurs as a result of injury takes place instantly, but a good deal of secondary damage unfortunately occurs when well-meaning citizens, bent on helping an accident victim, move them to a "safer" place or into a "more comfortable" position. Should a person suffer a fractured or dislocated vertebra, any movement at all could thrust a slightly damaged spinal cord against a sharp piece of vertebral bone or move one vertebral element across another and sever or severely compress the spinal cord (see figure 8.41).

Spinal shock is a loss of neural function due to just such a sudden compression. Just as a hard blow to the head can leave a person concussed for several days, sudden tremendous shocks in the spinal cord can render certain parts of it inoperative. Although generally considered a temporary condition, spinal shock can last as long as a year before normal function is restored to the nerves involved . . . if indeed normal function is ever restored. There are predictors that can sometimes alleviate the tremendous anxiety patients are bound to feel. For instance, the sudden reappearance of a simple reflex that had vanished is considered a good sign. Physicians become optimistic when that happens, because the usual result is recovery of normal cord activity, even below the level of compression.

If, on the other hand, the cord is severed, there is little that anyone will ever be able to do. Inevitably, all motor and sensory functions will be irretrievably lost in the region of the body below the transection.

Obviously, then, this is to be avoided at all costs. To help reduce the possibility of such a disaster, the most important aspect of treating any suspected spinal injury is to promptly immobilize the patient and do everything possible to avoid any kind of movement of the vertebral column.

Ruptured Discs

Back pain in middle-aged adults is so common that people today often think it is unusual if such a person does not complain, at one time or another, of having a "bad back." Probably the most common cause is muscular spasms in the lower back, and they can be extremely painful. The underlying cause is usually a rupture of one of the cartilaginous pads that separate the bony elements of the vertebral column. These pads—called **intervertebral discs**—also act as shock absorbers for the entire length of the spinal column. Naturally, the thinnest discs would be near the top of the cord, while the thick ones would be in the lower regions, since the lower portions of the backbone must support more weight. As people age, these discs get thinner and less resilient, until finally one or more of the lower ones may rupture.

Most people accept this horrid back pain as part of growing old. Hence, by the time medical aid is sought, the patient has a long history of back problems, mostly episodes of extreme back pain that come and go, each spell usually lasting a week or two. Often the pain can force the patient to realign his posture, placing unusual strain on certain muscle groups and resulting in muscle spasms. The best treatment is rest, followed by exercises designed to strengthen back muscles. Surgery is a last resort, since any surgery around the spinal cord is serious and often does not relieve the pain.

Headaches

It is hard to imagine anyone living to adulthood without having experienced a headache, and they can be caused by so many things that it would require a book to list them all. If we eliminate the really dangerous afflictions, there are only two groups of causes. They are termed **muscular** and **vascular,** and these categories embrace nearly all headaches that Americans routinely suffer.

Tension Headaches

Tension headaches are far and away the most common, and they embrace both of the common classes of headache. They are caused by a tensing of scalp or neck muscles, usually accompanied by vasoconstriction in the neck just below the head. Generally they are brought on by work stress or unusual worrying, and they can last as long as the muscles stay tense, usually only part of a day. When the muscles relax, the headache goes away. However, there are case histories of patients—particularly women—who have experienced continuous tension headache for periods up to four years.

Scientific evidence hints that it may not be a good idea to proffer any medication for such headaches, and the medical community generally agrees. Naturally, the most common treatment is carried out by the sufferers themselves through the purchase of over-the-counter medications. Researchers worry about this, since it tends to make a tension-sufferer dependent on regular administrations of analgesics. Physicians usually suggest psychotherapy or prescribe some type of general muscle relaxant, although neither of these is uniformly dependable.

Migraine

These headaches are definitely in the vascular group, because they tend to shoot bursts of pain through the patient's head—bursts that coincide with the heartbeat. Weird neurological disturbances usually proclaim the beginning of a migraine—often visual disturbances like shimmering waves of light, exploding flashbulbs, or parades of bright spots precede the actual pain. Sometimes they begin with motor aberrations—even partial paralysis—and it is not uncommon for migraine sufferers to experience extreme nausea during an attack. The word *migraine* is a contraction of the Greek *hemikrania,* which means "half a head," and they are so called because usually such headaches afflict only one side of the head and body.

Everyone has headaches, of course, and usually they are minor inconveniences. For real migraine sufferers, however, they are not minor. Often the pain lasts for an entire 24-hour period and is downright crippling. Victims are often rendered prostrate during this period, and if they are lucky, sleep will relieve the agony. Many migraine victims cannot sleep, however. They cannot lie still because they can't tolerate the pain, yet it hurts them to move. As a result, they wander around, lying down, getting up, moaning and miserable. While the headache is running its course, victims who do get up and stroll around are often helpless. They will spill drinks without realizing it, walk into posts or walls, and display slurred speech like a drunken person. As far as is known, migraine has never been fatal, although some victims consider this a mixed blessing.

Sufferers will probably not be cheered by the knowledge that such headaches have been with humanity for millenia. The Roman physician Galen described them in the second century AD, and prehistoric skulls with carefully trephined holes in them—holes obviously made while the owner was alive—suggest that maybe ancient medicine men were doing their best to relieve migraine pain ten or twenty thousand years ago. In a period of twenty thousand years you would think *someone* would discover a way to relieve such pain, but unfortunately it has not worked out that way. Even today, we have no consistently reliable method of combatting migraines. The biggest problem, of course, is that there is not a great deal known about them, although we do know a little. We know, for instance, that the pain is usually preceded by a gradual reduction in cerebral blood flow, and then, accompanying the onset of pain, there is a sudden vasodilation and a rush of blood into the vessels of the brain. We have clinical evidence to suggest that emotional states like depression or rage sometimes precede them, sometimes certain foods or perfumes seem to be around when they start, and occasionally a sudden foray into brilliant sunlight from the more dimly lit offices or factories where people work will touch off a migraine attack. Beyond that, we know very little.

The most effective treatments are preventive and symptomatic. Preventive steps would include eliminating foods, odors, or drinks that seem to be associated with the headache, avoiding sudden exposure to brilliant light when possible, and steering clear of stressful situations. Sometimes these precautions work, but not often. Symptomatic treatment is just as uncertain. Most **analgesics** (pain relievers) are ineffective. Over-the-counter drugs like *Midol*, *Anacin*, or other preparations favoring aspirin or acetaminophen (*Tylenol*) are of no value at all. Obviously some other *type* of drug must be utilized and most success has been experienced with vascular muscle relaxants and beta-blocking agents. Prescription drugs like the beta-blocker *Inderal* or monoamine oxidase inhibitors like *Nardil* will often—but not always—reduce the pain. Other successful treatments involve the use of vasoconstrictors like the ergot alkaloids. And in some cases, biofeedback conditioning has eliminated the headaches completely. Obviously, for migraine sufferers, treatment must be tailored to the individual.

Stroke

Stroke was the third leading cause of death in the United States over the last decade, and it is responsible for more than 200,000 deaths in this country each year. Medical personnel have estimated that more than two million Americans currently suffer from some neurological debilitation as a result of a stroke and that this number expands every year by 25 percent.

Most strokes are the result of **atherosclerosis** or "hardening of the arteries," a circulatory anamoly that will be discussed in detail in chapter 12. Embolism (the sudden clogging of an artery or vein, usually by a clot) and hypertension (high blood pressure) are other prime causative factors. Strokes, like most other diseases, vary in their severity. Some people can suffer a stroke without even realizing that it happened, while others, apparently healthy, will suddenly crash to the ground unconscious and dying, or will live permanently crippled as a result of sudden stroke. The problem is lack of blood flowing through cerebral capillary beds because of complete blockage of the artery supplying the area, or because an artery has had a "blow-out" and the blood is flowing freely onto the brain instead of going through the vessels. In either case, the nerve cells served by that blood vessel are starving for oxygen and fuel and often die. The symptoms that show up after the stroke can indicate pretty clearly how much damage was done and where it occurred.

If the region of destruction is fairly large, there really is not much that can be done. Vasodilators have on occasion been of some value, but they often lower arterial blood pressure and decrease cerebral flow, which is the worst thing that can happen following a stroke. Symptomatic treatment can be tried, and the patient should be kept comfortable, but despite all that medical science has discovered, the mortality rate for such patients has changed little since the late 1940s.

Epilepsy

Epilepsy is a common affliction, and it still has an unsavory reputation, despite efforts of the medical and scientific communities to educate the public. Unfortunately, it was associated centuries ago with mental deficiencies and is still viewed in this way by the majority of the nonprofessional population. The epileptic seizure is still known in these circles as a "fit" and is often mistakenly characterized as a period of screaming insanity during which the afflicted person has superhuman strength and can easily kill himself or others if they come near.

The disease itself seems to have an affinity for relatives of epileptics, but the statistics are not clear enough to conclusively state that it is genetically borne. No one really knows just how prevalent it is, mainly because many suffering from the disease hide it . . . they are afraid of the stigma it may attach to them. The estimated number of epileptics ranges all the way from 0.5 percent to 2 percent of the world's population. It is not restricted to any race or age group, although it seems to begin during a person's early years, since most epilepsy is diagnosed before the victim reaches the age of 20.

The most common type of epilepsy is known as **focal epilepsy** and is usually the result of a lesion caused by a head injury. The injury could be the result of anoxia (lack of oxygen), lack of adequate nutrients, excessive indulgence in alcohol, drug withdrawal, or anything else capable of damaging the central nervous system. The damage may occur prior to the birth of the victim or many years later. Usually the lesion can be located in the midbrain or the cerebrum. Every once in a while an epileptic will be found with lesions in the hindbrain or brain stem, but these are extremely rare.

Studies of neurons in the lesioned areas seem to indicate that the cells responsible for setting off epileptic seizures often have unusually low activation thresholds; hence they are easily discharged, and whole groups of them tend to fire rhythmically and indiscriminately once they start. In keeping with the earlier observation (chapter 7) that membrane permeability in excitable tissues is linked to the voltage across the membrane, the membrane permeability—and hence the electrolyte distribution in the cell—is abnormal.

Sometimes, we find that there is no brain damage of any kind, and yet seizures occur. Obviously, in such cases, the cause is a complete mystery.

Two main classes of epileptic seizures are recognized by the medical profession. These are **partial seizures** and **generalized seizures.**

Partial Seizures

During partial seizures, the victim is usually conscious throughout the entire attack, although he or she seldom recalls anything about what happened during the ordeal. It may begin with a light twitching of the fingers or a tic somewhere on the face. Then these slight motor disturbances progress relentlessly to larger and larger muscles—usually, but not always, on just one side of the body. Sometimes mental disturbances occur—like a sudden recollection of forgotten past events or even startling hallucinations. All this is forgotten when the attack is over. Recordings of the brain's electrical activity (EEG) during seizures indicate that they usually start with "spike-like" electrical patterns. The patterns often have peaks occurring at regular intervals, usually at frequencies ranging from two to ten per second, which explains why these types of seizures may be brought on by strobe lights, pounding music, or some other rhythmic stimulus. Rhythmic stimuli are not essential. Often, the seizures will occur spontaneously.

Generalized Seizures

There are two types of generalized seizures—*grand mal* and *petit mal.* Petit mal seizures usually produce a short loss of both awareness and the ability to voluntarily control any body functions. The periods of unconsciousness generally last only a half-dozen seconds, and the victim often doesn't know anything untoward has occurred, unless something momentous happens during those few seconds. This kind of seizure is quite common in children, and fortunately it usually disappears when puberty is attained.

Grand mal seizures are the classical "fits" that people usually think of when they hear the word epilepsy. Usually, but not always, the victim can feel it coming. Often the warning period is short-lived, and a period of unconsciousness quickly begins, during which the victim tends to lose control of bladder and rectal muscles and most other autonomic mechanisms, all the while experiencing wild skeletal muscle contractions that can grossly distort the body. Jaw spasms often lacerate the tongue, and attendants usually will force a wooden or rubber plug between the patient's teeth during the spasms to prevent oral damage. It is also important to keep the patient's breathing tubes open, which is usually accomplished by rolling the victim onto his or her side and letting any vomitus or salivary exudate leave the mouth. Usually the seizures only last a few minutes, but it is a period of intense activity for both attendants and the patient, and when it is over, the patient usually lapses into a period of deep sleep—sleep from which he or she cannot be awakened—for about half an hour. When they finally do wake up, they are nearly always confused and a bit shocked. They cannot remember anything that happened during the attack, but they recognize the signs if they have had seizures before.

Sometimes as simple a thing as a change of diet will reduce the number of seizures. This technique is more often successful with children than with adults. The most common adjustment is to increase fat intake and reduce body pH slightly. Drug therapy is more reliable for adult patients. Fortunately, there are several drugs available to reduce the incidence and the severity of the attacks, and more than 70 percent of those treated respond positively. Unfortunately, too many of the drugs have undesirable side effects. Things like barbiturates, for instance, will prevent attacks, but they also depress the conscious brain to the point where the patient is essentially unable to perform rationally. Patients will not take their medication because of these horrible side effects, so they remain essentially untreated. There are several new drugs being tested, among them the muscle relaxant carbamazepine which, although not without its own nasty side-effects, is more easily tailored to individual needs than the barbiturates. Should all else fail, sometimes surgery can reduce or even eliminate the incidence of attack.

Lou Gehrig's Disease

Lou Gehrig's disease, or **amyotropic lateral sclerosis,** is another degenerative disease afflicting mainly central nervous motor centers. The disease is fairly well known in this country despite its rarity because it is the affliction that killed the so-called Iron Man of the New York Yankees baseball club in 1941.

Amyotropic lateral sclerosis is a spontaneous and progressive deterioration of motor cells in both the brain stem and the spinal cord. The result is gradual loss of muscle coordination and motor control. It usually ends with the early death of the victim. Its rarity makes it doubly hard to diagnose and treat because of the lack of research and literature on the subject.

Diseases Affecting Peripheral Nerves

The neurological disorders discussed so far have all involved portions of the CNS, but there are a number of afflictions that concentrate their efforts on neurons outside the CNS. These are the diseases that tend to attack motor and sensory neurons in the body's periphery, usually by removing part or all of the myelin sheathing from the afflicted axons.

Multiple Sclerosis

Multiple sclerosis is by far the most common of these diseases, although it is by no means the only one. No one knows for sure what causes it, although recent evidence suggests that it is congenital. Workers in San Francisco report that they have succeeded in cloning a defective gene that they say is responsible for producing multiple sclerosis in mice. There is also evidence to support an opposing view—the contention that viral infections may trigger an attack by the body's own immune system on the myelin of the peripheral nerves.

Some statistics are available concerning the worldwide distribution of multiple sclerosis. Generally it attacks people between the ages of 20 and 40, seems to have a genetic link, and occurs in females a little more often than it does in males. It is almost nonexistent in tropical or frigid zones, confining its depredations, for some reason, to the temperate parts of the earth.

When it strikes, whatever mechanism it employs strips chunks of myelin from peripheral nerves in great patches, leaving behind a kind of scar tissue composed mainly of nonfunctional glial cells. During an attack, the afflicted neurons cease to function, and the patient loses feeling or motor control in the area served by the neurons. A remission almost always occurs following an attack, but the remission is never 100 percent, and the patient gradually deteriorates as recurring attacks take a relentless toll. Ultimately, myelin destruction spreads to the white matter of the CNS, and the neural deficiencies that follow are irreversible.

So little is known about why or how this destruction occurs that there is almost nothing that can be done, other than to make the patient as comfortable as possible. Early in the disease, medical science has reported limited success with a group of drugs known as **steroids,** which are isolated from certain cells of the adrenal glands, but in general, aside from keeping the patient's spirits up and encouraging exercise, there is very little that can be done.

Myasthenia Gravis

Myasthenia gravis is another insidious nervous affliction involving a progressive deterioration in the victim's ability to control his or her muscle movements. In this case, problems arise at the point where the motor neuron meets the effector muscle, and symptoms usually begin with extreme muscle weakness. It is caused by a flaw in the process of conducting the nerve message to the muscle it innervates, and no one really knows what that flaw may be, although there have been many suggestions. Some workers feel there is a dearth of neurotransmitter available, and their hypothesis has some experimental support. Remissions are often possible following treatment with drugs capable of destroying acetylcholinesterase, the enzyme responsible for breaking up acetylcholine. Other workers think the cause is a lack of viable receptors on the muscle side of the nerve-muscle junction. Whatever the reason, the direct result is rapid fatigue and an unusually prolonged recovery time from that fatigue.

Until recently, the mortality rate for myasthenia gravis was higher than it was for bubonic plague. Now, however, drug therapy has succeeded in prolonging life remarkably. This is extremely important, because if the patient can survive for eight or nine years, the disease assumes a benign aspect and seldom kills, although its victims must remain forever conscious of their physical limitations.

Some Diagnostic Tools

X Ray

Cerebral X rays have always been of tremendous value in diagnosing neural problems. They can pinpoint vertebral damage and possible trouble spots in a way no other process can, and more than one person is alive today who would have died without X ray technology. However, there are other methods in use today that have even greater versatility than the simple X ray.

The CAT Scan

The early 1970s produced a technology that made it possible to view layers of living tissue as if they had been sliced and mounted in sequence on a microscope slide. This is known as structural **tomography,** and it is made possible by bringing an individual layer of tissue into radiographic focus while leaving the layers above and below it blurred. The X ray film is rotated around a chosen body plane, while an X ray tube across from the film continually provides X ray images of the body. The planes of rotation and the rotations are selected, adjusted, and performed by computer, hence the name CAT scan, which is an acronym for *computerized axial tomography.* It is, for all practical purposes, an X ray cross section of a living body on any plane the technician chooses, and it differentiates between various tissues better than a simple X ray can. Neurologists use CAT scans extensively when searching for suspected tumors or blood clots in the brain or spinal cord.

The PETT Scan

The PETT scan has added still another dimension to the neurologist's arsenal in the war against central nervous diseases. With X rays—even with a CAT scan—one can view only the *structure* of the organ. With the PETT scan, one has an opportunity to glimpse an area of the body—including the brain—while it's working and *in situ.* The key to the process is a subatomic particle called a **positron.** Positrons are similar in many ways to electrons except for their positive charge, and they are emitted quite rapidly when thrust into certain compounds. The PETT scan (*Positron Emission Transaxial Tomography*) exploits this phenomenon in the following way:

An investigator carefully selects a substance to insure that it is something the organ being investigated normally uses in a specific way. That substance or a close analog is formulated with positrons and the resultant chemical is injected into the patient. The patient then inserts his body into the scanning device, and the pathway of the positron-emitting chemical can be followed by using a positron detector. This technique permits an investigator to note where the organ is concentrating the injected substance, and to determine whether the various parts of the organ are working normally. In the brain it's particularly useful, because nervous tissue has only one food—glucose. Nerve cells ignore both proteins and lipids as energy sources and restrict their efforts to gleaning all their ATP requirements from glucose stores. Consequently, injection of positron-containing glucose will permit positron-sensitive film to locate which structures in the brain are the most active and which are lying down on the job (see figure 8.42). It also tells workers which parts of the brain are responsible for certain specific activities. For example, if a subject being scanned is told to move his foot around vigorously, a worker can tell from a shift in sugar concentration which part of the brain is using the most energy; hence that must be the part that's telling the foot to move. PETT scans have been used to locate centers of epileptic activity. And by noting which brain areas might be functioning in unusual ways, psychiatrists report PETT scans have occasionally aided in diagnosis and treatment of some forms of mental illness. Since brain tumors are unusually active cell masses, they have proven invaluable in locating suspected tumors as well.

Figure 8.42 PETT scan from a human brain. The subject is given a dose of positron-emitting glucose compound, and after a short wait, radiation detectors are used to photograph the body area in question. Areas where activity is high will concentrate the positron-emitting glucose more than less active areas, and areas of high concentration show up in varying colors on the film. Since brain tumors are often tremendously active, such pictures can have enormous early diagnostic value.

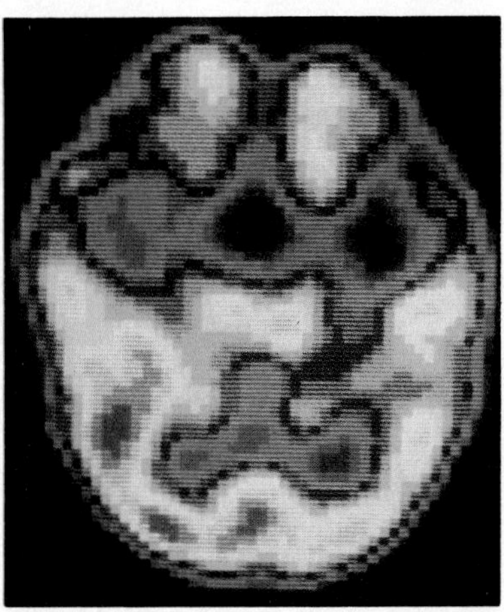

Nuclear Magnetic Resonance

Both PETT and CAT scanning are extremely important diagnostic tools, but they have one tremendous disadvantage: they both expose the patient's brain to unusual levels of radiation, and that is never a good thing.

Figure 8.43 An NMR scan of a human brain. This is the newest tool to be used to study brain activity. The subject's head is exposed to special magnetic fields that can cause certain atoms—like the hydrogen in water—to emit weak radio waves at specific frequencies. By analyzing these waves with computers, technicians can build an image showing the location and concentration of the organic molecules being investigated.

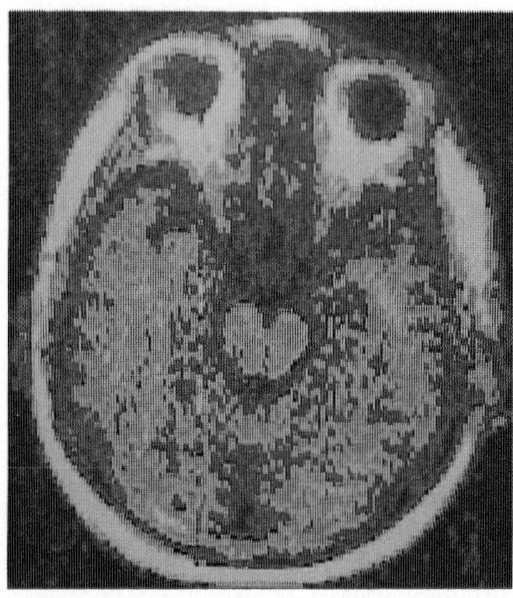

There is a newer technique that is being utilized with greater and greater frequency. It is called **nuclear magnetic resonance imagery,** and, as the name implies, it makes use of magnetic fields instead of radiation.

To be scanned, the individual is placed in a chamber that is exposed to a powerful magnetic field. This magnetic field distorts the electrical characteristics of the atoms within the chamber in a specific way. When the scanning equipment is turned on, a second magnetic field is established that rotates around the body and causes certain atoms, such as the hydrogen, nitrogen, and carbon atoms present in organic compounds and body fluids, to release very weak electrical signals at radio frequencies. A special antenna picks up these radio waves, which are amplified and then presented to a computer. The computer analyzes the radio data fed in and then creates a cross-sectional figure derived from that data (figure 8.43).

In addition to offering cross- and sagittal-section imagery, it also can analyze the radio waves emitted by some components of the organic compounds that are present, thus permitting technicians to obtain information about the chemical composition of the body region under investigation.

Electroencephalography (EEG)

EEG records are widely used in medical and research laboratories all over the world today, and their needle-waggings are of real value in diagnosis and research involving certain emotional and sleep states. Experimental psychologists often use them to determine things like the attention span of their subjects or to indicate the levels of sleep or wakefulness. Clinicians find them useful in diagnosing CNS disorders such as epilepsy.

EEG recordings are usually made by applying electrodes to various points on the outside of the skull and recording the voltage changes that occur between them. It is commonly believed that these potential alterations represent an algebraic summation of the electrical changes in all of the cells between the electrodes. This may well be true, but there is disagreement. Nevertheless, EEG patterns have definite meaning and are useful research and medical tools.

Sleep

Sleep is, without a doubt, one of the most enigmatic and perplexing of all mental states. We know almost nothing about it other than that it exists and that apparently all vertebrates—certainly all mammals—*must* have a given amount each day. No one knows why. It has been suggested that it is necessary to give the central computer (the brain) a rest from managing daily activities, but that cannot be correct, because the brain does not rest during sleep states—or at least, we don't *think* it does. Others feel that sleep is needed to "clear" the computer, whatever that means. Another, less arcane, suggestion is that sleep shuts down many body operations and permits the animal to pass normally inactive time periods in a state that requires the least energy. That, of course, does not explain why it is *essential,* but it makes a certain amount of sense.

As things stand, sleep and the reasons why it is required are beyond the powers of current science to explain. One interesting aspect of sleep, however, appears to be just as important as the sleep itself. I am referring to dreaming, another bewildering central nervous phenomenon. Evidence suggests that humans must sleep a certain number of hours each twenty-four-hour period, and that a certain percentage of that sleep must consist of the brain activity known as dreaming. Like many medical theories, evidence for this comes from someone's illness.

People suffering from alcoholism frequently experience particularly vivid, realistic hallucinations when they are between drunken stupors or are undergoing withdrawal. These hallucinations, known as *delirium tremens* or DTs, are thought to be dreams that the victim is experiencing while awake. According to this hypothesis, alcohol inhibits the process of dreaming, so that while drunks always seem to get enough sleep each day, they do not dream sufficiently. As is the case with most maladjustments, the body will tolerate this lack for only so long, and then it takes steps to remedy the problem. Since alcoholics *cannot* dream while intoxicated, and since they are always drunk when they are asleep, nature forces the dreams on them when they are awake and uninfluenced by alcohol.

Mental activity can interfere enormously with a person's ability to sleep. People who have experienced a particularly trying day, especially one that included frustration or intense mental activity, often find they cannot fall asleep. They spend the nighttime hours flopping back and forth on their beds, mentally confronting people or situations, or rewriting an unusually important report again and again while sleep consistently eludes them. When the daylight hours arrive and it is nearly time to get up, they fall asleep, only to wake up minutes later when the alarm goes off.

The problem is known as **insomnia,** and we know very little about how to alleviate it. Probably one of the most reliable cures is to rid the brain of all the wakeful activity that is taking place. There are many ways to do this. Reading sometimes works. A better method is to turn on a television movie and get swept along by its plot. One thing seems certain: *you must lie down.* Researchers report that efforts to keep people awake are never successful for very long if the subjects are permitted to lie down—even sudden, explosively loud noises will not prevent their falling asleep when they are flat on their backs.

Recently, researchers have succeeded in isolating a chemical that is thought to be responsible for putting people into a deep sleep for 6 to 10 hours out of every 24. The material is known as **factor S,** and while it is not commercially available, it is somehow comforting to know that it exists.

Sleep Stages

Experts have identified several stages of sleep through use of EEG recordings and a little analysis (figure 8.44). When a person is wide awake, the electrical summations seen on EEG are small, desynchronous waves of high frequency. When the person begins to relax and get drowsy, the EEG begins to show patterns of activity that begin to synchronize into spindle-shaped bursts appearing at fairly regular intervals. When sleep begins, much of the fine, high-frequency "noise" disappears from the EEG, and the waves begin to form simpler, more synchronous shapes. As sleep deepens, the waves get more and more synchronous until, in stage 4 sleep (deep, restful sleep), the EEG shows low-frequency, high-amplitude waves with synchronized peaks and valleys about a second apart. All of these stages are considered to be **normal sleep.**

Figure 8.44 EEG recordings. Alpha waves occur when a person is awake but completely relaxed and near sleep. Beta waves are typical of wakeful alertness. Theta waves, particularly in the hippocampus, are typical of arousal patterns. Delta waves indicate deep sleep.

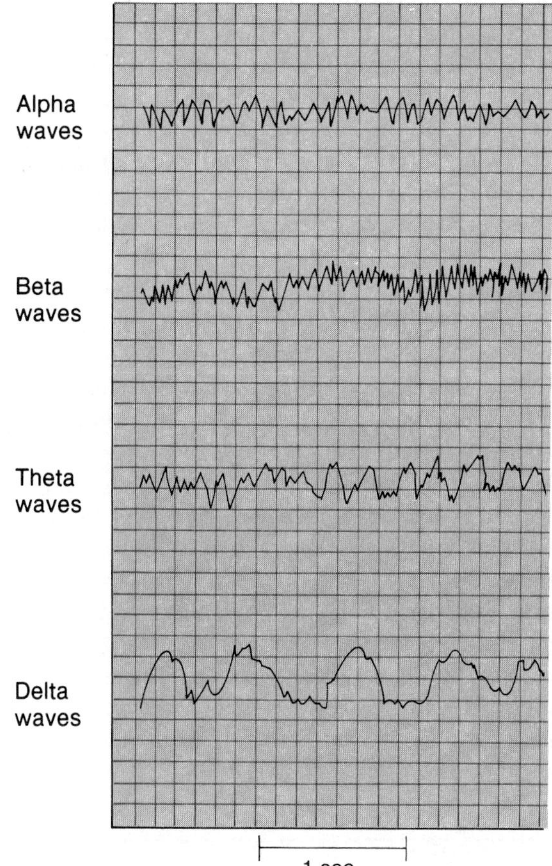

There is, however, another type of sleep that is quite common but is considered to be **paradoxical sleep** rather than normal sleep. It is known as **rapid eye movement** or **REM** sleep. People experiencing REM sleep are apparently in very deep slumber. Experiments show that it requires as much stimulus to awaken a person in REM sleep as it does to awaken the same person from stage 4 (the deepest) sleep. The EEG patterns, however, don't suggest this at all. Subjects in REM show EEG patterns that look like they have just drifted into a light slumber—hence the paradoxical aspect of this particular type of sleep.

Most workers feel that REM sleep is associated with dreaming, which, they say, accounts for the eye movements that are so obvious. The dreamer, they contend, is following the events he is imagining with his eyes. During a period of normal rest, the average person shows REM sleep patterns about every ninety minutes, and they usually last about fifteen minutes. The duration of the REM events often increases the longer the subject remains asleep.

REM sleep is apparently a greater percentage of the total sleep pattern in children than it is in adults, and the ratio gets smaller and smaller as the person ages. It is thought that this may be because children, particularly infants, require the extra dreaming because they are unable to process much of the information entering their brains from external stimuli.

Hypnosis

Hypnosis is related to sleep. The word itself comes from the Greek *hypnos* which literally means "sleep." Nevertheless, that is not, apparently, what hypnosis is. EEG records indicate that people in a hypnotic state are drowsy, but they are wide awake. Just exactly what is going on is dismayingly vague. People under hypnosis can be told they have just had twelve hours' deep sleep and, physiologically, they *have*. It can remove inhibitions, alter behavior, and, in the hands of a responsible clinician, it has proven a useful tool in the treatment of mental aberrations ranging from drug addiction to anxiety. Some practitioners have even suggested hypnosis as a possible preventive of migraine headaches, and there are indications that in a few cases, even *this* has worked.

Despite some successes involving hypnosis, considerable doubt has been cast on its effectiveness, possibly because of some of the fabulous claims some practitioners have made for it. Things like trips into another, previous life or regression mentally to a time when the subject was only five or six years old. Under hypnosis, some people claim to have recalled, almost to perfection, the tiniest details of specific days during childhood. They paint pictures of events that occurred in detail they couldn't begin to achieve when awake. The clinker is that these so-called perfect memories frequently include pseudo-memories . . . memories of things that never happened or people who did not exist. Such memories can be injected into the memory banks under hypnosis or during full wakefulness by just discussing them. They may even have their source in simple daydreams. Yet under hypnosis, these artificially induced memories are as vivid to the subject as an actual experience. Hence people insist that their visions are real, despite presentation of clear evidence that they are not. This is the primary reason why hypnotically induced testimony is not admissable in any court of law in this country. In keeping with this latter observation, it should perhaps be mentioned that this is also one of the reasons why polygraphs are considered unreliable as "lie detectors." Polygraphs can be completely baffled by hypnosis. Things that are patently untrue will consistently show up "true" on a polygraph if the subject has experienced it under hypnosis or has been told under hypnosis that it is true. People under post-hypnotic suggestion, people under the influence of relaxants or some other mind-dulling drug, and people who understand how the instrument works can all completely disrupt it.

Summary

Slow Potential Changes

In living systems, action potentials are initiated by slow alterations in membrane potential.

I. Neuronal Membranes
  A. These slow potential changes are the result of a stimulus, somewhere in the body, impinging on a specialized receptor, at a junction between two or more neurons, or between neurons and another organ.
  B. The stimulus represents energy presented in a nonelectrical form.
  C. The portion of the neuron that receives the stimulus transduces the energy into an electrical potential.
  D. Ionically, slow potential changes differ from action potentials. Action potentials occur because of a sudden passage of sodium through the membrane, and they end because of a sudden efflux of potassium. The ion movements of slow potential changes are separate, but they occur simultaneously.

II. Pressure Stimuli. A pressure stimulus represents a receptor stimulus.

The Receptor Potential

Receptor potentials are slow potential changes. Such a potential might develop as a result of pressure on the correct type of receptor.

I. Decremental Transmission. Action potentials are self-regenerating; their voltage does not change as they spread. Slow potentials lose voltage as they spread from their source.

II. Other Characteristics
  A. High Threshold. Action potentials cannot exist unless a certain minimum voltage change takes place on the membrane. This minimum voltage is known as the threshold voltage. Slow potentials require no threshold voltage change in order to develop.
  B. Graded Response. Action potentials are explosive, single-level changes in membrane potential. Slow potentials are smooth, graded alterations in membrane voltage.
  C. Duration Is a Function of Stimulus Change. The amplitude of a slow potential change is directly proportional to the strength of the applied stimulus.

Some Neuroanatomy

I. Primary sensory neurons accept stimuli from the environment.
II. Motor neurons carry instructions to muscles or glands.
III. Interneurons accept information from sensory neurons and pass instructions to motor neurons.

The Central Nervous System

The Spinal Cord

The spinal cord is the portion of the neural tube that is not inside the skull. It is a mass of nerve fibers that carry motor and sensory information between the CNS and the lower parts of the body.

I. Spinal Nerves. There are thirty-one pairs of spinal nerves. They spray from between the bony elements of the vertebral column to innervate various parts of the body. There are two roots associated with the spinal cord:
   A. The dorsal (posterior) root is associated mainly with sensory neurons.
   B. The ventral (anterior) root is associated mainly with motor neurons.
II. The Cranial Nerves. There are twelve pairs of cranial nerves. They all have their origin in the brain. With a single exception, they all innervate elements of the head, neck and upper thorax. The exception is the tenth cranial nerve (the vagus), which carries fibers throughout the thorax and abdomen. The cranial nerves carry sensory neurons, motor neurons, or both.
III. The Meninges. The brain and spinal cord are hollow. This means there are two surfaces, one inside and one outside. The hollows within the brain are called ventricles. Both surfaces of the CNS are covered with three membranes called meninges.
   A. The outer meninx is called the dura mater. It is a tough, fibrous membrane.
   B. The middle meninx is called the arachnoid mater. It is not as tough a membrane as the dura, but it is substantial.
   C. The innermost meninx is the pia mater. It is a delicate membrane, often only a single cell thick.
   D. The Brain's Shock Absorber. Between the arachnoid mater and the pia mater is the cerebrospinal fluid (CSF).
      1. The CSF is filtered from the blood inside the ventricles of the brain at sites called choroid plexuses.
      2. It is reabsorbed on the brain's outer surfaces at locations called arachnoid villi.
      3. The CSF serves mainly as a shock absorber for the brain. It also carries homeostatic information to certain brain areas.
   E. Central Nervous Circuitry

Passing Information from Nerve to Nerve

Most nerve-to-nerve signals are chemical, not electrical.

The Synapse

Nerves communicate with one another across specialized junctions known as synapses. There are two kinds of synapses: electrical and chemical.

I. Gap Junctions: Electrical Synapses. Electrical synapses are less abundant than chemical synapses. Electrical synapses are known as gap junctions. They are points of physical contact between membranes of adjacent neurons.
II. Chemical Synapses
   A. Chemical synapses are not points of physical contact between neurons; there is a space between neurons at a chemical synapse. Because a space exists, electrical signals cannot pass between neurons at such a junction. Information is passed by specialized chemicals called neurotransmitters.
   B. Because the neurotransmitters are assembled in the presynaptic neuron, chemical synapses are one-way transmission points.
III. Morphology of the Synapse
   A. There are three main elements in a neural synapse: the presynaptic element, the synaptic cleft, and the postsynaptic element.
   B. The presynaptic element contains the chemical transmitter.
   C. The postsynaptic element contains receptors designed to respond to the transmitter.
IV. Chemical Neurotransmission
   A. Influx of calcium into the presynaptic element stimulates opening of neurotransmitter "gates."
   B. Neurotransmitters are released into the synaptic cleft when an action potential arrives at the end of the presynaptic fiber.
   C. They diffuse across the cleft to the surface of the postsynaptic membrane.
   D. They fit themselves into receptors on the postsynaptic membrane and alter its permeability characteristics.
   E. Channels to both sodium and potassium open, and the resultant ionic movement produces a slow potential change known as a postsynaptic potential (PSP).
   F. Recovery. Special enzymes then break down the neurotransmitter, and it is carried back to the presynaptic neuron. Inside the presynaptic neuron, it is reassembled into neurotransmitter to be used again.
   G. Removal of Calcium. Calcium is removed from the presynaptic element by an unusual kind of exocytosis.
   H. The Postsynaptic Membrane and the PSP. Slow potential changes occur because of an increase in membrane permeability to sodium and/or potassium.
      1. Spatial Summation. Several adjacent PSPs can combine their effects to produce a summated depolarization.

2. Temporal Summation. Rapid bursts of neurotransmitter can also summate to increase or prolong their effects.
   a) Some PSPs stimulate the postsynaptic fiber, hence are known as excitatory postsynaptic potentials (EPSPs).
   b) Some PSPs inhibit the postsynaptic fiber, hence are known as inhibitory postsynaptic potentials (IPSPs).

The Significance of the Chemical Synapse

Some integration of neural activity is possible at the synapse because of the variable nature of the neurotransmitter quanta and the variability of the receptors.

Neurotransmitters

There are many different types of neurotransmitters. Some nerves release only one kind of neurotransmitter, while some can release more than one, thus increasing the integrating abilities of their synapses.

I. The Postsynaptic Membrane. Receptors respond in different ways to neurotransmitters. Many workers feel that the effect produced by the combination of neurotransmitter and receptor is the most important aspect of synaptic integration. Some neurotransmitters can reduce pain impulses sent into the brain from pain receptors in the periphery. The ability to reduce pain is known as analgesia, hence these neurotransmitters are analgesics.

II. Anesthetics. There are two basic types of anesthetics: local and general.
   A. Local anesthetics affect movement of the impulse along neural axons.
   B. General anesthetics tend to raise thresholds at central synapses.

Neuropeptides

Neuropeptides are the most recently discovered family of neurotransmitters. There is a large number of them, the most interesting of which is the enkephalins.

I. It's All In Your Head. Enkephalins are responsible for spontaneously dulling or eliminating the perception of pain in the central nervous system.

II. Acupuncture. Acupuncture is an ancient method of dulling pain by stimulating certain body areas with pins or needles. Its ability to eliminate the perception of pain may be due to the action of enkephalins.

III. Natural "Highs." Some neuropeptides have been associated with emotion. It may be that they are responsible for the feeling of euphoria that often accompanies vigorous exercise.

IV. Other Neuropeptides. Some peptide hormones are being investigated for their ability to function as neurotransmitters. Gastrin and cholecystokinin are two of them.

The Brain

The brain is the portion of the neural tube that is inside the skull. It is suggested that there may be ten billion neurons in the brain. The brain is what makes people individuals. Almost all neural operations have their centers in the brain. The largest mass of the human brain is collected in the zones known as the cerebral hemispheres, where all conscious operations occur. Memory centers are almost certainly in the cerebral hemispheres.

I. Memory. Memory is the essence of intelligence, but no one knows what it is. There are two kinds of memory: short-term and long-term.
   A. The short-term memory of the average person has a capacity of seven bits of information. Short-term memory patterns can be remembered for only a few minutes.
   B. Long-term memory is somehow permanently stored within the brain. It is not known how or where long-term memory patterns are stored or how they are retrieved.

II. Other Brain Parts. Other brain regions contribute to homeostatic processes and conscious operations in special ways.
   A. The Basal Ganglia. The basal ganglionic structures are formed of four main structures: the putamen, the globus pallidus, the caudate nucleus, and the corpus striatum. They are associated with control of muscle movement.
   B. The Thalamus. The thalamus is a cluster of nuclei. It is a major relay station and is involved in sleep/wake phenomena.
   C. The Hypothalamus. This is a major homeostatic center. Many endocrine loops run through the hypothalamus.
   D. The Limbic System. This area is deeply involved in emotions, learning, and the acquisition of new memory patterns.
   E. The Hindbrain: The Medulla, Pons, and Cerebellum. The medulla contains the centers that control heartbeat, respiration, and blood vessel tone. Even a tiny bit of damage in the medulla is fatal. The pons is a relay station for motor and sensory information. The cerebellum is involved in nerve-muscle coordination.

The Autonomic Nervous System

There are two functional branches of the nervous system: the somatic and the autonomic. Anatomically, the autonomic nervous system differs from the somatic nervous system as follows:

I. Somatic peripheral efferent neurons have their cell bodies inside the spinal cord, and their axons go all the way to their effector organs.

II. Autonomic efferents begin in the spinal cord, but there is a synapse between there and the effector organ.

III. There are two branches in the autonomic nervous system: The sympathetic and the parasympathetic. These two branches differ from each other anatomically and physiologically.
   A. Anatomically:
      1. Sympathetic neurons emerge from the spinal cord in the thoracic and lumbar regions. Parasympathetic neurons emerge from the spinal cord in cranial and sacral regions.

2. Sympathetic neurons characteristically have short preganglionic fibers and long postganglionic fibers. Parasympathetic neurons have long preganglionic fibers and short postganglionic ones.
3. Sympathetic preganglionic neurons often synapse with many postganglionic fibers. There is usually a one-to-one relationship between parasympathetic pre- and postganglionic neurons.

B. Physiologically:
1. Preganglionic neurons of both systems release acetylcholine (Ach) as their neurotransmitter. At postganglionic endings, the parasympathetic system still uses Ach as its neurotransmitter. But the sympathetic system uses norepinephrine for neurotransmission at its postganglionic endings.
2. The sympathetic system, when stimulated, fires everything at once. It is an emergency control system. The parasympathetic system tends to fire its neurons on a much more controlled basis. It handles mostly day-to-day homeostatic operations.

IV. Antagonistic Control Mechanisms. The sympathetic and parasympathetic nervous systems are antagonistic to each other . . . what one does, the other undoes, and vice versa.

Clinical Considerations

I. Tumors
II. Injuries
III. Ruptured Discs
IV. Headaches
  A. Tension Headaches
  B. Migraine
V. Stroke
VI. Epilepsy
  A. Partial Seizures
  B. Generalized Seizures
VII. Lou Gehrig's Disease: Amyotropic Lateral Sclerosis
VIII. Diseases Affecting Peripheral Nerves
IX. Multiple Sclerosis
X. Myasthenia Gravis

Some Diagnostic Tools

I. X Ray
II. The CAT Scan
III. The PETT Scan
IV. Nuclear Magnetic Resonance
V. Electroencephalography (EEG)

Sleep

I. Sleep Stages
II. Hypnosis

Review Questions

1. What is transduction, and how does it relate to neural receptors?
2. Discuss the membrane alterations and subsequent ion movements that occur when a receptor is stimulated.
3. What is meant by the term *decremental transmission?*
4. Under what circumstances can receptor potentials increase or decrease in intensity?
5. Which neuronal type—interneuron, motor neuron, or sensory neuron—is most abundant?
6. Of what cell types is the central nervous system composed?
7. How many cranial nerves are there in a human being? How many spinal nerves?
8. Draw a cross section of the spinal cord and label:
   a. the anterior (ventral) root
   b. the posterior (dorsal) root
   c. The central canal
9. What is a plexus?
10. Name the three meninges, and describe each one to the best of your ability.
11. Between which two meninges is the cerebrospinal fluid found? Describe the CSF.
12. What is the function of the cerebrospinal fluid?
13. What is a synapse? What two types of synapses are there in vertebrates?
14. Draw a diagram of a typical gap junction and discuss its operation.
15. Name the three main elements of a typical neural synapse.
16. Discuss the chemical transmission of information from a presynaptic neuron to a postsynaptic element.
17. What is a PSP?
18. Name two functions of the enzyme acetylcholinesterase.
19. What is the role of calcium in chemical neurotransmission?
20. Describe the phenomenon known as spatial summation. Distinguish it from temporal summation.
21. How do IPSPs differ from EPSPs?
22. Discuss the significance of the chemical synapse in as much detail as you can.
23. What is a neurotransmitter? How many have been identified?
24. What two broad groups of anesthetics are there? Identify them and discuss their effects on neurons.
25. What are neuropeptides?
26. Identify the major zones of the human brain.
27. Describe the location, morphology, and function of each zone you named in 26.
28. What is an engram? How does it relate to equipotentiality?
29. How does long-term memory differ from short-term memory?
30. How is the autonomic nervous system (ANS) distinguished from the somatic nervous system?
31. Name the two divisions of the ANS.
32. Discuss the three anatomical characteristics that distinguish the two branches from each other.
33. Discuss the function of each division of the ANS.

Chapter 9 The Special Senses

Study Hints

This chapter deals with three different types of sensory receptors: (a) receptors that provide us with information concerning contact stimuli, (b) receptors that provide us with information concerning the position of our limbs in spáce, and (c) receptors that provide us with information about things at a distance from us. Be sure that you can clearly distinguish them from one another. Pay particular attention to:

1. the difference between sensitivity and selectivity—and how the latter is achieved by the nervous system.
2. the importance of neural inhibition to perceptive clarity.
3. the two types of visual receptors, the neurons they synapse with, and their abilities.
4. the process of chemical amplification, such as is accomplished in the retina of the eye.
5. the role of pressure in the process of hearing.
6. the fact that equilibrium is a primary sense that is also centered in the ear.

Remember to look for similarities between the various kinds of reception in the distance receptors—it can simplify the process of learning. For instance, in both visual and auditory reception, the energy enters in a wave form; in both smell and taste, the energy is chemical, and reception must be accomplished in solution.

Objectives

When you have finished reading this chapter, you should:

1. be able to recognize the various types of cutaneous receptors and classify them on the basis of the stimulus detected.
2. understand the concepts of *mode* and *adequate stimulus.*
3. be able to trace the path of a light stimulus from the outside of the eye into the retina.
4. be able to explain how the visual receptors are stimulated and how they can amplify that stimulus.
5. be able to identify the receptors responsible for the sensation of pain.
6. know the major anatomical divisions of the ear.
7. be able to list the events involved in the perception of sound waves.
8. know the organs involved in equilibrium and be able to describe how they work.
9. know the four primary flavors classically identified and the three that have recently been proposed.
10. be able to locate the sensory receptors involved in the perception of smell and describe the neural pathway that funnels this information to the brain.

Visual receptors in the retina.

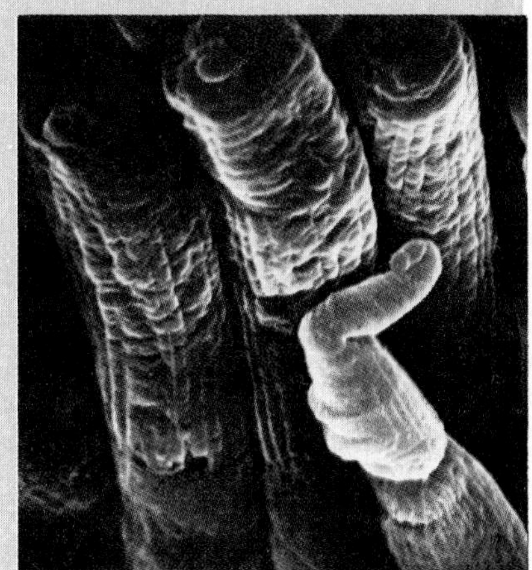

Introduction

Our nervous systems, as we have seen, can deal with many different kinds of problems and can utilize previous experience to modify behavioral patterns. Clearly, nervous systems can learn and can use newly learned facts to improve the whole organism's chances of survival. By accepting all kinds of stimuli and by comparing their meaning with learned experiences, animals can respond in ways best suited to maintaining homeostasis. Often the easiest and most beneficial response is behavioral. That's why we are made consciously aware of changes in our environment or potentially serious changes in conditions inside our bodies.

For example, when our body dries out more than is optimal, there are a lot of mechanisms that can swing into action to help reduce the problem. Autonomic mechanisms can kick in to reduce the amount of water lost in urine or to minimize the amount permitted to remain in the feces, but the quickest and most productive way to alleviate the problem is behavioral. Permit the organism's conscious brain to realize that it lacks water—make it thirsty. Thirst stimulates a behavioral homeostatic response: it drives the organism to drink. That replenishes the body's water supply quickly and easily, and the energy necessary to physiologically conserve water is never spent.

Nervous control systems use behavior as the first line of homeostatic defense. When supplies are low and food is needed to provide energy or raw materials, our conscious mind is made aware of hunger. When something is causing damage somewhere, we become aware of pain so we can move away from the source of the harm. Once the destruction has stopped, these same controls can start organizing other homeostatic mechanisms to repair any injury already done.

Behavior is the prime resource, but it's not the only one. Central control systems have lots of other homeostatic responses at their disposal, all of which are designed to maintain living systems at optimal operating efficiency. However, before they can respond to challenges from outside or inside the body, these central controls must be made aware of what is going on. To insure that the control centers are *always* aware of conditions affecting the organism, the body has been equipped with literally millions of the nervous accessories we call receptors. We have seen how receptors produce electrical signals (receptor potentials) and convert these into action potentials for transmission to these central control areas, but we have not studied just how they convert environmental energy into their receptor potentials. To do this, we need to take a much closer look at the receptors themselves.

Receptors

Our environments are, in a sense, determined by our receptors. We can accept and identify certain kinds of stimuli from our surroundings, and based on this information, we adjust our style of living. Some of these adjustments we are conscious of, and some are handled without our ever being aware of it. But whichever course is followed, it is followed in response to what receptors have told our central controls. Logically, then, if our receptors do not continually sample the environment, no adjustment is made, no matter how critical it might be. Each receptor has its own special job to perform, and each does it, all the time.

Not all receptors are equally important. In humans, our eyes provide the lion's share of our sensory information, and we have only two of them. Hence they are easily our most important receptors. Humans possess an acuity of vision that only a very few animals can surpass, and color vision not only provides clarity but also adds an esthetic quality to visual perception. But colors mean nothing to the color-blind dog. We may therefore pity the poor animal for being deprived of the wonders of brilliant color vision, yet we live our lives blissfully unaware of the enormous, rich panorama of clearly identifiable odors that the dog's nose detects. The shark's olfactory lobes dominate his brain. Who knows what esthetic input such incredible sensitivity might provide? We can only guess, yet we are given hints by the memories that an odor can awaken or by the intense hunger we can experience when we walk into a room laden with the scent of delicious food cooking. Each receptor has its own job to do, and each provides information that makes our environment whole.

Even if we ignore the restrictions that civilized life has placed on our sensory systems, humans tend to be unconsciously selective in the information that they take from their environments. We must miss a lot. For instance, people who have had certain forms of eye surgery can sometimes see radiation in the ultraviolet, and they tell fascinating stories about the world they see. It is tremendously interesting to speculate on what a dolphin's view of the world might be or what olfactory information might be presented to a hound "hot on the trail."

Environmental stimuli represent information that is brought into our brains by our peripheral receptors, and each bit is analyzed, compared, and integrated with earlier information that was collected the same way. With the exception of responses to sexual stimuli, our responses to what we perceive are always *homeostatic.* They are all intended to maintain our *milieu interieur* as close to the same as is feasible.

We should also be aware that usually an environmental stimulus stops at the receptor. Damaging stimuli will, of course, pass well beyond reception if steps are not taken to avoid them, but ordinary stimuli end when they encounter the receptors. Normally, sound impinges on our ears and stops there. The *perception* of sound is not the airborne sonic vibrations but rather an electrical interpretation of those energy waves. The flavor of a steak is picked up in our mouths, but our awareness of the taste results not from the delicious chemicals but from the action potentials that rush from our mouths to our brains.

Primary sensory neurons carry all the sensory information into the central nervous system, and **primary sensory receptors** are the specialized endings of primary sensory nerves. Not all incoming stimuli encounter primary sensory receptors. Some, like sonic waves entering our ears, are accepted by specialized epithelial cells and then are passed from them to the primary sensory neurons of the eighth cranial nerve. In this case, the receptors are known as **secondary sensory receptors.**

Our bodies are filled with nervous receptors of all kinds. We have receptors in our intestinal tracts designed to detect any number of things—pressure, acids, alkalines, water, fats—the list seems endless. There are receptors buried in tendons that tell us if our muscles are contracted, semicontracted, or totally relaxed. In our mouths, we have receptors that can detect the presence of certain chemicals by dissolving them in saliva and identifying them as flavors, and deep in our brains we have receptors that respond to changes in the osmotic pressure of the blood. We have receptors that are designed to detect low-frequency vibrations in the air—vibrations that might have their source miles away. Still others are sensitive to certain bands of electromagnetic radiation, and they can detect this radiation even though it was emitted by a source billions of miles away at a time when our ancestors were living in caves and wearing paint for armor.

Several methods have been suggested to classify receptors. They all have certain advantages. In one, the eyes, ears, and nasal receptors are classified as **distance receptors,** because they receive stimuli from somewhere outside the body—often from great distances away. The various receptors in our skin would be **contact receptors,** because the stimuli they are designed to detect must actually touch the organism. **Internal receptors** would, as the name implies, accept

Table 9.1 Some Ways of Classifying Receptors in the Human Body

Receptor	Example(s)	Adequate Stimulus	Perception
Classification System 1 (Functional)			
Distance	Eye, ear, nose	Varied	Varied
Contact	Meissner's, Ruffini's, Krause's	Touch, temperature changes	Varied
Internal	Pacinian corpuscles, pH receptors in gut	Pressure, acids	Varied
Classification System 2 (Functional)			
Mechanoreceptors	Pacinian corpuscles Meissner's corpuscles Ruffini's corpuscles Krause's corpuscles	Physical distortion of the receptor membrane	Pressure and touch
	Auditory receptors		Hearing
Chemoreceptors	Olfactory organs Taste buds	Chemicals in solution Chemicals in solution	Odor Taste
Photoreceptors	Rods and cones in the eye	Electromagnetic radiation	Vision
Pain receptors	Scattered everywhere	Damaging stimuli	Pain
Classification System 3 (Perceptive)			
Cutaneous receptors	All skin receptors	Varied	Touch, heat, cold, etc.
Proprioceptors	Muscle spindles Golgi organs	Movement and position in space	Location of arms and overall posture
Special receptors	Eye, ear, nose	Varied	Vision, hearing

stimuli from within the organism. Another method of classification involves the type of stimulus the receptors respond to. Receptors sensitive to alterations in things like oxygen content of the blood or the amount of pepper in the soup would be classified as **chemoreceptors,** because they respond to changes in the chemistry of their surroundings. **Mechanoreceptors** respond to movement or displacement of some part of the receptor, and **baroreceptors** respond to pressure changes, while our eyes are **photoreceptors** (see table 9.1).

Adequate Stimulus

The type of energy that a given receptor is specialized to respond to, whatever it may be, is known as its **adequate stimulus.** Each type of sensory receptor in a living system is designed to respond to a specific form of energy at a much lower threshold than other receptor types. As each receptor type increased its sensitivity to one form of energy, its ability to respond to other forms diminished correspondingly. For the eye, the adequate stimulus energy is the type of energy present in electromagnetic radiation in the visible spectrum. Light waves, even at extremely high intensities, are not detected by receptors in the skin unless they can increase the temperature and thus introduce a different form of energy. For the ear, the adequate stimulus is energy vibrations in the audible frequency range. For some skin receptors, it is light touch, while for others it is a sudden drop in temperature. Each sensory receptor has its own special adequate stimulus energy form.

This does not mean that specialized receptors cannot detect other forms of energy. What it does mean is that each type of receptor is designed to respond with greatest sensitivity to one particular kind. Highly specialized receptors will often respond to energy in forms other than their adequate stimulus, but their threshold for these other energy forms is much higher. Most receptors can be touched off by injury or mechanical distortion if it is strong enough. You have probably experienced this yourselves, although you may never have noticed it. When you close your eyes and rub against the eyelids, you are pressing against your eyeballs. Often, when you do this, your brain will perceive a series of multicolored flashes of light, and the harder you press, the more flashes you will see. Obviously, with your eyes closed, you are not actually "seeing" anything, but your retinal receptors are being stimulated by pressure, and the stimulus is powerful enough to cause your visual receptors to respond.

The Law of Specific Nerve Energy

It is important to realize that in spite of the fact that it is pressure that is stimulating your eyes, what you *perceive* is light. Obviously, perception does not depend on the stimulus, but rather on the nerves involved and the brain areas that the nerves run into. This observation has led to postulation of a physiological principal known as the **Law of Specific Nerve Energy** of sensory nerves. What this law states is that each individual sensory system has a specific function and will subserve *only that function*—no other. And it means that our perception of a stimulus depends on the nerves involved, not the stimulus. If we electrically stimulate a taste bud receptor in the mouth, the result will be flavor perception. A similar stimulation on the skin surface might result in the perception of cold or heat. A hard blow to the head produces explosions of light or the perception of unusual odors, and everyone has heard of amputees experiencing itching in nonexistent limbs. People feel these things because what we experience depends on the connections between the receptor and the brain. There seems to be little doubt that it applies in particular to the specialized receptors.

Since our brains perceive only a single sensation from most sensory receptors regardless of what stimulates them, it is interesting to consider what we might learn if we had the techniques. If it were possible, for instance, to attach the optic nerve to the auditory tract, then snip loose the auditory nerve and graft it into the optic tract, the subject would perceive light flashes when something nearby made a sound and would hear an explosion when someone flashed a bright light in his eyes. It would be fascinating to discover if light blue struck a chord as harmonious as its visual image, or if the color of F-sharp would be different if played an octave higher.

Mode (Sensation)

Our perceptive abilities, even taking our limitations into account, are as varied as our receptors . . . maybe a little more. Each specialized receptor has its own particular sensation, and there is no crossing over; a touch evokes a sensation totally unlike a sound, and everyone knows the hand cannot see. There is a word that describes the characteristics of a given sensation that permit us to distinguish it from other sensations. It is called the **mode,** and each sensation has its very own. The eye, regardless of how it is stimulated, responds with visual images, and we can distinguish these sensations from any other sensations. Thus the *mode* of the sensations elicited by the eye is visual; the mode of the sensations perceived by the tongue is gustatory—and as you know, the two are as different as night and day. There can be no variation in the *mode* of any given sensation, but there can be variation in the *quality,* and we can certainly detect changes in *intensity.* The crash of a thunderbolt differs in quality from the sound of a symphony orchestra playing Brahms' Lullaby, the taste of a ripe apple is quite different from that of onions, and the silhouette of an attractive member of the opposite sex looks nothing like a brightly colored seashell. Each is a variation *within* its own mode, a *qualitative* variation.

Stimuli of the same mode and quality can also vary *quantitatively* to some extent. It is often hard to evaluate such variation objectively, but there is no doubt that it can occur. A brightly lit room is not the same as a dimly lit one; a small firecracker is less noisy than a stick of dynamite, and a mild onion is more delicate than a pungent one. Yet despite such variation in intensity, science often has no way to quantify them.

How do you measure, for instance, the intensity of flavor in an onion? One person might refer to it as "very strong," while another might take a bite of the same onion and pronounce it "moderately strong." Obviously, terms like this are subjective evaluations and are not quantifiable. It may be that individual perception is subject to individual quantification, and there is really no valid, objective way to do it. After all, how does one establish a unit of sweet odor or a unit of onion flavor? About the closest we can come to quantifying sensations is to measure *stimulus intensity.* That is not hard to do and by determining how strong any individual stimulus must be to produce the very first sensation, we can quantify perception to some extent.

The Weber-Fechner Law

The **Weber-Fechner law** is an attempt to quantify abilities to **discriminate** between various intensities of stimulus perception. It states that *a perceptible change in stimulus intensity is always a constant fraction of the original stimulus.*

For instance, a person holds a 10-gram metal disc in his hand. The weight is increased by 0.9 grams, and no change in weight can be perceived, but when the weight is increased by a whole gram, it is detectable. From this data we would infer that an increase of 10 percent is detectable, but anything less than 10 percent is not. Now, according to the Weber-Fechner law, if that same person were to hold a 30-gram disc in his hand, he would not be able to detect an increase in weight of one gram, because one gram is not 10 percent of 30. Before he would be able to perceive any increase in weight, the disc would have to increase by 10 percent—to 33 grams.

Like all such so-called laws, the Weber-Fechner law is not without its exceptions. Generally speaking, however, it works very nicely over the middle stimulus intensities and is about the only means known of quantifying *relative* stimuli. The ratios vary for different stimuli. Also, naturally, they vary with individuals, although most usually fall within a small percentage range. For pressure stimuli, detectable increases usually must be about 3 percent of the original; for audible stimuli, about 5 percent; and for weight, about 2.5 percent.

The ability of a sensory receptor to perceive a stimulus is a measure of that receptor's **sensitivity.** One person might be able to detect a very slight sound that another cannot, and the second person's ears would be considered less sensitive than the first person's.

Selectivity is a different form of perception. It represents an ability to discriminate between two separate, but similar, stimuli that occur at the same time, fairly close to each other. It is not the same thing as sensitivity, a fact that is actually quite easy to demonstrate.

For example, the back of the average person's neck is extremely *sensitive;* you can feel a mosquito weighing 1/1000th of an ounce landing there. But if two mosquitoes landed on your neck a half-inch apart, it is not likely you would be able to detect the fact that there were two present and not merely one. The palm of your hand, however, has opposite capabilities. You probably would not be able to feel a mosquito landing on the inside of your finger near the palm of your hand, but the selectivity there is much greater than it is on the back of your neck. This is not difficult to illustrate. By taking an artist's compass and performing a simple experiment, you can easily determine the relative selectivity of various parts of a person's body. The test is called a two-point discrimination test, and it is very easy to do.

Figure 9.1 The two-point discrimination test of receptor selectivity.

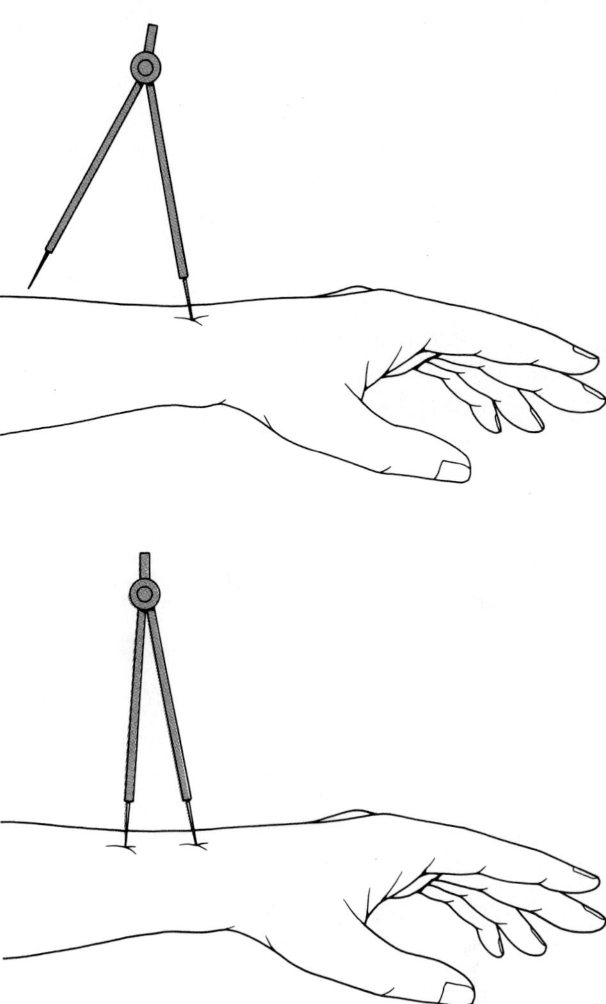

As illustrated in figure 9.1, you touch the subject's skin with one or two points, without the subject seeing which, and ask each time how many points the person feels. If he or she can detect only one point, gradually spread the compass tips further and further apart until you are satisfied the subject can really feel two separate stimuli. It varies from person to person, of course, but experience shows that a very sensitive area in the middle of the back is least selective; the compass points can be separated by 4 centimeters or more before the average person can discriminate between them. The fingertips, however—not always a very sensitive zone—can clearly detect the presence of two stimuli when they are no more than 3 mm (an eighth of an inch) apart.

Figure 9.2 In order to clearly distinguish between separate stimuli, there must be a different neuron innervating the region beneath each stimulus. Obviously then, the bigger the receptive field each nerve is able to cover, the less selective the area will be.

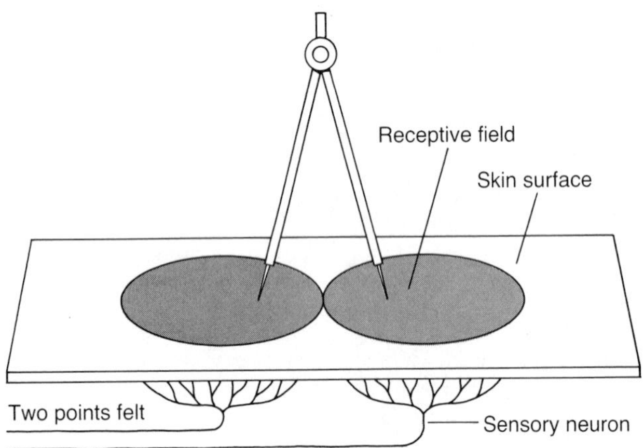

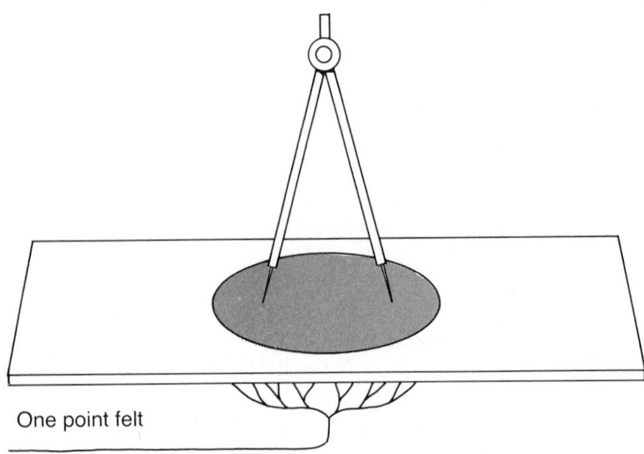

Figure 9.3 (*a*) A gross view of lateral inhibition. When an object touches the skin (*1*), receptors in the middle are stimulated more than neighboring receptors (*2*). Lateral inhibition in the nervous system (*3*) reduces input from these neighboring neurons even more. The sensation, as a result, has a sharper outline (*4*).

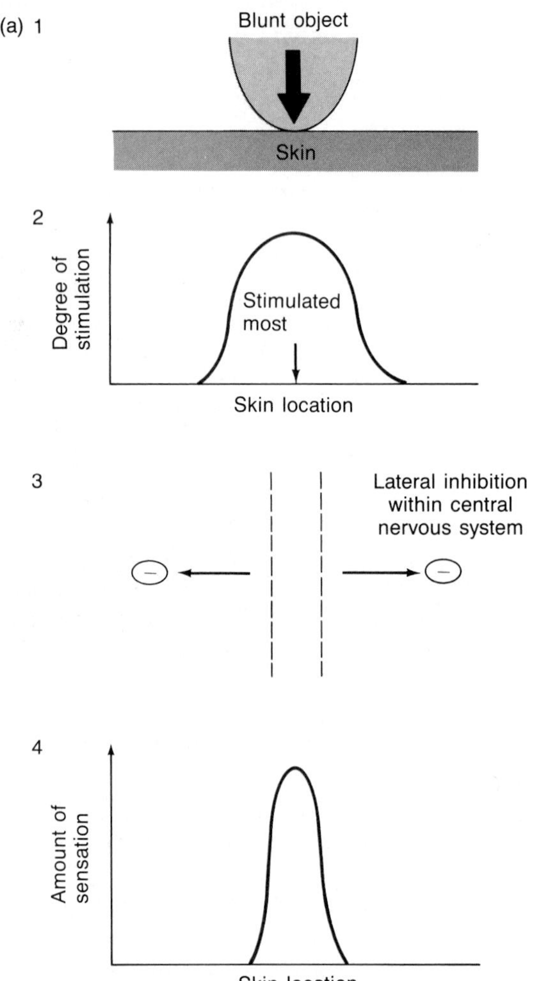

Receptive Fields

Selective ability depends on the number of nerve fibers that are devoted to a given skin surface area. The size of the skin surface that a given neuron innervates is known as the **receptive field** of that fiber. If a given area of skin has lots of nerve fibers innervating it, each receptor will be required to respond to stimuli on only a very small area. On the other hand, if there are only a few neurons running into a given zone, individual receptors will be responsible for a larger surface area. The size of the receptive fields in any given skin region determines the selective acuity of that portion of skin surface. Such fields are of particular importance for mechanoreceptors and photoreceptors, because they increase the *clarity* or *acuity* of the perception (see figure 9.2).

Lateral Inhibition

Sometimes the body can increase perceptive acuity by narrowing the receptive field even further through the phenomenon known as **lateral inhibition** (see figure 9.3). In an area where acuity of perception is really important, it is not uncommon for inhibitory collateral fibers to run from the axon of each sensory nerve to its nearest neighbors, so that when one is stimulated, it tends to inhibit those cells adjacent to it. This sharpens perception by rendering neurons incapable of sending messages concerning stimuli unless their receptor potential is strong enough to overcome the inhibition. That can only happen if the receptor is directly in the path of the stimulus.

Figure 9.3 (cont.) (*b*) A more detailed look at lateral inhibition. Nerves C, D, and E, directly beneath the blunt stimulus, are firing rapidly. Their frequency is sufficient to stimulate all inhibitory fibers. The intensity is such, however, that the inhibition provoked doesn't stop neurons C_2, D_2, and E_2 from becoming active. The stimulus intensity at *B* and *F*, however, is not as great. As a result, their impulse frequency is not great enough to fire the inhibitory neurons they synapse with, nor is it sufficient to overcome the inhibition administered by inhibitory fibers from *C* and *E*. The resultant sensation is a sharp outline instead of a fuzzy one.

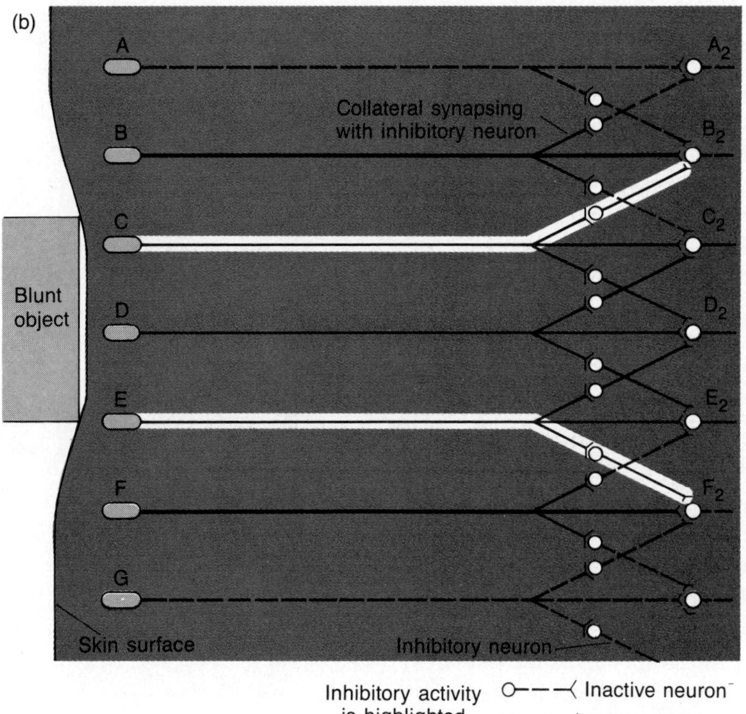

Adaptation

Most of us know that the only unpleasant part of taking a cool dip on a hot summer day is entering the water. Doing it all at once is easier than the slow torture of gradually getting our bodies wet a bit at a time, although that first plunge is pure torment. The sudden crash of water that is 30° or 40° F cooler than the surrounding air has been known to provide a nervous jolt that can actually render a weakened or aged person unconscious. Usually the swimmer is just momentarily dazed. The sudden barrage of nervous impulses hammer into the brain in such teeming profusion that they threaten to overwhelm all other sensory input. Still, it all passes quite rapidly. After the first jolt, the neural bombardment quickly slows, and the person becomes "used to" the coolness of the water. Walking into a dark movie theater after being in bright sunlight results in a period of blindness, and sometimes five or ten minutes is required before one can see properly.

We are always assured of one thing when confronted with a cold pond or a dark room—after a short period of adjustment, we will "get used to" our suddenly altered environment. Yet the cold water has not gotten any warmer, nor has the dark movie theater suddenly increased its level of lighting. The phenomenon is due to an interesting and poorly understood neural capability called **adaptation,** and it's one of the most important features of the nervous system.

It has to do with the fact that a large percentage of our body's receptors respond primarily to *change* in stimulus (see the box on page 188). They respond only fleetingly to unchanging stimuli and so are known as **phasic receptors.** Even **tonic receptors**—those that are intended to maintain a constant rate of fire under constant stimulus—show a sudden burst of unusual activity when the intensity of a stimulus changes. After the change is over, these receptors settle down to a new rate of steady activity, but while change is actually occurring, they bombard us with information.

Researchers are not really sure what happens when a battery of sensory receptors and their attached nerves undergo this process of adaptation. It is known (see figure 9.4) that the generator potentials drop off, and as a consequence, the action potentials slow down, but we do not know why. Nevertheless, adaptation is of tremendous importance to living systems. Just imagine how difficult it would be to survive in this world if our bodies were not able to adapt. Because of adaptation, we *are* eventually able to see—and see clearly—in a darkened theater. And we do not become permanently blinded when we step from the theater into the bright sunlight after the performance is over. Imagine how little enjoyment you would get out of a swim if you experienced a "first shock" neural bombardment all the time you were in the pool. As it is, we can take a cool shower or a hot tub in genuine comfort after going through the process of becoming used to the initial immersions. As we have already seen, one even gets used to pain. Pain is at its most intense during the administration of its stimulus, driving the person to avoid it. Afterwards, while it continues to make one unpleasantly aware of its presence, it does not (unless it is unusually severe) saturate or overload our sensory systems to the exclusion of everything else.

Tonic receptors are designed to keep us aware of things like the position of our limbs, which side is up when we are in the water, or the salt concentration of our blood. Such receptors are most abundant in the structures that are involved in adjusting muscle tension and body posture—the muscles, tendons, and ligaments—and, of course, our central nervous system.

Proprioceptors

Proprioceptors are involved in what is known as "deep" sensation. They are the **muscle spindle organs, Golgi tendon organs,** and **joint organs.** The muscle spindles are the most widely studied and are the sensory portion of a biological "remote control" sensory/motor pathway that is known as a *myotactic reflex.* This will be discussed later in this chapter.

Figure 9.4 The correlation between receptor potential amplitude and impulses generated along the corresponding axon in response to an applied, constant stimulus. This type of response is typical of a tonic receptor. Arrows mark the beginning and end of the stimulus.

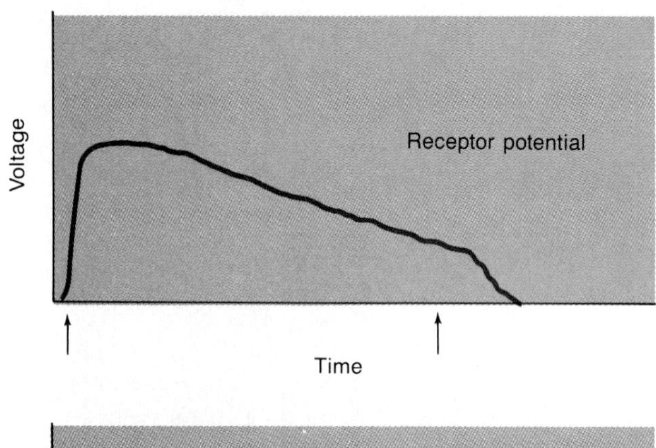

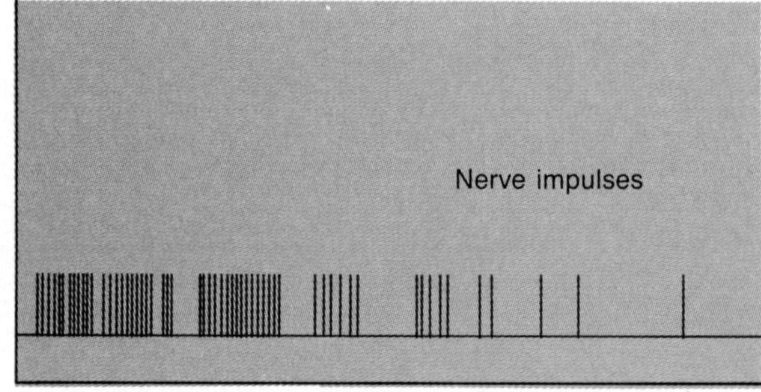

The Cutaneous Sensations

Our skin provides a home for millions of receptors. Some of them are highly specialized and some are not. Specialized ones are encapsulated in layers of connective tissue, each one with a different, obviously special, design. Presumably their construction is intended to enhance the likelihood of the detection of a specific stimulus. Others are simply bare nerve endings that look like they can respond to almost anything that provides them with extraneous energy (figure 9.5).

Taken as a group, these sensors, which cluster mainly in our body covering, mediate what is known as the *somatovisceral senses,* and they are unusual in that they operate individually. Instead of clustering together into specialized organs, each with a single

Figure 9.5 (*a*) Different types of dermal receptors and the types of stimuli they respond to. (*b*) A Pacinian corpuscle.

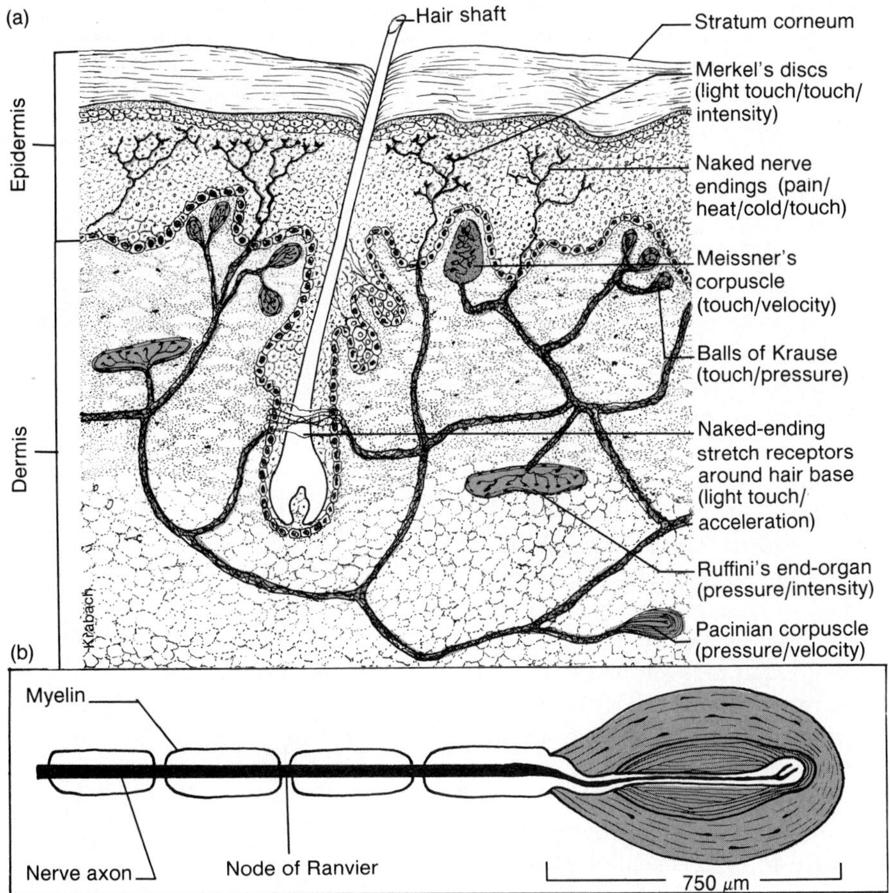

function, they are dispersed, with no apparent overall pattern, across the whole body surface. Nor are there any afferent nerves devoted exclusively to input from the body surface. Individual fibers arising from isolated cutaneous sensors join with afferent fibers of all types to form complex peripheral nerves and spinal tracts, which carry their messages to our conscious brains.

As shown in figure 9.5, there are no receptors in the *stratum corneum*, since this, the outermost layer of the epidermis, is dead tissue. It is constantly being sloughed off, so if there were any receptors present, they would be lost on a pretty regular basis, a thing the human nervous system would not tolerate.

Touch and Pressure

Special construction for special functions: The receptors that deal with specific sensations feature specialized endings and capsules of connective tissue (see figure 9.5). The skin is filled with receptors that respond to some physical distortion such as touch or pressure. They are known as *mechanoreceptors*, and they are selective enough to segregate four distinct degrees of touch that have been designated *pressure, touch, vibration,* and *tickle*. These degrees of touch also help categorize the various mechanoreceptors in the skin.

Meissner's corpuscles, for instance (figure 9.5*a*), are responsible for the detection of gentle to moderate touch, and they respond almost exclusively to *change*. They normally will adapt to a given stimulus within half a second, so they are considered *fast* receptors. Yet they are extremely delicate and can detect tactile stimuli as light as 5 mg (less than 1/5,000th of an ounce). They are abundant in the lips and around the nipples of the breast, so in addition to being quite discriminatory, those zones are also extremely sensitive. They are thought to be involved in perception of the *tickle* aspect of touch.

Despite their fast-adaptive response, Meissner's corpuscles are not as fast-acting as the **Pacinian corpuscles** (figure 9.5*b*). Normally when a stimulus impinges on Pacinian corpuscles, they will depolarize their axon only once or twice, and then adaptation takes over. They are generally deeper in the tissue than Meissner's receptors, and their morphology, consisting of many concentric layers, resembles a miniature onion bulb. They are especially abundant below the upper surface of the dermis, and their extremely rapid adaptive abilities has led to agreement that they are probably good at picking up *vibration*.

Pacinian corpuscles are not particularly sensitive, and they do not respond to light tactile sensations. Possibly the construction of the receptor (see figure 9.5) makes it less easily distorted by gentle touch. The outer membrane of the receptor must be distorted at least 100 Å out of position, and usually closer to 1,000 Å, before there is any axonal firing. That means pressures of on the order of 150 to 1,500 mg are necessary to produce receptor potentials of sufficient amplitude to fire axons connected to Pacinian corpuscles. For these reasons, Pacinian corpuscles are usually thought of as *pressure* rather than *touch* receptors.

Pacinian corpuscles may compensate somewhat for their lack of individual sensitivity by their tendency to converge on one interneuron. Fibers from several receptors will often synapse with a single interneuron, resulting in a summation of all their impulses at the synapse. Of course, convergence, while requiring less force per unit area to fire the postsynaptic fibers (see figure 9.6), does reduce the receptive selectivity considerably.

Ruffini's end organs, along with the **bulbs of Krause,** have traditionally been considered thermal receptors, the former to detect temperature increases and the latter to detect temperature decreases. Recent work, however, indicates that there are no specially constructed receptors for detection of thermal changes. Both Krause's and Ruffini's end organs are involved with tactile perception. Ruffini's are quite slow acting and are therefore considered to be receptors involved with *pressure intensity*. Krause's bulbs are moderately slow acting and are also involved in deep pressure reception and intensity.

Figure 9.6 An example of convergence effects. An application of 150 mg of pressure over an area large enough to stimulate only two Pacinian corpuscles (*1*) might not be enough to cause the postsynaptic neuron to fire and thus inform the brain of the presence of pressure. However, if that same amount were applied to an area large enough to fire six corpuscles (*2*), the resulting synaptic bombardment might summate enough to depolarize and fire the postsynaptic fiber.

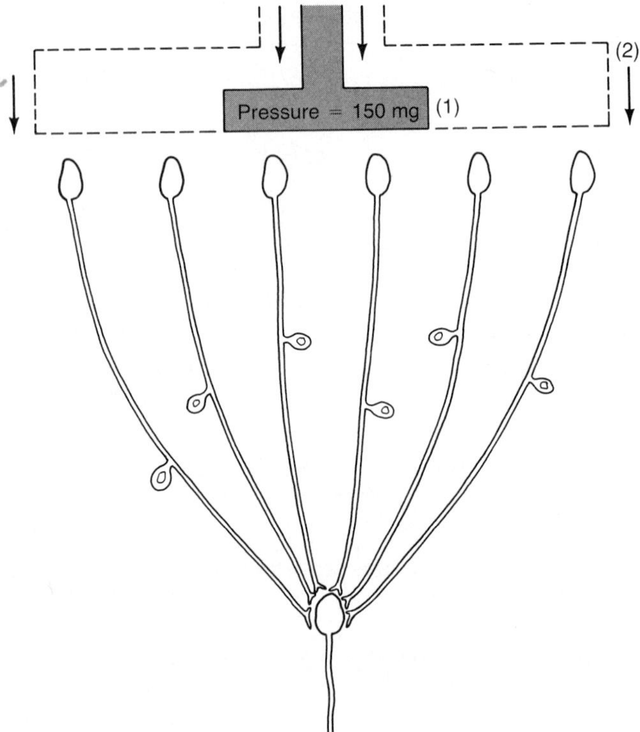

Merkel's discs are also moderately slow-adapting, tactile receptors. Buried just below the cornified dead layers of the epidermis, they are quite sensitive, responding to very light touch. They are generally considered to be touch/intensity receptors and have been compared, in this respect, with immature Meissner's corpuscles.

Nonspecialized Receptors

Right below the stratum corneum are clusters of apparently unspecialized neurons known simply as **naked** or **free nerve endings.** As tactile receptors, they are probably the most sensitive of all. These are capable of responding to the slightest breeze wafting across the skin surface, and, if the ending is wrapped around the base of a hair (see figure 9.5*a*), they can detect a floating speck of dust. They are exquisitely sensitive and extremely fast-acting receptors. A hair, for instance, will detect the distortion caused by a strand of spider silk, but will do so only for an instant, and it will not quantify the movement at all. Whether you bend the hair just a tiny bit or completely fold it over, the perception will be the same—and it will be gone in an instant.

Thermal Receptors

Many of the naked nerve endings serve as thermal receptors, some specializing in reception of *decreases* in temperature and others serving to detect *increases.* The former—the cold receptors—are quite a bit more abundant than the heat-sensitive ones and can conduct their information into the central nervous system six times as fast. Just why that should be isn't known. Both cold and warm receptors respond maximally to *changes* in stimulus, and they continue to produce a constant stream of signals even after adaptation has taken place. As you know, you experience the first shock of cold when you jump into a pool, and that quickly dissipates, but you remain conscious—on a lower level of course—of coolness all the time you are in the water. The same is true of hot bathwater—you are aware all the time that you are immersed in something pleasantly warm.

Surprisingly enough, it seems that the receptive fields of the thermal receptors are quite small—every bit as tiny as the receptive fields of many tactile receptors—not something a person would necessarily expect, since the nature of ambient heat and cold tends to be rather sweeping.

Pain and Painful Stimuli

As we all know, pain, despite its unpleasant nature, is essential for continued health. Without it, we would probably make very little effort to avoid damage to our body areas, and we could rapidly accumulate enough damage to destroy or seriously damage crucial body parts—which is exactly what happens when certain diseases, like leprosy, destroy the ability to perceive pain.

Apparently there is no adequate stimulus for pain. It is a primitive form of perception, and any form of energy, if it is intense enough, can produce the sensation we know as pain. Pressure, heat, and cold all result in pain if they threaten tissue damage.

Certain free endings are thought to be responsible for detecting damaging or painful stimuli. It is assumed they are pain receptors, because they are found mainly in areas where pain is one of the major stimuli—areas like the nerve in a tooth or the underside of the fingernail. They are rather unusual receptors in that they, or endings very similar to them, are often found clearly subserving functions other than pain. As noted above, naked nerve endings are wrapped around the base of the tiny hairs that cover the human body, and other naked endings terminate against the tough little saucer-shaped Merkel's discs imbedded in the epidermal layers of the skin. In both cases, the naked endings are obviously involved in perceiving very delicate touch sensations, not pain. That doesn't mean they are not pain receptors; they could be both. When functioning as tactile receptors they are clearly mechanoreceptors. When functioning as pain receptors, they serve as a kind of chemoreceptor, because they respond to certain chemicals released by damaged or dying cells. It is *possible* that they can pass along information about both pain *and* touch (see the following discussion of "A 'Law' Violated").

One of the problems is that no one is certain exactly what pain is. We know what its purpose is, we know that it is an unpleasant sensation, and we certainly try to avoid it. But some contend that it is not a separate, unique sensation. These workers hypothesize that pain is an exaggeration of ordinary, nonpainful sensations—like touch, for example— and one of their strongest arguments is the obvious ability of most people to distinguish between pain caused by scalding water and that caused by a cut or a sharp blow. They suggest that we perceive pain when some ordinary sensation becomes harmfully intense, in which case our brains are simply perceiving an unpleasant and warning aspect of pressure or heat, for example, from the regular touch or heat receptor.

This hypothesis still exists, although few today agree with it. Current evidence suggests that pain is just as specific a perception as flavor or vision. Nerve endings have been located throughout the periphery that evidently start working only when some tissue-damaging or potentially tissue-damaging stimulus takes place. These endings are called **nociceptors.** They respond only to *noxious* stimuli, and they are apparently as specific about this as Meissner's or Ruffini's receptors are about their stimuli. Some respond to damaging thermal stimuli, some to pressure damage, and some to noxious chemicals or to fluid spilling from ruptured cells. Thus, a person who has suffered a painful stimulus *should* be able to distinguish the pain of a cut from the pain of a burn, because there is a specific nociceptor for each of these injuries.

These facts could also suggest that the free nerve endings around hair bases are subtly different from the free nerve endings of nociceptors. Or it could imply that free nerve endings do indeed have more than a single function. Possibly the receptive events that occur in response to pain are different from those that take place in response to touch.

A "Law" Violated If the latter is true, it would be a violation of the specific energy law, but exceptions to such scientific "laws" are not all that unusual. Most eventually go down the drain or require considerable modification. The term *law* is hardly ever used today in describing new scientific principles, simply because there are almost always exceptions, and scientific principles are intended to be guidelines, not inviolate "laws."

There's a fair library of instances in the files of medical history that tend to support the contention that pain receptors are indeed separate from those of the other cutaneous sensations. People have suffered selective neural damage as a result of accident or disease and have been unable to feel pain, but they can still detect other tactile stimuli. They can distinguish heat from cold, can hold things and *know* they are holding them . . . some can even feel flies and other insects landing on the affected areas, yet they could suffer severe tissue damage without any sensation of pain.

On the surface, this would appear to be unequivocal evidence that pain receptors are indeed specialized, separate entities, at least in the skin; but it is not—not completely. There is another possible explanation. Maybe there are specialized pain tracts in the spinal cord but no special pain receptors in the skin. If the disease damaged these special pain tracts in the spine, the hypothesis would agree with the above observations. The receptors in the affected areas may all be working correctly and sending messages of pain to the spine when some painful stimulus occurs, but because the "pain tract" is damaged, none of these pain messages are relayed to the brain.

Cutaneous senses carry with them more than just the ability to perceive the proper sensation. Probably, because of the arrangement of the fibers and their relationship to their surroundings, the conscious brain can determine *where* on the surface of the body a given stimulus is being applied. There are receptive fields in the brain that respond to certain similar fields on the body surface, thereby permitting conscious **localization** of the stimulus. This is known as the **principle of tonotypic organization,** and it involves the spinal cord tracts for the senses as well as the cortical reception areas.

Figure 9.7 Aristotle's experiment.

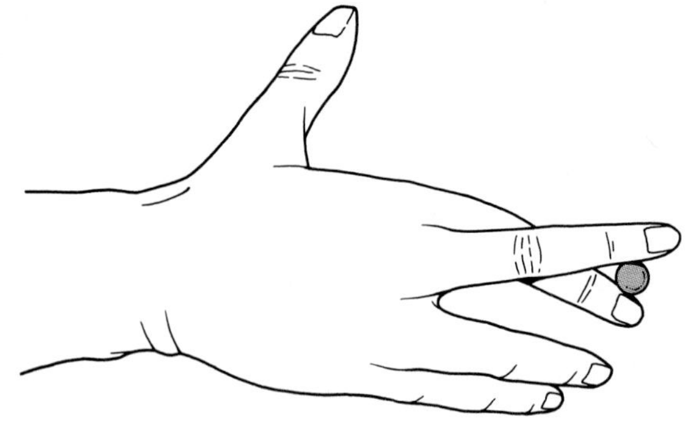

This ability to consciously localize various stimuli is related rather broadly to the ability to discriminate, and it is a valuable ability, although not uniformly dependable. All by itself it is sometimes inaccurate, and it is remarkably easy to deceive with or without the assistance of other senses. Aristotle noticed this and passed one deception down to us—one that he discovered sometime during the 4th century B.C. He noted that when you hold a spherical bead between the second finger and index finger while keeping both straight, you feel only a single stimulus. Yet if you cross the two fingers over one another and then inserted the bead as shown in figure 9.7, it feels like two separate stimuli instead of just one. In this case, the tactile senses can ignore the contradictory visual input.

On the other hand, sometimes visual input can completely confuse our perceptions when our bodies are arranged in rather unusual ways. By crossing our wrists, gripping our fingers together and twisting into the positon shown in figure 9.8, we can disorient our internal sensors and our eyes rather badly. Get a friend into this posture and then, taking care not to actually touch any fingers, indicate one and ask him or her to move it. The length of time it takes to adjust will probaby surprise both of you.

Input from a Distance: The Special Senses

It is beyond the scope of this textbook to delve into all the major sensory organs and detail all their functions, capabilities, and variability. Yet in view of the tremendous importance of the so-called **special senses** possessed by humans, I would be remiss to ignore them. It has been estimated that somewhere on the order of 75 percent of the average person's sensory input is visual, which confirms what all of us already know—our eyes are very important organs indeed.

There is nothing novel about vision . . . indeed, every animal phylum of which we are aware has representatives that feature this ability, and in the vertebrate phylum it is rare indeed to find a type lacking eyes. The fishes, amphibians, and reptiles not only have the capacity to see, but can see in color, just as

Figure 9.8 Touch/visual localization (see text).

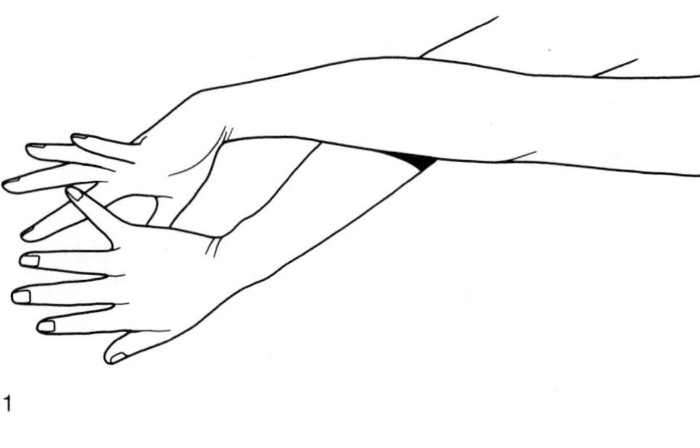

1

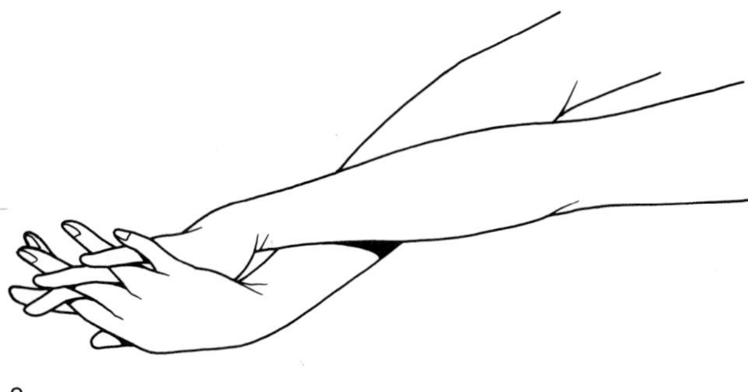

2

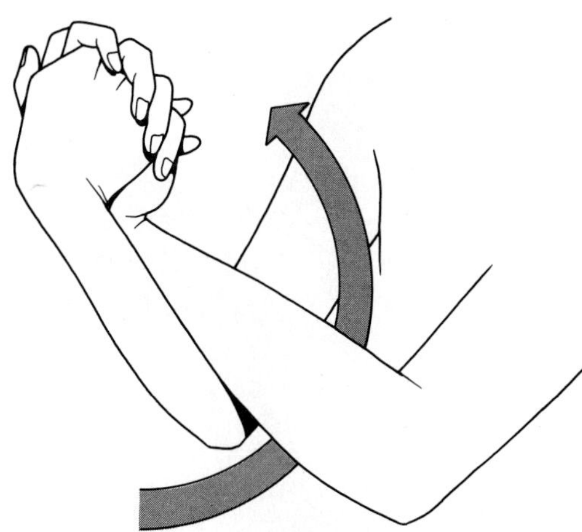

humans do. Birds rely on vision even more than people do, and in keeping with this observation, research indicates that many of them—especially the high-flying birds of prey like hawks and eagles—can see *better* than humans.

As far as we know, only the mammals have a large number of representatives that cannot see color, and this probably fits in with the life-style of many of them. It may, in fact, go back to the time when the earth was ruled by reptiles, and mammals were tiny, insignificant animals who often served as a dessert for some of the smaller dinosaurs. During those millenia, it was probably extremely dangerous for a small mammal to venture out of its burrow during the daytime when the reptiles were active. At night, however, it would have the world to itself. Once the sun went down, all but the largest reptiles would be relatively inactive, and the chances were that small insectivorous and vegetarian mammals could feed with impunity. Even those possessing color-sensitive receptors in the beginning would tend to lose them, since they would be of no value at night when the light was dim and they would be taking up space that could be utilized for low-illumination receptors.

Nocturnal activity is a behavioral ramification that still seems, among the vertebrates, to be almost the exclusive property of the mammals. Many mammalian herbivores living in forested areas and hot deserts remain in hiding during daylight hours, venturing out into open meadows or sand dunes to feed only during hours of darkness. As a result, their predators have become nocturnal also. Our household pets, both dogs and cats, are nocturnal in the wild and depend far more on their senses of smell and hearing than we do. In fact, of all the mammals, only those that are, or were, arboreal (tree-dwellers) seem to possess color vision and the daytime visual acuity of humans (excluding some of the bats).

The primates and squirrels, being essentially arboreal, possess color vision, and they rely on their eyes far more than they do on their sense of smell or hearing. This seems to be correlated with the fact that when bounding around in branches high in the trees, a sense of smell would be of limited value since there would be no continuous trails to follow from tree to tree. But the ability to spot ripe fruit a half-mile away, dangling among masses of other vegetation, would be important to survival, and a highly developed visual sense could provide such information. It could also locate approaching or hiding predators from the vantage point of a high tree, while they were still miles away. In the same context, should a predator get close enough to pursue an arboreal animal, judging distances accurately before leaping from one branch to another could mean the difference between living and dying; hence the retention of binocular vision (depth perception).

So human beings can see colors in three dimensions. And most of our sensory input is visual because, in our evolutionary past, it was crucial to our survival. We are very definitely visual animals.

The Eye

The visual organ is essentially a means of focusing light rays onto a receptor zone. The visual receptor zones are designed to break up these energy patterns into electrical impulses that can be transmitted to the brain and translated into recognizable forms. Regardless of what animal the eye is found in, the structure and functional principles all seem to be about the same, even in animals as distantly related to humans as the squid and the octopus. In all these organs, light enters through a pupil (which can dilate or contract to adjust the amount of light that enters) and is converged into a narrow beam. Then the image is inverted and focused by a lens onto a light-sensitive, pigmented "film" designed specifically for such stimuli (see figure 9.9). That is exactly the way a camera works—in fact, in many ways, our eyes are very like a camera . . . we even have lens caps in the form of eyelids.

Our eyes are not exactly like a camera, however—which is fortunate for us. For one thing, cameras, in order to clearly and sharply record what they "see," must be kept as still as possible. Even movie and television cameras come with tripods, shoulder rests—anything that will help the operator prevent them from moving up and down or around very much. Moving a camera blurs the image, and that's true of all cameras. A television camera that is being jostled around or one that is "panning" (swinging across) a large area cannot record what it picks up with clarity unless the movement is very slow. Every little jerk or twist distorts some part of the picture. (Everyone has seen pictures taken from a movie or TV camera when the cameraman was walking or running.) Generally, eyes handle movement much better than this. They can adapt rapidly to motion and often give a pretty accurate picture of what they see, even when the observer is leaping through a field or bouncing around in a car.

Figure 9.9 The human eye in sagittal section.

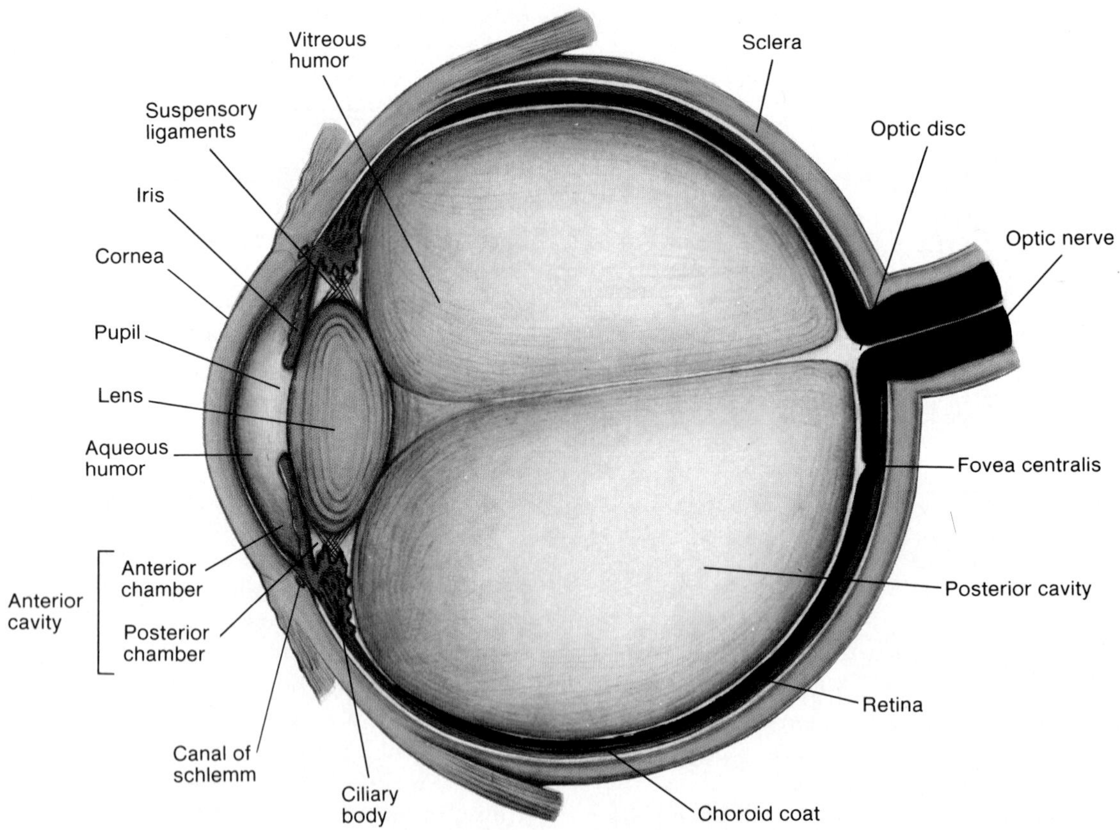

This, however, is not the biggest advantage that eyes have over a camera. The biggest advantage is the enormously wide angle of vision our eyes give us. Even the best cameras have very definite tunnel vision compared to an animal's eyes; they see only that which is in front of the lens. The eye can detect visual stimuli that are beside it. Try it and see. While looking directly ahead, stretch an arm straight out beside you and wriggle your fingers. Keep wriggling your fingers and gradually move your arm back until you can no longer see movement. It may surprise you to see how broad your visual field actually is.

Part of the reason for such a broad field is the eye's anatomy. The film inside a camera is a flat sheet directly behind the lens (figure 9.10). The photosensitive film in our eyes is mounted on a spherical background that wraps around the rear half of the eyeball, forming almost a full hemisphere around the rear and edges of the lens. Light beams entering a human eye from directly beside the person's head will stimulate receptor areas on both sides of the eyeball and provide images of a sort in the visual zones of the cerebral cortex. The images are blurred and out of focus, but they are images, and they provide us with a great deal of information . . . information that can promptly be brought into focus just by turning the head or the eyeball.

Figure 9.10 The wide-angle receptive field of the human eye.

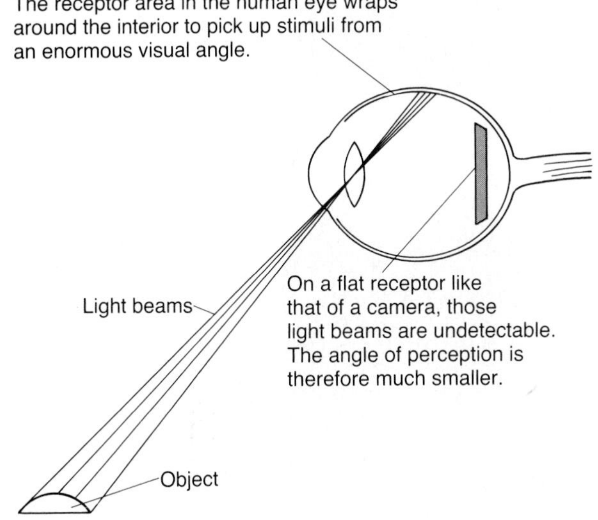

When light enters the eye, it *bends* or *refracts.* It is a little outside the experience of most of us to realize that light rays can actually be bent, but they can. We are all familiar with light rebounding from a mirror, but that is a matter of *reflection,* and light always leaves the mirror at the same angle that it entered. However, when light beams pass from one medium to another, such as water to air, or water to glass, they always refract a little bit. That's why it is so hard to hit something at the bottom of a clear pond or stream with a small rock; things always look closer than they actually are, because the light rays refract when they move between air and water (see figure 9.11).

Images enter the eyeball through the **cornea,** which is the outermost layer at the front of the eye. The beams then pass through a fluid so crystal clear that it casts no shadow and is almost invisible, a fluid called **aqueous humor.** Both the cornea and the aqueous humor refract the light beams a little before they (the light beams) are passed through the opening into the rear of the eye—the **pupil.**

Figure 9.11 Light rays bend when they move from one medium to another. If the person throwing the rock relies only on what he sees, he will underthrow the target; therefore he must compensate.

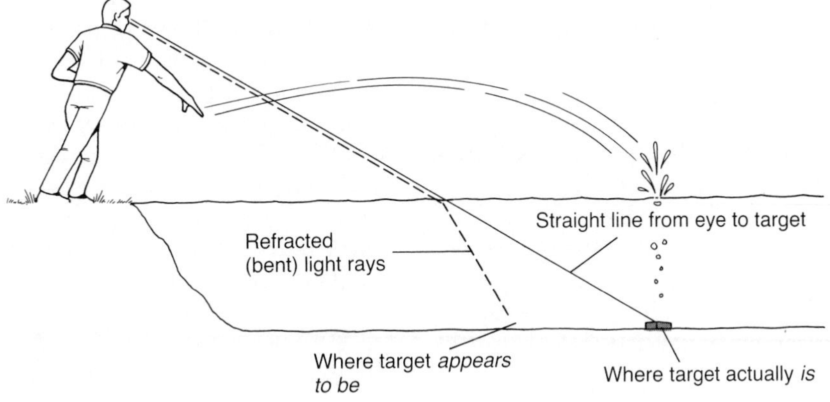

The amount of light that actually enters the eye is carefully adjusted by the **iris,** which is the colored part of the eye surrounding the pupil. If too much light is permitted to enter, all the receptors in the eye fire simultaneously, literally swamping any discriminatory abilities in a barrage of visual impulses—impulses that can actually be painful. On the other hand, if too little light enters, there will not be enough energy to stimulate the cells that provide us with the greatest visual acuity. The intensity of the light beams passing through the pupil is adjusted by widening or narrowing the opening. The adjustments are made via a reflex network that involves the two autonomic branches of the nervous system and two different sets of muscles in the iris (see figure 9.12). When the light is dim, sympathetic motor nerves stimulate the radial muscles to pull the pupil wide open. When the light is very bright, parasympathetic neurons stimulate constriction of the circular muscles, and the pupil shrinks in size.

Eye Color

Contrary to popular belief, there is only a single color-producing pigment present in the iris. The variation in eye color that we perceive is a function of the distribution of this pigment rather than a variation in its color. If the pigment is present in only the outer cell layers on the posterior surface of the iris, the eyes are blue. If it is present in all layers of the iris, the eyes appear brown. Naturally, there are all kinds of variations in the intensity of these colors. The more abundant the pigmented cells of the iris are, the darker the structure will appear. When the pigment is present only in the posterior epithelial layers, but the tissue there is unusually thick, the eyes take on a grayish cast, and if some pigment migrates in small streaks into the middle areas of the iris, the eyes often have a greenish hue.

The complete absence of any pigment—which occurs in albinos—produces the startlingly light pink eyes that are considered so cute in pet rats or rabbits. Pink eyes are not all that cute when a human has to live with them, however. An unpigmented iris is transparent; hence it cannot block out any light beams that might impinge on it. Obviously, then, it cannot fulfill its function as governor of the amount of light it allows to enter the eye. As a result, albinos are almost completely blind in bright light of any kind, and they have to wear heavily tinted glasses to see even in subdued sunlight. Furthermore, the enormous angle of visual stimulation (due to the huge lens opening) cuts down on their acuity of vision, so none of what they see is very clear or sharp. And despite popular rumor, they see no better at night than the average person.

Figure 9.12 Muscles of the iris alter the size of the pupil in response to light. Dim light stimulates contraction of the radial muscles, and the pupil opens wide. Bright light causes contraction of the circular muscles, and the pupil is reduced in size.

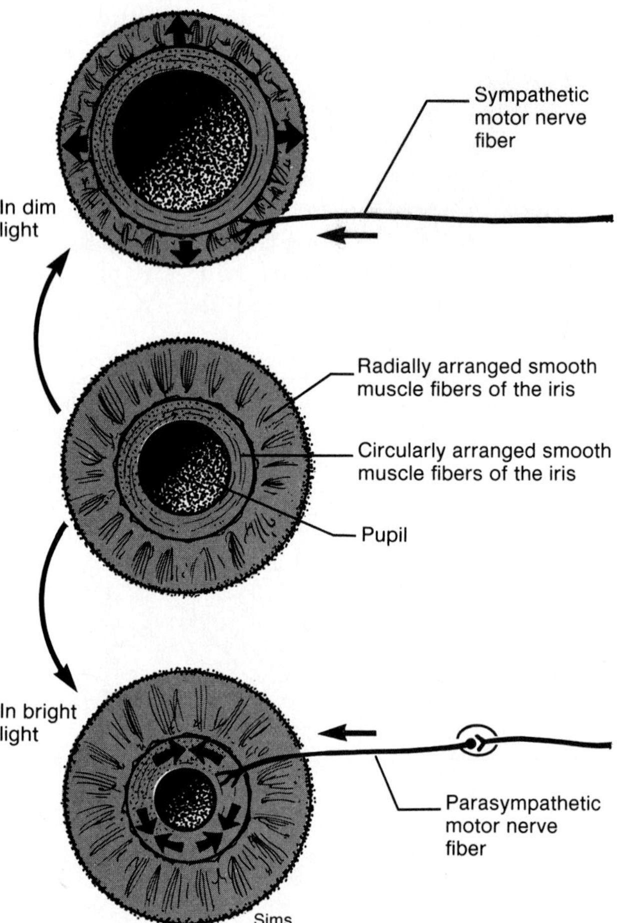

Inside the Eyeball

Having passed through the opened pupil, the light now must enter the **lens.** The lens is connected to masses of **suspensory ligaments.** These are typical ligamentous tissue—tough, inelastic fibers that form a kind of woven mat around the edges of the lens and hold it in place, directly behind the pupil. All light passing through the pupil must enter the lens before it can make any further progress, and the lens is responsible for the final, or "fine," focus. It adjusts by reflex to provide a clear, sharp image on the light-sensitive receptors at the back of the eyeball. Cameras, microscopes, telescopes—all man-made optical instruments—focus light beams by moving the lens back and forth. So do a lot of animals, like fishes, snakes, frogs, and others. But we do not. Humans do it a different way. Instead of moving the lens back and forth, humans change the *shape* of the lens by employing a relatively soft lens and pulling on the edges of it to make it longer and thinner, or relaxing and letting it return to its shorter, fatter egg shape.

Figure 9.13 Accommodation of the lens in the human eye. (*a*) When the object being viewed is approximately twenty feet or more from the eye, the ciliary muscles are relaxed and the suspensory ligaments pull the lens nearly flat. (*b*) When objects get closer, the ciliary muscles contract, opposing the tension applied by the suspensory ligaments and permitting the eyeball to relax into a more rounded shape. Both maneuvers are designed to focus the light on the retina by altering the amount of light refraction applied by the lens.

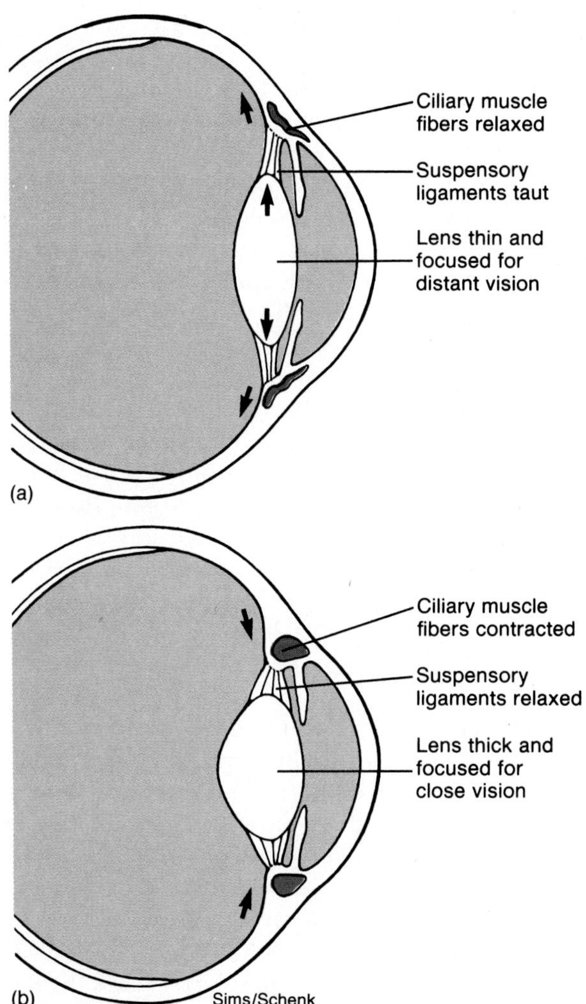

Figure 9.14 Various shapes pertaining to light refraction: (*a*) A lens concave on one side. (*b*) A lens convex on one side. (*c*) A biconcave lens. (*d*) A biconvex lens.

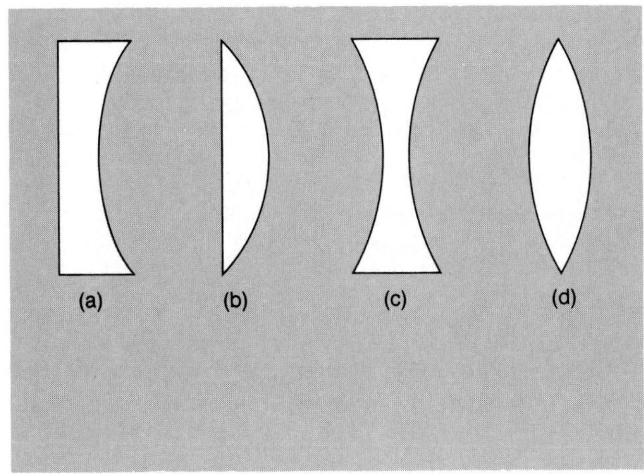

In sharks and snakes, the lens of the eye is as hard as a marble, and its shape never changes. To bring a visual object into focus, the lens moves either away from or closer to the light-sensitive rear of the eyeball. Our human conceit would have us insist that the mammalian way of doing it is best—that changing the shape of the lens is a more efficient and generally more desirable method of focusing than moving the lens back and forth. So it may prove, someday. Right now, students of optics can see no particular advantage to it, and there are some disadvantages. The biggest one has to do with the flexibility of the lens, which is absolutely critical. If the lens cannot alter its shape, then the eye loses its ability to adapt to changing distances, and the eye's focal length becomes fixed. Images a fixed distance away might be in focus, but nothing else is. As it turns out, the lenses in our eyes do just that—they harden as we get older, and we lose our ability to focus, particularly on objects that are near at hand . . . a distinct disadvantage for survival.

This shape adjustment is carried out by the **ciliary muscles,** which are connected to the suspensory ligaments and which completely surround the lens (figure 9.13).

Does the mammalian eye work better than that of the fishes or the snakes? Since we do not really know how these animals perceive visual images, we will probably never be able to answer that question. We know what *we* perceive, and we know how our cameras work, but with all these facts in mind, it is still terribly hard to figure out just which method actually is best.

It is not easy to bring all images into focus on a single plane and even harder to do so on a spherical one. Generally speaking, the edges of the lens tend to produce a sharper image than the middle does, and that is why the lens is biconvex in shape, so that the edges won't be as sharply curved and the refraction will be equal all the way across (see figure 9.14).

The *color* of the light can also cause blurring—a phenomenon known as **chromatic aberration.** For instance, blue and purple light waves bend a little more than red and orange ones do as they pass through the cornea and lens, and it would be most inconvenient for us to have all the reds, oranges, and yellows in focus while all the greens, blues, and purples were blurred. The lens partially eliminates the problem by filtering out some of the colors. The lens is tinted a very light yellow, and this yellow coloration tends to wash out the higher-frequency light rays—mostly the purples.

This method of correcting for visual aberrations also has its disadvantages. It does eliminate blurred images to some extent, but it also eliminates our ability to see some purples and blues, and the effect gets worse as time passes. As age makes its relentless advance, the original light cream tint of the lens begins to darken to a richer yellow, thereby filtering out still more of the high-frequency colors.

From the lens, the light beams enter the **posterior chamber** of the eye. This chamber, like the anterior one, contains another crystal-clear, nearly invisible fluid, this one called **vitreous humor.** Through it the refracted light beams pass, and finally they contact the photosensitive layer at the back of the eye—the **retina.** After passing the receptors in the retinal layer, they encounter a very thin layer of cells known as the **choroid coat.** The choroid coat consists of a layer of blood vessels intended for retinal nourishment and masses of nearly black, pigment-containing cells called **melanocytes.** These latter cells prevent reflections from blurring or obscuring images by absorbing the light beams and thereby eliminating them. They also help keep the interior of the eyeball darkened everywhere but where the images fall on the retina. Behind the choroid is the **sclera,** the tough, outer layer of the eyeball. On the front of the eyeball, these two layers are completely different in appearance and function. At the front of the eyeball, the sclera is the transparent cornea through which light beams must pass, and the choroid coat is the iris.

More than one physiology student has wondered just why it is people never have their vision obscured by all these layers of tissue. With all this material between the receptors and the light, how come no one ever sees it? On occasion, people do. If one *concentrates* on seeing them, under the right conditions, they *can* be detected. By staring hard at a colorless background like a white wall or a brilliant white cloud bank, you can usually make out the outlines of the blood vessels if you close your eyelids to a narrow slit and are aware of what you are searching for. Nevertheless, they certainly exist in our receptor fields all the time, so why don't we see them all the time? Unfortunately, no one has a really good scientific answer for this question. The best answer available is that the visual brain is "programed" to ignore them, although no one is really sure how this is accomplished.

The retina itself is composed of three layers of nerve tissue (see figures 9.15 and 9.16). The first layer (the one closest to the interior of the eyeball) consists of **ganglion cells** and their axons. The middle layer is made up of neurons known as **bipolar cells,** and the third layer consists of the receptor cells of the retina, the **rods** and **cones** that are photosensitive and provide us with vision.

The rods are relatively narrow cells, much more numerous than the cones, and they are responsible for providing us with visual capability in dim light. The cones are much fatter than the rods and so appear shorter, although in truth, both are about the same length. The cones are not nearly as sensitive to radiation as the rods are, but they are much more selective. It is the cones that provide us with color vision and our sharp, clear daytime images.

An individual human eye has more than six million cones and more than twenty times as many rods which, if translated into the jargon of photography, means that our retinas have an extremely fine "grain." These receptors form junctions with the bipolar cells along a complicated and often quite confusing synaptic lattice that reduces the number of neurons involved by a factor of about 8. The bipolar cells, in turn, synapse with just over a million ganglion cells, thereby reducing the number of neurons in the optic nerve to less than 1/100th the number of receptors in the retina.

The Photoreceptors

As we have already seen, other receptors, when touched by their adequate stimulus, react by producing a depolarizing potential. This slow potential change, if it is powerful enough, will stimulate action potentials in the sensory axon, and in this manner its information is relayed to the CNS. For some unknown reason, our photoreceptors appear to behave in the opposite manner.

When a normal eye is completely dark, there is a constant flow of electrical current through the photoreceptor membrane, and this keeps the membrane in a constant state of depolarization. The photoreceptor membrane potential, in the dark, is only about −20 mv, and there is a steady flow of inhibitory neurotransmitter from the receptor cell to the bipolar cells nearby. When light invades the interior of the eye, the photoreceptors respond, not by depolarizing, but by *hyper*polarizing—in other words, by *in*creasing their normal resting potential. Current flow through the membrane is reduced accordingly, along with a concomitant decrease in the amount of inhibitory neurotransmitter. The bipolar cells, as a result, can activate the ganglion cells. Receptor cells and bipolar

Figure 9.15 The various cell layers of the retina. Light enters from the bottom in this diagram. (*a*) Signals detected by several rods converge on, and activate, a single bipolar cell. Three bipolar cells, in their turn, converge on and feed information to a single ganglion cell. Thus the stimuli received by ten different rod receptors emphasize their information by feeding it to a single ganglion cell. (*b*) Cone vision seldom demonstrates such convergence. Each cone receptor usually stimulates a single bipolar cell, which in turn stimulates one ganglion cell. The cone plan reduces sensitivity, but it increases visual acuity enormously.

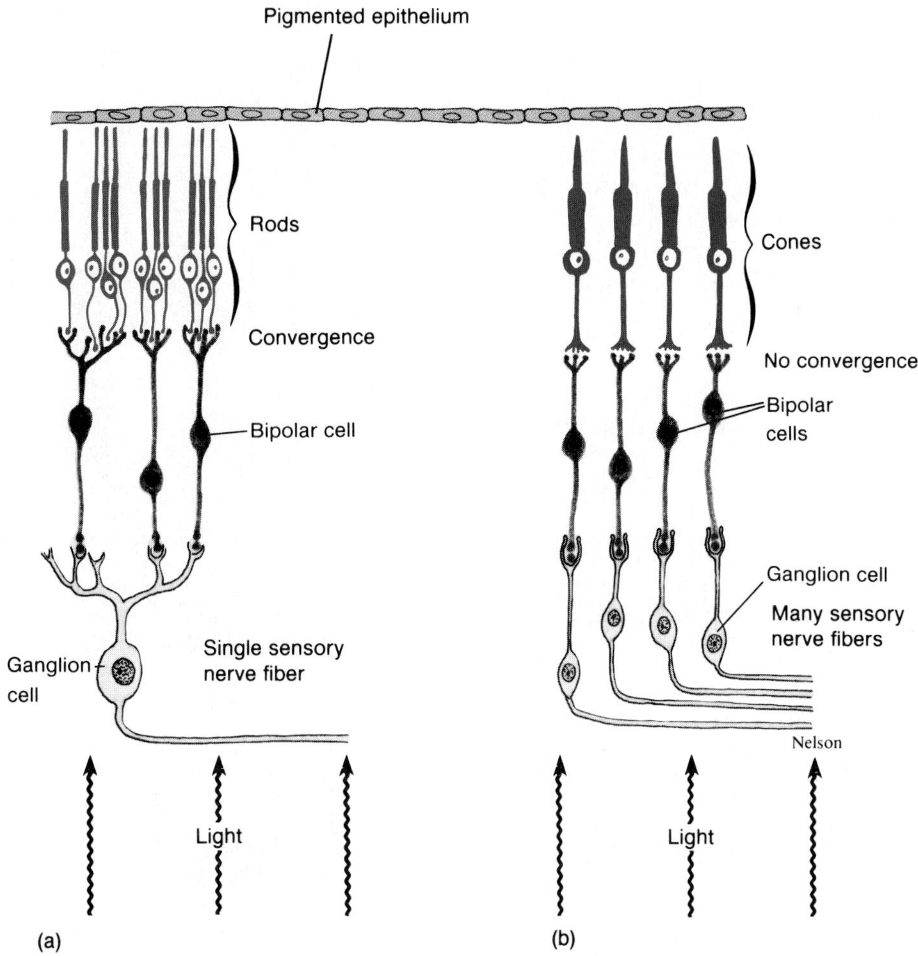

Figure 9.16 A light micrograph of the various retinal layers.

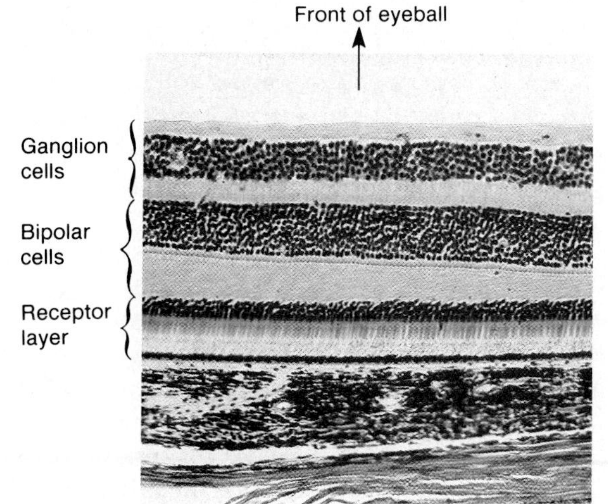

cells show only slow wave depolarizations; neither can produce action potentials. But the ganglion cells can produce action potentials and the final output from the retina is impulse activity along the axons of the ganglion cells. These axons, when they leave the eye, collectively form the optic nerve.

The electrical patterns are quantifiable. The more light that is present in the eye, the greater the hyperpolarization of the receptor and the smaller the amount of neuroinhibitor that is released. The smaller the amount of inhibitor that is released, the smaller the inhibition of the bipolar cells, and thus the greater the stimulation of the ganglion cells and the brain.

Rods

Rods are at least four times as sensitive as cones, and in dim light they are the only receptors that operate. Even in the dimmest light they will hyperpolarize, and action potentials can be detected along the optic nerve when light is nearly nonexistent. Visual acuity when light is sparse, however, is not very good, because often a single bipolar cell will receive input from several rods, and this naturally makes the image quite diffuse. Yet there is a reason for this morphological arrangement. Apparently, it is a matter of priorities. The image received in dim light may not be very clear, but the fact that a dozen or so receptors ultimately impinge on a single ganglion cell will summate, thus insuring that the individual will see *something*. This is why, in the absence of artificial illumination, things we see at night are so fuzzy and why they are nearly always colorless. It is a clear indication that even if the image is blurred, it is better to view a blurred image than to see nothing at all.

Animals that are instinctively nocturnal often have nothing but rods in their retinas. Dogs and cats have no cones in their retinas, and hence they cannot distinguish colors. While they are enormously successful hunters and can get along wonderfully during daylight hours, they see rather poorly compared to humans. It is not unusual for people to place a bit of food on the ground for a dog or cat to eat, and if the animal did not see it strike the floor, it is not able to find it with its eyes alone. It must sweep back and forth in the area, using its sense of smell for location. Yet at night, the ability of these animals to see is phenomenal. If there is the tiniest bit of light, the entire area opens up to their eyes, and they can locate obstacles and other large items in places that are so dark to a human it is like standing in a room full of ink. The American opossum is particularly adept at this, and its retinal morphology indicates why—sometimes as many as 800 receptor cells provide the stimulus for a single ganglion cell. In addition, these animals have something else, just behind the retina—something that humans lack. It is a layer of tissue known as a **tapetum.** The tapetum is highly reflective, and after the light has passed through the retina and hyperpolarized the rods there, it reflects back from the tapetum and strikes the receptors again. Each receptor therefore receives two stimuli from a single ray of light, doubling their photoreceptive energy input. The reflected light then passes out of the animals' pupils and is often visible to outside observers. The result is eyes that appear to glow in the dark—something human eyes do not do.

Cones

The cones of the retina differ morphologically from the rods, and they differ in their connections to the brain as well (figure 9.17).

More often than not, a single cone cell provides the only receptor input to a ganglion cell, which means that it must receive a powerful stimulus indeed if its information is to be transmitted to the optic nerve. For this reason, cones are useful only in relatively bright light, and they are usually concentrated in areas where the most direct beams will fall. In humans, the area of greatest concentration is the **fovea centralis,** or simply the **fovea.** The fovea is a tiny, saucer-shaped concavity covered by a yellow-tinted, transparent layer of tissue called the **macula lutea** that occupies about a square millimeter in the middle of the retina. The fovea is directly behind the lens, positioned to be right in the middle of the images that enter the eye. It is the focal point of our visual field—the center of optical precision. It's the optic zone where the highest concentration of visual receptors exists; hence it has the finest "grain" and is the point in the eye of greatest visual acuity. Nearly all the receptors in the human fovea are cones, and there are a great many of them packed into its square millimeter.

Figure 9.17 The photoreceptors of the human eye.

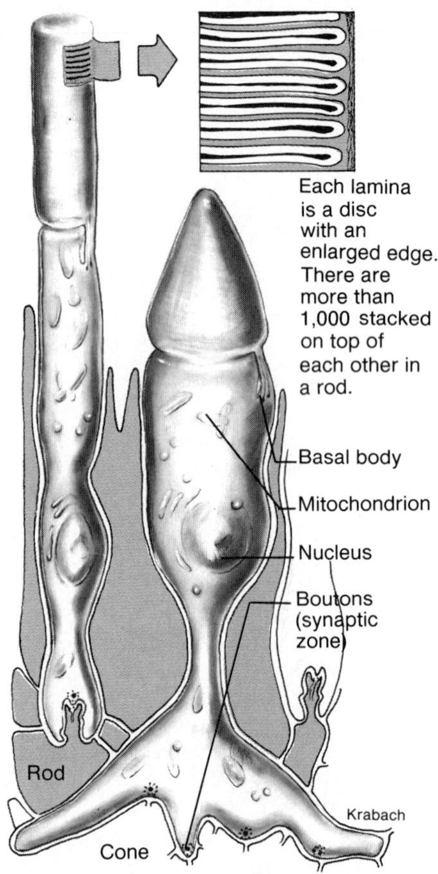

This is the part of the eye that perceives details for us. To objectively illustrate how small it is, pick a small word on this page and concentrate on it. Be careful not to let your eye vibrate or move at all, and note just how tiny the spot is that is actually in focus. As you can see, very little is actually in the center of your focus at any instant; if a word contains more than two or three letters, some will be outside the fovea. We can see whole sentences clearly because we move

Panel 9.1

Light: Wavelength and Color

In order to comprehend a little of how photoreceptors work and how various adaptations are made to changing intensities and types of light, we need to understand a little more about light itself. Most of us already know that light travels at a mind-boggling speed, faster than anything else we know of. Its velocity in a vacuum is 300,000 kilometers per second, which means if it could travel in a circle, it could go around the earth more than seven times in one second. While the beams of light are traveling at this incredible velocity, energy is also vibrating back and forth across the plane of movement (see figure 9.A). The frequency of these vibrations varies, depending on the characteristics of the radiation. The electricity that is in our homes, for example, travels *through* the wires at almost the speed of light, but it vibrates back and forth *across* the plane of travel fifty to sixty times a second, which is why it is called 60-cycle. The distance that the light is able to travel in the length of time required to complete one vibration is known as the **wavelength** of that particular frequency (see figure 9.B). In a 60th of a second, light can travel nearly 3,500 miles, so the 60-cycle electricity in our homes has a wavelength more than 3,000 miles long. Our early warning radar sets are called *microwave* because their wavelengths can be measured in micrometers. Radiation in the visible spectrum vibrates at rates that are even faster. Red light has the slowest rate of all visible radiation, yet its frequency is so incredibly high that it can complete one vibration in less than four trillionths of a second, giving it a frequency of 4,000,000 megacycles. The longest visible wavelengths are in the neighborhood of 680 to 700 nanometers (billionths of a meter). The yellow wavelengths are slightly shorter (600 nanometers), and they grade gently into the greens (520 nm), then the blues (465 nm). The shortest wavelengths that are visible are in the violet portion of the spectrum between 400 and 450 nm (see table 9.2). Photoreceptors in the human eye respond variably to these wavelengths of visible light, the variability depending on the types of chemicals the receptors contain.

Infrared is radiation with too low a frequency to be seen (too long a wavelength), but we possess other receptors that can detect it. When it strikes our skin, it can be clearly felt. Radiating heat is pure infrared.

Ultraviolet is radiation with too high a frequency (wavelengths are too short) to be visible, and unlike infrared radiation, our bodies contain no receptors that are sensitive to ultraviolet. We can, however, become belatedly aware of its presence by what it does to us if we lie too long in the sun on a warm day.

Figure 9.A A traveling beam of light radiation.

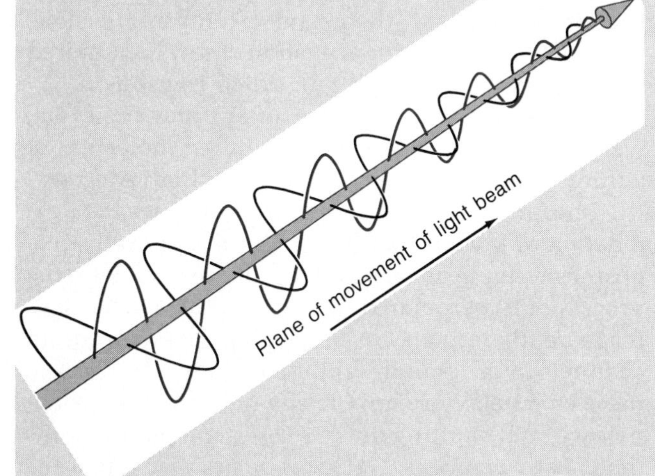

Figure 9.B The "wavelength."

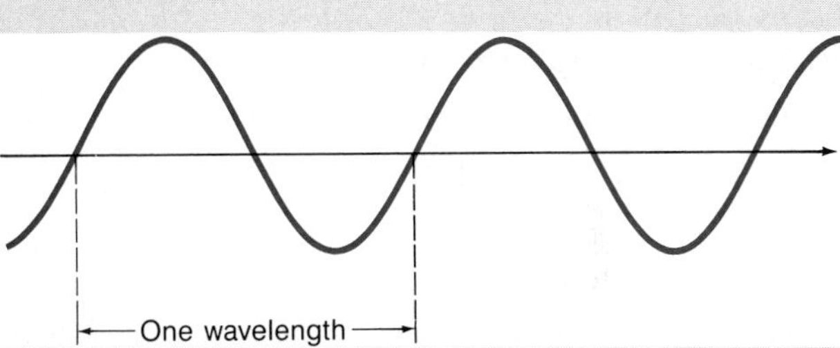

Table 9.2 Wavelengths of Radiation in the Visible Spectrum

Wavelength (nm)	Color
400 to 450	Violet
450 to 500	Blue
500 to 550	Green
550 to 600	Yellow
600 to 650	Orange
650 to 700	Red

our eyes back and forth across each word, and we can appreciate a massive outdoor panorama like the Grand Canyon by sweeping across broad areas, placing a sequence of individual spots successively on the fovea, thus bringing the whole thing into one perceptive focus.

Human reliance on the fovea centralis is profound. In the mid-1960s a trio of high school students got "stoned" on LSD, and in their hallucinatory fervor decided that the sun was the ultimate in beauty and design. To fully appreciate this revelation, all three of them spent five or ten minutes staring at the sun and commenting quietly on the beauty of the various emanations that they were seeing. Unfortunately, the lens of the human eye is an excellent "burning glass," and with the brilliance of the sun's radiation focused directly on the middle of the retina, it proceeded to burn out the fovea. Those three students are men now, of course, and are, for all practical purposes, blind. They have full vision everywhere except the fovea, which means everything they see stays in their visual periphery. When they try to bring something into focus in the manner that you or I would do it, it quickly flits into a black zone where there are no more receptors. Imagine having to spend your life being able to see things floating around the edges of your vision, but never being able to focus on it. It's a sobering thought indeed.

Visual Perception

Visual Pigments—the Energy Source

A **pigment** is a chemical compound that absorbs light. The color of the pigment is determined by the wavelengths that it reflects or transmits, not those that it absorbs. Plants appear green because the reds, blues, and purples are all absorbed, and only the greens are reflected. Blood appears red because the pigment in blood cells absorbs all the wavelengths except the red ones.

Rod Vision

The receptors in the human eye are referred to as photoreceptors because the adequate stimulus that initiates their response is radiation in the visible spectrum. But the electrical change that develops in the rods and/or cones when light strikes them is due to an alteration in a chemical—an organic compound produced in the eye. The compound in all rods is the same, and while it cannot separate colors, it is sensitive to all wavelengths of light except reds. It is known as **rhodopsin** or **visual purple** (chemically, 11-*cis* retinal). Normally, this compound is a deep red or reddish purple in color, but when light rays strike it there is a series of structural changes that ultimately splits it into two products: a colorless protein called **scotopsin** and a yellowish compound called **retinal** (retinene), which is derived from vitamin A. These changes in structure are called **bleaching,** and they release energy that ultimately changes the permeability of the receptor membrane and results in hyperpolarization of the receptor and an increased firing rate in the bipolar cell.

It takes very little light to bleach rhodopsin. If as little as one photon of light strikes every fifteen minutes or so, it is above threshold, and a response will develop. Night vision is usually fairly good when photons are striking single rods in the eye on an average of one every ten seconds.

This degree of sensitivity is hard to believe. There is energy, of course, in light photons, but not very much . . . certainly not enough to account for the response the visual rod is able to give. Sensitivity of this magnitude was difficult to explain, but when the answers finally came, they provided us with a remarkable view of natural design (figure 9.18).

Chemical Amplification

Each rod is a tiny chemical amplifier. A single photon of light changes a molecule of inactive rhodopsin into an active enzyme molecule. Enzymes, remember, are catalysts, and when catalysts are involved in reactions, they are not used up or changed, so they are available to catalyze as long as they last. The activated protein fraction of rhodopsin (scotopsin) is able, therefore, to catalyze the activation of several hundred molecules of a second protein called **transducin.**

Transducin, which is also an enzyme, then catalyzes the activation of several hundred molecules of a third compound, the enzyme **phosphodiesterase.**

Phosphodiesterase, in its turn, catalyzes the degradation of several hundred molecules of cyclic guanosine monophosphate (cGMP), and that initiates the process of hyperpolarizing the receptor. Cyclic GMP is apparently responsible for keeping open the sodium channels in the photoreceptor membrane. Without it, these channels close up. Closing of the sodium channels without shutting down the sodium pump means that positive charges (Na^+) will be pumped out of the receptor in large numbers, but very few new ones can leak in to take their place. As a result, the *interior* of the receptor gets more negative—it *hyperpolarizes* (figure 9.18).

This shutting down of sodium channels requires less energy than propagating action potentials, and this also contributes to rod sensitivity. Since each step can catalyze several hundred reactions leading to the succeeding step, the sequence is, in effect, a process of amplification. Each photon of light manages to degrade several hundred molecules of cGMP, which in

Figure 9.18 The radiation amplifier in the human eye.

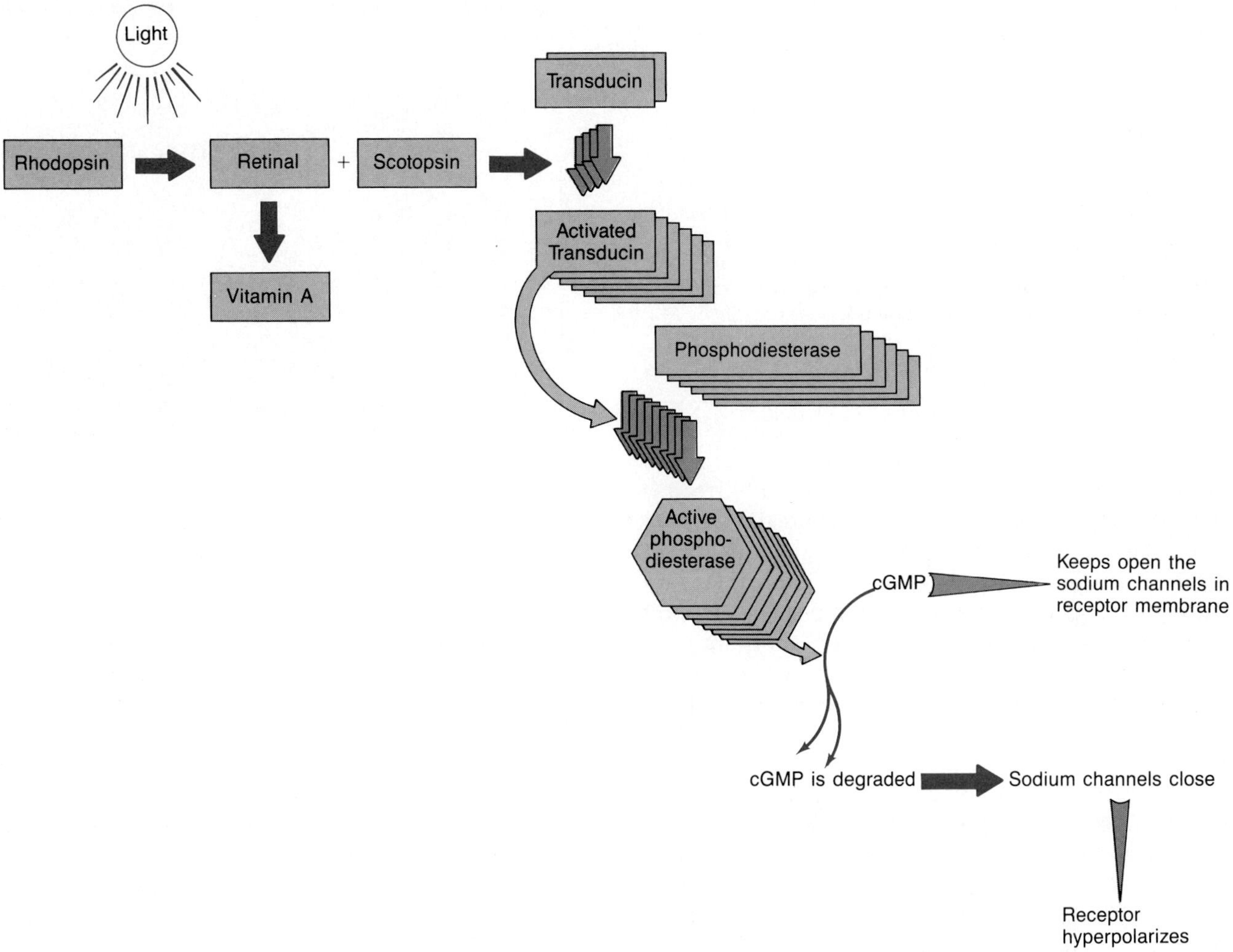

turn can block the influx of a million sodium ions through the receptor membrane. The eye's visual receptors can, through chemical manipulation, effectively amplify the energy in a single photon by a factor of one million.

In addition to rendering the rods extremely sensitive to radiation, this method of amplifying the stimulus is a tremendous energy saver in another way: it conserves rhodopsin. Since the ultimate result requires that only a tiny amount of rhodopsin be bleached, rods do not run out of rhodopsin unless it is daylight-bright. Viewing the surroundings in average night light, therefore, produces only very small quantities of scotopsin and retinal, and what little *is* produced is recycled to reconstruct the visual pigment (figure 9.19). Influenced by the correct enzymes and driven by ATP, rhodopsin can be reassembled in light or dark, and an equilibrium actually develops between the rhodopsin breakdown process and the rebuilding reactions. If the rate of breakdown is the same as, or slower than, the buildup, the eye remains dark-adapted. If the breakdown is more rapid than buildup, the degree of dark adaptation is reduced accordingly. In bright light, the bleaching of rhodopsin becomes almost total, sensitivity in the rods disappears, and the eye shifts from rod vision to cone vision.

Figure 9.19 Regeneration of rhodopsin.

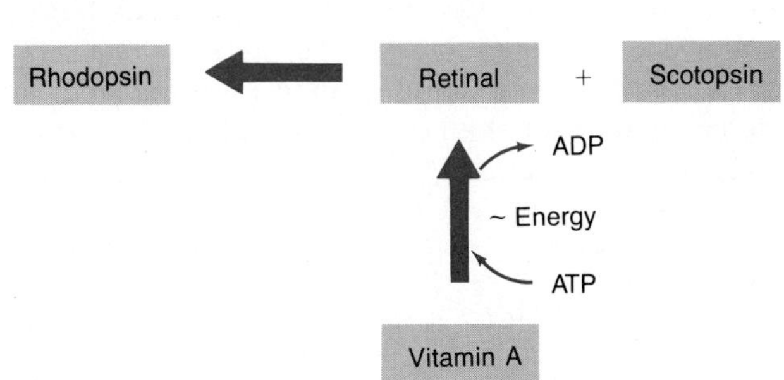

It usually takes a long time for a person's eyes to adapt to low intensities of illumination. This is mainly the fault of the rods, which take six to seven times as long to adapt as cones do. Even though they are not used much in dim light, cones will adapt to minimal lighting conditions in less than five minutes. Rods, on the other hand, require at least thirty and usually closer to forty minutes to become completely adapted to dark conditions after exposure to bright light. Not coincidentally, this adaptation takes about the same length of time as that required for reassembling rhodopsin in the rods. Since rhodopsin requires vitamin A as a substrate, people who suffer from a shortage of vitamin A usually take longer to dark-adapt than average people, and in some cases they cannot adapt at all. Vitamin A deficiency, therefore, is often suspected when the victim is, for all practical purposes, blind in dim light.

Cone Vision

As far as we know, the visual pigment in all rods is the same, whether in fish, bird, or mammal. There are some slight variations in the wavelengths the eyes of some animals will respond to, but rhodopsin throughout the entire vertebrate subphylum is pretty much the same. The cones, however, are more variable. Each cone is believed to contain only a single pigment, but different cones in a given individual can contain any one of three different types of pigments, and these variations are believed to be responsible for the ability to perceive colors. Cone pigments are composed of retinal and a protein, just as rhodopsin is, but the protein is different from the one present in rhodopsin and is variable from cone to cone. There are, in fact, three different protein groups, one for each color range. There are pigments that are red-sensitive (called **erythrolabe**), others that are green-sensitive (**chlorolabe**), and a third group called **cyanolabe** that is sensitive to light in the blue frequencies. The color our brain perceives depends on what combination of cones has been stimulated. If all are stimulated, the color we perceive is white. If none are stimulated, we perceive no color at all (see figure 9.20).

As we have seen, there are many similarities between technical aspects of modern photography and human vision. Here is another one. Black and white film is relatively insensitive to red wavelengths, which is why red lights can often be used in darkrooms when processing black-and-white film. Our black-and-white visual pigment, rhodopsin, is also insensitive to radiant energy in the low end of the spectrum, and red light (wavelengths longer than about 575 nm) will not bleach it. It was, and still may be, routine for naval personnel about to go on night watch to spend at least forty-five minutes in a room illuminated only by red lights so that their eyes will be *dark adapted* when they go on duty. Military aircrew (especially gunners) required to fly at night used to wear red goggles before going on duty, and the night instrument illumination was red. The red light stimulated the cones, so the individuals could see, but because it did not bleach the rhodopsin, it had no deleterious effect on night vision.

Figure 9.20 Absorption spectra of the visual pigments in cones. Note that although cyanolabe can absorb some ultraviolet, it never receives any because the yellow pigment in the lens blocks out all UV.

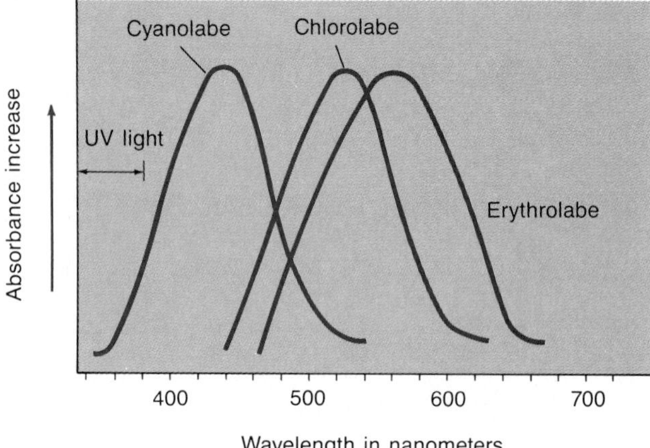

Binocular (Stereoscopic) Vision

Our eyes are set in the front of our heads in such a way that as long as we focus on objects twenty-five feet or less away from us, we view the objects in three dimensions—that is, we view them *stereoscopically*. This is because, when objects are within that range, each eye gets a different image of the objects (see figure 9.21). This is not difficult to check. With both eyes open, point directly at a distant object. Without focusing on your finger, try and note how many fingers you can see. With a little effort, you'll be able to detect two separate images . . . two different views of the same finger. Now close one eye. If you are still pointing at the object, open both eyes again and this time, close the other eye. Now look where you are pointing. Open both eyes again and pull in your focal point, focusing on your finger. See how the two images begin to draw into a single, three-dimensional image?

By focusing on your finger, you changed the tension on the ciliary muscles around the lens of your eye and altered the shape of the lens. Simultaneously, in some unexplained manner, your visual brain melded the two different views of your finger into a single three-dimensional object, clearly in focus. It seems obvious that two eyes are necessary in order to obtain the illusion of *depth* that is such an integral part of stereoscopic vision. Because of this, people who

Figure 9.21 Stereoscopic vision. As the figure shows, the closer the object being viewed is, the greater is the difference between the images seen in each eye. Focused at infinity (broken line), the objects appear two-dimensional because both eyes see the same figure.

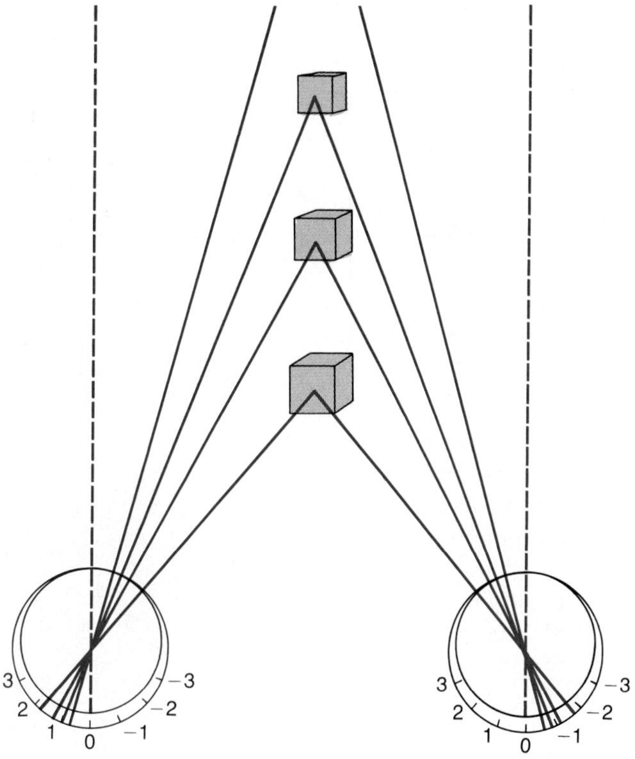

Figure 9.22 The pathway of visual images to the brain.

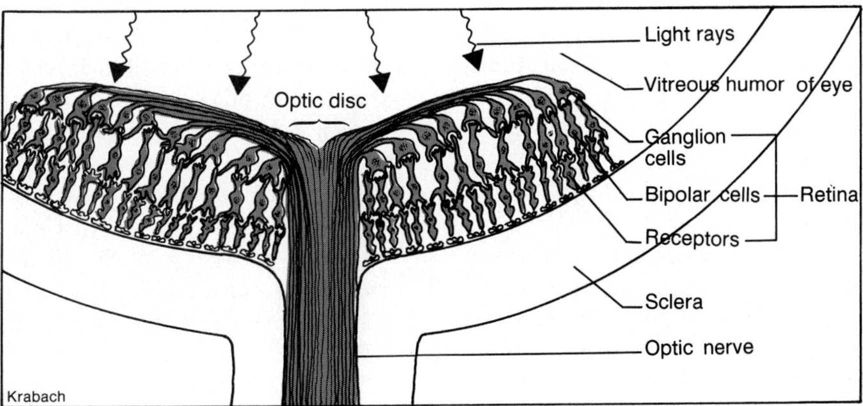

have lost an eye cannot see in three dimensions, although most of them can estimate distances by relating what they see to what they know of size changes and the distances involved. Still, it *is* a handicap, particularly in childhood, when abilities like catching balls or jumping across puddles are important.

The Pathway to the Brain

Once the visual impulses have been translated into electrical impulses in the ganglion cells, they are carried along ganglionic axons into the brain. Their pathway is a little strange to our logic, since it appears to be more complex than necessary (figure 9.22).

Figure 9.23 The blind spot. Close your right eye and focus on the cross. Starting with the page about six inches from your face, gradually move it back until the black ball disappears. It should vanish from view about a foot from your face. If you close your left eye, focus on the ball and watch the cross disappear.

As you have seen, the light enters the eyeball and, before it actually can activate any of the receptor cells, it must first pass through a layer of nerve fibers, then the layer of ganglion cells, then the bipolar cells, and finally, the receptors. In addition to the possible loss of some stimulus power from this arrangement, there is another disadvantage to it as well. The axons from the ganglion cells all run across the interior of the retinal layer, and to leave the eye, they have to turn in and go back through the retinal layer. This leaves a spot on the interior of the eye where there are no receptors at all: the so-called **optic disc** or **blind spot.**

It's a genuine blind spot, too. Light striking the eyeball there cannot register because there are no receptors to transduce it into nerve impulses. Like the adjustments involved in making two images into a single, three-dimensional one, our visual brains somehow compensate for this blind spot, and it never bothers us. However, figure 9.23 shows how you can become aware of it.

The Optic Chiasma

The enormous mass of fibers plunging through the eyeball at the optic disc is actually the optic nerve, and one such nerve leaves each eyeball. The two then intersect at the **optic chiasma,** which is below the floor of the *hypothalamus* (see chapter 8) and just rostral to the pituitary gland. In the optic chiasma, fibers from the inside of one eye cross over and join up with fibers from the outside of the other eye, so that each eye contributes about half its input to each side of the brain. After sorting themselves in the optic chiasma, the fiber bundles divide again into two separate **optic tracts.** A few nerve fibers course out of the optic tract at various points to take visual sensory input to reflexes, such as those responsible for opening and closing the iris, but the vast majority synapse in the **superior colliculus** of the thalamus with brain neurons that carry their information into the **visual cortex**—the **occipital lobe** of the cerebrum (figure 9.24).

Figure 9.24 The route of visual stimuli from the receptor cells to the visual cortex of the brain.

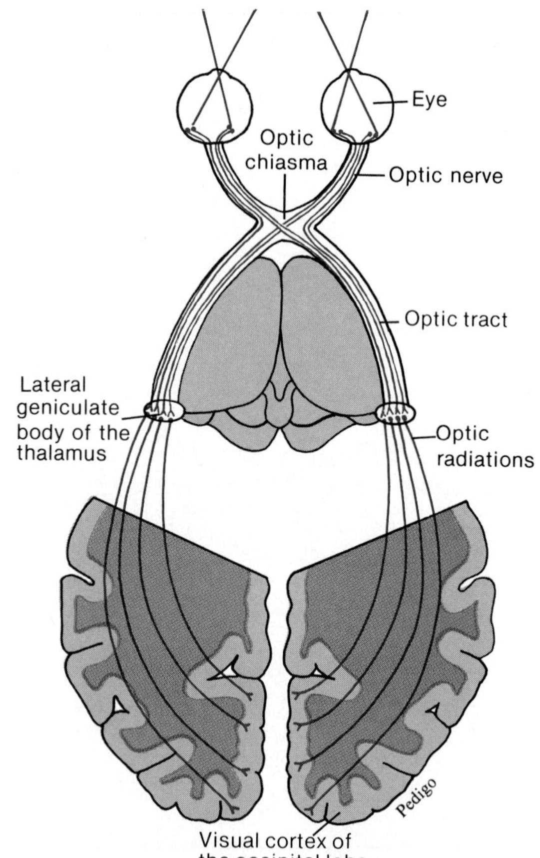

From what has been observed through experiments and analysis of the visual afferent pathways into the brain, it would appear that there are two separate regions in the visual field of each eye. One of these is called the **medial zone,** and the other, the **lateral zone.** When an object is viewed from less than twenty feet away, some light rays from it will stimulate receptors in the medial zone and some will stimulate receptors in the lateral zone of the retina. In the optic chiasma, fibers from the medial receptors will cross over to the other side of the brain, while those from lateral receptors will continue straight back to the brain without crossing over. This means that the right optic tract will carry visual information from the lateral receptors of the right eye and medial receptors of the left eye, and this information will be carried to the right side of the visual cortex. Naturally, the left optic tract will carry the remaining information from receptors in the other halves of the visual fields.

Most of this information is processed in the visual cortex, which is involved in conscious acknowledgment of the stimuli, and integrated with other information, such as that received from auditory, olfactory, or tactile centers. Some visual fibers plunge from the thamalus into the brain stem, where they are processed so that head and eye movements can be properly coordinated to keep objects in the visual field.

The auditory sense is in some ways more selective than vision. For instance, our ability to separate frequencies is much more powerful in our ears than in our eyes. Almost everyone can listen to a certain frequency of sound and know immediately if the frequency changes as little as 0.3 percent. That means that if a note held steady at 1,000 cycles per second (cps) were to increase in frequency by only 3 cycles per second, it would be immediately detectable as a slightly higher pitch. Such precision in frequency discrimination is almost impossible for our eyes. Almost all colors are composed of a mixture of many visible frequencies, and what we detect is a mixture. Thus there are many shades of red, just as there are many shades of purple or green or any other color. If we heard a burst of audio frequencies from an orchestra that was as diverse as most colors, we would be offended by the discord. Probably the only "pure" colors any of us will ever see are those produced by lasers— and even they contain more than a single frequency.

The Ear and Hearing

The first ear-like organs featured by vertebrates were almost certainly organs of equilibrium; they were not involved with detection of sound waves. If the fossil record is correct (and there's no reason to doubt it), the first vertebrates were fishes, and their "ears" were used to keep them upright. The organs designed to handle what we would call hearing were not in the skulls of these early fishes but rather in special ampullae imbedded beneath a line of unusual pores in the animal's side . . . as they still are. These **lateral line organs,** as they are called, are designed to detect compression waves moving through water, many of which are in about the same frequency range as sound. Air-breathing vertebrates, of course, have organs designed to detect similar vibrations in the air. As could only be expected, the two types of organs vary in accordance with the medium in which they carry out their function.

They have some rather striking similarities, however, particularly in their method of detecting the vibrations and transmitting them to the brain. In all vertebrates, the eighth cranial nerve is responsible for transmitting both sound vibrations and the stimuli involving equilibrium from the ears into the brain. In all vertebrates, including humans, there are still two separate branches of this eighth nerve: the auditory branch and the vestibular branch. Humans are not as dependent on their sense of hearing as they are on vision, but hearing is, nevertheless, extremely important, and our sense of equilibrium is critical.

The detection of sound vibrations in air is called *hearing*.

For some strange reason, the detection of similar vibrations by fishes, in water, is not considered "hearing." While purely a matter of semantics, it *is* a little surprising, because the sensory receptors involved are remarkably similar. As it happens, the same branch of the eighth cranial nerve is involved in both cases, and sound actually travels better in water than it does in air; certainly it travels faster. What is more, water-dwellers can use the energy waves directly, without having to rely on any amplifying mechanisms to increase the probability of detection.

Our ears are remarkably selective. In addition to their already-mentioned ability to detect small changes in frequency, their sensitivity to volume is also remarkable. Intensity changes as small as 0.25 decibels (see table 9.3 on page 273) are detectable. Even more amazingly, the ear can sort through an incredible mixture of frequencies produced by human

Figure 9.25 The human ear exposed. Note the eustachian tube, which connects the middle ear to the pharynx.

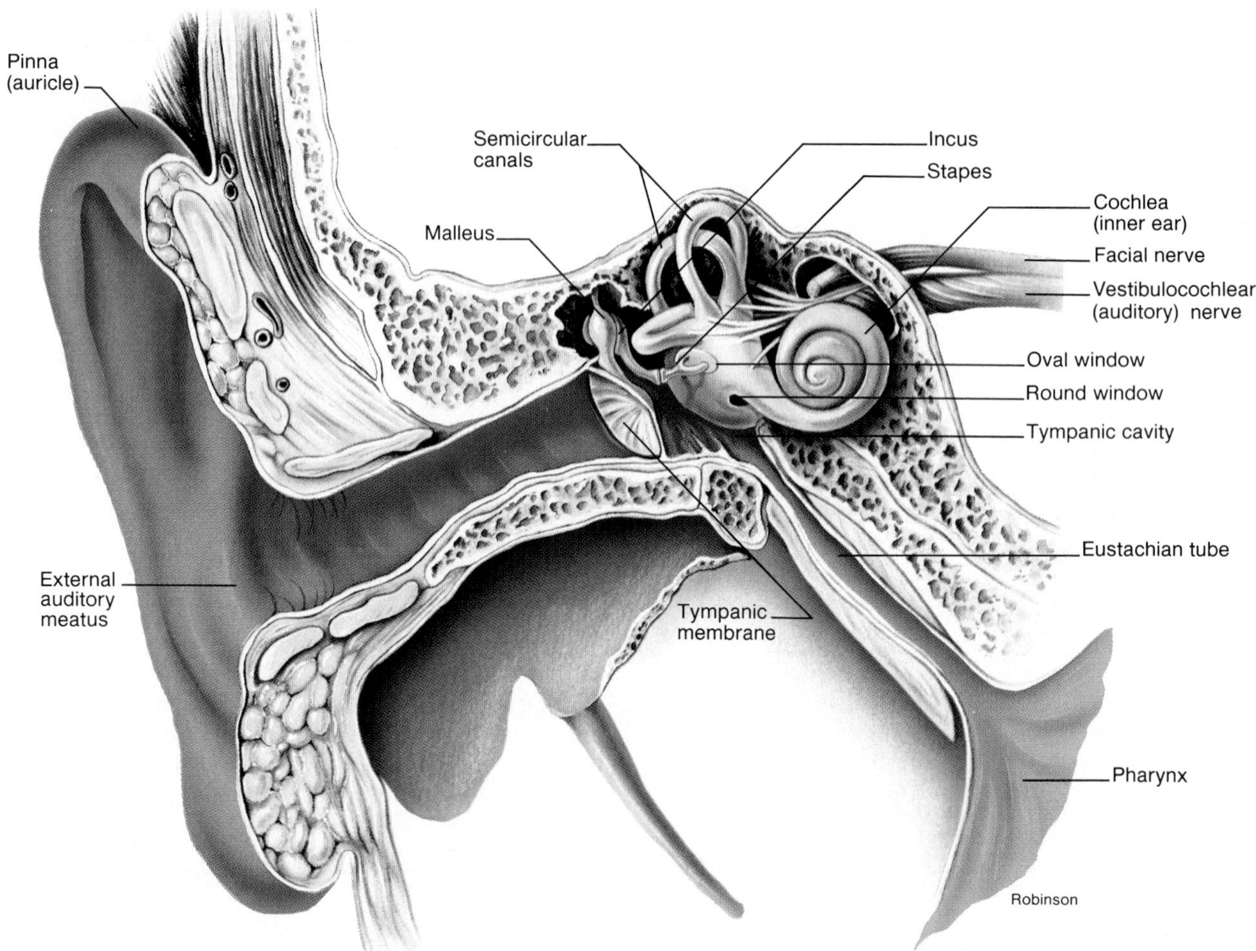

vocal cords and extract recognizable information. This last feature is extremely important, because without it, no coherent speech would be possible. It is really remarkable, and no one is sure how the brain does it, because speech patterns are so mixed and contain such diverse, scattered frequencies. Moreover, it makes no difference whether a man or a woman is speaking; normal speech can be easily understood by any listener, despite the fact that the frequency components that dominate the speech patterns of the two sexes often vary enormously.

Sound waves carried in the air contain very little energy. Most air-dwelling animals—including humans—possess in their ears an amplifying mechanism to enhance their ability to detect and analyze these waves. Like most mechanisms in biological systems, the auditory amplifier comes complete with a built-in "volume control" that operates automatically and can turn up or down, depending on just how loud the sound waves are. To understand how this is accomplished, you must learn a little about the anatomy of the human ear and the receptors involved (figure 9.25).

Some Aural Anatomy

The most obvious part of the mammalian ear is called the **pinna** (plural *pinnae*) or external ear; it includes the **auditory meatus** (pronounced *'mee-eight-us*), or external canal. The external ear ends at the eardrum or **tympanic membrane,** which also marks the beginning of the **middle ear.** In the chamber of the middle ear are the three bones or **ossicles** of the middle ear—the **malleus,** the **incus,** and the **stapes**—also known

Figure 9.26 The human middle ear, showing the arrangement of the ossicles. The stapedius and tensor tympani muscles are the ear's "volume control."

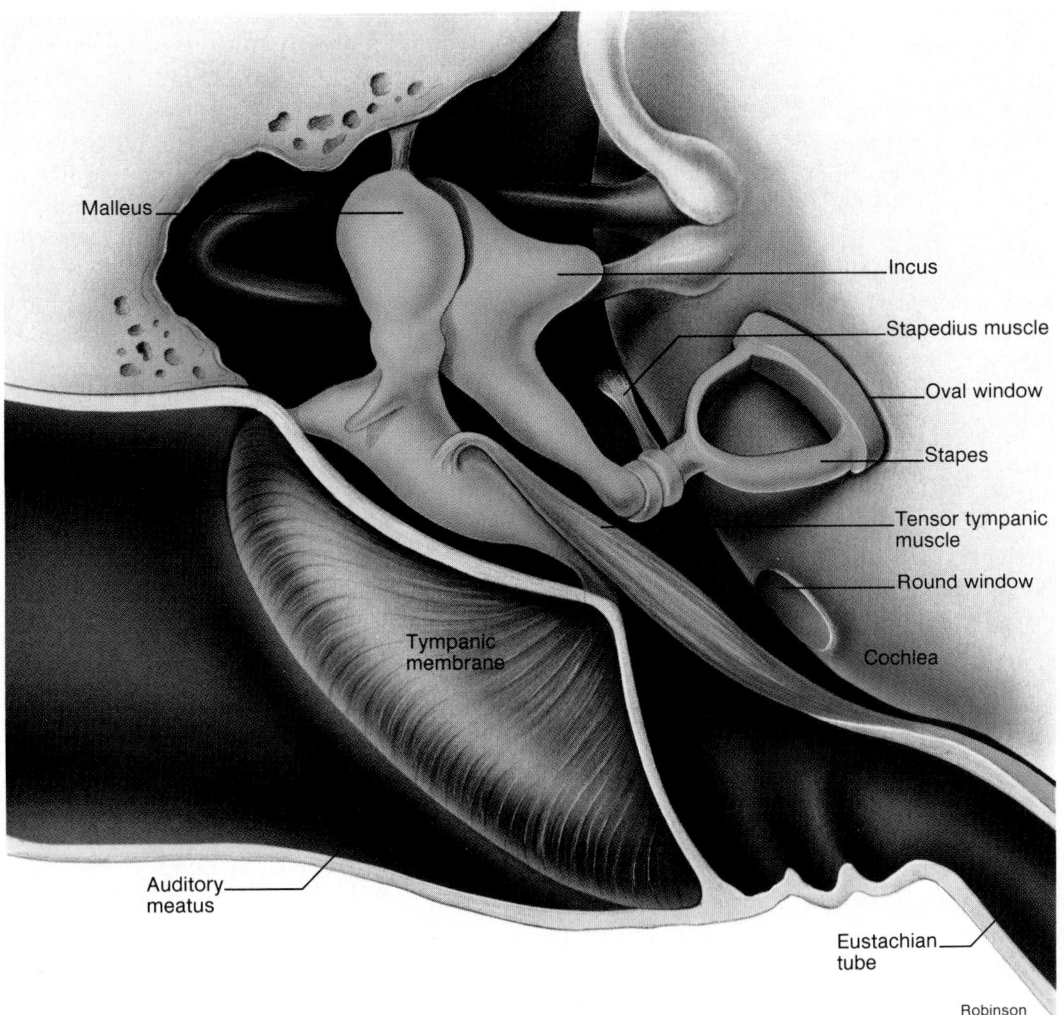

as the hammer, the anvil, and the stirrup. The **eustachian tube** (figure 9.26) opens into the middle ear, linking it with the pharynx, which is the back of the throat.

The stapes contacts the **cochlea,** a part of the **inner ear,** at the **oval window,** where it transfers its vibrations to the **endolymph,** a fluid similar to intracellular fluids, within the cochlea. It is in the cochlea—more specifically, within the **organ of Corti,** which is immersed in endolymph—that sonic energy vibrations are translated into electrical impulses for transmission and analysis by the auditory part of the brain.

On the upper edge of the cochlea are the three **semicircular canals,** which connect with the **vestibule** to form the **organs of equilibrium** in all vertebrates. They are encased, as is the cochlea, within a bony chamber inside the skull and are bathed by a liquid called **perilymph,** which is continuous with the cerebrospinal fluid. Like the auditory portion of the inner ear, the vestibule is innervated by a branch of the eighth cranial nerve. Reasonably enough, this is known as the **vestibular branch.**

Function

The External Ear

The pinnae are the first ear structures to encounter sound waves in the environment, and often they are pretty complex. With the exception of our seagoing relatives (whales, dolphins, seals, etc.), all mammals have external ears. They are designed to steer sound selectively into the auditory meatus, and through their ability to rotate, can aid in locating the source of the sound waves. Human ears are deficient in this regard. Compared to the huge ears on bats, rabbits, or deer, they are not particularly efficient as sound gatherers, and as we all know, human pinnae can't rotate the way many other animals' can. So our ability to localize sound sources is rather limited. Still, they do serve, in their limited way, to steer sound waves into the meatus and thence to the eardrum.

The Middle Ear

The eardrum is a fine membrane stretched taut across the ear canal, blocking the passageway completely and forming a boundary between the outer and middle ear. It's stretched tightly, very similar to the membrane covering a drum, and like a drum, when energy waves strike it, it vibrates. These vibrations are transferred through the middle ear to the inner ear by the three middle ear ossicles—the malleus, incus, and stapes—which are also the structures responsible for sound amplification. The vibrations caused by sound waves are transferred from about 60 to 70 mm^2 of the tympanic membrane by the malleus. It passes them through the incus to the stapes, which finally presents them in concentrated form to just over 3 mm^2 of membrane surface at the oval window of the inner ear. That boosts the volume by a factor of about 20, and in addition, there is an adjustable lever action between the malleus and the incus which can, if necessary, further magnify the movement. Travelling through the middle ear, therefore, sound waves can be amplified twenty or thirty times.

That is a maximum amplification figure. Sound is not always amplified that much. It depends ultimately on the intensity of the sound that enters the ear. As was mentioned before, the amplifier has a "volume control" built into it, and this control can turn the volume all the way up, or cut it down to a negative value. This volume control is a pair of tiny muscles attached to the malleus and the stapes (figure 9.26), and by contracting or relaxing they can alter the mobility of the ossicles relative to each other, thereby adjusting the degree of sound amplification. These muscles function to keep sound volume at optimum levels for everyday operations, but they perform their greatest service when massive volumes of sound enter the ear . . . sound waves containing potentially harmful amounts of energy. Confronted with such audio stimuli, the muscles contract, pressing the ossicles more rigidly against one another, thereby reducing their ability to conduct the waves through the middle ear and preventing damage to inner ear mechanisms. They cannot, of course, adjust to sudden, unexpectedly loud sounds, and that is why the sound of gunshots in a closed room can be so damaging, but they can adjust fairly well to constant loud noise.

Noises that are not so loud produce less profound contractions, and as entering sounds weaken, these muscles can relax accordingly, increasing the mobility of the ossicles and subsequently boosting amplification. Finally, with very soft sounds, the volume is turned up all the way. These same middle-ear muscles contract reflexly when people talk, chew, or swallow—again, apparently to prevent damage—and independent of the volume of sound entering the ear. This is why normal conversation is sometimes difficult to hear when you are eating.

While it is hard to gauge the volume of sound perception, it is possible to measure the energy content of audio vibrations. A table has been constructed using **decibels** as its unit. Decibel values of various sound levels are presented in table 9.3.

The utilization of these bones to amplify airborne sounds is extremely important and may be a major reason why mammals can analyze sounds so distinctly and hear so clearly. Reptiles, for example, have *inner* ear structures very similar to the mammalian one, but two of the three bones that comprise our *middle* ear are still part of the jaw in these animals. Since they lack the amplifying abilities of our middle ear, most reptiles are capable of responding only to very loud sounds in low frequency ranges—on the order of 200 to 300 cps—and frequency discrimination seems to be very poor.

As you can see from figure 9.26, the eustachian tubes run from the middle ear to the pharynx, opening to the throat on one end and the ear on the other. Since the throat opens to the air through the mouth, the eustachian tubes represent a link between the middle ear and the atmosphere. As such, they are involved in pressure equalization on both sides of the mammalian eardrum, and for organisms living in trees or in mountainous terrain—anywhere where the ear is exposed to constantly changing altitudes—their presence is critical.

Normally, the tubes are closed off at their pharyngeal end by a pair of flaps in the throat. The middle ear is thus hermetically sealed . . . not a good seal, since there are leaks present, but nevertheless, a seal.

Table 9.3 Decibel* Values for Sounds Ranging from Faint to Very Loud

Decibel Value	Examples of Such Sound Levels	Effect
140 decibels and up	Gunfire in a closed room; heavy artillery outdoors	Ear damage
120–140	A loud, high shriek in one's ear, like a siren or a jet engine	Painful
100–120	Rock and roll concert; nearby riveting	Deafening
80–100	Loud motorcycle rushing by; sheet metal factory	Uncomfortable
60–80	War movies; building construction zones	Loud
50–60	Normal conversation	Moderate
40–50	A library reading room; riding in a new car	Gentle sounds
30–40	Background sounds; an audible whisper	Quiet
20	Dusk in the country, sounds of country life	Peaceful
10	Gentle wind blowing across a wheatfield	Faint

*By convention, zero decibels (0 Db) is the least perceptible sound that can be heard. Each 10 decibel increase increases the volume by a factor of 10. Ten decibels is, therefore, 10 times louder than 0; 20 decibels is 100 times louder than zero, and 30 decibels is 1,000 times louder. Using this scale, the volume of music offered at a modern rock concert (which is usually between 100 and 120 decibels) is a million times louder than normal conversation. No wonder ear damage is so prevalent in the youth of the U.S.

It has also been noticed that normally friendly people tend to be less friendly and can get downright nasty when a loud noise has been going on for a fairly long time around them.

Air can leak through the eardrum, but only very slowly, so *sudden* pressure changes in the external environment can be painful—they could even be damaging were it not for the presence of the eustachian tube.

When we drive up a mountain, for instance, it is commonplace for our ears to begin to feel uncomfortable as altitude increases. This happens because although the air pressure all around us decreases as we climb higher and higher, the pressure on the inside of the eardrum is the same as it was when the climb began; air has not had time to leak out through the eardrum. The higher internal pressure causes the eardrum to bulge out, impairing hearing and causing discomfort. The higher one goes, the more the membrane bulges. Obviously, there has to be some mechanism that will speed up equilibration of these pressures. Sometimes it happens automatically, without any conscious help. A flap of tissue moves, air suddenly leaks into the eustachian tube, the eardrums "pop," and the discomfort disappears. More often, however, we help the process along by swallowing, or if that doesn't work, by yawning . . . both of which open the pharyngeal end of the eustachian tubes. Incidentally, this process of pressure equalization is difficult or impossible when someone has a nasal or pharyngeal infection, and flying can actually be quite painful when a person has a cold.

Sound Perception: The Inner Ear

The membrane contacted by the stapes covers the oval window and represents the beginning of the inner ear. It is in the inner ear that "hearing" actually begins, since this is where the various energy waves are converted to nerve impulses. The bones of the skull form a chamber for the inner ear mechanisms—a chamber filled with fluid perilymph. Immersed in this fluid are the sensing mechanisms—the snail-shaped *cochlea* and the *vestibular organs.*

The Cochlea

In Latin, *cochlea* means "snail," and that's exactly what it looks like, the coiled shell of a snail (figure 9.27*a*). It's a little more complex on the inside than a snail shell, however, in that there are three separate chambers coiled within. The **scala vestibuli** and the **scala tympani** occupy the top and bottom chambers (figure 9.27*b*) and communicate with one another through the **helicotrema,** a small opening near the tip of the cochlea. Both are filled with perilymph. The **cochlear duct** is separated from the scala vestibuli by **Reissner's membrane** and from the scala tympani by the **basilar membrane.** Within the cochlear duct is the organ of Corti (figure 9.27*c* and *d*), which consists of the structures that convert sound waves into nerve impulses.

You can understand something of the wave motion that takes place within these chambers if you picture a glass tube filled with water and covered with a membrane at each end—a membrane stretched tight, like a drum. If you push one membrane in, the one

Figure 9.27 (*a*) The inner ear and hearing. (Colored zones are filled with endolymph.) (*b*) A cross-section through the cochlea (enlarged). (*c*) The organ of Corti. (*d*) An electron micrograph of the organ of Corti.

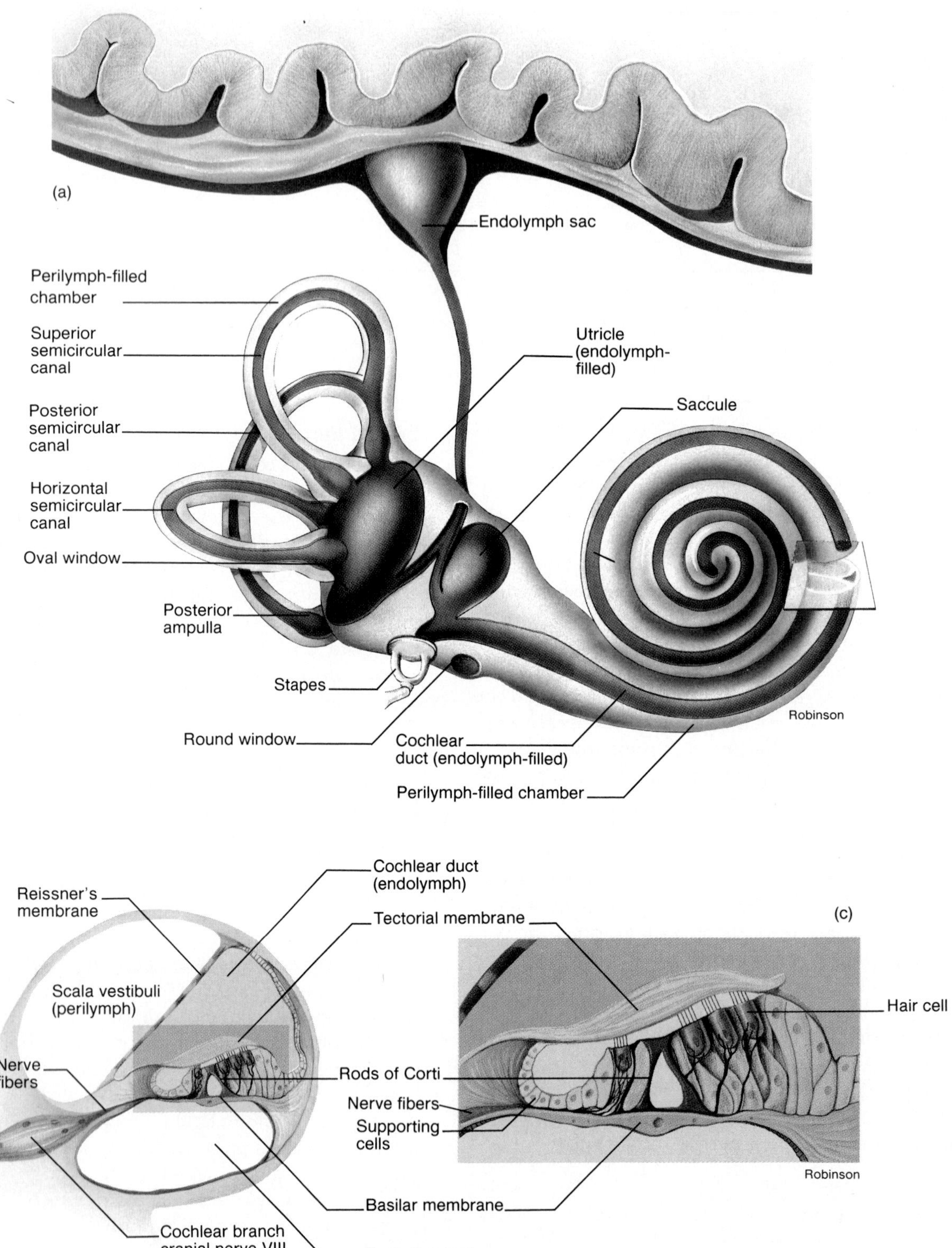

Figure 9.27 (cont.) (*d*) An electron micrograph of the organ of Corti.

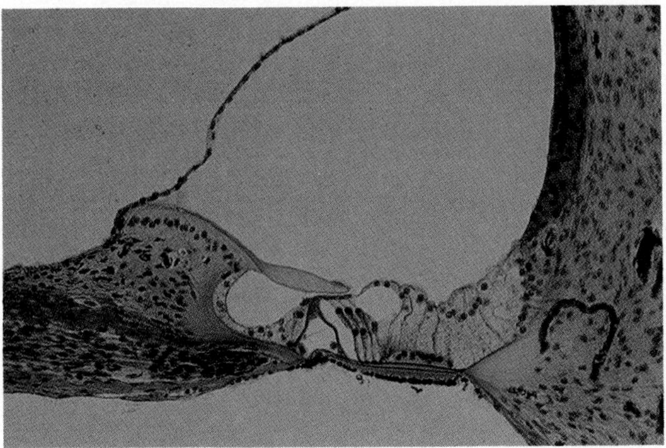

Figure 9.28 Pressure relationships between the two windows of the cochlea.

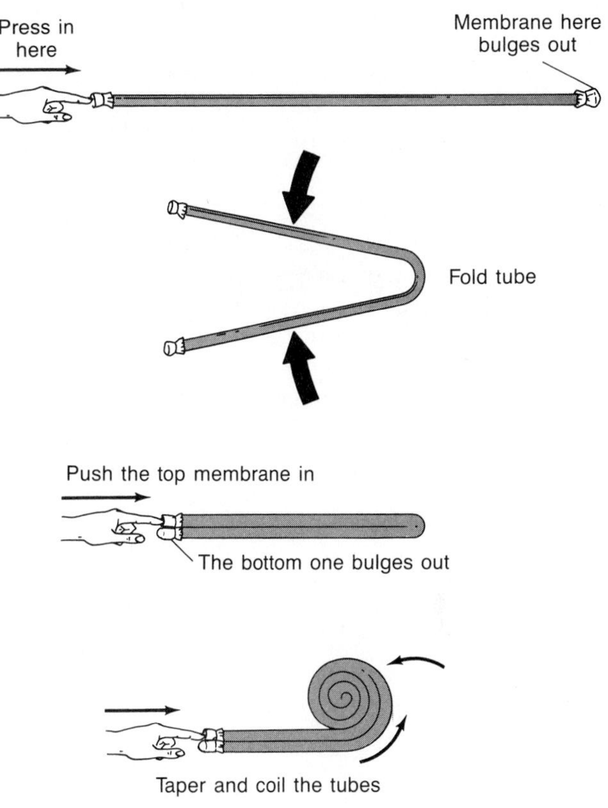

on the other end bulges out. If you pull one membrane out, the one on the other end will suck in (figure 9.28). Folding, tapering, and coiling the tube as diagramed in figure 9.28 shows a representative cochlear-like structure. The most significant difference is that between the two tubes of the living cochlea there is a pliable membrane instead of a solid piece of glass. The two rubber membranes covering the ends of the tube represent the membrane-covered **oval** and **round windows,** and these two membranes work in living systems just as those shown in the figure.

Sound waves enter the oval window from the stapes and are converted into liquid compression waves in the perilymph. Like all liquids, the perilymph cannot be forced into a container smaller than its own volume, so as the oval window moves, the round window follows. Inward movement of the oval window produces a pressure wave that runs through the scala vestibuli, turns at the helicotrema, and runs back through the scala tympani to the round window, which bulges out to accommodate the extra pressure. These pressure waves cause corresponding waves in both Reissner's membrane and the basilar membrane, and as these membranes displace, they cause corresponding compression waves to be established in the endolymph of the cochlear duct, which can move the tectorial membrane, displacing the cilia on the hair cells (figure 9.29). As figure 9.30 shows, the higher frequency vibrations tend to produce most of this movement in membranes near the base of the cochlea, whereas lower frequency vibrations cause greater movement in the more pliable membrane near the end of the coil. Regardless of the route followed, each part of the basilar membrane has its own particular resonant frequency, and the portion of it that vibrates is determined by the frequency of the waves entering. Researchers are reasonably sure that the frequency or *pitch* of a note is determined by the position, on the membrane, of the displaced hair cells.

The Auditory Receptors

The hair cells are *mechanoreceptors,* inasmuch as their adequate stimulus is physical displacement. They are receptors of auditory stimuli, and ultimately their movements are translated into action potentials and carried by cochlear fibers of the eighth cranial nerve into the auditory portion of the brain. The hair cells are **secondary receptors.** They hand their information to adjacent neurons in the form of chemical transmitters, and these neurons produce the electrical responses that the brain can interpret.

It seems, then, that both hearing and frequency discrimination depend to an enormous extent on the flexibility of the basilar membrane. Most humans are unable to hear sounds below 20 cps (although there are reports that exposure to subsonic vibrations is depressing; hence they must be detectable somewhere)

Figure 9.29 Sound waves entering the cochlea can bend the basilar and vestibular membranes down (*a*) or up (*b*), thus bending the cilia on the hair cells. Bending of the cilia produces a permeability change in the hair cell membrane, which results in a receptor potential. (*c*) Position of hair cells when silence prevails.

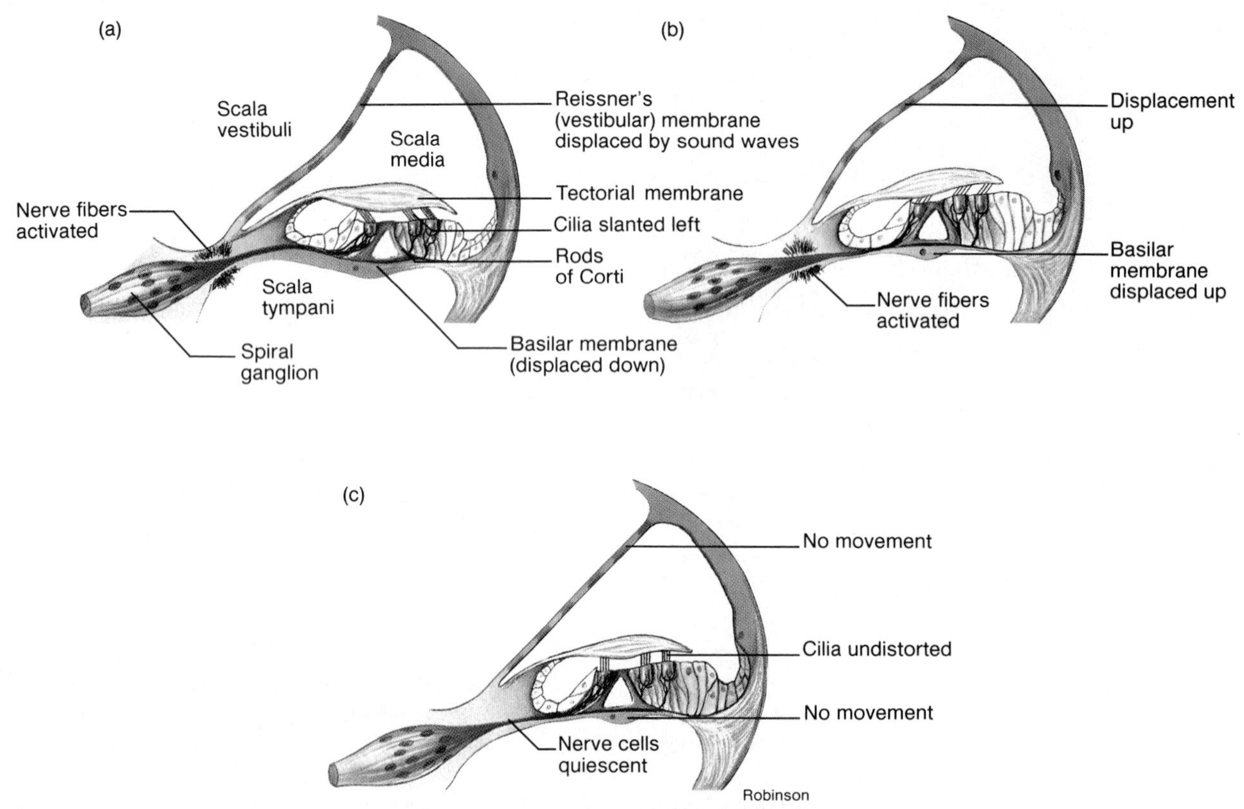

Figure 9.30 The cochlea, straightened out to show frequency discrimination in the basilar membrane. High-frequency vibrations (*line 1*) produce the greatest response near the oval window, at the base of the membrane. Moderate frequencies (*line 2*) are best detected in the middle portions, while lower frequencies (*line 3*) produce the greatest membrane distortion at the membrane's tip, near the helicotrema.

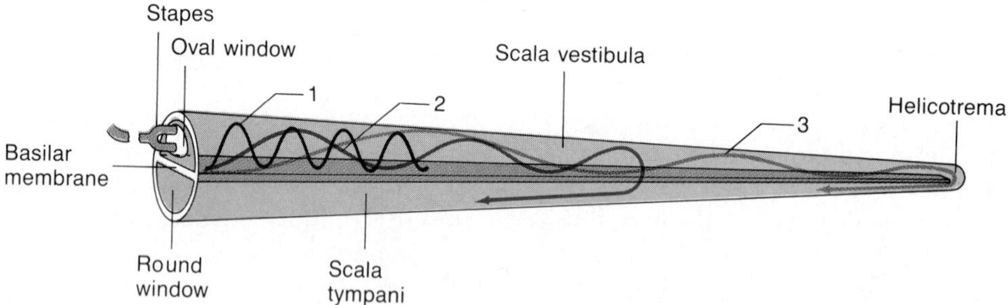

Panel 9.2
Echo Locating

Some animals possess an ability to analyze sound waves that is truly incredible. Principles that humans learned only in the last forty years have been used by some animals for millenia and may have been present eons ago. Bats, for example, use sound the way we use radar. When they are hunting in the twilight, they send out showers of high-frequency notes at specific intervals, and they can intercept and analyze these sounds as they reflect from objects around them. Using this built-in sonar, they locate flying insects with astonishing precision. Bats can fly with ease in total darkness, twisting and turning away from all obstacles, able to analyze their surroundings with sound.

And such ability is not restricted to fliers. It has been known for years that dolphins and porpoises are able to send complicated messages to each other using water-borne sound waves, and recently it was discovered that they can use self-produced high-frequency sounds to analyze their surroundings in murky waters. They simply emit these bursts of sound at regular intervals and locate objects the same way bats do, by analyzing the length of time it takes for the sound waves to bounce back to their ears.

People, of course, have been fiddling with this type of echo location since early in the twentieth century, and we are getting better at it all the time. Almost everyone knows what radar is, and it is nothing more than a high-speed echo-locator. It is much better known to the average person than sonar is, but in fact, echo-location using sound waves preceded radar by about twenty years. The British navy used sonar (they call it ASDIC) in World War I to help combat the U-boat menace, and although it was not very reliable, it nevertheless existed. Today sonar is quite precise. It is used by fishing boats to locate schools of fish, by treasure hunters to locate sunken wrecks, and by naval vessels to locate submarines. Yet despite all our improvements, we still lack the analytical ability of the cetaceans (dolphins, whales, etc.) and the tiny bats. Our best sonar can be misled quite easily by simple things like layers of different temperature in the water or clouds of bubbles. Radar still hasn't learned how to pick an aircraft out of a cloud of fluttering aluminum-foil strips. Dolphins are never bothered by such things, and a blindfolded bat can fly between strings dangling from the ceiling of a room and never strike a one. Nothing we have ever designed—neither audio equipment nor our most modern radar—can begin to approach this degree of precision.

---

or higher than 20,000 cps. Some animals can detect sounds as low as 10 cps, while most dogs and cats can hear sound frequencies as high as 42,000 cps.

Silent dog whistles depend on this ability. They produce notes on the order of 35,000 cps, much too high for *any* human to hear, but clearly audible to both dogs and cats. Contrary to popular belief, blowing such a whistle does not automatically attract dogs. As with any other stimulus, the animals must be taught what its note means. Also, it is worth mentioning that while most such whistles are well beyond the audible range of humans, every once in a while a cheap model will produce a note in the 22,000 cps range and some young children are able to hear it. They report that it is a really ear-splitting sound, so high-pitched as to actually be painful.

Hearing as a Sense

Aside from its obvious importance in communication, the value of hearing to humans is more limited than that of sight. It does not usually reveal its source or nature as faithfully as vision does. Sound waves tend to be more diffuse than electromagnetic radiation, and they bounce or are scattered by almost any solid object. Depending on the topography surrounding the receiver, the location of a sound's source is more or less detectable but often imprecise. Echoes can render this aspect of hearing faulty, and obstacles like trees, bushes, or buildings can "scatter" the sound all over the place, making it impossible to accurately zero in on origin or cause. Nor can our ears tell us how far away the sound might be, beyond telling us that something is either close, distant, or very distant.

Nevertheless, vertebrates in general place tremendous reliance on their sense of hearing, especially nocturnal hunters. Cats and dogs, animals that depend enormously on their sense of smell, rely a great deal on their hearing, too, because they can *hear* things happening much sooner than they can *smell* them, and sound often travels farther than odors do, particularly if the odor is a subtle one.

The Pathway Into the Brain

Nerve fibers from the hair cells are gathered into the cochlear branch of the vestibulocochlear (auditory) nerve and enter the brain at the medulla, progressing from there into the midbrain. There are some synaptic connections made here and there with minor nuclei, but most fibers continue through the thalamus into the auditory cortex, the **temporal lobe** of the cerebral hemispheres.

The auditory cortex is an area of considerable integration and analysis. It is here that grades of pitch are handled. Destruction of certain portions of this area result in loss of the ability to understand words and to distinguish between pitches of musical notes. These may be the speech centers of the cortex, although the process of speech is so complex and so strictly human that doing any definitive research in these zones has proven extremely difficult and mainly inconclusive.

Crossover

Crossovers provide the higher centers with some opportunity for comparison of the information received by both ears, thus making it possible to identify the direction from which the sound is coming. The first such crossover occurs in the medulla oblongata, and a second occurs after the fibers leave the midbrain, in a region known as the **inferior colliculus.**

The inferior colliculus is generally viewed as a rather rudimentary correlation center. Some fibers in this area are believed to mediate sound-associated reflexes, such as jumping or blinking at loud noises.

Equilibrium

The earliest vertebrates used their ears to keep their balance and to help them determine which direction was up. Modern, air-breathing vertebrates still utilize these organs for the same purpose, with a couple of sophisticated additions. Not only can we determine which way is up, but we can also determine whether or not we are moving, and in which direction. In other words, we utilize two separate sets of inputs for equilibrium—**static** and **dynamic.**

Static input tells us where we are in space. Are we standing on our heads or our feet? Are we lying on our right sides or our left sides? This is information that pertains to the body when it is motionless. *Dynamic input,* on the other hand, provides information concerning *acceleration.* When we suddenly begin to move in a given direction, we do not have to see things moving around us—we know we have begun to move because mechanisms in our inner ears tell us so. Not only that, we know the *direction* of our acceleration, and we can tell when we're slowing down and when we stop.

Constant velocity, however, is something our bodies are not able to sense. This is probably just as well. The earth is barrelling along in its orbit at more than 65,000 miles per hour while simultaneously spinning around on its axis at another 25,000 miles per day, and we are blithely unaware of both velocities. Because of this, we can avoid input that is of no value to us and keep our sensors available for other, more pertinent, information. Until the last couple of centuries, this was a lack that no one even suspected and certainly never missed. You can make yourself aware of a similar effect the next time you fly in commercial aircraft in smooth air. Once you have finished with the acceleration of take-off and climbing to altitude, the process of flying cross-country is generally without any awareness of motion at all. The airstreams at altitudes of 35,000 feet or more are usually so smooth that the aircraft's cruising velocity, being constant, is undetectable, and we are so high up that even our visual input is deceptive.

Static Equilibrium

The organs involved in static equilibrium consist of two bony chambers—the **utricle** and the **saccule**—located between the cochlea and the semicircular canals (see figure 9.27*a*). Inside each of these chambers is a liquid called **endolymph,** which is, in composition, very similar to intracellular fluid and is identical to the endolymph of the cochlear canal (figure 9.31). As figure 9.31 shows, these chambers communicate with each other, with the semicircular canals, and with the inner chamber of the cochlea as well. **Hair cells** (figure 9.31*d*) function as the sensory receptors within these chambers. They are imbedded in the walls of both chambers . . . not scattered loosely, but grouped in patches called **maculae** (fig 9.31*c*). The saccule has two such patches, the utricle, one. Covering the inner surface of each macula is a gelatinous material filled with tiny mineralized concretions known as **otoliths.** These otoliths rest on a bed of cilia projecting from the surface of the sensory receptors—receptors designed to indicate the position of the head with respect to gravity. If the head tips forward, obedient to gravity, these otoliths begin to drift rostrally, bending the cilia on the hair cells and sending signals to the nerve fibers at their base (figure 9.32).

Dynamic Equilibrium

Dynamic equilibrium is the province of the three semicircular canals. At the base of each of these there is a swelling called an **ampulla** (figure 9.31*a*), in which is imbedded a sensory receptor known as a **crista** (figure 9.31*b*). Like the hair cells of the maculae, these receptors are surrounded by endolymph and covered

Figure 9.31 The vestibular organs of the inner ear. (*a*) The organs of equilibrium. (*b*) The crista. (*c*) The macula. (*d*) The hair cell.

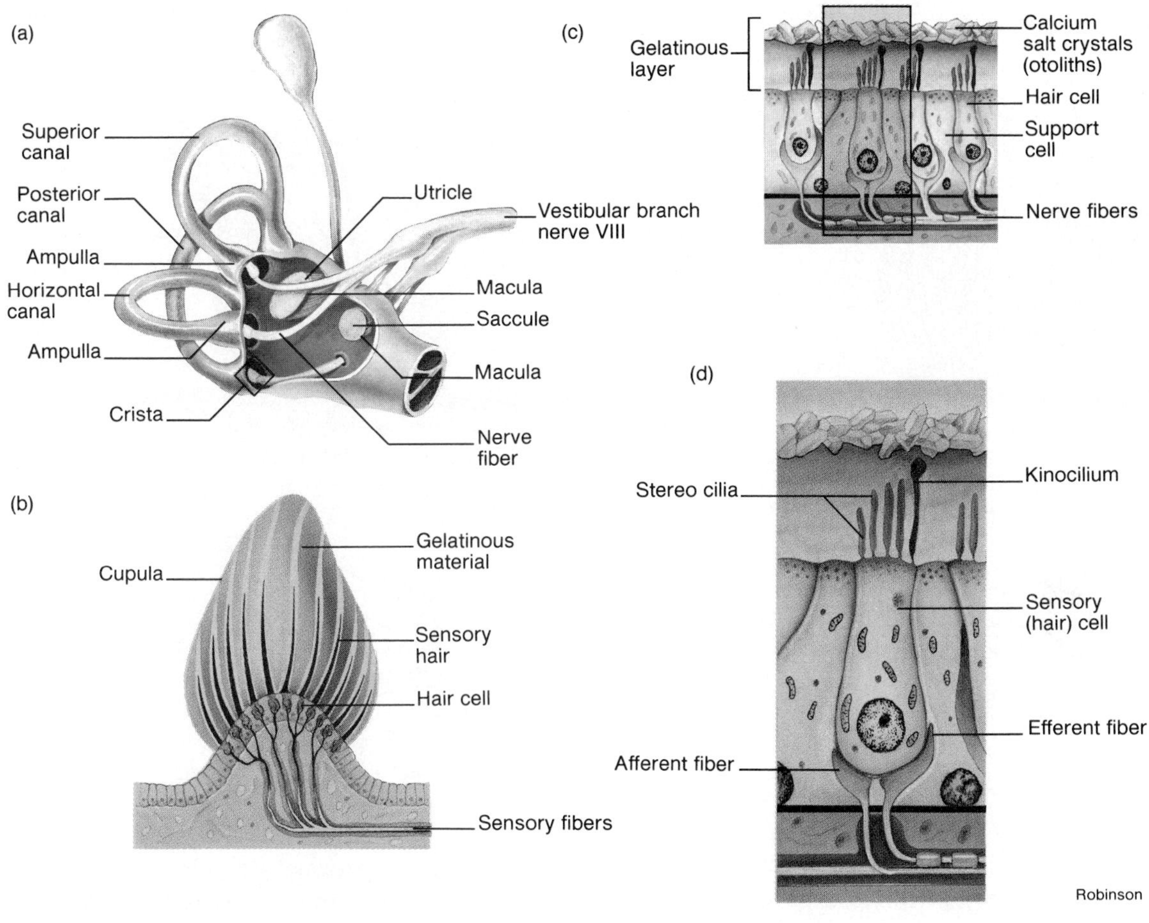

Figure 9.32 The static equilibrium sensors in action.

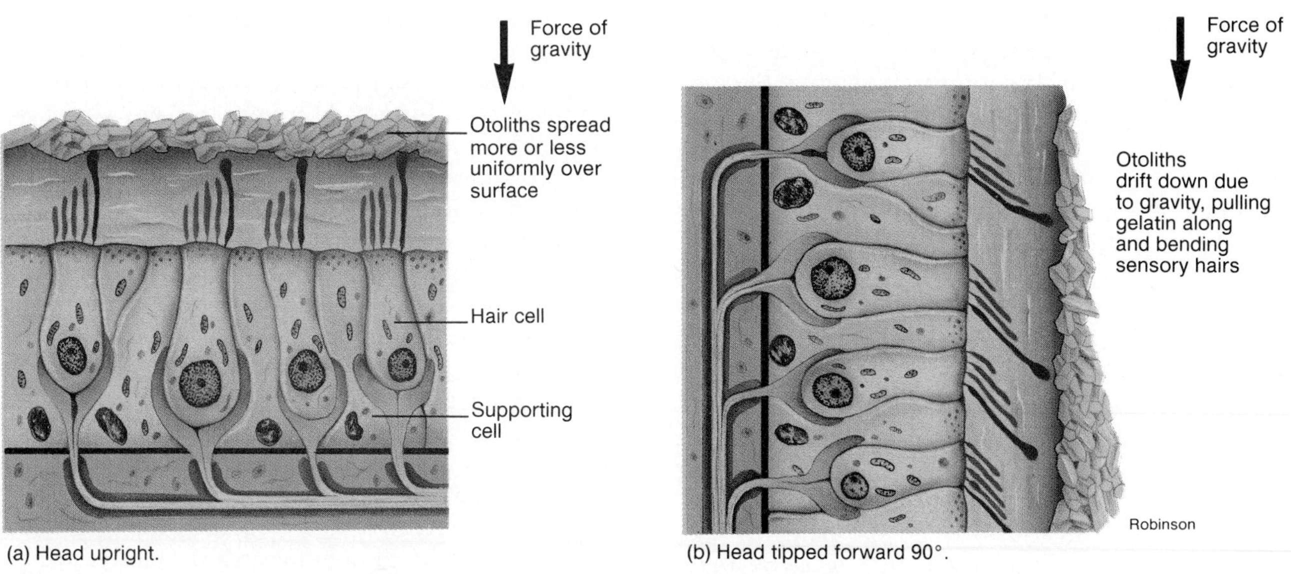

(a) Head upright.

(b) Head tipped forward 90°.

Figure 9.33 The sensory structures in the semicircular canals. (*a*) No movement. (*b*) Movement left. The endolymph and the water try to remain stationary as the head (and the glass) move left.

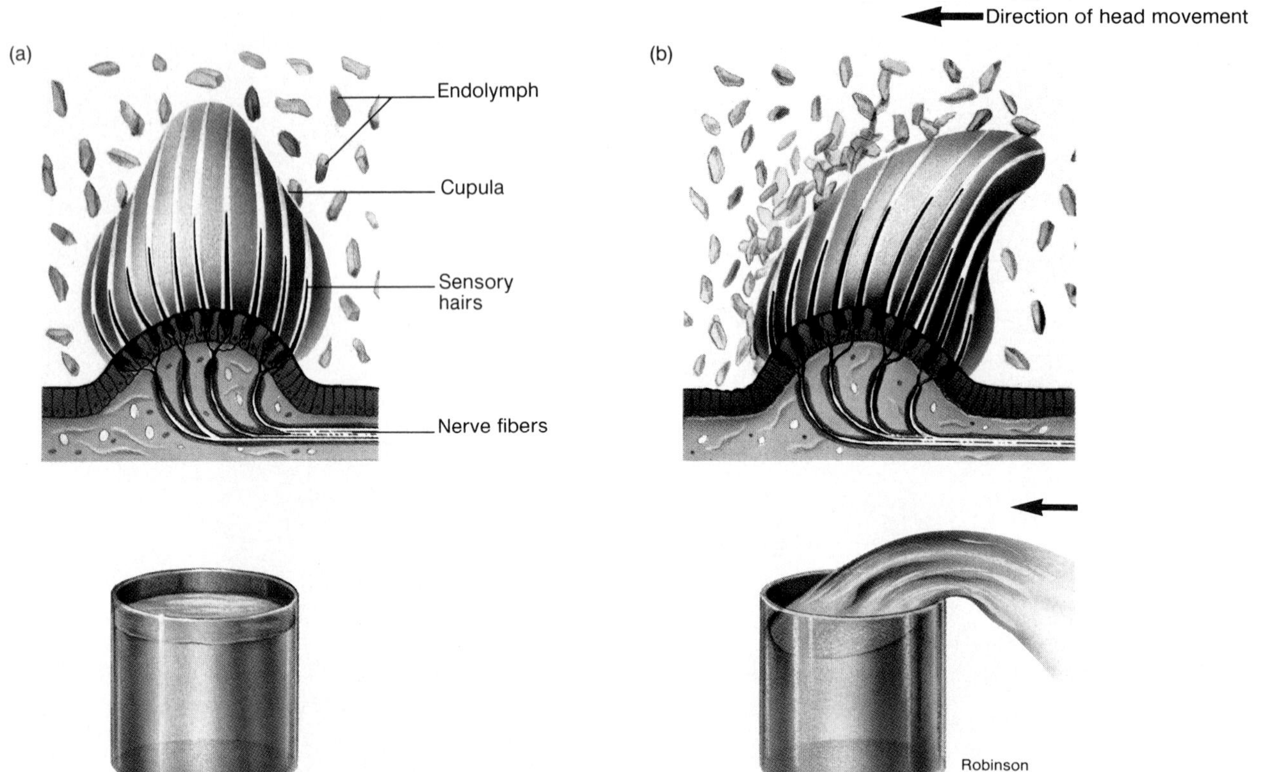

with an umbrella-shaped cupula that is filled with gelatinous material. When the head moves, the bone-encased canals move and pull the jelly-filled cupula with them. The endolymph inside the canals, however, being a liquid, doesn't move with the canals the way the cupula does. It tends to stay in the same place due to inertia, and the result is that the cupula bends under the pressure of the endolymph, displacing the sensory hairs within and ultimately sending the necessary information to the central nervous system (figure 9.33). The same thing happens if a full glass of water is suddenly moved across a table top: the glass moves and the water tends to stay where it is, spilling over the lip of the glass onto the table.

The "Tilt" Receptors

Like the auditory neurons that innervate the organ of Corti, the hair cells of the utricle, saccule, and semicircular canals are *secondary receptors,* not primary ones. The hair cells cannot produce action potentials; they are epithelial cells, not neurons. When their cilia are bent in one direction, they tend to produce slow *de*polarizations; when the hairs are displaced in the other direction, they *hyper*polarize. Whatever the information, it is passed on in the form of chemical transmitters that in turn produce the electrical impulses in the contiguous nerve cells.

The static and dynamic equilibrium sensors provide us with information all the time, yet probably less than 10 percent is ever *consciously* used. Most of this input is handled below the level of consciousness by elements in the brain stem. The information provided by the ampullae in the semicircular canals, for instance, is funneled through the cerebellum (see chapter 8), where it is integrated with visual input to predict the consequences of running, jumping, or other body movement.

Walking, for example, may appear to be a simple, relatively routine process, but it requires a lot of central nervous coordination—including some pretty good mathematical integration—to keep us from constantly falling down. Because we can walk without thinking about it, it seems like a smooth, effortless process, yet what it actually amounts to is a series of sequential shifts of the body's center of gravity. We hurl ourselves off-balance, thrusting our weight forward on a given line, and then quickly flip a leg under the new center of gravity to catch the shifted weight before we fall down. Walking receives very little conscious consideration, but the neural mechanisms of the inner ear, eyes, and cerebellum are working vigorously and in concert, all the time. As each movement occurs, stimuli from the semicircular canals and our eyes report the movement, and the cerebellum integrates it, stimulating all the necessary muscles, making all the major movements and the myriad minor tonic adjustments that keep us from losing our balance with each shift in position.

Chemoreceptive Senses

Chemoreception, as studied in humans, deals mainly with the senses of smell and taste. We tend to be more aware of these two senses than of our other chemoreceptive processes, because we use them consciously. Yet we have in our bodies many other kinds of chemoreceptors, and these work ceaselessly, monitoring the interiors of our bodies and making any necessary adjustments to maintain homeostatic consistency. As we have already seen, body cells relentlessly scrutinize the mineral content of extracellular and intracellular fluids, and there is abundant evidence to indicate that there is equally determined surveillance of oxygen and carbon dioxide levels, nutrient concentration, and waste production. All the information concerning these things is made available to our central nervous system through the efforts of chemoreceptors.

Our chemical senses diligently analyze the blood and lymph, probing for any kind of maladjustment. Some, like the O_2 receptors in the carotid sinus (see chapter 14), are fairly specific in their analytical abilities. Others are more general and will respond with equal fervor to potentially harmful concentrations of almost anything. Hence they are particularly responsive to unusually high levels of salts (osmotically damaging), acids, or alkalines (able to disrupt enzyme activity). Whenever such concentrations are detected, these receptors can set off compensatory mechanisms that will reduce the threat to the organism's well-being. The responses, therefore, are always directed toward homeostasis.

Although they often operate together, and both are designed to detect the presence of chemicals in solution, the senses of smell and taste are clearly separate in humans. The differences are actually quite profound. The receptors involved with the sense of smell look nothing like those responsible for taste; olfactory receptors are much, much more sensitive than our taste buds; and the information gathered by the two senses is carried on different cranial nerves and is processed by clearly different brain areas.

The Olfactory Sense (Smell)

Our sense of smell is generally considered to be, like vision and hearing, a *distance* sense. Chemicals transported in the air find their way into our respiratory tract, and if they are abundant enough, we may detect them. Their origin could be a few inches, or several miles, away. What is more, despite our olfactory shortcomings compared to dogs, the human nose is pretty good. Most humans can identify several hundred different odors, and with practice, people can become familiar with tens of thousands. Not only that but, depending on the substance involved, our noses can be remarkably sensitive. For instance, chemicals known as *mercaptans* are particularly offensive to most humans, and it has been calculated that the average person can detect them when there are only two or three molecules present in a noseful of air. We can detect the presence of ammonia when it represents less than 0.0001 percent of the atmosphere, and we can smell perfume from a lilac tree a half-mile away when the wind is right. It is absolutely mind-boggling to imagine what a *really* sensitive nose, like a dog or a cat's, might reveal.

Like vision, hearing, and equilibrium, olfaction is a primary sense, yet we know less about the sense of smell than any of them—at least from an objective standpoint. Possibly part of that reason is that in humans, it is a good deal less important than in most other animals.

Morphology

Mammalian olfactory receptors are very well protected. Not only are they buried within the bones of the skull, they are protected from the mainstream of air that enters the respiratory tree. It has been reliably estimated that less than 2 percent of the air we breathe in actually contacts the **olfactory epithelium** during normal breathing. For this reason, when we want to detect odors, we often must open our receptor epithelial layers and sniff carefully, causing little eddies in the incoming air as it passes over the receptor areas. The receptors are concentrated in the upper (superior) zones of the nasal cavities alongside the **nasal septum** (the bone between the nostrils). See figure 9.34.

The receptor cells themselves are **bipolar neurons** very similar in configuration to the bipolar cells in the retina of the eye. They are packed in between rows of columnar epithelial cells known as **sustentacular cells.** As figure 9.35 shows, the receptor cell itself is an elongated cell, the tip of which projects beyond the layer of sustentacular cells and into the film of mucus covering the interior of the nasal epithelium. Between ten and fifteen tiny cilia emerge

Figure 9.34 The olfactory epithelium. The ciliated receptor cells are supported and separated by columnar epithelial cells.

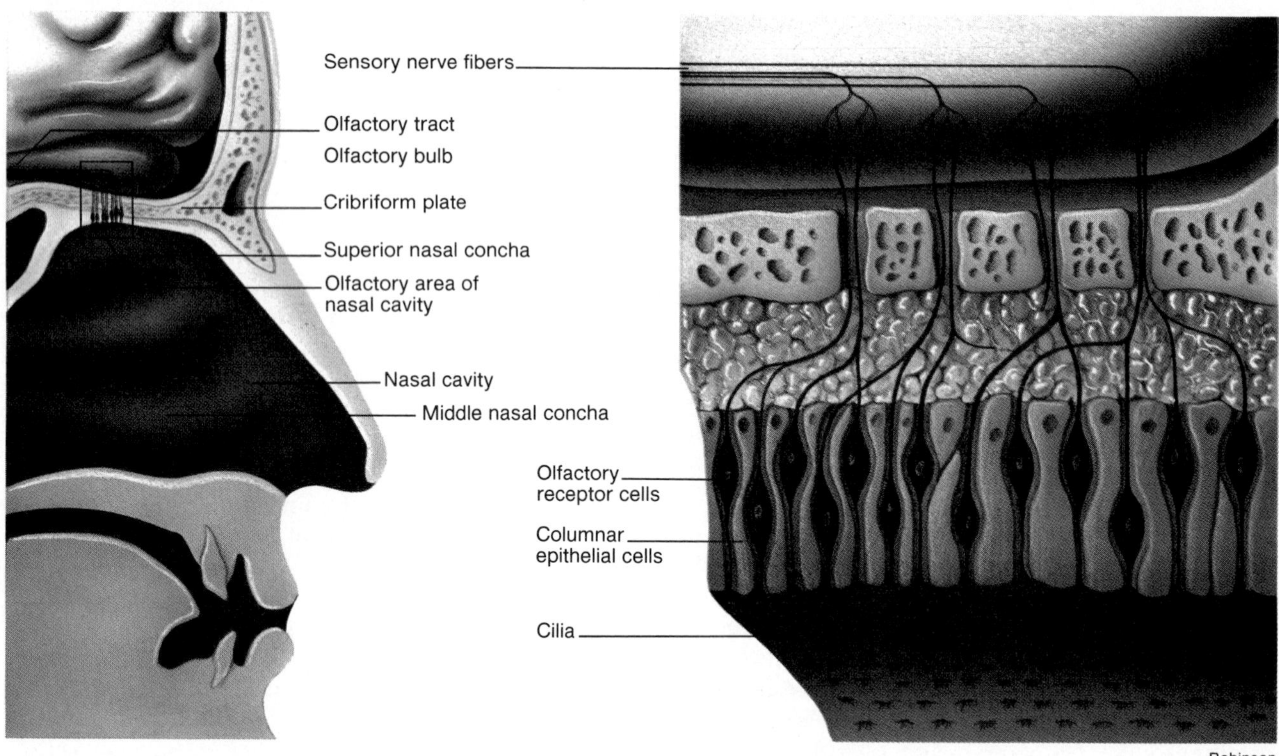

Figure 9.35 A region of olfactory epithelium.

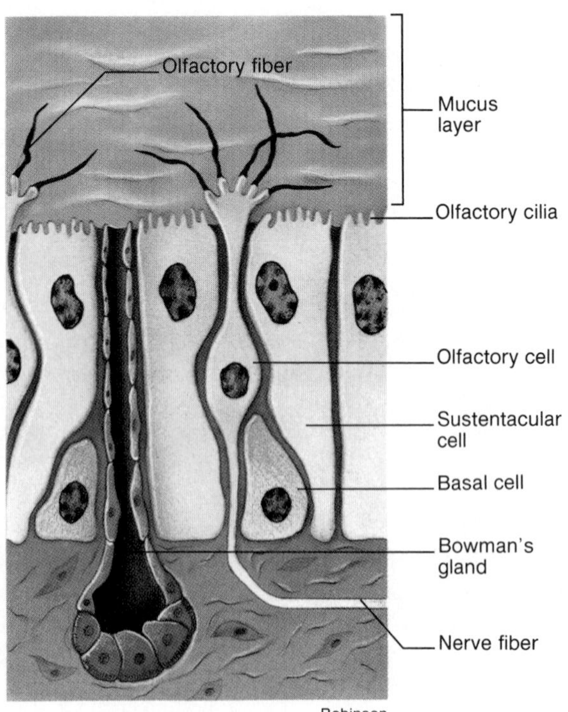

from the tip of each receptor cell, projecting well into the mucus layer. The mucus is produced by the sustentacular cells, by bundles of small **goblet cells** that abound in the epithelial layer, and by a structure known as **Bowman's gland.** The mucus is thought to have two primary functions: one to protect the epithelium from the drying forces that must be constantly at work as air flows back and forth across it, and the other homeostatic, since it provides the sensory portions of the receptor cells with a constant environment.

Basal cells are a type of developmental stem cell. Some workers think they become sustentacular cells, while others think they become olfactory cells. As you can see, more work is needed.

Molecules that enter the nasal epithelium enter in gaseous form, but in order to be detected, they must dissolve in the mucus, then migrate to the ciliar layers, where it is believed the chemoreceptors are located. Impulses originating in the neurons there travel to the **olfactory bulb** (see figure 9.34), and from there to the frontal lobes in the brain, where they are decoded.

Odor as a Sense

Regardless of our pride in our olfactory accomplishments, the information provided to us by the sense of smell is relatively scanty. Compared to other mammals, the sense of smell in humans is really undeveloped. Even if you manage to identify a source, you have very little information about its location, size, or distribution. In humans, the sense of smell probably functions mainly as an alerting sense—one that can suggest warning or pleasure and advise the subsequent use of more analytical senses.

The relative importance of the sense of smell to animals varies a great deal. Birds appear to ignore it almost completely. Even buzzards and vultures, carrion eaters whom you'd think would use that sense to locate food, apparently pay little attention to it. When monkeys and apes smell something, it is usually as an adjunct to other, more detailed analysis by eyes or taste. But to a dog or a cat, odor is the ultimate in identification analysis, and they depend on that sense more than any other. When you walk into your home, your dog will spot you with his eyes and see what is familiar. When you talk to him, it further supports his suspicion that it is really his boss, but until he can get a good whiff of your personal scent, he never really believes it. Even so, none of the air-breathers place the reliance on smell that fish do. A dog will lose a scent only a few hours after it was laid down, and if it is on hot pavement, it may disappear in less than an hour. Sharks can identify and follow a trail of blood for miles through turbulent water, and salmon can locate streams where they were hatched after spending years in the open ocean, thousands of miles away.

Analysis of Odors

No one really understands how odors are coded or what it is that gives a molecule its olfactory identity. There are so many different, clearly distinguishable scents that it is ludicrous to suggest there is a specialized receptor type for each. In any case, the receptors that have been investigated all appear to be the same. But it is not essential that we have different receptors. There are several theories as to just how animals might be able to qualitatively distinguish one odor from another.

The Shape Hypothesis According to the shape hypothesis, the coding of an aroma involves molecular *shape* . . . a disc-shaped molecule might smell musky, while one shaped like a keyhole is perfumey, like a flower. After an initial outburst of minor ridicule, the idea was given serious consideration because there is some experimental work to support it, at least in a broad sense. Some molecules with similar shapes apparently smell the same, even when they are enormously different chemically. See figure 9.36.

The Vibrational Theory Another theory states that odor sensing and variation may be due to the vibrational qualities of the molecules being sensed. As we know, every material thing vibrates, as long as its temperature is greater than absolute zero. The vibrational theory holds that quantized vibrational energy is transferred from an odor molecule to the receptor and that the quality of the odor can be correlated with the molecule's fundamental vibration frequency.

Figure 9.36 The "shape" or "stereochemical" theory of smell. These are the postulated receptor shapes in the human olfactory epithelium. The theory states that the odor we perceive depends on which receptor is stimulated. Hence, all molecules that can fit into a given hole (receptor) will smell the same. The better the fit, the purer the response. (Source: J. E. Amoore, *Proceedings from the Toilet Goods Association, Scientific Section Supplement 37,* pp. 1–20, 1962.)

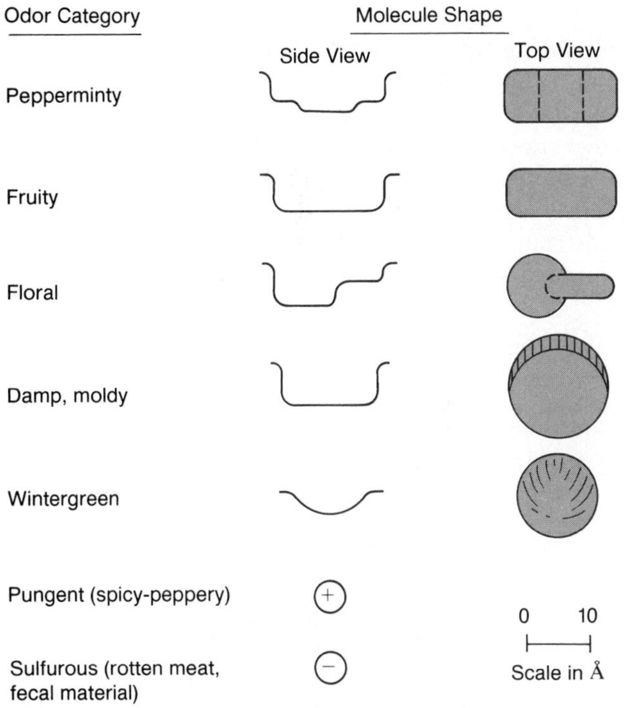

Odor Category
Molecule Shape
Side View
Top View
Pepperminty
Fruity
Floral
Damp, moldy
Wintergreen
Pungent (spicy-peppery)
Sulfurous (rotten meat, fecal material)
0 10
Scale in Å

Either of these theories could be correct—or neither. There are others that could be mentioned, but to what end? All have some experimental support, but none are free of problems. The simple truth is that we do not really understand why certain things smell different from others.

Our sense of smell appears to suffer more than most primary senses as we age. The bipolar cells responsible for smell reception are exposed to the external environment more than any other nerve cells in our bodies, and like all nerve cells, when they are destroyed, they are not replaced. In our civilization, there are many things that attack them—acid vapors, smog, noxious chemicals, automobile exhaust, and the most ubiquitous of all, tobacco smoke. A child's nose is much more sensitive than an adult's, and a country-dweller's more so than an urbanite's, but given time, all will deteriorate.

The Sense of Taste

Like the sense of smell, taste (or *gustation*) is extremely hard to study, because it is almost impossible to qualify. There really is no way to define a taste objectively. Even subjectively, about the only way to describe a flavor is to compare it with something else, and all that does is compound the subjectivity.

The **taste buds** in humans consist of long, narrow cells clustered around the end of a sensory neuron. Each cell has a series of hairlike ciliary processes that extend out of the taste bud into the interior of the mouth. These are believed to be responsible for detecting the chemical. They are modified epithelial cells, not neuronal cells, and hence are secondary sensory receptors. Taste buds are concentrated on the dorsal surface of the tongue, where there are about two thousand of them. They are present in lesser abundance on the roof of the mouth, where there are scattered patches of them, on the inner surface of the cheeks, and in the upper throat and pharynx (see figures 9.37 and 9.38).

Humans have traditionally been considered to have the ability to detect only four distinct flavors: **sweet, salty, sour,** and **bitter.** In the last few years, additional primary flavors have been suggested, and many workers are inclined to accept at least two of them—**soapy** and **metallic.** Whether or not the **"hot"** flavor so characteristic of spicy Mexican or East Indian food is a primary taste is currently being debated. It certainly can be detected by sensory receptors in the mouth, and it is a chemoreceptive sensation.

It was assumed for years that each primary flavor had a specific receptor that would not respond to any other flavor. More recent work, however, has modified this view. It is now thought that while there are different types of taste buds and that each responds *maximally* to a specific primary flavor, each of them will produce a response to *all* flavors. Nevertheless,

Figure 9.37 (*a*) The surface of the human tongue, showing the surface papillae. (*b*) A diagram of a taste bud, showing the pore at its outer surface through which a flavor may enter.

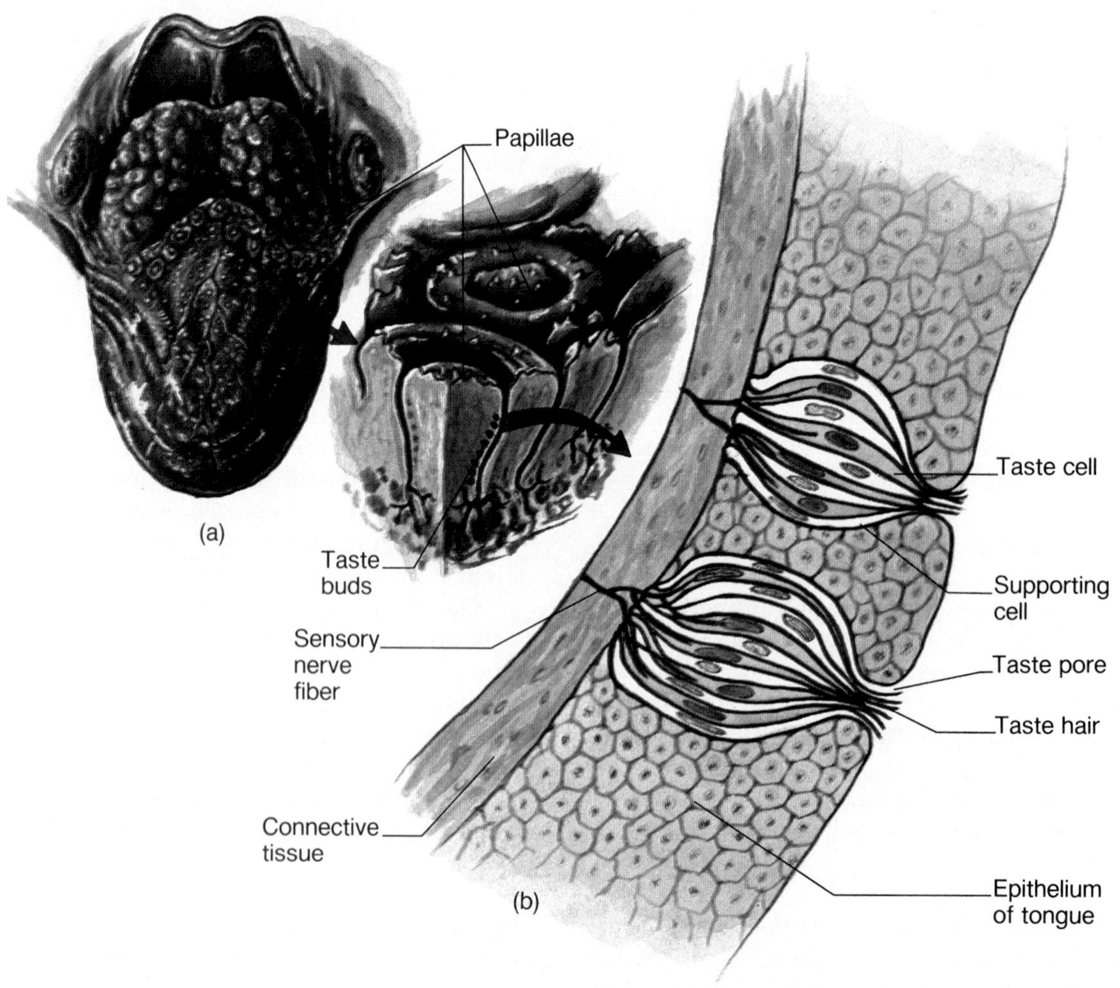

Figure 9.38 A microphotograph of taste buds.

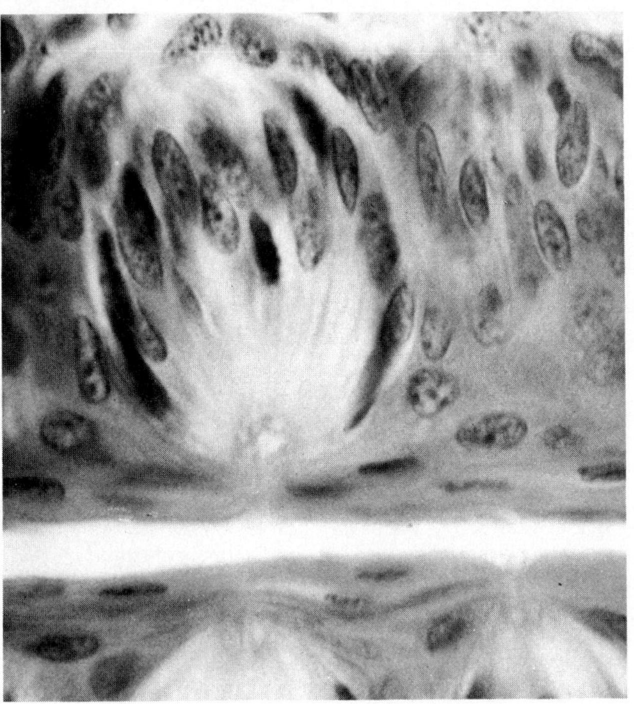

each type responds best to its own adequate stimulus, and workers have found that the types tend to cluster in certain areas. Sweet receptors are clustered on the dorsal surface of the tongue near to, but not on, the tip; salty receptors are on the edges of the tongue running all the way down the sides nearly to the throat; sour receptors (acid detectors) are on the edges and dorsal sides of the tongue, where they share considerable overlap with the salt receptors. The receptors most sensitive to the bitter flavor appear to be at the very back. The receptors that respond strongly to soapy (alkaline) flavors are right on the tip of the tongue, extending a short distance along the sides; then there is a break, and they appear again near the base of the tongue along the sides. Metallic ions are most easily detected along the lateral edges of the tongue, while the flavor known as hot seems to be most powerful on the edges of the tongue, the dorsal surface near the middle, and all along the cheeks. There are also some taste receptors in areas other than the tongue. No one will deny that they can clearly detect sour-tasting materials on their cheeks, and there is no doubt that there are some bitter receptors in the throat (see figure 9.39).

Figure 9.39 Receptor distribution patterns for the six primary flavors. Distribution of: (*a*) Sweet receptors. (*b*) Sour receptors. (*c*) Salty receptors. (*d*) Bitter receptors. (*e*) Soapy receptors. (*f*) Metallic receptors.

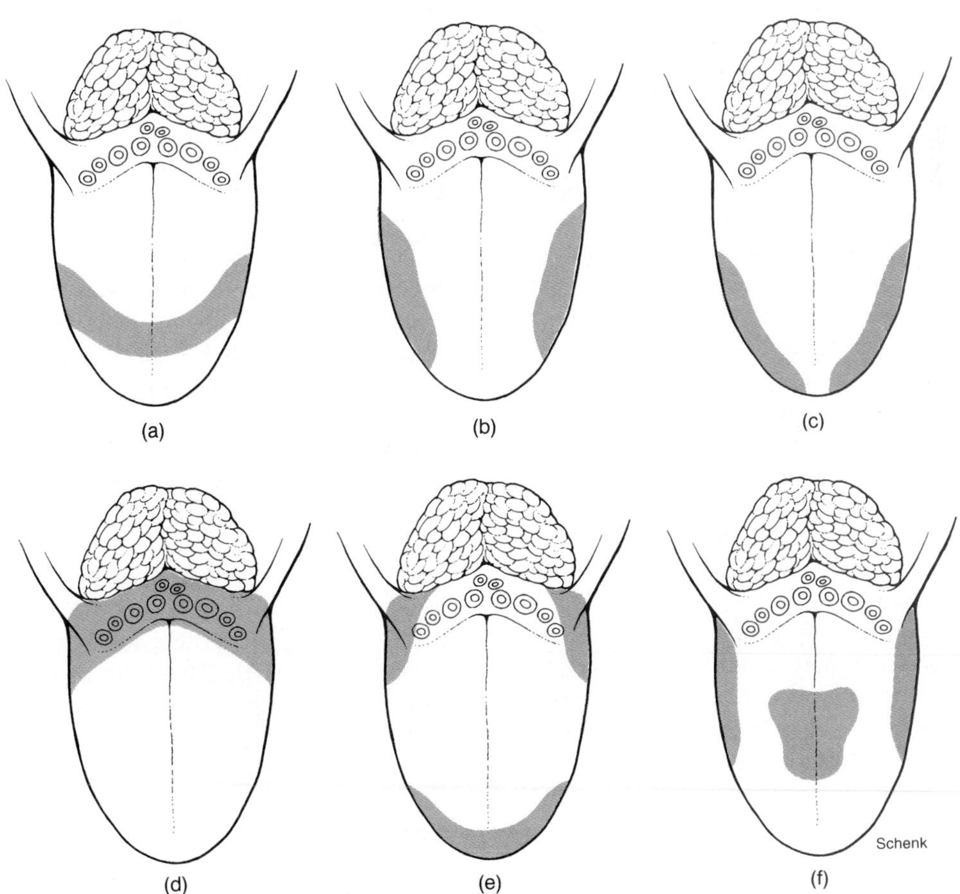

Morphologically, no one has been able to distinguish between sweet taste buds and sour, salty, or bitter, or any other taste buds. They all look the same, and they tend to cluster in mixed groups.

Sensory Innervation of the Tongue

No single cranial nerve is devoted to the taste buds, but there is plenty of innervation, nevertheless. Cranial nerves VII (facial), IX (glossopharyngeal), and X (vagus) are all involved. The facial nerve sends most of its sensory fibers into the apical or tip area of the tongue, while the glossopharyngeal and the vagus handle stimuli in the back and in the pharyngeal area. The information picked up by these nerves is run directly into the brain stem and is collated in the medulla oblongata before being sent into the higher centers for integration.

Taste as a Sense

As far as "taste" itself is concerned, we're dealing with a sensation that is tremendously subjective. Electrophysiological examination of taste buds can indicate whether or not a given flavor will stimulate a particular taste bud, but there is no objective way to evaluate the degree of flavor or to describe a mixture of flavors. The problem is compounded by the heterogeneity of the substances being tasted. Some foods stimulate only one type of taste bud, while others—most others—stimulate several. Sodium chloride is one of the rarer ones. Table salt tastes salty and *only* salty. There are apparently no other flavors mixed into the taste of table salt. This does not appear to be true of any other salty-flavored compound; all the rest seem to have other flavors mixed in. The inorganic salt KCl (potassium chloride), for example, tastes salty, but not as salty as NaCl, and as patients on sodium-free diets will tell anyone who will listen, there is an unpleasant, bitter aftertaste involved with KCl. Another inorganic salt—ammonium chloride (NH_4Cl)—tastes salty too, but this compound has a sour component mixed in with the salty flavor.

Things that are sweet appear to be a little more restrictive, qualitatively. Some are mixtures of other flavors, but many of them are only sweet. They usually differ in intensity of sweetness, however. The sugars fructose, sucrose, and glucose are all sweet sugars, but fructose is much sweeter than sucrose, and both are sweeter than glucose.

Most of the flavors people routinely experience are not merely sweet or salty. Nearly everything we eat is a combination of the primary flavors, and many involve the olfactory sense as well. Onions, for example, are beloved by all kinds of people, yet a person holding her nose cannot taste the difference between a chunk of raw potato and a piece of raw onion unless the onion is "hot." The familiar, distinctive flavor of the onion is heavily involved with the sense of smell.

With all our sophistication and analytical skill, flavors and taste remain almost completely subjective in their qualitative and quantitative characteristics. We can try to make objective evaluations, but they all remain subject to individual judgment. Trying to describe a unique flavor to a friend is extremely hard to do and may be impossible without comparing it to known foods. You might try it and see.

An interesting side note to all this is how other animals perceive various flavors. Cats, for instance, cannot taste sweet. Dogs are able to detect sweet flavors, yet for some reason they can't taste saccharin. Bitter substances will drive dogs half out of their minds, yet they seem only mildly sensitive to the flavor "hot." The new sweetener *aspartame* (sold commercially as Nutrasweet Brand Artificial Sweetener®), which is a combination of two amino acids, is providing some interesting observations. It was predicted that it would be virtually undetectable by cats, and it turns out that it is. This suggests that its sweet flavor is consistent from animal to animal. Yet dogs, which are not universally noted for their love of sweets, are passionately aware of *Nutrasweet* and will do almost anything to obtain it. Most dogs like sweet rolls and cakes, but they are not wild about them, and most don't care for straight sugar, honey, or syrup at all. In view of this, it is interesting to speculate as to what *Nutrasweet's* two amino acids might taste like to dogs. Does it taste sweet to them, or do they love it because it tastes like a particularly succulent cut of amino acid–rich meat? As we have stressed, flavors are subjective, and so we will probably never know.

Proprioceptors

A blindfolded person can easily stretch his hands out in front of him, then bring his hands together and touch the tips of his fingers. A person can close her eyes, stretch her arms out full length beside her, and in a single movement touch the tip of her nose with the index finger. These things are easy to do because we need not look at our limbs to know exactly where they are. We know because of the presence of a group of sensory systems called **proprioceptors** (*propri,* "self"). Proprioceptors are abundant in our voluntary muscles, and while they have considerable afferent input to the central nervous system, we're not conscious of any particular sensations from them. The afferent information is all handled by the CNS without involving our conscious brain at all, and it provides a steady flow of information concerning the position of our muscles. Proprioceptors are perpetual monitors. When a muscle moves, these receptors detect both the amount of change and the rate of change, and they inform the CNS. When muscles aren't moving, the receptors note that fact too, and proceed to record the amount of tension present and any other pertinent facts.

Proprioceptive afferents produce a never-ending stream of information that is integrated continuously and is used to fine-tune muscle movement or muscle tension, even while the individual is already moving. It is the kind of data that is necessary to be absolutely certain the movements will be appropriate to the occasion. When integrated with the input from our semicircular canals, it insures that a person can run without falling, stand or sit without toppling over, and know immediately where all his limbs are without having to check each one visually. Three different specialized receptors are involved in this process, and each has its own unique role to play. They are the **joint receptors,** the **Golgi organs,** and the **muscle spindle receptors.**

The joint receptors are located, as the name implies, in the soft connective tissue of the bone joints, and their job is to indicate the angle of the joint. Their response is slow, but it is precise. They are accurate to within a single degree.

The Golgi organs are present in the tendons that attach muscles to bones, and their adequate stimulus is stretch. It makes no difference whether the stretch is due to active contraction of the muscle or to a passive stretch caused by tension on some other muscle; the tendon organs record the information and pass it on to the CNS. What's more, thanks to their unusual design, they are able to distinguish between a muscle that is actively contracting and one that is passively stretching, and they include these coded data in their output. Obviously this information is essential to proper coordination of body movements, but it may be redundant.

The muscle spindle organs also distinguish between passive stretch and active tension on the muscles they innervate. These organs are imbedded in certain muscles and are arranged in parallel with the fibers they are anchored to (see figure 9.40). This arrangement permits them to stretch and contract along with the big muscle fibers—the **extrafusal fibers**—and in this way to detect and note every change. The spindles are the organs responsible for the familiar **stretch reflex.** When muscles are stretched, it excites the spindle receptor, which reflexly activates motor

Figure 9.40 The muscle proprioceptors. A muscle spindle, which is a modified muscle fiber, shown in position, next to the intrafusal fibers.

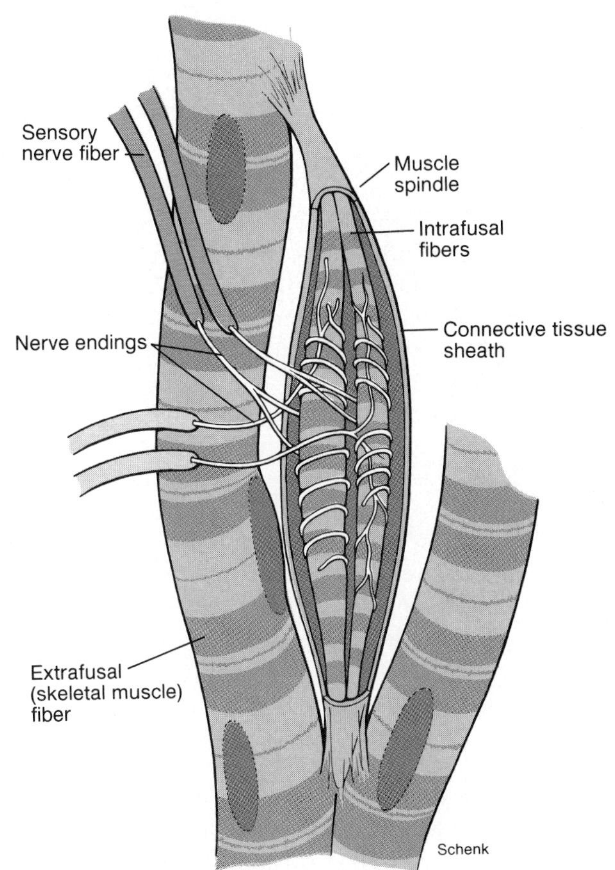

nerves of adjacent muscles, which produce contractions that resist the stretch. Simultaneously, the spindle receptors can activate interneurons nearby, thus inhibiting certain antagonistic muscles. The whole process is designed to achieve the desired amount of movement in any given muscle at any given time. The extrafusal fibers are responsible for changing the length of a given muscle, and the spindle organs are responsible for determining when the muscle has reached the desired length.

Together, all these proprioceptors are able to provide what has been called our *sixth sense*—the **kinesthetic muscle sense**—which furnishes us with automatic awareness of our body position. Without our having to look, our brain knows which muscles are contracted and which are not, the angle formed by each body joint, and the position of our limbs in space—all the information required for normal posture and body movement.

Clinical Considerations

Neural Disorders

When we think of pain, we tend to consider it a most unpleasant sensation; one that should be avoided at all costs. No one likes pain, emotional or physical, and in everyday speech, reference to pain is almost always disparaging.

Yet pain is one of our greatest allies. Far from being an undesirable facet of our existence, it is absolutely necessary for our well-being, and in spite of its unpleasant nature, it really is a critical survival mechanism. People hate being hurt. We avoid pain whenever possible, which means avoiding contact with things that might cause pain—and that, of course, is the point.

Pain indicates either damage or potential damage. It tells us that something very bad for us is happening. It tells us where and warns us that if it continues to happen, we'll probably be worse off for it. Without the sensation, some permanent damage can occur . . . and there are some diseases that will destroy not just pain, but all cutaneous (skin) sensations. They are among the most horrible diseases known to man. The best known of all may be the most feared disease in human history—leprosy.

Other diseases—plague, for instance—have killed more people, and many are more *certain* killers, but since biblical times, leprosy has been universally abhorred, feared, and shunned. Lepers are social outcasts even today. Victims can find neither work nor sociable company, and most are restricted to special colonies—*leprosaria,* as they are called. Fortunately, the incidence of leprosy, if not its severity, has diminished considerably over the years.

Leprosy, the Ultimate Painkiller

The organism responsible for causing leprosy is the only one known that seeks out and specifically attacks peripheral sensory nerves. Usually it destroys them in random patches, leaving behind areas where there are no sensory responses at all. Most people have a vision of lepers with toes and fingers rotting and falling off and huge sores all over their bodies. Sometimes this happens, although the disease is not the direct cause. It is the loss of the ability to feel pain in these areas that results in the horrible mutilation so often seen in leprosy patients.

Few things in this world can so graphically demonstrate the importance of a properly functioning nervous system. With the victims unable to feel pain, damage can occur to feet or hands without their being aware of it. Since they are not aware of it, they do nothing to prevent further damage or infection from occurring. They may have their hand in a mangling piece of machinery, and since they cannot feel anything, they may leave it there, permitting further mutilation to occur. They may suffer a severe burn on the foot, and, unaware of the damage, wander around for a day or so, peeling off damaged or traumatized skin layers and tramping dirt and infectious bacteria into an open, suppurating wound. A leprosy patient must be totally aware of his hands, feet, arms, and legs perpetually. He must make constant checks all the time throughout his life in order to avoid the kind of damage one usually associates with the disease. The number of painful experiences an individual must have during a normal day has staggered physicians who have seen a single day's damage to the limbs of careless leprosy patients.

We are fortunate indeed that the disease is as rare as it is.

Shingles

This is a viral infection of the sensory nerves of the periphery, and it seems to be restricted to people who suffered from *chickenpox* during their childhood. Apparently, in some people the virus is not completely eliminated from their bodies when they recover from chickenpox, and it lies dormant within them for years, probably nestled somewhere in the ganglia or the fiber bundles of peripheral sensory nerves. When it finally emerges, it assaults those ganglia and neuronal membranes, causing inflammation and concomitant pain in sensory root ganglia, the meninges, and the dorsal roots of the spinal cord. Usually the infection runs outward to the skin and is gone in a month or so. Occasionally, however, it spreads in toward the motor centers in the spinal cord, infecting the posterior horn of the gray matter and the ventral roots. In such cases, it can cause paralysis.

Eye Disorders

Trachoma

There are several infectious agents that attack the eyes. Probably the greatest cause of blindness in the world today is a disease called **trachoma** that is caused by an agent that is neither a virus nor a bacterium but is somewhere between the two. Since no one has given a name to forms such as this, it is referred to simply as an "agent." It is spread by contact and is most prevalent in areas of the world where personal hygiene is generally ignored. The organism attacks epithelial cells of the conjunctiva, causing reddening and swelling of the surface of the eye. If it is not treated rapidly, secondary bacterial infections usually begin, and the resultant scarring of the cornea leads to blindness.

Pink Eye

Pink eye, or **conjunctivitis** as it is more properly known, is, as the name implies, an inflammation of the conjunctiva. The most common causes are cold viruses, common bacteria, and occasionally, allergies. Fifty years ago, the disease was extremely painful, lasted about two weeks, and, because it is extremely infectious, usually necessitated the quarantine of the victim. Furthermore, its incidence in summer months was very high, particularly around public swimming pools. Chlorination of the water in public pools has eliminated these as an infection source, and while the disease is still pretty painful when it first takes hold, antibiotics can control it so effectively and so rapidly that quarantine is unnecessary.

Cataract

Eye infections are not as great a threat to sight as are functional disorders of the eye, and one of the most common of these is **cataract.** The name refers to a slowly developing loss of transparency in the lens. When the lens becomes opaque, light can't get through to stimulate the retinal layers behind it, and the individual becomes, for all practical purposes, blind. Sometimes its cause can be traced to an infection, but in the U.S., this is very rare. Usually it is a degenerative problem associated with old age. It is characterized by gradual, progressive loss of vision, and its opacity is so obvious that it can be seen clearly by observers as a gray blob in the middle of the pupil.

Replacing a natural lens that has become opaque has produced some unexpected results, particularly in the early days of the procedure. The replacement lenses were carefully crafted to be as much like the original as possible, but every once in a while, both the craftsman and the physician would forget the yellow tint. The result was more than a little surprising to all concerned. Because most of the patients were in, or past, their middle years, their own lenses were heavily tinted, and most had forgotten what the more exotic shades of purple looked like. Suddenly seeing them again was overwhelming, and there was a trend among all of these patients to fill their lives with things that were blue and purple. Even more interesting was the fact that many of them could actually *see* colors in the violet part of the spectrum that are invisible to even the youngest children. Vision in this ultraviolet range was imperfect because of chromatic aberrations, and so the images perceived were reported to have been fuzzy-edged and rather blurred, but their surfaces were "incredibly colored and unusually reflective."

Patients in whom a cataract is developing can be treated with vitamin C. The vitamin C concentration in the lens is thirty times what it is elsewhere in the body, and supplemental doses substantially slow the progress of cataract development. Should preventive therapy prove useless, surgery is indicated, and it usually consists of removing the affected lens and replacing it with a prosthetic lens.

Glaucoma

Glaucoma is also a functional problem, a disorder resulting from an increase in pressure in the anterior chamber of the eye (see figure 9.9). The cause is a narrowing or obstructing of Schlemm's canal, a small opening in the cornea near the outer edge of the iris. The aqueous humor that fills the anterior chamber of the eye normally circulates from where it is formed in the ciliary bodies, into the anterior chamber and out through Schlemm's canal. Normally, the rate of outflow equals its rate of formation, and pressure in all eye chambers is about equal. Any kind of obstruction in Schlemm's canal, however, means that the fluid cannot run out of the anterior chamber as quickly as it is formed, and pressure in the chamber goes up rapidly. Symptoms begin with a decrease in the patient's angle of vision, which means that his or her ability to see peripheral objects—objects at the edge of the visual field—diminishes. Eventually, if it is untreated, or if treatments fail, the eye becomes blind. This is a blindness due to damage to the head of the optic nerve, and once it has happened, nothing will restore sight in the afflicted eye. Obviously then, the sooner treatment is begun, the better. Anything that is able to open Schlemm's canal and thus relieve the pressure is indicated, and there are several drugs available that will do this. In cases where all else has failed, researchers have discovered that *tetrahydrocannibol* will sometimes alleviate the problem. To this end, it has become legal for certain patients, under special doctor's orders, to obtain and smoke marijuana.

Refractive Disorders

By far the most common visual disorders involve light refraction, and **myopia** or nearsightedness is the bane of young people in this country. The cause is one of two things. Either the eyeball is a little longer than it should be (see figure 9.41) or the lens or cornea is a little thicker than is optimum. Whatever the cause, the result is that the image entering the eyeball focuses in front of the retina, and the image that the retina receives is therefore blurred. It is easily corrected by a biconcave lens (figure 9.41). **Hyperopia** or farsightedness occurs a little less frequently than myopia, but it is not what one would call rare. It is usually a result of a foreshortened eyeball, but occasionally the cornea or the lens is too thin. The image

Figure 9.41 The most common visual afflictions and their corrective lenses.

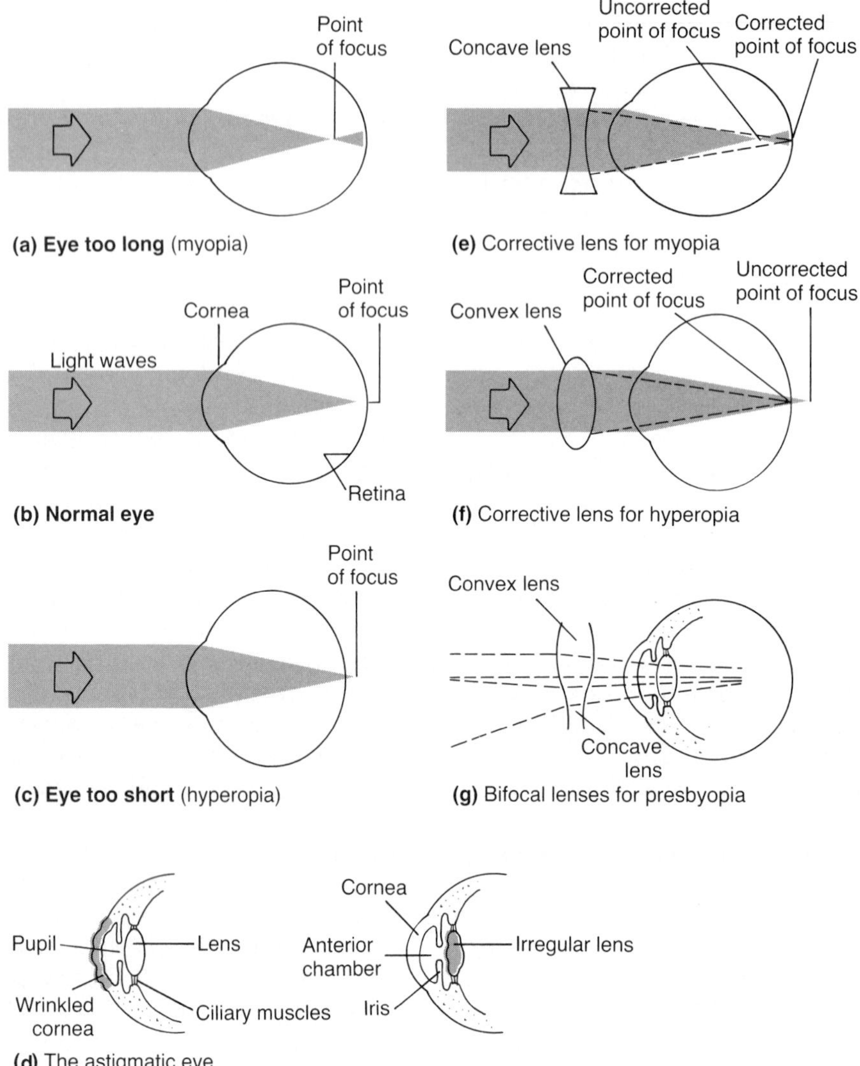

focuses *behind* the retina, and once again, the image that falls on the retina is blurred. Convex lenses will correct this condition.

Often the lens or the cornea becomes wrinkled or irregularly shaped, which means the eye will not be able to see a complete, focused image. Because of the irregular refractive pattern, part of the image is always out of focus. The affliction is known as **astigmatism,** and it is not unusual for a person to be myopic and astigmatic or hyperopic and astigmatic. It is unfortunate that it is so common, because it is a difficult condition to correct. Contact lenses apparently do a better job of correcting minor astigmatism than standard glasses do.

Age has debilitating effects on the eye as, indeed, it has on everything. As we know, it tends to intensify the yellow tint in the lens. In addition, as the years pass, the lens becomes gradually more rigid, rendering it progressively harder for the ciliary muscles to change its shape. A person's ability to focus on close images deteriorates along with it. A 9-year-old child can often see objects held only an inch or so away from the eyeball, whereas a 25-year-old won't focus clearly at distances much closer than about eight inches. By the time one reaches the age of 40, the lens has become even stiffer and is usually not able to focus on objects as nearby as two or three feet. By the age of 50, the lens of the average person's eye has gotten so rigid that it is almost impossible to adjust it very much; the person wakes up to find that his eye has a fixed focus and he is unable to focus on items that are either distant or close at hand. The condition is known as **presbyopia,** and if we live long enough it appears to be inevitable. It is the reason for the existence of *bifocal*—sometimes even *trifocal*—glasses. Such lenses are designed to concede the inflexibility of the lens and to provide two other zones of focus artificially. The top of the lens usually is slightly convex, to concentrate on things that are some distance away, while the semicircle along the bottom of the glasses is concave to permit focusing on objects nearby.

Disorders of the Ear

Sooner or later, almost everyone will suffer from at least one earache, and the most frequent cause, particularly in children, is infection. It does not take much of an infection to produce severe pain. For this reason, specialists warn constantly about blowing one's nose through a single nostril while holding the other, particularly when advising children on health procedures. Upper respiratory infections often invade the pharyngeal area, and the eustachian tubes connect the middle ear to the pharynx. Usually these tubes slope slightly downward from the ear to the pharynx, so that materials tend to run *from* the ear into the throat, not the reverse. However, increasing pressure in the pharynx by blowing one's nose can sometimes thrust materials back up the eustachian tubes and into the middle ear, where cold viruses or streptococci find a haven. As infection progresses, fluid accumulates in the middle ear, pressure builds up, the tympanic membrane gets inflamed, and the pain becomes intense.

Antibiotics are often effective in fighting off these infections, since they are usually bacterial, and as the pain and pressure disappear, much of the accumulated exudate runs from the ear down the eustachian tubes into the throat and is disposed of. In young children, however, the eustachian tubes are often horizontal or have very little slope downward into the pharynx. When this is the case, even the slightest inflammation will prevent the fluid from running out of the ear. It simply accumulates, gradually building up pressure within. The child complains of frequent headaches, and before long, parents begin to notice their child isn't paying attention to what they are saying. If they are alert, they will spot the fact that hearing is diminishing.

Treatment consists of administration of decongestants to help open the eustachian tubes, and this usually works. If it doesn't, and the tympanic membrane is actually bulging into the auditory meatus because of the pressure in the middle ear, surgery is often recommended to relieve the pressure and restore normal hearing. The surgery is simple, consisting of inserting a couple of very small teflon tubes through the tympanic membrane into the middle ear (called a **myringotomy**) to drain off the fluid. Ultimately, the tubes fall out, the membrane heals, and as the child grows, the eustachian tubes assume the adult position, running downward into the pharynx and reducing the probability of a recurrence.

Hearing Loss Due to Noise: Nerve Deafness

One of the toughest commands a parent can give to a modern child is *"turn down the stereo."* Yet it is a command that should be given, and care should be taken to warn teenagers of the danger of loud noises . . . not that such warnings would do any good.

Modern "rock" music is invariably run through huge amplifiers and blasts out of rock concert loudspeakers at volumes between 110 and 120 decibels. Teenagers purchase powerful amplifiers and audio equipment, and even if parents can get them to turn down the stereo, they will often clap a pair of earphones on their heads and continue to blast the noises into their ears. *Any* intense noise can cause irreparable damage to the inner ear. Sounds of 85 db or higher will sooner or later damage a person's ability to hear, no matter who they are. The lower frequencies disappear first, and afflicted teenagers often will play music with the bass turned up so loudly that people with normal hearing can barely hear the treble notes. Such hearing loss is known professionally as **sensorineural deafness,** because the damage that is done has been done to the nerve. It is usually accompanied by a sustained, shrill noise that only the victim can hear—a condition known as **tinnitus.**

Since the damage is done to receptor mechanisms in the inner ear, there is really no cure. Prevention is the key, but young people, intent on hearing their music and certain that nothing bad can ever happen to *them*, seldom consider that. It's a problem that will almost certainly plague us increasingly with time.

Conductive Deafness

As with the eyes, age gradually steals away various aspects of our sense of hearing. The most common form of hearing loss in this country is known as **conductive deafness** and involves the bones of the middle ear. The problem begins with the deposition of calcium salts at joints between the ear bones (**otosclerosis**), usually between the incus and the stapes. As these salts build up, they slowly render the bones less and less mobile, and hearing gradually disappears, often so slowly that the victim does not realize it is happening.

The most common remedy is the "hearing aid." These are usually small electrical mechanisms designed to accept airborne sonic vibrations and transfer them onto the bones of the skull—usually the mastoid bone just behind the ear. This bypasses the inoperative ossicles. Since the auditory nerve and the receptors inside the cochlea are all working nicely, all these hearing aids have to do is amplify the sound a little bit and impress it onto the skull bones, where the receptors can pick it up.

A more permanent way to correct the problem is with microsurgery, which consists of removing one of the affected ossicles—usually the incus—and replacing it with a prosthesis.

Age will often reduce a person's ability to hear high-frequency sounds, and workers in nursing homes and geriatric hospitals are instructed to address patients in tones as low as possible. Such routine hearing losses emphasize why sensorineural deafness may be a huge problem in forty or fifty years. Remember that when hearing loss results from continual loud noise, it is usually the lower frequencies that disappear first. An aging person who is already suffering from sensorineural deafness might become completely deaf when age steals the higher frequencies as well.

Motion Sickness

The built-in ability to detect accelerations coupled with man's ability to build automotive devices has, unfortunately, produced a nasty and unique affliction. Motion sickness is due mainly to our inability to correlate conflicting sensory input associated with movement. When on board ship, for example, whether enclosed in our cabins or out on deck, things appear stationary and homelike to our eyes. Our organs of equilibrium, however, are informing our brains that things are *not* stationary . . . that we are moving up and down, and from side to side. We feel this motion clearly, but intellectually we try to ignore it because we know that's the way it is supposed to be and everything is OK. Nevertheless, despite what we feel and know, our eyes keep telling us that we are *not* moving, and we are, after all, visual animals. All our instincts tell us to trust our eyes before any other senses. The resultant imbalance upsets our central perception, and we wind up seasick. Sometimes, if we get sick in our cabins, we can straighten things out by going on deck—not for the fresh air, as most people think, but to watch the horizon or the waves that are causing the boat's motion. Usually this does not help. The motion we see still doesn't agree with the motion we can feel and since we can't reconcile the conflicting inputs, we get terribly sick. But every once in a while, we may get lucky. The visual input agrees with the vestibular, and we are able to avoid the problem. Some people are better at this than others. These hateful people never seem to get seasick, although we are told everyone is susceptible. Conversation with those who are apparently immune seems to indicate that determination helps a lot. Most of them are aware of the cause, and they try very hard to understand what is going on. Whatever they do, it seems to work, for the same people always seem able to avoid motion sickness no matter how rough the voyage.

Disorders of the Nose

Probably the most common nasal problem in young children is the presence of some foreign object the youngster has jammed into a nostril and cannot get out. They can't tell a parent what they've done and the object stays where it is, gradually accumulating a coating of mineral salts and forming a boney capsule called a **rhinolith.** Usually the first hint a parent has that something is really wrong is a bloody, foul-smelling discharge, and the hint that one is dealing with a rhinolith and not a sinus infection or a bad cold is that the discharge comes from only a single nostril. Attempts to pull these things out with forceps usually just shove them further in, because they tend to conform to the shape of the nostril, so parents should be advised never to attempt it. Physicians have special instruments to handle such problems, and usually the removal is so painful that anesthetic is required, even in adults.

Nosebleed (Epistaxis)

Nosebleeds, as we all know, are very common and sometimes occur for no apparent reason. Bleeding nearly always is from a large mat or network of blood vessels just in front of the bony septum in the middle of the nose. Usually it can be stopped by pinching the upper nostrils for two or three minutes. Sometimes, however, it does not stop, and that's when a physician's help is required. The damaged site must be found, and when it is, it is usually cauterized to stop the bleeding. Usually in a young, healthy person, nosebleeds do not indicate a serious problem, but in people with hypertension or arteriosclerosis it often does. Such patients generally bleed from very high in the nose, and the bleeding is very hard to control, often requiring minor surgery and ligation of the ruptured vessels.

Colds (Rhinitis)

Colds are the most common upper respiratory tract infections, and the nose is the area that seems to be most prominently involved. The greatest misery that seems to emanate from the common cold is the familiar "plugged nose" and sinuses with the concomitant heavy drainage, constant nose-blowing, and the raw, red upper lip and external nares. There is nothing much that can be done to cure this affliction, and there is an old adage that's as true today as it was when it was coined years ago: "take good care of your cold and it'll go away in fourteen days. If you do nothing for it, it will take two weeks to go away."

There are some modern remedies that sometimes will reduce a few of the symptoms. Aspirin will help alleviate aches and pains. Some decongestants work. Alcohol, in the form of an ounce of whiskey or the like before bed, will often help the patient sleep, but nasal sprays and patent medicine "cold tablets" and "cold capsules" are generally worthless. The nasal sprays in particular are cautioned against because of their familiar "rebound" effect.

Sinusitis

Rebound occurs when homeostatic mechanisms try to adjust to an artificially induced abnormality. Nasal sprays cause powerful vasoconstriction in the sinuses and nasal cavities. The body's homeostatic mechanisms fight this effect by bombarding blood vessels in the area with instructions to dilate. When the spray's effects wear off, the homeostatic instructions are unopposed, and the resultant sudden vasodilation causes an exaggerated tissue engorgement in all the affected areas. Often, the rebound effect is worse symptomatically than the original cold-caused congestion.

Infections of the nasal sinuses are almost always bacterial invasions precipitated by a viral cold or the "flu." They almost always cause terrible headaches, and sometimes the pain is so intense that it is referred to the mouth, and patients feel like they have a toothache as well. Treatment usually consists of improving sinus drainage and getting rid of the bacteria causing the problem. Antibiotics and decongestants are dependable and ordinarily give fairly quick relief, but it's important to realize that bacteria often lay dormant in the sinuses and can reappear quickly. When antibiotic therapy is initiated, it is highly advisable to continue it for at least ten days.

Anosmia

Anosmia is the complete loss of the sense of smell. In the past, it was a rare problem, but with increased "snorting" of euphoric drugs by middle- and upper-class Americans, it has become rather common. It is not uncommon among chronic users of drugs like cocaine, amphetamines, or PCP (sernalyn), and sometimes it seems to be linked to tobacco, particularly if the patient smokes strong tobaccos in pipes or cigars and is given to exhaling the smoke through his nose. If drugs are not involved, far more often than not, the cause is never determined.

A chronic problem with the elderly can sometimes be caused by anosmia. Elderly people often have lost their sense of smell, and because of that, food tastes bland and becomes less and less appealing to them. Frequently, the biggest problem gerontologists must face is trying to get their elderly patients to eat enough to maintain themselves. To this end, it is suggested that their meals be made as visually attractive as possible.

Mouth Disorders

Very little is known about the pathology of taste buds, probably because the sense of taste is lost so slowly that patients do not realize it when it is gone. The feeding problem in elderly people suffering from complete or partial anosmia is, of course, exacerbated by a gradual loss of sensation in the taste buds.

Bad Breath

Foul-smelling breath is a problem that's more often imaginary than real. Mouthwash purveyors use all kinds of gimmicks to get people to use their products, but most enticements or warnings are pure hogwash. Few people need a mouthwash, and blaming bacteria in the mouth for "everyday bad breath" is nonsense. Even if true, no mouthwash would alleviate it for more than a few seconds, because any bacteria killed by the mouthwash are reestablished in the mouth with the first lick of the lips.

Occasionally, chronic bad breath is real, but unfortunately it will not be helped by mouthwash. It almost always has some deep-seated underlying cause that sweet-smelling "breath purifiers" only mask. Dental problems, tonsillitis, or sinus infections are often the cause, and occasionally disorders in the chest such as lung abcesses will produce a putrid odor. If a patient exudes a powerful odor of mouthwash every time he or she visits the doctor, an alert physician will often seek to discover why the patient is so concerned about bad breath.

Summary

Receptors

Receptors help to maintain homeostasis. They accept information from the environment (internal and external) and transduce it into electrical signal. There are various classifications of receptors:

I. Functional Classification. Receptors are categorized according to the type of energy they accept.
   A. Mechanoreceptors accept movement or distortion.
   B. Chemoreceptors accept and analyze chemical energy.
   C. Photoreceptors accept electromagnetic radiation in the visible spectrum.
   D. Thermoreceptors detect changes in temperature.

II. Perceptive Classification
   A. Cutaneous receptors. These receptors respond to contact stimuli.
   B. Proprioceptors. These receptors respond to stretch and tension.
   C. Special receptors. These receptors respond to specific stimuli. They are the eyes, ears, nose, and taste buds.

III. Adequate Stimulus. Adequate stimulus is the type of energy for which a given receptor is specialized.
   A. The Law of Specific Nerve Energy. This law states that an individual sensory system has a specific function and will serve only that function.
   B. Mode (Sensation). A receptor's mode is the sensation quality perceived by that receptor. Eyes perceive light, ears perceive sound. The eyes can be stimulated by things other than light, but they cannot feel nor hear. The quality of a sensation cannot be changed, but the intensity can.
   C. The Weber-Fechner Law
      Sensitivity is a measure of a receptor's ability to detect. Selectivity is a measure of a receptor's ability to discriminate.

IV. Receptive Fields. Selectivity depends on the number of nerve fibers present in a given area. The region on the skin surface that a given neuron innervates is called that nerve's receptive field.

V. Lateral Inhibition. Perceptive acuity can sometimes be enhanced by lateral inhibition.

VI. Adaptation. Receptors can "get used to" a particular stimulus. This phenomenon is known as adaptation.
   A. Phasic receptors respond maximally to change. They respond only fleetingly to constant values.
   B. Tonic receptors respond maximally to change but produce good responses to absolute stimuli as well.

VII. Proprioceptors. These receptors are involved in "deep" sensation.

The Cutaneous Sensations

Receptors in the skin can respond to heat, cold, tickle, vibration, touch, pressure, and pain. Collectively, these are known as the somatovisceral senses.

I. Touch and Pressure
   A. Mechanoreceptors in the skin detect tickle, vibration, touch, and pressure. These receptors are all morphologically highly specialized.
   B. Tickle, touch, vibration, and pressure receptors all respond to qualitatively similar stimuli. Each type can also detect quantitatively different stimuli.
   C. Vibration is detected by receptors with extremely high adaptability.
   D. Pressure is detected by receptors with extremely low adaptability.
   E. Meissner's corpuscles perceive mainly tickle.
   F. Pacinian corpuscles perceive mainly pressure and vibration.
   G. Ruffini's end organs and the bulbs of Krause are both involved in the perception of deep pressure and intense pressure.
   H. Merkel's disks are touch/intensity receptors.

II. Nonspecialized Receptors. These are the free nerve endings. In perception of contact, they are the most sensitive.
   A. Thermal Receptors. Naked nerve endings can respond to both increases and decreases in the skin surface temperature; thus they are both heat and cold receptors. They have no specialized structures. They respond most powerfully to changes in temperature. But they also provide information about absolute temperature values. Thermal receptors are distributed all across the skin surface.
   B. Pain and Painful Stimuli. Pain is detected by receptor endings called nociceptors. These receptors have no obvious specialized structures but appear to be free nerve endings. Pain has an important homeostatic function in that it warns of occurring or impending damage.

Input From a Distance: The Special Senses

I. The Eye. The eye provides humans with probably 75 percent of all sensory input. Light enters the eye through the cornea. It passes the iris and penetrates into the interior by passing through the pupil. The pupil adjusts the amount of light that enters the interior by expanding or contracting, as the situation demands.
   A. Eye Color. There is only one pigment involved in producing various eye colors. The variation perceived is due to the distribution of this pigment.
   B. Inside the Eyeball
      1. Physiologically, the eye is designed to accept and process light beams that enter the eye from distant objects.
      2. Light enters the eye and is bent slightly. The lens is pulled or relaxed to bend the beams so that they focus precisely on the retina. This ability is called accommodation.

3. The retina contains the photoreceptors that are responsible for transducing the electromagnetic energy into electrical signals that the brain can perceive and interpret.
4. The receptors are either rods or cones.

The Photoreceptors

The light that is arranged on the retina changes the characteristics of certain chemicals that initiate the production of neural responses.

I. Rods. Rods are responsible for our ability to see in dim light.

II. Cones. Cones provide us with color vision and visual acuity.

Visual Perception

I. Visual Pigments. Pigment colors are determined by the wavelengths they reflect or transmit.

II. Rod Vision

A. Rods possess a chemical called rhodopsin that is derived from vitamin A and is sensitive to very low levels of illumination. Rhodopsin is composed of a protein, scotopsin, and a pigment called retinene.

B. Chemical Amplification

1. Rods are tiny chemical amplifiers. They are capable of responding to a single photon of light and, through amplification, can make the brain aware of it. Rod vision is fairly good when a rod is struck by only one photon every ten seconds.
2. When light strikes the visual chemicals, they split into their components and initiate the electrical response in the receptor cell.
3. When the stimulus is over, the retinene and scotopsin are reassembled into rhodopsin once again, and the chemical is ready for another stimulus.
4. Splitting of rhodopsin is known as bleaching.
5. When the eyeball is dark, there is a steady flow of both K and Na current through the membrane of the receptor cells. The membrane potential is only about −20 mv. Bleaching of rhodopsin hyperpolarizes the receptor.
6. Waves of slow potential change spread across the receptor cell and the cell with which it synapses—the bipolar cell. Both the receptor and the bipolar cell are capable only of slow potential changes. The ganglion cells are the only cells within the retina that fire action potentials.

III. Cone Vision. Cones have different chemicals available that respond to light beams. They are called erythrolabe, chlorolabe, and cyanolabe and are sensitive to red, green, and blue wavelengths, respectively. Each cone possesses only one such chemical. Like rhodopsin, each of these breaks down into a protein and a pigment. The pigment—retinene—is the same in all the visual chemicals. The scotopsin is different in each.

IV. Binocular (Stereoscopic) Vision. Our visual anatomy is such that when objects are less than twenty-five feet away, we can see them in three dimensions.

V. The Pathway to the Brain

A. The optic nerve is formed by the axons of the retinal ganglion cells.

B. The Optic Chiasma

1. The optic nerves cross over at a point just beneath the hypothalamus. This crossover point is called the optic chiasma.
2. After passing through the optic chiasma, the optic nerves become the optic tract. The optic tract enters the brain.
3. Some optic neurons synapse with neurons in the thalamus. Others continue through the thalamus and make connections with neurons in the visual cortex.

The Ear and Hearing

The ear is responsible for detection of sound and maintaining equilibrium.

I. Some Aural Anatomy. Structurally, the ear consists of three separate regions: the external ear (pinnae, auditory meatus, and tympanic membrane); the middle ear (ossicles, oval window, round window, and eustachian tube); and the inner ear (cochlea, labyrinth).

II. Function

A. The External Ear. The function of the pinnae in humans is unclear, but it is thought to focus the sound waves to some extent. Sound waves pass the pinnae and enter the auditory meatus. The waves travel through the auditory meatus and strike the tympanic membrane, causing it to vibrate.

B. The Middle Ear. These vibrations are amplified by the middle ear ossicles and are transfered to inner ear through the oval window. The amplification factor is adjustable over a fairly wide range, and depends on the amplitude of the soundwaves entering.

III. Sound Perception: The Inner Ear

A. The Cochlea

1. The cochlea of the inner ear is filled with fluid called perilymph. When the oval window vibrates, it creates pressure waves in the perilymph. These pressure waves cause the round window at the other end of the cochlea to move in accord.
2. The same pressure waves cause the basilar membrane in the cochlea to move back and forth.

B. The Auditory Receptors. When the basilar membrane moves, the cilia on the surface of the hair cells are distorted (stretched). This distortion is the adequate stimulus for the hair cells. Slow potential changes result from this displacement.

IV. Hearing as a Sense. Hearing may be a human's second most important sense.

V. The Pathway Into the Brain. Sounds are processed in the auditory cortex of the brain. Crossover permits comparison of stimulus intensity from each ear.

Equilibrium

The semicircular canals, the utricle, and the saccule are the organs of equilibrium. They are located in the inner ear.

I. Static Equilibrium. Static equilibrium is monitored by special sensory cells in the saccule and the utricle.
II. Dynamic Equilibrium. Dynamic equilibrium (motion) is monitored mainly by sensory cells in the semicircular canals.
III. The "Tilt" Receptors. The sensory cells, called hair cells, are secondary receptors. Stretching of their cilia produces either slow depolarizations or slow hyperpolarizations, depending on the direction of stretch. Information concerning motion and balance is integrated in the brain and is used to coordinate walking and other day-to-day movements.

Chemoreceptive Senses

I. The Olfactory Sense (Smell)
  A. Morphology. Chemicals in the air enter the olfactory region through the external nostrils (external nares). They travel across the olfactory epithelium high up in the nose, then down into the pharynx through the internal nares. The information is sent through the olfactory bulb into the hypothalamus, the thalamus, the brain stem, and parts of the cortex.
  B. Odor as a Sense. The sense of smell is a primary sense, yet almost nothing is known of it. In most mammals, it provides nearly as much sensory input as vision. In humans, it is relatively undeveloped.
  C. Analysis of Odors. The coding of odor variation is largely unknown. Several theories have been offered to account for different olfactory identities.
    1. The Shape Hypothesis. This theory suggests that odors vary according to molecular shape.
    2. The Vibrational Theory. This theory suggests that the amplitude and range of molecular vibration determine its olfactory identity.
II. The Sense of Taste
  A. The gustatory receptor cells are in taste buds on the surface of the tongue. It is hypothesized that there are specialized receptors each designed to receive one primary flavor.
  B. There are at least four primary flavors, and there may be as many as seven. It is generally agreed that sweet, salty, sour, and bitter are primary flavors. Many researchers argue that soapy and metallic are also primary flavors. Some feel that "hot" as in "spicy" or "peppery hot" is also a primary flavor.
  C. Sensory Innervation of the Tongue. Three cranial nerves are involved in the transmission of taste. The VII (facial), the IX (glossopharyngeal), and the X (vagus) all have sensory fibers in the surface of the tongue. Fibers from these nerves run into the brain stem, and information is integrated in the medulla before proceeding to the cortex.
  D. Taste as a Sense. Flavors are usually combinations of the primary flavors, plus some olfactory input. Perception and interpretation of taste is almost purely subjective.

Proprioceptors

Proprioceptors are designed to permit the conscious brain to know the position of the limbs and muscles without having to use vision to locate them. There are three different kinds of proprioceptors: the joint receptors, the Golgi organs, and the muscle spindle receptors.

I. Joint receptors. Joint receptors are in the soft tissue of bone joints. They detect the angle of the joint.
II. Golgi organs. Golgi organs are in tendons; they respond to stretch. They tell when there is tension on a muscle.
III. Muscle Spindle Organs. Muscle spindle organs distinguish between active stretch (tension due to a contracted muscle) and passive stretch (tension due to a stretched muscle). They are protective in nature. When a muscle is being stretched abnormally, the spindle receptors can activate motor nerves that stimulate fibers to resist the stretch, thus preventing a muscle tear.

Clinical Considerations

I. General Neural Disorders
  A. Leprosy, the Ultimate Painkiller
  B. Shingles
II. Eye Disorders
  A. Trachoma
  B. Pink Eye
  C. Cataract
  D. Glaucoma
  E. Refractive Disorders
III. Disorders of the Ear
  A. Hearing Loss Due to Noise
  B. Conductive Deafness
  C. Motion Sickness
IV. Disorders of the Nose
  A. Nosebleed
  B. Colds
  C. Sinusitis
  D. Anosmia
V. Mouth Disorders
  Bad Breath

Review Questions

1. What is the difference between primary sensory receptors and secondary sensory receptors?
2. Identify various kinds of receptors and discuss the significance of their classification.
3. Define the term *adequate stimulus.*
4. What is the Law of Specific Nerve Energy?
5. What is a mode? How does it differ from adequate stimulus?
6. Distinguish between selectivity and sensitivity.
7. What is the Weber-Fechner law?
8. Define the following:
   a. receptive field
   b. lateral inhibition
   c. adaptation
   d. phasic receptors
   e. tonic receptors
9. Identify and describe the cutaneous receptors. Be sure to mention those responsible for detecting:
   a. touch
   b. vibration
   c. tickle
   d. heat and cold
   e. pain
10. Draw a longitudinal section of a human eyeball, naming all the important structures.
11. Trace the path of a beam of light entering the eyeball. Name the structures through which it must pass, and mention how each structure attenuates, modifies, or amplifies the light beam.
12. How many different eye-color pigments are there? Explain.
13. Name the types of visual receptors present in the retina of the eye. Discuss their major differences.
14. Name the visual pigments. Which is present in the rods?
15. Discuss the chemical process of rod stimulation. What effect does this have on the electrical characteristics of these receptors?
16. Describe the process of chemical amplification as it occurs in the retina of the eye.
17. Name the cone pigments.
18. Discuss the phenomenon known as stereoscopic vision.
19. What route do the retinal nerve fibers follow into the brain?
20. Through what brain structures does the optic nerve pass? What is its ultimate destination?
21. Draw a schematic diagram of the entire ear of a human being. Be sure to include:
   a. the external ear
   b. the middle ear
   c. the internal ear
22. Broadly discuss the function of each of these three parts of the ear.
23. Discuss in detail the structure and properties of the middle ear.
24. Where does the middle ear end and the inner ear begin? Draw a section of the inner ear.
25. Trace the progress of a sound wave through the organs of the inner ear. Be sure to diagram the receptor cells of the inner ear and be able to discuss their operation.
26. Trace the pathway of electrical impulses along the auditory branch of the eighth cranial nerve from the cochlea to the auditory cortex.
27. Name the two organs of equilibrium that are present in the inner ear.
28. Discuss the function of the utricle and saccule.
29. What is the function of the semicircular canals? Discuss.
30. Draw a section of the receptive area of the nose. Where, in the skull, are the receptive cells located?
31. What is the function of the sustentacular cells? Describe the perception of an odor.
32. What are the two major theories of scent differentiation?
33. Name the primary flavors that are classically accepted. What are the latest additions to this list?
34. Describe the sensory innervation of the tongue.
35. Identify and describe the function of the body's proprioceptors.

Chapter 10 The Endocrine System

Study Hints

The endocrine system is the second of the two major control systems in humans, the nervous system being the other. Like the nervous system, it strives to maintain homeostasis by speeding up or slowing down certain systems and by modifying behavior as necessary. When reading the chapter, do so with an understanding that while both systems employ neurochemical transmission, the endocrine system tends to rely more on chemicals to communicate and control, while the nervous system concentrates on electrical methods of communication.

1. Pay particular attention to what constitutes an endocrine gland.
2. Be sure you understand just how it is that endocrine glands manage to control other mechanisms. Remember that control of an organ's function usually means controlling some aspect of cellular operations within that organ.
3. Try to realize that behavior is merely another mechanism designed to maintain internal homeostasis. The only exception is sexual behavior, and even that, in a way, represents homeostasis within a species.
4. There are two major types of hormones. You may or may not be required to learn the chemical structures of these types, but you should certainly remember the group of compounds that each belongs in.
5. One important aspect of the activity of an endocrine gland is the mechanism that controls its secretions. *Pay particular attention to secretory regulation.*
6. This chapter will emphasize *feedback loops.* If you did not understand them before reading this chapter, be sure you do when you're finished with it. You cannot possibly understand the regulation of endocrine function without understanding the basics of feedback loops.
7. Probably the easiest way to remember the myriad things our hormones do is to focus on just what a particular endocrine gland is trying to accomplish. Once you know exactly what that is, a good many seemingly disconnected facts often fall nicely into place. For instance, the hormone insulin has a single broad goal—to lower the concentration of glucose in the blood. Keep that goal in mind while learning all the things that the hormone does, and they will be much easier to remember.
8. Remember, the endocrine system is a control system. It does not initiate processes or operations, it *accelerates* or *slows* those that already exist.

Objectives

When you have finished reading this chapter, you should:

1. have a general knowledge of how the nervous and endocrine systems control homeostasis and how they interact.
2. be able to outline a procedure that you might follow if you were trying to get the medical community to accept a structure you'd just found as an endocrine gland.
3. be able to describe the two different chemical classes of hormones.
4. be able to contrast the mechanisms of action of both major classes of hormones.
5. be able to describe the anatomy of the hypothalamus and its morphological and endocrine relationship with the pituitary.
6. know all the major endocrine glands and where they are located in the body.
7. be able to list the hormones and trophic hormones of the adenohypophysis and know their target organs and functions.
8. know the hormones of the neurohypophysis, their target organs, and their functions.
9. be able to describe the morphology and location of the thyroid gland and know the target and functions of its hormones.
10. be able to locate the parathyroid glands and know the function of their hormone.

Islet of Langerhans within the pancreas. The pancreas is a glandular organ in the abdominal cavity secreting hormones and digestive enzymes.

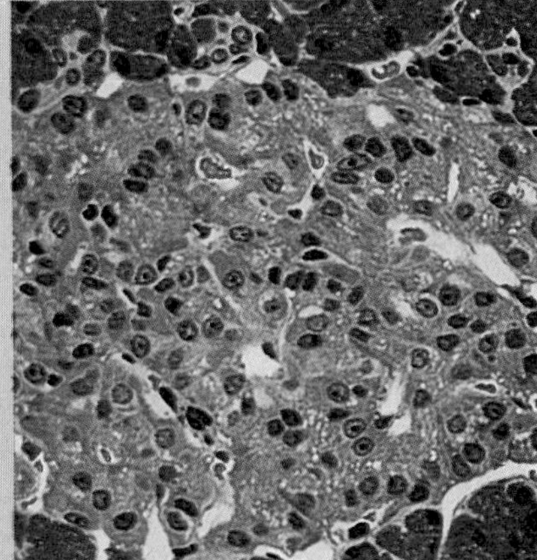

11. understand the relationship between calcitonin, parathormone, and vitamin D in calcium metabolism.
12. know the location and function of the adrenal medulla and its hormones.
13. be able to contrast the three groups of steroid hormones produced by the adrenal cortex and know which glandular layer produces each.
14. be able to locate and describe the importance of the thymus gland.
15. know the location of the pineal gland and be able to discuss what is known of its secretions.
16. be able to describe the location and importance of the islets of Längerhans and to name the hormones produced therein.
17. describe the metabolic effects of insulin, glucagon, and somatostatin.

Introduction

The development of organisms that possess an internal environment (Claude Bernard, arguably the greatest biologist of the nineteenth century, called it the *milieu interieur*) opened up the entire earth for colonization by living systems. Once multicellular organisms had established a medium in which the cells in their bodies could live, plants and animals did not have to stay in watery environments that were exactly the right temperature and where oxygen, nutrients, salts, and food were all dissolved in exactly the right concentrations. Furthermore, life was freed somewhat from absolute dependence on the capricious whims of the weather. Animals became able to insulate their bodies from these vagaries of nature, thereby maintaining their *internal* environment just the way their cells had to have it. And as long as they kept the external environment out, they could wander into areas where conditions were not ideal for life and where cells that were unprotected simply could not exist. They could live in desert areas where unprotected cells would dry up like tiny raisins. They could live in areas where temperatures plunged to 40 °C below freezing, secure in the knowledge that their external insulation would help prevent damage to the environment they had inside. And as long as they could maintain internal conditions, they could survive and prosper.

As we have seen from chapter 9, we have, built into each of us, nervous mechanisms that are designed to observe and analyze conditions outside of our bodies. These observations and analyses permit us to do things that will help us, while simultaneously letting us avoid that which might do us harm. There are nervous mechanisms intended to sample our internal environment as well, and adjustments are made by homeostatic machinery on the basis of their appraisals.

Human beings have another system that helps coordinate and modulate the various homeostatic mechanisms our bodies possess. This is the **endocrine system,** and while it does respond somewhat to external conditions, it concentrates mainly on adjusting processes that involve our internal environment. Instead of relying on electricity, as the nervous system does much of the time, endocrine control is exerted primarily through a battery of specific chemical messengers called **hormones,** and the primary transportation and information dissemination system is the blood and body fluids.

In a way, considering endocrine controls and the nervous system is like comparing the old stagecoach to the telegraph. We liken the endocrine system to the stagecoach. It carried the mail and all kinds of information between cities and towns, including instructions to city or other government officials. When important orders were handed to the driver in one city, he took quite a while to deliver them, but his coming was always a big thing, and orders were obeyed until the next stage came, so whatever the orders were, they lasted a long time. The telegraph, however, could carry messages rapidly. Instructions got where they had to go almost instantly and could be obeyed the same day they were sent. What is more, they could be modified quickly when something turned up that required a change in plans, and that is the way nerves work. Typically, most neural mechanisms respond to *change* in a given parameter. Adjustments are made rapidly and are of short duration. Our endocrine system, on the other hand, is inclined to respond more slowly than nerves usually do. Its controls are ordinarily able to deal with absolutes, its adjustments are made more smoothly, and, since any endocrine-inspired changes occur slowly, the effects often last a long time.

A Brief History

Endocrinology is not a particularly new science. From the earliest historical records it is obvious that ancient people knew what would happen if a man lost his testicles. Some ancient physicians even noted the similarity between human changes and the alterations that bulls and roosters underwent when they suffered similar losses.

A man bereft of his reproductive organs loses, of course, the ability to fertilize a female; but while important, that is not what people noticed. What they noticed was that young castrates lost or never developed all of the things that make a man *male*. Muscle tissues either never developed or became infiltrated with fat, the voice never deepened, no hair sprouted on their chests, and the distribution of fat deposits resembled those of women. The physical changes were fundamentally similar to those observed in some experimental animals. Roosters, for instance, when castrated lost their big, bright red combs and wattles—marks of their maleness. Along with the desire to mate they also lost their aggressiveness—both behavioral traits, but definitely male ones.

Early endocrinological discoveries weren't restricted to the reproductive glands. Greek physicians as early as 400 B.C. knew *diabetes mellitus* when they saw it. They had no idea what was causing the disease or how they might go about curing it, but they were able to recognize it. They recorded in detail its signs and symptoms as well as its progress and its inevitable, deadly outcome.

The first hints of true endocrinological research actually began in the last century when a physician named Berthold showed that the atrophy of a castrated rooster's comb could be prevented if some of the rooster's testicular tissue were grafted onto its body. Significantly, it didn't make any difference where on the rooster's body the tissue was grafted . . . in fact, Berthold grafted it under the skin just dorsal to the wings. He reported, apparently in some surprise, that these roosters not only retained the *appearance* of maleness, they also regained male behavioral traits. About the only thing they lost was the ability to fertilize females.

Despite some unusual opinions shared by early researchers, they eventually realized that there were several endocrine glands in the body and that they all seemed to have several things in common. For instance, diseases involving certain endocrine glands could be arrested by giving the patients homogenized gland or glandular extracts to eat. The interpretation of that event was inevitable: *Endocrine glands regularly release chemicals into the blood that are essential for the normal function of some part of the body.* This turned out to be a fundamental observation. Soon something else showed up, something that no one had thought of but that would prove to be equally important. Physicians treating endocrine diseases by administering glandular extracts noticed that when they overdid it, their patients developed different diseases. These diseases were familiar, but their cause and cure had been unknown. Now, suddenly, the cause was obvious, and the realization added another fundamental fact to the new science: *Disease states can result from too much of an endocrine gland's product as well as from too little.*

Thus began the final stage in the pioneering of endocrinology. The amount of endocrine product released into the blood had to be exactly right or the individual would get sick. Turn the controls up too high, and it's just as bad as turning them too low. Two of these early workers responsible for turning nineteenth-century theories into modern physiological concepts were W. M. Bayliss and E. H. Starling. The principles they established as a result of their experiments, although eighty years old, are still valid. Among other things, they established a set of criteria that is still considered, with some modification and flexibility, to confirm or deny the presence of a functioning endocrine gland (see table 10.1).

The final stage in the development of modern endocrinological theory emerged with the linking of hormonal regulation with the concept of homeostasis . . . the realization that the endocrine system is one of the master controls that balances the homeostatic mechanisms our bodies use to maintain the internal milieu.

An interesting sidelight to Berthold's research is found in the writings of a contemporary of his, a gentleman named Brown-Sequard. Noting the apparent sexual rebirth in animals that should be capons, Brown-Sequard, a 70-year-old libertine, began taking daily injections of canine testicular extracts, and despite his advanced years, he claimed to have completely regained the sexual prowess of his youth. His claim was supported by the testimony of his mistress, a woman almost fifty years his junior, who was apparently delighted with his experimental results. It is quite an example of the power of autosuggestion, and one must remember that despite our certainty that his sexual capabilities had nothing to do with the canine hormones, there was nothing phony about them. His mistress leaves no doubt about his ability to perform, so whether or not it was "all in his mind," it was real.

Table 10.1 Bayliss and Starling's Criteria

1. The presence and continued activity of the suspected structure must be essential for the proper function of the whole organism.
2. Definite, predictable consequences must result when the gland is removed.
3. It must be possible to counter these consequences by administration of an extract of the structure in question.
   This criterion was refined with the passage of time. Now there are two corollaries:
   a. The extract must be an "active" extract.
   b. The extract must be administered via the correct route.
4. It must be possible to show that there is something present in the blood draining the suspected gland that was not present in the blood entering the gland. Researchers would refer to this as an *arterial/venous* or *A/V difference.*
   This criterion has also required refinement: The arterial and the venous samples must be drawn at the same time.

The Endocrine System

The endocrine system consists of so many different kinds of cells, it is nearly impossible to keep track of them all. Some endocrine cells are scattered throughout other structures, single cells doing their jobs independently of their close neighbors. This is typical of the neuroendocrine cells in the hypothalamus. Others form clusters of similar-behaving cells buried in tissues that have their own, different jobs to do. Still others are discrete structures located strategically throughout the body. These latter are the endocrine glands, and although each is structurally autonomous, none of them operates for individual benefit. Each fits into the overall functional body plan, and there is a closely knit cooperation throughout that is designed to maintain a precise and smooth control over the body's homeostatic mechanisms. Each endocrine gland is capable of doing many things, and sometimes we do not really understand why they do some of them. Generally, though, we have at least a vague idea of what the gland is trying to accomplish, and that helps when detailed analysis of its abilities begins.

Interaction with the nervous system is common. For example, when danger threatens, there is an endocrine gland that swings into action to help the nervous system handle the emergency. With danger past, food begins to enter a placid intestinal tract, and neuroendocrine elements once again collaborate to digest the food and get it absorbed. The urge to become sexually active is mainly a nervous response, but it is the endocrine system that primes both the male and the female so the urge will occur. The structures and curves that make the female attractive to the male, and the angles and musculature that make the male look sexy, are products of endocrine activity. The *ability* to reproduce would be futile were it not for the united efforts of various endocrine secretions.

Gland Characteristics

The individual endocrine glands are quite diverse in size, and they originate in every type of embryonic tissue. But there are certain characteristics that all endocrine glands have in common. They are, fundamentally, **ductless glands** . . . none have obvious exits for the products they synthesize. It is the nature of endocrine secretions to have varying effects on organs and tissues scattered throughout the body; hence, directing them to a single target zone would defeat their goal. Endocrine cells synthesize their product and literally dump it out into the interstitial fluid, where it is picked up by the blood and distributed throughout the body.

Structure

Generally speaking, endocrine glands have two basic structural patterns:

1. clumped, like the lobes of a raspberry, around a central point, or
2. strung out in cords along blood vessels, the way peas are arranged in their pods.

Regardless of which of these two forms they assume, endocrine cells are never far away from a blood vessel. It is characteristic of endocrine glands that, without exception, all are **highly vascularized,** meaning they have an unusually abundant—sometimes even startling—blood supply. Such an enormous blood flow through them renders the gathering of their products quick and ineluctable.

Hormones

Starling coined the word **hormone** in 1905. It is a Greek word meaning something is "kindled" or "set in motion," and while it doesn't really fit with our modern concept of what is actually taking place, it's permanently engraved in biomedical jargon. The hormones synthesized by our endocrine glands can be segregated chemically into two broad classifications.

One major group is the **proteinaceous hormones,** which embraces all the endocrine secretions composed of amino acids. It is a big group with a broad range, extending from the amino acid hormone **thyroxin** of the thyroid gland to compounds that have dozens of such acids. There are subgroups galore clustered under the proteinaceous heading, and classification depends mainly on the size of the compound.

The other major hormone group is fatty in nature and includes all the **steroid hormones.** Hormones in this category cover a much narrower range than those composed of amino acids. They vary only slightly in size and composition and are all built around the same core—a nucleus of **cholesterol**—the compound with the nasty reputation that resides in such abundance in the membranes of our body cells.

In the hope of making things a little easier to understand, I have chosen a couple of common endocrinological terms and have applied them, along with the word *hormone,* specifically in this text. Each refers to a certain type of endocrine secretion, depending on function and/or source.

Hormone: The word *hormone,* used without qualifiers, designates all glandular secretions that have a direct effect on some homeostatic or reproductive mechanism or structure.

Trophic hormones: Some endocrine secretions serve to control the synthesis and secretion of other hormones. In this text, these "controlling secretions" will always be labelled *trophic hormones.*

Releasing hormones: There is a whole battery of endocrine secretions released by the hypothalamus, which, as you know, is part of the brain. These secretions are constituents of complex feedback loops controlling both trophic hormones and nontrophic hormones, and they often involve two or three endocrine glands. For the sake of order, these hypothalamic secretions are referred to consistently as *releasing hormones.*

All of the above secretions can quite correctly be termed hormones and in many textbooks, they are. I have merely chosen to consistently qualify that word for clarity and ease of understanding.

Function vs. Mechanism of Action

Hormonal *function* and hormonal *mechanism of action* are two fundamentally different considerations. "Function" refers to the job that the hormone does in the body; what homeostatic processes it is going to modify and its overall goal. (The *function* of insulin is to lower the concentration of glucose in the blood.) "Mechanism of action," on the other hand, is the means by which the hormone achieves its goal. How does it affect its target cells? What does it do when it arrives, and how is the cellular machinery changed?

Target Selection

Since hormones are carried by the blood, and the blood goes everywhere in the body, it follows that the hormones will be carried, eventually, to every cell. Yet no hormone affects *every* cell—not even hormones with the broadest activity range. They might encounter every cell, but they do not act on all of them. Why not? Why do hormones not become involved with all the body's cells instead of just a select few? Perhaps the easiest way to explain this would be to utilize an analogy.

Suppose we compare the hormones to groceries carried throughout the body by a delivery boy, the blood. There are lots of groceries in the delivery boy's truck, and each bagful is to be delivered to a specific address. The delivery boy will encounter dozens of houses as he drives along, but he does not necessarily deliver a bagful of groceries to each house. Only if the groceries are assigned to a house will they get delivered there.

This kind of outlook is convenient and is easy to picture, but while it paints an understandable picture, it really does not explain much, because unfortunately we do not know—yet—how hormones are addressed. We do, however, have some ideas.

Specificity The most common explanation involves what is called **specificity,** and it is said that when a target cell and a hormone interact, it is because they have a high degree of specificity for each other. Interactions between hormones and their target cells have been compared to two pieces of a jigsaw puzzle linked together, and maybe that's all there is to it. The hormone will not work when it bumps into a cell unless both the cell membrane and the hormone are the right shape. If the receptor and hormone are incompatible, the hormone will simply slide across the cell surface and pass on. If, on the other hand, the hormone can fit into some part of the membrane, it will slip into place and affect that cell.

Receptors

If the specificity theory is correct, and if shape is a factor, it is logical to suspect that proteins are involved somewhere, and the suspicion seems to be well-founded; all the receptors identified so far are proteins. Variability is also a characteristic of proteins, and that fits too; there are all kinds of receptors. It has been suggested that the cells in our bodies are covered—and filled—with receptors of one kind or another, and that sooner or later, something drifting by in the interstitial fluid is going to fit into every last one of them.

Generally speaking, receptors that are destined to link up with peptide hormones will be in the cell membrane simply because that is about as far as most peptides can go; they cannot penetrate the membrane. But not all hormones are forced to remain outside the cell, and neither are their receptors. Fatty hormones, for instance, can slip through the lipid bilayer of the cell membrane without significant difficulty, so their receptors are in the cytoplasm. There is even a hormone that must penetrate the nuclear envelope in order to find its receptor.

But regardless of its location, once hormone and receptor join together, they set off a chain of events within the cell involved.

The Mechanism of Action of the Peptide Hormones

Proteinaceous hormones that contain more than two amino acids are considered to belong in the **peptide** subgroup and, with acknowledged exceptions, the mechanism of action of the peptide hormones is fundamentally the same. Peptides are water soluble, so they cannot go through the cell membrane, and most are too big to slip through any of the pores. Whatever the hormones are going to do, therefore, has to be done to the cell membrane, and any internal effects will be a result of what has happened on the membrane. As it turns out, peptide hormone receptors are generally imbedded firmly in the cell membrane, with just enough sticking out into the interstitial fluid for the correct hormone to locate and recognize. What happens then follows a sequence more or less common to all of the peptide hormones. It involves what is known to endocrinologists as a **second messenger.**

The Second-Messenger Hypothesis

1. When the hormone links to the receptor, the resulting complex is actually a new compound with its own special characteristics and properties. These new properties include activation of an enzyme present in the membrane. The enzyme is called **adenyl cyclase.**
2. We're not sure exactly how the next step is accomplished. Adenyl cyclase could leave the membrane and enter the cytosol or it could just project an active "head" into the cytosol. Whichever of these is correct, it concentrates on groups of adenosine triphosphate (ATP) and removes two of the phosphate groups, thus converting it to **adenosine monophosphate (AMP).** Expressed simply, the reaction looks like this:

$$\text{ATP} \xrightarrow{\text{adenyl cyclase}} \text{AMP} + 2\,\text{phosphate groups}$$

3. This type of AMP is known as **cyclic AMP (cAMP),** and its job is to transfer the information brought by the hormone to the proper mechanism inside the cell. The mechanism then proceeds to do whatever it is the hormone does to that cell.

Figure 10.1 The "second messenger" cyclic AMP, and its role in the action of proteinaceous hormones. As the active cAMP builds up, it removes the regulatory subunit from the protein kinase. The cAMP is then deactivated to 5′ AMP by the enzyme phosphodiesterase.

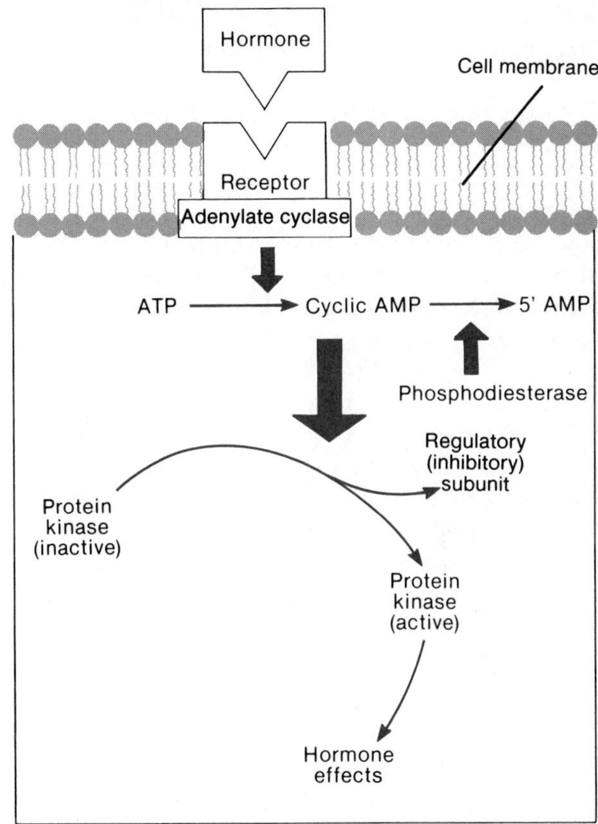

That is the sequence. The blood represents the *first carrier.* It delivers its hormonal message to a receptor on the surface of the cell. The resultant hormone/receptor complex hands it to the *second carrier,* the cAMP inside the cell membrane, and the cAMP then carries the message into the cytoplasm and sets the correct machinery in motion. The entire operation is known as the **second-messenger hypothesis** (figure 10.1).

The hormone itself is only a bit of information. By forming a complex with the receptor, it delivers its message to the cell and its job is done. Once adenyl cyclase and cAMP begin to run, any control the hormone might have had disappears, and events occur relentlessly. The hormone has turned on all the switches that it can control, and now other mechanisms have to take over.

Within the cell there are many enzymes. Some are active and some are quiescent, just waiting for instructions. **Protein kinases** are among the normally inactive enzymes that have to be switched on before they can begin operating, and cAMP is the switch. Protein kinases are formed of two different subunits, one known as the **catalytic subunit,** the other, the **regulatory subunit.** Cyclic AMP activates the catalytic subunit by locking onto the regulatory fraction and pulling it away. Once freed of the restricting influence of the regulatory residue, the catalytic subunit proceeds to do whatever it is that the hormone is supposed to do in that particular cell.

The Mechanism of Action of the Steroid Hormones

The steroid hormones operate quite differently from the peptide hormones. Since they are fatty in nature, they can go right through the cell membrane; hence the problem of how to get their message into the cell is easily solved. They carry it in themselves. They are free to circulate into and out of any body cell they encounter, without having to check receptor addresses in the membrane. The addresses they are looking for are not on the membrane but on receptors floating around in the cytosol, waiting for the hormone to come to them. Unlike membrane receptors, these cytoplasmic receptors don't seem to be restricted to any particular zone and apparently float around in the cytosol pretty freely. For this reason, they are known as **mobile receptors.** The performance sequence of the lipid hormones goes like this:

1. Being fatty, steroid hormones can dissolve in the lipid of the cell membrane. Hence they can migrate into the cell without any energy use or enzymatic assistance. Inside the cytoplasm, if they encounter the correct receptor, they lock into it, and a new compound forms (the hormone/receptor complex).
2. Using energy in a manner not clearly understood, this new compound then moves through the cytosol to the nucleus, where it slips across the envelope into the interior.
3. Inside the nucleus, the complex is able to influence certain genes on the DNA, and in this manner it changes the *rate* of synthesis of a certain kind of mRNA. No one is sure just how this is done, but there is little doubt that it is.
4. This mRNA then slips into the cytoplasm, where it stimulates the production of a protein that is characteristic of that particular steroid hormone (figure 10.2).

The peptide hormones lose control of events when they deliver their messages to the receptors. So do the steroid hormones. Once the hormone/receptor complex has formed, there is nothing more any hormone can do. Events proceed inexorably to their conclusion.

Figure 10.2 Mechanism of action of a typical steroid hormone. (*1*) The hormones arrive at their target cell. Being lipid, they penetrate the membrane easily (*2*) and form a complex with an appropriate cytoplasmic receptor (*3*). The complex then moves across the nuclear envelope (*4*) and links to chromosomal proteins (*5*). In some manner, this influences an increase in production of a strand of messenger RNA (*6*), which proceeds out of the nucleus (*7*) and stimulates synthesis of an enzyme characteristic of the hormone (*8*).

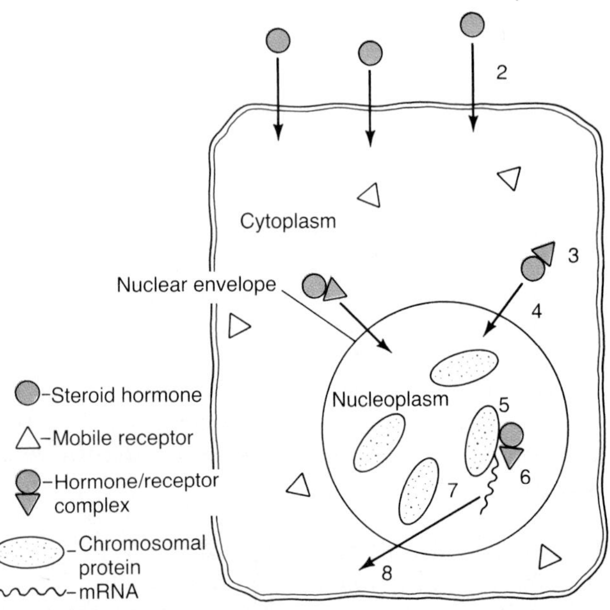

One rather important point perhaps has been brushed over too casually in our discussion of the activity sequences. Yet it should be emphasized, because it is important. Hormones don't *initiate* any given process, homeostatic or otherwise. It is their job to *regulate* the activity of homeostatic systems. Hormones are *control* mechanisms, not architectural, and they cannot design and introduce new systems. In the case of the steroid hormone activity sequence just described, it is important to note that they do not stimulate production of *new* strands of mRNA, but rather alter the *rate of production* of an mRNA type already being produced.

The proteins produced as a result of the presence of the hormone can take any one of several forms. As enzymes, they might produce some unusual activity within the cell or help in the synthesis of some particular compound intended for secretion. As structural proteins, they might become part of the membrane, influencing the movement of materials into or out of the cell. Or they might become other hormones, squeezing through a membrane pore, leaving the cell, carrying a message of their own to some other body area.

Hormonal Regulation

As I have already said, the endocrine system is essentially a communications network, and when you stop and think about all the links in such a network, it is not hard to find spots where something or someone can make a mistake. Anyplace where error can occur is a zone of variation; such zones are therefore the logical spots to insert some kind of control mechanism.

Regulating Hormone Production

Some of these control regions are obvious. For instance, the mechanisms within the gland that synthesize a hormone could always make a mistake and produce too much or too little, and that makes it an ideal place to put a regulator. Other mechanisms are responsible for gathering the raw materials that the hormone is made from, and they, too, represent control surfaces. By influencing either of these two operations, a regulator could alter the quantity of hormone produced.

Receptor Regulation

Another obvious place to regulate hormonal activity would be at the receptor where the hormone delivers its message to its target cell. There are several ways this could be handled. The most obvious way would be to alter some of the receptor's properties. For instance, changing the shape of the receptor would certainly alter the hormone's activity. Cells apparently never use this method, however, because serious problems could arise. Changing its shape or other recognition characteristics might make the receptor specific for some other hormone, and that would be bad indeed. Also, it is completely out of character; it represents a qualitative change. Hormones do not indulge in qualitative changes. As noted in the box on page 304, they do not initiate processes . . . they just modify the rate of activities that are already going on. With that in mind, it would seem that the best way to handle regulation at the receptor level would be to alter the number of receptors. That is more in character with hormonal operations anyway, because it doesn't shut off or initiate any process—it merely alters the rate. It appears that this is what our bodies do.

Feedback

For any control mechanism to work properly, it must have some means of determining how effective its activities are. Unless there is some way to detect the results of its operations, the regulator is not going to know when it is needed and when it is not, and that's no way to exert proper control. Imagine what the appliances in our homes would be like without some means of sensing the consequences of their efforts. Heaters and air conditioners would be a lot less useful if they could not sense changes in temperature; toasters would burn all the toast or would not toast it at all; washing machines would have to be carefully watched so they would not overflow and flood the laundry. But they don't do these things. All of our appliances work, and one reason is that they do have such sensors. We've had them in our machines for a long time. It has been seventy or eighty years since we first recognized the importance of feedback loops. Nowadays, we use them constantly, and we are very proud of the accomplishment.

The basic principles that are used in these appliances to make their operations so effective were invented long ago by our evolutionary mechanisms.

Loops

It will help you to understand the operation of these mechanisms if you realize at the beginning that they are *cyclic*. This is the reason that they are known as *feedback loops*. Since they run in a circle, it really doesn't matter where one begins to describe their workings. Most people prefer to start at the point where the sensor is inserted—the zone of stimulus input—and that is as good a place as any, so let's start there.

Anything that accepts an input is, by definition, a receptor, and in living systems the receptor almost always is a **transducer** as well. Transducers accept the energy from the system they're designed to monitor and pass it to a second system, usually in another form. In this case, the other form is a language that the next stage in the loop can understand.

The second stage is an **integrator.** This stage takes the message sent by the transducer, reads it, and decides what to do. If it decides that nothing needs to be done, then nothing is done. If, however, it decides to do something, it sends its own code message to the next stage in the loop—the **effector.** The effector receives the message, decodes it, reads it, and obeys it. Depending on the nature of the loop itself and the orders from the integrator, that response might support the original stimulus, in which case the feedback is positive. Positive loops are relatively rare in biological systems, but they do exist, as we have already seen in chapter 7. Usually, however, the instructions tell the effector to do something that will reverse the original stimulus, and the control is, therefore, a negative feedback loop (see figure 10.3).

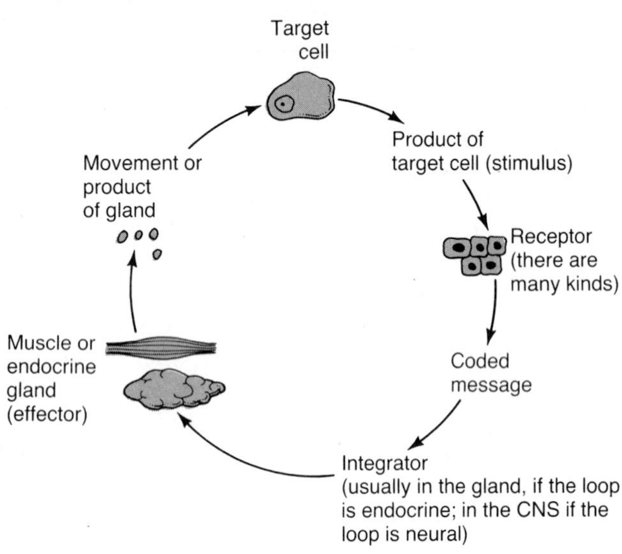

Figure 10.3 A typical feedback loop.

Figure 10.4 is an idealized pattern of a typical, endocrine-controlled homeostatic parameter. In this case, the diagram is that of blood glucose concentration, but it could be almost anything that is involved in homeostasis. As you can see, the levels of glucose in the blood are never constant but are always varying. This is as it should be. It is the function of the control mechanisms to see to it that variations are promptly responded to and that they never stray very far from optimal levels.

This is not our first contact with feedback systems, but it is our first concentrated look at them. Endocrine feedback loops are not all negative, but most of them are, and they're very effective. Sometimes these loops employ neural receptors as sensors to pick up stimuli; sometimes they do not. The loop that involves the thyroid gland, for instance, uses neural receptors to detect levels of thyroid hormone in the blood, and it bases its responses on this information.

Figure 10.4 An example of an endocrine feedback loop. This one shows a simplified schematic of the primary mechanisms that control blood glucose concentrations.

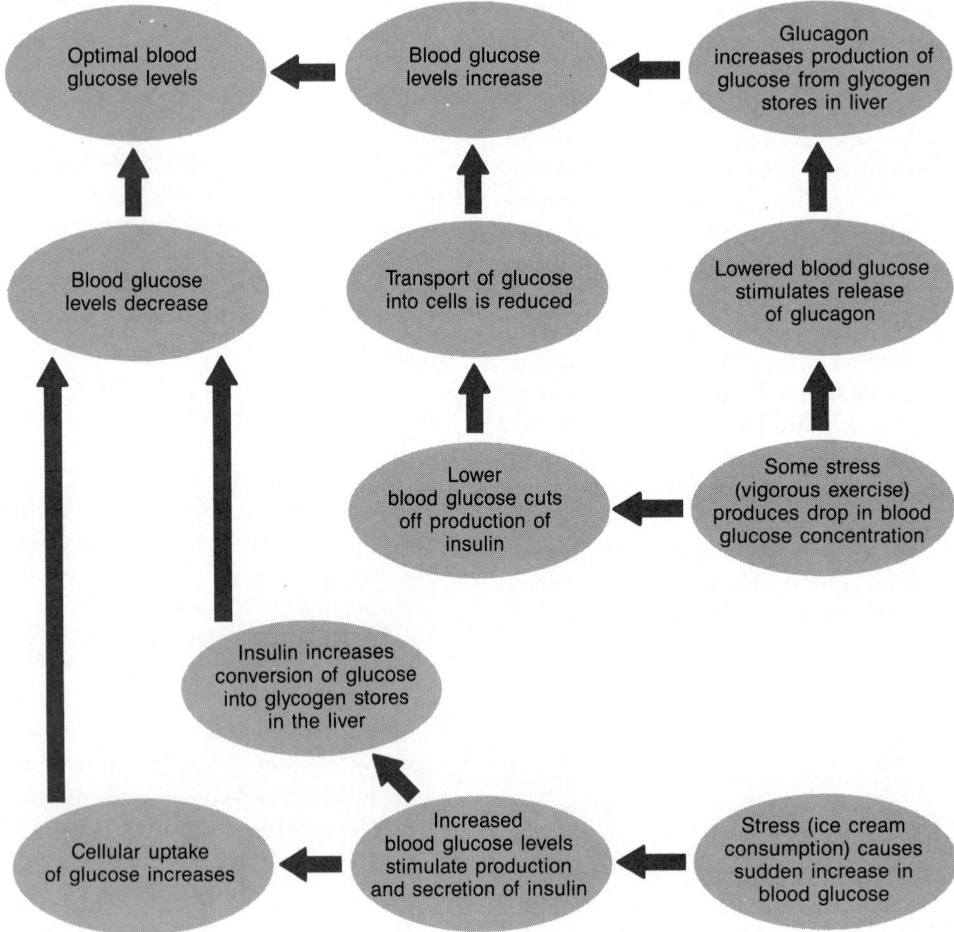

Other loops may rely exclusively on endocrine cells to detect changes in the parameter they are regulating. Whether these sensors are endocrine or not, they are all linked to integrators and effectors that can take appropriate action should any be necessary. If their interpretations indicate that some hormonal secretion is required, instructions are immediately sent to the proper cells to boost their synthetic and secretory efforts. The resultant hormones are picked up by the blood and circulate to the target tissues, where further processing occurs. The tissue responses will, in their turn, become the next stimulus sensed by the receptors, and the process begins all over again.

The Endocrine Glands

Glands are defined as biological structures consisting, at least in part, of epithelial cells that synthesize special chemicals made of raw materials obtained from the blood. These chemicals are then secreted from, or used by, the body in which the gland is found. Generally speaking, that certainly fits our body's endocrine glands. Of course, no one really believes that we have found all the endocrine glands that the human body possesses . . . they are still cropping up. We thought we had found them all by the mid-1950s, but in the 1960s workers discoverd a brand-new one whose existence had been totally unsuspected. Nor was that the last . . . there is one whose endocrine function was confirmed as recently as the late 1970s.

Most of our endocrine glands, however, were uncovered six or eight decades ago. Yet there are still mysteries associated with them, and their operations still receive considerable scientific scrutiny. For example, the endocrine function of the pancreas was confirmed before the turn of the century, but it still malfunctions with jolting frequency, and there remains no sure way to prevent its malfunction or to cure the results. A malfunctioning thyroid gland is usually rather easy to repair or to supplement, but we do not really know what its hormones do. For reasons like these, endocrinological research is a frontier science, and much needs to be done.

The major glands are as follows (see figure 10.5):

The **hypothalamus:** This is a brain structure and is, therefore, mostly nervous tissue. It is, as indicated in chapter 8, deeply involved in all autonomic homeostatic operations and represents a circuitous link between the endocrine system and the brain, particularly the cortical brain centers.

The **pituitary:** This is a dual gland that dangles from the floor of the hypothalamus just posterior to the optic chiasma. One part of the gland is derived from buccal (pronounced "byou-cl") ectoderm (the lining of the mouth). The other part is actually an extension of the hypothalamus. The pituitary gland is on the floor of the brain and is located just above the roof of your mouth.

The **thyroid:** A butterfly-shaped gland that wraps around the trachea (windpipe) just about where the larynx (voice box) is located.

The **parathyroids:** These smallest of all endocrine glands are located in close association with the thyroid gland. There are usually two pairs of them, and one pair is almost always imbedded in the tissue of the thyroid gland.

The **pancreas:** This is both an endocrine and an exocrine organ. It wraps around the upper curve of the small intestine. It would be huge if it were all endocrine gland. Most of the tissue, however, is involved in exocrine functions—in this case, the synthesis and secretion of digestive enzymes.

The **adrenals:** These are embryologically two, and functionally four, glands. They are located, as the name implies, on the dorsal surface of the kidneys.

The **gonads:** The male and female reproductive organs, the ovaries and the testes, sources of both the germ cells and the sex hormones.

Figure 10.5 The locations of the major endocrine glands (shaded).

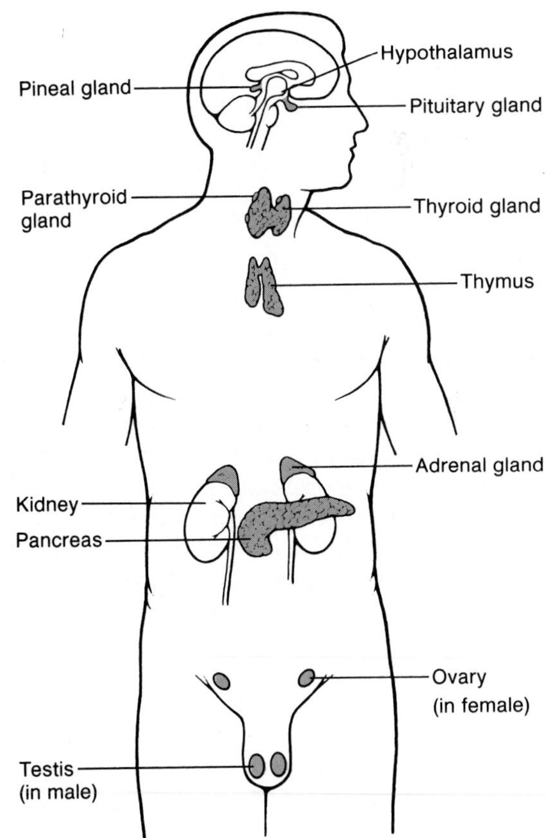

The **thymus:** This gland is located in the middle of the chest, just behind the sternum (breastbone) and between the lungs.

The **pineal:** The pineal gland is located in the roof of the third ventricle of the brain. It sits, therefore, deep in the brain tissue, just above the hypothalamus.

The Hypothalamus

The hypothalamus is considered by workers today to be the *endocrine control center,* because its releasing hormones control the secretions of the anterior pituitary. In addition, it contains the receptor cells for one of the hormones of the posterior pituitary and the integrating mechanisms for both.

The role of the hypothalamus as a control center was confirmed rather recently. It was suspected for years, but until early in the 1960s no one had been able to demonstrate just how it managed to do these things, mostly because the cells that synthesize and secrete the various releasing factors are not concentrated in any one place. Instead, they are scattered throughout the hypothalamic tissue. This made things extremely hard for researchers, who had to segregate the various secretions in order to analyze and identify them.

The hypothalamus represents the primary *receptor* for the loops that feed through it. It responds to so many stimuli that there sometimes seems to be no stimulus it will not accept. Some stimuli, such as the sex hormones, enter as blood-borne chemicals, some are variations in temperature, some are electrical signals from other parts of the brain, and still others trace their origin to receptors in structures like the great blood vessels emerging from the heart or entering the kidneys. Almost every hormone that exists seems able to influence it; the cerebrospinal fluid sends signals to it . . . there is even some evidence of osmoreceptors. So much information pours into the hypothalamus that it is hard to believe it's as small as it is.

Although they are circuitous and extremely hard to trace, there are solid neural links between the hypothalamus and higher brain centers. Experimental observations indicate that behavioral changes can be stimulated by the presence or absence of certain hormones and that most of the neural stimuli originate in the hypothalamus. Sex hormones are particularly effective in stimulating such changes, although all the steroid hormones seem to work.

Figure 10.6 shows the parts of the hypothalamus that have been associated with releasing hormones. They are actually areas more than they are discrete structures or clearly defined zones. Not all the cells

Figure 10.6 Hypothalamic zones that are involved in secretion or transfer of various releasing factors. (*a*) A line drawing and (*b*) a microphotograph.

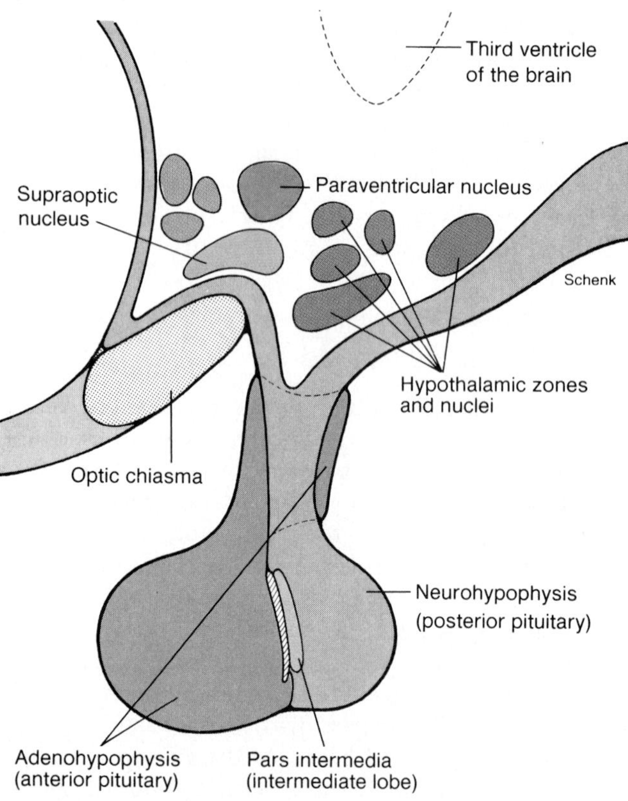

(a)

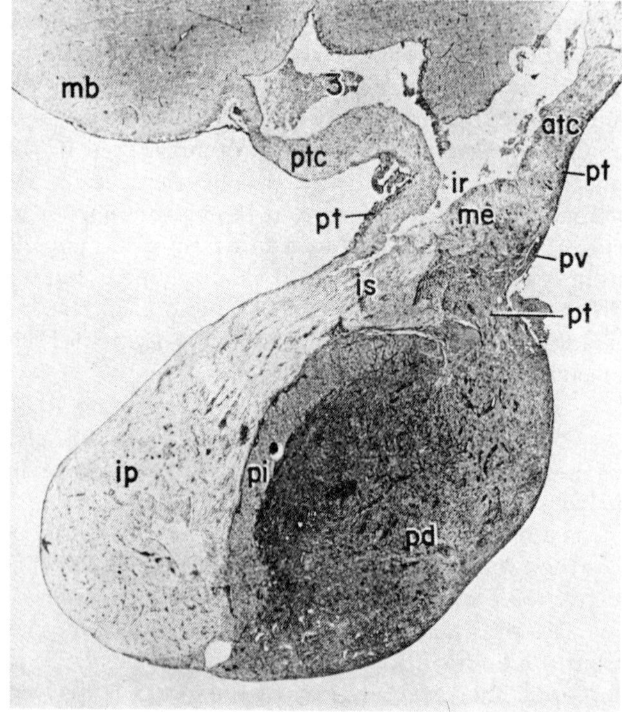

(b)

Table 10.2 Hypothalamic Factors

Hypothalamic Hormone	Pituitary Secretion It Controls
Thyrotropin-releasing hormone (TRH)	Thyroid-stimulating hormone (TSH)
Gonadotrophin-releasing hormone (GnRH)	Trophic sex hormones (FSH, LH)
Prolactin-releasing hormone (PRH) Prolactin inhibitory factor (PIF)	Prolactin (PRL) Inhibits release of PRL
Corticotropin-releasing hormone (CRH)	ACTH
Growth hormone inhibitory hormone (GHIH)* (also called somatostatin)	Inhibits growth hormone (somatotropin)
Growth hormone–releasing hormone (GHRH)	Growth hormone (somatotropin)
Melanocyte-stimulating hormone–releasing hormone (MRH)	Melanocyte-stimulating hormone (MSH)
Melanocyte-stimulating hormone–release-inhibiting factor (MIF)	MSH

*Somatostatin is the only hypothalamic factor we know of that is synthesized in any significant volume by cells outside the hypothalamus. It is synthesized in the pancreas, the gastrointestinal epithelium, and many other locations as well. As might be expected, somatostatin has profound effects in structures other than the pituitary.

in these areas do the same thing, nor do they necessarily secrete releasing factors. Some areas function as relay stations or as interfaces between other zones. This does not mean that there are no discrete nuclei in the hypothalamus, because there are a few, but in general, the secretory cells of the hypothalamus are scattered all over, and their functions are diffuse.

The factors elaborated by the hypothalamus are listed in table 10.2. Please note that not all of them are excitatory in their action . . . which incidentally calls in another "jargon alert." The factors that are excitatory are the *releasing hormones;* those that are inhibitory are known as **release-inhibiting hormones,** and one or the other is apparently involved with all but one of the anterior pituitary secretions.

The Pituitary Gland

Prior to the discovery of the hypothalamus's endocrine roles, the pituitary was viewed as the body's "endocrine control center," and today, despite having lost some grandeur to the hypothalamus, it is still considered by most workers to be the *master endocrine gland.* Certainly its secretions regulate the synthesis and secretion of many of the glands in the endocrine system, and it seems able to respond to feedback control. In fact, it does so many things that for several years it defied research efforts to uncover all the things it was involved with. A man named John Smith finally hit upon the idea of removing the gland (hypophysectomy), then listing all the things that went wrong. This procedure (called the **ablation technique**) finally led researchers to the answers they had been looking for.

Smith's list of observed malfunctions in his hypophysectomized rats sounds like the aftermath of a national disaster. Growth in the young stopped; adults immediately became anorexic (pathological loss of appetite and weight); in females the estrous cycle stopped; in males the testes shriveled up and sex drive vanished; body muscles were infiltrated with heavy loads of fat and became too weak to support the organism; the thyroid gland atrophied to a point where it nearly disappeared, as did the outer layers of the adrenal glands; symptoms of severe thyroid and adrenal disease appeared; the body lost almost all its sodium and retained vast quantities of potassium; water loss from the body was so profound that the blood actually became syrupy, and the kidneys shut down due to lack of filtration pressure. Mortality rate was 100 percent and always from kidney failure.

Obviously, the pituitary is an important gland.

The Adenohypophysis (Anterior Lobe)

The adenohypophysis (anterior lobe) is the portion of the pituitary that originates in buccal ectoderm. It develops embryologically from a dimple of tissue (Rathke's Pouch) on the roof of the fetal mouth. As growth proceeds, this pouch breaks from the oral tissue and migrates to the floor of the hypothalamus, where it attaches. The adenohypophysis is therefore not neural tissue, despite the fact that it is attached to the brain. There are no neural fibers running into it—its only communication with the brain is chemical. Control is exerted by chemicals synthesized in the hypothalamus, which enter the pituitary via the hypothalamo-hypophyseal portal system (figure 10.7).

Figure 10.7 The hypothalamo-hypophyseal portal system.

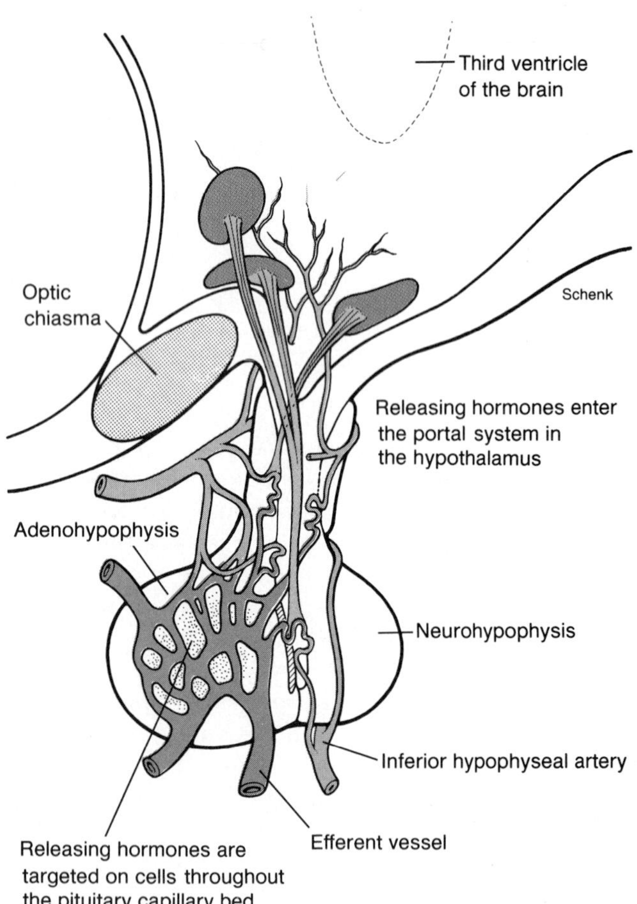

This is a particularly rich system of capillaries and tiny blood vessels that picks up releasing hormones in the hypothalamus and transports them to their target cells in the adenohypophysis.

The adenohypophysis releases four trophic hormones and two nontrophic hormones, all of which are peptides. They are listed in table 10.3.

Some interesting secretory patterns can be seen in the hormones of the adenohypophysis. For instance, in women, the gonadotrophic hormones have a lunar (thirty-day) rhythm—a rhythm completely lacking in men. Other hormones have a *circadian* (literally "about a day"), or daily, pattern. Some of the rhythms are so short that they often appear sporadic, but they are not; even the most abbreviated are rhythms. Many endocrine cells in the adenohypophysis secrete their hormones in bursts every half hour or so.

Pituitary hormones are all proteinaceous. Hence, generally speaking, the actions of all of them on their target cells involve the "second messenger."

Table 10.3 Secretions of the Adenohypophysis

Hormones
1. Growth hormone or somatotropin (STH)
2. Prolactin (PRL); also called lactogenic hormone (LGH)
Trophic Hormones
1. Thyroid-stimulating hormone (TSH)
2. Adrenal corticotrophic hormone (ACTH)
Two gonadotrophic hormones:
3. Follicle-stimulating hormone (FSH)
4. Luteinizing hormone (LH)

Somatotropin (STH)

Somatotropin is a fairly large peptide hormone with a molecular weight of about 23,000. Like the other hormones of the anterior pituitary, it is controlled by a hypothalamic releasing hormone, but unlike the majority of adenohypophyseal secretions, somatotropin is a *hormone,* not a *trophic* hormone . . . it does not regulate other endocrine glands.

Its Function in Children STH has tremendous, sweeping effects all over the body. As its old name (growth hormone) implies, in children its overall goal seems to be growth. To accomplish this, it is involved in stimulating mitosis—mainly in the skeleton, but also in muscles, connective tissues, internal organs . . . in fact, about the only tissue that is not affected is nervous tissue. At the cellular level, STH increases the rate of protein metabolism, especially the protein matrix in the bones. It speeds the cells' ability to accumulate amino acids, and it stimulates the incorporation of these acids into proteins. Under its influence, bone and body cells rapidly grow, and with increased size comes the stimulus to divide. STH helps that process directly by stimulating the synthesis of DNA and encouraging increased production of new varieties of RNA. Under the influence of STH, growth rolls along at an unusually high rate.

Its Function in Adults But if growth is its job, what does STH do for adults in whom growth is completed? Does STH secretion cease once a person has attained his or her full growth?

Not at all! In the adult, STH has another chore. It still involves protein metabolism, but this time its goal is different. Instead of building new cells by increasing their protein content, in adults it helps prevent unnecessary breakdown of cellular protein during periods of fasting. As we all have seen, glucose is used by the body cells for fuel, and its consumption is fairly rapid, even when the individual is inactive. During a meal, as food is being absorbed in large quantities, foodstuffs load up in the blood to be carried to our biological storehouses. Excess glucose can be toxic if permitted to remain in high concentration, so it must be converted either to the polysaccharide glycogen or to body fat. Glycogen is synthesized first and is stored in various places, mainly the liver. When body cells are burning glucose, it disappears from the blood and is replaced by breaking down glycogen. As long as glycogen is available, that's where the blood gets its glucose.

However, when glycogen stores are depleted—which happens during dieting or short fasts—some other glucose source must be found. Fatty acids cannot be converted to glucose, but amino acids can—a process called **gluconeogenesis**—and so in the absence of glycogen, amino acids are converted to glucose. This process, if not regulated, could result in excessive loss of important body proteins.

STH provides the regulation. It reduces the ability of body cells to burn glucose, so glucose is not taken out of the blood quite as quickly. That means gluconeogenesis will slow down, blood glucose will not fall as quickly, and protein consumption will be reduced. But the body cells still must have energy—that hasn't changed—and since they cannot get all that they need from glucose, they shift gears. Instead of concentrating on glycolysis, they begin producing ATP from their fat stores. Here again, STH exerts its influence. It accelerates the breakdown of fat stores and helps mobilize fatty acids for consumption by the cells. Glucose consumption is not totally depressed, of course, because hormones do not work that way . . . they're regulators, remember, not initiators. But it is reduced to the point where the body is burning about three times as much fat as it is protein, and that's good.

So while STH regulates growth in children, its major function in adults is regulating metabolic priorities.

Somatotropin Regulation As with any regulatory mechanism, it must be possible to turn STH on and off as needed. That means there must be some way to determine its effects on the machinery it's trying to control, and of course, there is. There may actually be some means of monitoring size in children so that growth can be shut off at the proper time, but if there is, it has not yet been discovered. What we do know is that STH responds to levels of blood glucose and rate of protein depletion in body fluids. The feedback loop is diagramed in figure 10.8.

Figure 10.8 The somatotropin feedback loop. Since this is a negative feedback loop, increases in the stimulus (blood glucose) would result in a decrease in effector (pituitary) activity. Similarly, a decrease in blood glucose would increase pituitary secretion of STH.

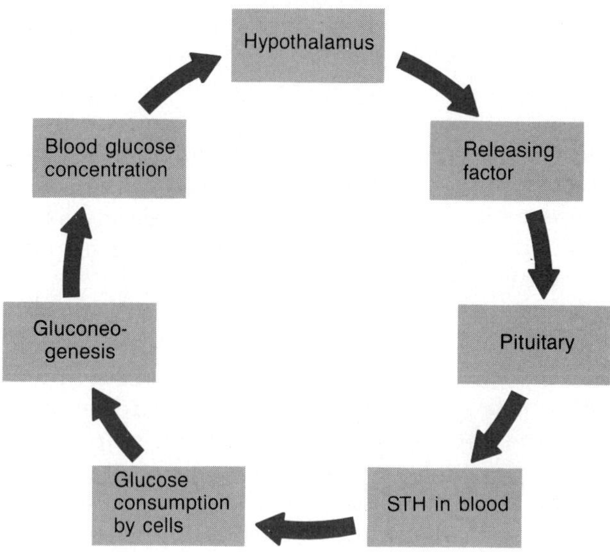

Prolactin (PRL)

Prolactin is the only other nontrophic hormone produced by the adenohypophysis, and it is surprisingly similar to STH in its size and general chemistry. It is considered a *mammotropic* hormone, because it directly affects the growth and development of the mammary glands. Its primary function, however, seems to be its **lactogenic effect,** meaning that it stimulates activity of the milk-producing cells in the female breast.

We also have a fairly good idea of what it does in males—male rats, at least. As with the females, it seems to exert its greatest effects after the mating process is over, although its activity seems to involve behavior more than anything else. It seems to suppress the aggressive attitudes so blatant during the mating process and to replace them with a gentler, homemaking spirit. This makes sense, because a parent who is always angry and looking for a fight does not need to be handling the children. It has this effect on other mammals too—at least, those mammal groups in which males help care for the young. There is also reason to believe that it works the same way in birds, so its "parental" effects are quite universal.

This does not, however, include humans. In human males, we do not really know what prolactin does. Obviously it is not going to produce milk from a nonfunctional mammary gland, so if it works at all, it must be focusing on something else. It is possible that it does nothing directly.

It may have some *indirect* effects, however, and they involve mating rather than parenting. We have reasonably good evidence to suggest that it enhances the effects of the gonadotrophins, increasing the output of both spermatozoa and testosterone. It almost certainly supports growth and secretory activity of the prostate gland and the seminal vesicles, so whether or not its role in reproductive activity is direct, it is obviously important.

The Prolactin Feedback Loop Prolactin's regulation involves both endocrine and neural machinery. Suckling is the stimulus for prolactin secretion in nursing mothers. The specific stimulus is applied to tactile receptors in the nipple and/or the areola around the nipple. It is carried by special nerve tracts into the hypothalamus. Its relationship with the hypothalamus is rather unusual in that the prolactin regulatory mechanisms seem to be exclusively inhibitory . . . at least, that is what the evidence implies. Some workers question this interpretation, and they have a reason.

Immediately after giving birth to a child, the mother's prolactin-synthesizing pituitary cells begin producing prolactin in enormous quantities, and it pours into the new mother's blood in such a flood that it seems unlikely that merely cutting off an inhibitory hormone could account for it all. If that is true, then there must be a factor somewhere that increases PRL synthesis and production. There is no other evidence for the existence of a stimulatory factor, nor do we know what form it may take. It was included as a releasing hormone in table 10.2 because many people expect to find one sooner or later, but it is possible that no such factor exists.

As for the inhibitory factor—its existence seems to be fairly well established, and we may even know what it is. Current evidence indicates that the neurotransmitter *dopamine* is either a constituent or is the factor itself, because it definitely depresses the prolactin-synthesizing cells in the pituitary.

The Trophic Hormones

Thyroid-Stimulating Hormone (TSH) TSH is a little different from most proteinaceous hormones in that it is associated with some carbohydrates as well as amino acids, making it a **glycoprotein hormone.** It is designed to control the secretions of the thyroid gland, and in this, it is about as complete a trophic hormone as can exist. When TSH is present in the blood, the thyroid gland:

1. works more vigorously to accumulate the substrates it uses to make its hormones,
2. synthesizes and secretes these hormones at an accelerated rate, and
3. experiences an increase in mitosis among the secretory cells, thereby increasing size and weight of the glandular tissue.

It would appear that the thyroid gland can do almost nothing without TSH.

TSH Regulation: TSH secretion is strongly influenced by the thyroid releasing factor mentioned earlier in this chapter. The loop is as follows:

1. The hypothalamus releases TRH according to receptor information.
2. TRH stimulates the release of TSH.
3. TSH stimulates an increase in the release of thyroid hormones.
4. These thyroid hormones (not TSH) have a negative effect on the hypothalamic sensors.

For the majority of the pituitary hormones, that is a pretty standard picture. The hormone released by the affected gland is the feedback stimulus for hypothalamic sensors, which in turn control all the rest. There is a complicating factor in the thyroid loop, however. This is not the only feedback loop involved in the control of TSH secretion. There is evidently a second loop—one that bypasses the hypothalamus completely and operates directly on the TSH-producing cells in the pituitary gland. The effect is negative, like the hypothalamic loop, but workers are not really sure why it exists. It seems to function mainly as a high-speed, direct-contact control and is apparently intended for quick, short-term alterations in levels of thyroid hormone.

An Out-of-Control Mechanism: There is another compound in the body that focuses its efforts on the thyroid gland. It is a protein molecule known as **long-acting thyroid stimulator (LATS).** It is usually found in the blood of patients suffering from a disease caused by too much thyroid hormone. LATS belongs to a class of chemicals known as *immunoglobulins* (see chapter 17), and its source is still a mystery.

Adrenal Corticotrophic Hormone (ACTH) ACTH is a fairly large, polypeptide hormone, and it may be the best known of all the pituitary hormones. Scientists knew it existed more than fifty years ago, and not just in animals but in humans as well. Its presence was first suspected when Smith's hypophysectomized rats suffered a near-complete loss of the adrenal cortex. This information was quickly coupled with the observation that human patients with pituitary atrophy nearly always showed adrenal atrophy as well, and under the circumstances, workers would have been pretty dumb not to have tied this together.

ACTH operates on the adrenal cortex in much the same way as TSH affects the thyroid. The core of the gland—the medulla—isn't affected by ACTH at all.

As with all the trophic hormones, ACTH has a whole battery of effects on its target cells.

1. It stimulates the accumulation of the substrates necessary for hormone synthesis.
2. It stimulates the synthesis of the hormones.
3. It increases the secretion of the hormones.
4. It increases the growth of adrenal secretory tissue by stimulating mitosis in the cells there.

ACTH Regulation: The feedback mechanisms that control ACTH secretion are remarkably similar to those involved in TSH control. Levels of adrenal hormones in the blood apparently represent the feedback stimulus, and as with the thyroid, there are two separate control loops. There is one that goes through the hypothalamus and involves a releasing factor and a second one that bypasses the hypothalamus and works directly on the pituitary.

The Gonadotrophic Hormones Like TSH, both the follicle-stimulating hormone (FSH) and the luteinizing hormone (LH) are glycoproteins. Also like TSH, the carbohydrates make up about 7 to 8 percent of the molecule, and the rest is amino acids. Both of the gonadotrophic hormones are big, double-stranded molecules, and both have molecular weights of around 32,000 daltons.

They are designed to supervise and guide the secretions of the gonads. Since males and females are very different in their cycles of sexual activity, the secretion of both FSH and LH depends to some extent on a person's gender. Prior to puberty, there is no secretion of either; in fact, their secretion signals the end of childhood and the onset of puberty.

In girls, with the first surges of gonadotrophins, the menstrual cycles begin. This cycle rotates around a lunar, or 30-day, hub, and it is the hypothalamus that establishes and controls it through the pituitary. FSH starts things off. One of the first things it does is to select an egg to work on from the thousands of eggs inside the ovaries. Human ovaries contain, in fact, around 300,000 eggs. That represents 300,000 potential menstrual cycles, yet if we assume that an average woman has forty years of reproductive life, she has time for only about 520 such cycles. That means that most of the eggs will never be used, so those that *are* used become doubly important. Just what criteria FSH uses in selecting an egg, no one knows. It is possible that there are none—that the eggs are picked completely at random, and that pure chance determines the genetic makeup contributed by the female. It is also possible, although purely speculative, that there is some detailed scrutinizing of the egg and its genetic material, and the final selection is determined by some unknown but desirable characteristics. Whatever the mechanism, it is the FSH that uses it to select the egg, and under its influence the chosen follicle begins to mature, and the egg it contains begins to ripen.

LH enters the pattern shortly after FSH does, and it starts to surge about the time FSH levels begin to drop a little. You might say that LH picks up where FSH leaves off. That is not completely accurate, however, because LH seems to concentrate its efforts on the cells that produce female hormones, while FSH appears to concern itself mainly with the egg and the cells that directly support it. Nevertheless, as LH levels continue to go up, FSH levels steadily drop, until LH becomes the dominant gonadotrophin. Because it focuses on the hormone-producing cells, there is an increase in the output of female sex hormones. During this surge, the egg completes its ripening and quickly bursts from the follicle, beginning the process known as **ovulation,** during which it journeys into the fallopian tubes, where it waits to be fertilized. The empty follicle, meanwhile, fills with secretory cells and begins to develop into a functioning endocrine gland. Influenced by LH, these cells fill with the yellowish, oil-soluble hormone known as **progesterone,** and the structure takes on a different function and a brand-new name—the **corpus luteum,** which means "yellow body."

As could only be expected, the function of gonadotrophins in males is both similar to and different from their job in women. For one thing, when FSH flows in women, a single germ cell develops; when it flows in males, its influence results in the production of germ cells by the billions. In women, viable reproductive cells are produced at the rate of one every thirty days or so, whereas in men, germ cell production is a process that continues on a more or less constant basis. In boys past the age of puberty, the gonadotrophins are not involved with a lunar cycle. There are some circadian rhythms, but even they are not uniformly dependable.

As to similarities, FSH and LH appear to concentrate on the same *types* of cells in both sexes. The major focus of FSH in females is the germinal epithelium, and that is essentially the same target as in males. In boys, FSH promotes the descent of the testes from the abdominal cavity into the scrotum, and it can increase the size and weight of the gonads. In men, it's responsible for stimulating the germinal cells in the seminiferous tubules to produce **spermatozoons,** the primary male reproductive cells.

In males, LH has a different name, but its primary target is, as in females, the hormone-producing interstitial cells. Hence its name—**interstitial cell-stimulating hormone (ICSH).** ICSH stimulates the synthesis and secretion of the gonadal hormones (see figure 10.9). It is also able to stimulate the repair of damaged male accessories, and its ability to accomplish this is sometimes amazing. If only a few cells of testicular tissue remain in the male scrotum, LH can stimulate regrowth of a completely new, functioning testicle.

Gonadotrophic Feedback Loops: Both LH and FSH are under the control of the same hypothalamic releasing factor, LHRH. There have been many attempts to find a separate releasing factor that involves only FSH, but none have been successful up to this point. The loop itself appears to be relatively simple. LHRH responds to blood levels of the primary sex hormones, and the hypothalamus is evidently not bypassed at any point. The controlling stimulus for release of LHRH is low levels of estrogens in the case of women, testosterone in men.

Figure 10.9 The gonadotrophin feedback loop. The broken line indicates an abbreviated feedback loop that may involve direct stimulation of the hypothalamus by the gonadotrophins. This loop is currently under investigation.

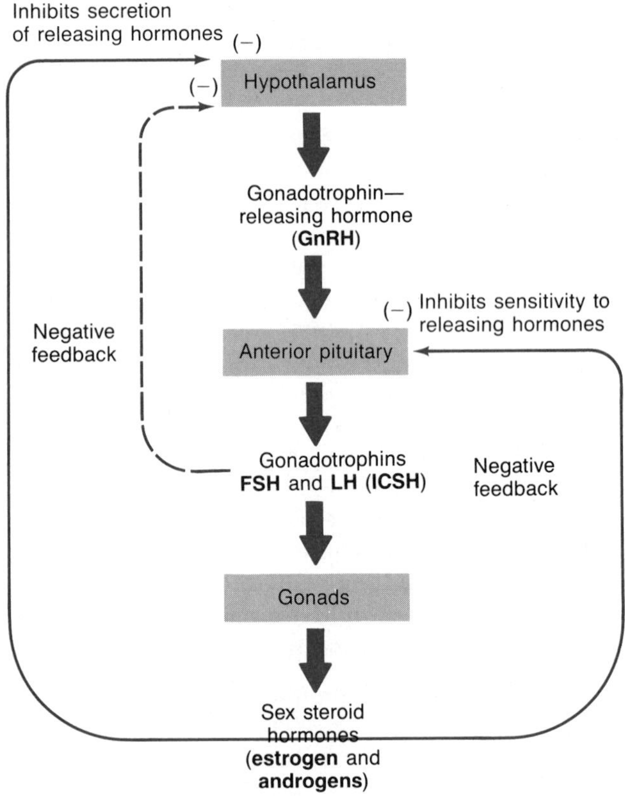

Modern oral contraceptives operate by disrupting the cyclic release of LHRH, and they do this by "fooling" hypothalamic cells with gonadal hormones. "The Pill" contains the female sex hormone and injects its influence into the feedback loop right where it begins. Taking sex hormones orally raises their blood levels considerably, and sex hormones have a negative feedback effect on the hypothalamus. These high levels of female sex hormones tell the hypothalamus that it need not stimulate the release of FSH or LH, and so it doesn't. The result is FSH never selects and ripens an egg, and LH never stimulates ovulation or development of a corpus luteum. Since there is no ripe egg in the fallopian tubules for a sperm to fertilize, no amount of sexual activity can result in a pregnancy.

The Pars Intermedia (Intermediate Lobe)

This is a relatively minor bit of pituitary tissue in humans—in fact, in all mammals. In reptiles, however, it dominates the entire gland. Almost certainly this is because the pars intermedia is the source of a hormone called **melanocyte-stimulating hormone (MSH).** MSH stimulates a group of cells known as **melanocytes** to alter certain of their states.

Melanocytes

Melanocytes contain a dark brown pigment called **melanin** and are imbedded by the millions in the epidermal layers of the skin. Humans everywhere have about the same number of melanocytes, but the amount of melanin that the cells contain can vary from group to group. Negroid groups, for example, have a lot of such pigment. Neither orientals nor caucasoids have as much as the negroid peoples, but they can have a great deal nevertheless. Actually, both groups vary quite broadly. For example, caucasoids from the Indian Peninsula or Middle Eastern countries often have enough melanin to produce dark brown complexions, while Nordic blondes typically possess considerably less. People with reddish hair and the typical Celtic complexion have the least of all, except in isolated patches called *freckles.* Within the range limits that exist for an individual's human group, their skin shade can vary over a rather broad range, depending at any given moment on the distribution of melanocytes and the pigment within each cell.

When the pigment-containing granules are clumped together, only small surfaces are exposed, and the cells appear light or even transparent. When the granules scatter and spread out, maximum surface area is exposed, and the light-absorbing properties of our skin surface are altered. MSH spreads out the granules. The more MSH that is present in the blood, the more the pigment granules will disperse, and the greater their dispersion, the more deeply colored and opaque the skin surface will appear. MSH is also able to increase pigment synthesis within the melanocytes, and it can increase it to such an extent that extra pigment can be passed to structures outside the melanocyte.

To present some sort of picture of what is going on, imagine you had a pure white handkerchief one foot square. In the middle of this cloth, you placed one cubic inch of black carbon powder similar to the type used in copying machines. As long as that cubic inch of powder stays clumped in a small area, a visitor, when asked the color of the cloth, will call it white. But fold the cloth over to form a bag and shake it up to disperse that cubic inch of powder, then lay it back down again. That same person who a moment before called the cloth white, would now call it black or at least gray, because the powder would cover the entire surface and would have colored it. The amount of black powder hasn't changed, but now it is dispersed and is much more prominent. That is very similar to what happens in a melanocyte when MSH stimulates dispersion of the pigment granules.

MSH Regulation

Darkening of the skin (tanning) is associated with exposure to the sun; that much we know. We also realize that darkening the skin through the tanning process is probably a protective mechanism. The high-frequency, short wavelengths of light contain a great deal of energy—so much, in fact, that they can damage body chemistry by knocking proteins and other biochemicals apart. Dark pigments absorb radiation, and it is assumed that MSH darkens the upper, dermal layer of the skin to protect the living dermis beneath it from harmful, high-energy radiation that could cause damage. Tanning as a result of lying in such radiation is, therefore, a perfectly logical homeostatic precaution. However, the precise stimulus that increases MSH synthesis and secretion and thus darkens the skin has been very hard to isolate. There is little, if any, doubt that solar radiation is responsible, and the most effective fraction is the UV band, but no one has been able to find the receptors in humans. Almost every logical alternative has been suggested and tested, but to date, none of them has produced any decent supporting evidence. The most obvious receptor is the eyes, of course, but tanning can occur quite nicely when the eyes are completely covered. In some animals, the pineal gland is involved, and its response to visible light, particularly in reptiles, has been confirmed, but there is no reason to believe it is involved in humans—not as a receptor, at any rate . . . it is much too deep in the brain for any solar radiation to reach.

The activities of the adenohypophysis are illustrated in figure 10.10.

The Neurohypophysis (Posterior Pituitary)

The posterior lobe of the pituitary gland is actually a short extension of the hypothalamus, which means it is part of the brain. At least half of it is made up of

Figure 10.10 The hormones of the adenohypophysis and their main target tissues.

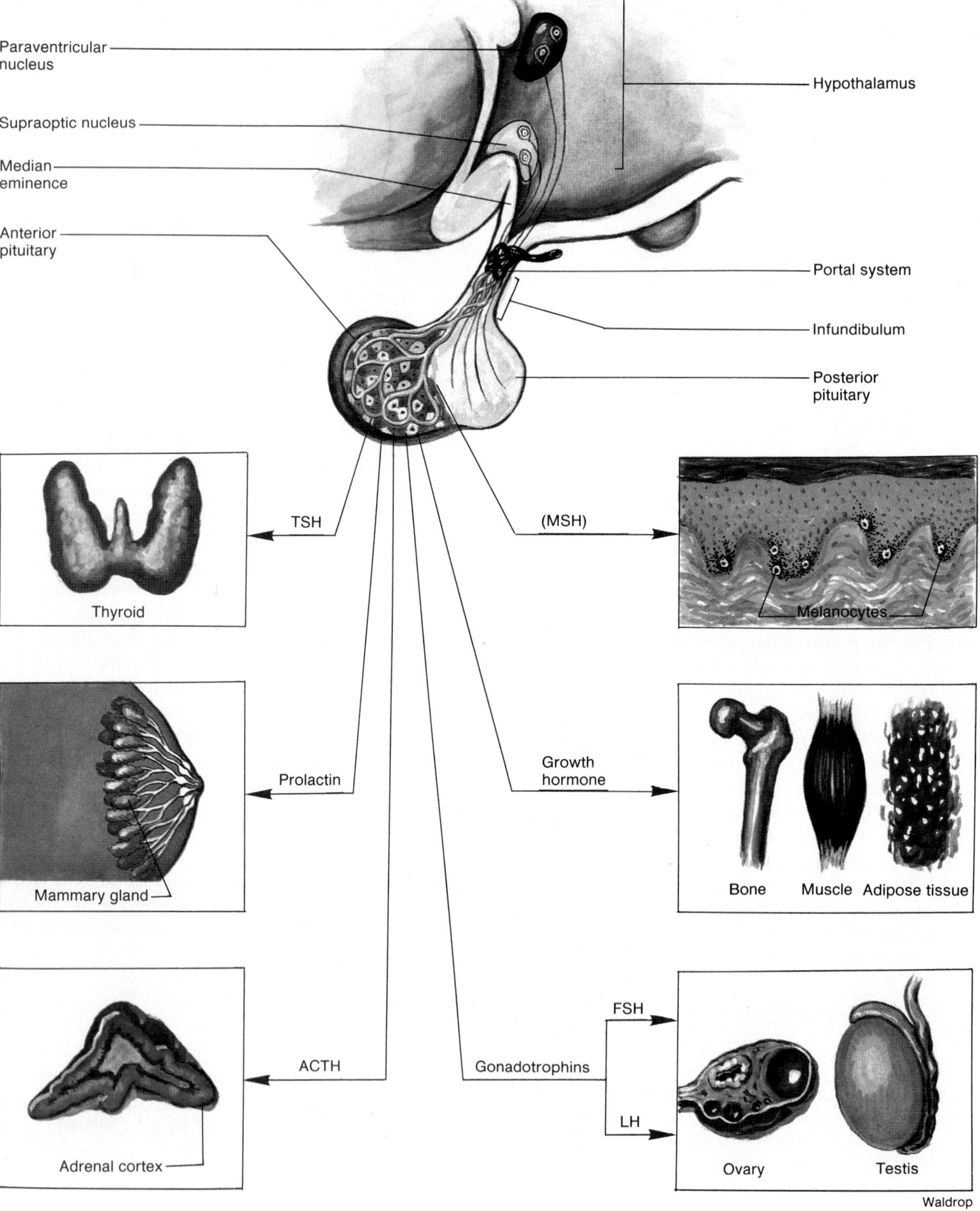

nerves or nerve axons, and there are firm neural connections between it and other portions of the brain (figure 10.11).

It was the neurohypophysis and its associated hypothalamic nuclei that gave researchers their first firm evidence of the phenomenon called **neurosecretion:** the release of special chemicals by neurons. The secretory neuron represents a combination of two classic cell types. They are neurons, and so are able to receive stimuli from adjacent nerve cells and transmit these stimuli as electrical signals. They are also endocrine cells, and like all endocrine cells, they synthesize a specific chemical that they release into the blood. Such cells are known today as **neuroendocrine cells.**

Figure 10.11 The neurohypophysis (posterior pituitary) showing the two hypothalamic nuclei with which it is most closely associated.

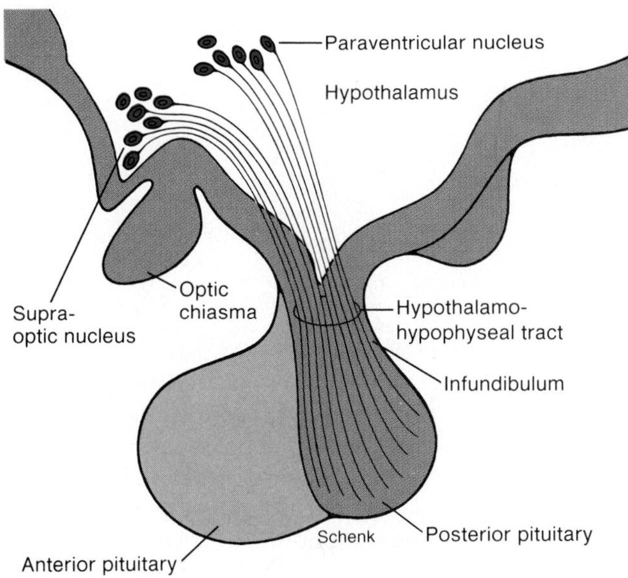

There are two hormones that are released by the neurohypophysis. Both are small peptides, and while they are secreted into the blood from the pituitary gland, they are actually synthesized in the hypothalamus. Two pairs of large nuclei—the **supraoptic (SON)** and the **paraventricular (PVN)**—are responsible (figure 10.6). The nerve fibers that pack the neurohypophysis have cell bodies in these two nuclei, and since all the DNA, ribosomes, and mitochondria are in the cell body, this is where the synthesis would have to be done.

Hormonal Synthesis

The hormones are synthesized in the soma of the neurons packed into their respective nuclei. They are packaged by their Golgi apparatuses in an inactive form and activated as they migrate down the axons into the posterior lobe of the pituitary where they are stored.

Both neurohypophyseal hormones are octapeptides, and each has a molecular weight of about 1,000. Chemically they are very similar. Functionally, they are quite different. The hormone synthesized in the SON is called **vasopressin** or **antidiuretic hormone (ADH),** while that from the PVN is called **oxytocin.** Both are fairly strong smooth muscle stimulants and cause widespread contraction of such muscle, particularly in peripheral blood vessels. ADH, however, has a more profound role to play in the kidney, where it stimulates the increased retention of water that might be lost through urination (figure 10.12). We will discuss this action in more detail in chapter 16.

Figure 10.12 Where the neurohypophyseal hormones oxytocin and vasopressin exert their effects.

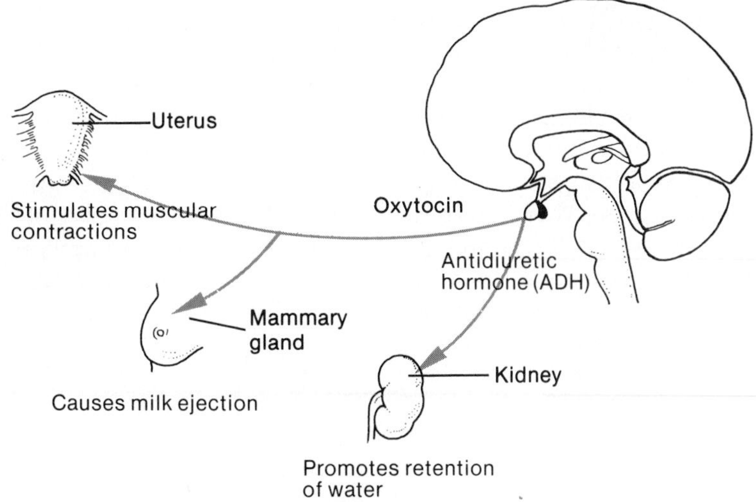

Oxytocin is not restricted to causing the contraction of blood vessel walls, either. Like vasopressin, it has some specialized functions. In females, it plays a major role in both the instigation of labor during childbirth and the secretion of milk following parturition. Levels of oxytocin start to surge shortly before labor begins, and it works to hasten the expulsion of both the infant and the placenta during parturition. Once parturition is finished, oxytocin collaborates with prolactin to stimulate the increased synthesis and secretion of milk from the mammary gland; in fact, without oxytocin, milk will not flow at all.

Evidently, both ADH and oxytocin have myriad other functions, most of which are still under investigation. Both can, and probably do, function as neurotransmitters, and they apparently also serve as substrates for the **catecholamine** neurotransmitters—epinephrine and/or dopamine. They seem to have considerable influence on important higher brain functions as well. Vasopressin, for instance, has been shown to augment both short- and long-term memory, and the effects last a very long time—in fact, its reputation in this line is so good that it has been used to treat amnesia patients, with considerable success. Oxytocin—so similar in structure, yet so different in activity—seems to antagonize this attribute of vasopressin. In fact, it opposes the establishment of long-term memory patterns so vigorously that it has been suggested by some psychologists that certain learning problems in children could be due to its presence in their systems. Oxytocin also is involved in altering certain behavior patterns concerned with reproduction. There is little doubt that it's at least partly responsible for instigating "maternal behavior" in rats, and it may have a soothing effect on human mothers while they are nursing.

The Neurohypophyseal Feedback Loops

Since both hormones are synthesized in the hypothalamus, it naturally participates in their regulation, but there are no releasing hormones involved. There are direct neural contacts between the hypothalamus and the posterior pituitary gland, and these contacts serve as the controlling release mechanisms. When either hormone is needed, action potentials travel from the cell bodies to the nerve endings in the neurohypophysis, and the hormones are then released into the blood. Apparently, except for the stimulus, one cell type furnishes all the mechanisms used in feedback control: the receptor cells also function as the integrators, and all evidence to date indicates that the receptor cells are the same cells that synthesize the hormone.

Figure 10.13 The antidiuretic hormone feedback loop.

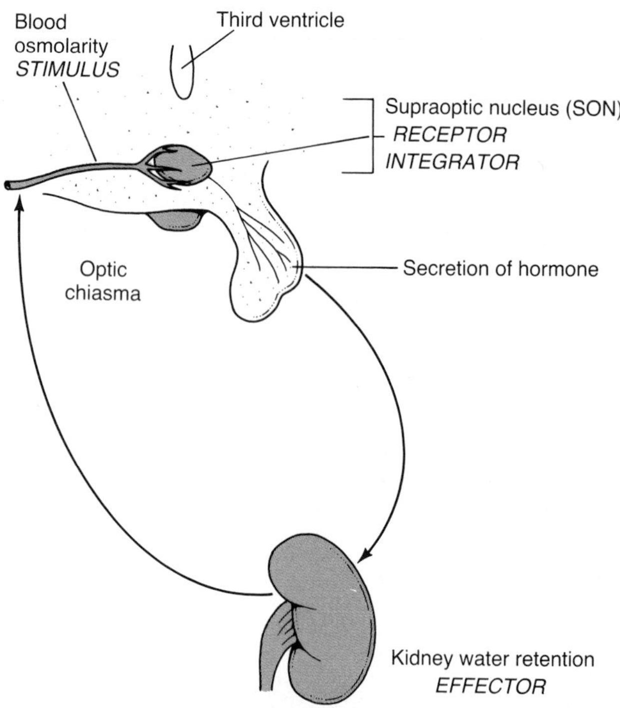

Vasopressin (ADH) The primary stimulus for the secretion of ADH is evidently an increase in the osmolarity of the blood flowing through the hypothalamus. Receptor potentials appear in the neurosecretory cells of the SON when the blood's osmotic pressure increases. An increase in blood osmolarity is an indication that water supplies are running a bit low and that water must be conserved, so ADH is released to stimulate increased retention of body water. When blood osmolarity drops, it is a clear indication that water supplies are building up. If they become excessive, neurohypophyseal secretion shuts down, permitting a heavy outflow of dilute urine from the excretory system (figure 10.13).

Oxytocin Oxytocin is not influenced by blood osmolarity. Evidently, its primary stimulus is the stretching of the muscles of the uterus as its contents approach term, information that is relayed via a specific nerve tract into the paraventricular nucleus. Apparently, when the muscles wrapping the uterus and its contents reach a certain length, information to this effect is sent to the neurosecretory cells of the PVN, oxytocin is released, and labor begins. (This, of course,

Figure 10.14 The oxytocin feedback loop.

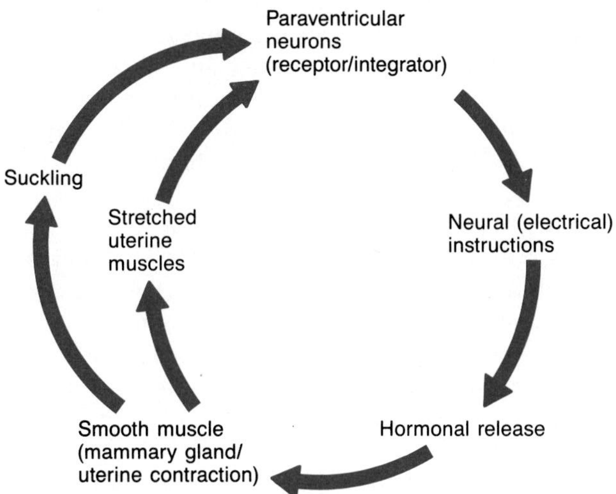

could explain why multiple births are so often premature. When more than one fetus occupies the interior of the uterus, the increased presence produces a greater stretch and therefore stimulates a premature release of oxytocin, which in turn begins the heavy muscle contractions that signal the onset of labor.)

Once the childbirth is completed, oxytocin continues to be released at low rates which, as we noted above, helps provide adequate milk for the nursing infant. This is important, of course, but there is considerable evidence to indicate that the continued outflow of oxytocin has a more immediate function. Recent work suggests that it stimulates postpartum contractions of the uterus that return that organ to its original size. In the process, it constricts any broken uterine blood vessels, thereby reducing the possibility of uncontrollable postpartum hemorrhage. The controlling feedback loop is shown in figure 10.14.

Most endocrinologists no longer consider the pituitary the endocrine control center, because the hypothalamus controls it. One should be careful, however, not to let semantics diminish the importance of a gland that obviously exerts profound control over so many aspects of homeostasis. Gonadal hormones, the adrenal cortical hormones, thyroid secretions, growth hormone, mammary milk production and release, and a large percentage of water reabsorption by the kidney are all powerfully influenced by the pituitary gland. Without it, a person would die in a few days. Control center or not, it is still a master gland and is obviously critical to our continued survival.

Figure 10.15 The location and morphology of the thyroid gland. (*a*) The position of the thyroid gland with respect to the trachea and layrnx. (*b*) Simplified drawing of a microscopic view within the thyroid. The colloid represents a hormonal storage compound.

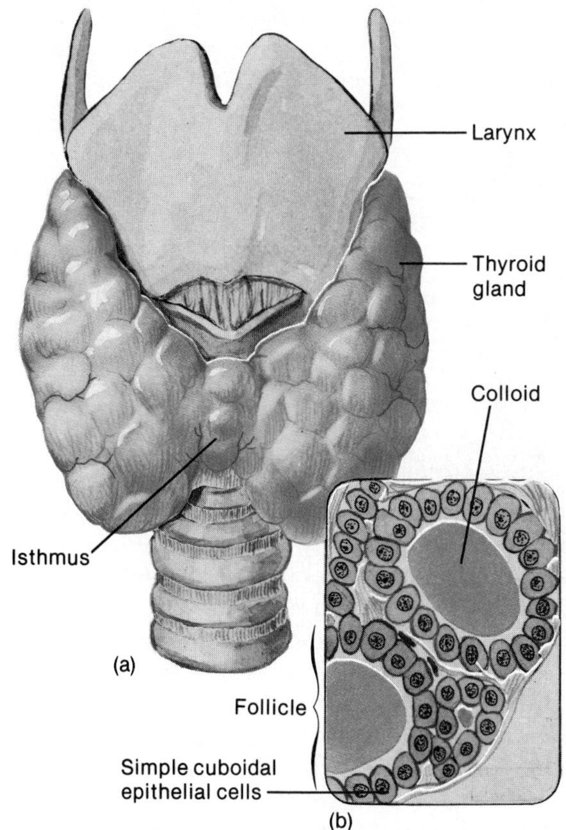

The Thyroid Gland

The thyroid is a diffuse, rather spongy gland with an enormous blood supply (figure 10.15). The name means "shield-like," referring to the fact that it is shaped like the old rawhide shields carried by ancient Spartan warriors.

As you can see, it resides in the throat at about the level of the larynx and actually wraps around the trachea (windpipe). It starts functioning about the third month of fetal life and immediately becomes involved with so many aspects of cellular and intercellular operations that science has not yet pinned them all down. The fetus must provide its own thyroid hormone, because for some reason it is not able to use its mother's. Researchers are not sure why, but the easiest explanation is that maternal thyroid hormone cannot cross the placental capillaries from the mother's blood to the baby's. This is surprising, because thyroid hormones are much smaller than many compounds that cross easily, but there are precedents for such phenomena.

Figure 10.16 The follicles of the thyroid gland. In this photomicrograph, the lumina within the follicles are filled with a fluid known as *colloid*, which contains the thyroid hormones.

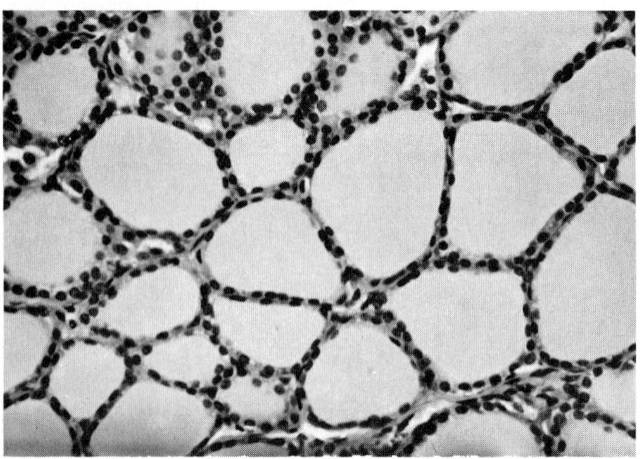

Morphologically, the thyroid belongs to the "clump" or "raspberry" type of endocrine gland. In this case, there are many such clumps—called **follicles**—microscopic baskets of cells surrounding a central cavity (figure 10.16). There does not appear to be any particular uniformity about the size of these follicles, nor is their shape consistent, but they do have some common characteristics. They are all hollow spheres, they all contain the same substance, and they are all very heavily vascularized. In fact, the amount of blood that flows through the thyroid gland is ten times the amount that flows through the liver, a much larger organ.

Between the follicles are groups of cells called **extrafollicular cells** that were ignored by science for forty years because they seemed to have no function. Not until the late 1950s did it become apparent that they were responsible for the synthesis of a new and different hormone whose presence no one had suspected.

Inside each follicle is an aqueous dispersion called simply **colloid.** In addition to water, colloid is made up of a large molecule known as **thyroglobulin.** It is a glycoprotein consisting of five thousand amino acids arranged in four chains, and about 10 percent of it is carbohydrate. Of those five thousand amino acids, only about 150 are potential thyroid hormone molecules. The purpose of the others has never been determined.

Thyroid Hormones

The thyroid gland produces several hormones. Of those that contain iodine, all are quite similar chemically (figure 10.17), and all have qualitatively similar functions.

The only noniodinated hormone released by the thyroid gland is calcitonin, a recently-discovered product of the interfollicular cells. It is a much larger polypeptide and bears no functional relationship to the others at all —in fact, it is such an alien that when thyroid hormones are discussed in the endocrinological community, it is never part of the conversation. We, too, will ignore it for the time being.

The iodinated hormones have various names, but they are all the same except for the location of the iodine atoms that are hooked onto them. They are built on a simple amino acid nucleus (tyrosine), and all of them are critical to health and life-quality. They are responsible for a seemingly diverse series of activities throughout the entire body, not all of which have been worked out.

In mammals, including humans, they are definitely involved in the regulation of cellular metabolism, a function easily confirmed. In the absence of thyroid hormones, the metabolic rate drops alarmingly low, yet simple oral administration of the hormones will promptly restore it to its original rate. Its function in the lower vertebrates is quite variable, and in the amphibians it has the most unusual role of all.

Iodine: The Mystery Element

The critical element in the synthesis of the thyroid hormones is **iodine.** It is ingested in the foods we eat as an iodide salt, and it is quickly concentrated in the cells of the thyroid gland. In fact, the ability to accumulate iodine against a powerful concentration gradient is the thyroid gland's chief accomplishment, for apparently lots of other cells in the body can make the thyroid hormones.

The physiological role of iodine has never been determined. Researchers do not know what it does, where or how it works, nor do they know why it has to be iodine that is used, but there is no doubting its importance. The thyroid hormones are inert without it. Just moving it around a little bit can be critical. If a single iodine atom is removed from the top ring of **thyroxin** (called a T_4 hormone because it contains four iodine atoms—see figure 10.17), it is changed to the T_3 compound known as **triiodothyronine** or **TRIT.** That is not much of a change chemically, but physiologically it is drastic. TRIT has several characteristics, including roughly ten times the activity rate of thyroxin, that render it distinctly different from any of the other T hormones. Taken all together, the properties of TRIT have led many workers to feel that TRIT is the *only* active T hormone—that the other forms are merely storage forms. That may or may not be true, but there is no arguing with the fact that very little of the circulatory or stored hormone is in the form of TRIT. Most of the body's iodinated hormones are in the T_4 form, and certainly there is no quarrel

Figure 10.17 The major hormones of the thyroid gland. The movement of a single iodine atom can make an enormous difference in hormonal activity. Thyroxin is only one-tenth as active as TRIT, and reverse TRIT has less than one-hundredth the activity of TRIT.

Thyroxin (a T_4 hormone)

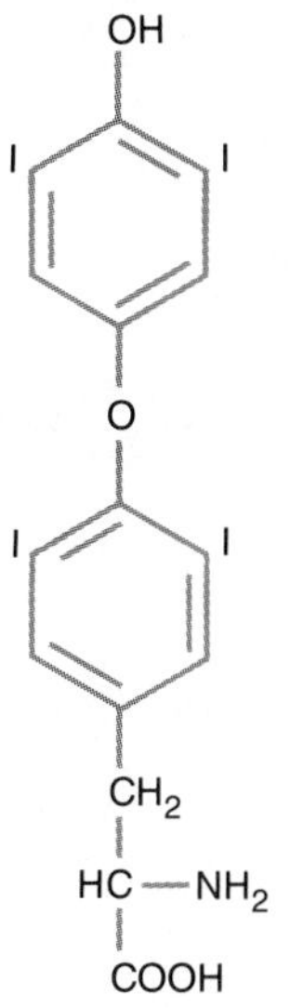

Triiodothyronine (TRIT) a T_3 hormone

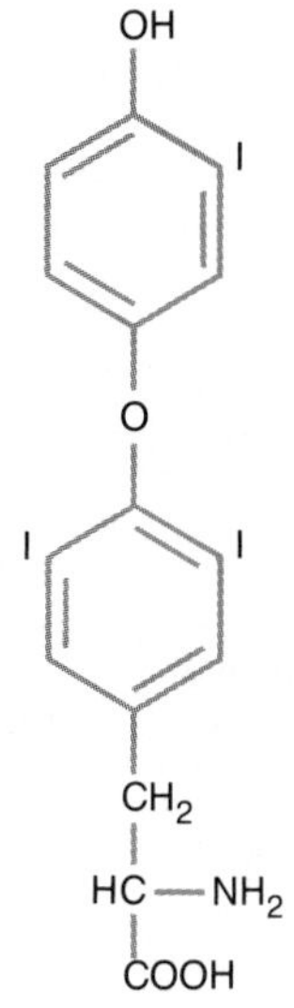

Reverse TRIT

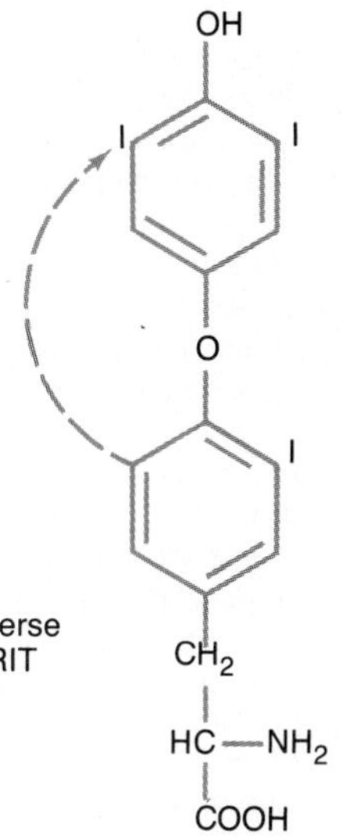

over their lower activity. Researchers generally regard thyroxin as a comparatively inactive molecule that is present in the blood in relatively large amounts, thus representing a large storage reservoir—one that is immediately available in any kind of emergency. When needed, all a cell has to do is deiodinate the molecule from T_4 to T_3 and it is ready to use.

Once inside the cell, the T hormones increase oxygen uptake by body cells, stimulate their ability to break up carbohydrates and fats for fuel, and increase the synthesis of mitochondrial DNA. Levels of metabolic enzymes inside the cell's mitochondria increase, too, probably due to the activity of T hormones. All these activities put together represent an increase in cellular metabolic rate, which means increased production of both ATP and heat.

T Hormones: Mechanism of Action

The thyroid hormone may be the most unusual of all the proteinaceous hormones in its mechanism of action. The thyroid hormones resemble the lipid hormones in their ability to penetrate the plasma membrane, but once in the cytoplasm, their activity is unique. Utilizing an energy source that has not yet been identified, they make their way to the nuclear envelope, which they penetrate with apparent ease, and bind to protein **nuclear receptors** that are in contact with the nuclear DNA. In a manner not clearly understood, they increase the production of a special strip of mRNA, which then migrates into the cytoplasm, where it guides the synthesis of special enzymes (figure 10.18).

Figure 10.18 Mechanism of action of the thyroid hormones. T_4 (or T_3) hormones approach the membrane. T_3 hormones enter the cell immediately, but T_4 hormones are deiodinated in the membrane. Inside the cell, the T_3 hormones migrate to the nucleus and enter. Inside the nucleus, they bind to protein receptors that are in contact with strands of DNA. The protein/hormone complex in some manner increases the production of a strip of RNA.

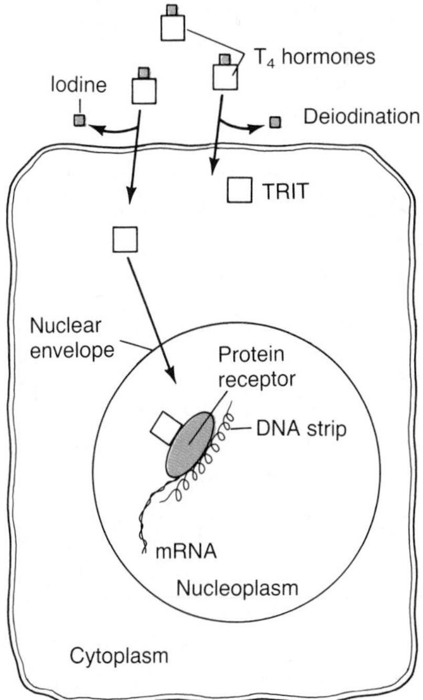

It seems reasonably certain that when the ambient temperature is low and the mammalian body is beginning to cool too much, there is a general increase in metabolic rate that might be due to the activity of the thyroid. Shivering is a common response. It is rapid muscle activity which, like any other activity, requires energy. As the muscle cells oxidize fuel to obtain this energy, they create extra heat along with it, boosting the body's internal temperature. Heat production and the maintenance of their high body temperature is the main reason that mammals and birds require so much more food than reptiles or amphibians. It has been estimated that more than 70 percent of the energy we obtain from food is used to maintain our high internal body temperature and that this percentage goes up when it is cold outside. It is, if you'll pardon the pun, food for thought. Maybe the answer to burning extra body fat and reducing obesity is to exercise someplace where it is really cold. Certainly, exercise alone does not consume an awful lot of calories—a person has to run a couple of miles just to burn up three or four hundred. Maybe a half-hour swim in water that is about 55° to 60° F will burn off a lot more by stimulating increased metabolic effort to keep warm.

Increasing cellular metabolism is the thyroid function that we understand most completely, but it is certainly not the only function. The T hormones do much more than increase metabolic rate. During early childhood, they are essential if heart, lungs, brain, and the intestines are to develop properly, and they are particularly effective in the brain. There is no increase in the number of brain cells after birth, but there is a great deal of architectural adjustment—like elongation of neuronal fibers and establishment of new synaptic connections. Apparently the T hormones play a major role. What is more, their operations are *time* dependent, meaning thyroid hormones must be present in the correct quantities when they are needed, not earlier and certainly not later. Infants who lack the hormone at the critical time will never achieve proper brain development, even if the system is flooded with T hormones later on.

Calcitonin (CT)

As mentioned previously, calcitonin is produced in the extrafollicular cells of the thyroid gland. It is not involved at all in metabolic rate, cellular development, or any other endeavor that seems to occupy the iodinated hormones. Its function involves calcium metabolism; it serves to lower the levels of dissolved calcium in body fluids when they get too high. CT was discovered in the 1960s almost by accident, and its complete structure was only recently elucidated (figure 10.19). There are several reasons for such a late identification. The main one is that the existence of the hormone was not suspected, because removal of the thyroid gland produced no disruption in calcium metabolism.

Figure 10.19 The amino acid sequence of the hormone calcitonin.

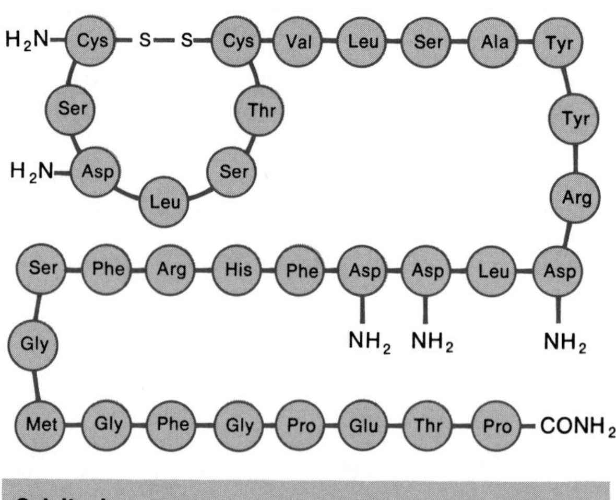

That suggests that the hormone is not essential for any particular body function, an observation that clearly violates Bayliss and Starling's first criterion. Yet it fits all the other criteria, so it is generally conceded to be a hormone.

There is considerable dispute about the nonessential nature of CT. Why does it appear to be relatively innocuous in mammals? No one is really sure, but several suggestions have been offered. It has, for instance, been suggested that CT is an evolutionary relic that was essential way back in our evolutionary past but has no significant function in humans any more. This is possible, of course. Yet it is hard to reconcile with the fact that humans have many elaborate mechanisms that regulate the release of calcitonin, and pound for pound, we release more CT than any other vertebrate. Another possible explanation is that its essential nature is masked by the operations of CT-producing cells that may be present elsewhere in the body. Maybe removal of the thyroid gland results in no calcium disruption because CT is still present—limited amounts being produced by the thymus gland and a few other body cells. As you can see from the divergence of these two theories, there is a lot we do not know about calcium metabolism and its regulatory mechanisms.

Calcitonin Function

We know a little. We know that CT reduces blood calcium levels by opposing the effects of several substances designed to *increase* calcium levels in the blood. Most of these substances increase blood calcium by stimulating activity in a group of bone cells called **osteoclasts.** Osteoclasts break up the calcium salts that form the "cement" in bone and release the freed calcium into the blood, so opposing their activity will inhibit the release of calcium. Calcitonin further augments this effect by reducing the ability of the small intestine to absorb calcium from foodstuffs, thereby depressing any tendencies for dissolved calcium to increase. But these effects are inhibitory, and apparently they are essentially passive. When CT is injected into a subject, blood calcium levels drop rapidly, which suggests that some active removal mechanisms must exist. Yet none have been found. There do not appear to be any reactions that stimulate the flushing of dissolved calcium out of the kidneys or force increased activity of the bone cells that use calcium.

Calcitonin Regulation

It has been assumed for years that increased blood calcium is the stimulus for the release of CT, but this has been questioned recently as being too simplistic. For example, CT levels increase substantially during pregnancy. It has been assumed that its purpose is to protect the mother against excessive bone demineralization while the skeleton of the fetus is being built, and since that is certainly reasonable, no one argues that point. However, during pregnancy there is usually a noticeable *lowering* of calcium in the blood as it passes through the placental circulation, and the potential mother requires a much higher-than-normal calcium intake just to maintain normal levels. If increased calcium stimulates CT release, why would CT levels go up during that time, when calcium is so low?

The fact is that the mechanisms underlying CT release are not really known. There is some experimental evidence to suggest that both nervous and endocrine activity can control it, possibly better than levels of blood calcium, but the evidence is shaky. Obviously, a lot more research is needed.

The Parathyroid Glands

The parathyroids are the smallest of the endocrine glands, weighing just over 1 mg each, but they are far from the least important. They are on the posterior surface of the thyroid gland, and the superior (upper) pair is often imbedded deeply in thyroid tissue (figure 10.20). The only hormone released by this gland—as far as is known—is a peptide called **parathormone (PTH)** that contains eighty-four amino acids. Like calcitonin, PTH is involved in calcium metabolism, but its actions are antagonistic to those of CT. The function of CT is, as we have seen, to reduce levels of dissolved calcium in our body fluids; the function of PTH is to increase them.

Calcium

Calcium is a tremendously important ion. It is involved in nervous activity, muscle activity, synaptic transmission, oxidative phosphorylation, blood clotting . . . the list is endless. Yet despite its strong tendency to polarize, it is not particularly soluble in

Figure 10.20 The parathyroid glands in humans. The superior (upper) pair is usually imbedded deeply in the tissue of the thryoid gland.

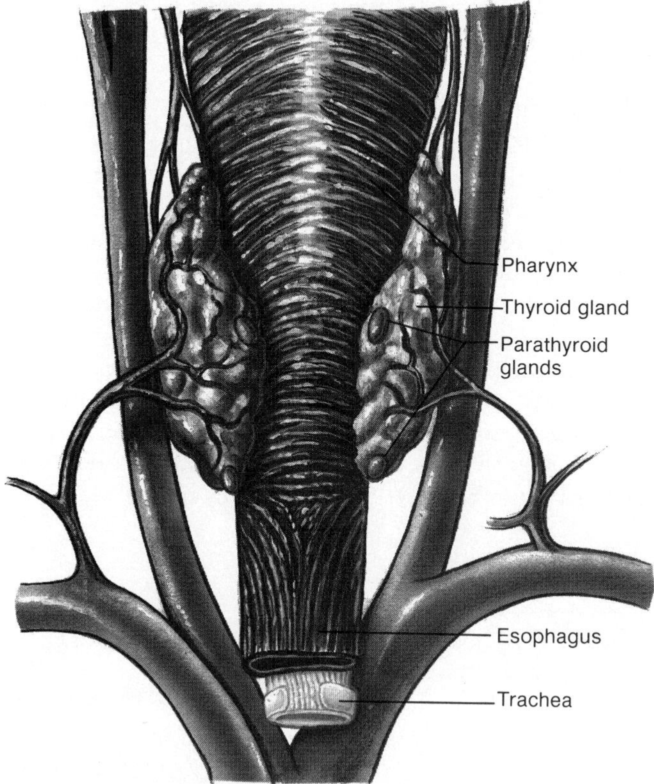

neutral or alkaline watery dispersions, which is what blood is. In fact, if we were to take a calcium salt and try to dissolve it in human plasma, we would only be able to get about 7 mg to dissolve in 100 ml of blood (such a concentration is referred to by the medical community as *7 mg percent* or *per deciliter*). As it turns out, however, normal blood concentration in humans is between 9.5 and 10.5 mg/dl, and that much simply will not dissolve without some catalytic manipulation of the aqueous environment. Obviously, something is doing just that, and that something is PTH.

Calcium vs. Phosphate

Calcium and phosphate are reciprocal ions, meaning that their solubilities in blood plasma are related. The blood will only dissolve so much of both of them, so when the concentration of one goes up, the other must go down. Therefore, before the blood concentration of calcium can increase, there must be some simultaneous lowering of dissolved phosphates. PTH utilizes this phenomenon in its adjustment of dissolved calcium. To do this, it exerts its physiological dexterity on both the bones and the kidneys.

The kidneys play important roles in regulating blood phosphates. They can adjust rapidly to sudden changes in blood phosphate concentrations and can alter phosphate excretion rates very quickly. Normally more than 75 percent of the phosphates that enter the kidney return to the blood, and when blood phosphates drop unusually low, that reabsorption figure rises to nearly 100 percent. PTH can change all this by its mere presence.

PTH Function

When PTH is present in the blood, osteoclastic activity in the skeleton is stimulated. As I mentioned earlier, osteoclastic activity results in the breaking up of bone salts and the release of increased quantities of both calcium and phosphate into the blood. That could present a problem, because all that extra phosphate turning up in the blood, if left alone, would reduce calcium levels instead of boosting them. PTH takes care of the problem by inhibiting the ability of the kidneys to return phosphates to the blood. As a result, all the extra phosphate plus a little more is excreted quite rapidly. Still operating in the kidneys, PTH also works to activate a **vitamin D** substrate that collaborates with PTH to increase blood levels of calcium.

Vitamin D

Despite its name, vitamin D is not, strictly speaking, a vitamin. Vitamins are, by definition, substances that the body needs, but cannot synthesize, and we can synthesize vitamin D. Most physiologists and biochemists today tend to view vitamin D as a hormone—a steroid hormone with the name **calciferol.** Calciferol, like all the steroid hormones, is built on a nucleus of cholesterol. But unlike the other steroids, it requires one thing that the body cannot take in and store, and that is sunlight. Sunlight stimulates a critical step in the manufacture of calciferol, and if sunlight is not present, its manufacture stops. Once sunlight has irradiated and altered the growing molecule, the final synthetic steps can proceed. The last step in calciferol synthesis is called *calciferol activation* and is accomplished in the kidney under the influence of PTH (figure 10.21).

Figure 10.21 The role of vitamin D (calciferol) in absorption of calcium from the intestine.

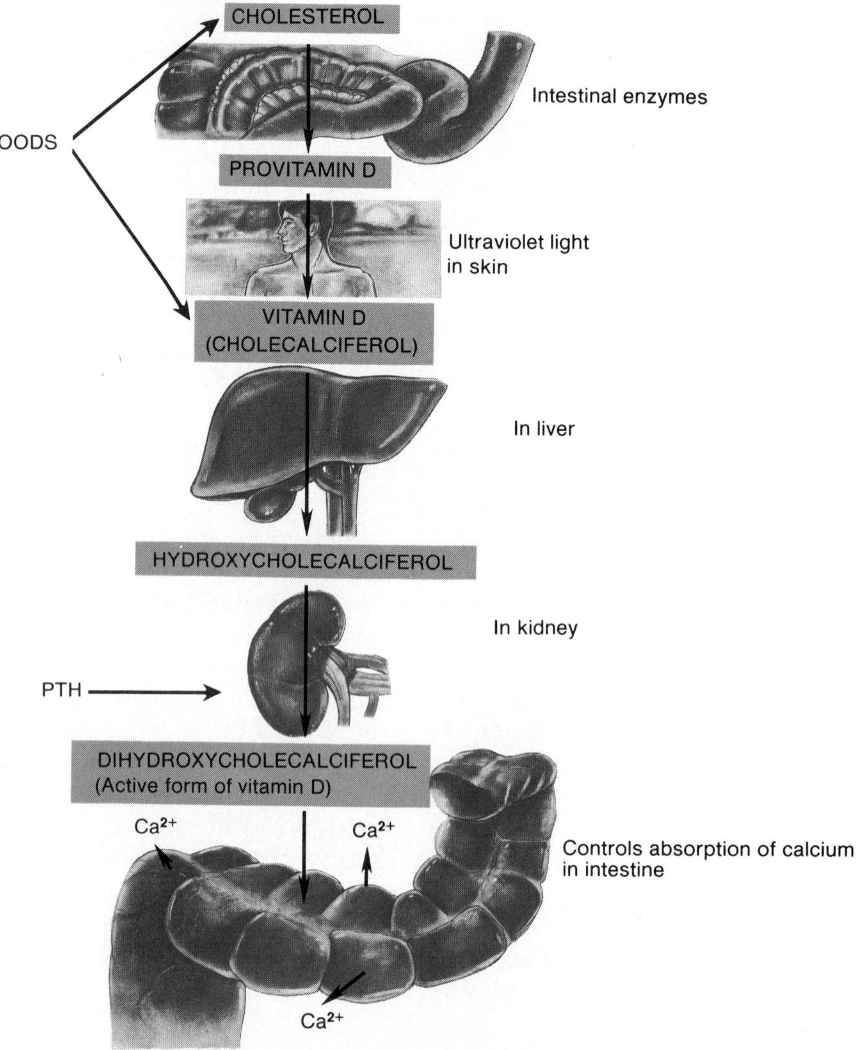

Once activated, calciferol stimulates the absorption of calcium in the small intestine; in its absence, only small amounts are taken up from ingested food. So we can say that once it is activated by PTH, it proceeds to pay back its debt by augmenting the efforts of PTH. PTH operates mainly on the skeleton and in the kidneys to increase blood calcium; calciferol helps by increasing raw calcium uptake from the gut (figure 10.22).

Parathormone Regulation

The parathyroids are independent of the hypothalamo-hypophyseal regulatory system. As far as is known, they respond directly to changes in the concentration of blood calcium, increasing PTH output when the calcium drops and reducing it when blood calcium is up (figure 10.23).

The Adrenal Glands

The adrenal glands are pyramid-shaped glands located along the upper border of the kidneys, forming a sort of triangular, spongy cap (figure 10.24). Embryologically they are two completely separate glands, and functionally, they are four, although their role as a sex-hormone producer is minor. The outer layer of an adrenal gland is the **cortex,** and it forms a thick "peel" around the core, or **medulla.** The glands have a tremendously rich blood supply, so rich that no organ in the body can match it—not even the thyroid.

The Medulla

The adrenal medulla is as much a part of the nervous system as it is an endocrine gland. It is, in fact, a modified sympathetic ganglion, and its cells are essentially postsynaptic sympathetic neurons. Preganglionic fibers from the thoracic region of the spinal cord innervate the adrenal medulla, and these fibers come straight from the spinal cord. They pass through a major sympathetic ganglion near the cord, but they do not synapse there. Instead, they course directly into the adrenal, where their terminals release acetylcholine onto the cells of the medulla.

Figure 10.22 The role of parathormone in calcium metabolism.

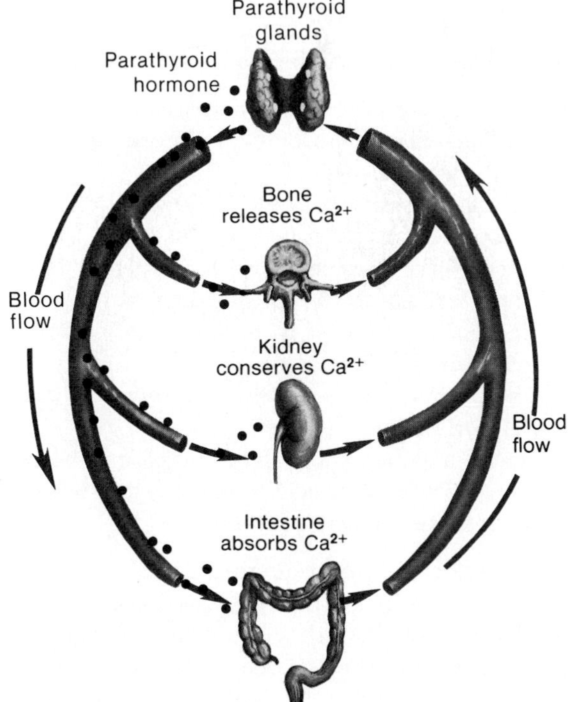

Figure 10.23 The parathyroid hormone regulating system. As far as is currently known, the parathyroids operate independently of both hypothalamic and pituitary secretions.

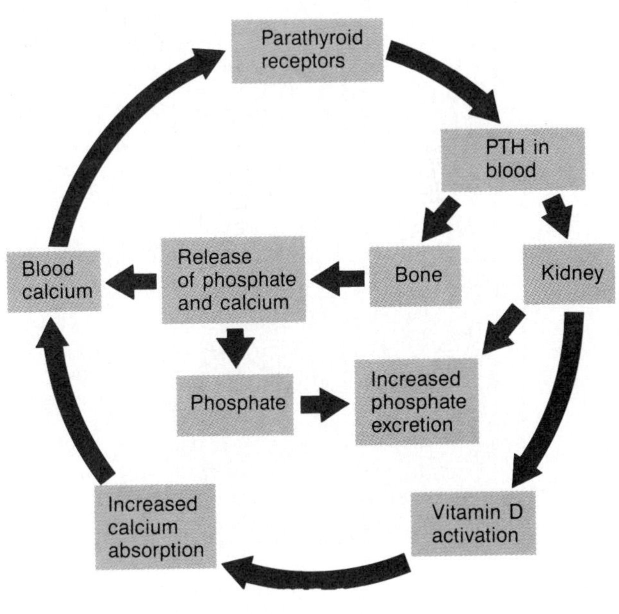

Figure 10.24 The location and structure of the adrenal glands. Note the three separate layers of the adrenal cortex.

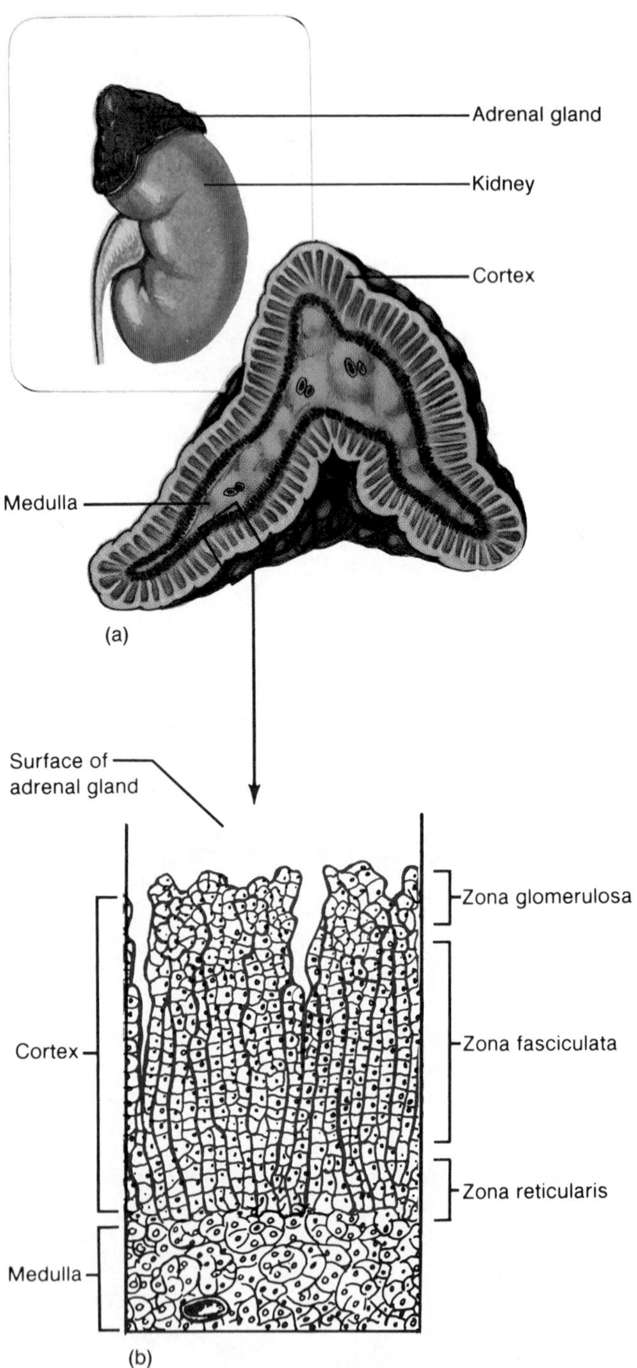

Figure 10.25 The two hormones of the adrenal medulla. Of the two, epinephrine is by far the more abundant.

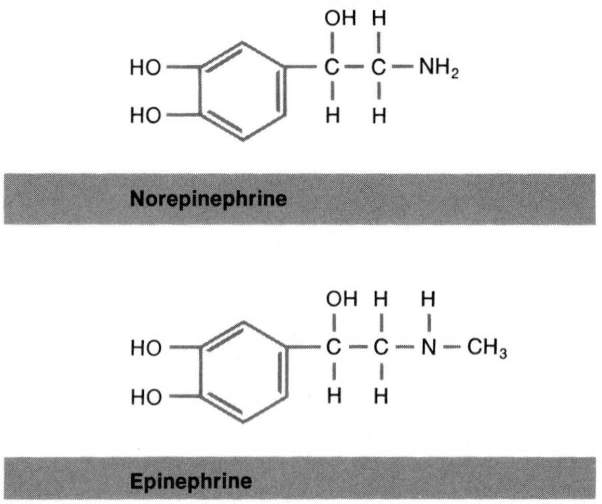

Norepinephrine

Epinephrine

Medullary Hormones

The adrenal medulla is often described as a **sympathomimetic** gland, meaning its hormones mimic the activity of the sympathetic nervous system. The cells of the adrenal medulla synthesize and secrete two catecholamines, epinephrine and norepinephrine, both of which serve the nervous system as neurotransmitters. Both are synthesized in the medulla, but the amount of norepinephrine is limited; the main hormone is epinephrine (figure 10.25). When properly stimulated, the adrenal medulla releases its hormones into the blood, and they circulate throughout the body, adding their influence to the already-profound activity of the sympathetic nervous system. As we know from chapter 8, this includes many separate operations, but they are all involved in the "flight-fright-fight" syndrome.

When epinephrine levels in the blood are high:

1. Blood flow to the brain increases.
2. The heart beats more deeply, more rapidly, and with greater power.
3. Arterial pressure and blood flow to skeletal muscles increases.
4. The subject breathes more rapidly, and the air tubes leading to the lungs dilate.
5. There is an increase in blood glucose, providing extra fuel for muscle cells.
6. The pupils of the eyes dilate to permit a broader field of vision.
7. There is even a short-lived increase in body temperature, because increased temperatures favor faster muscle contractions.

The effects of norepinephrine are different from those of epinephrine, but the differences are mainly quantitative in that they tend to concentrate on slightly different operations. Both chemicals are involved in preparing the body to face an external emergency.

As with the activation of the sympathetic nervous system, body zones that play no role in emergency activities are shut down. When the medullary

Figure 10.26 Some of the steroid hormones and their parent, cholesterol.

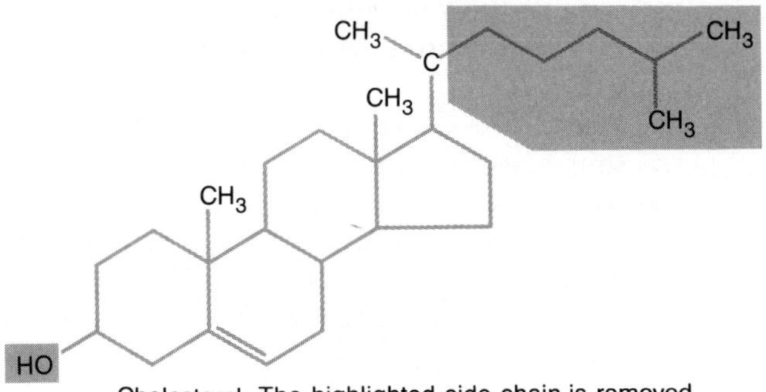

Cholesterol. The highlighted side chain is removed to produce steroid hormones, and the highlighted position on ring A is a frequently altered site.

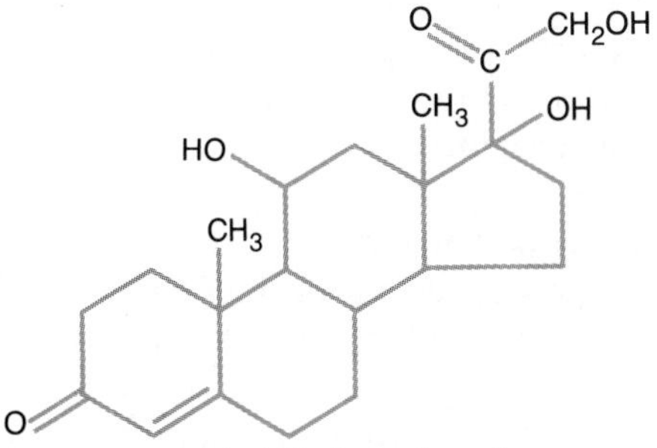

Cortisol (Hydrocortisone)

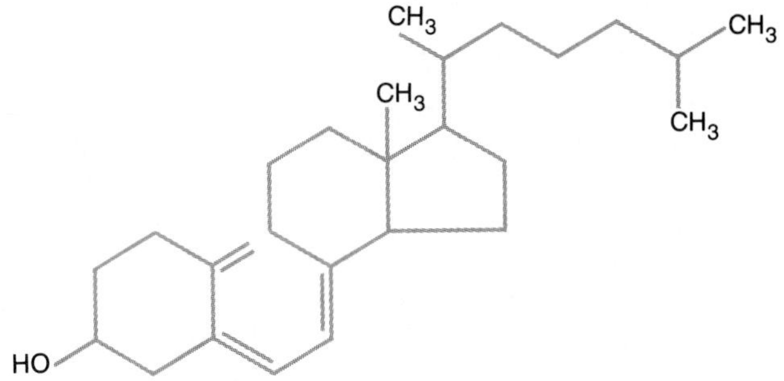

Vitamin D_3 (Cholecalciferol)

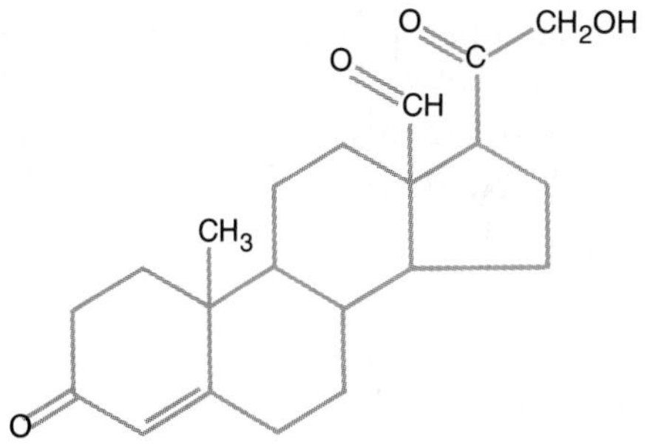

Aldosterone

hormones are flowing, blood flow to the viscera is drastically reduced, activity in the stomach and intestinal tract grinds to a halt, and the formation of urine in the kidney nearly stops. This latter has the effect of reducing water loss, but consciously, it does not *feel* like water is being conserved. The shutting down of all water-loss mechanisms means that, among other things, salivary secretion virtually stops, and the subject feels dry and thirsty, with a swollen tongue and a dry, "cottony" mouth.

Medullary Regulation

Epinephrine is released from the adrenal medulla whenever the sympathetic neurons going into it are firing. They fire whenever some emergency situation occurs or is perceived by the various receptors available to the central nervous system. Anything that frightens or unduly angers a person constitutes a stimulus for the release of epinephrine into the blood and increases the synthetic activities of adrenal medullary cells. Once the emergency is past, the neural bombardment ceases, and the secretion of epinephrine stops. Recovery from the "3-F" reactions is unusually fast, thanks to the activity of MAO enzymes (see chapter 8) in the body fluids and medullary cytosol.

Despite all their neuronal properties, the cells of the adrenal medulla are considered endocrine, and the adrenal medulla is considered an endocrine gland. As with all nerve cells, cells of the adrenal medulla are unable to divide, and this is about the only typical endocrine-cell characteristic that they lack.

The Adrenal Cortex

The outer wrapping of the adrenals is a capsule of connective tissue that encloses the entire gland. Underneath this is a mass of epithelial tissue that forms a three-layered cortex of irregular shape around the medulla. The outermost layer of this ephithelium is the **zona glomerulosa,** which encloses the thickest layer, the **zona fasciculata.** This layer, in its turn, wraps around the inner one, the **zona reticularis** (figure 10.24). All three layers are involved in the synthesis and secretion of the steroid hormones of the adrenal cortex.

Adrenocortical Hormones

Steroid hormones are lipids, and they are all built on a cholesterol nucleus. The hormones are synthesized by stripping cholesterol of its side chains, then making a few additions and deletions (figure 10.26). Upwards of thirty different steroids are synthesized by cells of the adrenal cortex, but they all belong to three major groups:

1. Sex hormones
2. Hormones involved in carbohydrate metabolism, the **glucocorticoids**
3. Hormones involved in electrolyte metabolism, the **mineralocorticoids**

The Mineralocorticoids

The latter group is synthesized in the glomerulosa, the outermost layer of the cortex, and its most abundant and most active hormone is **aldosterone** (figure 10.26). Mineralocorticoids concentrate on regulating the movement of small electrolytes from one body compartment to another, and in humans, they operate primarily in the kidney. Under the influence of aldosterone, much of the sodium in the kidney filtrate is reabsorbed by the kidney and returned to the blood. In exchange, aldosterone transports potassium into the kidney filtrate for disposal through urination.

Mineralocorticoid Regulation

The trophic hormone ACTH can stimulate the synthesis and release of aldosterone, but only for a short period of time, and its effects are not very profound. Evidently, the primary stimuli in the regulation of the mineralocorticoids are blood pressure and blood chemistry. Some of the chemoreceptors responsible for this are right in the adrenal gland, and they respond directly to increases in blood potassium, decreased blood sodium, or both. The other receptors—those responsive to blood pressure—are present in a group of blood vessels at the entrance to the kidney's blood-scrubbing units, the juxtaglomerular elements (see chapter 16). When properly stimulated, these units initiate an involved series of reactions, ending in peripheral vasoconstriction, release of aldosterone, and an increased thirst drive. The sequence is as follows:

A decrease in either blood pressure or blood volume stimulates pressure receptors in the kidney to release an enzyme called **renin** (pronounced *reen-in*), which lops a few molecules off a minor blood protein called **angiotensinogen,** thus converting it to **angiotensin I.** Circulating in the blood, angiotensin I migrates to the lungs, where it is changed by enzymes there into **angiotensin II,** the active form of this compound. Angiotensin II, moving through the blood, accomplishes several things:

1. It serves as a trophic hormone, stimulating the synthesis and release of aldosterone from the adrenal glands. This results in the conservation of both sodium and water by the kidney and permits their retention by the blood.
2. It elevates both systolic and diastolic blood pressure.
3. It increases the contractile force of the heart, thus boosting blood pressure.
4. Its presence in the blood flowing through the hypothalamus results in acute thirst, producing immediate drinking behavior if water is available (thus increasing blood volume and pressure).

Renin is released, therefore, when there are indications that blood pressure and possibly blood volume are lower than either should be, and it has a single goal—the maintenance of proper blood volume and pressure throughout the body (figure 10.27).

The Glucocorticoids

The zona fasciculata of the adrenal cortex synthesizes a body of hormones that are concerned primarily with carbohydrate metabolism and hence were given the name *glucocorticoids.* The most active of these is **cortisol** (hydrocortisone—see figure 10.26). They are also involved to a somewhat lesser extent in both amino acid and lipid metabolism. Like all the steroids, they are fatty hormones and so are able to slip through the membranes into the cytosol of their target cells before linking onto their receptors.

Their main objective seems to be maintaining proper blood glucose concentrations. This is achieved, as far as we can tell, through gluconeogenesis and by the reduction of glucose consumption by body cells. They accomplish this in the following ways:

1. They boost the activity rate of enzymes responsible for converting amino acids to glucose.
2. They slow protein synthesis in body cells, making the amino acids that would be used in constructing proteins available for gluconeogenesis.
3. They divert free amino acids away from protein-synthetic pathways, thereby providing more substrate for gluconeogenesis.
4. They reduce the ability of body cells to take up glucose. This may seem inconsistent, but it's not. By slowing the movement of glucose into cells, they enable blood glucose to increase.
5. They increase the utilization of fatty acids as fuel molecules, thereby sparing glucose.
6. They increase the conversion of free glycerol into glucose.

Figure 10.27 The regulatory mechanisms involving the adrenal's mineralocorticoids.

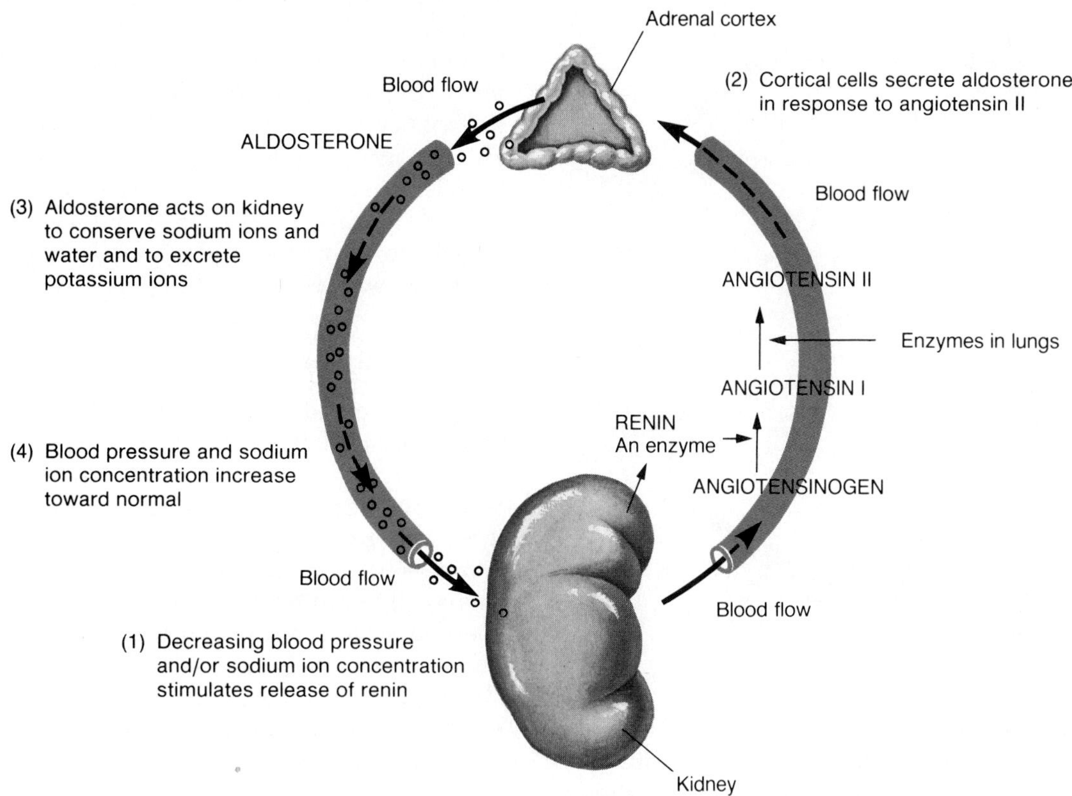

It is fairly well known that hydrocortisone (cortisol) is used to soothe inflamed tissue, and in sports medicine it reduces the effects of rheumatoid afflictions like tennis elbow, pitcher's elbow, and various knee problems.

For soothing inflammation, hydrocortisone is quite useful if used with discretion. Inflammation is the result of a response to injury, and in many cases, it can really hurt. Hydrocortisone tends to soothe the sensitive tissues and reduce the inflammation. One must not forget, however, that inflammation is mainly a defensive process that is ultimately beneficial to the person, and it should not be casually treated.

The use of hydrocortisone in rheumatoid or arthritic conditions like tennis elbow is more specific. Certainly its anti-inflammatory activity is useful, but its main effects are not related to its anti-inflammatory attributes, but rather to its ability to break up proteins and promote the conversion of amino acids into glucose (gluconeogenesis.) Ordinarily, hydrocortisone is injected directly into the afflicted joint. In its presence, the protein matrix of the rheumatic or arthritic tissue is disrupted, and the amino acids are freed and taken to the liver, where they can be converted into glucose. With much of the arthritic tissue converted to sugar, the afflicted joints can move without pain. Unfortunately, administration of hydrocortisone does not attack the underlying cause of the condition—it merely reverses the symptoms temporarily. Relief usually lasts only about four or five hours, which is just about enough time to make it through a baseball game or a tennis match.

Glucocorticoid Regulation

The glucocorticoids are part of the hypothalamo-hypophyseal feedback loop. As such they are controlled by secretions of the pituitary gland. ACTH stimulates cholesterol accumulation by the steroid-synthesizing cells, increases the rate of both synthesis and secretion of glucocorticoids, and promotes the growth of the zona fasciculata and the zona reticularis of the adrenal cortex. The glucocorticoids, in their turn, exert a negative feedback effect on the receptor cells of the hypothalamus. The entire loop is shown in figure 10.28.

Sex Hormones

There are sex hormones produced in the zona reticularis of the adrenal cortex. Not many, it is true, and their influence during a person's reproductive life is minimal, yet they are present. In women, the adrenal cortex is the only source of the male hormones, just as it is the only source of female hormones in men. Generally speaking, their effects are negligible except when their synthesizing cells are malfunctioning.

Figure 10.28 Glucocorticoid-regulating feedback system.

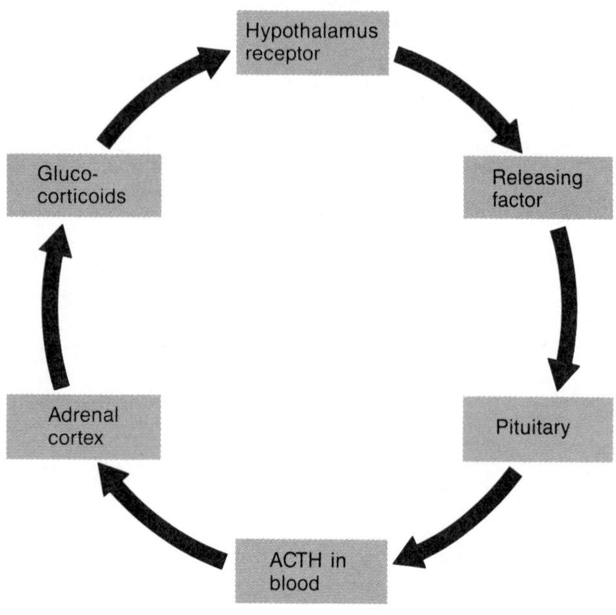

The Gonads

The reproductive organs—the testes in the male and the ovaries in the female— besides containing all the germ cells, are very important endocrine glands. Unlike most such glands, however, removal of the gonads does not threaten life or even life quality; people can live long, productive lives without any gonads. What is more, depending on the age of the individual involved when the gonads are lost, it may not even reduce sexual activity. It would in any animal *but* humans, and its failure to diminish the sex drive is indicative of how powerful that drive is in human beings. It appears to be much stronger than it is in any other animals we know of, and this, as we will see, may be one of the reasons that the human race is currently standing in greater command on this earth than the most powerful dinosaur ever did. The endocrine operations of the gonads are concerned almost exclusively with the urge to mate and with sexual activity. We will deal with these compounds and what they do in chapter 18.

The Thymus Gland

The thymus gland is structurally rather like the thyroid gland. It is flattened and double-lobed . . . a little broader than the thyroid, but still shaped like a butterfly. It is also quite diffuse—even spongy—and is located between the lungs in the thoracic cavity. Like all endocrine glands, it is well supplied with blood vessels. In addition, there are several lymphatic afferents entering it. This gland and its secretions are heavily concerned with the body's immune system; hence we will deal with it in detail in chapter 15.

The Pineal Gland

The pineal gland is located on the roof of the third brain ventricle, deep in the brain between the two cerebral hemispheres. It forms a tiny knob that extends into the gray and white matter of the thalamus. It has only recently come to the attention of endocrinologists because, like calcitonin, it doesn't adhere to Bayliss and Starling's criteria very well. Its removal does not produce any particularly deleterious results—in fact, unless you know exactly what you are looking for, its removal doesn't produce any results at all. Even if it does produce them and they are recognized, replacing the gland does not always reverse them. Furthermore, many of the hormones it makes are synthesized in other parts of the body.

Nevertheless, the tendency today is to accept it as a bona fide endocrine gland. It is part of the brain; hence it is mostly neuronal tissue, and several biologically active compounds have been isolated from the efferent blood draining it. Not a great deal is known about these compounds, however, and there are some pretty good reasons why this is so. Because of the gland's location, these compounds are *very* difficult to isolate, and when they are obtained, the amounts are very small. Also, there are so many nerve axons entering and synapsing in the pineal gland that it is hard to separate materials these neurons might have brought in with them from what was actually synthesized by pineal cells. Nevertheless, there are some peptides that seem to originate in the pineal gland, and they are implicated in either endocrine function or hormone synthesis. **Melatonin (MLT)** appears to be the major secretion. It has been recognized as *the* pineal hormone, and it seems to have some definite effects. No particular effect has been detected in males, but it seems to alter sexual activity in females of many animal species. Whether it affects human females is uncertain.

The belief that human reproductive activity is not influenced by light is so deeply ingrained that it is hard to contradict, but it seems to be wrong. Human reproductive systems are almost certainly affected by photoperiods. For instance, it was reported years ago that Eskimo women living in their traditional way outside the settlements did not menstruate during the four months of continual darkness that persists during a northern winter. It was suggested then that this was due to the lack of a day-night cycle, and although the suggestion was rejected by most workers, it seems to be true.

Melatonin Function

Apparently, MLT can suppress the secretion of estrogens in women by inhibiting the secretion of gonadotrophins. The feedback stimulus is inversely related to light entering the eye: the more light that enters, the less the pineal gland is stimulated. Thus, when day length increases, MLT secretion is inhibited, and the longer the day, the greater the reduction of MLT. Less MLT means more gonadotrophins, and in nonhumans, that nearly always means greater sexual activity. The connection between the eyes and the pineal gland has not yet been traced, but it almost certainly is neural. Research in this branch of endocrinology is continuing.

Atypical Endocrine Structures

There are other structures that secrete bona fide hormones, but they cannot really be considered endocrine *glands,* since they are heavily involved in other physiological operations. The lining of the stomach, for example, secretes a special hormone when the right kind of food enters, and parts of the intestine have hormones of their own. Researchers are also aware that the kidney secretes at least one hormone-like compound, and the human placenta produces gonadotrophins and sex hormones during pregnancy. These structures as well as their endocrine functions will be considered in the chapters dealing with the systems of which they are part.

Nonhormonal Chemical Messengers

Neurotransmitters are bearers of intercellular information, and they are synthesized by specific cell types. What is more, they are often important homeostatic regulators, and some, such as adrenalin, are viewed as hormones when circumstances are correct. Why, then, are they not *always* considered hormones?

It is a matter of convention. If a chemical simply leaves the cell where it was synthesized and diffuses through interstitial fluids to its target cell, it is a neurotransmitter, not a hormone. If the same chemical is liberated by the same group of cells and is picked up by the blood to be carried to a target cell, then it's a hormone. According to the rules, the chemical must enter the blood and be carried to its destination in the circulatory system in order to be considered a hormone.

The Endocrine Pancreas

I have chosen to deal with the endocrine pancreas last, not because it is less important than any of the others, but because it is almost impossible to discuss the endocrine pancreas without dealing with the most prevalent and deadly endocrine disorder we know of—**diabetes mellitus**—and clinical aspects of each chapter are reserved for last.

The pancreas is a large, diffuse organ shaped somewhat like a hatchet and nestled in the upper curve of the small intestine, just below the stomach (figure 10.29). Unlike the glands we have already discussed, the pancreas is not solely an endocrine structure. It's an extremely important digestive organ, and as such it synthesizes a barrage of enzymes designed to break up the nutrients that we ingest. This aspect of pancreatic function will be discussed in detail in chapter 15.

Pancreas Morphology

The pancreas consists of masses of exocrine, enzyme-producing cells with their accompanying ducts all leading out of the organ. These ducts are destined eventually to join one another (anastomose), forming the larger pancreatic duct. In between these cell masses are packages or clumps of very different cells that are segregated by connective-tissue enclosures.

Figure 10.29 The location of the pancreas in the human abdomen.

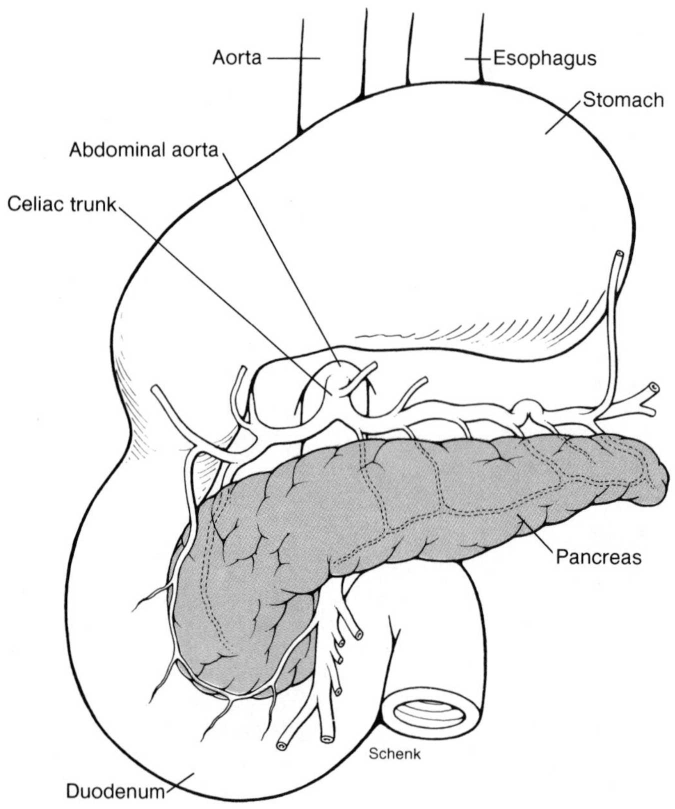

These isolated cell packages form small islands of endocrine tissue in between the digestive cells (figure 10.30). They are called the **islets of Langerhans,** and the cells they contain are responsible for the synthesis of at least three different hormones. The largest of the islet cells are known as **alpha (α) or A_2 cells.** They represent about 25 percent of the total number and synthesize the hormone **glucagon.** The **beta (β) cells** are much smaller than the α cells, but there are so many of them that they constitute about 70 percent of the mass of the islets. Beta cells are responsible for the synthesis and secretion of the best-known of all the pancreatic hormones—**insulin.** The remaining cells are known as **delta (δ), D,** or **A_1 cells,** and they are responsible for the synthesis of the hormone **somatostatin.** A variation of the D cells may also be responsible for the synthesis of a gastrointestinal hormone known as **gastrin.**

The Pancreatic Hormones

All the pancreatic hormones are large polypeptides. Two of them, insulin and glucagon, are involved in the metabolism of carbohydrates, fats, and proteins. The third is somatostatin.

Somatostatin

Somatostatin does so many things in such widely divergent body areas that it is hard to promote a single most important function. However, since it is mostly secreted immediately following a meal, and since most of its activities seem to be aimed at lowering the level of nutrients in the bloodstream, it would appear that its main goal is to reduce the possibility of hyperglycemia (high blood sugar) following meals. To this end, it slows gastric and intestinal muscle activity, it inhibits the secretion of almost every digestive enzyme in the entire gastrointestinal tract, it retards the absorption of nutrients even after they've been broken up, and when secreted in small quantities, it can inhibit the hyperglycemic activity of glucagon.

Figure 10.30 The islands of endocrine cells between the ducts and the enzyme-secreting tissues of the pancreas. (*a*) The pancreas in position within the abdomen, and a microscopic drawing of the pancreatic secretory cells. Note the lack of an obvious exit from the hormone-secreting zone. (*b*) A photograph of the structures shown in *a*. How much can you identify in the photograph?

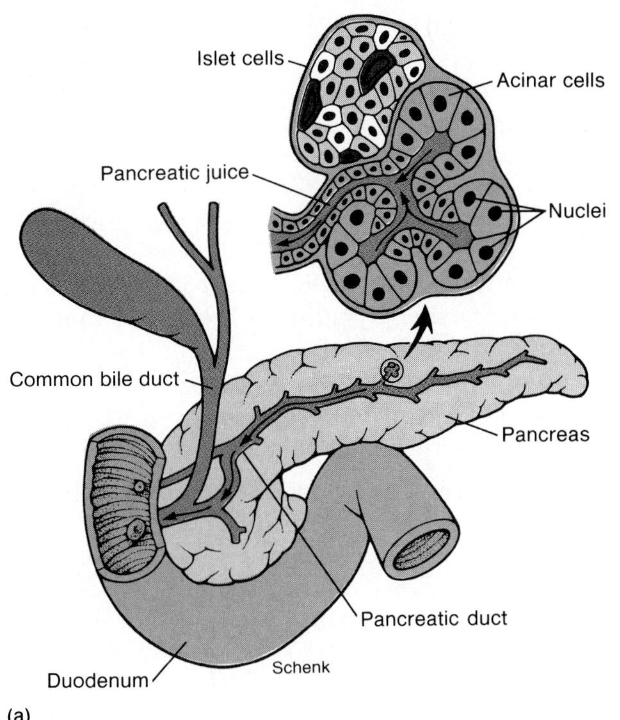

(a)

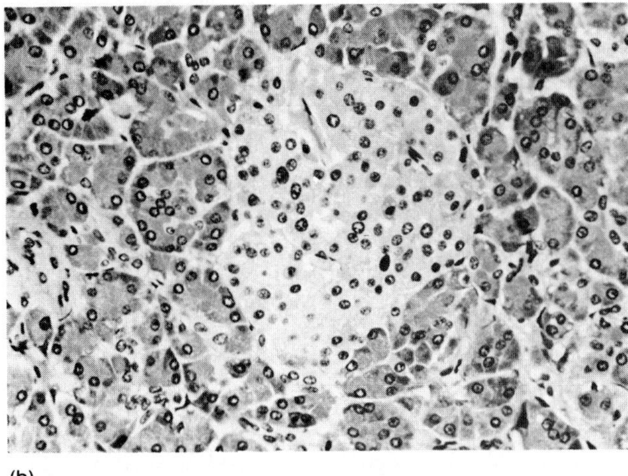

(b)

Somatostatin also works outside the abdominal area, and it has many sources besides the pancreas. As was mentioned earlier, it is synthesized in the hypothalamus. When released there, it enters the hypothalamo-hypophyseal portal system, inhibiting the activity of TSH and STH (which accounts for its name). It operates as a neurotransmitter elsewhere in the brain, and even in the pancreas it has ancillary activities. It can, for instance, influence the secretory rates of its companion cells in the islets of Langerhans directly, without entering the bloodstream (this is called a *paracrine* effect).

There is a fourth hormone that is synthesized in the pancreas. It may be synthesized by some of the islet cells, but there are cells outside the islets that seem to be responsible for most of its secretion. It is called simply **pancreatic polypeptide (PP),** and although there is some evidence that it can inhibit the secretion of certain pancreatic digestive enzymes, its function is largely a mystery. It is most actively secreted following high-protein, low-carbohydrate meals. Although falling levels of blood glucose seem able to stimulate its release, it is not clear whether the secretory cells are directly controlling its release or the sensors are elsewhere and its release is controlled by neural impulses.

Glucagon

Glucagon is a small protein. The mechanisms it stimulates are mainly breakdown or catabolic processes, and it accelerates these with the apparent object of preventing blood glucose levels from getting too low. What it does depends on the amount of hormone that the pancreas secretes.

The initial response to a gradual drop in blood glucose is gentle. Low levels of glucagon stimulate the conversion of liver glycogen into glucose, thereby increasing glucose concentration in the blood. When glycogen stores begin to run out and get too sparse to maintain glucose levels, glucagon secretion increases. Higher hormonal levels accelerate the conversion of amino acids and glycerol molecules into glucose, and if this still is not adequate, even greater amounts of glucagon are secreted. Maximal discharge stimulates the breakdown of fat, thereby providing more glycerol for gluconeogenesis and fatty acids for β-oxidation.

Glucagon Regulation

As far as we can determine, the main glucagon control loop does not involve the hypothalamo-hypophyseal axis. There are some nuclei in the hypothalamus (the ventromedial nuclei) that can stimulate glucagon secretion to some extent, but their effect is not very profound. Glucose levels in the blood represent the main motivating force for glucagon secretion or inhibition. The stimulus is apparently a drop in blood glucose, and the sensors are the α cells, the same ones that synthesize glucagon.

Insulin

The most plentiful cells within the pancreatic islets are also those that most often malfunction, and the hormone they produce has activities that are unique. The β cells synthesize and secrete insulin. Insulin is the only hormone known whose goal is to lower blood glucose concentrations.

Insulin Function

Like somatostatin, insulin is involved in so many operations that sometimes it seems that it exists for no other reason than to complicate the science of endocrinology. Nevertheless, for all its myriad activities, it seems always to have a single goal—the reduction of basic nutrient particles in the blood, especially glucose. To this end, it influences the metabolism of all the organic groups and selectively stimulates the movement of certain compounds across cell membranes into body cells. In fact, it does so many things that a tabulation is essential.

1. Insulin increases the movement of blood glucose into storage areas in the liver and muscles, then stimulates its conversion into the storage molecule, glycogen.
2. It stimulates the movement of glucose from interstitial fluid into the cells.
3. Within the cell, insulin stimulates an enzyme known as **glucokinase** into increased activity.
4. Glucokinase then catalyzes the phosphorylation of glucose into glucose 1-phosphate. Phosphorylated glucose cannot cross the cell membrane; thus the sugar is locked into the cell.
5. It boosts the activity of enzymes of the glycolytic pathway, thereby increasing the rate of glucose breakdown and the production of ATP.
6. It increases the uptake of glucose by adipose (fatty) tissues so it can be converted to glycerol.
7. It then stimulates the conversion of glycerol into neutral fat molecules.
8. It stimulates the movement of amino acids into cells and enhances their incorporation into proteins.
9. It inhibits gluconeogenesis, even in glucose-free media.
10. It can influence nucleic acids to increase protein synthesis, thereby utilizing both free amino acids and glucose.
11. More protein synthesis means increased tissue differentiation and growth.
12. It stimulates the appetite.

Many of these activities are directly involved in the assembly or repair of body cells. Others aid in stockpiling raw materials and tend to stimulate the production of energy for use in cellular projects or to provide protection against excessive tissue breakdown. Because all of these are necessary in the construction or maintenance of tissues, insulin is considered an anabolic hormone, meaning that it is involved mainly in constructive operations in the body—in building things up, as opposed to breaking them down.

In the absence of insulin, all these operations break down or run in reverse. The result is diabetes, one of the deadliest diseases known to humanity, which will be discussed shortly.

Insulin Regulation Insulin is not part of the hypothalamo-hypophyseal feedback loop, and there do not appear to be any trophic hormones involved in its control. The stimulus for insulin release seems to be constituents of the blood plasma—mainly glucose, but also amino acids and fatty acids. It has not been confirmed, but there is also reason to believe that elements of the autonomic nervous system exert a "fine control" on insulin secretion and play a role in both suppressing and stimulating insulin release.

Clinical Considerations

Diabetes Mellitus

Of all the endocrine disorders, diabetes mellitus is the most common, and that is unfortunate, because it is incurable and deadly. Our struggle against it has been going on since the dawn of recorded history, yet despite the best efforts of science, it is still the number four killer in the U.S. (See panel 10.1.)

There is still a great deal about diabetes that we do not understand, but the symptoms, signs, and clinical course of the disease are all thoroughly catalogued. There are actually two separate types of diabetes. By far the more severe is **insulin-dependent** (once called *juvenile-onset diabetes* because it was thought to be more prevalent in young people). The other is **non-insulin-dependent** (old name, *adult onset*).

Insulin-Dependent (Type I) Diabetes

We know almost nothing about the insulin-dependent form. We have no idea at all what causes it, although we have a pretty good handle on what does not cause it. It is probably the result of genetic programming; hence it is likely to run in families, although no one really understands the mechanisms. There is no obvious connection between the disease and obesity, dietary habits, hygiene, or patient activity. What happens is that for some clouded, puzzling reason, patients suddenly lose all, or most, of their pancreatic β cells, and insulin simply disappears from the bloodstream. The results are dramatic and overwhelming.

When insulin is absent, all phases of metabolism are affected. One of the first and most overt signs is that the victim's urine is packed with sugar. The reasons, considering insulin's action, are not hard to trace.

1. Glycogen is no longer synthesized. Instead, the glycogen molecules that are already assembled and stored in the body are rapidly broken down, converted to glucose, and reinjected into the bloodstream.
2. The ability of glucose to penetrate cell membranes is reduced. Glucose that should be converted to energy by body cells instead stays in the blood.
3. Since it cannot enter the cells, glucose levels in individual cells drop too low. To correct this, protein synthesis stops, and amino acids stored in the cells begin to undergo gluconeogenesis to boost intracellular glucose.
4. Unfortunately, this does no good. Insulin normally activates some of the glycolytic enzymes in the cytosol; in its absence, they become nearly inert. So while there is lots of glucose inside the cells, it cannot be used. Instead of correcting a problem, gluconeogenesis aggravates one that already exists. Glucose piles up in the cell in such quantities that the cell cannot hold it all, so it begins to leave. This adds more sugar to the blood, further increasing the rapidly developing hyperglycemia.
5. The cells, meanwhile, are getting desperate for an energy source. Since glucose cannot be used, safety-valve mechanisms swing into action to make fats available. Neutral fats in the various storage areas of the body start to break up, releasing glycerol and fatty acids into the blood in large quantities.
6. These emergency mechanisms promptly convert the newly available glycerol into glucose, increasing the blood load even more.
7. The body cells accept the fat and burn it as rapidly as possible, but without the calming influence of insulin, the fat mobilization runs amok and there is far too much in the blood for the cells to keep up with. Fatty acids enter the liver in such quantities that the liver sometimes becomes plugged with fat.
8. To make things worse, the heavy oxidation of fatty acids produces large numbers of ketones as by-products of fat catabolism, and they begin to build up in the blood. The body recognizes the danger, and they are eliminated everywhere they can be, including the lungs. The acetone being eliminated in the diabetic's breath is clear and unmistakable—a second diagnostic sign.
9. The heavy glucose load in the blood cannot be reabsorbed by the kidney mechanisms, and much of it is lost in the urine. The osmotic pressure of these huge sugar concentrations draws large quantities of water into the urine to alleviate the osmotic gradient. The extra water

Panel 10.1

From Ancient Egypt to the Present: A 4,000-Year Battle with Diabetes

The signs and symptoms of diabetes mellitus were familiar to the ancient Egyptians and were described before the Israelites began their long trek away from Pharaoh. It was well-known in Europe before Alexander began his conquests, while most Europeans still lived in caves. Greek physicians mentioned it so often it must have been common throughout the Mediterranean, and its ravages were repeatedly described by the doctors of Rome.

We lose sight of it through the Middle Ages, yet while it is not mentioned in any of the sparse writings of that period, we can be sure it was there. In 1614, the beginning of the Renaissance, we are given a glimpse of it—enough to know that it was still around and still killing. A London physician named Willis mentions a patient who died shortly after he saw him. He writes: "The urine was wonderfully sweet, as if imbued with honey or sugar. . . ." Obviously, he had tasted his patient's urine . . . and by doing so he noted the most unmistakable and characteristic sign of the disease. This had been the diagnostic method used by the Ancient Egyptians, and 4,000 years later it was still the only certain key to its detection.

As modern times approached, the characteristics of diabetes became clearer and clearer. In 1776, English physicians demonstrated that the urine of diabetics contained real sugar, and from that day on, the disease was known as *sugar* diabetes. But still, no one knew what malfunction produced it.

In 1889, Von Mering and Minckowski, two scientists working on the physiology of digestion, surgically removed the pancreas from several experimental animals and within two days detected the signs of diabetes in all of them. The pancreas was thus firmly linked to the disease, and a rush to find a cure began. There was no lack of funds. A diagnosis of diabetes was a sentence of death, and anyone could get diabetes, so contributions were abundant. It was well-known that drinking extracts of thyroid gland could cure thyroid diseases; in the hope that it would work with diabetics, pancreatic extracts were prepared and people drank them desperately, but to no avail. None of them worked; people still died. Physicians, reasoning that maybe the digestive powers of the stomach destroyed the pancreatic extracts, tried injecting them, but the preparations either killed the patient or did not work

is supplied by body fluids, which means a heavy water loss from the kidneys . . . patients urinate large amounts, frequently. This causes an increase in thirst, and victims find themselves constantly drinking, yet always thirsty—a third diagnostic sign.

10. High levels of ketones in the circulation tie up hydrogen ions and produce an alkalosis in the blood that rapidly leads to coma and death. This, in fact, is the most frequent cause of death in untreated diabetics.
11. The tremendous water loss can be just as bad. As the body tissues are broken down with greater speed, weakness forces the patients into bed, and from that point, deterioration is rapid. They cannot drink enough water to keep up with their urinary loss; blood osmolarity rapidly climbs, producing dehydration, shock, coma, and death due to kidney failure (see figure 10.31).

Exogenous Insulin Injections of insulin immediately bring everything back to normal again, but in cases of severe diabetes, this does not last long. Unfortunately, injected insulin is quickly used up; when it is gone, glucose surges, and all the life-threatening signs begin to develop again. This is the problem we have today with diabetes. Exogenous insulin saves lives, but there is no feedback control—no way to prevent it from getting into and out of the patient's blood too fast.

Deadly Glucose Glucose is an essential fuel molecule that people simply cannot live without, but when it is present in too high a concentration over long periods of time, it is a poison. It thickens blood vessel walls, making it difficult for nutrients and wastes to be exchanged, and it produces major circulatory problems, especially in the limbs and the retina of the eyes. Diabetes-induced gangrene can cost patients their legs, and diabetic retinopathy is the biggest single cause of blindness in this country. It all could be prevented by keeping glucose concentrations stable, but that might mean four or five injections a at all. Scientists began to realize that whatever antidiabetic substance the pancreas made, it was mixed in with the pancreatic digestive enzymes and was similar enough to be able to avoid any separation procedures. It seemed that they had hit a wall.

Rummaging through the literature in the early 1920s, the Canadian physician Frederick Banting chanced upon some microscopial research done in 1869 by Paul Längerhans. In his notes, Längerhans observed that there were tiny "islets" of cells distributed throughout the pancreatic tissue in scattered lumps. They were, he said, separate from the major enzyme-secreting cells, and they did not seem to have any means of getting their products into the pancreatic ducts. To determine whether or not these islets were involved in the production of digestive enzymes, Längerhans tied off the pancreatic ducts in several experimental animals. He reasoned that by tying off the ducts he would block the movement of anything they produced, and the chemicals would pile up, permitting him to identify them. Instead, all the exocrine cells atrophied and became nonfunctional, while the islet cells prospered. There was no extra production of the secretory granules as he had anticipated; the islet cells merely stayed the same. Längerhans mentioned this in a small note, and then passed on to other things. He could not know that the simple experiment that he considered a failure was the key to isolating the endocrine secretions of the pancreas.

Banting and two of his colleagues (Doctors Best and MacLeod) repeated the experiment on a number of animals, permitting the exocrine cells to atrophy, and then made extracts of the pancreas. To their delight, the extract worked. When it was injected into experimental animals, all the signs of diabetes vanished . . . but only temporarily. It did not take long for them to realize that they had not discovered a cure and that the extracts were going to have to be administered every day. Still, it was infinitely better than dying, and since they had purified the extract and thoroughly tested it, they were ready to try it on a human.

The first injection of insulin was given to a human diabetic patient on January 11, 1922. The patient had been declared terminal, and like all diabetics in those days, was drifting rapidly away. The response was immediate and breathtaking. A man inches from death recovered much of his old vitality, he ate his first meal in days, and his urine showed a complete absence of glucose. Banting knew, of course, that these effects were only temporary, and the injections would have to be repeated for the rest of the man's life. But the patient didn't care, and neither did his family. He had been prepared for death—no one had ever recovered from diabetes before—but he got up and walked home, armed with hypodermic materials and his pancreatic extract.

There are those today who feel that it might have been better if Banting had never discovered insulin. They reason that its discovery removed the threat of immediate death and thus plucked away the driving sense of urgency that prevailed prior to 1922. Needless to say, this line of reasoning has left diabetics and their loved ones cold, but it does make a good point. With the threat of immediate, certain death gone, the money supply for research dried up and stayed dry for twenty-five or thirty years. Who knows what might have been found during those thirty relatively inactive years if diabetes had still meant sure death?

day. One injection a day over a period of years can cause severe muscle deterioration . . . four or five a day for any length of time is out of the question. There must be some way to monitor glucose concentration in the blood on a constant basis and deliver insulin to a patient in proper amounts the instant that it is needed. Unfortunately, no one has yet discovered just what that way might be.

Non-Insulin-Dependent Diabetes (Type II)

Not all forms of diabetes require insulin. In fact, non-insulin-dependent diabetes (adult-onset) is the most common form and while its *precise* cause is not known, it is associated with a variety of things.

1. The tendency to develop the disease almost certainly is inherited, since it runs in families.
2. Most victims are obese when it strikes.
3. More often than not, this form of diabetes is not caused by a shortage of insulin . . . in fact, such diabetics frequently have high blood levels. The problem appears to be that their body's cells do not respond to the hormone anymore, so the patients are diabetic even though their pancreatic β cells are working normally.

Fortunately, this form of diabetes is much less severe than the insulin-dependent form, and patients can usually be maintained quite safely through careful manipulation of diet, exercise, and weight control.

Glucagon

Problems involving hyper- or hyposecretion of glucagon have not been reported in the medical literature. However, at least one important research laboratory has offered the suggestion that many of the problems associated with severe diabetes are due, not to an absence of insulin, but to a hypersecretion of glucagon (compare figure 10.31 with figure 10.32). Workers in this laboratory contend that by reducing glucagon secretion, all the severe problems of diabetes can be eliminated, and even the most insulin-dependent diabetic can then be stabilized with diet alone. Research indicates that this may well be true for dogs and rats, but in humans, the evidence is not as convincing.

Figure 10.31 The inexorable progress of diabetes mellitus.

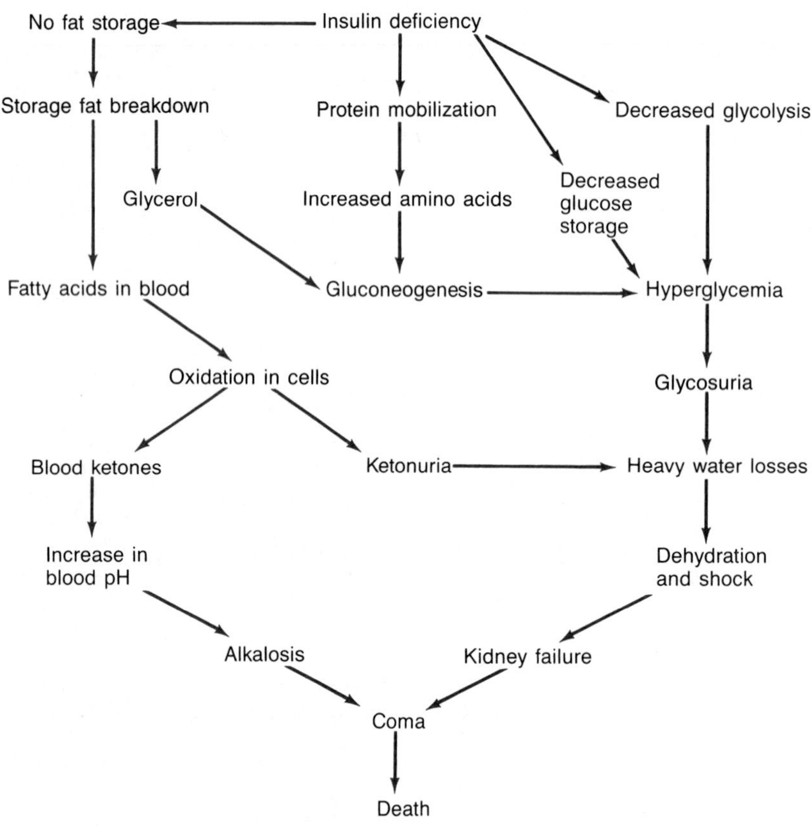

Figure 10.32 The effects of unopposed hypersecretion of glucagon. How similar is this to diabetes (figure 10.31)?

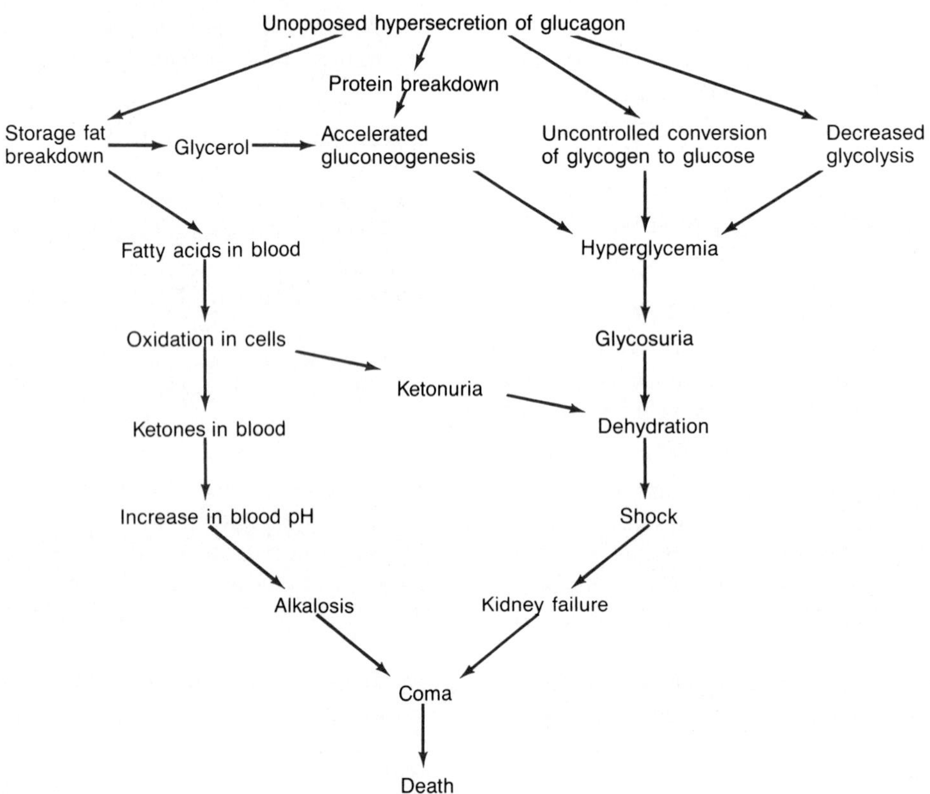

The Pituitary

Pituitary malfunctions are not as common as endocrine problems, but they do occur, and when they do, they are serious. Because of the location of the gland, any surgical procedures are extremely difficult, and because of its cellular dispersal, it is almost impossible to deal with any single adenohypophyseal problem without disrupting all the other hormones.

STH

STH (growth hormone) can become too abundant or too scarce, and the results in either case depend to a great extent on just when during a person's life cycle the malfunctions occur.

During the period of growth, *hyper*secretion of STH results in what is known as a **pituitary giant.** Such people often top eight feet in height. They usually have considerable muscle weakness, and their hands and feet are too heavy for them to maneuver properly. Most pituitary giants live abbreviated lives, usually dying in their early twenties.

*Hypo*secretion of STH during growth results in a **pituitary dwarf.** This is an unfortunate nomenclature, since it calls up the picture of people with abnormally short bodies, arms, and legs and the normal-size head. These so-called "little people" are not suffering from pituitary abnormalities—would that they were, for we might be able to help them. Real pituitary dwarves have normal body proportions, but are much smaller than normal (figure 10.33).

Until recently, there was little that could be done to help either condition, but in 1984, scientists at the Salk Institute in San Diego announced that they had analyzed growth-hormone releasing hormone and had succeeded in genetically engineering the compound in bacteria. This permits mass-production and makes it available for use in abnormally small children.

No serious problems have been reported as a result of hyposecretion of STH in adults, but hypersecretion, while it does not always seriously affect health, can be terribly disfiguring.

Figure 10.33 A typical pituitary dwarf (left) and his twin sister.

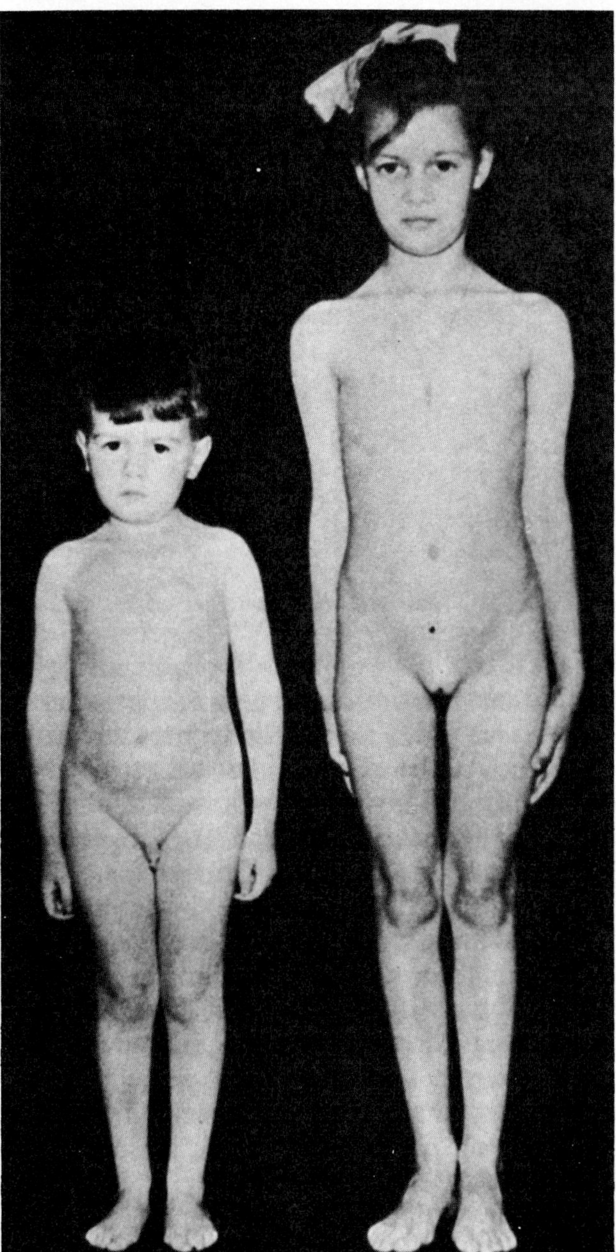

Acromegaly Gonadal hormones seal off the ends of our body's long bones and put a period to growth; thus we achieve adulthood. This eliminates the possibility that too much STH might produce a gaint, since the long bones cannot grow. But where growth *can* be stimulated, it will occur. The facial bones can all grow, and they do. The nose broadens, brow ridges get thicker, and an ape-like appearance develops and is exaggerated by abnormal growth of the jaw and its tendency to become underslung. The hands and feet grow, fingers and toes thicken, and tasks requiring finger dexterity become difficult. Often the ribs elongate, crowding the heart and lungs, and thickening of the cranium can compress the brain and cause shattering headaches and hallucinations. Frequently the larynx enlarges, the voice deepens to startling depths, and the hair gets coarse and lusterless.

Figure 10.34 The disfiguring effects of acromegaly (right).

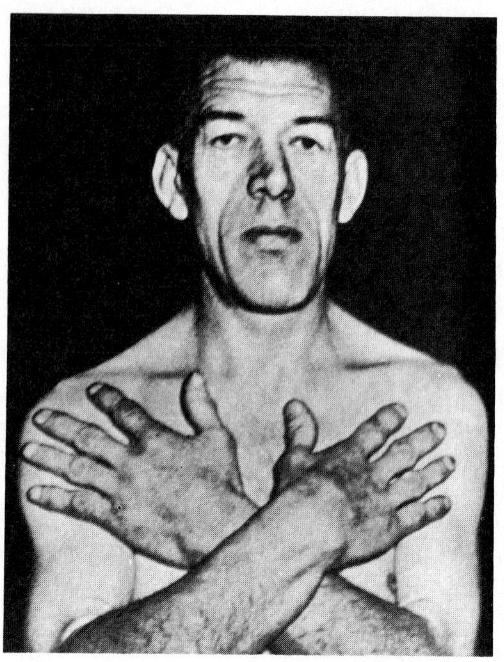

The affliction is known as **acromegaly,** and the alterations are characteristic (figure 10.34). Unfortunately, treatment is drastic and uncertain. Radiation of the pituitary gland *may* work, but it usually doesn't. Hypophysectomy (removal of the pituitary gland) is a last resort.

Trophic Hormones

Any of the trophic hormones may be hyper- or hyposecreted, but since such problems are reflected in the corresponding activity of the glands they control, they will be discussed with the pathology of the individual glands.

The Neurohypophysis

Diabetes Insipidus

Hyposecretion of vasopressin (ADH) results in the disease known as diabetes insipidus. (In medical jargon, the term diabetes without any qualifiers refers to the pancreatic malfunction, whereas diabetes insipidus is referred to as simply *D.I.*) The disease can strike without warning, and in fact it usually does. So sudden is its onset that most victims can tell their doctors not only the date but the precise hour when it hit them. The diagnostic sign is a massive loss of water in the urine (called **polyuria**). Those who completely lack ADH must drink more than ten gallons of water a day just to replace the amount lost through urination. Obviously, a normal life for such patients is impossible. Their days and nights are dominated by the need to urinate constantly and just as constantly replace the loss by drinking. Regular sleeping periods are not possible, and they cannot ever be very far away from the necessary facilities.

If the problem is lack of ADH, powdered, exogenous hormone can be administered by "snorting," but this frequently produces intolerable nasal irritation. Synthetic ADH is available as a nasal spray, and it is effective. Also, there is an injectable form available, a single shot of which often lasts as long as three days.

Hypersecretion of ADH

This has been implicated in compulsive dieting. Women suffering from what is known as **anorexia nervosa** are thought to have abnormal levels of ADH in their circulation. Whether this is an effect of the problem or part of the cause is currently under investigation.

The Thyroid

Malfunction of the thyroid gland is almost as common as problems with the insulin system, but the results aren't nearly as serious. The most common such affliction stems from a systemic lack of iodine, and while it is disfiguring, it is easily corrected.

Common Goiter

When a person fails to ingest enough iodine, the thyroid gland cannot synthesize enough hormone, and the result is a dearth of T_4 and T_3 hormones in the

Figure 10.35 Victims of common goiter. The cause? Dietary iodine deficiency.

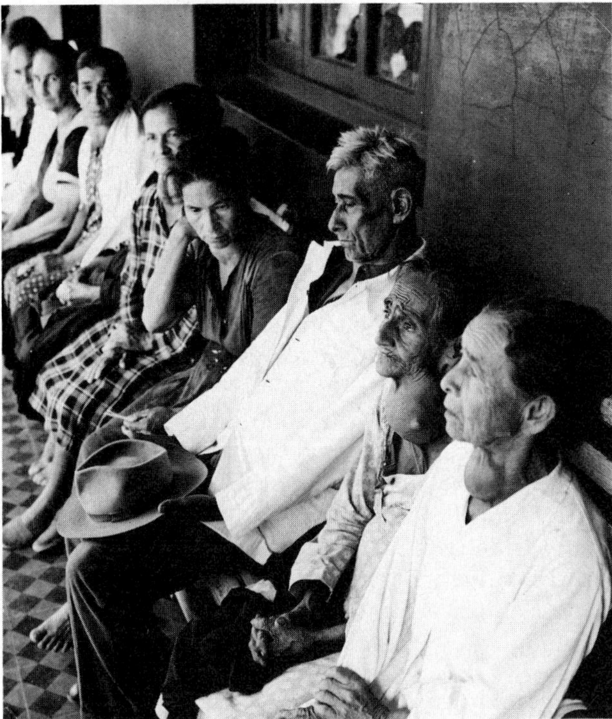

Figure 10.36 The disfiguring exopthalmia (pop-eyes) common in Graves' disease.

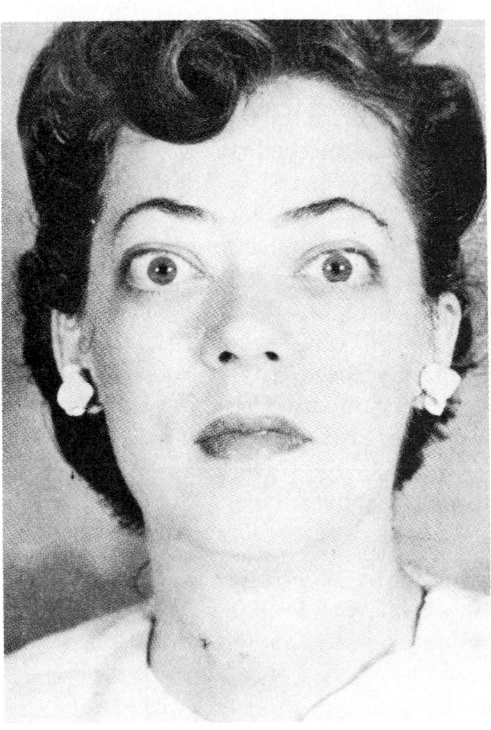

bloodstream. This fact is promptly picked up by elements of the feedback loop, and the response is predictable. The sensors in the hypothalamus, noting that hormonal levels are too low, increase their release of TRH. This extra TRH stimulates the secretory cells of the pituitary gland to increase their output of TSH, and it is this high level of TSH that causes all the problems.

You will recall that TSH normally stimulates the accumulation of iodine, but since there isn't any iodine, it cannot do that. TSH also stimulates the synthesis and secretion of thyroid hormones, but there isn't enough iodine to make any hormone, so it can't do that either.

The only thing left for TSH to do is to stimulate cellular proliferation in the thyroid gland, and that it does. The result is that the thyroid begins to grow and grow . . . and it continues to grow until the extra tissue is able to collect enough iodine to manufacture sufficient hormone. At that point, the gland may be as big as the patient's head (see figure 10.35). It should be understood that there is no problem other than the swollen neck. Levels of thyroid hormone in the blood and metabolism are usually normal, so there are no further pathological signs or symptoms.

Eliminating common goiter is simple. Provide sufficient dietary iodine, and it will dissapear in a few weeks.

Toxic Goiter

The affliction known as a toxic goiter is very different from the common goiter. It has many forms and more than a single cause. Usually the problem is the thyroid gland itself. It is often larger than normal (although never as large as a common goiter) and is secreting tremendous quantities of hormones. There are two problems that commonly cause toxic goiters, and they have been given the names **Plummer's disease** and **Graves' disease.** Of the two, Graves' disease is the more serious.

Graves' Disease The cause of Graves' disease is not clearly understood, but it is not thought to be the result of a malfunction of the hypothalamo-pituitary-thyroid axis. Current opinion suggests that it is a malfunction of some immunological mechanism that has not been elaborated. Graves' disease patients have a hypersecreting thyroid, but they also suffer from a disfiguring exophthalmia ("pop-eyes") and often **myxedema,** an affliction that is characteristic of hypothyroidism, as we'll see shortly (figure 10.36).

All this is believed to be due to the circulating antibody known as long-acting thyroid stimulator or LATS. Nothing is known of its origin or what the stimulant is that caused its appearance, but LATS is apparently able to clamp onto the TSH receptors on the thyroid gland and stay right there, turning everything on. It seems that anything TSH can do, LATS can do more of. It increases substrate accumulation in the thyroid gland, it stimulates the biosynthetic machinery, and it increases the gland's output of thyroid hormones. It could be considered an alternate regulatory mechanism for the thyroid gland, except for one thing—there are no feedback mechanisms to control the output of LATS, and so it runs completely out of control. Under the influence of LATS, T_3 and T_4 hormones are pumped out so rapidly and in such quantities that the follicle interiors are almost completely devoid of colloid. Levels of thyroid hormone do not merely get high, they get super high, and they stay super high, because there is nothing the patient produces that can shut down the production of LATS, and doctors do not know how to do it artificially. The cumulative effects are much different from those produced naturally by TSH, and they can be dangerous to life.

1. Patients are restless, irritable, and hyperactive. They tend to be impatient with almost every problem and are given to fits of uncontrollable anger.
2. In keeping with this tendency toward hyperirritability, they cannot sleep well. They spend most nights sleeping for fifteen- to thirty-minute periods interspersed with an hour or two of restless wakefulness.
3. During activity periods (which may or may not be during daylight), they have very short attention spans. Movements are rapid and uncoordinated, and tremors persist to the point where it is difficult for victims even to drink a cup of coffee without shaking quantities out of the cup.
4. Contractions of the heart increase in strength, and often the heart rate is abnormally high. Blood pressures increase and cardiac output is higher than normal.
5. The metabolic rate is so high that the individual feels hot when the temperature is 65 to 70° F, and heavy sweating is common.
6. Patients can ingest five heavy meals a day without any increase in weight. In fact, dehydration and burning of fat stores can be so intense that the patient may actually lose weight despite daily consumptions of five to six thousand calories.
7. Exophthalmia is a phenomenon that is specific for Graves' disease. It does not occur in Plummer's disease. What causes the exophthalmia is not known, but it is not thyroid hormones.

Plummer's Disease The cause of Plummer's disease is usually restricted to one or two nodules in the thyroid gland that have begun to hypersecrete for no particular reason. The nodules are almost always tumorous and are usually benign. The excess hormones they produce usually inhibit the feedback loop, and TRF and TSH both disappear from the blood.

Treatment As far as Plummer's disease is concerned, treatment is relatively simple. Injections of radioactive iodine is the treatment of choice. If all goes well, the radioactive iodine will be concentrated mainly in the hyperactive cells of the thyroid and will destroy them. It doesn't, however, always go well, and if it fails, surgery will almost always correct the problem.

Graves' disease is harder to treat. Sulfur-containing drugs will depress the gland's synthetic processes, thereby alleviating the symptoms of toxic goiter, but they are not a cure, and they have some nasty side effects. Radioactive iodine sometimes works, but when it does, the result is sometimes hypothyroidism a year or two later. In patients under 21 years of age, surgery is frequently used and usually produces very good results. The success rate is between 91 and 98 percent.

There is, unfortunately, a nasty complication of Graves' Disease called **thyroid storm** that occasionally strikes. This is a sudden onset of exaggerated hyperthyroid symptoms that can result in cardiovascular collapse and atrial fibrillation. It is a particularly lethal complication of toxic goiter, with a mortality rate of upwards of 25 percent, even if treatment is prompt.

Hypothyroidism

Called **myxedema** (*myx, "mucus"; edema, "swelling"*) in adults, and **cretinism** in children, hypothyroidism is more common than toxic goiter, and the obvious signs are almost the precise opposite:

Myxedema

1. The individual becomes sloppy, indolent, and always sleepy. Hearing becomes less acute, and visual perception is impaired.
2. The facial expression is flat and emotionless; there is a general puffiness around the cheeks and under the eyes that was originally believed to be due to the infiltration of mucus under the skin (which is responsible for the name *myxedema*).
3. The heart rate and the strength of the beat are reduced, and both cardiac output and blood pressure are reduced.

4. The body temperature is abnormally low. The skin surface feels cold and clammy, and the patient complains of chills in temperatures of 80 to 85° F.

Treatment: Supplemental doses of thyroid hormone can be taken orally and will completely reverse the symptoms. It must be carefully monitored to avoid provoking symptoms of toxic goiter, but is generally the preferred route.

Cretinism In children, hypothyroidism can be much more serious than in adults; if left untreated, it can result in permanent, serious structural damage. Apparently, the thyroid hormone is necessary for proper development of the infantile skeleton, of muscles, and of gonads. Untreated victims never grow normally and oftentimes do not exceed thirty inches in height. Thyroid hormones also apparently stimulate dendritic and axonal growth in the central nervous system, and without them, millions of CNS synaptic connections are never made, resulting in significantly diminished mental abilities (see figure 10.37).

Treatment Treatment of the afflicted child with proper hormones can make a dramatic difference in muscle and skeletal development, but after a certain time, the brain damage cannot be corrected.

Parathyroid Glands

Hypoparathyroidism

A person completely deprived of parathormone usually dies within forty-eight hours in tetanic convulsions. The disease most often occurs following thyroid surgery and is a result of damage to, or accidental removal of, one or more of the glands. Occasionally it may occur spontaneously, but this is rare. More commonly, PTH is gradually reduced, and the patient, while not totally deprived of the hormone, is definitely hypoparathyroid. The first signs are:

1. Hyperexcitability of muscles. Tapping the finger on the face produces exaggerated contractions of facial musculature (called **Chvostek's sign**), and tremors of the fingers, lips, and tongue are common.
2. Often these signs are followed by a hyperirritable gut, and vomiting and diarrhea are common.
3. Chronic hypoparathyroidism often results in uncontrollable spasms of the jaw that make clear speech almost impossible, and hair and fingernail growth slow drastically. Damage to the skeleton is common.

Figure 10.37 A cretin infant. Note the protruding tongue and the puffy, blank features. If left untreated, this child will suffer disastrous mental damage.

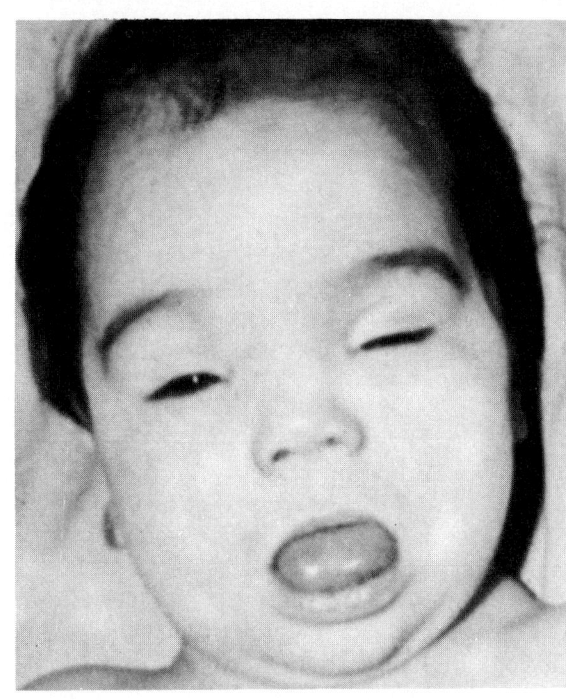

Treatment The administration of exogenous PTH is seldom the answer. The major problem is that parathyroid glands do not store much hormone, so it is extremely rare and prohibitively expensive. The problem is exacerbated by the fact that PTH is species specific, meaning that each species of mammal has a slightly different kind. As it turns out, all mammalian PTH will work in humans, but it *is* different, and because of this, immune reactions often develop quickly. Fortunately, high-calcium diets with supplemental vitamin D almost always will relieve the symptoms and restore normalcy, although care must be taken to avoid giving too much vitamin D (vitamin D intoxication).

Hyperparathyroidism

The cause of hyperparathyroidism has never been determined, but the signs are usually clear-cut. When there is an abnormally high PTH output, one of the first signs is abnormally high blood calcium. This can cause anorexia and sometimes polyuria. Intense thirst is common and is usually accompanied by dehydration, constipation, and high fever. Headache, muscular weakness, and memory loss are also common. If the condition persists without treatment, there will eventually be deposition of calcium salts in the soft tissues of the body, particularly in the kidney. Once deposited in the kidney, calcium can't be removed by physiological mechanisms, and it can impair renal function. Calcium salts are frequently deposited in the walls of arteries and can stiffen the walls, making them unresponsive to vasomotor commands.

Treatment Surgery is almost always recommended and is usually successful if all the hypersecreting cells can be located and removed. This is not as easy as it sounds. Abnormally functioning parathyroid glands are not always where they should be, and locating them without damaging the thyroid requires considerable experience and knowledge.

The Adrenal Glands

The Adrenal Medulla

Loss of the adrenal medullary hormones is rapidly compensated for by the sympathetic nervous system, which promptly increases its secretion of noradrenalin. Loss of the medulla is therefore not a life-threatening condition, although some abilities are lost. It's difficult, for example, for such patients to engage in strenuous physical activity, and their ability to function normally in cold climates is impaired. Cuts resulting in moderate blood loss are extremely difficult to cope with and can produce shock long before it would occur in a normal person. There is also a distressing tendency to become hypoglycemic for no apparent reason.

Treatment consists of care by the patient to avoid unusual or traumatic situations.

Hypersecretion of the adrenal medullary hormones is considered a more serious affliction. Such patients show a chronic "flight, fright, fight" syndrome—increased peripheral blood pressure, high blood sugar, increased heart rate, and a chronic gastrointestinal discomfort due to a general slowdown of digestive operations. The problem is usually a hypersecreting tumor on the medulla, and its cure is surgical removal.

The Adrenal Cortex

Addison's Disease Much more serious problems develop with the loss of the adrenal steroids. Loss of either the glucocorticoids or the mineralocorticoids is often fatal. The affliction is known as Addison's disease and can be caused by malfunctioning adrenal glands or inadequate ACTH. About three-quarters of the cases are due to the deterioration of the adrenal cortex for some unknown reason or because of an infection. The loss of glucocorticoids in Addison's disease is usually exacerbated by a deficiency of the mineralocorticoids as well.

The obvious signs are:

1. Hypotension and profound disturbances in carbohydrate, fat, and protein metabolism.
2. Chronic hypoglycemia and inadequate deposition of liver glycogen.
3. Resistance to infection is not good, and the patient cannot cope with stress.
4. Body temperature is subnormal and physical exertion cannot be tolerated.
5. The absence of aldosterone results in an unusually high water loss in the urine.
6. Potassium, ammonium ions, and hydrogen ions are retained in body fluids, while sodium is lost at a very high rate. The result is an abnormally low volume of extracellular fluids and a rapid loss of blood pressure. The unusual retention of K^+ in the interstitial fluids depresses heart function, while the lowered Na^+ in the body reduces the sensitivity of the blood vessels to vasomotor controls.

There is a handy way to determine whether the disease is an adrenal problem or is due to pituitary malfunction. If the problem is the adrenal cortex, the low serum levels of cortisol will result in abnormally high blood levels of ACTH and abnormal stimulation of melanocytes. This often produces unusual pigmentation, especially in areas of high pigmentation anyhow, like the areolas of the breasts, and the lips and gums. If a hypofunctioning pituitary is the problem, pigmentation doesn't occur, nor does the mineral imbalance that is so disastrous in primary Addison's disease.

Untreated Addison's disease results in profound muscle weakness and tremendous pain in the lower back and legs. Severe circulatory problems develop—low blood pressure, low cardiac output, and a reduced blood volume. Collectively, these will ultimately result in kidney shutdown and death.

Treatment is the same whether the disease is caused by a malfunctioning adrenal cortex or insufficient ACTH. Hormone replacement therapy consists of oral doses of hydrocortisone, and if the dosages are high enough, aldosterone replacement therapy is not required . . . why is not known. There are seldom any complications to hydrocortisone administration once the dosage has been adjusted, and as long as such therapy is carefully maintained, the prognosis is excellent.

Cushing's Disease: Adrenal Cortical Hyperfunction As with *hypo*function, adrenal *hyper*function may be due to an overactive pituitary, or it may be the adrenal cortex. Regardless of which it is, the cause is usually a hypersecreting tumor. Usually, the tumor is on the adrenal gland. The signs are:

1. Sharply increased appetite and a rapidly developing obesity.
2. Fat deposition increases abruptly and is abnormal. Very little is deposited in the legs, buttocks, or arms. Most is spread across the face and the back of the neck, resulting in a characteristic "moon face" or "buffalo hump."
3. Skeletal muscle begins to waste away, and this results in profound weakness.
4. Wounds occur easily and heal only with great difficulty.
5. The living layer of skin gets thin, and bruises occur frequently, producing the familiar purple striations known as "stretch marks" in places where they seldom are seen.
6. Menstrual irregularities occur, and females often begin to display signs of maleness (called **virilism**).

The virilism is due to the presence of unusually high levels of testosterone in the bloodstream. Regardless of a person's sex, the adrenal cortex produces both sex hormones. The amounts are small, and in a normally functioning person, their effects are never seen. However, when the adrenal is hyperfunctioning, there are unusually large amounts of both produced. The amount of estrogens is about the same as that of testosterone, and on that basis one might think that a person would begin to show female secondary characteristics as vigorously as they would show those of the male. That doesn't happen, however, because for some reason the liver selectively destroys estrogens at a much higher rate than it does testosterone, and that latter hormone begins to appear in large quantities in the blood. In a man, of course, that does not matter, but in a women, baldness, a hairy chest, and beard growth do matter and can be psychologically disastrous.

Treatment is aimed at eliminating the cause of the problem. If it is severe, surgery is used to remove the offending tumor, and even partial hypophysectomy can be successful if the neurosurgeon is experienced and good. If adrenalectomy becomes necessary, patients can be maintained as an Addison's disease patient would be.

Summary

A Brief History

Outlines the discovery of the endocrine system and historical efforts to learn about it.

The Endocrine System

- I. Gland Characteristics
  - A. Endocrine glands synthesize and secrete chemicals into the blood. They are clusters of secretory cells that have no obvious exits for the products they synthesize.
  - B. Structure. Generally speaking, there are two types: clumps of cells, like a raspberry, around a central area; or strung out in cords along blood vessels.
- II. Hormones. Hormones are chemicals that carry information or instructions involving homeostatic mechanisms or structures. These chemicals fall into one of two major groups: proteinaceous (amino acids and conglomerates of amino acids) or steroid (fatty). The steroid hormones are all built on a cholesterol nucleus.
  - A. Function vs. Mechanism of Action. Function refers to the job the hormone does. Mechanism of action describes how it does its job.
  - B. Target Selection. How the hormones identify their target cells.
    1. Specificity. Specificity refers to an affinity possessed by targets and hormone. It is like the interlocking of pieces of a jigsaw puzzle.
    2. Receptors. Receptors are the sites on target cells that the hormone identifies and locks onto.
- III. The Mechanism of Action of the Peptide Hormones
  - A. Peptide hormones are water soluble, so they cannot penetrate the membrane. Whatever they do must therefore be accomplished on the outer surface of the cell membrane.
  - B. The Second-Messenger Hypothesis. When the receptor and hormone lock together, they stimulate production of a compound inside the membrane. This second compound carries the hormone's message into the cell.
- IV. The Mechanism of Action of the Steroid Hormones Steroid hormones are fat-soluble, so they can penetrate the cell membrane; hence their receptors are inside the cytoplasm of the cell. The receptor/hormone complex forms in the cytoplasm, and the complex moves into the nucleus. It stimulates increased production of a certain kind of mRNA, which produces a protein that is characteristic of that particular hormone.

V. Hormonal Regulation. There are several places where hormone levels can be affected.
   A. Regulating Hormone Production. This can be influenced by increasing or reducing substrate availability. It can also be influenced by speeding or slowing utilization of substrates.
   B. Receptor Regulation. Regulating receptor number would affect the hormone's influence on its target cells.

VI. Feedback Loops. Feedback loops are cyclic; hence the name *loops*. They have a receptor, an integrator, and an effector that feeds back into the receptor.
   A. If the results of the effector activity support the original stimulus, it is a positive feedback loop.
   B. If the results of effector activity oppose the original stimulus, it is a negative feedback loop. Most biological loops are negative.

The Endocrine Glands

I. The Hypothalamus. This is part of the brain. It is a crucial control center.
II. The Pituitary. This is a double gland that dangles from the floor of the hypothalamus. It is called the master gland.
III. The Thyroid Gland. Located in the throat at about the level of the larynx.
IV. The Parathyroids. The smallest endocrine glands. They are close to the thyroid.
V. The Pancreas. A large, diffuse organ in the abdomen.
VI. The Adrenals. A dual gland located on the upper surface of the kidney.
VII. The Gonads. The reproductive organs.
VIII. The Thymus. Located in the middle of the chest, just behind the sternum.
IX. The Pineal Gland. Deep in the brain, just dorsal to the hypothalamus.

The Hypothalamus

Because the hypothalamus is part of the brain, it is the central integrating and coordinating structure for neuroendocrine operations in the body. Many of its secretions control operations of the anterior lobe of the pituitary gland (the adenohypophysis).

The Pituitary Gland

I. The Adenohypophysis. Has been called the "master gland" because it controls so many other endocrine glands. It controls secretions of the thyroid gland, the adrenal cortex, and the gonads. It also releases hormones that have a homeostatic function.
   A. Somatotropin. Somatotropin is a large peptide hormone. It is also known as growth hormone.
      1. Its Function in Children. In children, somatotropin stimulates growth in all tissues, especially bone.
      2. Its Function in Adults. In adults, somatotropin controls metabolic priorities by controlling glucose catabolism and lipid breakdown.
      3. Somatotropin Regulation. Somatotropin responds to glucose levels in the blood. It is not known how its growth-controlling abilities are regulated.
   B. Prolactin
      1. Prolactin is also known as the mammotropic hormone or the lactogenic hormone. It stimulates milk synthesis in the female breast. It may also stimulate parental behavior (as opposed to mating behavior).
      2. The Prolactin Feedback Loop. Suckling is the prime stimulus for the production of prolactin. The only hypothalamic factor associated with prolactin is an inhibitory factor.
   C. The Trophic Hormones
      1. Thyroid-Stimulating Hormone. Thyroid-stimulating hormone (TSH) controls most aspects of thyroid endocrine activity.
         a) TSH Regulation. TSH is regulated through the hypothalamus.
         b) An Out-Of-Control Mechanism. An immunoglobulin known as LATS sometimes takes over control of the thyroid. This is a disease condition.
      2. Adrenal Corticotrophic Hormone (ACTH). ACTH is a fairly large, polypeptide hormone. It controls the endocrine operations of certain layers of the adrenal cortex. ACTH is regulated through the hypothalamus.
      3. The Gonadotrophic Hormones. There are two gonadotrophic hormones—follicle stimulating hormone (FSH) and luteinizing hormone (LH).
         a) FSH exerts its primary effects on the germinal epithelium in both males and females.
         b) LH exerts its primary effects on the hormone-producing cells of the gonads. Under its influence, a new endocrine gland develops in females—the corpus luteum, source of progesterone.
         c) Gonadotrophic Feedback Loops. The gonadotrophic hormones apparently have a single hypothalamic releasing factor, which controls both of them.

II. The Pars Intermedia (Intermediate Lobe)
   A. Melanocytes. Melanocytes are cells in the skin. They contain a dark brown pigment called melanin. When stimulated, melanocytes spread their pigment throughout their cytoplasm, darkening the skin.
   B. MSH Regulation. The stimulus for MSH secretion seems to be ultra-violet radiation on the skin surface. The receptor is not known, nor is the controlling neural pathway (if any).

III. The Neurohypophysis (Posterior Pituitary). The neurohypophysis is an example of a neuroendocrine gland. Its cells are functioning neurons as well as endocrine cells. Its hormones are synthesized in the hypothalamus, transported down nerve axons into the neurohypophysis, and stored there.
   A. Hormonal Synthesis. One of these hormones is called oxytocin. It controls smooth muscle

contractions, particularly in the uterus and around the lactogenic glands of the breast. The other hormone is called vasopressin (antidiuretic hormone, ADH). It produces antidiuresis by limiting water loss via the urine.

B. The Neurohypophyseal Feedback Loops. Suckling provides the stimulus for oxytocin release. A neural pathway carries the stimulus to the hypothalamus, where integration takes place. Increased blood osmolarity is the stimulus for vasopressin release.

The Thyroid Gland

I. Thyroid Hormones. There are two main types of iodinated thyroid hormones: those that have four iodine atoms (called T_4 hormones) and those that have three (called T_3 hormones).

A. Iodine: The Mystery Element. Iodine is a critical element in the synthesis of thyroid hormones. The T_3 hormones are the most active. They regulate basic metabolic rate and, in infants, the development of bones, muscles, and the nervous system.

B. T Hormones: Mechanism of Action. The iodinated thyroid hormones are amino acids, and they can penetrate both the plasma membrane and the nuclear envelope. Inside the nucleus, they link onto nuclear proteins and influence the production of mRNA.

II. Calcitonin. The thyroid also produces a hormone called calcitonin.

A. Calcitonin Function. Calcitonin reduces levels of ionic calcium in body fluids. It is unusual in that its absence does not seem to disrupt life or life quality significantly.

B. Calcitonin Regulation. The feedback loop is largely unknown, but it does not appear to involve the pituitary.

The Parathyroid Glands

These are the smallest endocrine glands, weighing just over a milligram each. They are involved in calcium metabolism.

I. Calcium. Calcium and phosphate are reciprocal ions, meaning their solubilities are related.

II. PTH Function. Parathyroid hormone (called parathormone or PTH) is a polypeptide. It can mobilize calcium from the skeleton. It is crucial to the activation of vitamin D (calciferol).

A. Vitamin D. Vitamin D is not really a vitamin. It is a steroid hormone. It augments the effects of PTH.

B. Parathormone Regulation. Parathormone is not controlled by the pituitary or the hypothalamus. It secretes its hormones according to levels of Ca^{2+} in the blood.

The Adrenal Glands

The adrenal glands are located along the upper border of the kidneys. They are formed of two layers: the medulla and the cortex.

I. The Medulla. Is the center or "core" of the adrenal gland.

II. Medullary Hormones

A. The medulla secretes catecholamines, mainly epinephrine and a little norepinephrine. These hormones are sympathomimetic in their action (imitate the sympathetic nervous system). They prepare the body to handle emergency situations.

B. Medullary Regulation. Control is exerted by neurons of the sympathetic nervous system. Hormones are released in response to external emergency.

III. The Adrenal Cortex. The adrenal cortex is functionally a treble gland.

IV. Adrenocortical Hormones. The cortex secretes steroid hormones of three different groups: (1) the mineralocorticoid hormones, which control electrolyte metabolism, (2) the glucocorticoid hormones, which are involved with glucose metabolism, and (3) small quantities of sex hormones, both male and female.

A. The Mineralocorticoids. The mineralocorticoids are secreted from the outer layer of the cortex.

B. Mineralocorticoid Regulation. They are controlled by blood volume, sodium and potassium content, and blood pressure. There is a very complicated loop present that involves at least two other hormones, renin and angiotensin.

C. The Glucocorticoids. Glucocorticoids are secreted by the middle layer of the cortex.

D. Glucocorticoid Regulation. Secretion of the glucocorticoids is controlled by the pituitary-hypothalamic axis.

E. Sex Hormones. The sex hormones of the adrenal cortex have no appreciable effect during the reproductive life of the individual and may have none when it is over.

The Gonads

These structures secrete the hormones peculiar to sex.

The Thymus Gland

The thymus is located in the middle of the thoracic cavity. It is concerned with immunity.

The Pineal Gland

I. The pineal gland is located on the roof of the third brain ventricle. It seems to be a genuine endocrine gland, although this is debated. It secretes a substance known as melatonin, which may be a hormone.

II. Melatonin Function. Melatonin is able to suppress estrogen secretion in women. It seems to be inhibited by light. The greater the day length, the greater the inhibition of melatonin.

Atypical Endocrine Structures

These are structures that secrete hormones but are deeply involved in other functions.

Nonhormonal Chemical Messengers

To be a hormone, a chemical must enter the blood after secretion and thus be carried to its target.

The Endocrine Pancreas

The pancreas has both an endocrine and an exocrine function.

I. Pancreas Morphology. The endocrine function is accomplished by small islands of cells between the exocrine systems. These islands are known as the islets of Langerhans. There are three kinds of cells in the islets:
   A. Alpha (α) cells, which secrete the hormone glucagon
   B. Beta (β) cells, which secrete the hormone insulin
   C. Delta (Δ) cells, which secrete the hormone somatostatin

II. The Pancreatic Hormones. Insulin and glucagon are involved with protein, carbohydrate, and lipid metabolism. Somatostatin is involved in many activities.
   A. Somatostatin. Somatostatin is synthesized in many other areas as well as the pancreas. It seems to be mainly a selectively inhibitory hormone, operating on other hormones.
   B. Glucagon. Glucagon increases the content of nutrients in body fluids through the stimulation of catabolic activity in liver, muscle, and other target areas.
   C. Glucagon Regulation. Glucagon is not controlled by pituitary secretions. It responds to varying levels of various nutrients—chiefly glucose—in the blood.
   D. Insulin
      1. Insulin Function. Insulin is the only known hormone whose function it is to lower blood glucose. It does this in a variety of ways, most of them involved with increasing anabolism in its target tissues throughout the body.
      2. Insulin Regulation. Insulin is not part of the hypothalamo-pituitary axis. Its stimulus is increasing levels of nutrients—mainly glucose—in the blood.

Clinical Considerations

I. Diabetes Mellitus
   A. Insulin-Dependent Diabetes
      1. Exogenous Insulin
      2. Deadly Glucose
   B. Non–Insulin-Dependent Diabetes
   C. Glucagon
II. The Pituitary
   A. STH
      Acromegaly
   B. Trophic Hormones
III. The Neurohypophysis
   A. Diabetes Insipidus
   B. Hypersecretion of ADH
IV. The Thyroid
   A. Common Goiter
   B. Toxic Goiter
      1. Graves' Disease
      2. Plummer's Disease
      3. Treatment
   C. Hypothyroidism
      1. Myxedema
      2. Cretinism
V. Parathyroid Glands
   A. Hypoparathyroidism
   B. Hyperparathyroidism
VI. The Adrenal Glands
   A. The Adrenal Medulla
   B. The Adrenal Cortex
      1. Addison's Disease
      2. Cushing's Disease

Review Questions

1. What is the general function of the endocrine system?
2. Describe the morphological characteristics of endocrine glands in general terms. Be sure to include the two structural patterns.
3. What is a hormone? Name the two basic types.
4. What is the difference between a hormone's function and its mechanism of action?
5. How do hormones recognize their target cells?
6. Describe the types of receptors present on cells.
7. What is the second messenger hypothesis?
8. How does the mechanism of action of the steroid hormones differ from that of most proteinaceous hormones?
9. Describe a typical endocrine feedback loop.
10. Name the major endocrine glands.
11. Discuss the endocrine function of the hypothalamus in as much detail as you can.
12. Name the divisions of the pituitary gland.
13. Describe the actions of the nontrophic hormones produced by the anterior lobe of the pituitary. Be sure to include:
    a. the function of both in adults and children, males and females, and
    b. how they are regulated.
14. What trophic hormones are secreted by the pituitary gland?
15. Describe the regulatory operations of each of the trophic hormones. Be sure to include:
    a. how they affect their target tissues (you may have to list these),
    b. the hormones they control, and
    c. their feedback systems.
16. What is MSH? Discuss its source, function, and feedback control.

17. What hormones are released by the posterior lobe of the pituitary? Name each, and discuss it. Be sure to include:
    a. where each is synthesized,
    b. the stimulus to which each responds,
    c. where each is stored until its release, and
    d. the feedback loops involved.
18. Where is the thyroid gland located? Describe its structure.
19. What two types of hormones are synthesized in the thyroid gland?
20. Discuss the function and feedback loops involved with the iodinated hormones.
21. Discuss the function and feedback loop involved with the other thyroid hormone.
22. With what major mineral are the parathyroid glands concerned?
23. Discuss the function and regulation of the parathyroid hormone.
24. Where are the adrenal glands located? Describe their structure.
25. What is the function of the adrenal medulla? Discuss its regulation.
26. What three groups of hormones does the adrenal cortex release?
27. Discuss the function and regulation of the three types of adrenal cortical hormones. Be sure to include:
    a. renin and angiotension, their source and effects,
    b. the effects (or lack of them) produced by ACTH, and
    c. the sex hormones.
28. What is the location, structure, and function of the thymus gland?
29. Where is the pineal gland located? What is its function?
30. Discuss the location and morphology of the pancreas. What portions are endocrine in nature?
31. Name and describe the three major cell types in the endocrine areas of the pancreas.
32. Name the three major hormones produced in the endocrine pancreas and their cellular source.
33. What are the functions of glucagon? How is it regulated?
34. Describe the hormone somatostatin. What are some of its functions?
35. Describe the hormone insulin and tabulate its functions.
36. Describe the consequences of insulin lack.

Section III

Motion and Motor Control

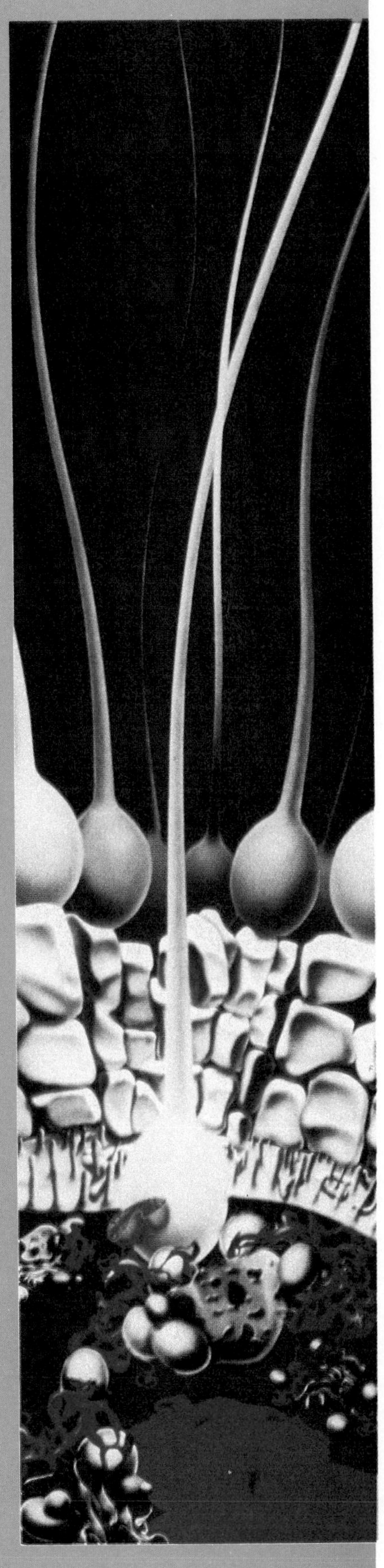

Chapter 11

Muscles and Movement

Study Hints

While reading this chapter, you should keep in mind that in its own way, muscle is just another homeostatic mechanism—one that enables the entire organism to move in order to collect food and water. Obtaining food is an elaborate homeostatic process, and like all the rest, it is a cooperative effort, with muscles playing a major part throughout, especially in the final stages.

And their role does not end when the food is eaten. In our digestive systems, other muscles assist in moving the food through the tract and in breaking it up so it can be absorbed. The whole pageant is designed to make certain that our cells always have an adequate supply of food and water, and muscles help insure that procuring these supplies will be easy and efficient.

Objectives

When you have finished reading this chapter, you should:

1. be able to describe the morphological differences between the three types of muscle tissue found in vertebrates.
2. be able to describe the functional differences between the three types of vertebrate muscle.
3. understand why muscles must have an antagonistic muscle or force to oppose them.
4. have a solid grasp of how contractile proteins interact with each other to produce movement in muscles.
5. be able to explain the relationship between the sarcoplasmic reticulum and the T system in skeletal muscle.
6. be able to explain the role that calcium plays in muscle contraction.
7. be able to explain how muscles are able to grade their movements and force so that we don't use as much energy to lift a pencil as we do to lift a barbell.
8. understand the role of ATP in muscle contraction and relaxation.
9. be able to describe the different types of skeletal muscle and know where in the body you would find each.
10. know the basic structural, chemical, and contractional differences between skeletal muscle and smooth muscle.
11. be able to describe the structural and contractile differences between the two types of smooth muscle.

Myosin filament in striated muscles.

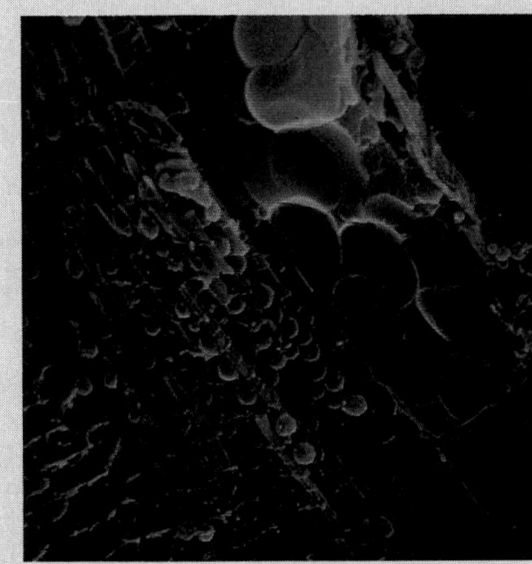

Introduction

Our muscles have gifted us with movement. Not just the ability to move from place to place, but movement *inside* our bodies. Our blood moves through its vessels because of a muscle's efforts, food moves through our digestive tracts for the same reason, and we are brought into the world thanks in great part to the efforts of the muscles of the female uterus.

Like almost every other body process, muscle is essentially a homeostatic system intended to keep our internal *milieu* constant. It accomplishes this by providing us with motion. Motion gives us the ability to move from place to place for the purpose of gathering food and water, and that's a homeostatic operation. We gather food and water in order to insure that our body cells will always have an adequate supply of nutrient. The voluntary muscles move our bodies from place to place so that when all the food is gone from a given place, we can go somewhere else where it is not all gone, thereby making food more abundant. Once food has been obtained and consumed, a different type of muscle moves it through the gut, mixing and churning, aiding in breakup and absorption, so it will be available to our blood in a form the cells can use. By providing blood with movement, muscles make it possible for our cells to obtain their nutrients without having to go out themselves and look for it. As long as we can provide our cells with adequate food, the cytosol will not become depleted, and an adequately stocked cytosol is an important aspect of homeostasis.

Motion, although crucial, is not the only advantage that muscle provides us with. Sheets of skeletal muscle provide protection for the abdominal organs and cushion the shock of blows that might be administered to the limbs or upper body. In humans, skeletal muscle is our primary source of internal heat and is thus critical in our thermoregulatory operations.

The Tissue

Muscle is considered a tissue in its own right. Its special properties are unique enough and sufficiently important to put it in a category by itself, and we will view it from this perspective.

Muscles are tremendously powerful, and each type can apply this power in its own way. The muscles that move our bones can get into action with astonishing speed, and although their activity does not usually last very long, while they work they can exert tremendous force. The muscles that move the food through our gut are capable of exerting considerable force, but it is applied much more slowly and smoothly and can be maintained for long periods of time without tiring. The muscle that comprises our heart works with surprising, monotonous regularity, minute after minute, year after year.

What separates muscle from all the other tissues is its ability to shorten all its constituent cells cooperatively and with tremendous force. Cells that are long and thin when relaxed can suddenly become short and thick, and in the process they can exert a lot of power. In this, as a tissue, muscle is unique. Other body cells contain microtubules and microfilaments that can contract when necessary to change cell shape; some can even move the cell from place to place. But only a few microtubules contract at a time, and as far as the cell is concerned, it is an individual effort. When muscle cells contract, *all* of its contractile mechanisms work simultaneously, and it is rare indeed when a muscle cell contracts alone. Usually many cells work together to produce a cooperative force.

Categories of Muscle

Grossly speaking, there are three types of muscle. These categories were created in the very early days of physiological research; hence the distinctions depend entirely on morphological differences that were clear when viewing them through light microscopes. Functional characteristics were not weighed too heavily when the original discriminations were made, but it turned out all right, because there are fundamental functional differences between each of the three types. There are also some important similarities. For example, they all share the most important characteristic, namely, the ability to shorten with power—that is what makes them muscles—and all of them use the same contractile mechanisms to perform this feat. Along with these biochemical and mechanical responses, the electrical activity is fundamentally the same.

Figure 11.1 Five skeletal muscle fibers are visible in this view. Note that each one has multiple nuclei and cross-striations.

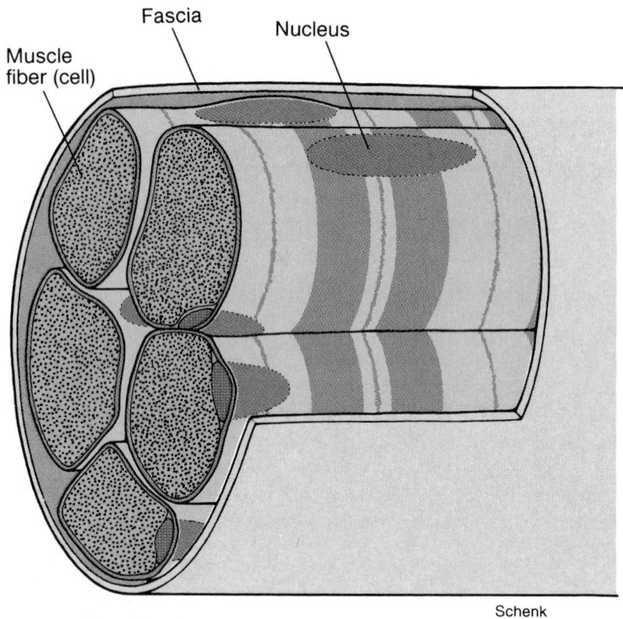

Aside from their individual appearance, the most obvious differences between muscles are their anatomical locations and the jobs they have to do, and these differences seem fairly obvious. The functional dissimilarities are subtle, and not nearly as apparent to the casual investigator. Things like the speed of response to stimulus, the energy source, and the manner in which the initial stimuli are applied are less easily distinguished, but they are nonetheless real.

Skeletal Muscle

The largest, and hence the most obvious, muscle mass is **skeletal muscle.** This is the contractile tissue that we consciously control and that provides us with the ability to move our whole body. It is also known as *striated* muscle and sometimes as *voluntary* muscle, and while both of these latter names are accurate, they have limitations. The name "striated" was applied because of the muscle's appearance under a light microscope. Under low or high power, obvious bands or striations are clearly visible, running in concert and at precise intervals across each muscle fiber (figure 11.1). These striations are so clear-cut and so regular that it would have been incredible if they were not somehow incorporated into the name. So it is appropriate . . . yet it is not a *distinguishing* name, because the patterned striations are shared by one other muscle type, cardiac muscle. There is, however, only one type of muscle that is associated with the bones of our bodies; therefore the name *skeletal* seems to be best.

Figure 11.2 Skeletal muscles (such as the biceps brachii shown here) exert their force against bones, setting them in motion. Contraction of the muscle shown here would pull the radius and the humerus toward each other, rotating on the hinge between them.

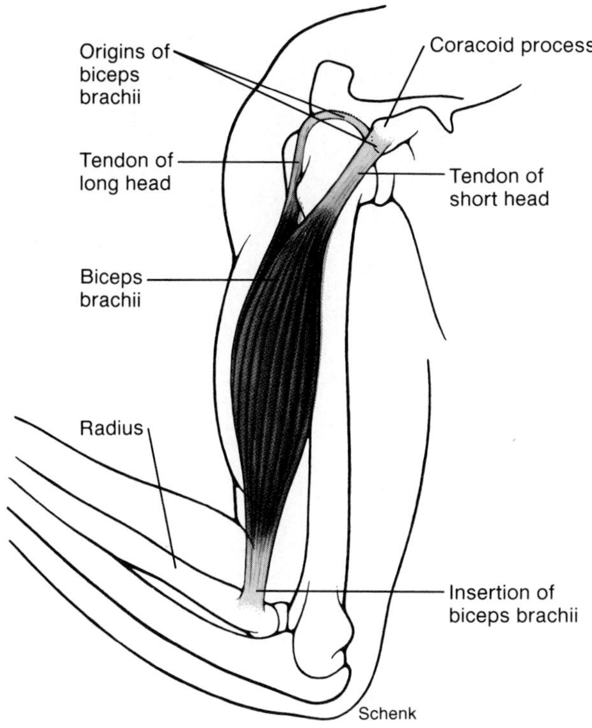

Skeletal muscles move us around. They exert a force on the bones they are attached to, and by setting these shafts in motion, they permit us to move (figure 11.2).

There are more than six hundred skeletal muscles which, when working in concert with the skeleton, give human beings independent motility. They are all sizes and shapes. For instance, the muscles that hold our heads upright are large, straplike muscles. Those that move our arms and legs are great, bulging muscles, tapered at both ends and wide in the middle. The muscles that lift our eyebrows in astonishment or raise a lip in a sneer are tiny, three-quarter-inch-long strips that look like flexible, flat toothpicks.

Vertebrate skeletal muscles can change from a state of complete relaxation to maximum contraction in about two-hundredths of a second, and they have tremendous speed and power. But their stamina is not quite as impressive. Maximum, sustained contractions of skeletal muscle gulp energy in such enormous quantities that oxidative metabolism is not able to keep up. As a result, sustained contractions usually do not last very long, but while they do, the power they can achieve is astonishing. Most skeletal muscles can exert forces of up to 1,000 times their own weight.

When muscles begin to work, the blood flow to them increases, carrying more oxygen to the working tissue, so that more energy will be available if needed. However, when muscles become highly active for extended periods of time, the aerobic production of ATP cannot keep up with the energy demands, and the muscle must begin to rely on its glycolytic operations to provide the necessary high-energy molecules. Glycolysis, you will remember, can remove accumulating end products from the glycolytic pathway and shunt them onto a lactic acid "siding," out of the way. The result is an accumulation of lactic acid in the muscles, which is transferred, as quickly as possible, to the blood.

If muscle activity continues at a very high rate with no significant breaks for rest, lactic acid will continue to build up. Eventually it will accumulate to a point where muscle pH may decline and inhibit the enzymes that are involved in contractile processes. The result is that the muscles can no longer achieve full or prolonged contraction, and muscle *fatigue* sets in. If, however, the intense activity isn't too prolonged, glycolysis is usually able to provide all necessary energy, even when the aerobic pathways have been overwhelmed. That extra energy is reflected in the quantity of lactic acid that accumulates during activity. When the exercise is over, extra oxygen must be inhaled to "burn off" that lactic acid and to rebuild the muscle's stores of high-energy compounds. The amount of extra oxygen required is determined by the volume of accumulated lactic acid; hence the lactic acid accumulation is often referred to as an **oxygen debt.**

Smooth Muscle

The second most abundant contractile tissue in the body is quite a different kind of muscle. Since it is not under conscious control, it is often referred to as *involuntary muscle,* and because it is so abundant around the GI tract, it has also been called *visceral muscle.* Yet it is not the only involuntary muscle in the body, and since it is abundant outside the viscera, these names lack distinction. The name **smooth muscle** is preferred for this type, because it is devoid of the regular, cross-striation patterns so obvious in skeletal muscle and is arranged inside of us in smooth, glossy sheets. Since no other muscle shares this characteristic, smooth muscle is the most delineative name (figure 11.3).

As is true of all muscles, the primary job of smooth muscle is to contract, but some contractile characteristics are quite different from those of skeletal muscle. For instance, skeletal muscle contractions can be, and often are, explosive, while those of smooth muscle are applied slowly and smoothly. Also, generally speaking, smooth muscles are not as strong as skeletal muscles, yet sometimes their force can be imposing. There are exceptions, of course, to all of these generalizations. Contractions of an offended digestive system can occasionally be rapid, and their power is

Figure 11.3 Photomicrograph of smooth muscle cells. Notice that these cells lack striations and contain single, centrally located nuclei.

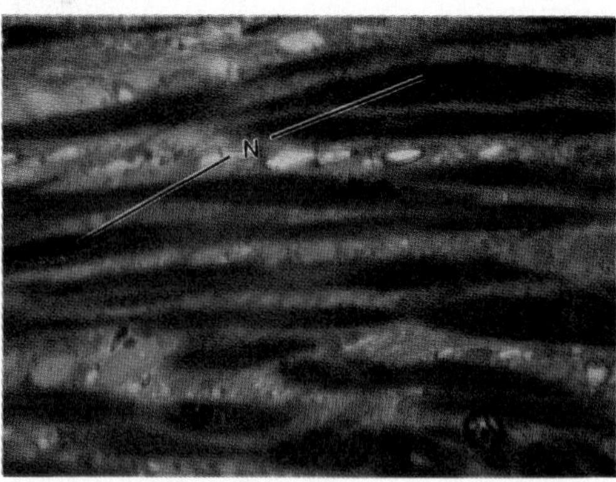

often quite impressive when expelling food from either end. Noteworthy also is the power available in the smooth muscle of the uterus. It rivals the strongest skeletal muscles in our bodies . . . and its stamina surpasses them all.

Cardiac Muscle

Cardiac muscle is unique to the vertebrate heart. Because of its appearance (figure 11.4), it used to be thought of as a combination of smooth muscle and skeletal muscle. Certainly its function seemed to be a combination of the two. But in fact, about the only thing it has in common with either muscle type is its contractile mechanism. Today, it is looked upon as absolutely unique and deserving of a category of its own.

Cardiac muscle beats, it seems, inexhaustibly, day after day, year after year. Yet it is not, as some people seem to believe, tireless. It is able to beat incessantly because it *never maintains a contraction*. It contracts, then just as promptly relaxes . . . and it has relaxation periods that are roughly twice as long as its work periods, so it actually gets plenty of rest. Nevertheless, when it is called upon to contract (which is about every nine-tenths of a second), it must do so without fail. There are no periods of prolonged contraction, true, but there are no prolonged rest periods available, either. It must be ready to go at the proper time.

Furthermore, its rest periods and its work periods are strictly outlined—the muscle rests, then it must contract before it can rest again. The periods of inactivity are short, but regular. Cardiac muscle is unlike smooth or skeletal muscle in that it cannot rely on anaerobic metabolic pathways to provide its energy; hence it must never—*ever*—fail to get all the oxygen that it needs. Cardiac muscle is the only muscle in our bodies that is unable, except in disease states, to achieve a state of sustained contraction, and it has other properties as well that render it unique. These are dealt with in detail in chapter 13.

Figure 11.4 Cardiac muscle. Note the multiple cell-to-cell contact points.

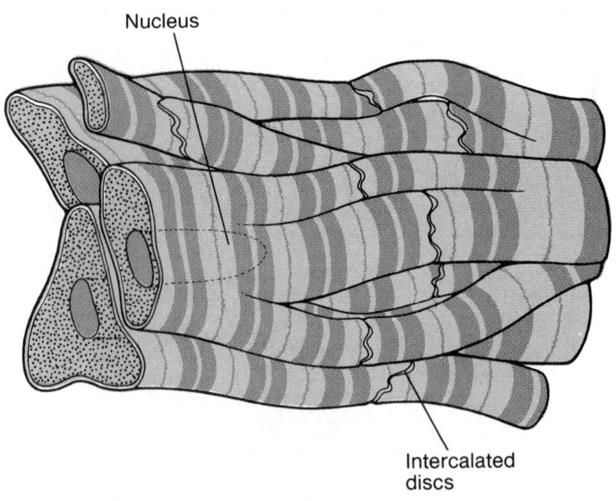

The Most Important Property

Easily the most important characteristic of muscle tissue is its ability to shorten with tremendous force. This property is fully exploited. By skillfully attaching muscles to our body's skeletal supports, nature has provided vertebrates with a system of motility that is remarkable in its effectiveness. Muscle cells that are long and thin when resting can, with the proper stimulus, suddenly shorten, become thick, and pull with tremendous force. Once the stimulus is removed, they promptly relax. *But they do not stretch back out to their original resting length.*

No Ability to Push

Muscles cannot return to their stretched-out length after contracting because *muscles are not able to push—they can only pull.* With the exception of the heart, no innate mechanism has ever been found that will actively stretch out a muscle. After a muscle has relaxed, therefore, if there is no outside force available to stretch it out, it will remain in its shortened condition. It will be soft and flaccid. There will be no tension involved nor any resistance to pull. An external agency can easily stretch the muscle back out again to its original long, thin state, but a muscle cannot stretch out by itself, because it simply cannot actively elongate.

Antagonistic Muscles

That is why we have *antagonistic muscles* throughout our bodies. There are no muscles anywhere that don't have some mechanism or provision built in that will provide for stretching them out again after they have

Figure 11.5 (*a*) Antagonistic muscle activity in the arm. (*b*) Antagonistic muscles in the leg.

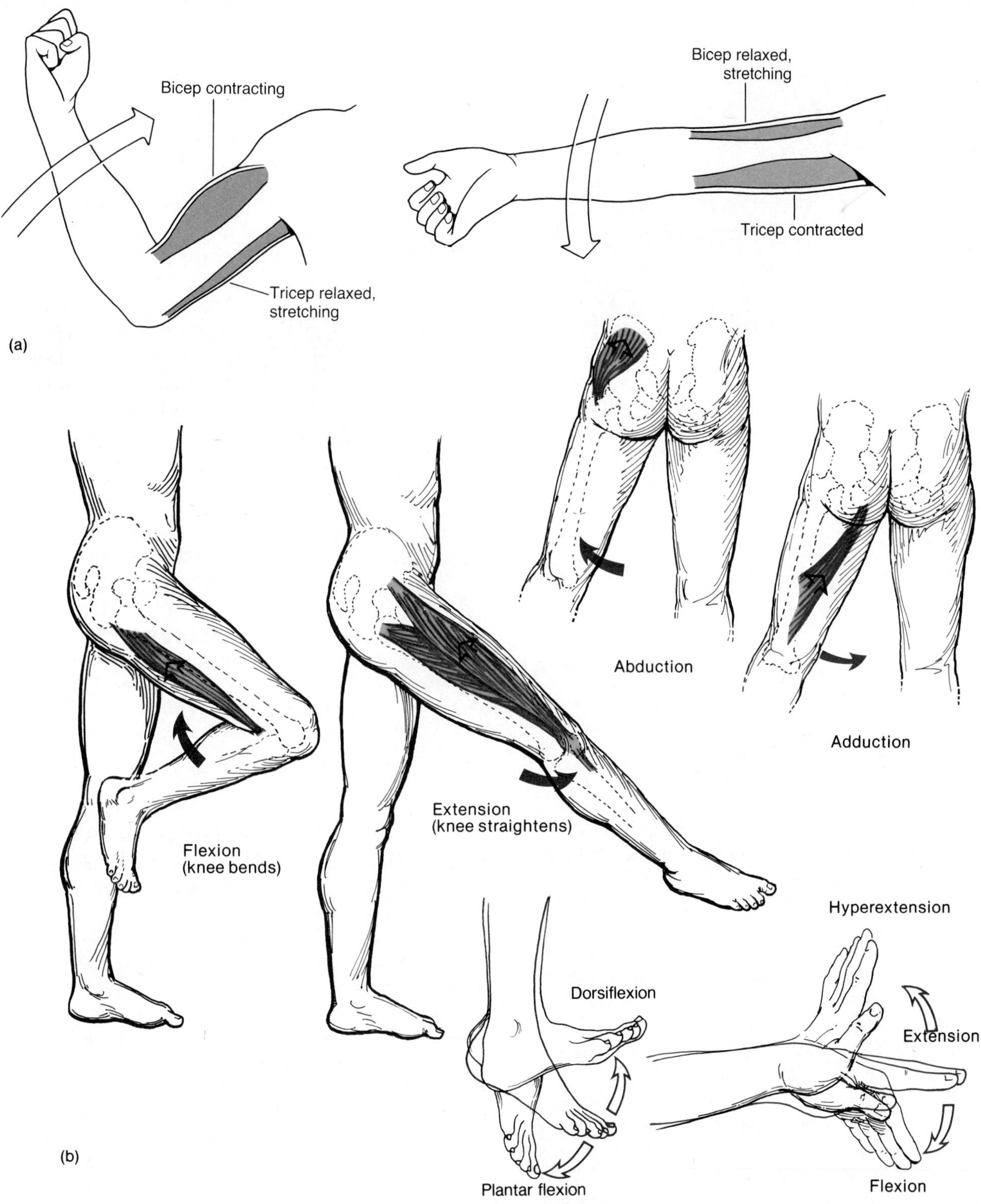

contracted. Most of our skeletal muscles have antagonistic muscles to do this. For example, the **bicep** muscle of your upper arm will pull your hand toward your shoulder, but when you relax your bicep it won't stretch your arm out again (figure 11.5*a*). Try it sometime when you're lying down and don't have the assistance of gravity to pull your arm straight. The only way you can straighten out your arm is to contract the

Figure 11.6 A skeletal muscle dissected. (*a*) A whole muscle, excised from the body. (*b*) A fasciculus teased out of the muscle and opened, showing individual fascia. Opening the fascia shows the individual fibers and eventually the myofibrils, the muscle's contractile units. (*c*) A schematic of the protein arrangement that produces the banding patterns.

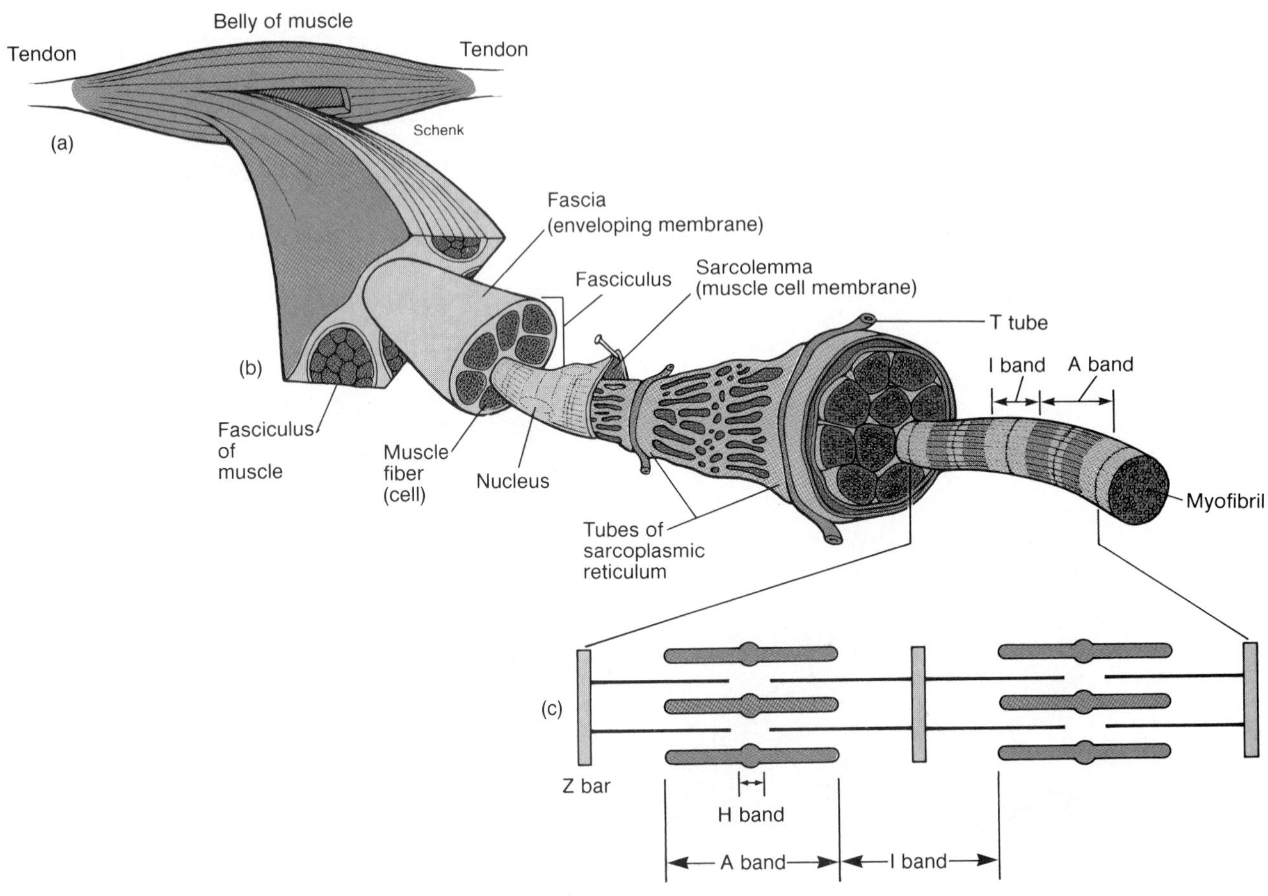

tricep muscle on the back of your arm. Conversely, when the tricep has contracted and relaxed, it can only be stretched out again by pulling it with your bicep.

This is the way all our body muscles operate. For each of them there is a force of some kind, usually a muscle, that opposes their action and will therefore be able to stretch them out again. The smooth muscle sheets of the intestinal tract are arranged in such a way as to oppose each other. Our blood vessels have the pressure of fluid flowing through them to stretch them out, and so, to a slightly more limited extent, does our heart. Secretory glands stretch out when they fill with fluid, and our diaphragm has pressure from the abdominal muscles below to push it back into its dome-shaped revetment in the thorax. There must always be something available to stretch a muscle out so it can do its job.

Micro- and Ultrastructure

To grasp the significance of muscle morphology and the role it plays in muscle function, we need to dissect and inspect it at the microscopic level. Since much of the microscopial and physiological work has been done with skeletal muscle, it seems reasonable to use it for our discussion.

If we were to take the limb muscle of some animal—say, a steer—we could see its characteristic spindle shape quite easily (figure 11.6). The thick part is called the *belly* of the muscle, and if we cut it across, we can see that it is internally subdivided into several compartments. These compartments are called **fasciculi,** and a cursory investigation will show us that they, in their turn, are further subdivided into muscle **fibers.**

Figure 11.7 The repeating bands of a muscle's sarcomeres.

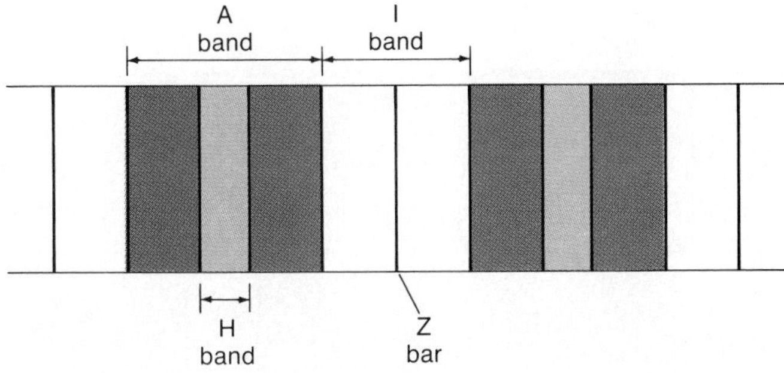

Figure 11.8 A thick myofilament. The contractile protein myosin is shown in clusters as they are arranged in a skeletal muscle fiber.

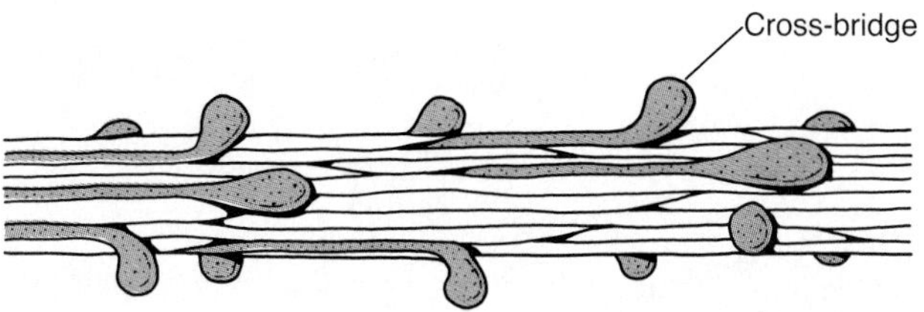

One very important point—when we are dealing with skeletal muscle, the terms *fiber* and *cell* are synonymous. Muscle fibers start out embryonically as strings of cells that butt up against each other, end-to-end. At this stage in their development, each cell has its own nucleus, and each one functions as an individual unit. But as the muscle fiber matures, these individual cells lose their end membranes and coalesce into one very long, single cell with many nuclei. In this form, each fiber—since it is now all one cell—can function as a unit. This kind of anatomical arrangement is known as a **syncytium** (*syn*, "together"; *tium*, "belonging"), and a skeletal muscle fiber is most assuredly an anatomical, as well as functional, syncytium.

Inside the Muscle Fiber

If we tease apart a muscle fiber, we will see first of all that it is surrounded by a plasma membrane. The muscle cell membrane is essentially the same as any other cell membrane in its basic chemistry, but because it surrounds a muscle cell, it is known as the **sarcolemma** (*sarco*, "flesh"; *lemma*, "husk" or "peeling"). Similarly, the cytoplasm of the muscle cell is known as **sarcoplasm** (figure 11.6).

Sarcoplasm is not *exactly* like the cytoplasm of a typical cell; there are some obvious differences. For one thing—and this is very obvious indeed— we can see an unusual sequence of dark and light bands running in perfect register across the entire fiber from one side to the other and in perfect sequence for the entire length of the fiber.

Myofibrils

As we continue our dissection of the muscle fiber, we see that the fiber is subdivided into parallel bundles grouped together in much the same way the fibers are collected into fasciculi (figure 11.6). These tiny bundles are the **myofibrils** (*myo*, "muscle"), or functional units of the muscle fiber, and like the muscle fibers, they are cylindrical in shape. The myofibrils run parallel to the long axis of the muscle fiber, and the elements within each fibril are carefully aligned with respect to each other. It is this military alignment of the internal elements that is responsible for the striations that course across the muscle fiber with the regularity of marching men. In early years, these striations were thought to be unique to skeletal muscle and, as was noted before, the patterns that resulted were responsible for giving the name *striated muscle* to this tissue. The fact that they seemed to form units that occurred over and over again along the entire length of the fiber suggested that each repeating unit had an individual role in the contractile process.

The lightest of these striations is known as the **I band,** while the darkest regions are the **A bands.** In the middle of the A band there is a thin region of slightly lighter density that is known as the **H zone,** and dividing the I band into separate halves is a thin line called the **Z bar** that separates each repeating unit from its neighbor. These units are known as **sarcomeres** (figure 11.7), and within each sarcomere are the myofilaments.

Myofilaments

Myofilaments are the **contractile proteins,** the fundamental contractile elements of muscle tissue, and when studied by means of electron microscopy their unique morphological characteristics are clearly visible (figure 11.8). The thick filaments are composed of the protein myosin, and in the A band of the myofibril, these myosin filaments overlap the thin filaments. Throughout this zone of overlap, small proteinaceous projections stick out of the thick filaments as the head of an ax projects from its shaft. These myosin projections are known as **cross-bridges** and are functionally critical to muscle activity.

All the contractile proteins are fibrous (which means they are longer than they are wide), and in the zone of overlap, they are arranged side by side in a pattern that is so precise that it has got to be functional (figure 11.9). It is, as we will see presently.

Figure 11.9 The regular arrangement of contractile proteins in muscle. (*a*) Drawing of a single contractile unit, showing how thin filaments surround the thick center. (*b*) A photomicrograph of two fibers in cross-section. Note the thick fibers surrounded by the thin in each contractile unit. (SR = sarcoplasmic reticulum.)

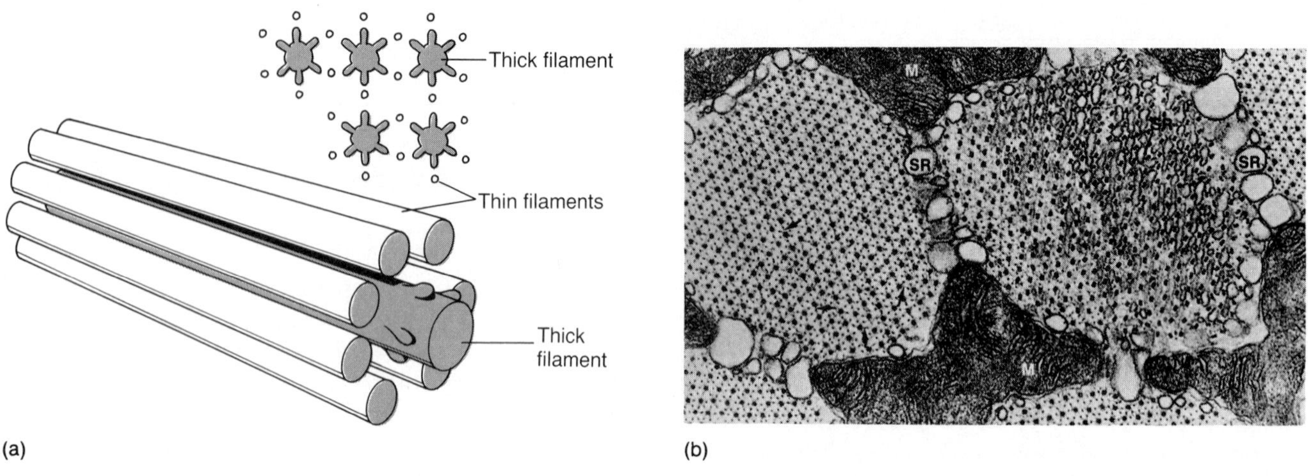

Figure 11.10 The globular protein actin as it is arranged in muscle fibrils. The darkened globes are troponin protein complexes, while the thin, light strands lying in the groove between the actin strips are tropomyosin, the fourth contractile protein.

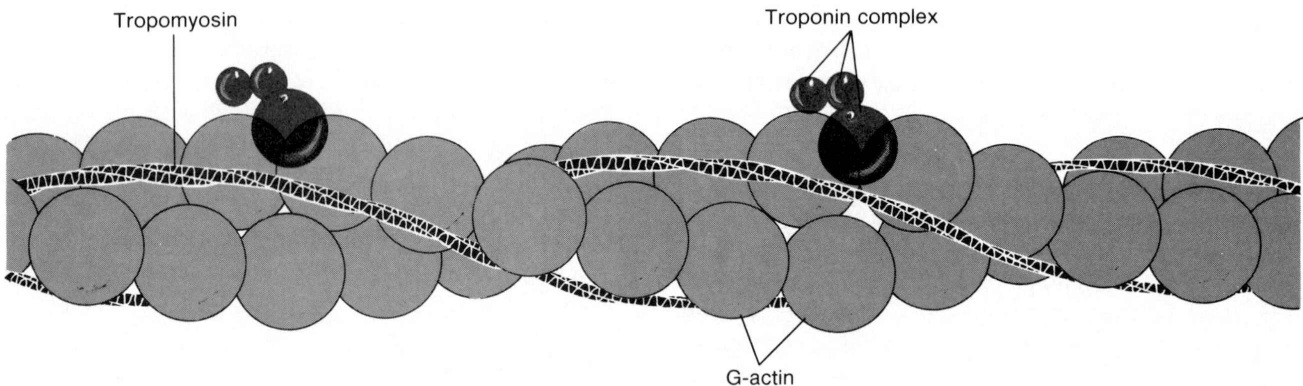

The Contractile Proteins

Muscle and nervous tissue have a great many things in common. They may not *look* very similar, but analysis shows that they are both about 75 percent water and 25 percent solids. Furthermore, of that 25 percent that is solids, most of the minerals and small organic molecules are distributed in similar proportions. The main difference between the two tissues relates to the large organic components. In nervous tissue, most of these are lipid. In muscle they are almost all protein, more than 80 percent, in fact, and almost all of that protein is contractile. Contractile proteins are not unique to muscle; they are found in lots of other cells. But they are not nearly as abundant or as ordered in other cells as they are in muscle tissue. There are four of them in skeletal muscle: **actin, myosin, troponin,** and **tropomyosin.**

Actin

Actin is a spherically shaped protein that has a molecular weight of about 46,000. In this form it is known as **G actin** (G for Globular) and contains about 220 amino acids. In muscle tissue these spheres polymerize (remember that word?) into long strings of globular proteins strung together to form a double helix—like two strings of identical pearls twisted around each other (figure 11.10). This form was given

Figure 11.11 A myosin molecule as it is arranged in the A band of a muscle fiber.

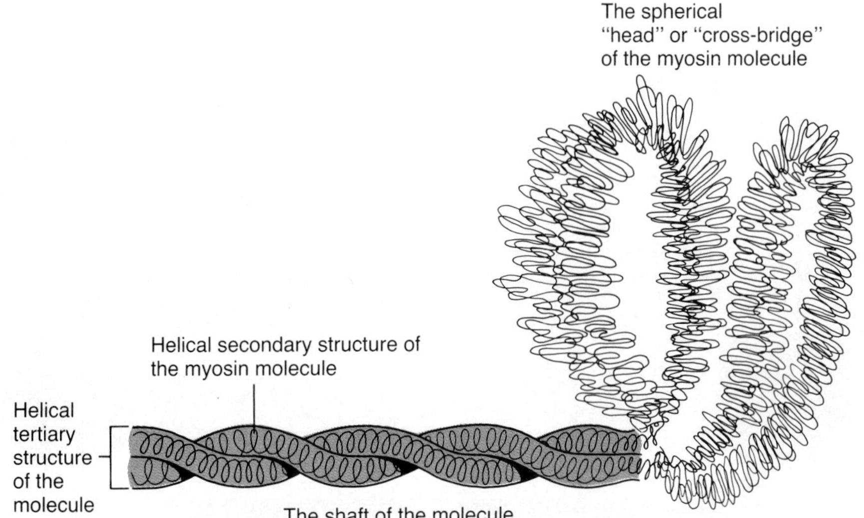

the name **F actin** (F for Fibrous), and the globes of G actin are the *monomers* (another word you should remember) of the F actin strips. These twisted strings of actin beads form the backbone of the **thin filaments** that make up much of the A band and the whole of the I band in skeletal muscle.

Myosin

As I said earlier, each thick myofilament is composed of myosin—about two hundred molecules of myosin, to be precise. Individual molecules of myosin are bigger than molecules of actin. In fact, myosin is the longest unbroken chain of amino acids that is known. More than two thousand amino acids are strung together in an alpha-helical shape to form a myosin molecule. The shaft of the molecule is formed of two alpha helices twisted around one another in a tertiary structure that resembles the strands in a thick rope fiber. The other end opens out as if it had been pounded with a hammer, spreading the amino-acid strings out into a globe-like shape (figure 11.11). Possibly to enlarge the head, there are two additional polypeptide chains, each with a molecular weight of about 17,000. Taken as a unit, the whole structure rather resembles a short-handled golf club.

For a structural protein, myosin is unusual in that it seems to have enzymatic activity. The head part of the molecule is apparently capable of hydrolyzing ATP and releasing that molecule's stored energy. This hydrolysis takes place as soon as ATP is bound to the myosin molecule, and when the ATP splits, its energy shifts into the myosin, which then becomes a high-energy compound. The myosin remains in this charged state until it is able to form chemical bonds with an actin molecule and produce an organic complex called **actomyosin.**

At first glance (figure 11.12), it would seem that such a linkage would be easily accomplished, because *in vivo,* actin and myosin are very closely associated, and if they have any affinity for each other at all, the link should happen. Such an evaluation is accurate. If there were nothing to prevent it, they would quickly combine and the energy stored in the myosin would be released, but in resting muscle, that does not happen. The complex is prevented from forming by a second pair of muscle proteins—troponin and tropomyosin.

Tropomyosin

Tropomyosin is a filamentous protein with a molecular weight of about 130,000. It consists of two identical peptide strands wrapped around each other. It spontaneously forms a complex with troponin when the two molecules are mixed. Once formed, the complex lies on the outermost surface of each thin filament, spanning seven of the actin globes, effectively fencing them off from the "heads" of the myosin molecules. In living tissue, this is the way it is always found.

Figure 11.12 In the A band, myosin and actin are arranged in such a way as to permit the myosin cross-bridge to contact actin and form the complex actomyosin. (Arrows indicate direction of movement.)

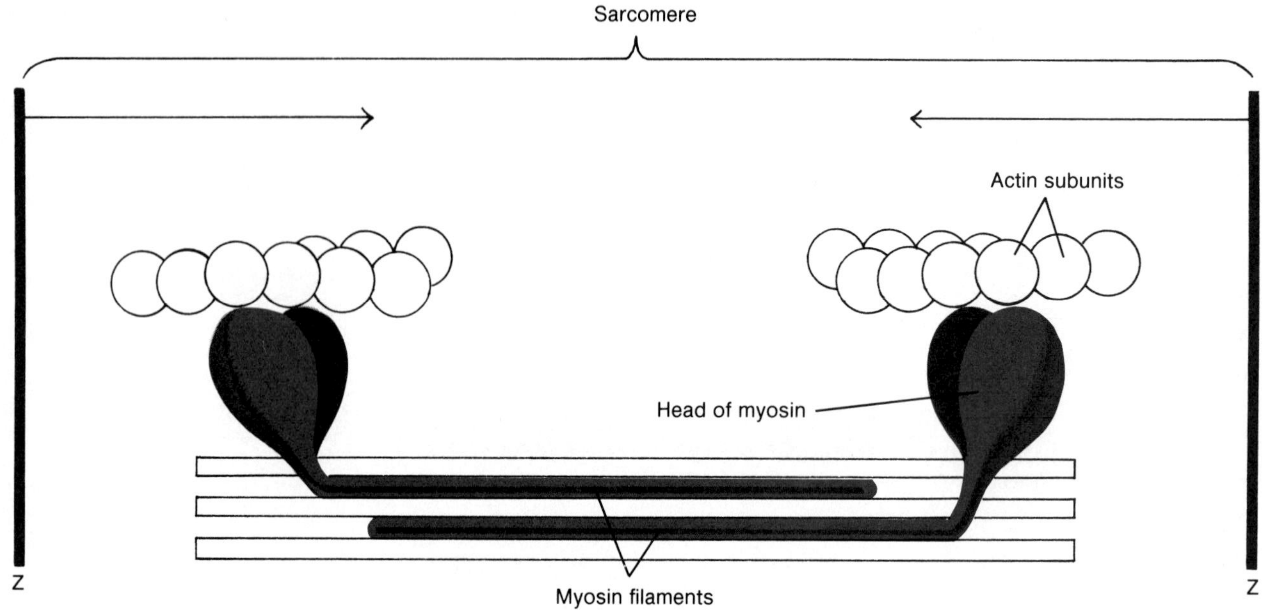

Figure 11.13 The troponin/tropomyosin complex, showing the position of the three troponin subunits.

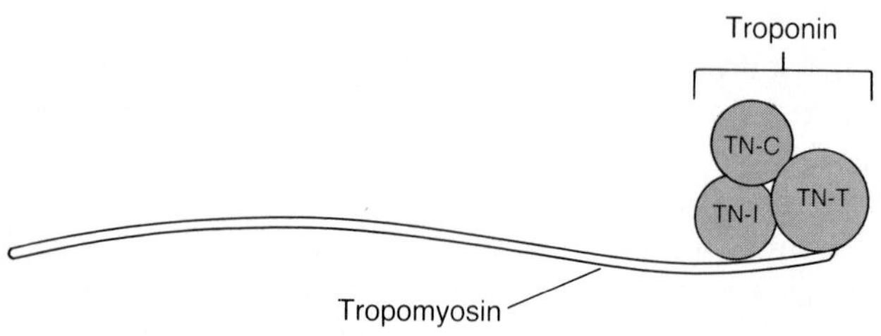

Troponin

Troponin is the smallest of the contractile proteins. It is a globular peptide with a molecular weight of only about 86,000. It is a complex molecule composed of three subunits: troponin T (TN-T), troponin C (TN-C), and troponin I (TN-I). *In vivo,* when it is complexed with tropomyosin, the two compounds resemble a long-tailed pollywog (figure 11.13).

So these are the contractile proteins of the muscle, and these are the compounds that give muscle its ability to shorten with power. We knew of the existence of these compounds for years, but it took the electron microscope to tell us what they did and how they worked. The key was found in the way all these proteins were arranged with respect to each other, a design that is crucial. It is precise, and the precision is essential if the muscle is to do its job.

The Contractile Process

Figure 11.10 shows the relative positions of the actin globes, the myosin molecules, and the troponin/tropomyosin complex. Note the fact that the tropomyosin is not in the "groove" between the beads of actin but is aligned across the outer surface. When the muscle is relaxed, the troponin/tropomyosin complex is linked to the actin molecules, and the tropomyosin molecule lies along the outer surface of the actin globes, held in place by its TN-T subunit. In this position, the tropomyosin strip is between the "heads" of the myosin molecules and seven of the actin globes, preventing a bond from forming between actin and myosin. Tropomyosin thus functions as the regulator of the relaxation phase of muscle activity.

With tropomyosin in the way, actomyosin cannot form, and because actomyosin cannot form, the energy necessary to produce movement in the muscle remains stored in the myosin molecule and is not released. Obviously, in order for the muscle to become active, something will have to move the tropomyosin out of the way.

The Action of Ionic Calcium

There is such an agent. It is ionic calcium, and it is normally not present in the sarcoplasm. But troponin subunit TN-C has a tremendous affinity for ionic calcium, and when it is present, they bind tightly together. This bonding changes the shape of the troponin molecule and forces the tropomyosin molecule to roll slightly. Instead of remaining in normal

Figure 11.14 The formation of actomyosin. (*a*) The position of the actin globes, troponin, and tropomyosin when calcium approaches. The linking of Ca^{2+} and troponin causes the tropomyosin to roll (see arrows). (*b*) A cross-section of a single actin globe showing the position of tropomyosin and myosin prior to the linking of troponin and calcium. In *b*, calcium is approaching. (*c*) Tropomyosin rolls out of the way when Ca^{2+} binds to troponin. Actin and myosin now have a free path to each other, and actomyosin can form.

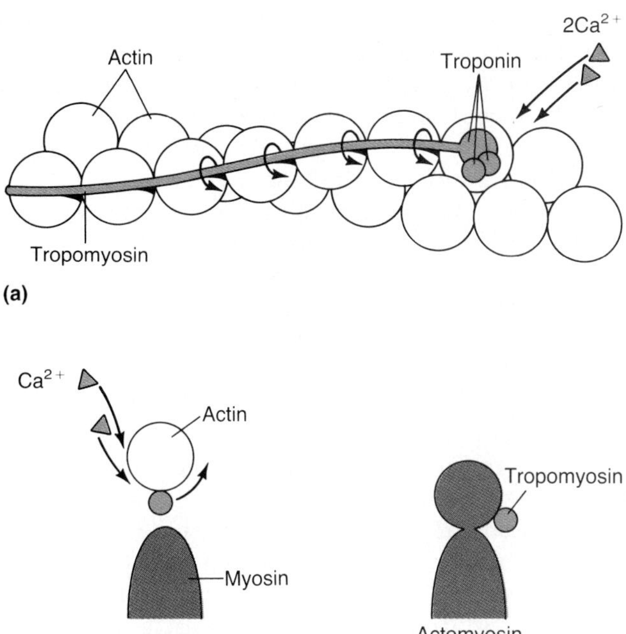

Figure 11.15 The events evolved in muscle contraction: (*a*) An ATP molecule is split by the ATPase present in the "head" of the myosin molecule, and its energy is transferred to the myosin. The myosin is thus "charged." (*b*) When calcium appears, its linking with TN-C causes the tropomyosin to roll down between the actin strands, permitting actin and myosin to contact one another. When actomyocin forms, the energy stored in the myosin head is released. (*c*) The chemical energy is changed to mechanical energy (movement), and the head of the myosin bends, pulling the thin filament past it. Meanwhile, a new ATP molecule arrives to recharge the myosin. (*d*) The binding of an ATP molecule causes the actomyosin complex to separate into its myosin and actin components, thus permitting this activity to occur again.

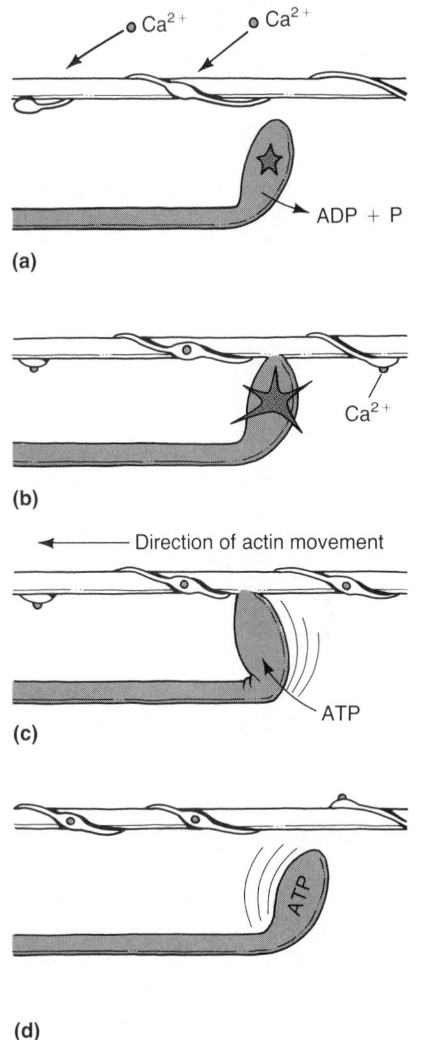

resting position along the outer surfaces of the actin globes, it snuggles down deep in the groove between the strings of F actin, out of the way of the myosin head (figure 11.14).

As we noted earlier, the actin and myosin molecules have considerable affinity for one another, and as close as they are in muscle, they would quickly form a complex if they could. When calcium is present, the tropomyosin filament rolls out of the way, and with it out of the way, the complex can now form. The head of the myosin molecule promptly links to an actin globe, forming a cross-bridge between the two filaments. The instant the complex forms, the myosin molecule releases the stored chemical energy it obtained from ATP, and this is promptly converted to motion, bending the head of the myosin molecule and pulling the actin past it (figure 11.15).

The Dual Role of ATP

As I have suggested, as soon as ATP binds to myosin, its energy is transferred to the myosin molecule, where it is stored. The energy is released from the myosin molecule only when actomyosin is formed. However, once the energy is released and the head of the myosin molecule bends over, the actomyosin is stable and will neither straighten out nor break apart until another ATP molecule binds to the myosin head. The binding of a new ATP molecule renders the actomyosin complex unstable, and it separates, permitting the myosin head to physically snap back to its original position. In that position, if calcium is still present and the tropomyosin strip is out of the way, the process will repeat itself.

ATP, therefore, has two hats. When it attaches to the myosin molecule, it provides the necessary energy for the movement of muscle contraction. If a new molecule of ATP does not hook onto the myosin head after it has moved, the cross-bridges will not separate, and the muscle cannot relax. ATP is therefore directly involved, in different ways, in both contraction and relaxation.

ATP is thus part of a phenomenon that puzzled medical personnel and research scientists for centuries. Within a few hours of death, muscles of the corpse lock firmly into position and will not relax—"death grips" are famous. It is possible to open such grips—to move the locked muscles—but it is not easy, and it cannot be done without tearing muscle fibers. The state is known as **rigor mortis,** and until recently its cause was merely guessed at. Often some pretty weird speculations were forthcoming—like the suggestion that the rigidity was due to all the blood clotting in the blood vessels and becoming hard. It is only in the last ten or fifteen years that we have really understood what the cause is and what is involved.

Immediately after death, muscles relax completely. (The idea of a dead person's facial muscles clamping into expressions of horror and fear at a ghastly, oncoming fate is all very dramatic, but simply not true.) However, as the muscles begin to deteriorate, calcium begins to infiltrate through decomposing membranes and the muscles contract in disorganized twitches. As the ATP is used up (remember, the person is dead; there is no more ATP forthcoming), the actomyosin molecules form stable bonds that cannot be broken. With no ATP to break the myosin and actin apart, the result is a contractile rigidity—a powerful rigidity produced by tightly cramped muscles. Whatever position the muscles were in when the ATP was used up is where they stay. As time passes and the muscles begin to decompose more thoroughly, the actin-myosin bonds gradually break apart and the muscles relax again. Within obvious limits, pathologists can tell from the degree of rigor mortis approximately how long a corpse has been dead.

One further comment is required with respect to muscle movement before we pass on to controlling mechanisms. As all the illustrations have shown, there is considerable regularity to the arrangement and alignment of all the contractile proteins in a muscle. However, there is a degree of irregularity in one phase of the arrangement, and it is not one that was produced casually.

Consider this: If all the myosin molecules formed complexes with actin at the same time, and all moved their heads simultaneously, muscle movement would progress in a series of tiny jerks. That does not happen, however, as we know. Muscle contraction is a smooth, flowing process, and much of this is due to the scattered arrangement of the myosin heads and the way they are oriented throughout each muscle fiber.

The myosin molecules are present in clusters in the muscle fiber, gathered together like a bunch of golf clubs with their heads sticking out in apparent disorder (see figure 11.8). Because of this dispersed arrangement, while one head is bending, another may be just forming actomyosin, while still others are binding to ATP or breaking free of the actin and returning to the original relaxed position, preparing to form another junction with actin and bend again. It is this uncoordinated movement of the millions of myosin heads that keeps our muscle movement smooth and sustained instead of jerky.

The arrangement of muscle fibers and the way their contractile mechanisms are designed makes their operation automatic. All you have to do is turn the mechanism on, and it will run by itself just as long as there is ionic calcium (Ca^{2+}) and ATP available to provide motion and relaxation.

In a way, the contractile process is like a machine gun. When one pulls the trigger, the gun begins to function and it will continue to function as long as the trigger is depressed. The mechanisms within the muscle fiber are much like those within the gun . . . pull the trigger and things happen relentlessly. The trigger that sets off muscular contraction is the electrical activity transmitted to the muscle fiber by its motor neuron.

The Neuromuscular Junction

The motor neuron enters the muscle fiber at a highly specialized structure known as the **neuromuscular junction** or the **nerve/muscle end plate.** At this site, the nerve axon branches, and the branches fit into recesses in the muscle fiber membrane, forming a junction similar to an ordinary chemical synapse (figure 11.16).

As you can see from the figure, there are myriad mitochondria in the terminal element of the nerve axon. The sarcolemma is highly convoluted beneath the terminal of the nerve, forming several **secondary synaptic clefts** beneath the **primary cleft.**

The process by which an electrical signal moves from a relatively tiny nerve fiber into the much-larger muscle cell has been thoroughly worked out. When an electrical signal arrives at the terminus of the nerve, a burst of the tiny packages of acetylcholine (quanta) is released into the myoneural cleft. The transmitter depolarizes the sarcolemma immediately adjacent to the myoneural junction, and an action potential is thus generated along the sarcolemma. This electrical activity then initiates the contraction.

Figure 11.16 The neuromuscular junction, showing the terminal of the motor neuron and the "motor endplate" of the muscle fiber. Note the elaborate folding of the sarcolemma under the primary synaptic cleft.

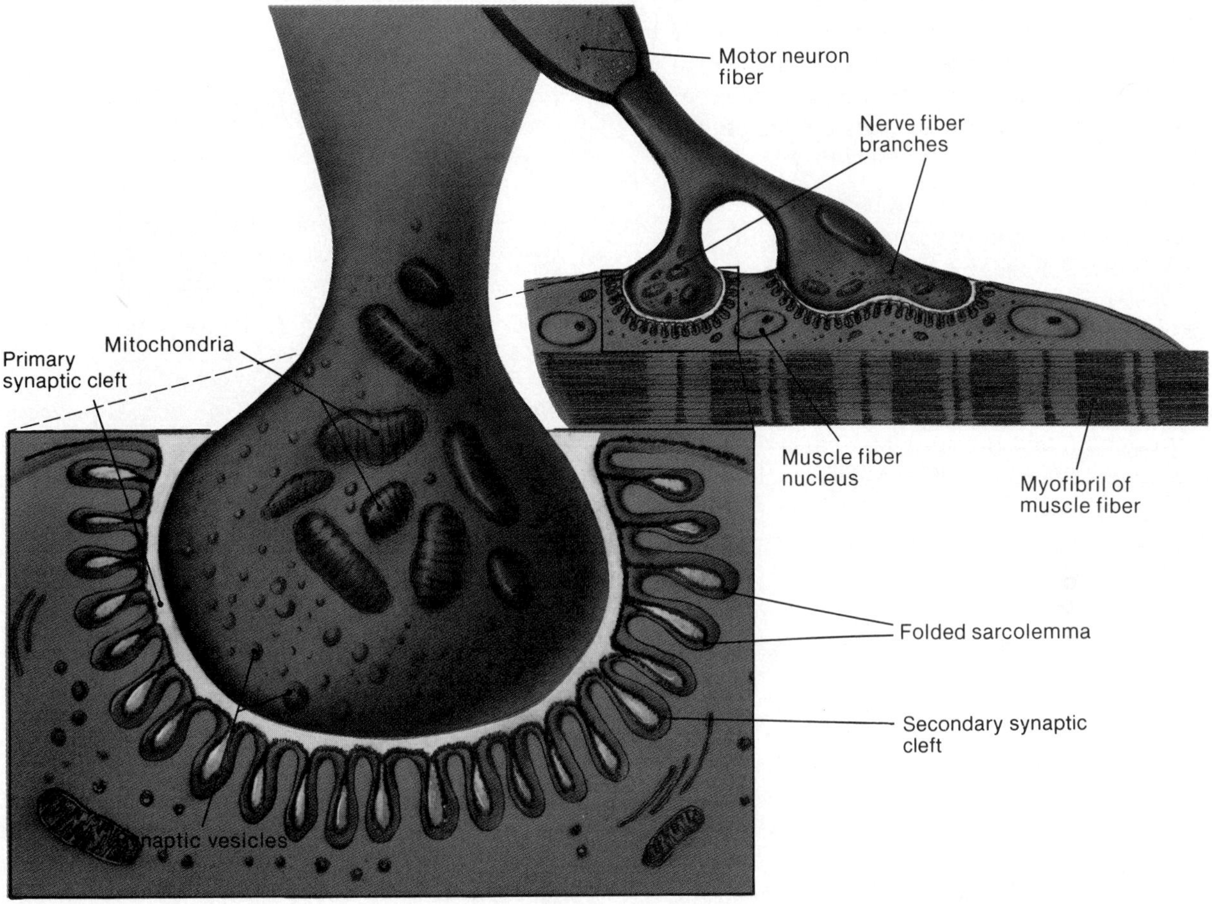

This part of the control process at least seems quite straightforward, and to this point, it is. However, there are some important questions that now must be answered.

One is, how does the depolarization manage to reach all myofibrils in the fiber simultaneously? We know that the entire muscle fiber contracts as a unit—it *always* does. When electrical stimulation occurs, all the myofibrils in the fiber go to work simultaneously; any other approach would constitute an inefficient system. Yet there is no way to avoid the fact that the action potential is a membrane phenomenon—we *must* keep that in mind (see chapter 6). Cell membranes—and the sarcolemma is no exception—are no more than 100 Å thick, while muscle fibers can be 200 μm in diameter. The action potential might spread across the entire sarcolemma, depolarizing it rapidly and completely (figure 11.17), but the sarcolemma represents only a surface film on the muscle fiber. How does the action potential manage to pass its instructions on to the myofibrils deep in the middle of the fiber?

Figure 11.17 The action potential is the signal to contract, and when it is received, the whole fiber responds. But the action potential exists only on the membrane. How does it signal myofibrils deep in the fiber?

Muscle fiber cross-section

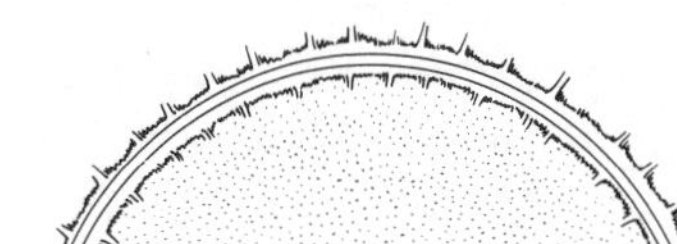

Another problem involves the manipulation of calcium. Dissolved calcium is a major factor in the control of muscle movement. The contractile process cannot begin without it, and it promptly stops when calcium is no longer present. It seems reasonable to infer that anything able to control the movement of calcium into and out of the sarcoplasm will control muscle movement. A pair of questions arise immediately when considering such a control:

1. Where does the calcium go between contractions, when the muscle is relaxing? and
2. How does it manage to penetrate into all the nooks and crannies of the muscle fiber almost instantaneously?

We know that such an influx occurs, because it *must*. The mere fact of contraction demands the presence of calcium, and the simultaneous movement of all the myofibrils in the fiber suggests that all the movement of calcium in and out of the sarcoplasm takes place synchronously and is orchestrated with extreme precision.

The T System and the Sarcoplasmic Reticulum

The electron microscope has provided most of the answers. It shows that there are two separate systems of tubes running almost everywhere throughout the fiber (figure 11.18). They are the **sarcoplasmic reticulum** and the **transverse** or **T tubules,** and they represent both a ubiquitous telegraph system to handle the distribution of instructions and the plumbing scheme necessary to dispense the calcium.

Sarcoplasmic Reticulum

The sarcoplasmic reticulum is the endoplasmic reticulum of the muscle cell. Since everything inside the muscle fiber seems to be arranged in highly organized patterns, it is not surprising to find that the sarcoplasmic reticulum is also. Its channels run mainly parallel to the myofibrils, spreading out in a hairlike network that penetrates everywhere. Periodically, at the Z bar and the H band, the reticulum opens into a perpendicular array of tubes that dives into the myofibril, providing cross connections between the longitudinal channels and forming an uninterrupted network of fine membranous tubes throughout the entire fiber. The ionic calcium needed to control the activity of the contractile proteins is stored in this reticulum, mostly in slightly swollen "pockets" at the Z bars, the so-called **terminal cisternae.** While the muscle is in its relaxed state, this calcium remains quietly dissolved in the fluids of the reticulum. It is in fairly high concentration there, whereas in the sarcoplasm there is almost none present. Thus there is quite a diffusion gradient for calcium between the two compartments. It would love to rush from the confines of the sarcoplasmic reticulum into the low-calcium sarcoplasm, but it cannot, because the walls of the reticulum won't let it. Before it can enter the sarcoplasm, something must change the permeability of those walls.

Figure 11.18 Line drawing of a half-dozen myofibrils, showing the network of sarcoplasmic reticulum and the transverse (T) tubules.

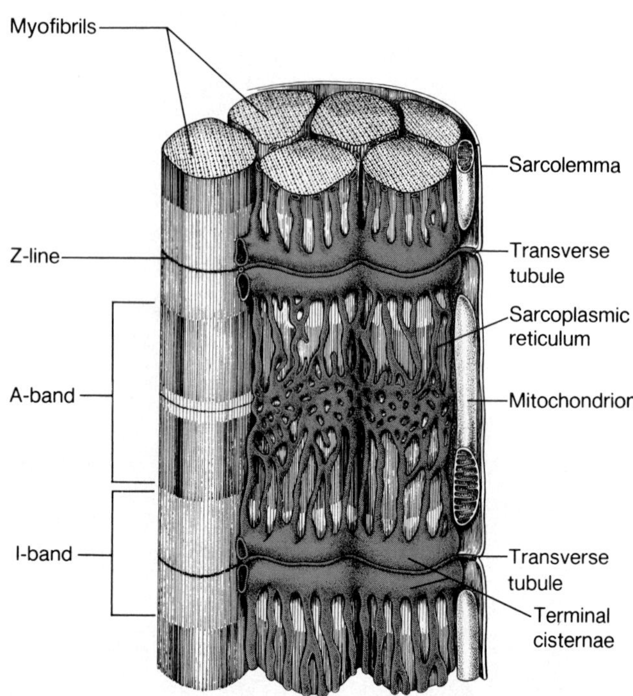

The Transverse Tubules (T) System

Researchers were aware of the existence of T tubes in the 1920s, but until the electron microscope permitted a close look at it, no one knew what its function might be. It was known only as a member of an unusual arrangement of tiny vacuole-like inclusions called the "triad of spores," but no particular role was hypothesized.

Andrew Huxley supplied part of the answer when he noticed, while stimulating myofibrils with a microelectrode, that he could get contractions deep in the muscle fiber only if his tiny stimuli were applied at the Z bar. With Huxley's work in mind, researchers utilizing the electron microscope began looking in the vicinity of the Z bar for some structure that was not present anywhere else. Whatever they found had to meet two other conditions as well. First of all it had to be continuous with the sarcolemma, and secondly, it had to penetrate into the deepest confines of the muscle fiber. They found the T system.

The T system is continuous with the sarcolemma. It is as if someone took a fine, blunt probe and pushed microscopic tubes of sarcolemma deep into the cell, forming a hair-thin network that suffuses the entire fiber at the Z bars. This is the membranous communication network that carries the depolarizing voltages to the innermost fibrils. When the action potentials from the motor nerve spread across the muscle membrane, they run along the walls of the T system as well, because after all, it is *part* of the membrane. The impulse gets into the interior of the fiber as quickly as the membrane can depolarize, which is very fast indeed. To carry its message to the center of the fiber, it has to travel, at the most, only about 50 μm, and at a conduction velocity of 100 meters/sec, it could go that far in five millionths of a second. The depolarization of the entire muscle fiber including its deepest interior would therefore require less than a millisecond.

The Calcium Bullet

This electrical activity is transmitted to the sarcoplasmic reticulum and "pulls the trigger" of the contractile system. Jerking this physiological trigger results in an increase in the sarcoplasmic reticulum's permeability, and calcium channels open up in the membrane. With nothing to stop it, dissolved calcium rushes into the sarcoplasm, and the individual ions are promptly grabbed by the molecules of troponin. The tropomyosin cylinders roll deep into the slots between the actin strands and complexes of actomyosin promptly form. The result is, as described previously, a movement of the filaments sliding across each other.

Very little calcium is required to produce contraction throughout the entire fiber. Tropomyosin is a pretty long molecule, and when it is pulled out of position by a troponin/Ca^{2+} complex, it uncovers quite a length of actin. A total of seven actin globules is exposed, and this means that seven actin-myosin contact points can form as a result of the formation of a single troponin/Ca^{2+} complex.

As long as the motor nerve is sending impulses into the muscle tissue, the calcium channels in the sarcoplasmic reticulum will remain open, and the contractile processes will continue to operate. Actinomyosin will form, ATP will bind, and the crossbridges will continue to flip back and forth, pushing against their companion actin molecules. When the impulses stop, the calcium channels in the reticular membrane close, and an energy-consuming system begins to pump furiously, quickly moving all the calcium back into the cisternae in the sarcoplasmic reticulum, where it is stashed away until it is needed again. With the exit of calcium, the tropomyosin fibers leave the groove between the actin filaments and take up position once again across the outer surface. Once this occurs, and each actomyosin molecule breaks apart, its components *stay* separated, because tropomyosin is now in the way, and things quietly return to a period of relaxation. The calcium pumps work very fast indeed, but they still require more time to get all the calcium out of the sarcoplasm than was required for it to diffuse in; hence the relaxation process takes a little more time than contraction does, but not much.

Energy Supplies

During Relaxation

The only energy source that can be used to produce movement of the contractile proteins is ATP. As we have seen, it is hydrolyzed to charge up the myosin molecule, and nothing else aside from ATPase, the enzyme that hydrolyzes it, will bind to myosin. So without ATP, there is neither movement nor relaxation. Unfortunately there is not very much ATP in muscle tissue. Oh, there is plenty available for minor jobs, and of course there is no shortage when the muscle is relaxed. But just in case a period of furious activity *should* develop, the fuel-consuming mechanisms in muscle take advantage of inactivity to stockpile some energy, and they store it in a form that other cellular mechanisms cannot use. When muscle cells oxidize their fuels, instead of using all the energy to make ATP molecules, they lock most of it into a high-energy phosphate compound known as **creatine phosphate.** Muscles cannot store much ATP, but they can store a lot of creatine phosphate, and a considerable supply of energy is amassed in that compound, which represents a quick-energy reservoir.

Because of this earmarked energy hoard, the muscle will be able to sustain itself for a considerable period. The available ATP is not abundant and is consumed in a couple of seconds, signalling the muscle's stores of creatine phosphate to start contributing. They do, transferring their energy to the ATP molecules so the muscles can use it. The transfer is accomplished quickly and efficiently. If the intense activity doesn't last more than ten or twelve seconds, this mechanism handles everything smoothly (figure 11.19).

Figure 11.19 Energy produced by aerobic and anaerobic fuel consumption is used to generate creatine phosphate and ATP when the muscle is not working. When activity is high, creatine phosphate transfers its stored energy to ATP, thus providing a short-term, emergency energy stockpile.

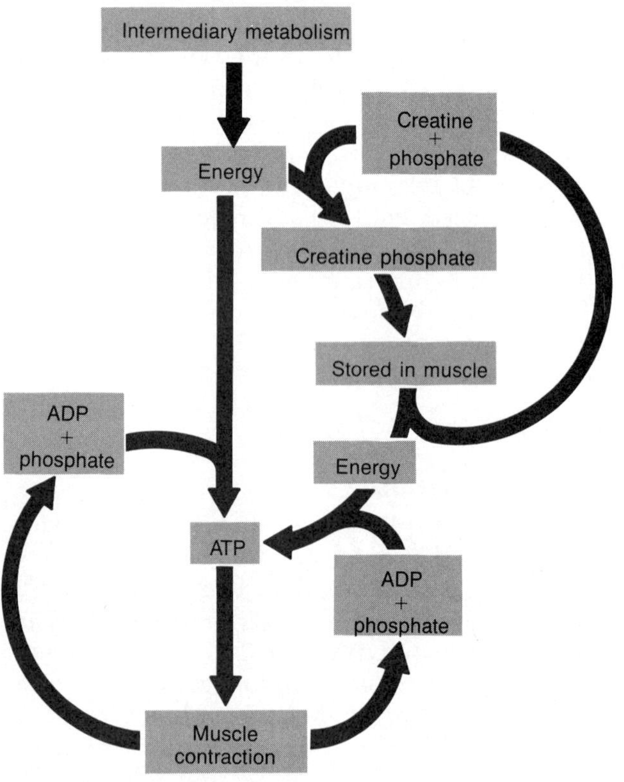

Prolonged Activity

However, when extended operation of the muscle is needed, the situation changes. Both the ATP and the creatine phosphate can be used up in a few seconds, and the muscle must rely on its fuel-burning mechanisms to produce the energy that is necessary to continue working. This is when the situation begins to get complicated. You will recall from chapter 5 that there are two phases to energy production by the cell. The first phase (anaerobic activity) takes place in the cellular cytoplasm and produces large quantities of ATP but at *very* low efficiency levels. The second phase is aerobic and must take place in the miniscule volumes of the cellular mitochondria. Mitochondria produce ATP at extremely high efficiency, but their ATP-production systems need oxygen to run correctly, and that is where a problem arises.

The main problem is oxygen! The oxygen is brought into the muscles by the blood. As we will see (chapter 12), oxygen is carried in the red blood cells and is released into body areas that need it. Unfortunately, when a muscle is really working, its powerful contractions ordinarily constrict the arterial vessels running through it, reducing blood flow substantially. Lack of adequate blood means a reduced supply of oxygen, and since the muscles are already being overwhelmed by demands for ATP, any reduction in oxygen availability means the aerobic metabolic reactions cannot run fast enough to keep up.

Fortunately, the anaerobic ones can—for a while. Considering the amount of glucose they consume, they do not provide much ATP, but there is usually lots of fuel available, and plenty of room for the reactions to occur. Anaerobic metabolism can supply the necessary ATP for a while. How long depends on things like age, physical condition, and the violence of the ongoing activity. The blood carries the lactate away as quickly as it can, but if the contraction is maintained constantly, lactic acid and other waste metabolites can induce alterations in muscle pH and osmotic pressure. This, coupled with the reduced supply of oxygen and lowered availability of nutrients, results in the onset of relaxation. The individual, try as he might, just cannot maintain contraction—not without a rest.

The phenomenon of fatigue is not clearly understood, and there is little doubt that it is at least partly a behavioral phenomenon. Nevertheless, it is no coincidence that the difficulty that accompanies sustained muscle contraction is linked to the inability of the circulatory system to provide its necessary services. As the waste products accumulate and the energy stores disappear, the muscles begin to hurt so much that the individual is psychologically unable to maintain the contraction.

The cause of the pain is not completely clear. It is thought to be due partly to the circulatory problems already mentioned and partly to the accumulation of a substance known as *P substance* (see chapter 9). Whatever the cause, the pain in a continually contracted muscle inevitably becomes so intense that the subject is absolutely incapable of maintaining contraction beyond a certain point. (The soreness that is so obvious in muscles after performing vigorous, unaccustomed work does not, apparently, have the same cause. It is believed to be the result of damage to the contractile elements produced by unaccustomed deprivation of nutrients plus an accumulation of interstitial fluids during and immediately following the exercise.)

Oxygen Debt

Vigorous, sustained exercise results in the rapid accumulation of lactic acid in the blood. That, as we have seen, represents an oxygen debt, and sooner or later, debts must be paid. Everyone knows that one inevitable result of a vigorous burst of exercise is heavy breathing. After a quick, 100-meter dash or swim, even the healthiest athletes stand around for about ten minutes, panting, breathing deeply, moving air in and out of the lungs at a high rate. The exercise has built up tremendous accumulations of lactic acid, and it has to be removed.

There is only one direction it can go; it must first be converted to pyruvate. Once back in the metabolic mainstream, the pyruvate can either be oxidized to produce ATP, or converted back to glucose.

Oxidizing all the accumulated pyruvate to ATP would produce far more energy than the body could possibly use or store, so only a little takes that route—about 20 percent of it, to be exact. Oxidizing 20 percent of the pyruvate provides more than enough energy to recharge all the phosphate molecules in the muscle and get things back to normal, and the energy left over is used to convert the 80 percent of lactic acid that remains back to glucose. Once the lactic acid is all gone, the oxygen debt vanishes.

As was stated above, how rapidly a muscle tires depends to some extent on the individual's physical condition. There has been some work done to discover just what does happen in muscle tissue as a person "gets into shape." What takes place in the muscle that permits it to operate longer anaerobically without fatiguing? As you can imagine, this is extremely hard to research. The work a researcher can do with humans is quite limited, and despite what you may think, it is not easy to get caged experimental animals to exercise until they are in good physical condition. As a result, we know only a little about this phenomenon.

We know, for instance, that athletes, when they exercise, produce less lactic acid than a person who is out of shape, and we know why. As training proceeds, the individuals will be able to place greater demands on their muscles, and energy demands by the most-used muscles increase. The circulatory system responds by increasing the number of blood vessels that enter and leave the muscle as well as the number of capillary beds within. Conditioned muscles produce less lactic acid, because their oxygen supply at any given time is considerably greater than that of unconditioned muscles. We also know that a conditioned muscle can tolerate greater concentrations of lactic acid than a poorly conditioned muscle can. We do not know why.

Grading the Contractions

When a muscle fiber contracts, it gives everything it has. As with nervous tissue, a living muscle fiber has only two natural states, "on" or "off." It is either contracting as hard as it possibly can, or it does not contract at all; there is no in-between.

Yet we all know that living systems can grade their muscular activity. When we pick up a pencil from a table, we are not exerting as much lifting power as when we pick up a heavy saucepan from a stove or a spare tire from the trunk of the car. In actual operation, there is plenty of in-between regarding muscle contraction, so the question is, "how come? Do muscle systems *in vivo* disobey the all-or-none law that applies to them *in vitro?*"

Not at all! It is all a matter of numbers. Each time a muscle fiber contracts, it gives everything it has, so the key to grading a whole muscle's contractile power depends on the *number* of fibers that contract at any given time. When you pick up a paper clip, you only activate a few fibers. When you pick up a barbell, you activate more.

The terms *in vivo* and *in vitro* are used with such abandon in biological research that it is probably a good idea to be sure we understand their meanings.

In vitro means literally "within a glass," meaning it is the kind of thing a researcher might see in a test tube or in an artificial environment. Experiments are often performed in which some body organ or tissue is removed from an animal and mounted in a nutrient medium. No matter now similar to body fluids or how benevolent the medium, the organ is considered to be in an artificial or *in vitro* situation.

In vivo means "in life" and pretty well speaks for itself. The tissue or organ being investigated is in position in the organism, within its normal environment.

Motor Units

Whole muscles are divided functionally as well as morphologically. Just as there are bundles of fibers organized into anatomically distinct *fasciculi,* there is a functionally distinct organization in which each separate group is known as a **motor unit.** The number of muscle fibers present in each motor unit varies tremendously. One motor unit may have only a few (the extrinsic muscle of the eyeball has a motor unit with just seven); another may have hundreds (the gastrocnemius of the leg has one with 1,700), depending on the muscle and its location in the body. Nor is there any particular anatomical arrangement for the motor units *within* a given muscle—a single motor unit may have fibers in each of a dozen fasciculi.

There is one point of anatomical unity, however, and it is related to the motor neurons that innervate our muscles. A single motor neuron and all the muscle fibers it innervates constitute a motor unit. The greater the number of motor units activated at any time, the more force the muscle will be able to apply to a given task. The smooth response to increasing demands on a muscle—like the accelerating motion that occurs when a ball is thrown hard—reflects the harmonious,

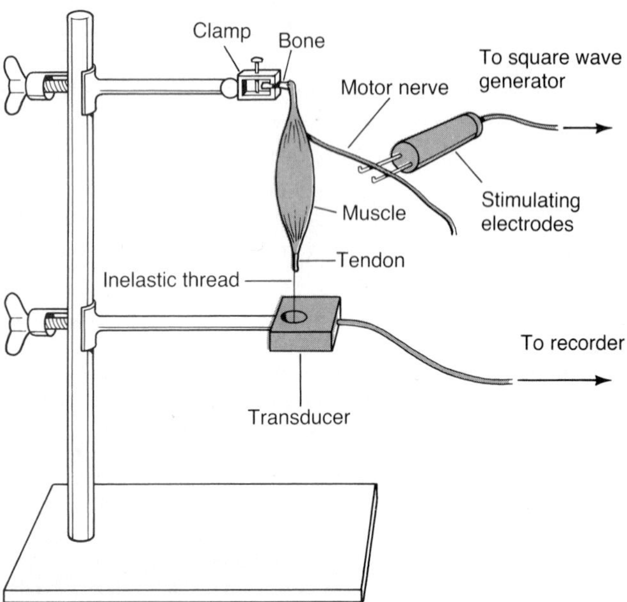

Figure 11.20 Frog nerve-muscle preparation. The transducer is designed to convert pressure into electrical signals, which can then be converted to pen movement or tension readout. Such transducers can permit movement under variable loads or clamp down hard and permit no movement.

sequential mobilization and relaxation of individual motor units as they gradually build up, peak, then slowly reduce the contractile power in the muscles of the arm.

Some Experiments and the Facts Derived from Them

One learns about the unknown by pursuing a sequence of logic known as the scientific method—by finding a problem and solving it methodically through experimental observation and strict control. We have applied these methods to physiology, of course, and there are patterns in the results that we have obtained from experiments with muscle—in fact, some of the patterns are particularly clear.

Threshold Voltage

By removing living muscles from animals and placing them in artificial situations, we can isolate functions and often eliminate many variables. For instance, we can measure the amount of voltage that the motor nerve applies to a muscle to make it fire, but that does not tell us very much. But, if we eliminate the neural stimulus by just disconnecting the motor nerve from the muscle, we can replace the motor nerve with a pair of electrodes that we attach to the muscle ourselves. That way we can apply known amounts of

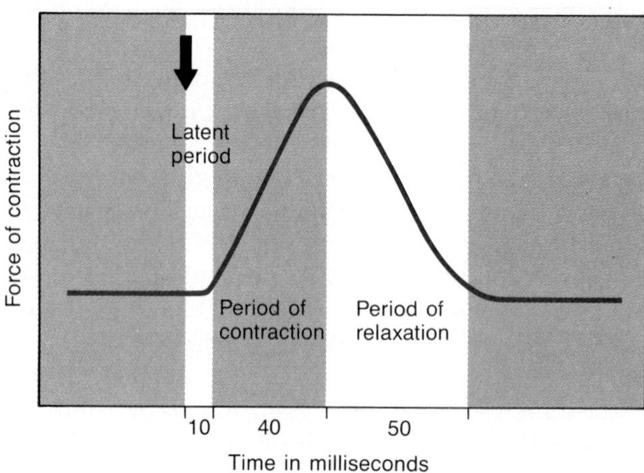

Figure 11.21 A single muscle twitch. The arrow pointing down indicates the point at which the stimulus is applied.

electrical energy directly to the muscle and, by varying the strength (voltage) of the electrical signal sent into the stimulating electrodes, we can determine exactly how much voltage is required to fire the muscle. We work this out by applying single shocks and starting with a very low voltage. At low voltages, the muscle will not fire; hence it will not contract, so we gradually increase the voltage until the muscle moves. The voltage value at that precise point is known as the **threshold voltage**—the minimum amount of voltage necessary to produce an action potential along the sarcolemma of the muscle.

Muscle Twitches

The phenomenon known as the **muscle twitch** is something that almost never happens *in vivo,* but from it we have gleaned much information about muscle function. We obtain such an action by producing a stimulus that will cause the muscle sarcolemma to depolarize *just once.* A twitch consists of the muscle's response to that single depolarization. The muscle—usually dissected from a frog or some other cold-blooded vertebrate—is mounted as shown in figure 11.20, and a single, above-threshold stimulus is applied. The sarcolemma depolarizes and the muscle follows with its response movement. It produces a pattern as in figure 11.21. This twitch was obtained from a frog muscle maintained at 25° C. On an average, such a twitch is complete in about a tenth of a second (100 msec). Broken down, it shows the following events: After the stimulus is applied (arrow), there is a brief period (about ten msecs) during which the impulse is spreading throughout the muscle and the various chemical changes preceding movement are taking place. This is known as the **latent period,**

Figure 11.22 (*a*) An afterloaded muscle. (*b*) A preloaded muscle.

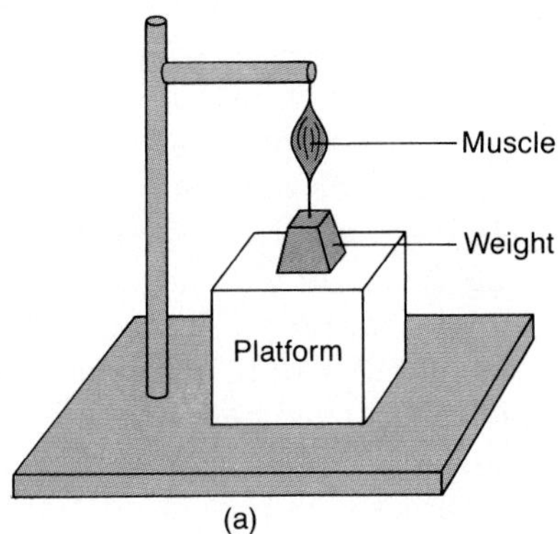

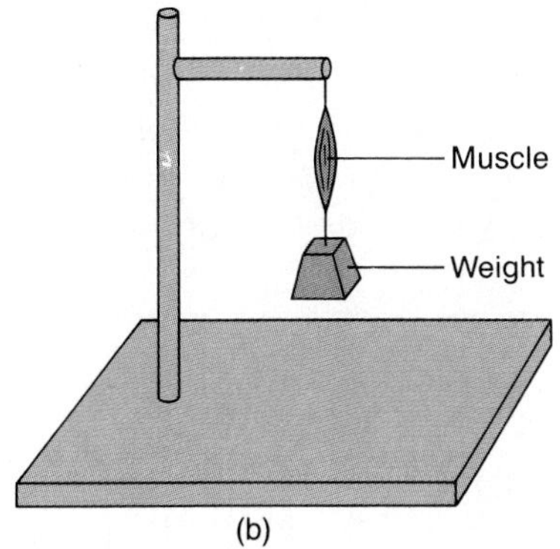

and it is followed by a **contractile period,** which lasts about 40 msecs. A **relaxation period** of an additional 50 msecs completes the twitch pattern.

As I have indicated, twitches do not usually occur in living systems, so it would be reasonable to ask why we bother with such a thing in experimentation. The answer is quite simple—because we can learn from it. For instance, we can learn by varying the way the load is applied (see figure 11.22).

Muscle Loading

In *(a),* the weight is attached in such a way that the muscle is not stretched by the weight at all. It is put in place when the muscle is relaxed and then is tied firmly to the tendon and arranged so that the muscle will "feel" the weight as soon as contraction begins, but not before. Because the muscle won't feel any load until after it has begun to move, it is referred to as an **afterloaded** muscle.

In *(b),* the same weight is tied to a relaxed muscle, but this time it is permitted to hang freely, stretching the muscle out. In this state, the muscle is said to be **preloaded.** When both preparations are twitched, we can see immediately (figure 11.23) that the preloaded muscle can do more work (see chapter 6) than the afterloaded one without consuming any more energy.

Experimental Observations Applied

What practical value is such information? Well, for one thing, it explained why the muscles in our bodies are always stretched out in their natural state; prestretching increases their working efficiency.

When a limb bone is broken, the muscles have to be pulled back into their normal state when the bone is set, and that requires considerable force . . . so much, in fact, that when a thigh bone is broken, mechanical assistance is often necessary to pull the leg out to a point where the physician can set the bones end to end. Even after the leg bones have been properly reset, it is frequently not enough to just immobilize them. Often a constant pull is required to prevent the muscles from dragging the newly set bone out of position, and this is why we sometimes see patients with broken legs lying in bed with a leg suspended by a rope from a pulley with a weight dangling from the rope's other end.

Figure 11.23 Twitches of pre- and afterloaded muscles compared.

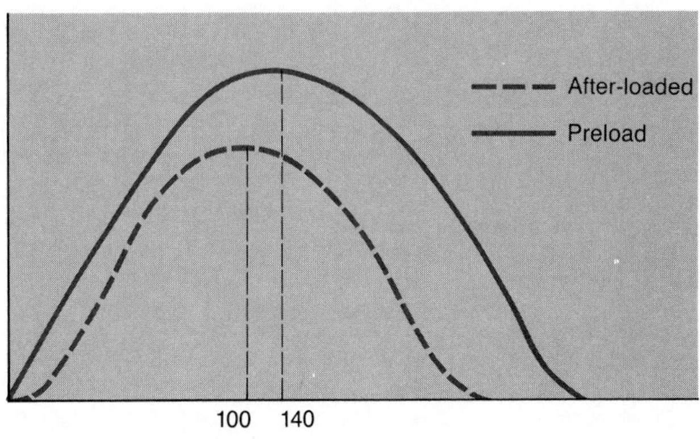

We have learned other things as well from such experiments. For example, we have learned a little about how our bodies control muscle movement. Obviously we do not move in twitches. Our muscle contractions are smooth and sustained, and considering the fact that depolarizations do not last very long, we really need to know how a series of individual depolarizations manages to produce a smooth contraction instead of a series of jerky ones. By applying multiple, above-threshold stimuli to muscle preparations and watching the muscles twitch, we uncovered an answer to that question, too.

Figure 11.24 Myograms of frog muscle preparation. (*a*) A series of twitches. (*b*) Treppe or the "staircase phenomenon." (*c*) Incomplete tetanus. (*d*) Complete tetanus.

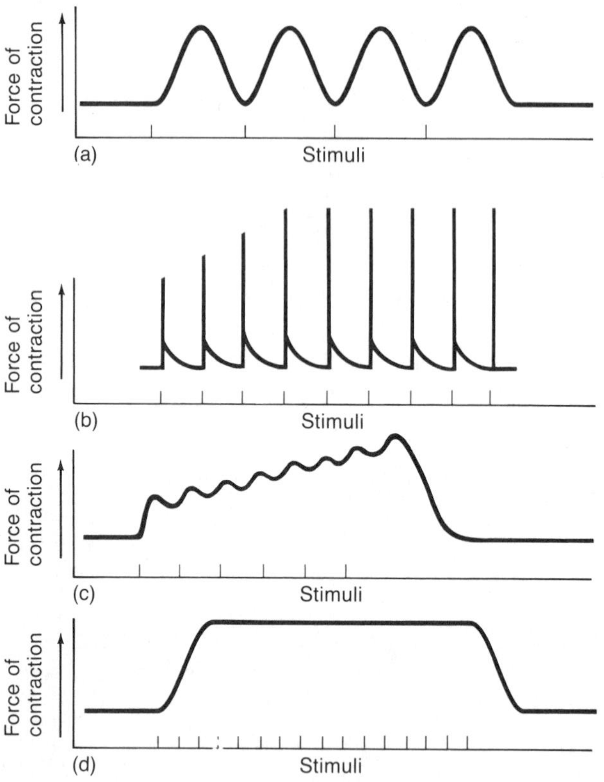

At first, the stimuli merely produced a series of identical twitch patterns (figure 11.24*a*), but as the stimuli began to get closer and closer together, a strange thing happened. The individual twitches began to show an increase in amplitude (figure 11.24*b*). In 11.24*c*, the twitches have fused together and are producing a more powerful contraction. If you look carefully, you will see that the amplitude of each twitch is no higher than before, but each one is building on the previous one so that the overall contraction is greater than any single twitch. This is a process called *summation*, a word we have already encountered. In this case, we are obviously dealing with a temporal summation, since the additive effects are achieved only when the twitches are applied at short time intervals. Stimulating at an even higher frequency produces what is called a **fused contraction, tetanic contraction,** or **tetanus.** In such contractions, the individual twitches *fuse* into a summated, unbroken contractile wave (figure 11.24*d*).

This tetanic contraction illustrates the way our muscles work in our bodies—*in vivo.* (Don't let the name intimidate you. Tetanus *is* the name of a rather nasty disease, but tetanic contractions in muscles are only vaguely related and are hardly ever the result of some illness. They are merely smooth, sustained contractions.)

See what you can learn from experiments?

Let us consider what we have discovered so far concerning the ability of muscles to provide our bodies with practical, smoothly functioning operation. Obviously, we must be able to control muscle contraction in several ways, and we've seen how we accomplish some of these.

We can vary the *force* of muscle contraction by varying the number of motor units we use for a given task. If we need only a slight contraction for some tiny job, we mobilize only a few motor units. If we have a big job to do, by increasing the number of such units, we can significantly increase the force we apply. This latter process is known as **spatial summation** or **recruitment,** because we are employing an increased number (or volume) of motor units.

By increasing the *frequency* of stimulation, we can produce larger contractions than we can in a series of separate twitches, and the contractions are smooth and sustained in all the motor units we use. These phenomena are the result of **temporal summation,** so called because we produce the total result any given fiber is capable of by increasing the number of stimuli per unit time. Temporal summation produces tetanic contractions, and this is the kind of contraction that our bodies normally employ. Twitches are rare, and they are never voluntary. Every once in a while you might experience one—like a "tic" in your cheek or your eyelid—but you cannot produce them whenever you feel like it, and you often can't make them stop, either.

Higher Control of Skeletal Muscles

The major brain areas concerned with controlling skeletal muscles include the basal ganglia, the reticular formation, the cerebellum, and a portion of the cerebral hemispheres known as the **motor cortex** (figure 11.25). The latter is, of course, the zone responsible for voluntary motion and hence is probably responsible for integrating the necessary information that will result in carefully controlled self-willed movement.

The lower brain centers, particularly the basal ganglia, are involved in coordinating movements that are semi-involuntary, like walking, running, standing up, or swimming. These latter are movements that required conscious thought when first learned, but their operations have become so deeply imprinted that they are now handled with very little awareness. You do not, for instance, consciously will your body to fall slightly forward and then flip your leg and foot out to catch yourself before you fall down. You do all this automatically when you walk, and little thought beyond thinking "walk" is required. There are no

Figure 11.25 The motor control areas of the brain (shaded).

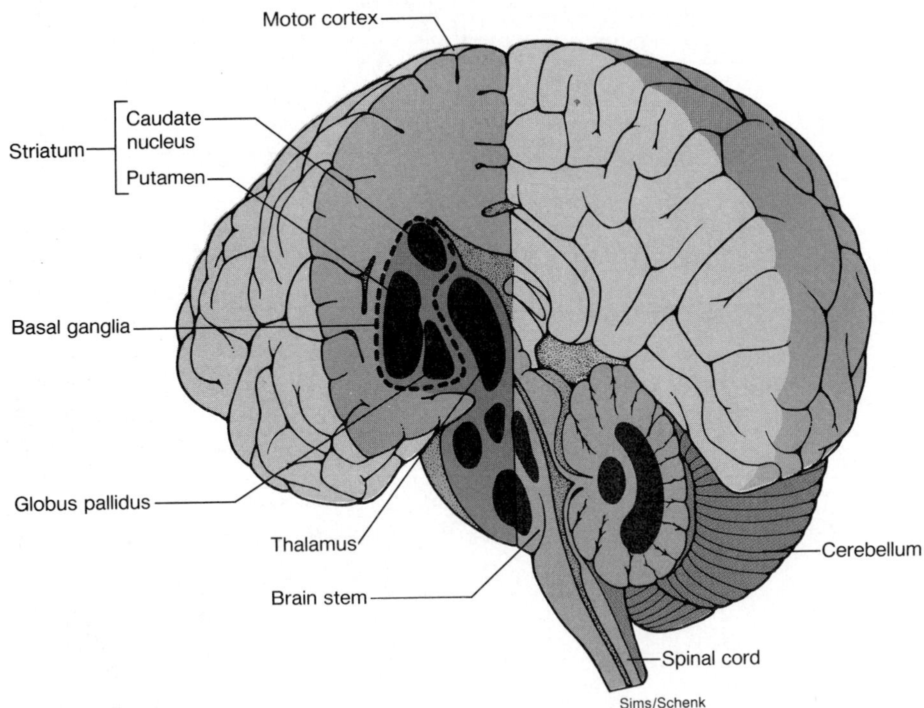

motor fibers originating in the cerebellum, yet that brain structure is nevertheless responsible for keeping all the separate, individually jerky, movements smooth and well-orchestrated. Apparently it harmonizes movement through its influence on higher centers in the thalamus and basal ganglia.

Voluntary motor impulses originate in the cortex and make their way through the various structures via the **pyramidal pathways.** These pathways begin in the motor cortex (the precentral gyrus), proceed through the midbrain and the cerebellum, cross over to the other side of the brain, and proceed down the spinal cord and end in the ventral horn. The pathways thus include **upper motor neurons** (the pyramidal fibers) and **lower motor neurons** (the α fibers that directly stimulate muscle contraction). The lower motor axons are considered to be the final common pathway for contraction once the neural impulse leaves the cell bodies in the spinal cord. A complete schematic for voluntary movement is offered in figure 11.26.

Proprioception

The Muscle Spindle

Muscle spindles are among our body's proprioceptors (see chapter 9). They are shaped like elongated, thin footballs about 4 mm long and 0.2 mm in diameter, and they lie in the muscle parallel to the contractile fibers. They are constructed of specially modified muscle fibers called **intrafusal fibers** (*intra,* "within"; *fus,* "a spindle"). These fibers are collected into bundles that are thin on each end, expand into a broader middle zone, and are encapsulated within a fibrous coating. Like the other fibers in the muscle (the *extrafusal* fibers), the spindles are anchored at each end. Spindles have no directly associated tendons but instead are linked by very thin, threadlike fibers that insert into the extrafusal membrane near the tendons, thus indirectly anchoring them to bone.

Spindle Innervation

The spindles are innervated by both motor and sensory fibers, but the innervation is not like that of the other fibers in the muscle. Spindles have their own set of special neurons. The sensory neurons keep the central nervous system apprised of the muscle's length at any given time and/or note when muscle length is changing; hence the spindles are viewed as *length receptors.*

There are two types of sensory fibers involved with the spindles. The *primary sensory fibers* or *annulospiral endings* are coiled around the central zone of the spindle; the *secondary fibers* or *flowerspray endings* innervate the intrafusal fibers on either end (figure

Figure 11.26 A schematic of the voluntary pathways involved in controlling skeletal muscle movement.

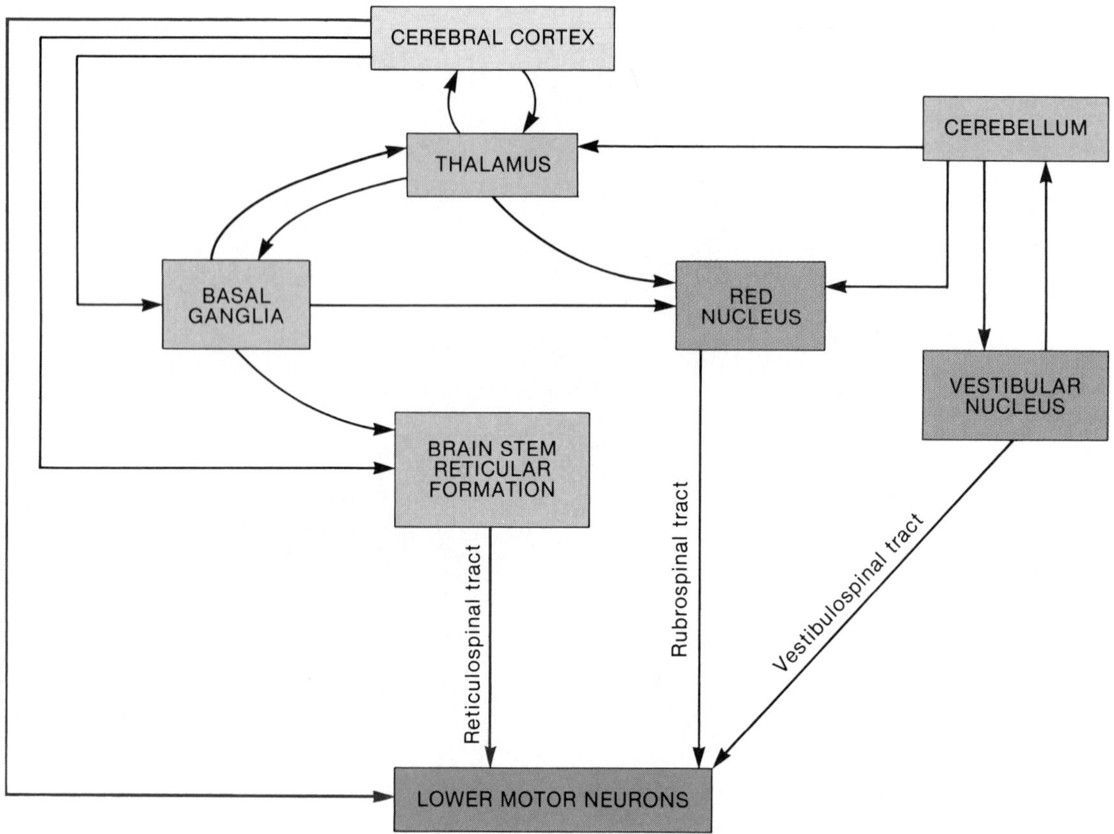

11.27). When the muscle is at rest, the spindle discharges at a fixed rate, sending its signals along sensory nerves into the spinal cord. The rate of discharge is partially determined by the length of the muscle. If it is relaxed and stretched out, the rate of discharge will be greater than if it is relaxed but *not* stretched; thus the CNS is kept informed of the spatial orientation of the muscle. Both primary and secondary fibers are involved in disseminating this information.

Should the muscle suddenly be stretched, the primary fibers in the spindle apparatus send a volley of action potentials into the spinal cord. The secondary fibers change their rate of fire also, but much more slowly than the primaries and only after the muscle has established itself at a new length. If the muscle should suddenly shorten, once again the primary neurons would send off volleys of information during the change, while the secondary fibers would slowly decrease their rate of fire until they settled on a new, slower firing frequency . . . one that would be indicative of the new, shorter muscle length. Thus the secondary fibers are *static indicators.* They keep the CNS informed of the length of the muscle at any given time. The primary endings, on the other hand, are *movement indicators.* They inform the CNS when muscle length is changing, and they continue giving out this information as long as change continues.

Spindle fibers are capable of independent contraction when properly stimulated. Intrafusal fibers are innervated by motor neurons that have been designated **gamma (γ) type motor neurons.** It is important to note that these fibers are not the same as those that innervate the extrafusal fibers of skeletal muscle. The γ fibers are smaller in diameter than the **alpha (α) fibers** of the skeletomotor neurons, and their conduction velocity is less than half that of the larger fibers. The γ fibers terminate on the intrafusal fibers a short distance away from the swollen middle of the spindle. When they discharge, the ends of the intrafusal fibers contract, pulling on the central zone and stretching it, thus stimulating the sensory fibers located there.

Spindle Operation

Sudden, short changes in muscle length can stimulate the spindle into activity. Should some outside force (like a physician's hammer striking the tendon in the knee) suddenly stretch the muscle, the primary fibers release a volley of sensory impulses. In the spinal cord, this information is relayed through a

Figure 11.27 The structure of a muscle spindle, showing sensory and motor innervation.

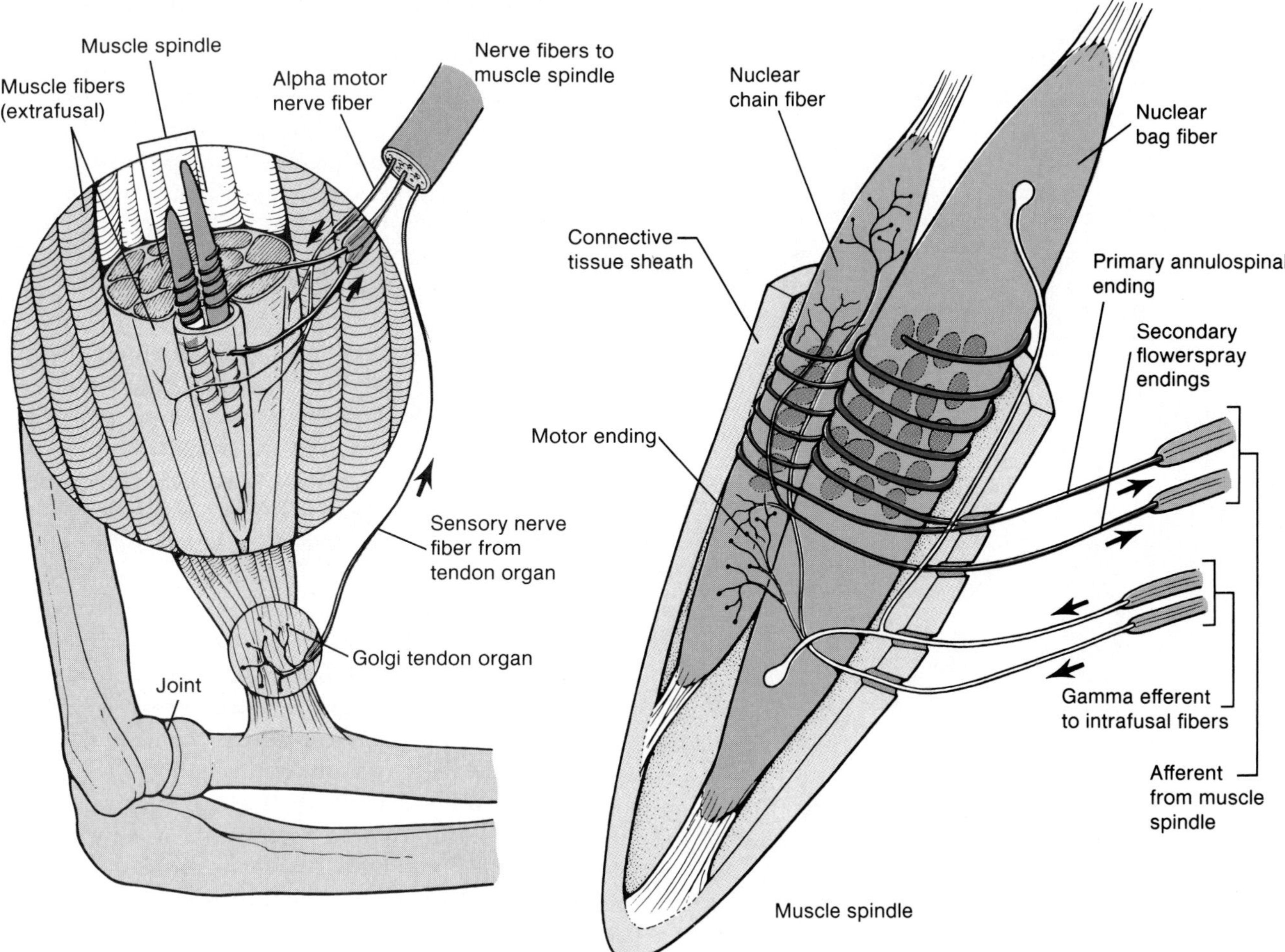

monosynaptic pathway, to the skeletomotor neurons of the same muscle. The extrafusal fibers in that muscle promptly contract, thus reducing the stretch on the spindle. The reflex has thus signalled a change in muscle length and has attempted to return the muscle to its control length as established by the gamma motor neurons.

Golgi Tendon Organs

There is a second group of receptors in skeletal muscles that aids in proprioception. These are the **Golgi tendon organs,** which are imbedded, as the name implies, in the tendons on either end of a skeletal muscle. Unlike the spindle organs, which are connected in parallel with the extrafusal fibers, the Golgi tendon organs are connected in series. Thus, when the muscle fibers contract, the Golgi organs are stretched (figure 11.28) and begin sending information regarding muscle tension into the CNS. This information is relayed to spinal interneurons, which are designed to inhibit the skeletomotor neurons that drive the muscle. If the tension on the muscle begins to approach dangerous levels, these inhibiting signals increase until they can override the contractile signals from the motor neurons driving the muscle. The Golgi organ is thus able to keep the CNS informed about the amount of tension on the muscle and to protect the muscle from damage.

Isometric vs. Isotonic Contractions

When a muscle is clamped into position as in figure 11.20, we can arrange things experimentally in one of two ways. If we choose, we can leave the muscle free to move or we can clamp both ends tightly so movement is impossible. If we permit movement, then, when we stimulate it to contract, it is said to be contracting **isotonically.** Movement, therefore, employs isotonic contractions, and this is the kind we usually experience—after all, muscles are intended to produce movement.

Contracting muscles don't always move, however. Sometimes, no matter how much force we apply, we just can't move certain things. Have you ever tried to pick something up, and no matter how hard you struggle, no matter how much force you apply, that thing just will not budge? Those efforts—increased muscle tension, but no muscle movement—cost you energy . . . as much, or more, than a comparable iso-

Figure 11.28 The orientation of spindle fibers and Golgi tendon organs. The spindles are arranged in parallel with the muscle fibers (*a*) so that when the muscle contracts (*b*), tension on the spindle is reduced. The Golgi organs are in series with the muscle fibers (*c*); hence, when the muscle contracts (*d*), the Golgi organs are stretched.

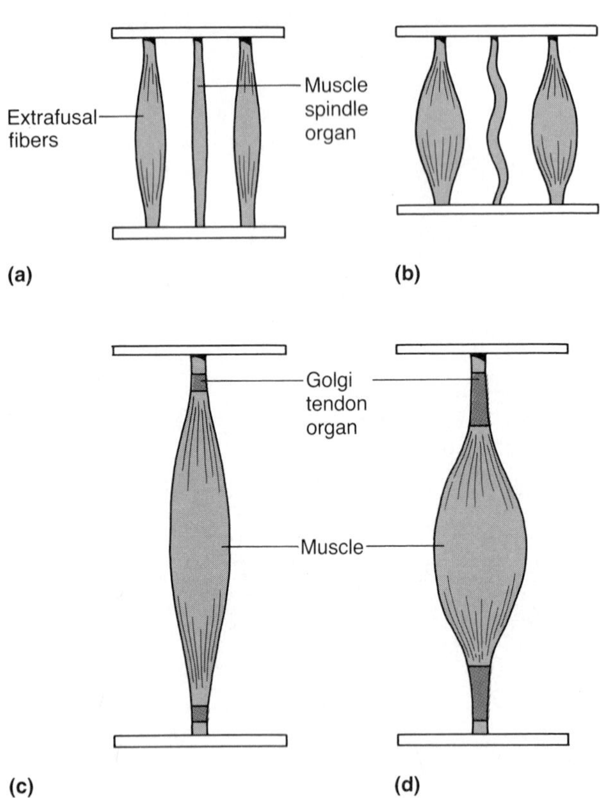

tonic contraction would. Such motionless contractions are called **isometric,** and since they use a lot of energy and stress the muscles without much movement, they are often the types of contraction recommended by exercise enthusiasts for home exercise programs (figure 11.29).

Muscle Tone

Muscles are seldom completely flaccid. Even when the body is relaxed and there are no conscious muscle contractions, there are almost always a few fibers within the muscle that maintain a contraction. Not enough to interfere with blood flow through the muscle or to deplete the ATP or CP stores, but enough to sustain a constant degree of tension within the muscle as a whole.

This partially contracted state is known as **muscle tone** or **tonus,** and it is due to a steady barrage of impulses applied by motor fibers according to instructions from interneurons within the spinal cord. It is present to some degree on nearly all muscles and can be detected even when the subject is lightly asleep. Tonus is responsible for preventing your knees or hips from folding over when you stand upright. You don't have to think about it, it is accomplished unconsciously. Tonus holds your head up when you are sitting or standing, and it provides partial tension in muscles of the trunk when someone is carrying you.

The reality of tonus is easy to see when attempting to lift an unconscious person. Movies and television show such individuals being carried with relative ease in a normal manner, employing two arms and cradling the person across them, but it would never happen. When a person is unconscious, there is no muscle tone at all. You cannot cradle such people in your arms, because their legs straighten out and their trunk collapses. They simply fold up, offering no resistance, and you cannot even *lift* them. You can't lift them by gripping them under their arms, either, because the muscles in their shoulders and upper torso are completely relaxed, and the arms simply flip up over their head. When there is no muscle tone present at all, the body and limbs feel like loose rubber appendages and offer no resistance whatsoever.

Myoglobin

Within nearly all skeletal fibers there is a pigment known as **myoglobin.** It is related to hemoglobin, the pigment in our red blood cells (see chapter 12), and like hemoglobin, it is capable of combining with oxygen and releasing it under the right set of circumstances. As we will see in the next chapter, oxygen is not very soluble in water, and only a little can be stored in our body fluids. So we use special chemicals to carry it and store it within our bodies against a time of deprivation. Myoglobin is one such molecule, and it holds oxygen with a firm grip. By the time our blood has passed through all the organs it must traverse and is heading back to the heart, it has only a little oxygen left in it, yet myoglobin can remove oxygen from venous blood and charge up to nearly complete saturation at the low oxygen concentrations normally present there. The pigment is able to move freely through muscle cells, and for that reason is believed to have the ability to carry oxygen from the blood straight to the muscle mitochondria. It is considered, therefore, more than merely a storage molecule for oxygen. It represents an important means of accelerating oxygen transport beyond the abilities of simple diffusion.

Types of Skeletal Muscle

When large limb muscles are dissected out of an experimental animal like a rat or a rabbit, it is apparent, upon teasing them apart, that there is more than one kind of skeletal muscle fiber. The gastrocnemius muscle (the muscle of the calf) has a large number of lightly colored fibers and only a few that are dark red

Figure 11.29 Isotonic and isometric contractions. (*a*) An isotonic contraction: Muscle tension is constant but length changes. (*b*) An isometric contraction: Muscle length is constant but tension changes.

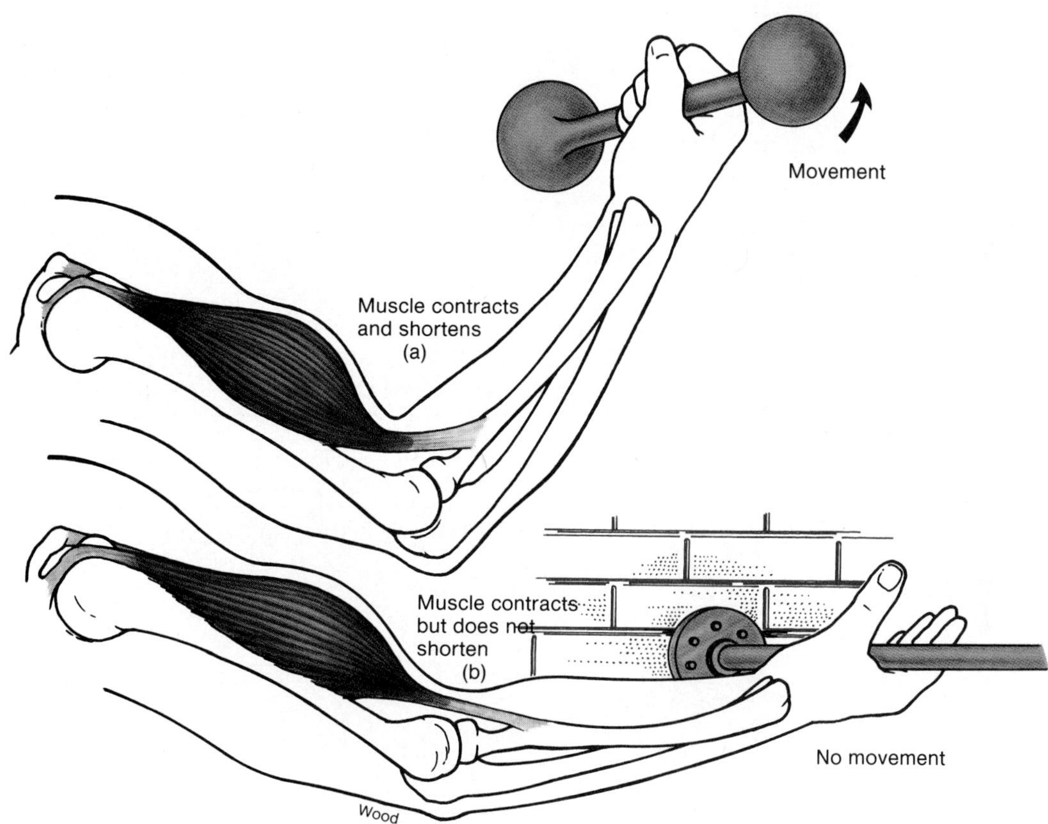

in color. On the other hand, the *extensor digitorum* (the muscle that straightens out the toes) has a preponderance of deep red fibers and shows them clearly. Skeletal muscle fibers vary in color according to the amount of myoglobin that each contains. There are white fibers with large diameters and very little myoglobin, and there are smaller red fibers that contain a great deal.

White muscles are known as **phasic muscles,** meaning they are designed to operate in vigorous, but short-lived, bursts of maximum effort. White fibers have a smaller blood supply, less myoglobin, and fewer mitochondria than red fibers, but they have a huge glycogen supply and an abundance of glycolytic enzymes, suggesting that anaerobic metabolism is more important to them than aerobic. Everything about them hints of speed—even the neurons that innervate them conduct their impulses more rapidly than those innervating the red fibers. White muscles contract very rapidly, produce great power, and they give out quickly. The flight muscles in the breasts of many ground-feeding birds are white muscles. Quail, partridge, pheasant, turkey, and chickens are all ground-feeding birds that tend to *stay* on the ground except in dire emergency. They take to the air for short periods of furious flight intended to remove them from immediate danger and land them a short distance away where they can quickly hide in the underbrush. Fast-acting muscles like the gastrocnemius and the pectoralis in humans are also heavily supplied with white fibers.

Red fibers, viewed broadly as a group, tend to contract more slowly than white. They are intended to maintain their contractile activity over long periods of time, and consistent with this function, the blood supply is rich, mitochondria are abundant, and myoglobin is plentiful. Red fibers are common in muscles that maintain tonic contractions over long periods of time, and in humans the *extensor digitorum,* a muscle in the front of the calf, is one such. Red fibers are also abundant in muscles that are intended to maintain intermittent activity for long periods of time, like the flight muscles of a goose or the swimming muscles of a tuna.

As usual, there are exceptions to the above-stated generalization. Although most red fibers contract rather slowly, not all of them do, and recent electron microscopical work has revealed that there are actually three groups of skeletal muscle fibers: the *fast-twitch red, fast-twitch white,* and *slow-twitch red.* Their characteristics are outlined in table 11.1.

Table 11.1 Characteristics of Skeletal Muscle Fibers

	Fast-Twitch Red*	Slow-Twitch Red	Fast-Twitch White
Diameter	Smallest diameter	Intermediate	Largest diameter
Contraction velocity	Rapid	Slow	Fastest
Mitochondria	Abundant	Abundant	Only a few
Z line thickness	Very broad	Intermediate	Narrow
Stamina	Good	Fair	Poor
Blood supply	Very high	Very high	Poor
ATPase activity	Rapid	Moderate	Rapid
Glycogen supplies	Moderate	Scanty	Abundant
Glycolysis capacity	High	Moderate	Very high
Myoglobin content	Very high	High	Low
Energy source	Aerobic	Aerobic	Mainly anaerobic
Twitch response	Rapid	Slow	Very rapid

*Fast-twitch red muscles are relatively rare in humans. The fast-acting muscles in humans are mainly white.

Figure 11.30 Smooth muscle. Note the lack of obvious cross-striations and the smooth manner in which each cell fits in with the others.

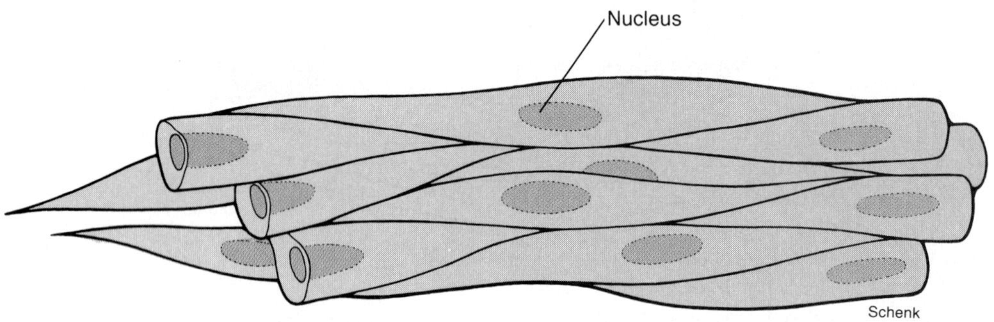

Smooth Muscles

Histologically, smooth muscle appears as layer after layer of flat sheets of smoothly interlocking, spindle-shaped cells (figure 11.30). These sheets wrap around the various tubes in our bodies that carry fluids about; they also enclose the glands or goblet-shaped organs that may, on occasion, require some assistance in squeezing out their contents.

Smooth muscle contains the same types of contractile fibers that give skeletal muscle its striated appearance, but because they are finer and arranged more randomly, their orientation patterns are not easy to see, even under high magnification. In addition, there are no Z lines in smooth muscles; thus there are no sarcomeres. Smooth muscle is the only type of vertebrate muscle that lacks clearly visible striations.

Visceral Muscle

There are two types of smooth muscle in human beings. One type is known as **visceral muscle** and is the type pictured in figure 11.30. As you can see, sheets of visceral muscle are composed of spindle-shaped cells that fit smoothly into place against their neighbors, forming close contacts at many points along their surfaces. There are gap junctions at these contact points that permit electrical stimuli to pass quickly and easily from cell to cell. Visceral is by far the most abundant type of smooth muscle. It is wrapped around tubes like our digestive tract or blood vessels (figure 11.31), or around secretory glands like the gallbladder or mammary glands. When this muscle type

Figure 11.31 Visceral smooth muscles wrap the gastrointestinal tract, providing the power that moves the food through the gut independent of gravity.

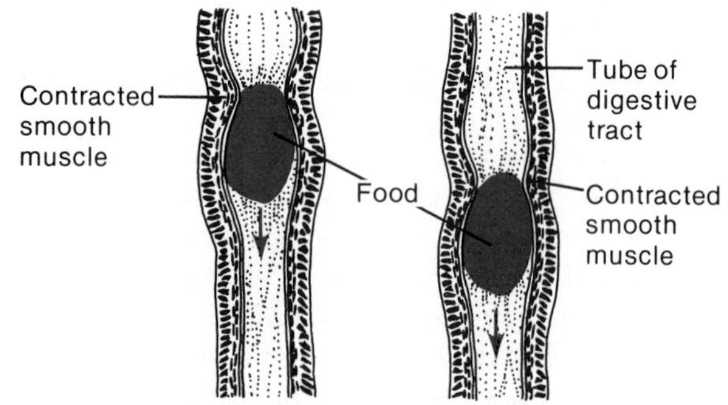

Figure 11.32 A multiunit smooth muscle. Here, two sets of such muscles work antagonistically to control the pupillary opening. (*a*) The first set contracts, the second relaxes, and the pupil constricts. (*b*) The second set contracts, the first set relaxes, and the pupil dilates.

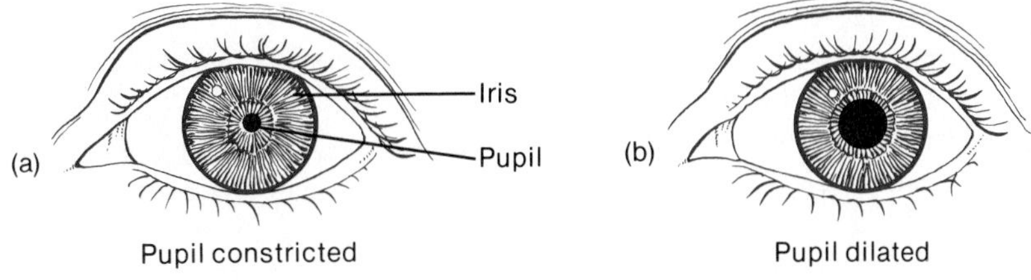

Figure 11.33 Electron micrographs of smooth muscle. (*a*) A longitudinal section showing a whole thick filament (between arrows). (*b*) A cross-section showing the relationship of the thick and thin filaments to each other. The arrows indicate thick filaments, and the blurred gray areas are "dense bodies."

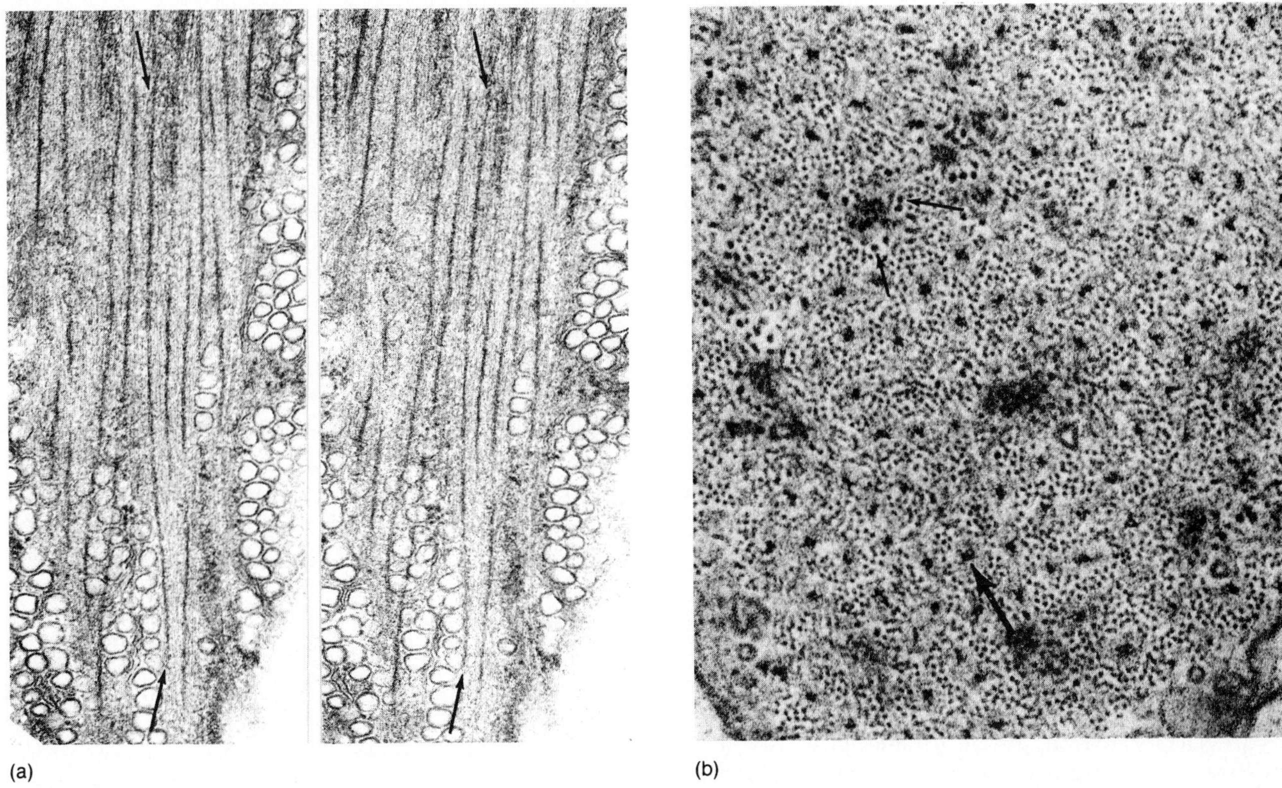

contracts, it does so much more slowly than skeletal muscle does, and the contractions usually require *much* less energy per unit time, so they can last longer.

Multiunit Muscle

Multiunit muscle is the other category of smooth muscle. In this type, the smooth cellular organization characteristic of visceral muscle is absent. The contractile fibers are separate or are arranged in bundles of just a few fibers instead of being organized into sheets. Their requirements for contraction are likewise a bit different. Multiunit smooth muscle fibers are responsible for opening and closing the iris of the human eye and for manipulating the diameter of arteriolar blood vessels (figure 11.32).

Smooth muscles are, chemically, almost the same as skeletal muscles. Actin is present, as is myosin, although their arrangement is different. Because there are no Z bars in which to anchor, the filaments of actin are frequently inserted into structureless masses called **dense bodies** or into the muscle cell membrane (figure 11.33). Smooth muscle does contain tropomyosin, but it lacks troponin, the protein that links with calcium ions and sets off contraction in skeletal muscle. There is another present, however, that is just as good. It is called **calmodulin,** and it serves essentially the same function as troponin, linking up with ionic calcium and permitting the myosin, tropomyosin, and actin to play their roles.

The contractile properties of smooth muscles as a whole are quite different from those of skeletal muscle. In smooth muscle cells, the sarcoplasmic reticulum is poorly developed and may leak badly. As a result, when an action potential is propagated in a smooth muscle cell, calcium leaks in very quickly. Many researchers think that the calcium plays the major role in depolarizing the membrane. Both calcium and sodium ions enter the cell, of course, and whether calcium is responsible or not, the membrane is depolarized. The smooth muscle cell is so much smaller than a skeletal muscle fiber that the calcium can diffuse all the way into the cellular interior without the aid of the sarcoplasmic reticulum. But it takes a lot longer to reach all parts of the cell than it does in skeletal fibers. The latent period in most smooth muscle cells can be fifty times longer than it is in white skeletal fibers—as long as 300 msec in some.

Relaxation is handled by two Ca^{2+} pumps; one pumps calcium back into the sarcoplasmic reticulum, and the other simply pumps it out of the cell. Both pumps are much less active than their counterparts in skeletal muscle; hence the process of relaxation requires a good deal more time in smooth muscle than it does in skeletal.

Stimulation of Smooth Muscles

Skeletal muscle, if it is not stimulated by its motor nerve input, simply does not work, and this is also true of *multiunit* smooth muscle. Multiunit muscles must have some instructions from nerve fibers or they will not contract. Multiunit muscle cells are innervated by parasympathetic or sympathetic nerve endings, each with its own nerve supply. When the correct stimulus is forthcoming, these muscles fire standard, all-or-none action potentials, and the contraction response is much like that of skeletal muscle.

In visceral smooth muscle, usually only a few cells are innervated, and the myoneural junction is not as complex as the skeletal neuromuscular end plate. The autonomic fibers lie in grooves along the surfaces of their muscle cells, and there is often a very broad area of contact between nerve and muscle (figure 11.34). As is the case with somatic motor neurons, neurotransmitter is released at the nerve terminals when an action potential passes along the nerve fiber. The neurotransmitter norepinephrine is released by the sympathetic fibers, while acetylcholine is the parasympathetic messenger. Since so few fibers are innervated, once the initial impetus is given by the neurons, the stimulating impulses must pass from cell to cell through the gap junctions between them. As a result, the contractions that follow the electrical activity fan out in concentric circles from the point of initial stimulus, producing a smooth, wavelike series of contractions.

Spontaneous Stimulation

The visceral type of smooth muscle does not require stimuli from motor nerves; in fact, about half its contractions occur without any neural input at all. These contractions seem to have an intrinsic stimulatory source, which is to say, they come from within the muscle mass itself. They are apparently orchestrated by certain cells or patches of cells considered to contain *pacemaker* types of contractile myofibrils. These cells are almost like receptors in that they tend not to generate action potentials themselves. Instead they produce waves of slow potential change that spread periodically across their surface membranes.

The membrane potential of these cells is not a constant value as it is in their neighbors. Instead it is a regular variable, and no one really knows why, although it has been suggested that possibly their sodium/potassium pumps work intermittently. Whatever the cause, their membrane potentials tend to vary in a wavelike manner, increasing and then decreasing in a perpetual series of rhythmic pulsations. The slow depolarizations that come every half-wave evidently have enough amplitude to stimulate action potentials in nearby cells, and these action potentials spread from cell to cell through gap junctions. The result is wave after slow wave of spontaneous activity spreading outward from the source and travelling in slow undulations all across the mass of smooth muscle.

Chemical Stimulation

Many chemicals can produce a reaction in visceral smooth muscle, and the blood is filled with them. Hormones of all kinds—acetylcholine, angiotensin, epinephrine, vasopressin, and oxytocin—can all produce a response in smooth muscle, and it is not always stimulatory. For instance, epinephrine will relax bronchiolar and gastrointestinal musculature, while acetylcholine has the opposite effect. But norepinephrine is not always a muscle relaxant, since it causes muscles around peripheral blood vessels to clamp down very hard on their arterioles. Similarly, acetylcholine can stimulate considerable activity in the visceral muscles of the intestinal tract, or it can relax the smooth muscles around arterioles. Just why certain hormones can act differently on two separate groups of smooth muscles has never been completely explained, although it is suggested that one group of muscles will have an inhibitory receptor for norepinephrine while another will have an excitatory receptor for the same chemical. Apparently they

Figure 11.34 (*a*) Microphotograph of an autonomic nerve (N) terminating in a visceral muscle mass. (*b*) Line drawing of an autonomic motor nerve terminating on smooth muscle cells. Can you identify the cells in the photograph?

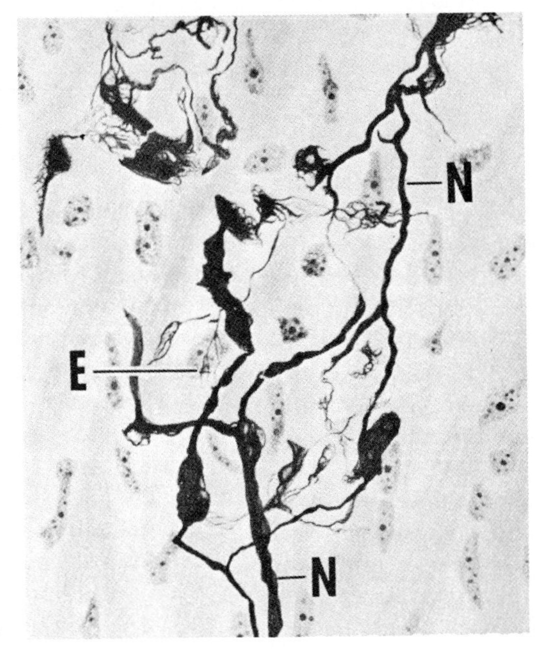

(a)

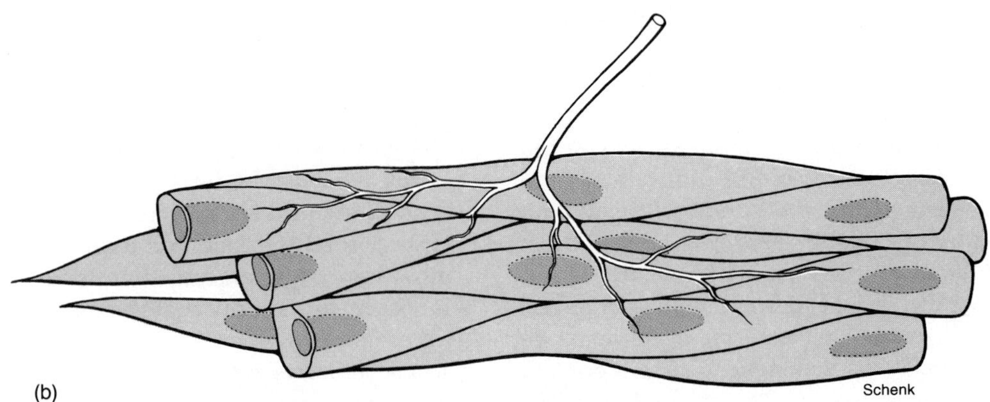

(b)

stimulate activity in the smooth muscle cells they touch by increasing the permeability of both the membrane and the sarcoplasmic reticulum to calcium ions.

Mechanical Stimulation

An important stimulus in the viscera is mechanical—the sudden expansion of the gut as it fills. This stretches the muscle cells lining it, and stimulates them to contract. This fact, coupled with the muscle sheet's tendency to contract in rhythmic waves, is essential; smooth muscle cells are so small that it takes billions of them to form a sheet big enough to wrap just a couple of feet of intestine, and there simply are not enough motor nerve fibers available to innervate all those cells. When a portion of intestine stretches to accommodate food that is entering, its surrounding muscle cells are stimulated into activity. Their depolarization is passed to adjacent muscle cells through gap junctions, and the contractions fan out in pulsating waves. Because most stimuli are passed from cell to cell through these gap junctions, the contraction of a sheet of smooth muscle is almost always slow and wavelike, no matter where the stimulus comes from.

Fortunately, smooth muscles are a good deal less resistant to stretch than skeletal muscles are. Considerable force is needed to stretch out a skeletal muscle, but very little is required to force a sheet of smooth muscle to expand. As we will see when we investigate the digestive and circulatory systems, this characteristic is also requisite; it permits these tubes to fill with food or blood with very little resistance.

Clinical Considerations

Generally speaking, skeletal muscles are so heavily supplied with blood that invasion by microorganisms is rare. Our skeletal muscles do give us problems, of course, but they tend to be functional problems rather than infectious ones.

Cramp

One of the less popular muscle malfunctions is the common cramp. Anyone who has ever come flying out of bed in the early morning hours with the calf muscle clamping down on nothing at all is well aware of how painful this condition can be. Unfortunately, not much is known about muscle cramps—not the spontaneous type at any rate. It is tempting to think that possibly the muscle has run out of ATP and so is locking into a contracted state until ATP is resupplied, but that does not seem likely. If that were truly the cause, one would think that a temporary cutting off of circulation to any limb would produce a cramp, but it usually does not. Mostly, the limb simply "goes to sleep"—the recovery from which is sometimes rather painful, but nothing like the pain of a real cramp. Furthermore, it takes a couple of hours for rigor mortis to set in when a person is dead. Why should a perfectly healthy person with normal, unobstructed circulation suddenly find that a muscle as large as a calf or stomach muscle has been deprived of ATP?

The problem is exacerbated by the observation that researchers have been unable to cause muscle cramps to occur in experimental animals. As you can imagine, it is nearly impossible to induce a natural cramp, and one cannot stand around looking at a rat or a mouse with hope in one's heart until one of them has a cramp. The only way we will ever figure out what is happening is to experiment on a cramped muscle, and if we cannot get a muscle to cramp so we can investigate fully, we may never figure it out.

Charley Horse

Charley horse is a bit easier to analyze. Usually, it is due to internal damage of some kind, often in the large muscle of the thigh (quadriceps). Tearing of a muscle fiber or a blood vessel in the muscle is the most common cause.

Tears and Separations

Muscle tears are not unusual, and as people get bigger and stronger, they are becoming more and more common. Suddenly placing contractile stress on a muscle that has not been "warmed up" can often tear it, and tears take a long time to heal. There is another cause, however, and it is raising more and more concern in the medical community. Men—particularly professional athletes—are getting so big and so powerful through the use of concentrated exercise and (unfortunately) anabolic steroids (specifically testosterone) that the muscles may be getting *too* large. Our skeletons are not large enough or strong enough to handle some of the tremendous pressures these oversized muscles can produce, and it is becoming increasingly evident that our tendons are not large enough or strong enough, either. It has been known for decades that humans, in moments of panic or insanity, can lift or throw objects that they could not begin to move under ordinary conditions. The hypothesis is that they can do so because, in the emotion of the moment, they are able to activate every single motor unit in the muscles they are using, giving them, for just a few seconds, "superhuman" strength. Unfortunately, sometimes these same people tear their muscles or tendons badly in their charged efforts to accomplish abnormal feats of strength, because neither the muscles nor the tendons anchoring them to the skeleton are powerful enough to withstand such stress.

People who work on their muscles regularly are not quite that badly off, because as the muscles increase in strength, so do the tendons and, to a lesser extent, the bones. But until recently, humans never achieved the levels of strength that scientifically designed exercise programs can produce, and questions have been raised as to whether the tendons or bones can ever adapt to such power. It is possible that they cannot.

Paralysis

When we hear the term *paralysis*, the first thing that springs to mind is the picture of a person whose muscles are totally flaccid and unable to contract. This is most assuredly paralysis, but it is only one form. Paralysis means simply that the muscle cannot perform its function—which is, naturally, motion. A person whose muscles were all tightly cramped would be paralyzed just as surely as the person whose muscles were all flaccid, and he would be hurting a good deal more. With this in mind, let us investigate some of the things that can cause paralysis.

Curare Poisoning

Curare is a poison that was, and may still be, used by the Jivaro Indians of South America. It is a paralyzing agent of a type that is known as a **competitive inhibitor.** It works in the following way:

As we all know, when a motor impulse arrives at a skeletal myoneural junction, there is a corresponding release of acetylcholine (Ach) into the synaptic cleft. That Ach attaches to receptors on the muscle side of the cleft, and if there is enough of it, it will cause the sarcolemma to fire. That is a normal contractile operation, and curare prevents it by competing with Ach. It happens that the receptors on the muscle are just as attracted to curare as they are to Ach, and as soon as a receptor opens up, curare molecules attach themselves to it. They do not have any effect on the muscle, so the victim does not need to fear a cramp . . . but the curare will not let go. It stays right there, anchored to the Ach receptors. There are no enzymes available to break it up, so when the motor nerve fires and Ach moves into the cleft, there are no receptors available—no place for it to go. The nerve can send repeated instructions down to the muscle, but because those instructions cannot get to the muscle, nothing happens. Without rapid treatment, a person paralyzed by curare will smother in a few minutes, because the muscles involved in breathing will not operate.

There is a synthetic curare used in surgical operating theaters. Its trade name is **Flaxedil,** and it is used to relax muscles that have to be pulled aside in order for the surgeon to get into the desired area. Naturally, patients who are given this have to be watched carefully, and artificial respiration must be maintained until it wears off, which normally takes only a few hours.

Botulism

This is one of the deadliest diseases known to humankind and one of the few to involve skeletal muscles. The bacteria responsible for the affliction are not normally pathogenic forms; they have no invasive capability. Their destructive power is in a toxin they produce after being forced to live under mainly anaerobic conditions. This is not a condition that crops up often, and when it does, it usually does not affect people because it nearly always occurs in the soil. Occasionally, however, during a canning process, sterilization procedures will be inadequate and some of the bacteria will be sealed, alive, in the newly canned food. That is when their toxin gets into a position to harm people. The poison is the strongest natural toxin known, so powerful that one ten-thousandth of an ounce of crystallized toxin could kill the entire population of Los Angeles County. It attacks the terminal endings of motor neurons and prevents the release of acetylcholine, effectively paralyzing the muscles involved. Curare is metabolized slowly, but it will usually disappear in a few hours; botulism toxin doesn't get metabolized sometimes for weeks, and once it becomes fixed to the motor nerve endings, it will simply stay there. Prolonged paralysis can kill even when the patient remains in intensive care, mainly due to respiratory problems that develop (see chapter 14).

Tetanus

This is another bacteria-produced infection that does not involve truly pathogenic bacteria. As with botulism, the cause is a toxin secreted by the bacteria that attacks the nervous system. Unlike botulism, however, tetanus toxin doesn't produce a flaccid paralysis. It prevents certain nerve cells in the spinal cord from producing inhibitory motor impulses, and the result is hard, tetanic contractions of all affected muscles. The first signs usually involve the jaw musculature, hence the old name of the disease—**lockjaw.** As with botulism, once the toxin is fixed in the nerves, it takes weeks for it to come out. This disease isn't much of a problem today, but in ages past, it used to kill wounded soldiers by the thousands. The disease organism lives in the soil and often enters open wounds as a result of contact with the earth, which was a pretty common occurrence until recently. Victims used to die in terrible agony: every muscle in their bodies cramped tightly into position; back bent like a bow, arms bent at the elbow and legs stiff as boards . . . even the feet were flexed so that the arches were hypercurved.

Man-Made Poisons

Nature normally provides enough difficulties for us to overcome without our producing any more, yet we do, usually in our development of new ways to kill people. One of the ghastliest forms of such mass murder involves what is known as *chemical warfare.* It involves poisons that are intended to paralyze the victims one way or another, and the so-called "nerve gases" do just that. They produce a spastic paralysis similar to that of tetanus, but the cause is quite different. These gases are designed to destroy acetylcholinesterase and thereby render it impossible for a person to relax his skeletal musculature or any other mechanism stimulated by Ach. Despite its name, the material is not really dispersed as a gas, but rather as a fine mist, and it need not be breathed. A single drop landing anywhere on the outer surface of the body is sufficient to kill.

Obviously science has not learned merely to kill. Common sense alone would suggest that a lethal gas that kills everything alive and for which there is no antidote would be utterly devastating to the attacker as well as to the victims of the attack. Consequently, for every nerve gas that has been developed, there is an antidote. Atropine, for instance, injected immediately upon exposure to the nerve gases described above, will counter the action of the gas. In fact, military personnel are all supplied with vials of atropine and injection kits for just such an emergency.

Not everything about poisons is bad. Curare is, as I said, used to relax muscles during surgery, and poisons like botulism toxin can isolate certain myoneural mechanisms and hence are tremendously useful in nerve-muscle research . . . science has found a use along these lines even for the venom of the black widow spider and the deadly tetrodotoxin of the puffer fish.

Muscular Degeneration

Regardless of the reason, if a muscle is not used for any significant length of time, it will degenerate (*atrophy*). Anyone who has ever seen a paraplegic's leg musculature will remember the glossy-smooth skin surface and the almost complete absence of any muscle bulges. Such muscles have not merely shrunk in size. The protein fibers have broken up and been replaced with adipose tissue or tough connective tissue, and the muscles are, for all purposes, no longer muscle. The atrophy is so complete that should some neural recovery make it possible for these muscles to become active again, they might never make it.

When spinal damage occurs, it is precisely this kind of wasting away that a physical therapist struggles to avoid while everyone—especially the patient—waits to see if the nerves will regenerate and move the muscles again. Massage helps retain the blood supply into the muscle, but only real movement of the afflicted muscles can avoid the breakdown of fibers. Naturally, the patient cannot move the muscle, but the therapist can stimulate it artificially with spot electrodes and can retain muscle workability temporarily by making it work against a load.

Summary

The Tissue

Muscle is a separate tissue. It is unique in its ability to shorten with power.

Categories of Muscle

The three types of muscle are skeletal, smooth, and cardiac. They all share the ability to contract with power.

I. Skeletal Muscle
   A. Skeletal muscle represents the largest tissue mass in the body. It is under voluntary control for the most part.
   B. It is attached to bones. Movement of the whole body is provided by setting the shafts of bone in motion.
   C. Skeletal muscle can go from relaxation to complete contraction in less than a quarter of a second.

II. Smooth Muscle. Smooth muscle lines internal organs and glands, including the gut. Its contractile strength is less than that of skeletal, but its stamina is greater.

III. Cardiac Muscle. This is a muscle type that is unique to the vertebrate heart. It beats on a regular basis, day after day, minute after minute. But is not inexhaustible; it rests between contractions. And it cannot function anaerobically. It must have plenty of oxygen.

The Most Important Property

The ability to contract is the most important property of muscle.

I. No Ability to Push. Muscles cannot push; they can only pull.

II. Antagonistic Muscles. Because muscles cannot actively lengthen, every skeletal muscle has a muscle that opposes its action. This is known as an antagonistic muscle. Antagonistic muscles move limbs in such a way as to lengthen or straighten out the opposing muscle.

Micro- and Ultrastructure

Muscles are divided into compartments. The largest compartments are called fasciculi. Each fasciculus is subdivided into fibers, and each fiber is further subdivided into myofibrils. Each skeletal muscle fiber is an individual muscle cell.

I. Inside the Muscle Fiber. Fibers are surrounded by plasma membranes and are filled with cytoplasm (called sarcoplasm), just like other body cells.

II. Myofibrils. Myofibrils are cylindrical in shape and are filled with myofilaments, which are the contractile proteins of the muscle. Myofilaments are aligned in such a way as to produce repeating bands or striations across the entire muscle fiber.

The Contractile Proteins

There are four contractile proteins in skeletal muscle: actin, myosin, troponin, and tropomyosin.

I. Actin. The thin myofilaments are composed primarily of actin.

II. Myosin. The thick myofilaments are composed chiefly of myosin. Myosin features cross-bridges that reach the thin filaments. The cross-bridge region of the myosin molecule has ATPase activity.

III. Tropomyosin. Tropomyosin is a filamentous protein with a molecular weight of 130,000.

IV. Troponin. Troponin and tropomyosin complex with each other and are associated with the thin filaments.

The Contractile Process

Actin and myosin have considerable chemical affinity for each other. When mixed together they will complex to form the compound actomyosin. Actomyosin does not form in a resting muscle because tropomyosin lies between the actin and myosin filaments. Therefore, to get actomyosin to form, the tropomyosin must be moved.

I. The Action of Ionic Calcium
   A. Ionic calcium has a very high affinity for troponin and complexes with it readily.
   B. When a troponin/Ca^{2+} complex forms, tropomyosin rolls away from its resting position along the thin filament.
   C. When tropomyosin rolls away from its resting position, actomyosin can form. Actomyosin is a stable compound.

II. The Dual Role of ATP
   A. When actomyosin forms, the cross-bridges use the energy from ATP and bend, forcing the thin filaments to slide past the thick filaments.

B. If ATP is available, it will bind to the cross-bridge segments of the thick filament.
C. Binding of ATP makes the actomyosin complex unstable, and it breaks apart.
D. The cross-bridge snaps back to its original position, and the process repeats.

The Neuromuscular Junction

Motor neurons enter muscle fibers at a highly specialized structure known as the nerve/muscle end plate. The junction is activated by acetylcholine in much the same way as a neural synapse is activated by a neurotransmitter. The electrical impulses travelling through the muscle set the contractile process in motion.

The T System and the Sarcoplasmic Reticulum

I. The Sarcoplasmic Reticulum
   A. Is highly organized in skeletal muscle tissue. It runs mainly parallel to the myofilaments, but crosses them at the Z bars and the H bands.
   B. During noncontractile periods, the sarcoplasmic reticulum houses most of the calcium that is necessary to activate contractions.
   C. Calcium is released from the reticulum when a depolarization occurs.
II. The Transverse Tubule (T) System
   A. The T system runs across the myofilaments at the Z bars. It is continuous with the plasma membrane. The T tubules are responsible for transmitting the membrane depolarization deep into the muscle fiber.
   B. The Calcium Bullet. When the muscle's trigger is pulled (depolarization), calcium is released from the sarcoplasmic reticulum, and contraction proceeds.

Energy Supplies

I. During Relaxation. Energy for the contraction is supplied by ATP. ATP is not stored in large quantities. Creatine phosphate (CP), another high-energy compound, is. CP transfers its energy to ADP, recharging it and making it possible for the muscle to obtain energy for contraction.
II. Prolonged Activity
   A. During prolonged contractions, skeletal muscle is often unable to obtain enough oxygen, and it gets its energy from anaerobic metabolism.
   B. Oxygen Debt. Anaerobic activity permits a buildup of lactic acid and creates an oxygen debt within the body. The oxygen debt is paid off by rapid breathing and increased heart rate.
III. Grading the Contractions. When a muscle fiber contracts, it contracts as hard as it can. Muscles obviously do not use all the power they are capable of every time they contract. There must be some means of grading the contractile power of whole muscles.
IV. Motor Units. Contractions are graded by varying the number of motor units that are activated during the contraction. A motor unit is a single motor nerve and all the muscle fibers it innervates.

Some Experiments and the Facts Derived From Them

I. Threshold Voltage. Muscles have a threshold voltage just as nerves do. It is defined as the minimum voltage necessary to depolarize the muscle fiber.
II. Muscle Twitches. Muscle twitches result from a single depolarization of a muscle. Twitches show that muscles have a latent period. The latent period is the delay between the depolarization and the onset of movement.
III. Muscle Loading. Preloaded muscles can do more work than afterloaded muscles, and they use no more energy. Preloaded muscles are muscles that are stretched out before the stimulus is applied. In living systems, skeletal muscles are prestretched.
IV. Experimental Observations Applied
   A. When stimuli are applied to muscles at a high frequency, the muscle twitches can become additive, producing a greater degree of contraction than any individual twitch. This is known as summation.
   B. If the stimuli are applied quickly enough, the contraction becomes smooth and unbroken. This is known as a tetanic contraction.

Higher Control of Skeletal Muscles

I. Control of skeletal muscles is mostly voluntary; hence the control center is in the cerebral cortex, in a zone called the motor cortex or precentral gyrus.
II. From the motor cortex, the controlling neurons course through the thalamus, the basal ganglia, and the medulla, and thence into the spinal cord. This is known as the pyramidal pathway.
III. The motor neurons that innervate the muscles are known as alpha fibers or lower motor neurons.

Proprioception

I. The Muscle Spindle. Muscle spindles are specialized fibers arranged parallel to contractile fibers in skeletal muscle.
   A. Spindle Innervation
      1. The spindles are innervated by three different kinds of nerves: the gamma motor neurons, the flowerspray sensory fibers, and the annulospiral sensory fibers.
      2. The flowerspray endings provide the CNS with information about the length of the muscle at any given time.
      3. The annulospiral endings tell the CNS when muscle length is changing.
   B. Spindle Operation. Sudden changes in muscle length can stimulate the spindle's activity.
II. The Golgi Tendon Organs. The Golgi tendon organs are imbedded in the tendons of the muscles. They provide information concerning the amount of tension on a muscle at any given time.
III. Isometric vs Isotonic Contractions
   A. Isotonic contractions are defined as contractions that result in a change in muscle length but no change in tension. They result in movement.

B. Isometric contractions are defined as contractions that result in a change in muscle tension but no change in length. The muscle is rigid and unmoving.

IV. Muscle Tone. Muscle tone or tonus is a constant, partial contraction of a muscle that provides living rigidity to the joint where it is attached. It helps keep the head upright and aids in walking and standing.

V. Myoglobin. Myoglobin is a special muscle pigment that is similar to hemoglobin in that it can store oxygen.

Types of Skeletal Muscle

There are three types of skeletal muscle: fast-twitch red, fast-twitch white, and slow-twitch red.

I. Fast-twitch red has a rich blood supply and lots of mitochondria. It is capable of sustained activity for long periods of time.

II. Fast-twitch white has a weaker blood supply and very few mitochondria. It is capable of very rapid, short bursts of activity that spend tremendous amounts of energy.

III. Slow-twitch red has a rich blood supply and lots of mitochondria. It is capable of sustained contraction, but its work onset is slow.

Smooth Muscles

Smooth muscles are usually arranged in sheets. The cells are small and they interlock. There are two types of smooth muscle, visceral and multiunit.

I. Visceral Muscle. Visceral is typical of the muscles that wrap the digestive tract and other large internal organs such as the uterus.

II. Multiunit Muscle. Multiunit is the other type of smooth muscle. The cells are not arranged in sheets, but rather in fine fibers. They are typically found wrapped around arterioles. They are also responsible for opening and closing the pupil of the eye. Multiunit muscle cells are all innervated.

Stimulation of Smooth Muscles

In visceral muscle, innervation is sparse. Only a few cells out of a large mass will actually be innervated. Communication between cells is by way of gap junctions.

Multiunit muscles are always stimulated by neural input.

I. Spontaneous Stimulation. Visceral smooth muscle is often stimulated intrinsically, by pacemaker cells.

II. Chemical Stimulation. Visceral smooth muscle responds to hormones and neurotransmitters.

III. Mechanical Stimulation. Visceral muscle can also be stimulated to contract by stretching.

Clinical Considerations

I. Cramp
II. Charley Horse
III. Tears and Separations
IV. Paralysis
    A. Curare Poisoning
    B. Botulism
    C. Tetanus
    D. Man-Made Poisons
V. Muscular Degeneration

Review Questions

1. What are the three categories of muscle? On what basis were they established?
2. Describe the major characteristics of all three types of muscle.
3. What is an antagonistic muscle?
4. What is the function of antagonism?
5. Why is antagonism necessary?
6. Draw a picture of a muscle and include:
    a. fasciculi
    b. fibers
    c. myofibrils
7. Draw a picture of a myofibril, showing clearly the striations. Be sure to identify each striation.
8. Of what chemicals are the myofilaments composed?
9. Name and describe the contractile proteins in as much detail as you can.
10. Discuss the importance of calcium to the contractile process.
11. Describe the morphology of a myoneural junction.
12. How does the tiny motor nerve transfer an electrical signal to the relatively huge muscle fiber?
13. Describe the process by which the electrical signal is able to penetrate into the interior of the muscle fiber.
14. What is the function of the T system?
15. What role does the sarcoplasmic reticulum play in the contractile process?
16. What molecule provides myosin with the necessary energy for a contraction?
17. How is that molecule recharged?
18. What is the role of creatine phosphate in the contraction process?
19. What is the main cause of the development of an oxygen debt during prolonged contraction?
20. How is an oxygen debt dispelled?
21. How is it possible for muscles to grade their contractions so that they are not using maximum power all the time?
22. Describe the advantage of prestretching a skeletal muscle fiber.
23. How does the muscle spindle operate to control muscle activity?
24. What is the purpose of the Golgi tendon organ?
25. Describe the types of skeletal muscle and discuss the characteristics of each.
26. Describe the differences between smooth muscle and skeletal muscle. What contractile protein is present in smooth muscle that is absent in skeletal muscle?
27. Name the different types of smooth muscle and discuss their characteristics.
28. How does the stimulation process of smooth muscle differ from that of skeletal muscle?

Section IV
Fluid Homeostasis

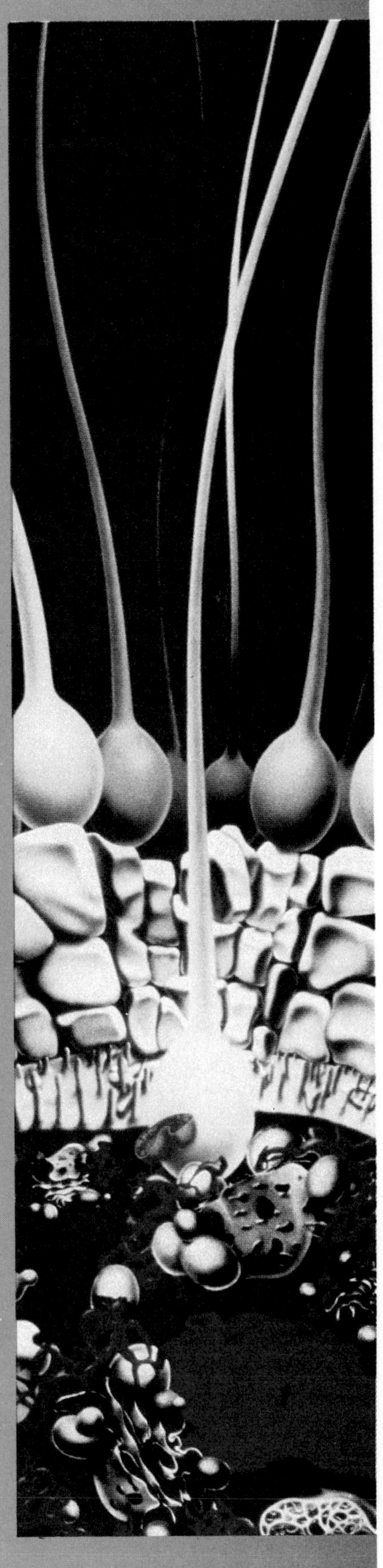

Chapter 12 Lymph and Blood

Study Hints

1. Try to grasp the concept of fluid compartments within living mammals.
2. Fluid and particulate exchange in living systems takes place between compartments. Be sure you understand how this is accomplished and how it is controlled.
3. Pay particular attention to the fact that exchange of materials, in the capillary beds and elsewhere, is a constant, dynamic process. Movement into and out of the vessel is rapid and continuous, and oxygen, carbon dioxide, nutrients, and wastes are constantly exchanging along the entire length of the capillary.
4. It is important to realize that humans have two circulatory systems and that they are not the same. Learn the difference between lymphatic and blood circulatory systems.
5. The blood does much more than transport oxygen. Make a special effort to understand the unique functions of the liquid fraction of the blood (plasma) and the role it plays in the maintenance of homeostasis.
6. There is only one type of red cell, but there are several types of white cells, and each is unique. Study the identifying characteristics and the unique function of each type.

Objectives

When you have finished reading this chapter, you should:

1. know what constitutes a fluid compartment in the body.
2. know which of the compartments is largest and be able to explain how they differ from each other.
3. be able to explain how the compartments achieve and maintain their differences in content, yet simultaneously interact so thoroughly as to almost mix with each other.
4. be able to describe the major morphological differences between the red and white blood cells.
5. be able to list the various white blood cells and explain the particular function of each of the types.
6. be able to describe the role that the formed elements of the blood play in resisting mechanical damage and bacterial invasion.

Red blood cells within a small vein.

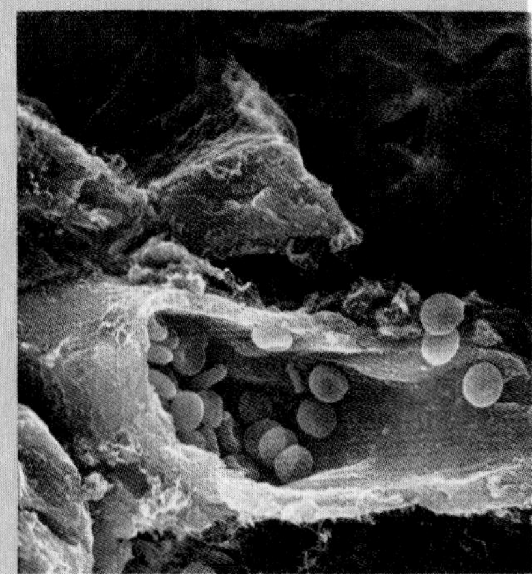

Introduction

By now you should be familiar with the structured particles inside the cell: particles made of proteins, lipids, carbohydrates, and/or nucleic acids, all meticulously arranged into the intracellular organelles. In addition, you should understand that while we do not know why or how it happens, in one way or another the interaction of these particles represents life. As you know, they are immersed in and nurtured by a fluid matrix, the cytosol. The cytosol is a furiously active aqueous dispersion. All the biosynthetic and catabolic activity within each cell takes place, for the most part, in the cytosol, as its bustling energy-producing machinery clearly demonstrates. But we must not lose sight of the fact that its major function may be to provide a generous and indulgent environment for the living particles it bathes. The cytosol actually touches these particles, and so its composition must be most strictly controlled, permitting only the smallest of changes. Its volume is pretty large, and that helps, but it must be able to obtain provisions the instant they are needed and to promptly dump trash before it can accumulate. It is maintained in these efforts by the interstitial fluid. Washing around the outside of the body's cells, the interstitial fluid insures that nutrients and essential minerals are always available and that waste products never pile up to the detriment of cellular life.

But the interstitial fluid is not of infinite size and capabilities—in fact, its total volume is relatively small. All the waste products it accepts from the cellular interiors must be disposed of quickly, or it will become polluted. Also, the nutrients so liberally dispensed must be replenished, or the interstitial fluid will be depleted. Obviously something must, in its turn, maintain the interstitial fluid.

That job is handled by the blood.

As it moves through its appointed rounds, the blood unloads nutrients of all kinds into the interstitial fluids and takes from it accumulated waste products. It does both jobs with the same kind of generous abandon that the interstitial fluid exercises with the cytosol—nothing is withheld; no waste is refused. Thus the interstitial fluid is nurtured in the same way that it pampers the cytosol.

But, by unloading its nutrients and accepting all kinds of draff, the blood is now confronted with the same problems—avoiding pollution and replenishing its nutrients. To deal with this, there are specialized areas where raw materials are supplied in abundance, zones where waste products can be unloaded and structures where the blood can be scrubbed clean. How and where this is done is what this chapter is all about.

The Fluid Compartments

If an average, 150-pound human being were completely dehydrated and the solid material set aside, we would find slightly less than 90 pounds of water in our collection vats. If it were then possible to separate this water into compartments depending on which part of the body it came from, we would note immediately that most of the fluid is inside body cells. This is the **intracellular compartment,** and it contains about 62 percent of the body water—in this case, that would amount to a little over 55 pounds. The remaining 35 pounds is outside the body cells, in what is known to physiologists as the **extracellular compartment.** Of that volume, only about 6 liters (7 pounds) is blood.

There is another compartment that we, as physiologists, sometimes recognize. It is known as the **transcellular compartment,** and while it is not exactly a morphological space, it probably is a physiological one. It includes cerebrospinal fluid, the aqueous and vitreous humor of the eyeball, the pleural fluid around the lungs, digestive fluids, and the sacs-full of lubricating fluid between the movable joints of our long bones. In the example we are using, it would embrace about a pound and a half of water.

The Interstitial Fluids

Of the thirty-five pounds or so of extracellular water, only a little more than six pounds is in the blood. The rest of it is interstitial fluid—the mass of liquid that enfolds our body cells and functions as a buffer or transition zone between the blood and the intracellular compartment. As far as the cells are concerned, it represents an inexhaustible warehouse of raw materials and a limitless dumping ground.

It is neither, of course. As you can see from the numbers I have cited, the volume of interstitial fluid is relatively small, and it must handle a prodigious volume of waste materials. But it is not a stagnant pond. It may not rush from place to place as quickly as the blood, but it's not inert. It moves, circulating through the body organs, flowing smoothly over tissues, bathing all the living cells in the body. Cells eject waste products as rapidly as they are produced, yet the wastes never become concentrated in any particular zone because of the constant motion of the extracellular fluid—always churning, mixing. It cycles repeatedly through zones where it comes into contact with the blood, and in these areas, it exchanges things. Its dynamic nature is neither surprising nor unprecedented, for the interstitial fluid is a component of one of the body's two major circulatory systems.

The Lymphatic Circulation

The interstitial fluid belongs to the lymphatic circulatory system, an *open* type of system that appeared very early in evolutionary history. That, of course, makes it primitive. But primitive or not, if we judge an organism's success in this world by its numbers, then the open circulatory system has got to be considered a consummate achievement, because it is possessed by an awfully large number of animals. All insects, lobsters, crabs, spiders, and the sundry other small multilegged invertebrates that crawl, ooze, rush about, or drift have this circulatory plan for their body fluids, and for them, it is the only one. It is not exactly the same as the human lymphatic circulation, but there are many similarities.

The Open Plan

In this kind of system, the circulating fluid is pumped by a strong heart into large arteries, which subsequently break down into smaller and smaller vessels. Ultimately these small vessels simply end, permitting their contents to pour out into the extracellular spaces. The liberated fluid then streams gently through the body cavities past tissues and individual cells, exchanging materials as it meanders along. Its motion tends to be relatively deliberate, and pressure is low, but movement is constant, and the fluid has a definite destination. This destination turns out to be large body pools or **sinuses** (*sinu,* "a hollow") in which this free-moving fluid eventually collects. As more and more fluid moves into these internal "caves," accumulating pressure gradually pushes it into veins that carry their contents, at extremely low pressure, back to the heart to be pumped out again.

Humans have a circulatory system something like that. The origin is a bit different and there is a means of replenishing its stocks and cleaning it up while it is out there percolating through the tissues, but in its essentials, that is the way it works. We call it the **lymphatic circulatory system.**

The Lymph

Lymph is an **ultrafiltrate** of the blood, which simply means that it is produced by straining blood through an extremely fine filter. Its source is any one of the millions of capillary beds in the human body through which the blood must flow and through which the lymph is filtered. We will discuss the mechanics of its filtration a bit later in this chapter, but for now let us consider the overall plan of the system. We will begin our investigation at the point where the lymphatic fluid is formed—the millions of capillary beds distributed throughout the body.

Figure 12.1 The formation of interstitial fluid and lymph in a capillary bed. Arrows indicate the direction of fluid flow.

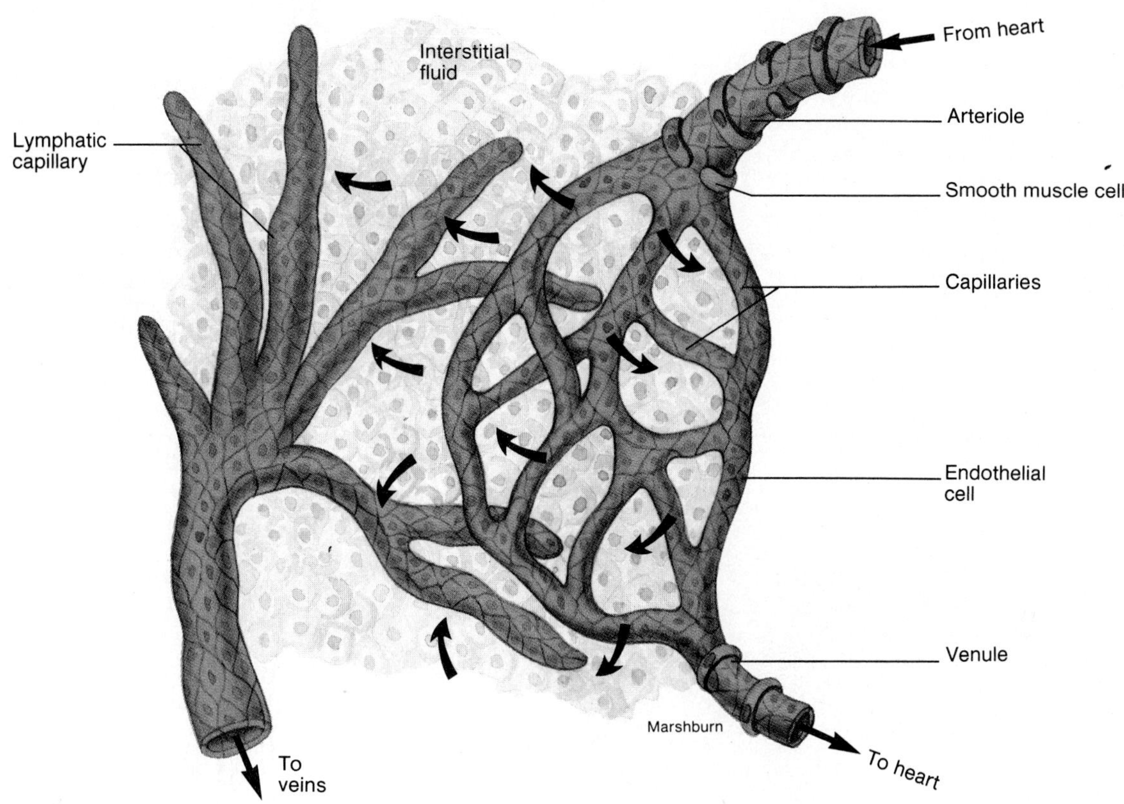

In composition, lymph is a good deal like the liquid fraction of the blood (plasma) from which it is filtered, except for a lower protein content. It even contains all the chemicals necessary to initiate the formation of a clot, so leakage of interstitial fluid can be minimized should injury occur. Once outside the blood vessels, the filtrate follows a definite, if very short, itinerary through the body, ending up in a variety of extremely small sinuses surrounding the lymphatic vessels (figure 12.1).

As the figure shows, lymphatic capillaries are unusual vessels. For one thing, they have no openings in their tips—we cannot really call them ends, since they are actually the beginnings. The interstitial fluid enters these lymphatic capillaries in pretty much the same way it left the blood, by passing through a filter. Capillaries of the blood circulatory system filter the plasma and form the lymph, and they are quite selective in what they will and will not permit to pass. In terms of selectivity, the lymphatic filter is not quite as finicky as the blood capillaries. Lymphatic capillaries are composed of overlapping endothelial cells arranged so that they lay across one another, each sheathing the next in much the same way shingles overlay each other on a roof (figure 12.2). And like shingles, the arrangement permits a one-way flow of materials. Things can get *into* the vessels fairly easily,

Figure 12.2 Schematic diagram showing the layering of epithelial cells in a lympatic capillary and illustrating their unidirectional nature.

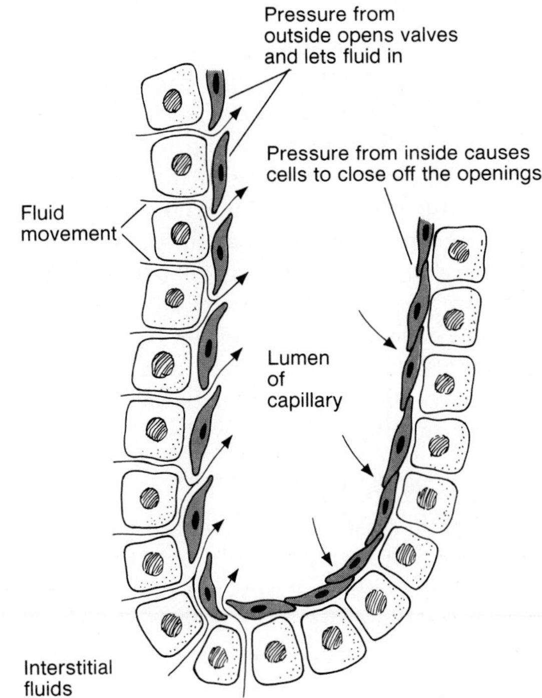

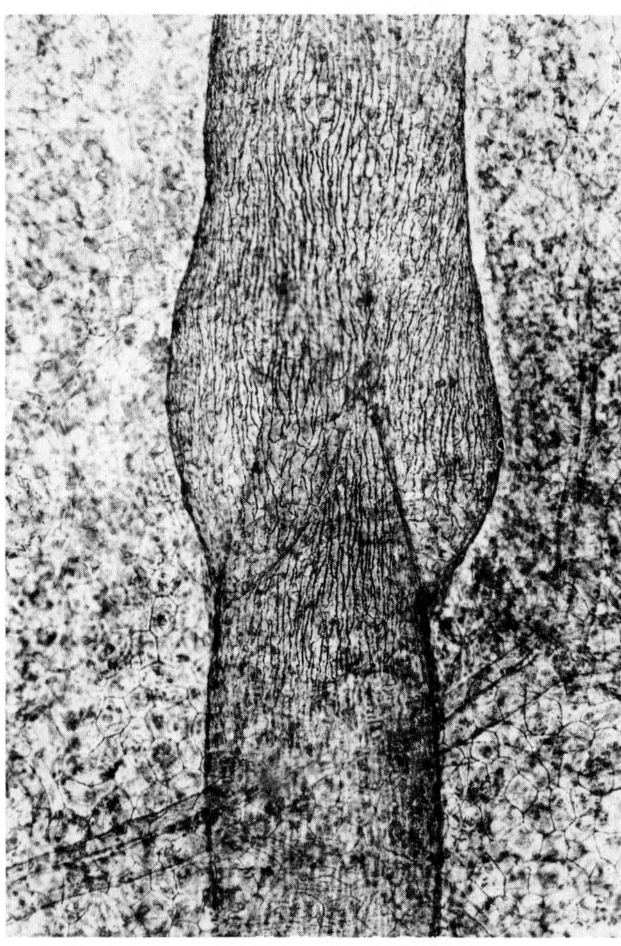

Figure 12.3 A microphotograph of a lymphatic vessel showing the flaplike valve. You should know the function of this valve.

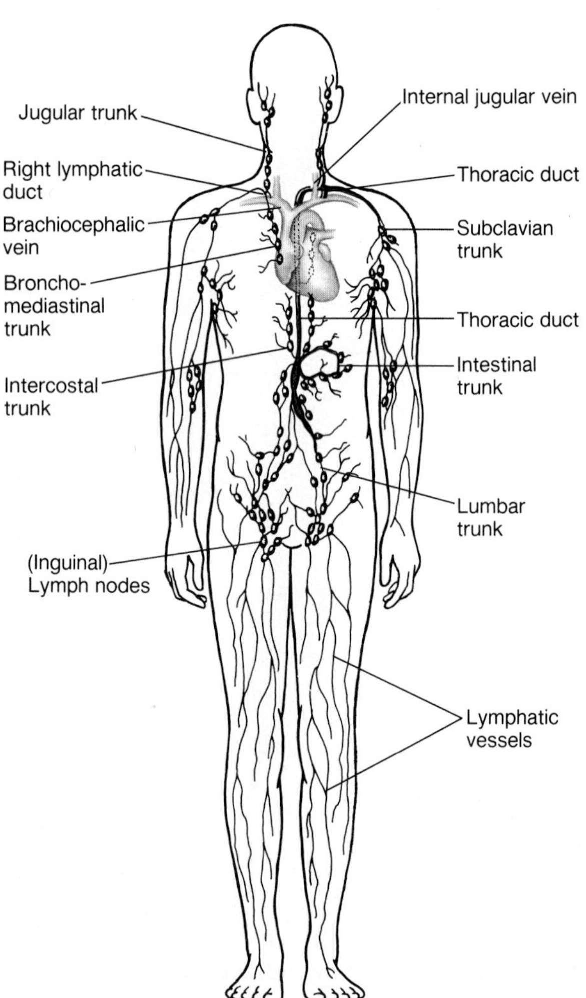

Figure 12.4 The lymphatic circulation in the human body.

entering without difficulty by opening the flaps of the cells, but should they try to get back out again, like the hair of a cat that is stroked backwards, the cells rise up and obstruct the flow (figure 12.2).

When things are moving in the right direction, however, this kind of filter is relatively permissive. Its openings into the system are large, so everything but the very largest proteins can get inside. As a result, the lymph and the interstitial fluid are essentially the same. Those large openings let bacteria in, too—bacteria that cannot get into the blood but want a free ride to a new home. Hitchhiking in the lymph seldom does them much good, as we will see.

Lymphatic Propulsion

The lymphatic vessels themselves are quite similar to blood veins, although perhaps a little flimsier (figure 12.1). Like veins, they possess lots of one-way valves in their interiors to prevent a backward flow of fluid (figure 12.3), but unlike the blood, lymph does not move because of pressure supplied by the heart. In fact, there are no special organs to pump lymph. It seems to depend exclusively on the mechanical activity of nearby skeletal muscles to push it along, although some experiments have hinted that when necessary, the lymphatic vessels are capable of contracting and providing a **slight** thrust. The evidence for this is meager, however (see box), and even if it is true, the force provided cannot be very profound, since the musculature in the lymph vessel walls is sparse indeed. In any case, lymphatic flow is much, much slower than that of blood. For example, in the **thoracic duct** (see figure 12.4), the largest of the lymphatic vessels, the velocity of flow is between 3 and 4 mm per second, which means about two liters of lymph move through it in a period of twenty-four hours. By contrast, about five liters of blood pour from the great veins into the right atrium of the heart every **minute.** Obviously, compared to the velocity of blood flow, the lymph barely crawls along.

Figure 12.5 (*a*) The arrangement of the larger lymph nodes of the human body. (*b*) The pattern of lymphatic drainage from the breast, showing the smaller nodes and emphasizing their ubiquitous nature.

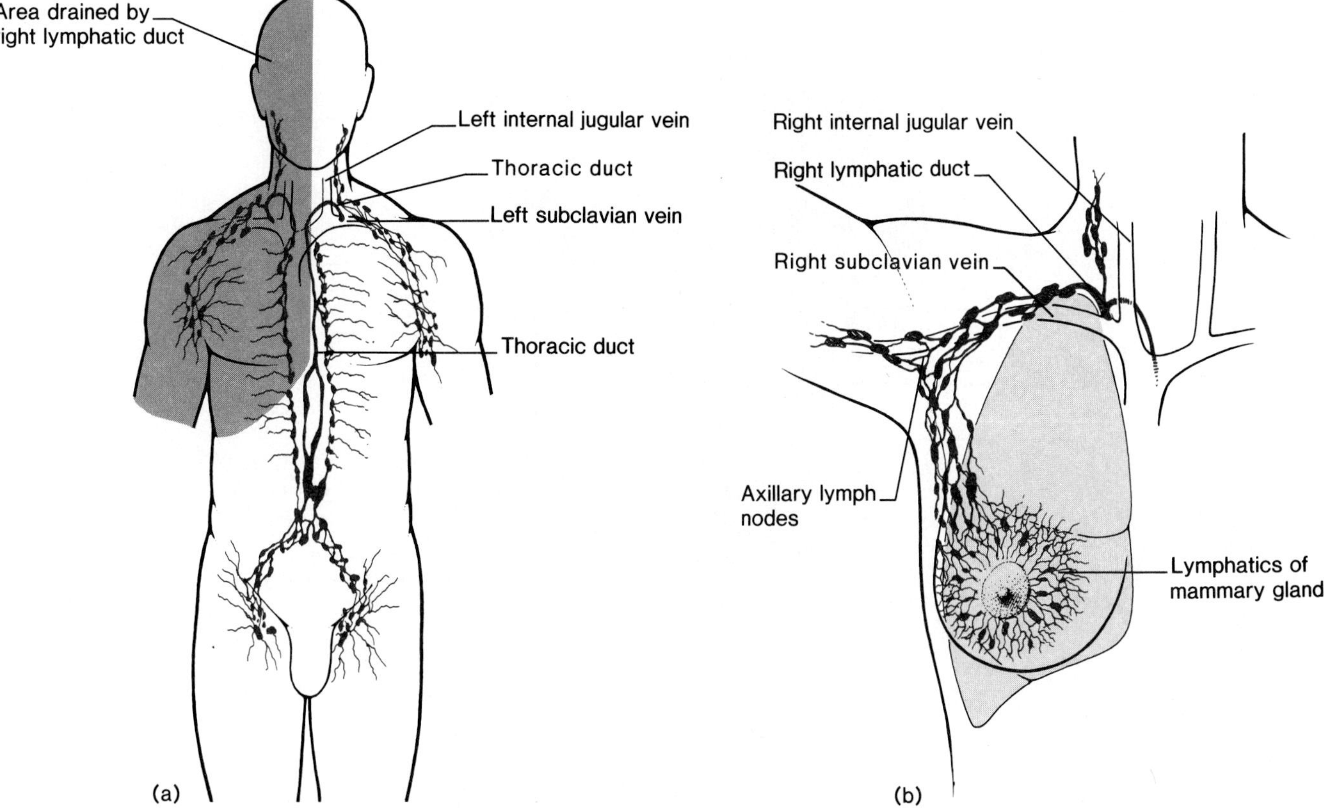

Evidence opposing the suggestion that lymphatic vessels move their contents by contracting:

1. In a resting limb, there is no flow of lymph whatsoever. The lymph tends to pool at the site of the valves in the vessels and can cause considerable distension.
2. The flow of lymph seems to increase and slow in accordance with an increase or a reduction in the flow of blood through the veins. There is no doubt that the skeletal muscles provide the lion's share of the motive power to the blood in the veins.

Lymph Nodes

As the lymph makes its way languorously through the long, narrow tunnels formed by its vessels, every once in a while it breaks out into a large "room" (figure 12.5). These "rooms" are the **lymph nodes,** and our lymphatic system is arranged in such a way that all of the lymph must pass through at least one such node before it returns to the blood.

The rationale is simple. In the nodes, the slow-moving fluid is subjected to several decontamination procedures, including a thorough ultrafiltration to remove large foreign particles. Masses of white blood cells called **lymphocytes** rove around in the interior of these nodes, and they check each immigrant thoroughly, searching for aliens. Should any be found, there is no thought given to deportation. They are immediately attacked and killed by elements of the body's immune system, then promptly eaten by white blood cells with tremendous appetites. Our lymph nodes are frequently the scenes of tiny but very deadly wars, with troops in the form of bacteria and white blood cells snuffing out by the thousands. There is no quarter in these conflicts. It is total annihilation that the body wants, and it either gets it, or the body succumbs.

As a result of the tremendous amount of energy being spent during these conflicts and the quantities of toxic substances released, the lymph nodes often swell; sometimes they get hot and sore. This can alert medical practitioners to the fact that there is an infection in the body before it has had a chance to take hold and do some real damage. Furthermore, because of the way the lymph nodes are arranged, they can give us a general idea of where this infection might be. When we come down with sinus ailments, tooth abscesses or ear infections, it is common for the lymph nodes in the neck and ear regions to become swollen, hot, and very tender (a condition called **adenitis**). Leg

Figure 12.6 A sagittal section of the head, showing the respiratory tract from the external nares (nostrils) to the trachea.

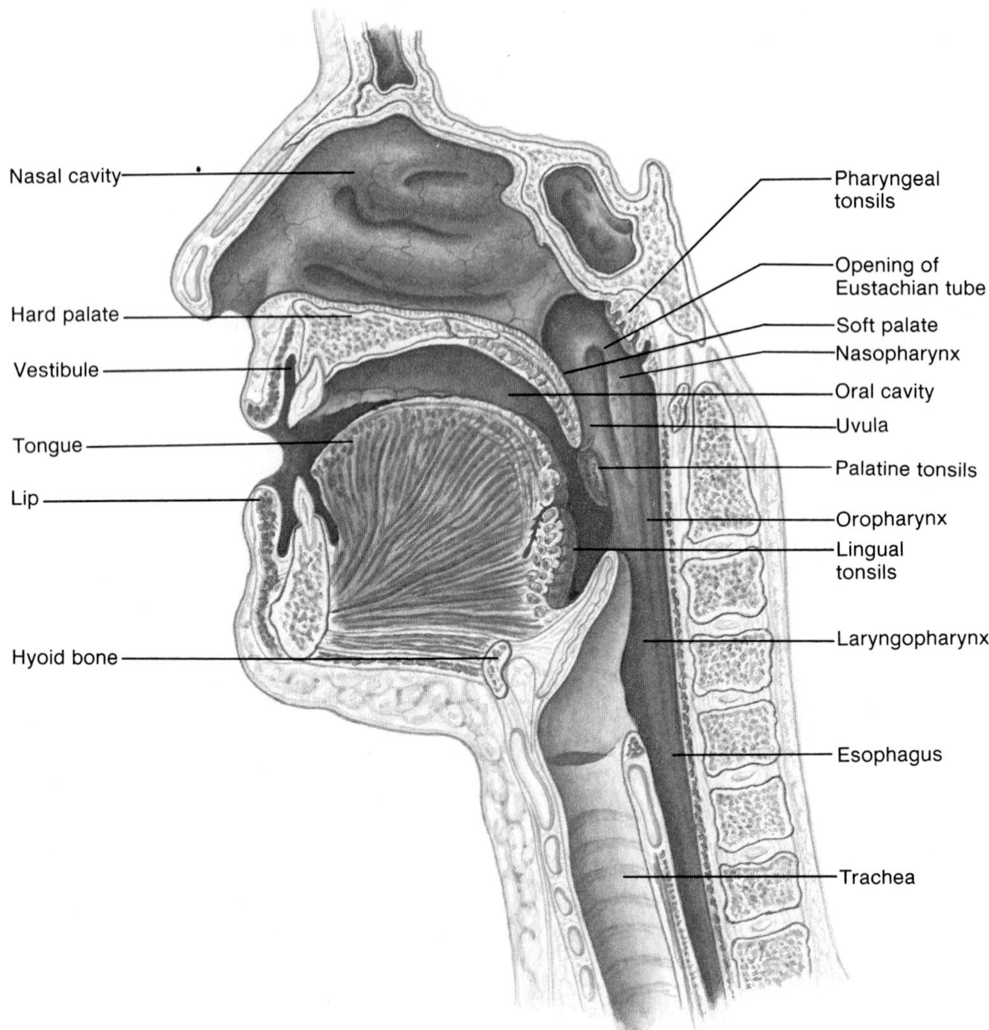

or foot infections will cause nodes in the groin to swell, while finger or hand infections will produce swelling of the lymph nodes in the armpits.

Lymph nodes are also present in the mucous membranes of the throat and nasal mucosa, where they are known as **tonsils** (figure 12.6).When upper respiratory infections are present, it is not unusual, especially in young children, for bacteria or viruses to become concentrated in the tonsils. When this occurs, the tonsils become inflamed and very painful. They often swell to enormous size, sometimes occluding almost the entire oropharyngeal entryway, obstructing eating and sometimes breathing. The condition is, of course, known as tonsilitis, and thirty years ago the tonsils were routinely removed at the first hint of such swellings. Indeed, it was rare for a child to reach puberty and still have his or her tonsils. Today, most pediatricians resist removing these pieces of lymphatic tissue for as long as they possibly can, because the feeling is that their continued operations probably serve a protective function.

All the materials that have squeezed through the lymph nodes and successfully passed their various check points rejoin the blood through openings in the right and left subclavian veins, just before the venous blood enters the right atrium of the heart (figure 12.7).

Blood—the Closed System

As you should infer from the discussion of the lymphatic circulation and the formation of interstitial fluid, the primary function of the blood is to maintain homeostasis in the fluid that bathes the cells. The most important organ in the circulatory system is felt, by popular consensus, to be the heart; after all, the heart pumps the blood all through the body, and it most assuredly is an indispensable part of the system.

But actually, the business end of the circulatory system is not the heart, but the capillary beds that are scattered by the thousands throughout the body. The exchange of materials between the blood and the interstitial fluids occurs in these capillary beds, and

Figure 12.7 The lymphatic and blood circulatory systems: a schematic diagram.

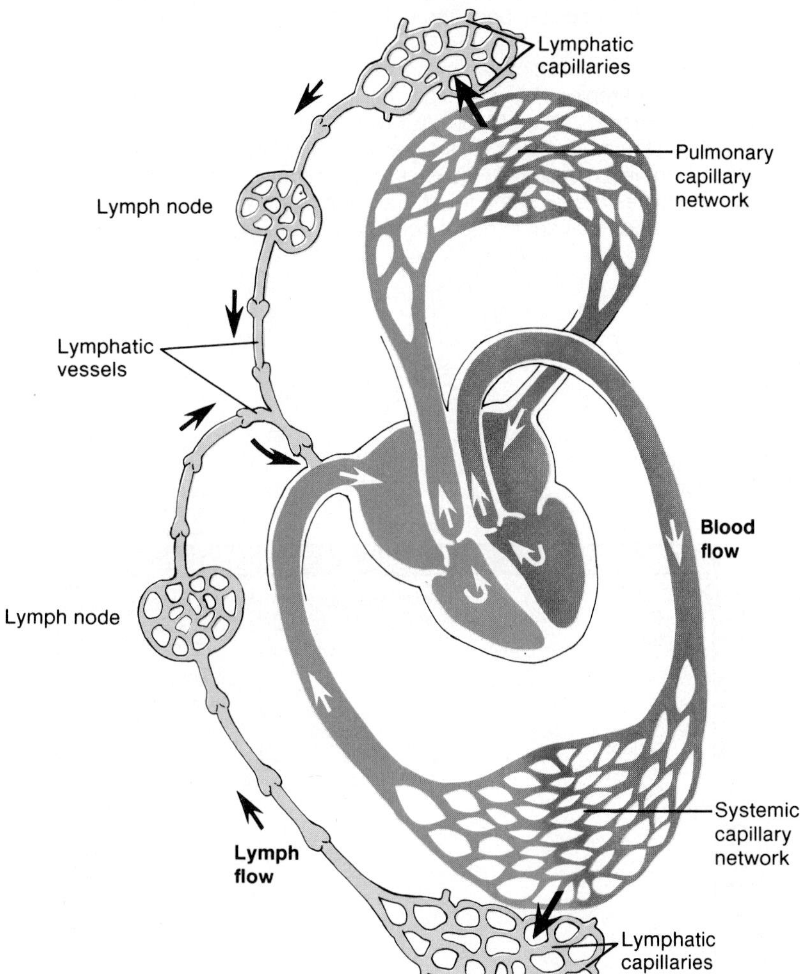

when you get right down to it, this is the reason that the blood exists. Let us view the overall pattern of body supply and demand and see where the blood fits in (figure 12.8).

The blood was not always viewed as it is now. Today, the idea that the blood flows in a never-ending stream through our bodies, ultimately winding up where it started, is accepted without question. But during most of the vast span of human history, this was neither common knowledge nor was it acceptable. In fact, until well into the last century, the medical attitude toward the blood was based more on superstition than on scientific knowledge. Until the seventeenth century, doctors thought that blood flowed from our hearts out to our muscles and was "used up" out there; nobody thought any of it came back to be used again. Until the middle of the last century, the most common means of treating illness was to bleed the patient painlessly in order to "balance his humors" (see the following box), and no one had any idea what it was the blood actually did. The discovery that the blood flowed in a circle only made things worse in the beginning, because it seemed to indicate that the blood did not do *anything*.

The "balanced humors" view of blood's function dates all the way back to the fifth century B.C. It was apparently adopted by (or originated with) Hippocrates (of the famous oath), following the philosophic view that everything material was composed of just four elements—earth, air, fire, and water (see figure 12.9). Hippocrates extended this philosophy to physiology, suggesting that all human life was dominated by four humors—blood, yellow bile, black bile, and phlegm. According to him, as long as all four humors were in proper balance in the body, the human was healthy.

Therefore all illness, whether disease or the result of an injury, was due to one of the humors being out of balance with the rest. The affliction would be characterized by whichever humor was present in excess. If phlegm was excessive, the patient would be *phlegmatic* (sluggish or unconscious); if black bile were the culprit, the patient

Figure 12.8 Overall schematic of body supply and disposal systems. (*1*) The cytosol maintains the intracellular organelles. (*2*) Interstitial fluids provide the never-ending supply of materials for the cytosol and carry away wastes promptly. A constant production of these fluids takes place in the capillary beds throughout the body, and they are constantly removed after they have made a circuit and completed their job. This keeps the fluids moving and insures that no "backwaters" develop that might result in stagnation. (*3*) The blood encounters this slowly moving interstitial fluid constantly throughout the body, and at each exchange area it removes any wastes and replenishes supplies. (*4*) Rapid movement of the blood permits it to flow quickly to replenishment areas and "sewage treatment" zones. The body's warehouses and dumping areas are strategically located, but they are stationary; hence the fluid must come to them. (*5*) Inside these warehouses, the blood is reprovisioned. In the "sewage treatment" zones, any materials present in excess are removed. Some of these materials will be recycled, but those that are truly wastes will be disposed of. (*6*) Wastes are excreted into the environment, and provisions are drawn from environmental sources. The warehouses and dumping grounds are in direct contact with the external environment.

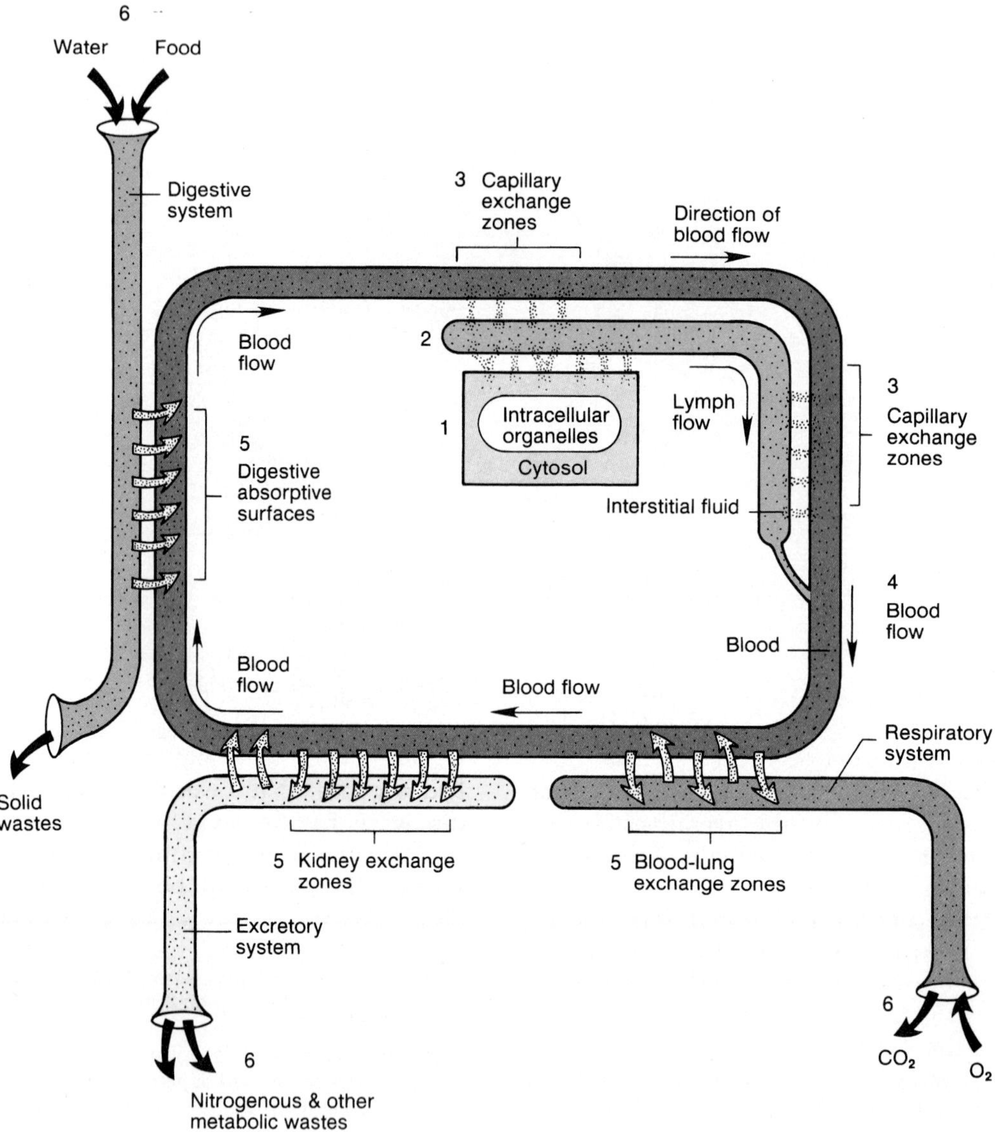

would be *melancholic;* if there was too much yellow bile, the patient would be *choleric* (ill-tempered or insane); and if blood was excessive, the patient would be *sanguine* (hopeful, confident, cheerful, etc.). The cure for any illness, then, was simple; drain off whichever of the humors was present in too great an abundance.

Unfortunately, it wasn't easy to drain off excess bile, and while a patient might be urged to cough up phlegm, the physician could not drain it. Actually, when they stopped to think about it, physicians discovered that they couldn't drain off black or yellow bile, nor could they change the volume of phlegm. But they *could* drain blood, and this became the doctor's art—the universal causative agent. The idea was that the sick person had too much blood, and by removing some, the physician would restore humoral balance.

The Roman physician Galen reinforced these principles during his lifetime (130–206 A.D.), and throughout the Middle Ages and well into the Renaissance, it was worth a person's life to challenge his writings. So, whenever a person became ill with something unfamiliar to physicians—which was almost everything—it was standard practice to open a vein and bleed the person for a while. It is hard for us, today, to imagine a situation where the removal of some blood would do anything but harm the patient, yet for 2,000 years it was more than just a routine procedure—it was the *universal specific.* The concept hung on with such tenacity that older surgeons working with both armies during the Civil War were still bleeding patients sick with "fevers" in the hope of curing them.

All kinds of theories were offered to explain what the blood was for, and a few of these ideas are reflected in some of today's common expressions. They include behavioral traits ("there is bad *blood* in him . . ."), character ("his *blood* is obviously noble"), and close relationships ("we are *blood* relatives"). But no one really knew, of course, what blood's function was.

The problem was that no one knew about the capillaries. They could see blood in arteries and they could see it in veins. Workers watched it and saw that arteries carried the blood *away* from the heart and got more numerous and much smaller; then they ended, and the blood inside them apparently just disappeared. Presently it showed up again, this time inside the veins and moving *toward* the heart. For a while, it was a colossal mystery, and some of the theories about what was going on were really wild. It was not until Italian microscopist Marcello Malpighi discovered capillaries that it became possible to ascertain just what blood *did* do.

The theory that was most generally accepted until the seventeenth or eighteenth century was Galen's. Galen was a dogmatic person, and he had few doubts about how a living body worked. He discussed the blood thoroughly in his writings, noting that it moved through vessels (any fool could see that it did), but he never detected a circular movement. It was his opinion that blood was made directly from food. This synthesis was accomplished in the gut, and the brand-new blood then went into the *veins.* The arteries, according to him, did not carry blood. While our veins were filling with blood, the arteries picked up air in the lungs (he called this air *pneuma*), and they carried just this pneuma. The destination of both veins and arteries was the muscles, where they dumped their loads. In the muscles, blood and pneuma were activated by mixing—this provided movement for the muscles—and the movement used up the mixture. There was no return to the gut or the lungs, and the heart was not involved in the movement of blood.

The ability of some of our ancestors to sideslip embarrassing questions was remarkable. Galen was once asked by a colleague why, if arteries carried only pneuma, they bled in spurts when they were cut. Galen replied that there were connections between the arteries and veins, and when an artery was cut, the pneuma—which was under considerable pressure—rushed out so fast that it sucked the blood from the veins. The pauses between spurts of blood represented bubbles of pneuma escaping.

Figure 12.9 The four elements and the four body humors. To the ancients who devised this scheme, all disease could be classified according to whichever humor was in excess.

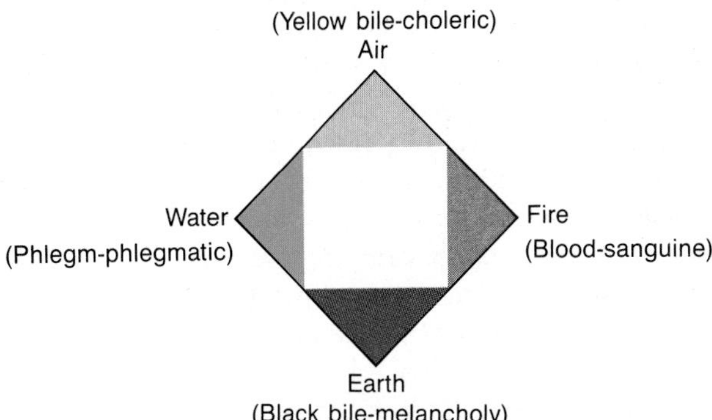

The capillaries were the key, of course, and in retrospect, it is not surprising that they were so hard to find. Generally speaking, they are so small that a half-dozen of them glued together would barely equal the thickness of a fine, blonde hair. Yet they are the business end of the circulatory system. All the other vessels—arteries, arterioles, venules, and veins—are merely pipes that carry their contents from capillary bed to capillary bed, over and over again. It is in these beds that researchers first saw the reason for blood's existence and discovered what was going on.

The Main Transportation Line

The blood, loaded down with cargoes of oxygen, fuel, and raw materials, makes trip after trip into these capillary beds, where it liberally dispenses its precious freight and picks up waste for the return trip.

Having handled the job of refurbishing the interstitial fluid, the blood is now loaded with debris and depleted of supplies. It must now restore its vitality. To accomplish this, it enters other capillary beds in supply areas or in "sewage treatment" areas.

The first stop-off for this venous blood is the lungs, where one waste product—carbon dioxide (CO_2)—is unloaded, and fresh stores of oxygen are picked up. The kidneys "scrub" the blood clean of metabolic wastes and carefully balance its chemical content so that it is not carrying too much or too little of anything. Fuel and raw building materials are collected in the capillary beds around the digestive tract after food has been broken down to chemicals that the blood can carry. Other organs like the liver, pancreas, and gallbladder are also involved in helping load up the blood with provisions. In fact, that is the reason they exist: to help refuel the blood after it has cleaned up and stocked the interstitial fluid. As you can see, it all comes down, ultimately, to homeostasis.

Blood as a Tissue

Originally, blood was viewed by both physiologists and anatomists as a connective tissue, and there are still many who think of it as such—it does, after all, have many of the general characteristics of connective tissues. Despite this, other workers consider it sufficiently distinctive to belong in a category by itself, and the two positions are not incompatible as long as the blood's uniqueness is recognized. Blood has characteristics possessed by no other tissue in the body. For one thing, it is the only tissue in the body that is basically a fluid. It has a large fluid matrix with a large number of cells swimming in that fluid; there are many types of cells, and they have a variety of functions. About 45 percent of the total blood volume is made up of cells or cellular material. The other 55 percent is a protein-rich, watery dispersion. This is the **plasma**, and it is *not* the same thing as **serum** (see figures 12.10 and 12.11). Serum is obtained by permitting the blood to clot and then lifting out the clot and all the elements that have adhered to it. The process of clotting removes a protein that is present in plasma.

Figure 12.10 Blood consists of an aqueous dispersion called plasma and a mass of formed (cellular) elements.

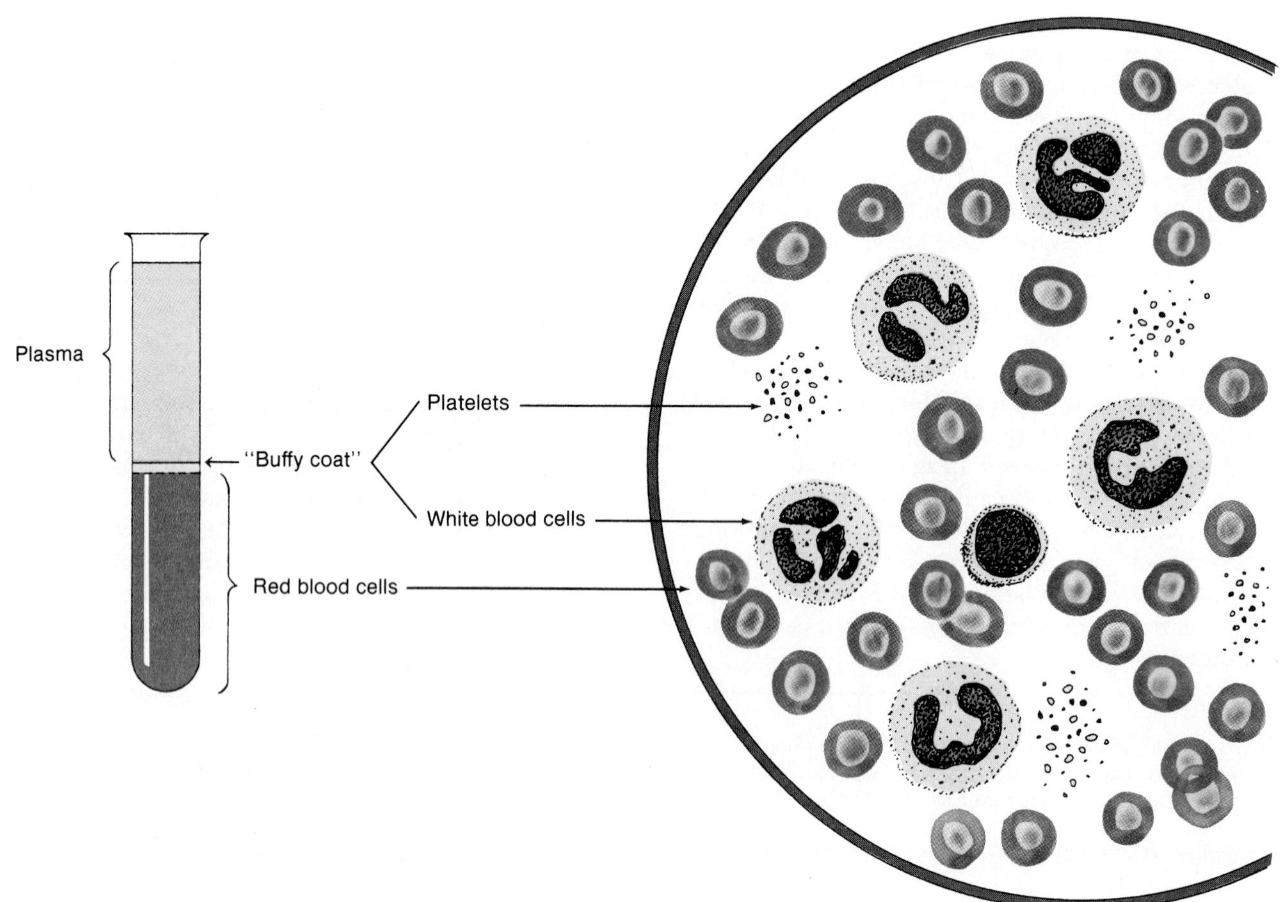

Figure 12.11 If a blood-filled capillary tube is centrifuged, the red cells become packed in the lower portion, and the percentage of red cells (hematocrit) can be determined.

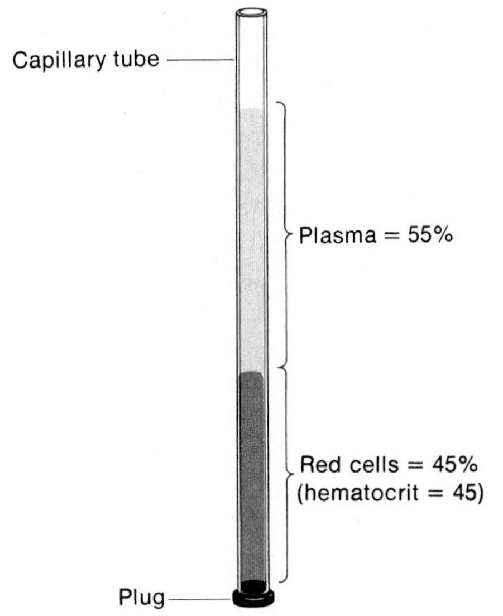

Plasma

Functions and Restrictions

Plasma has many functions. It operates as an intermediate, or a *buffer,* between the cellular elements of the blood and other body fluids—anything carried on or in any of the cells must first enter the plasma. It represents a storage reservoir for many hormones and other chemicals that can be selectively moved to their target tissues when they are needed. It is the major transportation system within the body, and in this regard it also functions as a communications network. There is very little that moves that the plasma is not involved with. It also represents the fulcrum of a series of equilibria between the blood cells, the interstitial fluids, and all the organ systems where there are capillary beds (figure 12.12).

Continuity between various compartments and organs must be maintained. That, after all, is what the blood is for, and it does its job meticulously. Wastes, hormones, and other chemicals pour into the plasma in a never-ending stream, while simultaneously, provisions and critical supplies are ceaselessly being

Figure 12.12 Plasma—the intermediate between red blood cells, lungs, and interstitial fluid.

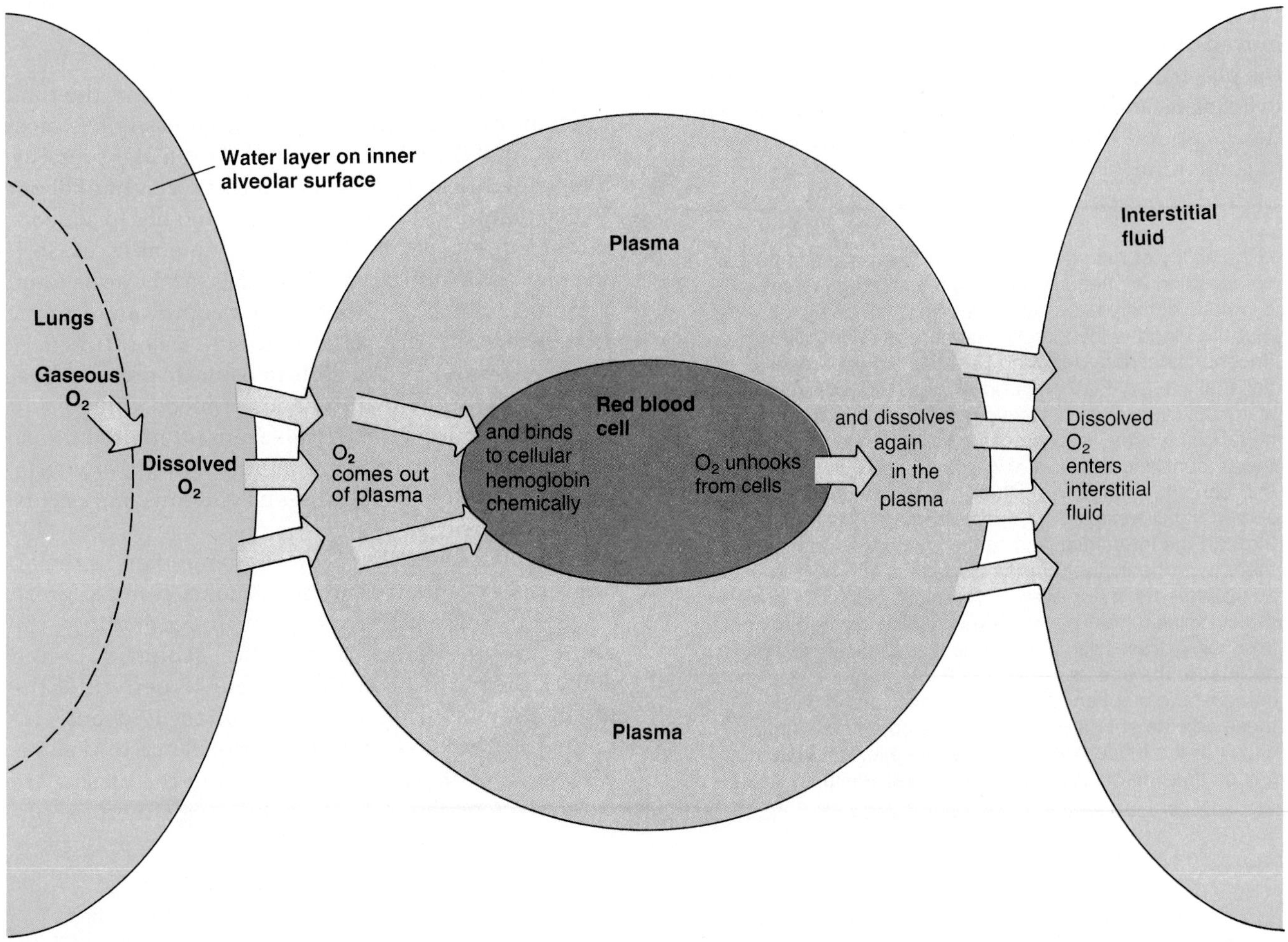

withdrawn. Along with the entering materials comes change of various kinds, including pollution. Supplies that are constantly off-loaded subject the blood to shortages. Yet like all body fluids, plasma has tolerance limits, and these limits must not be violated. This means that not only must the plasma drop off its freight and pick up the intercellular scourings, it must do so without altering its osmolarity, its pH, or the concentrations of hundreds of other substances. This is a prime directive, hence it must be obeyed. Therefore the plasma itself must accept perpetual inspection and incessant manipulation. Quality checks must never cease, and any qualitative or quantitative adjustments that are deemed necessary must be accomplished instantly and with precision.

It is a tremendous job. To begin with, plasma is a pretty complex dispersion, and it contains a large variety of substances. Mostly, of course, it is water—nearly 90 percent of it—with various solids, liquids, and gases broadcast all through it. About 70 percent of those solids is protein, while 10 percent consists of inorganic salts. The remainder is lipid micelles, hormones, carbohydrates, amino acids, waste products—anything that can use the blood as a vehicle and needs to relocate will be there. Many of these materials will vary in amount, depending on where the blood has just been and what the body cells have removed, but it is important to realize that nothing is added or removed casually. Every time something enters or leaves the plasma, some sort of compensatory adjustment has to be made, and everything carried in the plasma, with the exception of the waste materials, has a function of some kind.

The ability of the plasma to adjust to changes in its own composition is phenomenal. One moment an increase in synthetic activity in some tissue might suddenly require that the blood unload large quantities of amino acids. Seconds later, blood flowing past the gut may receive an unusually heavy load of carbohydrates or lipids, and inches away the liver might be pumping out acids and other metabolic wastes. In each case, there will be a variation in the amount and the kind of solutes present in the plasma that can alter things like diffusion potential or osmolarity. If something is removed from the plasma and is transferred through the interstitial fluid to the interior of some cells, there must be instant compensation in all three compartments. If, for example, a solute particle is given to the cytoplasm, that particle's osmotic influence disappears from the extracellular compartment. If some correction is not made, the effects will be felt throughout the body. Our homeostatic mechanisms are so sensitive and efficient that these adjustments are often achieved during a single circuit of the blood without noticeable effort and without any compartments slipping outside their tolerance limits.

Plasma Chemistry

The only significant difference between the plasma and the interstitial fluid (lymph) is the protein content. Lymph, you will remember, is filtered from the blood in the capillary beds. The small molecules—amino acids, sugars, minerals, hormones—tend to be equally distributed in both compartments, while the large molecules, mostly proteins, stay in the plasma because they are too big to get through the capillary filter. Collectively, plasma protein has several functions. It can serve as a buffer, it can help maintain optimal blood and interstitial fluid volume through its osmotic influence, and it can even function as substrate material if the body should run disastrously short of amino acids. Individually, the plasma proteins have a broad and interesting variety of functions, including such things as forming blood clots and resisting bacterial attack.

The Plasma Proteins

Since it is the function of the blood to transport materials throughout the body, there are bound to be many, many chemicals dispersed in the plasma—far too many for us to cover. Even the proteins are present in such profusion that we cannot begin to consider them all. However there are three *groups* of proteins that completely overwhelm all the others in terms of abundance, and these we must investigate. They are **albumin,** the **globulins,** and **fibrinogen.**

Albumin represents about 45 percent of the total solids in the plasma, which makes it easily the most abundant of the proteins. Of the three major proteins, it is the smallest, having a molecular weight of about 70,000 daltons. Still, that is a little too big to squeeze through the pores in the capillary membranes, so it stays locked inside the blood vessels. At the same time, there is so much of it that it has a significant osmotic influence, and this relates to its major function. Mainly, it provides the **colloid osmotic pressure** that aids greatly in the maintenance of blood volume and in the absorption of materials from interstitial fluids. Albumin also functions frequently as a *carrier protein,* attaching itself to such things as vitamins, fatty acids, and hormones.

The blood *globulins* are not as abundant as the albumins; hence their osmotic influence is not as great. There are three different groups of globulins—the **alpha** (α), the **beta** (β), and the **gamma** (γ)—and among them, they constitute about 18 percent of the blood proteins. At least one of them is deeply involved in the development of resistance to disease. Almost all of the antibodies found in the plasma are derivatives of the γ fraction, although there is evidence that the β globulins occasionally play a role in antibody production. Both the α and the β globulins function also as carrier proteins, often linking up with and transporting small ions that are unable to dissolve in the near-neutral body fluids. All three types of globulin serve as substrate sources when the body needs raw materials. Like the albumins, the α and β fractions are synthesized in the liver. The γ globulin, however, is synthesized by special cells in the body's lymphatic tissue.

Fibrinogen makes up about 3 percent of the plasma proteins, and fibrinogen is the difference between plasma and serum—it is present in plasma, absent in serum. Fibrinogen is the soluble protein that changes into an insoluble gel called **fibrin** when the blood coagulates. The formation of fibrin is the final reaction in a whole series of carefully orchestrated biochemical events that ultimately lead to clot formation, and of them all, it is the only one that gives any *visible* indication that something has occurred.

There are other plasma proteins, of course. They are present in much smaller amounts and do not have much of an effect on the way the blood, as a tissue, behaves during its travels through the body, but some of them are quite important for other functions. *Complement,* for example, is intimately involved with the body's immune capabilities, particularly the repelling of bacterial invasions; *prothrombin* is one of the chemicals involved in clot formation, but it is well up the line from the fibrinogen/fibrin conversion; *angiotensinogen* is a plasma protein that we should remember from chapter 10; and there are various carrier proteins designed to transport all sorts of materials, including hormones. The blood transports literally thousands of materials.

Nutrients

The plasma is filled with nutrients intended for immediate use by body cells or for storage in some organ or specific body zone. Amino acids are abundant. So are glucose, phospholipids, vitamins, fats, minerals—almost everything that moves in the body is carried where it is going by the blood.

Cholesterol and Triglycerides

Fats are transported in the plasma attached to protein carriers—a necessary precaution because of the tendency of fat-soluble molecules to pass through membranes without resistance. Immediately digested fats are present as tiny fat droplets surrounded by a protein coat. These droplets—called **chylomicra**—are the form in which fats are absorbed from the gut, a process that is aided by two other plasma phospholipids, **lecithin** and **cephalin.** Generally, chylomicra are present only after a meal, and they rapidly disappear.

Other fats are more permanent occupants of the bloodstream. These are attached to various blood proteins and have been categorized according to the amount of protein in each transported molecule. **High-density lipoproteins (HDL),** which carry cholesterol, have a lot of protein and relatively little fat. **Low-density lipoproteins (LDL)** have more fat and less protein and, like the HDL, they are designed to transport only cholesterol. A third type of carrier, the **very low-density lipoprotein (VLDL),** is reserved for the transport of neutral fats and glycerides.

Minerals

The plasma always has a fairly high concentration of mineral electrolytes that are being moved around. Calcium, sodium, potassium, and chloride are always present, as are magnesium, zinc, iodine, and other trace elements. In addition to whatever specific functions they possess in their target cells, minerals have a profound influence on pH, and they can exert extremely high osmotic pressures under the right conditions; a change of only a few molecules per 100 ml of blood can significantly alter the osmotic characteristics of the plasma. For these reasons, the electrolytes are stabilized throughout the body fluids and maintained with a precision that is mind-boggling.

Nitrogen and Other Gases

Several gases are carried in solution in the plasma. The most abundant is nitrogen, because most of the gas that enter the lungs is nitrogen. Oxygen is, of course, present, as is carbon dioxide, although most of the latter is carried in the form of bicarbonate.

The Formed (Cellular) Elements

There are three types of formed elements in blood; two are cells, and the third is a cellular fragment. With only one exception, all of them are synthesized in the marrow of the long bones, mainly those of the chest. The whole cells are separated into two broad categories on the basis of their color. (See table 12.1.)

The Red Blood Cells

The red cells or **erythrocytes** (erythro, "red") are easily the most numerous, outnumbering the white cells by at least six hundred to one; within the confines of the circulatory system, the number is closer

Table 12.1 Formed Elements of the Blood

Component	Description	Number Present	Function
Erythrocyte (red blood cell)	Biconcave disc without nucleus; contains hemoglobin; survives 100–120 days	4,000,000 to 6,000,000/mm^3	Transports oxygen and carbon dioxide
Leukocytes (white blood cells)		5,000 to 10,000/mm^3	Aid in defense against infections by microorganisms
Granulocytes	About twice the size of red blood cells; cytoplasmic granules present; survive 12 hours to 3 days		
1. Neutrophil	Nucleus with 2–5 lobes; cytoplasmic granules stain slightly pink	54%–62% of white cells present	Phagocytic
2. Eosinophil	Nucleus bilobed; cytoplasmic granules stain red in eosin stain	1%–3% of white cells present	Helps to detoxify foreign substances; secretes enzymes that break down clots
3. Basophil	Nucleus lobed; cytoplasmic granules stain blue in hematoxylin stain	Less than 1% of white cells present	Releases anticoagulant heparin
Agranulocytes	Cytoplasmic granules absent; survive 100–300 days		
1. Monocyte	2–3 times larger than red blood cell; nuclear shape varies from round to lobed	3%–9% of white cells present	Phagocytic
2. Lymphocyte	Only slightly larger than red blood cell; nucleus nearly fills cell	25%–33% of white cells present	Provides specific immune response (including antibodies)
Thrombocyte (platelet)	Cytoplasmic fragment; survives 5–9 days	130,000 to 360,000/mm^3	Clotting

to one thousand to one. They constitute about 97 percent of the blood's formed elements, and they exist almost exclusively to perform the all-important job of transporting oxygen (figure 12.13).

It would be reasonable to assume that the life span of these cells would be short, partly due to feverish overactivity and partly because they have no nuclei when they are released into the circulation. Remember, it is the DNA that handles the day-to-day decisions in every living cell, including the blood cells, and it is the DNA that tells the cellular machinery what to do when an emergency of any kind arises. Should damage occur anywhere in the cell, it is the DNA that tells the cell what it must do to repair the damage; if anything unusual is needed, it is the DNA that metes out the instructions for synthesizing or capturing it. Without its DNA, the healthiest cell is a dying entity, and without its nucleus, it has no cellular DNA. Yet surprisingly, erythrocytes manage to stay alive and functional within the circulatory system for an average of about 120 days. This may not seem like a very long time, but compared to the life spans of the other cellular elements in the blood, it is a very long time indeed. Most white blood cells, for instance, manage to remain viable for only about two weeks, despite the fact that they possess fully functional nuclei.

Just why the nucleus is removed from the erythrocytes has never been satisfactorily explained. Many hypotheses have been advanced, including some very learned ones. Some workers have suggested that removal of the nucleus permits greater miniaturization of the cell, rendering it capable of squeezing through narrowed vessels. A smaller size would also make it possible to concentrate larger numbers of cells in a given volume of blood, thus increasing its maximum oxygen-carrying capacity. It is further suggested that the surface-area-to-volume ratio is greater because of the biconcave shape that results when the nucleus is withdrawn. This would make penetration of oxygen into the depths of the cell more uniform and rapid.

Certainly these hypotheses may be true, yet they still leave room for wondering. As far as is known, mammals are the only vertebrates that possess anucleate red blood cells. Fishes, amphibians, reptiles, birds—all of them—have red cells with nuclei. These animals are present in enormous numbers on the earth, so the lack of anucleated RBCs does not appear to have affected their ability to survive. It cannot be an adaptation for endothermy (warm-bloodedness), because bird erythrocytes have nuclei, and endothermy in birds is just as highly developed as it is in humans. So perhaps the most honest way to explain it is to simply say that while everyone agrees there is

Figure 12.13 (*a*) The morphology of a human red blood cell. (*b*) Scanning electron micrograph of human red blood cells.

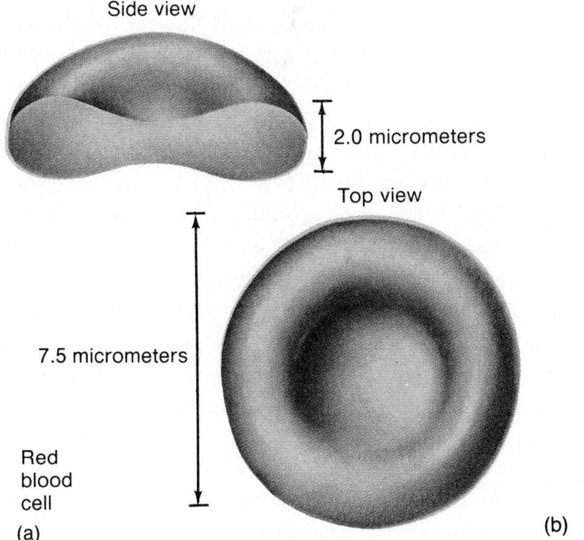

probably some sort of advantage to having red blood cells without nuclei, we don't know precisely what that advantage may be.

One thing is certain. Lacking nuclei, our erythrocytes are short-lived. The average life span is said to range from 100 to 130 days, but that number was established some thirty years ago, and it may be a bit optimistic. Current evidence suggests that most red cells do not last quite that long. Every time a blood cell slips into the capillaries of active muscle tissue, it runs the risk of having a muscle contract and squeeze it. When that happens, the membranes are often torn or stretched beyond repair, and that necessitates their removal from the circulation.

Respiratory Pigments

The function of the red blood cells is to transport oxygen from the lungs to the interstitial fluid, and in this, they require the assistance of an unusual chemical known as a **respiratory pigment.** All of the more highly organized animals have a respiratory pigment in their blood. Some organisms—like people, for instance—keep their pigment locked up in cells, while others let it run freely in their blood. Some organisms—like people, once again—have a respiratory pigment with an *iron* base for carrying their oxygen, but not all organisms use iron for this purpose. The arthropods, for instance, have a blood pigment with a *copper* base, and others, while they use iron, lock it up in a different organic superstructure. Respiratory pigments vary broadly from group to group.

Figure 12.14 The meandering hemoglobin molecule.

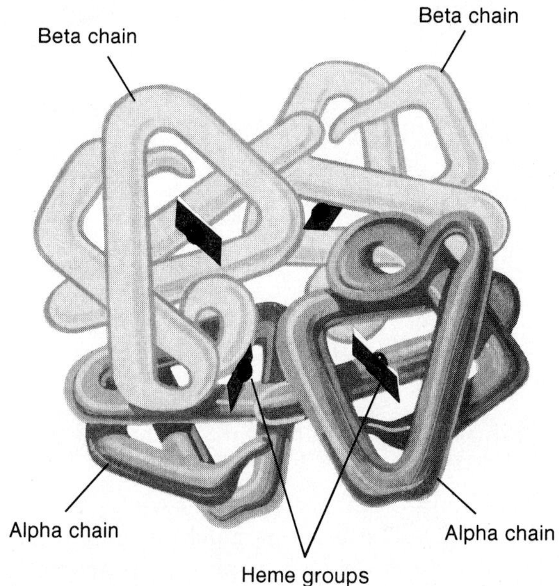

Hemoglobin

Our iron-based respiratory pigment is **hemoglobin** (Hb), and it is a combination of two separate chemical modules. The largest fraction is a protein known as **globin.** Globin is a large serpentine tangle of amino acids and is the part of the molecule that is crimped and pleated. It has been thoroughly analyzed, and its meandering, irregular shape is familiar to biological scientists everywhere today (figure 12.14).

Figure 12.15 Heme, the non-globin portion of hemoglobin. Heme contains the iron to which oxygen is bound. When hemoglobin is broken up, the iron is removed, and the rest of the heme molecule is converted to biliverdin, then bilirubin, and is disposed of in the GI tract.

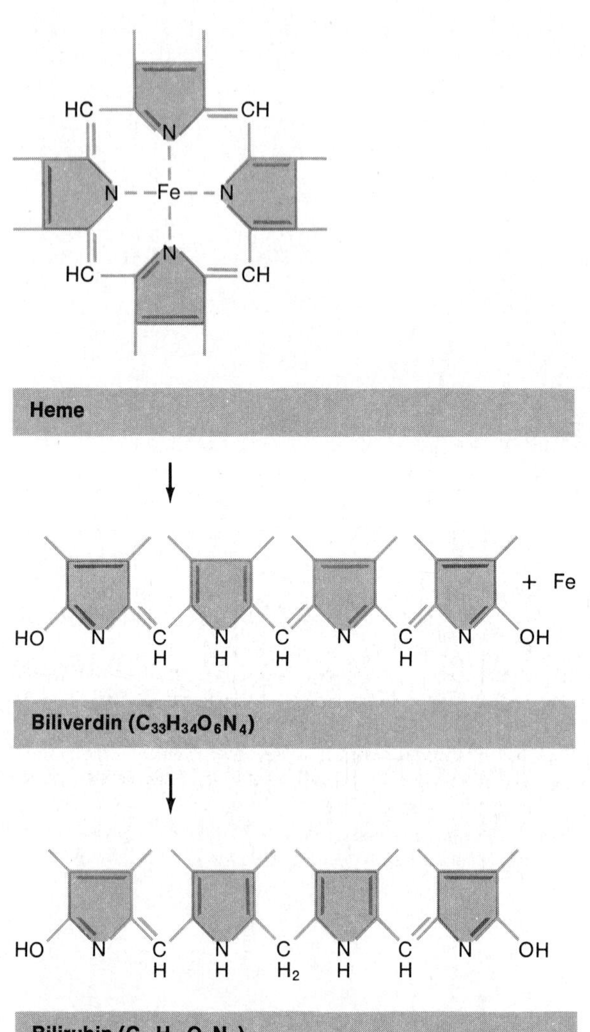

The nonprotein parts are known as the **heme** (figure 12.15). The heme is much smaller than the globin and not nearly as complex in its geometry. It is the heme molecule—or more specifically, the iron part of it—that is responsible for the red color of the blood, and it is the iron that plays the central role in hemoglobin's relationship with oxygen.

Iron is able to get a covalent grip on *molecular* oxygen (O_2, not O)—a grip strong enough to hang onto it through the curves and rapids of the arteries and arterioles, yet docile enough to release it at the proper time, deep in the tissues of the body. There are four of these nonprotein groups in every hemoglobin molecule; hence each Hb molecule can carry four molecules of oxygen. (Because the bonds holding the oxygen are covalent, there is neither loss nor gain of electrons. As a result, the iron molecule does not undergo *oxidation,* but rather is *oxygenated.*)

We have an idea of how long the average body cell can live without energy, and by extension how long it will last without oxygen. It's not very long. Obviously, gathering and providing oxygen is crucial to the continued survival of the body. The tremendous importance of this element is underscored again and again by the provisions made by physiological mechanisms for obtaining and transporting it. The red blood cells are by far the most abundant cells in the blood, and their interior is jam-packed with hemoglobin. The reason for the existence of all this pigment is singular—it was designed to transport oxygen. Without it, high levels of activity in large animals, maybe even homeothermy and high levels of nervous activity, would not be possible.

As molecules go, hemoglobin is fairly large. Yet molecules in general are so tiny that there are more than 300 million hemoglobin molecules packed into every little erythrocyte. Such figures have little meaning, as we all know, but sometimes they can help put things into proper perspective. In this instance, they can give some idea of the unbelievable efficiency and industrial power of the biological engine.

Responsible researchers calculate that about three million erythrocytes are broken up by the body every second, so just to keep up with attrition, three million new ones must be released each second into the blood. Therefore, the body's synthetic mechanisms have to produce hemoglobin at the rate of 900 trillion molecules every *second* just to maintain a normal blood level of this important pigment. Yet despite this enormous capacity, our biosynthetic machinery always runs just quickly enough. If it were to run too slowly, it would not be able to match the rate of erythrocyte fragmentation; if it ran too fast, it would pump so many red cells into the circulation that the blood could become syrupy.

Yet one could quite reasonably ask why the body bothers to synthesize the globin . . . why it wastes energy on such an enormous molecule when the relatively tiny heme carries all the oxygen. This is a legitimate question and deserves an answer, because the energy cost of constructing such a huge molecule is indeed high, and as we have seen, the body's requirements are staggering. Why, indeed, construct such a big molecule?

The answer seems to lie in the fact that the iron molecules within the hemoglobin mass must remain in the *iron two* (Fe^{2+}—*ferrous*) state. Should the iron molecules become oxidized to the *iron three* (Fe^{3+}—*ferric*) state, they would be unable to hold oxygen and would be physiologically useless. Any contact with free water oxidizes (rusts) ferrous ions, so water must not be allowed to touch them. That's a prospect that is extremely hard to avoid in view of the fact that the cytosol of the red blood cell is mostly water and must remain so. Under the circumstances, it would seem unlikely if not impossible to prevent contact between the two.

It is the big globin molecule that handles that job! Its tertiary arrangement tucks the iron-containing heme molecules deep inside a densely packed mass of tightly twisted amino acid strands, and there they remain, effectively isolated from their aqueous surroundings (see figure 12.14). They can shift up near the surface of the hemoglobin molecule for split seconds only when oxygen enters and when it is discharged.

Red Cell Count

According to medical convention, blood cell counts are expressed in terms of their number per **cubic millimeter** (mm^3). There are about five million erythrocytes in every mm^3. Now, that is an enormous number of cells to be packed into any volume, but this volume is *small.* To give you some idea of just how small, a mm^3 of water is just about enough to sit on the head of a straight pin without overflowing and running off. Five million is a tremendous number of such cells to be in such a small volume of blood. Obviously, the importance our bodies attach to the transport of oxygen and the facilities that support such transport is enormous.

Don't rush past the blood-count figures without being sure you are absolutely clear about the volumes involved! It is awfully easy to confuse the term milli-*liter* with cubic milli-*meter,* and the two are not even close to the same thing. A milliliter is very nearly identical to a cubic *centimeter,* and there are 1,000 cubic millimeters in one cubic centimeter. That means quite naturally that there are 1,000 cubic millimeters in a milliliter. In volumetric terms, the mm^3 could be correctly called a *microliter,* but not a ml.

Also, it should be realized that the figure of five million red blood cells/mm^3 isn't exactly right; it's merely a rough average. The actual count depends on sex and age, and even then the range is rather broad. Children have counts that range from 4,500,000 to 5,200,000, adult males from 4,600,000 to 6,200,000, and adult females from 4,200,000 to 5,400,000.

Erythrocyte Synthesis

Erythrocytes are assembled in the marrow or spongy portions of certain bones in our bodies. Early in life, the marrow of almost all our long bones (any bone that is longer than it is wide is a "long bone") is able to produce the necessary cells, but as we mature, the marrow in those bones gets increasingly fatty and gradually loses its synthetic ability. In mature adults, about the only places where erythrocyte synthesis occurs is in the marrow of bones like the sternum, the ribs, certain vertebral elements, and parts of the skull.

Our red cells begin life as fully nucleated cells called **erythroblasts,** which bud off undifferentiated **stem cells** (or **hemocytoblasts**) in the bone marrow. These erythroblasts undertake a frenzied program of protein synthesis, furiously producing hemoglobin and structural proteins. All this frantic synthetic activity culminates in a burst of spirited mitotic divisions, during which the importance of the nucleus steadily diminishes. The final mitotic division strips out the nucleus completely, and the finished red cell is thrust into the circulation as the familiar, biconcave disc loaded with the material necessary to perform its job (figure 12.16).

Control of Erythrocyte Production

The production of erythrocytes is obviously a monumental task requiring perpetual efforts by the synthetic tissues and huge stores of energy, but despite its tremendous production records, the synthetic machinery normally doesn't run at full throttle. We know from certain disease states that it can go faster, so it must be governed—it cannot be permitted to run out of control any more than it can be allowed to slow down.

It seems that it seldom does, either. The number of erythrocytes in the circulation of a normal person remains remarkably constant day after day, month after month. The most profound and direct control over erythrocyte production is exerted by a chemical—the hormone **erythropoietin** (or *erythrocyte-stimulating factor*—**ESF**). This is a glycoprotein hormone that is apparently secreted by the kidney in response to either a dearth of red blood cells, tissue anoxia, or both. (There are a lot of things that could produce anoxia in kidney tissues, some of which will be discussed in the clinical applications section of this chapter.) The target of the hormone is the erythrocyte-producing zone of active bone marrow, specifically, the hemocytoblasts. In the presence of ESF, the hemocytoblasts increase their production of erythroblasts, which in turn release larger numbers of erythrocytes into the circulation. Increased production continues until oxygen delivery to the kidneys is back to where it should be, at which point the negative feedback mechanisms swing into action, and the secretion of ESF stops.

Androgenic hormones also have a stimulatory effect on ESF production, and it has been suggested that this is the reason why men have a higher average RBC count than women. (You will recall from chapter

Figure 12.16 The stages of development from hemocytoblast to erythrocyte.

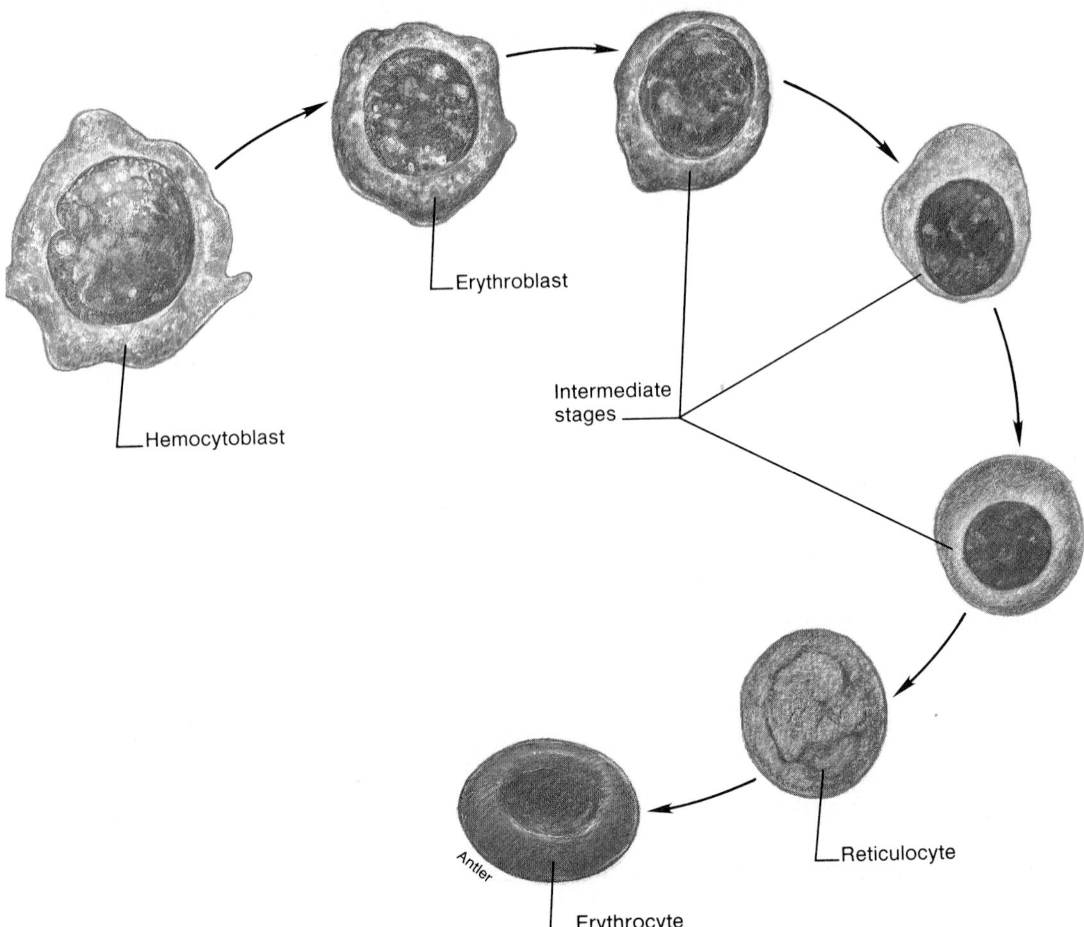

10 that androgenic hormones are the steroids responsible for, among other things, increasing muscle mass.)

The Breakdown of Erythrocytes

They do not live long, but while they do, erythrocytes must perform a prodigious amount of work. Therefore, as they develop, the DNA assembles the necessary materials that may be needed in the future. When they are finally released into the circulation, each erythrocyte contains a supply of already-synthesized enzymes for energy production and minor cell repair, and these enzymes last a surprisingly long time. Nevertheless, time ultimately has its effects. The enzymes must either wear out or get damaged, because by the end of their third month, most circulating erythrocytes look the worse for wear. Ultimately their vigor declines, membranes get more and more fragile, and finally they break up.

Most damage occurs while the cells are squeezing through some tight spot like a contracting muscle or the filtering system of the kidney or spleen. Sooner or later, the unusual pressure in such areas is too much for worn-out cells, and they simply burst. The contents fan out in the plasma and could be lost except for the activities of phagocytic white blood cells collectively called **reticuloendothelial cells.**

These cells ingest the free hemoglobin molecules by the thousands and promptly begin salvage operations. Very little is wasted. The molecule first is separated into the heme and globin fractions. Then the globin is thoroughly digested, and its amino acids are added to the body's free amino acid pool. The iron is also retained. It is carefully freed from its heme and immediately linked onto a β globulin derivative, a protein called **transferrin.** It is carried in this form to iron storage areas, mainly in the liver, where it is released from its transferrin carrier.

Figure 12.17 A simplified schematic of erythrocyte breakup and the fate of hemoglobin.

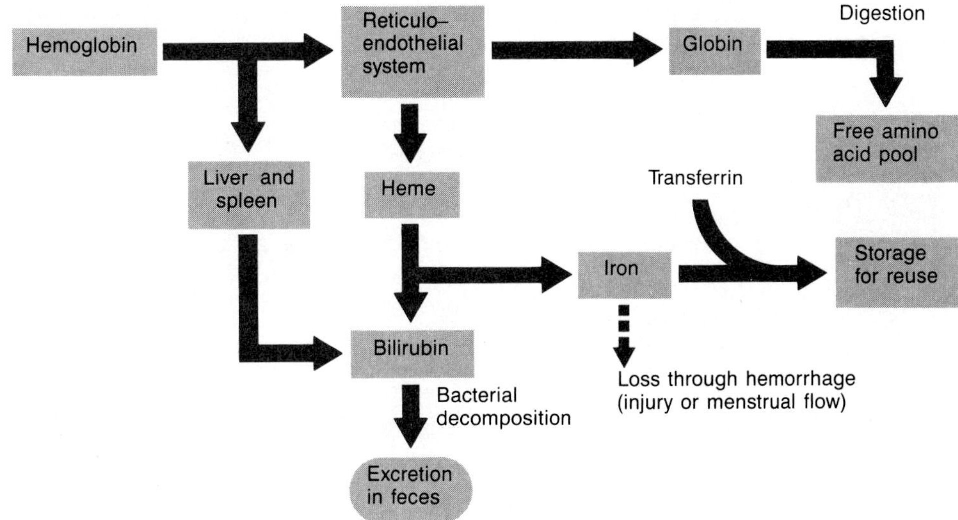

All that remains is the iron-free heme, and it is the only part of the entire hemoglobin molecule that the body makes no effort to salvage. It is decomposed to **biliverdin** and **bilirubin** and is discarded as waste through the bile ducts (figure 12.17). Within the intestinal tract, some of the bilirubin is reabsorbed and is responsible for the characteristic yellow color of urine.

The heme molecules are decomposed to bilirubin and biliverdin by reticuloendothelial cells, which ultimately ship it to the liver (see figure 12.15). The liver empties them as waste products into the small intestine, and most are eliminated in the feces. Since they are passed down the bile duct, they are considered the liver's **bile pigments,** and they have considerable value as medical diagnostic tools. The action of bacteria in the gut produces breakdown products, at least one of which is a very dark brown. This is the main pigment in the stools and is what gives them their characteristic brown color. Should disease or malfunction render the liver incapable of excreting these pigments, they back up into the liver and work their way once again into the blood, imparting a yellowish tint to the whites of the eyes and the skin, a characteristic of the condition known as **jaundice.** With the bilirubin absent, the stools, instead of being their usual brown, turn the color of a clay flower pot. This will be discussed in more detail in the clinical considerations portion of the chapter.

Raw Materials and Nutrients

The volume of substrate required for hemoglobin synthesis is, as you can imagine, enormous. It is so enormous, in fact, that it is not likely that our bodies would be able to consistently obtain the necessary raw materials, especially the iron, from outside sources. It seems fairly clear that the body's perseverance in capturing and recycling worn-out erythrocytes is the only thing that makes it possible for the synthetic machinery to keep up with erythrocyte destruction. Very little substrate material is wasted. Nevertheless, no machinery is 100 percent efficient, and the human body is no exception. Losses cannot be avoided; hence fresh ingredients must be regularly ingested to replace material that is discarded or lost.

Iron is a prime ingredient in hemoglobin, and as we all know it is considered an essential mineral in the human diet. It is retained so intensely that we really do not need very much—in fact, about the only way it gets lost is through hemorrhage, which is why women need more iron than men. Due to the menstrual cycle, women hemorrhage regularly. Men hemorrhage only due to injury, and that is not, hopefully, every thirty days.

A careful analysis of body contents shows that, in terms of total metal content, there is very little iron in the healthiest of people, male or female. If it were possible to melt down a human being and extract the iron, we could get about four grams of pure metal—less than one-seventh of an ounce—less than the weight of a nickel coin. Of that skimpy four grams, more than two is locked up in hemoglobin. There is a little in the cytochromes, and there is some in the muscle pigment myoglobin. Most of the remainder (about 30 percent of the total) is stored in the liver. The liver incorporates iron into a compound called **ferritin,** and in this form it serves as a storage depot. When needed, it is easily and quickly mobilized (see figure 12.18).

Figure 12.18 Life cycle of a red blood cell. (1) Essential nutrients are absorbed from the intestine; (2) nutrients are transported by blood to red bone marrow; (3) red blood cells are produced in red bone marrow by mitosis; (4) mature red blood cells are released into blood and circulate for about 120 days; (5) damaged red blood cells are destroyed in liver by macrophages; (6) hemoglobin from red blood cells is decomposed into heme and globin; (7) iron from heme is returned to red bone marrow to be reused, and biliverdin is excreted in the bile.

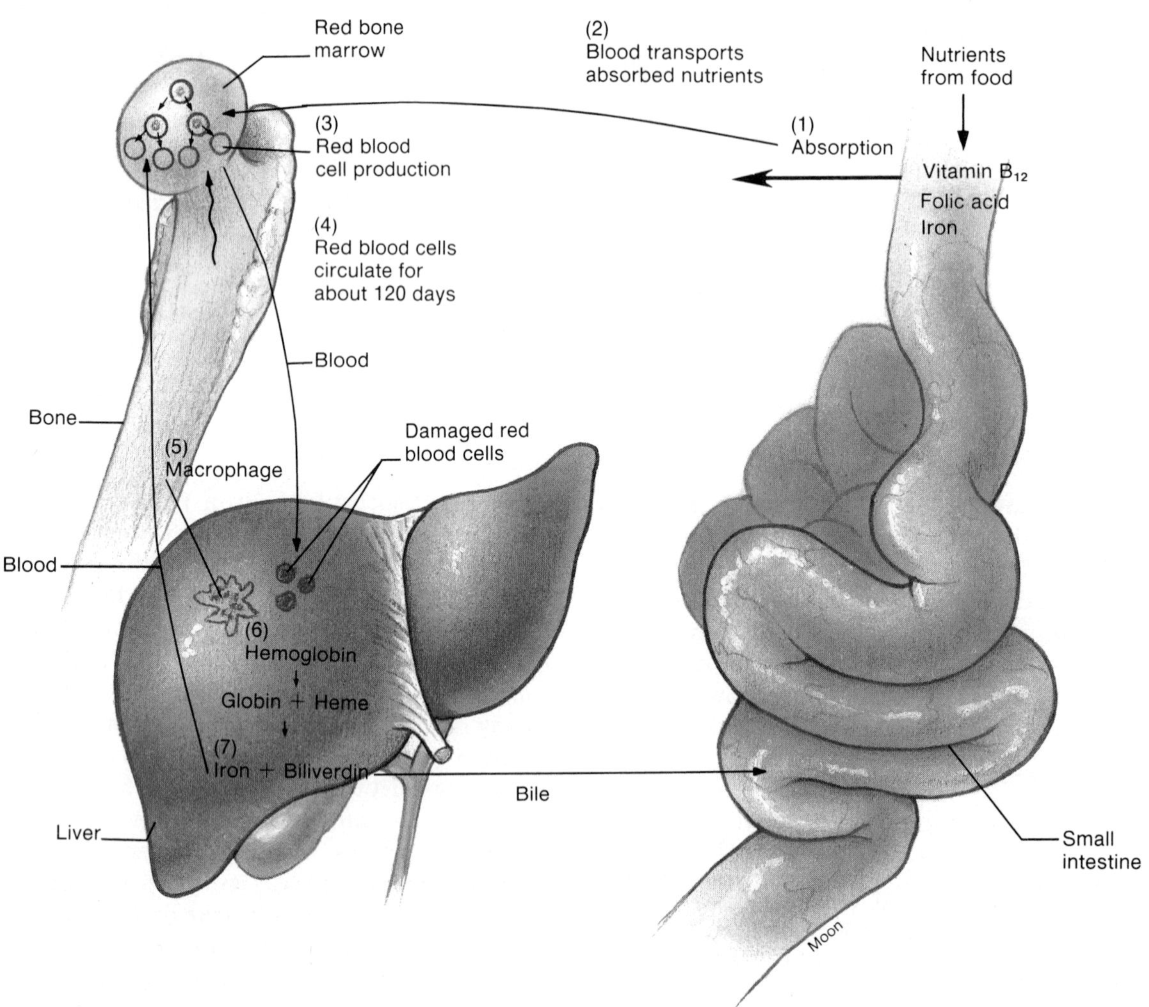

The Role of Vitamins

Some vitamins are intimately involved in hemoglobin synthesis and hence are considered essential in our diets.

Vitamin B_{12} (cyanacobalamin) is one such. This particular vitamin—often called the *anti-pernicious anemia vitamin*—is essential for DNA synthesis, so in fact it is involved in the growth of every tissue in the body, not just erythrocytes. Erythrocytes themselves do not have any nuclei, but their precursors all do, so production is not possible without the nuclear DNA. When there is a shortage of any critical material, its lack is most keenly felt where the greatest manufacturing activity is going on. When we recall how much hemoglobin is needed every second and how many erythrocytes must be released into the blood in that same period of time, it is obvious that if B_{12} is not present, its absence will be noticed more quickly in areas of erythrocyte production than anywhere else.

Folic acid, another of the B-complex vitamins, is also involved in the maturation of nuclear DNA, and its involvement may be a cooperative one with B_{12}. Like B_{12}, its absence has a profound effect on the body's ability to produce any additional cells, and its absence is noticed first in blood-synthesizing areas. (See table 12.2.)

The White Blood Cells (Leucocytes)

The other formed elements of the blood are the white blood cells (**leucocytes**—also spelled *leukocytes*) and **platelets.** Since the latter are not really cells but are rather cellular fragments, we will deal first of all with the leucocytes.

Table 12.2 Dietary Factors Affecting Red Blood Cell Production

Substance	Source	Function
Vitamin B_{12}	Absorbed from small intestine in the presence of intrinsic factor	Necessary for the synthesis of DNA
Iron	Absorbed from small intestine; conserved during red cell destruction and made available for reuse	Necessary for the synthesis of hemoglobin
Folic acid	Absorbed from small intestine	Necessary for the synthesis of DNA

From John W. Hole, Jr., *Human Anatomy and Physiology,* 4th ed.

In the blood of an average healthy male we expect to find about five million red cells per cubic millimeter; in a female, maybe a half-million fewer. In the same cubic millimeter we would find only four to six *thousand* leucocytes. Based on numbers alone, it would certainly seem that the primary function of the blood revolves around the function of our erythrocytes.

But in biological systems, success is not always determined by numbers alone, and this is a definite case in point. It would be a mistake to consider the leucocytes unimportant. It is true that a lack of leucocytes would not result in an individual's death quite as quickly as a dearth of erythrocytes would, but it would be just as certain. Our white cells represent our only protection against parasitic invaders—both large and small—that every minute of every day threaten our existence.

Morphology

Leucocytes are quite a bit larger than erythrocytes, and unlike their red colleagues, they possess a nucleus. White cells have been separated into two categories on the basis of morphological differences. This may not be particularly appropriate, but it is at least convenient.

One of the groups is noted for a comparatively clear cytoplasm and so has become known as the **agranular** group. Along with this agranular cytoplasm, these cells usually feature a single nuclear mass. The second group of white cells are the **granular leucocytes,** and as the name implies, their cytoplasm contains an abundance of darkly staining granules. (See figure 12.19.) They show a definite nuclear bifurcation, which produces two-lobed (sometimes three-lobed) nuclei, a phenomenon that accounts for their alternate name—**polymorphonuclear leucocytes.** Often, the nucleus of these leucocytes is indicative of the age of the cell, the older ones usually featuring more lobes.

As we have already mentioned, the separation into these two groups is based entirely on the morphology of these cells and was made years ago when leucocyte function was pretty much a mystery. From a functional point of view, therefore, it is not surprising that this separation is rather worthless. The primary mission of all our blood's white cells is to provide us with protection against foreign invaders and to clean up debris in the form of dead or useless cellular material.

Agranular Leucocytes

Agranular leucocytes are subdivided into two smaller groups, the **monocytes** and the **lymphocytes.** The lymphocytes are functionally quite unique. Their operations are complex and so important that they deserve to be treated separately. We mention them here for the sake of thoroughness. They will be dealt with in detail in chapter 16.

Monocytes

Monocytes, which constitute about 4 percent of all leucocytes, are **phagocytic cells,** which means their function is to *eat*—a somewhat understated observation. They do not just eat. Given the opportunity, they will eat themselves to death! All by itself that would be a noteworthy accomplishment, but the body's monocytes have other interesting capabilities as well. Not only do they feature prodigious appetites, but they also have a kind of Jekyll/Hyde personality that they succeeded in hiding from researchers for a long time. Work with leucocytes during the last twenty years or so has unravelled some mysteries that perplexed workers for decades. The monocyte/macrophage mystery was one of them.

Monocytes had long been recognized as an individual type of leucocyte. Their function in the circulation seemed lackadaisical, but reasonably important, and was thought to be pretty well established years ago. Broadly speaking, they were identified as reluctant phagocytes—reluctant because they were not very *active* phagocytes, but they were phagocytes, nonetheless. In the 1960s, researchers suddenly discovered that the monocyte's job *in*side the circulatory system was strictly secondary. Its primary role was *out*side—in the interstitial fluid—where it operated as the huge, voracious **macrophage.**

Macrophages

Workers knew of the existence of this enormous phagocyte in the last century, but its origin was pretty much a mystery until the early 1960s when, thanks to radioactive-tracer research undertaken in Holland, its secret identity was uncovered. It turns out that, like some of our best comic-book heroes, the monocytes

Figure 12.19 The origin and development of the formed elements of the blood.

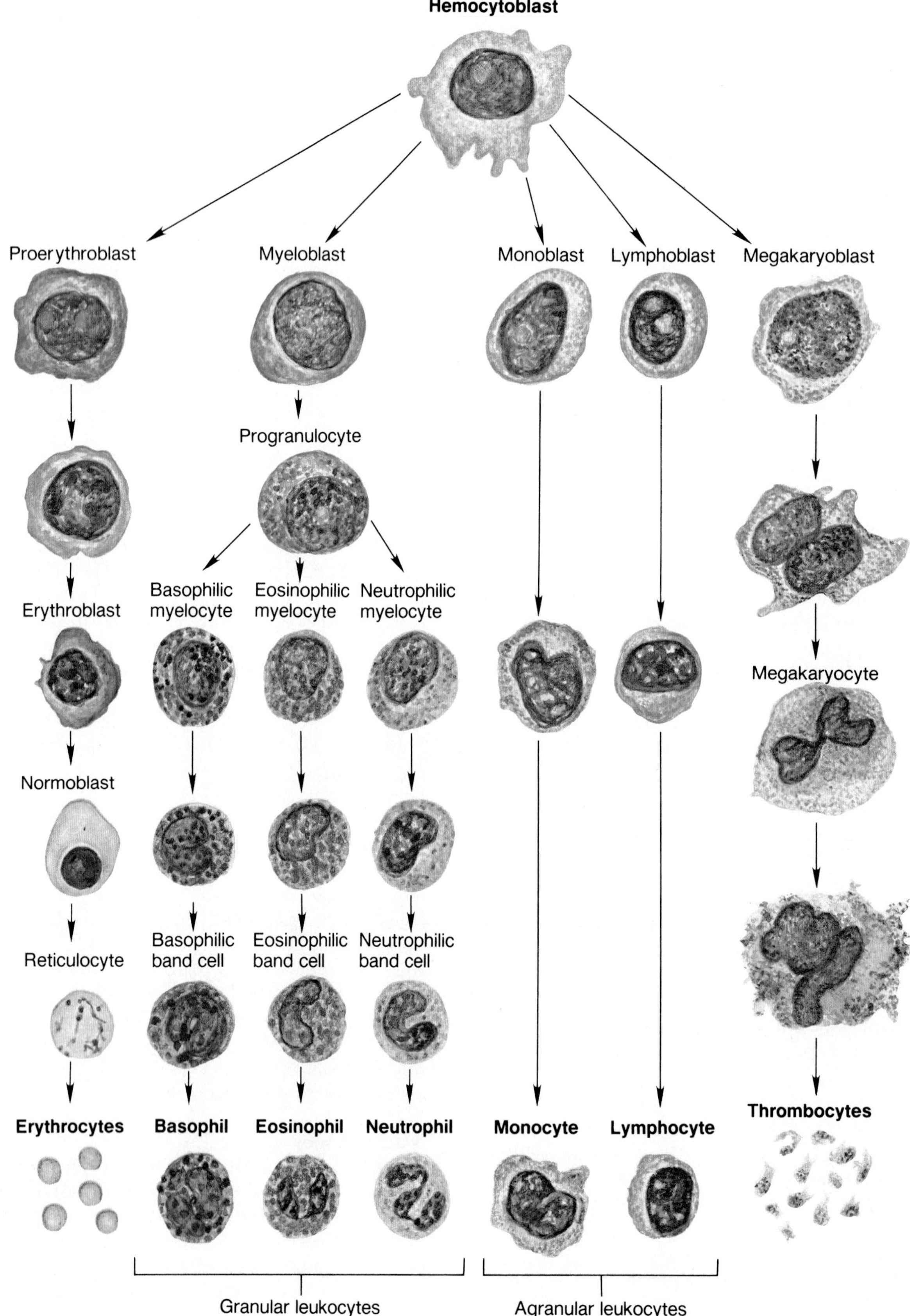

Figure 12.20 Development of macrophages from monocytes. All of these cells except the macrophages are capable of mitosis, and at least one macrophage stage can also divide.

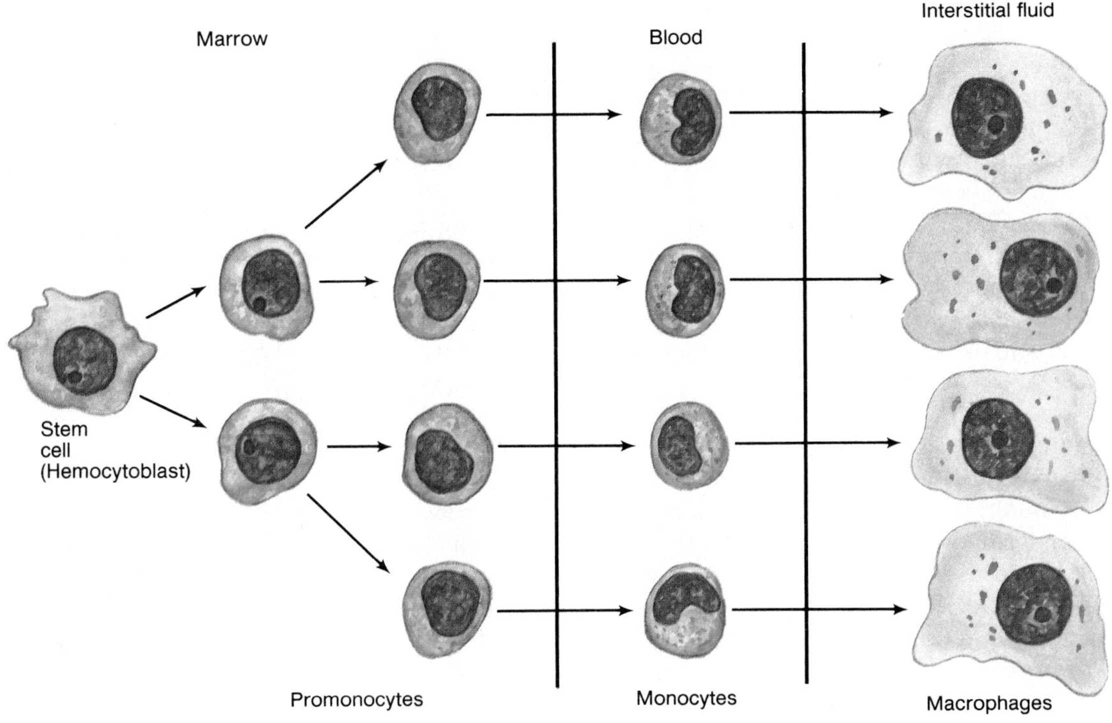

have a dual personality. As do most blood cells, monocytes originate in the red marrow of the long bones, and since almost none are stored, they are released into the blood as soon as they are complete. They circulate freely for about thirty-two hours, and then they slip out of the blood vessels into the interstitial fluid. Once outside the blood, like Superman in a phone booth, their size and powers change dramatically.

They expand several diameters in size and often become multinucleate (figure 12.20). Granules begin to show up in the cytoplasm, and the appetite increases to the point where they become furiously, almost desperately, phagocytic—the ideal macrophage. In this form, they wander everywhere, rummaging through the upper reaches of the respiratory tract, cleaning up bacterial colonies that might be threatening to establish themselves in the pharynx or in the nasal sinuses. They constantly patrol the bronchiolar and alveolar regions of the respiratory tree, gulping down debris too small to have been trapped by hair filters or respiratory mucus—they go, literally, everywhere—even into the brain, where they are known as **microglial cells.**

Macrophages can undergo mitosis and in that way can sometimes increase their numbers, but current evidence indicates that they don't do this very often. Usually they remain in the tissues and simply die there, doing their duty. They eat voraciously, snapping up everything they touch as long as they are alive, and when they are actively feeding, that is not very long.

Their life tends to be short, ranging from a minimum of a few weeks to several months—unless they start eating in the interim, in which case they die quickly, stuffed full of dead bacteria or cellular debris that they have ingested. Normally, macrophages never return to the blood, although reliable workers have reported that some do. When they return, they apparently resume their meeker, milder role; but by then their lives are nearly over.

Granular Leucocytes

The granular leucocytes consist of three cell groups, separated this time on the basis of their affinity for various dyes. Those that stain darkly with alkaline stains are called, logically enough, **basophils.** The **eosinophils** are so called because they have an affinity for *eosin,* an acidic stain used very commonly in cytological studies. **Neutrophils** take up neither acid nor basic dyes.

Neutrophils

Neutrophils are far and away the most abundant of the leucocytes. Fully 70 percent of the white cells can, at any given time, consist of neutrophils. Like the monocytes, neutrophils are phagocytic cells, but unlike the monocytes, they do not normally leave the circulatory system to forage among the interstitial jungles. They are produced continuously in the bone marrow and fed into a neutrophil "pool," from which they are released as needed into the circulation. Those that enter the circulation either circulate freely in the blood or set up temporary headquarters in various capillary beds throughout the body. There they sit, waiting until an alarm bell rings somewhere, indicating an invasion is occurring and that they are needed.

The Phagocytic Leucocytes There are a good many similarities between the neutrophils and monocytes. Both move around in the same manner, throwing out pseudopods and squeezing around like toothpaste moving back and forth in a tube with the lid screwed on. They both are liberally endowed with lysosomes, both have huge appetites, and both are phagocytic-type cells. However, we should realize that while these phagocytic leucocytes are able to ingest large food particles, they do not have to. It must be remembered that blood cells spend their lives in a food-rich medium. Energy-producing carbohydrates and all the necessary raw materials are available anytime they are needed. If a blood cell requires nutrients, it activates the appropriate carrier proteins or simply opens its selective floodgates and lets whatever it requires diffuse into its interior. Despite this, macrophages loaded with digestive enzymes and lysosomal weapons wander through the tissues like street fighters that are out looking for trouble—it is eminently fitting to consider them active predators. But that designation is not quite appropriate for the neutrophils.

Neutrophils tend to be more circumspect than the macrophages; they generally wait to be called before they rush into a fight. They do sweep the circulatory system clean as they are carried from place to place in the blood, but until an infection is located, they tend to stay pretty much where they are, "in reserve," as it were. When an infection does turn up, there is a general mobilization. All the neutrophils, those stored in the capillary beds and even those stashed away in the bone marrow, break free of their temporary anchorages and rush into the fray wherever it may be. The combat zone is almost always outside the circulatory system, and that means there is a mass exodus of white cells from the blood.

This sudden loss of white blood cells is sometimes detectable in the early stages of infectious disease. It is followed by a general increase in serum white-cell counts as the bone marrow steps up granulocyte production. The increase in white blood cells resulting from this boosted production is often one of the more reliable early indications that an infection is present and the body is fighting back. When the neutrophil pool in the bone marrow becomes depleted, production areas in the bone marrow begin cranking them out at an ever-increasing rate, sometimes reaching numbers as high as thirty to forty thousand per cubic millimeter in a case of serious infection. By the time the infection is beaten, the casualty rate among the phagocytic cells may be in the billions.

Eosinophils

Eosinophils are the most visually striking of all the leucocytes when they are properly stained. Their cytoplasm is loaded with large, bright, reddish-orange granules, and the two-lobed nucleus often resembles a sad pair of eyes. It is as if an unhappy owl with the measles were staring out of the microscope at the observer. Only about 2 percent of all leucocytes are eosinophils, but despite their small numbers, they are very important to the defense mechanisms of the human body.

Eosinophils, like the neutrophils and monocytes, are phagocytic. However, current evidence suggests that their appetites are much more restrained than those of either of their colleagues. It appears that they confine their eating habits to two items—certain blood-borne macroparasites and the debris left over after antibodies and bacteria have slugged it out and both have lost. The defunct product of these latter, lethal combats is known as an **antigen/antibody complex,** and during bacterial invasions there can be a lot of this around. The general feeling is that eosinophils, instead of wasting their energies trying to eat *everything,* restrain their appetites until they are needed to perform their specialty, and then they go to work.

But they have other, unusual functions as well. Eosinophils are evidently capable of inactivating some of the products of allergic reactions. They are able, for instance, to neutralize histamine and a substance that is known as *slow reacting substance of anaphylaxis* (SRS-A). Because of this ability, they are thought to play a very important role in reducing the severity of allergic reactions, and there is reason to believe that some lymphocyte activity can attract them. We will discuss this in chapter 16.

Basophils

Basophils are the rarest of all the leucocytes, usually constituting less than 1 percent of the body's white cells. The nucleus is irregular in these cells; it often assumes a rough crescent shape, although lobes are occasionally visible. Like the eosinophil, basophils have a cytoplasm crowded with fairly large granules, and with the standard blood-smear stains, the granules stain a deep violet-blue. These cytoplasmic granules are loaded with various enzymes and three unusual chemicals: **heparin, serotonin,** and **histamine.**

Basophils are very similar to a group of cells called **mast cells** that congregate around the basement membranes in certain capillary beds. They are so similar, in fact, that there is a suggestion they are related to the mast cells in the same way monocytes are related to macrophages . . . or possibly both arise from the same stem cells in the bone marrow. Despite the similarities, there are often—but not always—some differences between the two. For instance, details of their microstructure are usually different.

It would seem that *secretion,* not ingestion, is the primary function of basophils. The granules in most granular leucocytes are lysosomes, but this is apparently not the case with basophils. In these cells, the granules are evidently materials synthesized within the basophil and destined for secretion into the interstitial fluid. The secretions are mainly histamine, SRS-A, an anticoagulant that may or may not be heparin, plus a substance that attracts eosinophils. Histamine is deeply involved in allergic reactions, as most of us know. It mainly serves as a vasodilator, sometimes with such effectiveness that capillary walls actually stretch to the point where they become leaky. SRS-A causes constriction of the small breathing tubes (the bronchioles) and can produce some nasty asthmatic reactions. We will discuss all of these substances in more detail in the section on allergies (chapter 16).

Platelets

Platelets are produced in the bone marrow from the disintegration of a cell known as a **megakaryocyte.** Megakaryocytes develop from stem cell hemocytoblasts, as do erythrocytes, and they are the largest cells present in the bone marrow. Probably because of their huge size, their structure and function were elucidated relatively early in blood research. Before the beginning of the twentieth century, it had already been discovered that megakaryocytes were the source of one of the blood's smaller formed elements—the *platelets.* It is not clear what stimulates them to behave differently from those hemocytoblasts that produce erythrocytes, but sooner or later something happens, and they do. The result is a megakaryocyte, a cell with a diameter of up to 80 μm (the RBC has a diameter of about 7 μm). As a beginning, the megakaryocyte undergoes an unusual kind of cell division—a *pure* mitosis only—no division of the cytoplasm at all (see figure 12.21).

Figure 12.21 The release of platelets. (*a*) A megakaryocyte in normal bone marrow. (*b*) A mature megakaryocyte showing demarcation membranes in the periphery. (*c*) A megakaryocyte releasing platelets.

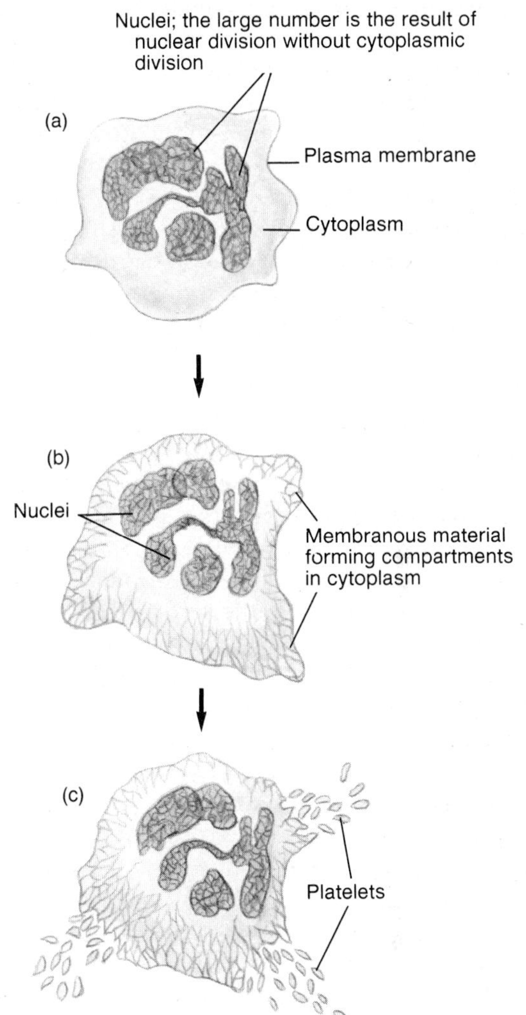

After several such divisions—usually eight—fragments of membrane begin to appear in the outer cytoplasm. These are not parts of a damaged cell membrane; that is still intact. These are apparently newly synthesized chunks of membrane called **demarcation membranes,** and they are intended for a specific purpose. Eventually they link within the cytoplasm at specific points, forming walled-off cubicles within the cell. Gradually these individual cubicles are shed, releasing platelets into the blood. As they flake off, they leave behind broken membranes and cytoplasm exposed to interstitial fluids. At this point, nearby macrophages rush in quickly to gobble up the lobulated nuclear chunks, but they pay no attention to the newly formed cubicles of cytoplasm that drift out of the marrow.

These cubicles are the platelets, and in a normal person, they are far more numerous than the leucocytes. Normal platelet count is about 250,000 mm^3, but they are so small (only about two microns in diameter) that their total volume is only a few teaspoonfuls.

They have no nucleus, therefore no DNA and no ability to synthesize proteins or repair damage. In this respect they are somewhat like the erythrocytes, but unlike the latter, they have no emergency enzymes for repair of even minor damage. As a result, they last only a few days, and when they die, they are not selectively dismantled. They are routinely eaten by phagocytes as soon as they wear out, if they are not consumed before then in the line of duty.

Despite their tiny size, there are well-defined organelles within the platelet cytoplasm. There are lots of endoplasmic reticular channels and sacs filled with materials to be secreted. There are dense granules containing calcium and some serotonin and lighter granules containing a variety of other substances. Also, there are lots of mitochondria, and there is an abundance of ATP and ADP in a concentrated mixture, suggesting a high rate of energy consumption. Platelets also contain a good supply of lysosomes.

The most unusual thing found in platelets is **contractile proteins** . . . the same kinds of proteins that make muscles contract. In fact, with the exception of muscles, platelets contain more contractile protein per unit volume than any other tissue. This suggests that one of their most important functions involves contracting, and in a sense, that is true.

This contractile ability is easy to see when you watch blood form a clot *in vitro*. A few drops of fresh blood placed on a glass slide will clot into a solid gel in about ten minutes. About forty minutes after that, you will be able to see clearly that the clot has decreased in size and in the process has wrung out a clear, yellowish fluid. The blood has formed a natural clot, and formation of that clot has stimulated the platelets. Once the clot has formed, things begin to happen within the platelets. First of all, those that are actually touching the clotted material become sticky on their outer surfaces and adhere to the clot. Then they begin to contract, pulling the clot into a smaller and smaller mass, wringing out the serum as they do.

This is an interesting and rather dramatic process to watch, but it is not what normally happens *in vivo*. In living systems, platelets have more important work to do than merely become involved in wringing serum out of clots. When some injury occurs that punctures a blood vessel but does not break or tear the vessel completely in two, platelets form the body's first line of defense. A leaking vessel needs to be sealed immediately, and the clotting process often takes a fairly long time. Platelets can plug the leak without waiting for the blood to coagulate.

Platelet Plugs

Our blood vessels are lined with overlapping endothelial cells. These cells cover the entire inner surface of the vessel, so the blood never comes into contact with the wall of the blood vessel itself as long as this lining is intact. But when the vessel is cut, things change. With the vessel wall cut, the blood can contact not only other cell types, but their contents, too. Damaged cells release, among other things, a protein called **collagen,** and there is lots of it coating the outside of the cells that form the vessel wall (figure 12.22).

Contact with collagen makes platelets sticky, so they stick to the wall of the blood vessel. As other, unconcerned platelets try to flow past, they get stuck on the sticky platelets, and that makes them sticky, too. Before long there is a logjam of platelets crammed into the hole, all of them stuck to each other, except for those on the edges, which are glued to the vessel wall. The mass is known in medical circles as a **platelet plug,** and once it has succeeded in closing off the leak in the vessel, the platelets that make up the plug begin to contract and pull the edges of the hole closer together so a tissue bridge can form and permanently seal the leak.

Only now does a clot form.

Plugging circulatory leaks with certain formed segments of the blood is nothing new as far as animals are concerned. Even insect blood is able to plug leaks. Insects do not have platelets as we do, but they do have certain blood cells called **amebocytes** that do for them what the platelets do for us. If the amebocyte finds a leak in the circulation or in the insect's body wall, it forms the initial plug! Of course, we must remember that insects are generally pretty small and no really complex mechanism designed to plug up large holes is necessary—most clots in people are bigger than the whole insect.

In larger animals it is often necessary to seal fairly big holes, and they must be sealed more completely and permanently than a simple cellular plug might be able to do. Even so, platelets or their kin provide the anchor for the clot to adhere to. In frogs and birds their relatives are whole cells called **thrombocytes,** and like human platelets (also called thrombocytes, incidentally), they can plug up small holes. Avian and amphibian thrombocytes are more stable than mammalian platelets, however, and it's a fact that in both these groups of animals, clotting occurs at a much slower rate than it does in mammals. No one is sure why.

Figure 12.22 The formation of a platelet plug.

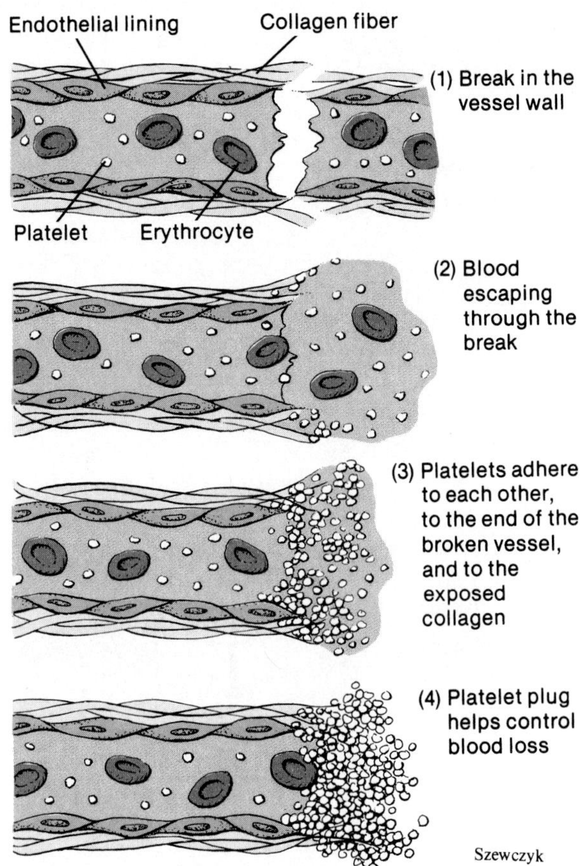

Coagulation of the Blood

Normally the circulatory system is self-sealing. Whether the sealing agent is a platelet plug or a blood clot, damage to blood vessels in a normal, healthy person is handled rapidly. Once the holes are sealed, the contractility of the blood vessel walls and platelets will pull the edges of the wound together and hasten permanent repair, but the primary long-term sealant is the blood clot, which makes it extremely important to us.

As I mentioned earlier, the formation of a clot is a complex sequence of enzymatically controlled reactions, and the only reaction in the entire sequence that is visible is the last one, the conversion of fibrinogen to fibrin. This is the biggest reason why the elaboration of clot formation required so much research and took so long to finish. If there is no way of detecting the existence of a given reaction, how are you supposed to experiment with it . . . especially when you don't know what is involved or what it does? To early researchers there was little doubt that several reactions preceded the fibrinogen to fibrin conversion, and most were convinced that there were some special chemicals that had to be present in the blood in order for clots to form, but they had no idea what they were. With perseverance, creative reasoning, some luck, and a lot of hard work, the keys were eventually found.

When the early work on blood chemistry began, almost nothing was known about coagulation. Hemophiliacs (bleeders) were beyond help in these years, because medical practitioners had no idea how to correct the problem. Their lives were precarious in the extreme, even if they were born into wealth and power, because the slightest thing might injure them fatally. This was very bad luck for the victim, but for medical researchers, it was very good luck. The only way many of the clotting reactions could ever have been elaborated was through the use of blood lacking some coagulating factor. The blood, of course, had to be contributed by individual "bleeders," and here research ran into another burst of good fortune . . . there are a lot more kinds of bleeders than you might think.

Early researchers noticed that blood samples taken from two hemophiliacs would sometimes coagulate when mixed. This immediately suggested that each one lacked a different factor, and it provided more fuel for research. As the puzzle began to unravel, more and more laboratories joined in, and while that hastened the discoveries, it added a complication. At one point, there were dozens of laboratories in the world doing independent research on this problem, and as each one uncovered and identified one of the factors involved in the process, they gave it a name of their own. With so many people working on the same thing, there were often ten different names for each factor and a barrel of confusion for the people trying to assemble the collective knowledge into a single cohesive unit.

After considerable work and a good many years, the process is fairly well understood now and the nomenclature more or less standardized. In order to offend no one, all the names were discarded, and each factor was instead given a number. At the time of this writing, there were thirteen numbered factors and a couple whose existence was being debated.

Two separate pathways lead to the production of a blood clot, and we will roughly outline both of them. The terms **extrinsic pathway** and **intrinsic pathway** refer to clotting reactions occurring under slightly different conditions. The extrinsic pathway is followed when clots form *outside* the circulatory system as a result of cuts or tears in vessels. Intrinsic clotting is that which takes place *within* the circulatory system. The intrinsic pathway is pretty slow compared to the extrinsic, mostly because of the ability of the latter to bypass several of the reactions that take place when the clots are internal.

The Extrinsic Pathway

Because of the presence of fewer reactions, the extrinsic pathway is the less complex of the two. This is the biochemical pathway followed when there is fairly extensive tissue damage, and **tissue factor (thromboplastin)** is released in abundance from damaged cells. The result is a series of reactions that will, in the presence of ionic calcium, produce **prothrombin activator.** Prothrombin is the next character in this sequence. It is an α globulin derivative, is produced by the liver from vitamin K, and is a normal fraction of blood plasma. Catalyzed by prothrombin activator and aided by calcium ions, prothrombin is converted to **thrombin,** which in turn catalyzes the conversion of **fibrinogen** into the insoluble **fibrin.** This final conversion is the visible culmination of the sequence. Figure 12.23 shows the process in detail.

The formation of fibrin is not the end of hemostatic activity when injury occurs. The thready strands of fibrin are sticky, and they adhere firmly to the damaged surfaces of the blood vessels, lying down on top of each other, criss-crossing and thickening until a solid net of fibrin threads has spread across the surface of the cut. White cells, erythrocytes, and platelets are trapped on the inner surface of these threads and thus are not lost to the blood.

The size of the clot depends on the amount of tissue damage that initiated the process, although not directly. While it is true that the amount of prothrombin activator that is produced depends on the amount of damage done, the clot is usually disproportionally large. This is due to a positive feedback loop that develops as clot formation takes place. Once thrombin is produced in the circulation, it stimulates a factor involved in its own production.

The Intrinsic Pathway

When thromboplastin is *not* present, several alternate reactions must take place, and each requires a specific enzyme. This is the **intrinsic pathway,** and it is the route that must be followed when blood clots within the circulatory system or when internal bleeding occurs. It is possible to rupture vessels of the circulatory system and to release blood into the intercellular spaces without damaging cells and releasing thromboplastin. When this happens, blood may have to clot intrinsically because thromboplastin is lacking. When blood clots form intrinsically, a clotting factor called the **Hageman factor** fills in for the missing thromboplastin. It does the job nicely, but the process can be extremely slow, much slower than the extrinsic reactions (figure 12.24).

Figure 12.23 The sequence of hemostatic events following injury to a blood vessel. This is the extrinsic pathway.

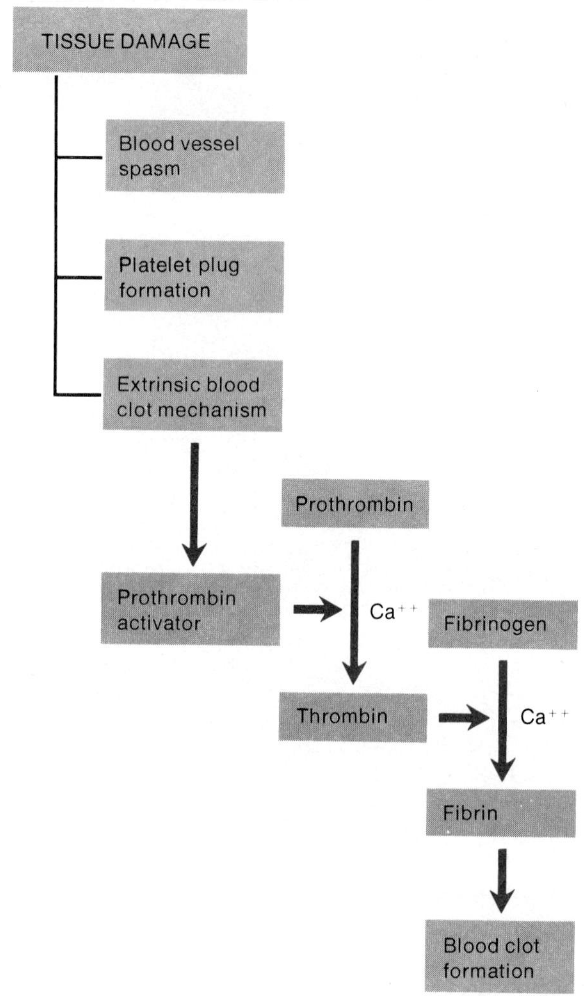

Functions of the Clot

The series of reactions seen in a test-tube sample of clotting blood start to occur in the body after the clot has formed. Many, many platelets are trapped in the sticky mesh of the fibrin, and the contractile proteins within these elements now to go to work. The result is that the entire mass of the clot is reduced, the edges of the tissue rift are pulled closer together, and serum is wrung out of the mass. Shortly thereafter, specialized cells known as **fibroblasts** begin to congregate within the clot, and they start production of fibrous connective (scar) tissue throughout, sealing the wound permanently.

A Clotting Problem

The extrinsic pathway provides a shortcut past many time-consuming intrinsic reactions, but blood does not *always* clot extrinsically when tissue damage occurs. Prothrombin has to be present in abundance, and some tissues have less than others. Muscle tissue,

Figure 12.24 The intrinsic blood-clotting pathway. This is not always initiated by injury but rather by contact with an unusual surface or foreign object.

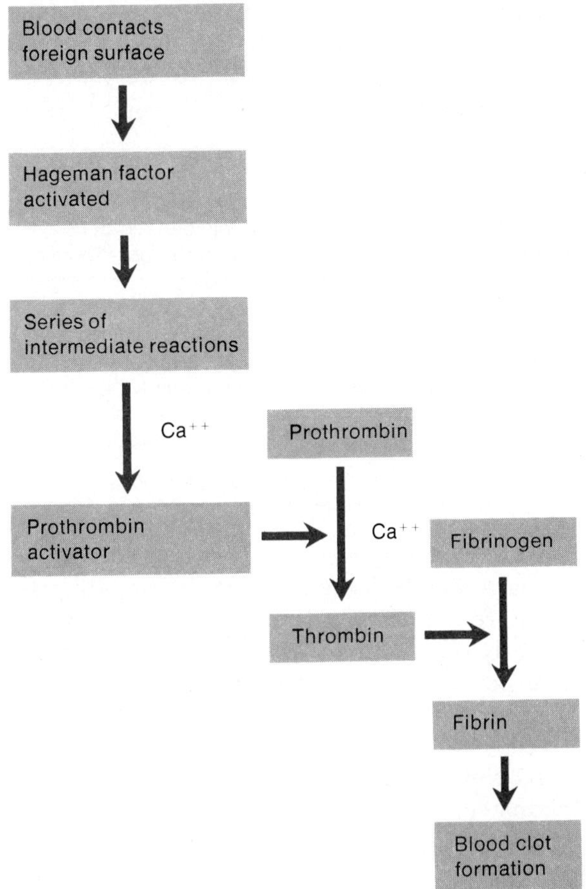

lung tissue, placental tissue, and some tissues of the gut have plenty, but there is very little in body joints and in blood vessels within the skull. As a result, bleeding into the interior of the skull when there is no nerve tissue damage will not activate the extrinsic system. Sometimes a heavy blow to the head won't damage the brain tissue but will rupture cerebral blood vessels and release large quantities of blood into the brain case. In such circumstances, the intrinsic clotting system is the one that must produce the coagulum, and sometimes that takes too long. What is more, in addition to being time-consuming, it involves more reactions, so there is more to go wrong. This is one of the major reasons why cerebral hemorrhage is so life-threatening.

Clotting is one of our body's defense mechanisms, and as such, it can be life-saving. Under certain conditions, however, the formation of clots can be highly undesirable—in fact, when clots form on the inside of blood vessels, they can be downright dangerous. Any unusual particle can be a problem if it begins to move freely in the bloodstream (where it is called an **embolus**), and when a clot forms on the inside of a vessel, there is a possibility that chunks will break free. A small piece of clot can easily plug small blood vessels, and if one happens to plug a vessel in the lungs, it can kill. If the whole clot (a **thrombus**) breaks free, it can dam up small cerebral or cardiac arteries, resulting in stroke or heart attack. Obviously, intrinsic clots can, if not properly handled, be extremely dangerous. Fortunately for us, we have a built-in protection against such things, and while this protection doesn't always work, it probably operates far more often than any of us realize.

Removing the Clot

The human body keeps a clot dissolver available and ready to go when it is needed. Its inactive precursor is known as **plasminogen,** and like fibrinogen and prothrombin, it is always present somewhere in the plasma. It is a fairly large glycoprotein (molecular weight about 92,000 daltons), synthesized by the liver and certain granulocytic leucocytes. All that is necessary to turn it on is an activating stimulus. Sometimes such a stimulus is present in specific tissues, but more often it is found in the cells that make up the walls of blood vessels. As soon as these cells touch the fibrin of a blood clot, they release the activators, and any plasminogen in the area is converted to active **plasmin,** which begins dissolving the clot.

Of course, there are times when dissolving a blood clot is not a good thing. We must remember that clots are temporary patches over damaged areas. They are intended to protect those areas until permanent repairs can be made. Therefore, while they ultimately have to be removed, they must not be dissolved until they have done their job. This has been taken care of, too. Plasminogen is not an abundant blood protein—in fact, its availability is quite limited. In addition, activated plasmin is an unstable molecule, and its own instability often breaks it up before it can dissolve very much fibrin. Finally, if some of it should slip away from the clot's proximity without falling apart, there are some specific plasmin deactivators in the general circulation that prevent it from going very far.

The dissolving of a clot is thus kept isolated and slow. It is desirable that the removal process be both. Plasmin is now commercially available (thanks to genetic engineering techniques), and will surely be a boon to cardiovascular medicine.

Other Anticlotting Factors

Because of the potential dangers posed by unwanted clots, plasmin is available to break them up after they have formed. Other protection is available to the body in the form of chemicals that prevent clots from forming in the first place. Among the most powerful of these is *heparin,* which we have already seen is a secretion of basophils and mast cells.

Heparin operates through a plasma protein called **antithrombin III,** which it activates to disrupt the coagulation reactions. Antithrombin III opposes the activity of thrombin, thereby blocking the conversion of fibrinogen to fibrin. As an exogenous anticoagulant, heparin is extremely effective and is used extensively in both medical practice and laboratory research.

The best anticoagulant in the circulatory system, however, is still the lining of the blood vessels. These overlapping connective tissue cells are so polished and smooth that they present no disturbance for platelets to focus on, no nucleus for the formation of a clot. As long as they remain so, there is nothing for the other anticoagulants to do.

Calcium

Blood without calcium will not clot. As can be seen from figures 12.23 and 12.24, calcium is required in both the extrinsic and intrinsic pathways. This fact is extremely important to medical practice, because calcium is easy to eliminate. If we add oxalates or citrates, calcium can be bound, and this technique is used by blood banks in this country to prevent whole blood from coagulating during storage. If you are ever privy to a pint of whole blood, look on the label. Somewhere, you will see the notification that the blood has been "citrated" or "oxalated."

Clinical Considerations

Hemophilia

Most of us are familiar with the condition known as **hemophilia.** People suffering from this affliction are unable to stop bleeding once it gets a good start, because their blood will not coagulate. Several thousand such unfortunates are born every generation, and until our modern medical era none of them lasted very long. Sooner or later they would fall down or get struck by something falling and suffer a damaging bruise. For a normal person, a black eye or a "sucker punch" to the stomach would mean a bellyache or a sore face for a day or so. A bruise, we must remember, is caused by internal bleeding. Normally, a clot forms before much blood can be dumped into the tissues. We get enough clotted blood under the skin to give the "black and blue" appearance, but that is all. Not for hemophiliacs. Since their blood cannot clot, they will rapidly bleed to death if they are not hospitalized quickly following such relatively minor accidents.

Although most of us are not aware of it, there are different kinds of hemophilia. The most common form is known as *hemophilia A.* This type of hemophilia is sex-linked, which means the genetic defect is carried on the female (X) chromosome. Females are almost never victims of such a disease, but they can be carriers, handing down the affliction to 50 percent of their male offspring.

Victoria I, England's queen through most of the nineteenth century, was a carrier of this genetic defect, and its rapid, near total, spread through the great houses of Europe shows how profound inbreeding was among the European nobility. Victoria's daughters were wed to royal families all over Europe, and they carried hemophilia A to their offspring and their offspring's offspring. It has been a royal "Achilles' Heel" ever since. Today, nearly half of the males descended from the royal houses of Russia, Germany, Serbia, and Austria-Hungary are bleeders, while their sisters are carriers.

For years it was assumed that people with hemophilia A simply lacked one of their clotting factors, but recent work tells us that this is not so. Apparently such patients have all the necessary factors, but for some reason, one of them doesn't work, and the form of the defect is not clear. Since the factor involved is not part of the extrinsic pathway, cuts are not a problem for its victims. But bruises or blows to the abdomen, back, and head—especially the head—are deadly. After suffering such a blow, the victims bleed uncontrollably into their deep tissues and rapidly die if not treated immediately.

As might be expected, hemophilia, when it occurs in females, is particularly deadly, since they are in danger of bleeding to death with each menstrual period. Fortunately, hemophilia A is extremely rare in women. But there are other kinds of inherited hemophilia, and in these, the defect is not carried on the sex chromosomes, so they are as likely to occur in females as in males. Since treatment consists of replacing the deficient factor via transfusion or injection when the patient is hemorrhaging, the life quality of female patients is not good, and their lives are seldom very long.

Acquired Clotting Deficiencies

Clotting deficiencies are not restricted to inherited, or even permanent, defects. Sometimes a common disease can produce a temporary hemophilia. Most such diseases involve the liver, for the simple reason that many of the clotting factors are synthesized there. As a consequence, then, anything that damages or stresses the liver can reduce the output of one or more clotting factors and deactivate the mechanisms. Cirrhosis and hepatitis, therefore, can be complicated by uncontrollable internal hemorrhage.

Vitamin Deficiency

Even something as simple as a vitamin deficiency can produce hemophilia. **Vitamin K** is an essential substrate in the synthesis of prothrombin, and if there is any shortage of this vitamin, bleeding problems can occur at any time; they are especially likely during surgery. Fortunately, this bleeding problem is rather easy to solve. Oral administration of vitamin K usually relieves the condition and restores normalcy.

Hemotoxins

Many of the poisons injected into mammals by venomous reptiles are designed to disrupt circulatory flow, and nearly all of them contain powerful coagulants. Obviously, anything that plugs up a blood vessel will hasten the death of a prey animal, so the venoms of most pit vipers (rattlesnake, cottonmouth, copperhead) have at least one factor that is similar to thrombin in its activity, catalyzing the formation of fibrin. Other toxins in the venom do other things. For example, rattlesnake venom, in addition to the coagulant, usually contains enzymes that shatter erythrocyte membranes and break down the blood vessel walls, causing fluid loss and heavy swelling in the vicinity of the bite.

Anemia

Anything that reduces the ability of the blood to carry oxygen is called **anemia.** Anemia produces all kinds of signs and symptoms in humans, among them general lassitude, overall loss of physical strength, and a tendency to tire easily, but the most reliable sign is pallor; pallor in the gums or the nail beds is most reliable. Often the faculty to think clearly seems to decrease, and overall ability to perform effective labor is reduced. *Anemia* is an extremely broad term, and it embraces a large number of different kinds of afflictions. We cannot possibly examine all of them, but some are pretty common and should be mentioned.

Anemias are classified according to the appearance of the red cells. The terms **cytic** and **chromic** are commonly used, and these refer to the size and color of the erythrocytes. Generally, in medical literature, there are three broad classifications—**microcytic hypochromic anemia** (small cells lightly colored), **macrocytic normochromic anemia** (large cells, normal color), and **normocytic normochromic** (normal cells) **anemia.**

Iron-Deficiency Anemia

This is a *microcytic hypochromic* anemia and the one that seems to crop up most often in our society. Its symptoms are often about the same as those resulting from inadequate sleep or moderate nervous tension. As a result, purveyors of patent medicines constantly struggle to convince tired Americans that their problem is inadequate iron. Unusual, catchy phrases have been dreamed up to attract buyers—things like "tired blood," for example—and incredibly, they work. People who would be better off going to bed three hours earlier will try instead to reduce their fatigue by ingesting iron sold to them by advertisers who neither know nor care if their product works. Because of these intensive sales efforts, iron-deficiency anemia has become an "everyday affliction" for many Americans, yet it is unlikely that many actually suffer from it. Iron is so intensely retained in the average human's body that, barring some horrible dietary deficiency or absorptive malfunction, none of us should need very much of it in the form of a supplement. Please do not misunderstand; everyone needs dietary iron. But there should be more than enough in a normal diet in the U.S.

Occasionally there *is* an unusually high requirement for iron. Sometimes women experience especially heavy menstrual periods. Sometimes the iron intake in the diet is marginal, and there is a stress of some kind—like an infection—that afflicts the bone marrow. When things like this happen, supplements are a good idea, but usually, they are unnecessary.

One thing all of us should get used to is reading the labels on medicine bottles to see what they contain and how much—and here is an instance when it is really important. Supplemental iron is available in pharmaceuticals in several forms. *Ferrous sulfate* tablets will provide the most iron and will do so rapidly, but ferrous sulfate is an inorganic iron and can have some unpleasant side effects. If taken on an empty stomach it can make one quite nauseous, and even if it is taken with food, it often causes diarrhea, making the feces gray and unpleasantly sticky. Unless the need for iron is immediate and desperate, organic compounds like *ferrous gluconate* or *ferrous fumarate* are the supplements of choice. They normally will provide all the extra iron an individual will need and will do so without causing gastrointestinal upset. The selection of an iron supplement should depend on what the tablet contains, and not on an advertising gimmick.

Hemorrhagic Anemia

Hemorrhagic anemia is a *normocytic normochromic* anemia, usually the result of blood loss. The most common agent is accidental vessel puncture due to a cut or a heavy blow, although sometimes the problem is functional—things like undue menstrual flow, spontaneous abortion during pregnancy, or bone marrow failure. When there is a large blood loss from the circulatory system for whatever reason, several automatic, protective mechanisms usually come into play. First of all, blood pressure promptly drops, which permits interstitial fluid to enter the circulatory system in abnormally large amounts. This reduces the pressure around body cells and permits some movement of intracellular water into the extracellular compartment. Both help increase blood volume and avoid circulatory collapse, but despite their protective intentions, these unusual fluid movements can produce some side effects that need to be handled with care. For one thing, they produce a craving for water. This is not psychosomatic. The need is quite real, and if such patients are conscious, they should be given all the water they can drink.

Even if the victim gets large quantities of water and plasma volume expands to normal, the new equilibrium provides no relief from the anemia. Body water has been replaced, but not the lost blood cells. Without erythrocytes, there is not much the body can do that will help the blood carry more oxygen, so the patient becomes anemic. Fortunately, barring complications, the condition is a temporary one. Normal, healthy individuals will compensate for the blood loss quickly as the body's homeostatic feedback loops swing into action. Kidney cells, when deprived of adequate oxygen, produce erythropoietin, which stimulates bone marrow cells to increase their efforts, and erythrocytes begin to pour into the blood in increased numbers. The high-powered synthetic activity can deplete the liver's stock of ferritin overnight, and this is when supplemental therapy with ferrous sulfate is advisable. Once the cause of the bleeding has been repaired, unless the blood loss has been enormous (more than a pint), the body will replace most of the lost cells within a forty-eight-hour period.

Pernicious Anemia (Lack of Intrinsic Factor)

While not the most common form of anemia, pernicious anemia afflicts many thousands of Americans every year. It is a *macrocytic normochromic* form of anemia, meaning the cells are the right color, but are a little too big. Usually there are not enough of them, either; blood workups often show that the red cell population has dropped. In such cases, the erythrocytes are unable to carry very much oxygen, and they break apart more easily than healthy erythrocytes. Administration of exogenous iron will not improve the patient's condition. The trouble is more basic, arising in the bone marrow where the cells are assembled. The developing red cells are much larger than they should be, yet their nuclei are abnormally tiny and clogged with pigment. The cause is nutritional.

An Old Wives' Cure that Works Many years ago, long before we were even aware that vitamins existed, some village matriarchs knew that they could cure anemia by feeding patients dried meat, like beef or venison jerky, *soaked in the gastric juices of a pig.* To medical professionals of the nineteenth century, and early twentieth centuries, it sounded like old wives' tale foolishness. To most people today, it sounds even worse—like prescribing wing of bat or pollywog's tail. The first response of a modern patient, if told to eat such a concoction, would be to find another doctor. Most so-called old wives' tales really are nonsensical, but in the dozens and dozens that exist, there are bound to be some that really work, and this is one of them. Today, we know why.

Intrinsic Factor The direct cause of pernicious anemia is an inadequate supply of vitamin B_{12}. Sometimes the patient simply is not ingesting enough of this vitamin, but usually that is not the hitch. Anything of an animal source—eggs, milk, butter, cheese, and of course, meat—has more than enough B_{12} to meet minimum daily requirements, so unless people are incredibly strict vegetarians, they will ingest enough B_{12}. The problem is that the vitamin is not getting from the digestive tract into the blood.

These patients lack a gastric secretion known simply as **intrinsic factor (IF).** Intrinsic factor is secreted by mucosal cells in the ileum of the stomach, probably the same cells that secrete the powerful stomach acids. If IF is not present, any vitamin B_{12} that is ingested is promptly destroyed. When IF is present in the stomach, it binds the vitamin tightly in a protective cup and transports it intact through the acid of the stomach and past the digestive enzymes of the small intestine. Deep in the small intestine, near its end, in fact, the IF/B_{12} complex finally encounters receptors that represent a target rather than a danger zone. These receptors promptly bind to the B_{12} and carry it across the gut into the blood. It is not known whether the entire complex is moved across the gut or whether the IF is broken free and released before the vitamin is bound, but one way or the other, the vitamin gets into the blood. Once there, it is taken up by many body tissues, including the red bone marrow, where it promptly solves the erythrocyte assembly problems and restores the blood count to normal.

Aplastic Anemia

Like hemorrhagic anemias, aplastic anemias are *normocytic normochromic* diseases. They are the result of bone marrow defects, but unlike pernicious anemia, these are not correctable through dietary manipulation. The problem is more malignant and deep-seated than simple diet. For some reason, there is a general reduction in the blood-cell-producing areas in the bone marrow, and the result is not merely an inadequate number of erythrocytes. Rather, we see an affliction called **pancytopenia** (*pan,* "all"; *penia,* "poverty")—a dearth of *all* blood cells. Medical literature mentions many causes of aplastic anemia, and only a few types have responded well to treatment. Some do not respond at all.

Most of the time, aplastic anemia is a secondary result of some other problem. Viral hepatitis, for instance, as well as a few bacterial infections can sometimes be responsible, but the most common causes today are chemical and/or physical agents encountered in our highly technological environments. Sometimes these are prescribed drugs, such as antibiotics or anticonvulsive agents, which are prescribed with perhaps more abandon than they should be. The American Medical Association has published a list of such drugs; at last glance there were nearly 350 on it, including such commonly prescribed things as penicillin, chloramphenicol, and epinephrine. But these cases are pretty rare. More often we suspect that aplastic anemia patients, particularly young ones, have contracted the disease by abusing some euphoric chemical. There is abundant evidence to indicate that toluene and benzene derivatives, both of which would be encountered in glue- or paint-sniffing, can do tremendous damage in blood-producing zones of the bone marrow.

Radiation has been blamed for some aplastic anemias, but not all radiation can do it. Brief exposure to the kind of high-energy bursts that would be encountered in nuclear-reactor accidents usually kills very quickly. This kind of radiation destroys the blood's ability to clot or to resist disease, and patients die quickly of internal bleeding or some horrible affliction that their immune systems cannot fight. That is not the kind of radiation that produces aplastic anemias.

Anemia-causing radiation is a low-level radiation—one that does not contain much energy—and it often doesn't attract any attention until it is too late. Radiation levels way below those that are normally considered lethal work their insidious witchery over long periods of time on unsuspecting victims. In the 1930s and 1940s, after years of working in plants where radium dials for watches were produced, assembly-line workers came down with untreatable aplastic anemias and everyone wondered why. By the early 1950s, we knew. Apparently the stem cells in our bone marrow can survive short bursts of high-level radiation but are destroyed or damaged by low-level radiation if they are exposed to it long enough.

Sickle-Cell Anemia

If iron-deficiency anemia is not the anemia best known to the American public, then **sickle-cell anemia** is. Sickle-cell anemia was identified in 1949; it was the first known example of a blood disease caused by a structural defect in the hemoglobin. The number of such diseases, known today as **hemoglobinopathies,** is now up in the dozens, but sickle-cell anemia is easily the most publicized.

Sickle-cell anemia is primarily, but not exclusively, a disease of negroid humans whose family trees are rooted in west Africa. It is the result of an almost undetectable change in the amino acids of the globin. There are 287 amino acids in a hemoglobin molecule, and of that huge number, just one, a single molecule of *glutamic acid,* has been replaced by a molecule of a different amino acid—*valine.*

The flexibility of modern technology makes it hard for most of us to accept the idea that out of 287 basically similar parts, a serious malfunction could result if one of these parts were swapped for another one that was only slightly different. We are taught from childhood to improvise, and we know from experience that improvisation often works. Trading similar parts back and forth or manipulating one slightly to make it work usually is acceptable. Now, suddenly, we are confronted with a specificity that is marvelously perceptive and remarkably sensitive. Both glutamic acid and valine are amino acids, and they are not very different structurally. But our body has selected the chemicals it needs with extraordinary precision, and it seems that even the tiniest alteration can destroy or disrupt specific functions.

Sickle-cell anemia is a good case in point. Sickle-cell hemoglobin so closely resembles the conventional molecule that unless subjected to stress, it behaves in a normal manner. However, if blood oxygen is drained by unusual tissue demands and it becomes necessary for the hemoglobin to maximize its oxygen-carrying efforts, the sickle-cell hemoglobin collapses and draws its host cell into the characteristic sickle shape (figure 12.25). In this form, the cells are rigid and tend to clump together, forming dams in small arteries and arterioles all over the body and producing what is known as a **sickle-cell crisis.** These crises can be very serious indeed; arterial plugs in the heart or brain can be lethal. In other organs and tissues they cause intense, razor-sharp pain and sometimes severe damage.

Sickle-cell anemia has been one of the most informative afflictions ever studied by biomedical scientists. It introduced us to hemoglobinopathic diseases, which occur as a result of structural problems with hemoglobin. In addition, it presented us with an example of a much more

Figure 12.25 (*a*) A light micrograph showing a "sickling" red blood cell among several normal cells. (*b*) A group of normal and (*c*) a group of sickled erythrocytes as seen by a scanning electron microscope.

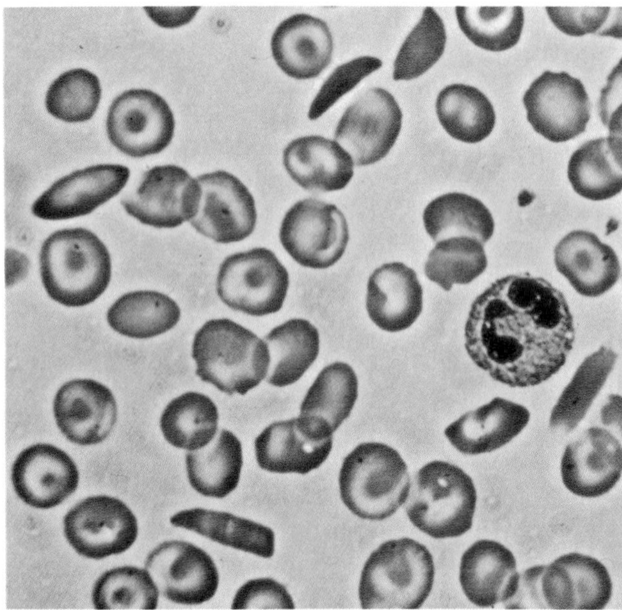

(a)

(b)

(c)

general biological principle. Biologists have known for years that when an inherited trait is damaging or disadvantageous to a population, it is usually blotted out in the normal course of events. Occasionally, however, a trait will show up that is certainly a disadvantage under average circumstances but provides huge advantages under unusual conditions. When this happens, the trait is almost always retained in the population, despite the fact that it can be a problem. Sickle-cell anemia is one such hereditary affliction. The only population of people on earth that has retained this trait are those who live in west Africa or whose recent ancestors lived there. Certain portions of west Africa are crawling with a particularly deadly form of malaria. For centuries, Europeans, traders from the Middle East, and blacks from other parts of Africa refused to enter, because so many of them died. Yet the area was populated heavily by people who seemed to have no problems with this affliction. Scientists pondered this for a hundred years in vain. Not until the 1950s did they find the key.

It turns out that nearly every native there is a carrier of the sickle-cell trait, but they don't have the disease themselves. There are no people in the population with active sickle-cell anemia, nor are there any who are not carriers. Why? Because both of those conditions are lethal in this relatively primitive society. In the uncivilized state that prevailed in that region for so many millenia, individuals who had active cases of sickle-cell anemia simply died of that disease. Those who were born normal, i.e., were not carriers, caught malaria, and they died too. The *carriers* got malaria alright, but for some unknown reason its effects were no worse than a case of mild influenza, and all of them survived, permanently immune. Every generation would lose half of its children to sickle-cell anemia or malaria, but the other half would live. What's more, they lived under a protection that no monarch or show of military might could provide . . . no outsider could enter their homeland and survive. Prosperity was assured, as long as they stayed where they were.

Leucocyte Disorders

The most common white-cell aberration (not really a disorder) that is encountered occurs when some microorganism decides to invade the body. Often the first indication that an infection has begun to take hold is a suddenly elevated leucocyte count. This can happen in a matter of hours, because many of the infection-fighting white cells are already synthesized and are merely waiting around to be released. Infections stimulate the bone marrow to dump its reserve into the bloodstream and increase its production of neutrophils, often elevating the white-cell count to as much as 500,000 per cubic mm, an increase of 10,000 percent above normal.

Leukemia

True disorders of leucocytes are almost always related to some production variation, and the best known is the deadly **leukemia** (*leuc,* "white"; *emia,* "blood").

There is nothing new about this disease. It was described thoroughly by Virchow in 1847—in fact, it was he who named it after observing patients whose blood was flooded with worthless white cells. Its cause is not known, and although some workers feel that there may be an inherited predisposition toward contracting it, there is very little empirical evidence to support this. Environmental factors like chronic exposure to mild radiation seem to be involved, although this is hard to pin down, because the disease may not appear until years after such exposure. Chemicals like benzene, toluene—even the antibiotic *Chloromycetin®*—have been cited as possible causes, with evidence accumulating that they are indeed involved. Natural causes have been quoted also. Viruses were long ignored as leukemia-causing agents, but they have certainly been implicated in animals, and there is a hint that immune deficiencies—including *acquired immune deficiency syndrome* (AIDS)—may also produce leukemias.

Leukemia features runaway production of useless white blood cells, sometimes granulocytes, sometimes lymphocytes. Whether the disease takes an acute form or follows a chronic track, the prognosis is poor, and while some survive for as long as ten years, most victims succumb in two or three years.

Treatment is drastic and temporary. It consists of radiation or chemicals designed to kill any rapidly proliferating cells, which is why both hair and fingernails often break and fall out during treatment. Remissions occur more often than not, sometimes complete remissions, but they are nearly always temporary. Leukemia was once thought to be a disease of childhood, but that is not true. There is really no age group, sex, or race that is safe. Although some *types* of leukemia appear to concentrate in certain age groups, the entire population is equally susceptible to one or another.

Research is continuous, and there have been some hopeful advances. Bone marrow transplants are becoming more common and are showing real promise, particularly in very young patients. Chemotherapy is also improving, and the results, while uncomfortable for the patient, are encouraging. Physicians today feel that if a patient can survive for five years, there is a good chance a cure can be effected.

Nevertheless, leukemia continues to be a heartless killer, and the mortality rate is discouragingly high. And although we are learning a great deal, nothing has been discovered yet that can reduce the incidence of the disease.

Cholesterol

Few things in medical science have generated as much controversy and have spun off as much quack advertising as saturated fats and cholesterol. Both of these materials are present in the plasma pretty much all the time. The saturated fats (often called *triglycerides*) may have been ingested or they may have been synthesized for storage by our own bodies. Cholesterol may also have been ingested, but our bodies synthesize it in large amounts as a building block for steroid hormones, cellular membranes, bile acids, and a few other things. The reason for such intense interest in saturated fats and cholesterol is that they have both been implicated in heart and arterial disease.

Coronary artery disease is the major killer in this country and in much of the Western world—in fact, circulatory problems of all kinds are prevalent and dangerous. There seems to be very little doubt that a high level of cholesterol in the bloodstream is a powerful indicator that such disease is either present or on its way. Cholesterol, before it enters the bloodstream, has got to be hooked onto protein carriers, and apparently the type of carrier the fat is gripped by determines whether it is considered "good" or "bad." The high-density lipoprotein carrier (HDL) is apparently the desirable type. No one is really sure why, but evidently when cholesterol is carried in the form of HDL, it not only is not any kind of health threat, but it can even sweep off cholesterol deposits that are already in place on the interior of an artery.

On the other hand, low-density carriers (LDL) are bad news indeed. Apparently, cholesterol carried on LDL can, and often is, released on the interior wall of the blood vessels it is moving through, damaging the vessel and encouraging the formation of scar tissue. These are the arterial "plaques" medical people talk about in concerned whispers, and as they grow, they become more and more of an impediment to the flow of blood through the vessel. Any time a tissue becomes unusually active, it requires additional oxygen, and to get that, the blood flow must increase. If there is a large arterial plaque occluding the vessel, it won't get the extra blood, and the tissue it supplies may suffer—even die. When such a plug forms in the coronary arteries, the result is the familiar "heart attack."

Total blood cholesterol is the most common analysis ordered by physicians, and if it is high, a competent doctor will then get a *differential analysis.* The differential tells her whether or not the high cholesterol levels are a problem. Apparently, if the HDL levels are high, it really doesn't matter how high the total cholesterol levels are. But if the LDL levels are abnormal, the subject is a candidate for a cardiac infarction and had better start doing something about it quickly.

The third type of lipoprotein carrier is known as very low-density lipoprotein (VLDL), and it carries almost no cholesterol at all. These are the lipoproteins that move neutral fats from place to place through the circulatory system, and nobody is really sure what role they play in the development of arterial plaques . . . maybe none at all.

Current medical opinion is that a high dietary intake of saturated fats stimulates the production of LDL and then loads the carrier with cholesterol. This may or may not be correct. Certainly there is very little doubt that high LDL blood concentrations are correlated with cardiovascular problems, but what might cause elevated LDL blood levels is debatable. Most medical people feel that saturated fat ingestion is an aggravating circumstance, although a good many researchers tend to disagree. The opinion of the latter group is that any fat can be a problem, and eating unsaturated fats is just as bad as eating saturated ones.

In any case, there are two points over which there is very little disagreement: (1) high blood levels of HDL usually mean there is no imminent cardiovascular problem, and (2) lowering blood levels of LDL can prevent or reduce the severity of heart attacks.

Drugs are available that will reduce blood LDL levels quickly and effectively, but they are expensive, and most have some rather unpleasant side effects. If the medical profession is correct (and it may not be), then the cheapest way to lower blood concentrations of LDL is to reduce saturated fat consumption and replace it with unsaturated oils, mostly plant oils. Corn, soy, sunflower oils—all are mainly unsaturated, and so are peanut oils, although these are not quite as good. It is often said that animal fat is dangerous and plant oils are safe, but you have to be careful about generalizations, because not all plant oils are unsaturated, and some are really nasty. Palm oils and coconut oil, for instance, contain more saturated fats than an equal volume of thick cream, and that is a lot.

Many foods have been touted at one time or another as having the ability to reduce LDL levels, and some of them really can. Oat bran and pectin do it by sweeping cholesterol out of the small intestine before it has a chance to be absorbed, and several other kinds of high-fiber foods are supposed to be good at this, too. Olive oil is also reputed to have the ability to reduce blood LDL, but the best of all (surprise) is *fish oil.*

There is a mounting body of evidence to indicate that persons eating two or three meals of fish per week can substantially reduce the risk of cardiovascular problems. This, when first announced, was particularly intriguing, because fish are animals, and animal fat has always had an unsavory reputation. In this case, however, we find an important exception.

Not only is fish oil unsaturated, but it contains a chemical that is missing even in unsaturated plant oils. This chemical (called **eicosapentaenoic acid**) not only lowers LDL levels, it actively inhibits the deposition of plaque on arterial interiors and inhibits platelets from getting sticky, thus reducing the probability of clots forming on any roughened plaque deposits that may already be present. And as if that were not enough—it also reduces blood pressure and arthritic inflammation.

Most Americans do not care very much for fish . . . in fact, one of the recommendations one often hears in restaurants when fish is discussed is that "it doesn't taste *fishy*." This is unfortunate, because the greatest natural source of fish oil is "fishy-tasting" fish. Salmon, mackerel, herring, and other deep water fish are all good. Cod are not so good because most of their oil is in the liver, and cod-liver oil, taken in excess (if anybody would want to), could result in vitamin A poisoning. Shellfish and crustaceans are also good, despite a high cholesterol content.

An interesting sidelight to this whole story is found in the tale of the fish known as **menhaden.** The menhaden is a herring, which means it is related to the sardine, the shad, and the European pilchard. For some strange reason, menhaden cannot be sold for food in this country, so the large numbers that are netted are usually sold in Europe. Europeans then reduce it to oil, hydrogenate it a little bit, and convert it to margarine. Obviously, American margarine manufacturers are missing a sensational advertising coup by failing to coerce our government into permitting them to do the same thing here. Imagine being able to advertise a margarine that not only does not contribute any saturated fats but *lowers* blood cholesterol and helps reduce the probability of cardiovascular disease.

Summary

The Fluid Compartments

There are three main fluid compartments in the body: the extracellular, the intracellular, and the transcellular.

The Interstitial Fluids

These are the fluids in the open tissues spaces. They function as an intermediate between the blood and the fluids within the cells.

The Lymphatic Circulation

I. The Open Plan. This circulatory plan involves releasing the fluids into sinuses or open spaces in the tissues of the body.

II. The Lymph

  A. Lymph is an ultrafiltrate of the blood. It is picked up from the tissue spaces by special vessels known as lymphatic capillaries.

B. Lymphatic Propulsion.
Propulsive force for the lymphatic circulation is probably provided by skeletal muscles.

III. Lymph Nodes. Lymph nodes are chambers through which lymph is filtered. They represent zones of filtration and purification.

Blood—the Closed System

Blood is the primary transportation system for the movement of materials throughout the body. Capillaries, the smallest vessels, are the entities in the system where material exchange takes place.

I. The Main Transportation Line. The blood provides both supplies and a waste-dumping zone for the interstitial fluid.

II. Blood as a Tissue. Blood is a separate, full-fledged tissue. It is 45 percent formed elements and 55 percent plasma.

Plasma

I. Functions and Restrictions. Plasma is the fluid portion of the blood. It is responsible for the dispersion and transportation of all minerals, raw materials, and waste products throughout the body.

II. Plasma Chemistry. Plasma is 90 percent water and 10 percent dissolved materials. Of the dissolved solid material, 70 percent is protein.

III. The Plasma Proteins

A. Albumin.
Albumin is the most abundant of the plasma proteins. It plays many roles. Probably its most pervasive is maintaining proper blood volume through its osmotic influence.

B. The Blood Globulins. There are three globulins: alpha (α), beta (β), and gamma (γ). All serve as substrate material for protein synthesis. All are involved in immunological reactions. Alpha and β globulins also serve as carrier proteins.

C. Fibrinogen. Is involved in clotting.

IV. Nutrients. The plasma carries nutrients both for immediate use by body cells and for storage.

V. Cholesterol and Triglycerides. There are three main protein carriers for fats: high-density lipoproteins (HDL), low-density lipoproteins (LDL), and very low-density lipoproteins (VLDL).

VI. Minerals. The plasma contains high concentrations of mineral electrolytes.

VII. Nitrogen and Other Gases. These are mainly carried in solution.

The Formed (Cellular) Elements

The Red Blood Cells.
RBCs are anucleate, pigment-containing cells synthesized in bone marrow. Their life span is approximately 120 days on an average.

I. Respiratory Pigments

A. Hemoglobin is an iron-based pigment that forms reversible covalent bonds with molecular oxygen.

B. There are 300 million hemoglobin molecules in each RBC.

C. Hemoglobin is synthesized at the rate of 900 trillion molecules per second in a normal, healthy human being.

II. Red Cell Count. There are approximately five million RBCs in every mm^3 of normal human blood.

III. Erythrocyte Synthesis. Synthesis takes place in the marrow of long bones. It begins with nucleated hemocytoblast (stem) cells and ends with anucleate erythrocytes.

IV. Control of Erythrocyte Production. The synthesis rate of RBCs is carefully regulated to insure that there will be neither too many nor too few.

V. Breakdown of Erythrocytes. Worn-out RBCs are not disposed of. They are carefully taken apart, with the amino acids of the globin and the iron from the heme fraction salvaged for future use.

A. Raw Materials and Nutrients. Most is retained from careful RBC breakdown, but some supplemental iron is needed, especially by women.

B. The Role of Vitamins. Vitamin B_{12} and folic acid are required for DNA synthesis.

The White Blood Cells (Leucocytes)

I. Morphology. There are two groups of leucocytes: the agranular and the granular.

II. Agranular Leucocytes. There are two; the monocytes and the lymphocytes. Lymphocytes are involved almost exclusively in the immune responses.

A. Monocytes. Monocytes are phagocytic cells. They remain within the bounds of the circulatory system. When monocytes migrate outside the circulatory system, they become macrophages.

B. Macrophages. These are wanderers throughout the interstitial spaces, actively phagocytizing anything that they deem out of place. They have a short life (one to three weeks) and seldom become monocytes again.

III. Granular Leucocytes

A. Neutrophils

1. These are the most numerous of the leucocytes. They are phagocytic.
2. The Phagocytic Leucocytes. This section deals with the similarities and differences between the macrophages and neutrophils.

B. Eosinophils. These leucocytes are involved in clearing up immune precipitates and macroparasitic invasions. They are also involved in control of some allergic reactions.

C. Basophils. These are the rarest of the leucocytes. They are involved in secretory operations, possibly during inflammatory reactions.

Platelets

I. Platelets are produced in the marrow of the long bones. They are cellular fragments. They contain much ATP, glucose, and contractile proteins.

II. Platelet Plugs. Platelets serve to plug holes that may occur in blood vessels.

Coagulation of the Blood

There are two separate reaction pathways that can lead to the formation of a clot.

I. The Extrinsic Pathway. This is the pathway followed when tissue damage occurs and thromboplastin is released from damaged cells.

II. The Intrinsic Pathway. This pathway is followed when thromboplastin is not present, as when internal bleeding has occurred.

III. Functions of the Clot
- A. The clot provides a site at which scar tissue can begin to form.
- B. A Clotting Problem.
  Blood doesn't always clot when it should, and sometimes it clots when it shouldn't.

IV. Removing the Clot. Removal of the clot is accomplished by a chemical called plasmin. Plasmin is formed from a plasma protein (plasminogen) when it is needed.

V. Anticlotting Factors
- A. There are several chemicals in the cytoplasm of body cells and in the blood that will prevent blood from clotting.
- B. Calcium. Without calcium, blood will not clot. Tying up all available calcium is therefore a fine anticoagulation operation.

Clinical Considerations

I. Hemophilia

II. Acquired Clotting Deficiencies
Vitamin Deficiency

III. Hemotoxins

IV. Anemia
- A. Iron-Deficiency Anemia
- B. Hemorrhagic Anemia
- C. Pernicious Anemia
  1. An Old Wives' Cure that Works
  2. Intrinsic Factor
- D. Aplastic Anemia
- E. Sickle-Cell Anemia

V. Leucocyte Disorders
Leukemia

VI. Cholesterol

Review Questions

1. Identify and discuss the two types of circulatory plan present in human beings.
2. What is lymph, how is it formed, and where is it found?
3. Describe the movement of lymph through the body.
4. What is a lymph node? What are the functions of these nodes?
5. What are the two main fractions of whole blood?
6. Of what does plasma consist?
7. What is plasma's function?
8. Name the three main types of plasma proteins.
9. Describe and state the primary function(s) of each of these proteins.
10. Discuss the fat, mineral, and dissolved gases carried in the plasma.
11. How are the formed blood elements categorized? Name these categories.
12. Describe the morphology of the erythrocyte.
13. What is a respiratory pigment?
14. What is the respiratory pigment in red blood cells? What is its function?
15. How much respiratory pigment can each RBC carry?
16. What is a normal RBC count in human beings?
17. Discuss the process by which RBCs are synthesized in bone marrow.
18. How are the RBC numbers regulated?
19. Describe the process of breaking up RBCs. Which products are salvaged and which are not?
20. Which vitamins are necessary in the synthesis of RBCs?
21. Identify and discuss the two major categories of leucocytes.
22. Describe the morphology and function of the monocytes.
23. Describe the formation and function of macrophages.
24. Name the granular leucocytes and the function(s) of each.
25. Describe the morphology and synthesis of platelets.
26. What is a platelet plug? Discuss its cause and formation.
27. Draw diagrams of the two pathways that lead to the formation of a blood clot.
28. How are clots removed when their job is done?
29. How are clots prevented from forming by hospital workers who must store whole blood?

Chapter 13 The Circulatory Plan

Study Hints

The overall goal of the circulatory system is to maintain homeostasis in the interstitial fluids and in the intracellular compartment.

1. Work on understanding why it is that two separate pumps are needed in the human circulatory system.
2. The blood is pumped out of the heart in a stop-and-go pressure pattern and it enters the arteries that way. Yet when it moves through the capillaries, it does so in a relatively steady stream at a constant pressure. Be sure you know why.
3. Be sure that you understand clearly what is responsible for the *diastolic* pressure in our arterial system and that you know the difference between it and *systolic* blood pressure.
4. Learn what factors can change the blood pressure and remember which of these factors has the greatest influence.

Objectives

When you have finished reading this chapter, you should:

1. be able to explain why changing blood vessel diameter is able to alter pressure so effectively.
2. be able to trace the route blood follows from the peripheral vessels back to the major veins, through the heart and lungs to the major arteries.
3. be able to explain the entire cardiac cycle.
4. know why relaxation of the heart is just as important as contraction.
5. know how the autonomic nervous system is able to modify the heartbeat and what stimuli have the greatest effect.
6. be able to explain how the body is able to vary blood pressure both selectively and generally.
7. know why, from a functional standpoint, hardening of the walls of blood vessels can create a dangerous health problem.

Capillary network.

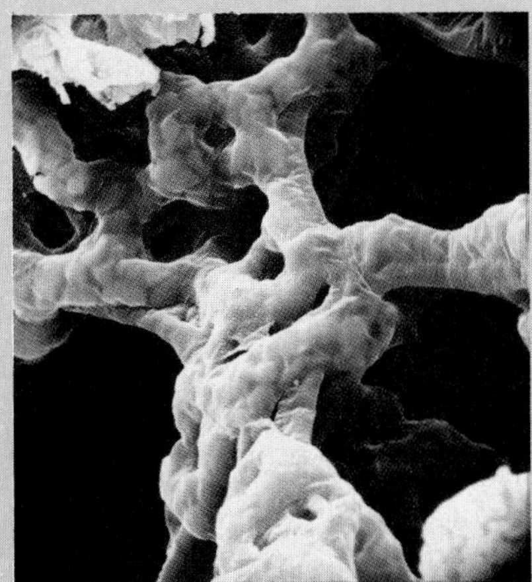

Introduction

Why a circulatory system? Before you can fully appreciate the answer to this question, you must first understand the magnitude of the problem. By investigating the obstacles that confronted our evolutionary ancestors and the solutions that developed, we may better appreciate the problems that a circulatory system must face and the solutions the human circulatory system has devised to solve them. Obviously the big problem is providing the living cells and their internal organelles with a source of nutrients and a waste-dumping ground. There are hundreds of smaller problems that arise in the search for a comprehensive solution to the big one.

Development of a Circulatory System

The Simplest Solution

If the organisms are small enough, specialized circulatory systems are not necessary. Nutrients can be provided and wastes can be discarded without expending energy to move them. Diffusion will take care of most of it—diffusion from and into the medium in which these organisms live. In this respect, life is simpler for them than it is for us. They do not have to worry about transporting materials throughout their bodies. All they need is a medium that has food in it and is so large that the dumping of their waste products will not pollute it. As long as it can do the job, diffusion is an energy-efficient process; hence it is the method of choice.

But there are problems with using diffusion exclusively, and the biggest one is that it places inconvenient limits on body size or shape. As long as the organism remains microscopic, diffusion works nicely. But when organisms begin to grow, the efficiency of diffusion transport begins to diminish. One way to solve that, of course, would be not to grow. That would be a good idea, except for one thing: there is a premium on size.

It seems that the least successful forms of life are those that change the most as a result of natural selection. The changes that take place occur because they enhance that life-form's chances of survival, and *an increase in size* is evidently an easy change to make—usually easier than a change in body design. And it presents its recipients with a significant advantage . . . if nothing else, it will reduce predation.

As modern engineers have discovered, however, one cannot simply increase an object's overall linear dimensions and expect everything to continue working the same as it always has. Things are never that simple. When the earliest single-celled organisms sought to increase their survival rate by expanding their size, they were immediately confronted with the problem of how to move materials back and forth between their interiors and the environment. The problem is associated with *surface-area-to-volume ratio* (remember that?). As size increases, this ratio decreases to a point where the distance from the outside to the interior is simply too great for diffusion to be practical.

The Problem of Growing—a Few Solutions

The problems presented by this diminishing ratio can be countered within limits by assuming a flat shape. If the animal is flat enough, it can spread out over a pretty wide area and still indulge itself through simple diffuson. Once again, however, the solution is self-limiting. The organism is restricted to a flat—and *very* thin—shape. If being shaped like a piece of tissue paper is too restricting, there are a couple of alternatives:

1. live in a medium where essential materials are very rich, or
2. find a way of moving lots of nutrient rapidly past the feeding body parts.

Choice one is not really practical because there are too many built-in disadvantages. First of all, finding a soup-thick nutrient would be hard to do. Then, even if one found such a place, continued existence would be terribly insecure. Competition would be tremendous, and even if you happened to be the most successful organism of all, you'd still be vulnerable to anything that might interfere with the high concentration of foodstuffs. Anyhow, the presence of large concentrations of nutrients would not give any enhanced means of dumping the waste products that would certainly accumulate. Survival would be very chancy.

Choice two would be a much more logical one. Not only would it provide the necessary materials, it would also solve the problem of waste disposal. Sponges adopted this technique more than a half-billion years ago, and they are still around, so it obviously works. Once again, there are disadvantages to such a restricted life-style. Like a sponge, any organism adopting that option would be anchored in one place throughout its life, performing the same chores with unending monotony. Plainly there is little possibility of ever provoking the evolution of sensory organs for the detection of food, or muscles to help pursue it, much less an intellect. In fact, intelligence would probably be a disadvantage, because if you thought about your life for any length of time, you might go crazy. Just sitting around, being part of the same old landscape day after day, watching nutrients go by and snacking every now and then might not be everyone's idea of gracious living. If an animal wished to have abilities like independent movement and some measure of freedom from random environmental fluctuations, it would have to do more than the sponge . . . something a little more innovative . . . a bit more *creative*.

An Alternative Modified

One could slightly alter choice two, moving the nutrients past the feeding parts. If the whole organism were encased inside a protective shell, the nutrients could be concentrated in an internal medium and presented to the individual living parts of the organism in that fashion. That way all kinds of problems could be avoided and some real advantages obtained. The size of the protective shell could be increased so that the advantages of size would be achieved, while at the same time, the individual cells inside the shell would not have to grow, because diffusion could handle their individual exchange problems. It would free the organism from the sponge-like life. Individual cells would be anchored in position inside the shell, and they would be dependent on *their* environment, but that environment would be of their own manufacture. The whole organism would be free to move about from place to place. Its dependence on its immediate environment would be vastly reduced. When a given environment became unsatisfactory, the whole organism could get up and move to a better one. By enforcing a little internal cooperation, the internal environment could be kept unchanged, and the nutritious medium inside could supply everything necessary. It would have to be replenished periodically, of course, just as it would have to be swept clean of debris, but if that could be done, the whole organism would have some measure of environmental independence.

The Medium

The medium would have to be nutritious, of course, and there are some other prerequisites that would have to be satisfied before such an organism would be able to carry around its own personal environment inside its body. It would have to be a thin fluid—the thinner the better—so it could be moved without using too much energy. The pattern of movement would have to be extensive, because it would have to wash every cell in the body constantly. Since it would be carrying all kinds of foods and waste products, it would be handy if it could dissolve most of these. All these requirements taken together pretty well restrict the choices of available medium. It would almost have to be an aqueous one, since water is about the only thing that satisfies all the requisites.

A Pump

Such an organism would gain no real freedom if the movement of this special internal medium were left to chance. Stagnation could be fatal, because wastes would surely concentrate someplace, and there would undoubtedly be local shortages of nutrients. There would have to be a better way; that kind of design is simply too capricious. A pump would solve the problem nicely. It would cost a little energy, but it would be worth it, because it would provide the nutritious medium with a dependable way of getting around.

Blood Vessels

Obviously, a pump would have to have an entrance and an exit in it so that the fluid could get in and out, and it would be nice to have tubes to carry the medium to and from the pump. A complete set of tubes or pipes could carry the fluid back and forth, taking nutrients deep into the body and carting waste products away. More than that, tubes could segregate their contents from the fluid sloshing around the outside of the cells. Tubes would also mean that replenishment zones and sewage treatment structures could be visited regularly, *after* the medium had run past the cells that were feeding and dumping wastes.

Recycling

And that brings us to another point. Once the nutrient medium has been organized and enclosed in its tubes, it would be a waste of everything, including energy, to permit it to be lost after washing internal structures just one time. If it meets all the criteria mentioned up to this point, it is worth saving, so obviously there should be provisions made to recycle it. To use the same fluid over and over again requires a means of washing out the toxins and waste and replenishing its supplies.

As you can easily see, we have just described the philosophy behind the development of the blood and the circulatory system.

A Brief Summary of the Situation

We have seen in previous chapters that our intracellular organelles and the cytosol never demonstrate any concern over where they are going to get their fuel molecules, oxygen, or the various building blocks they might need to maintain their organization. They apparently operate on the assumption that everything will be right there when they need it, and there are many systems available to see that whatever they might need is always present. The interstitial fluid provides the services for the cytosol, while the blood is designed to see that the interstitial fluid never wants for anything.

The System as a Whole

The blood is mainly a transportation system with a subsidiary role as a communications network (chapter 11). It functions in much the same way as the fuel lines function in a car. Like those metal fuel lines, the blood network carries the refined fuel molecules from the processing plants or storage tanks outside the body into the tiny places where the energy is released.

The fuel transport system in an automobile, however, is a one-way system, and it has a pretty easy time of it when compared to the tremendous problems the human circulatory system has to overcome. The number of parts the blood has to stock and cart around and the complexity of the machinery it services make the operation of an automobile pale by comparison. No car that was ever built operates with the perpetual, frenzied vigor of the human body. Every single body cell—and there are trillions—represents a tiny oxygen- and fuel-consuming engine, and every one of them needs individual attention. For example, each group of cellular engines often operates at a different speed than its neighbors, so the flow of fuel needs to be adjusted differentially in order to conform to the special requirements of each separate part. To this end, regulating mechanisms in the head and throat must send chemical instructions and information to organs in the abdomen, where spare parts and roughly refined fuel molecules are prepared. Elsewhere, glands all over the body release chemicals designed to adjust cellular activity and priorities. All of these mechanisms, plus a good many others, trust the blood to handle their transportation and communication chores, and it must deliver these messages with care, since each must get to the correct place. Obviously, the blood has to be able to do more than just carry things around blindly.

The circulatory system must handle all of its chores dependably and without oversupplying or starving anything. Everything, everywhere, requires constant monitoring, and there must be unbelievable flexibility throughout the system. The blood vessels carrying the blood must be able to adjust to increased or decreased pressures, they must be able to expand or shrink as their loads vary, and they must be capable of switching large volumes of blood from one vessel to another at a moment's notice.

And it is not just the vessels carrying the precious fluid that must be instantly compliant. The various chemicals that make up the blood must be tractable also. The hemoglobin, for example, must be able to alter the amount of O_2 it releases, and it must be able to adjust to changing demands immediately. Carbon dioxide must be packed and shipped out when it accumulates, and if there is a sudden surge in CO_2 production, that must be handled smoothly and instantly.

The Circulatory Plan

The circulatory *plan* is very important. We need to know where the blood goes on its never-ending travels and what is accomplished at every way station and turnoff it encounters. The number of problems that need solutions is legion. For instance, in its trips through the body, the bloodstream cycles again and again through tissue exchange areas, where it picks up large quantities of waste materials. Removing all this waste prevents the interstitial fluids from becoming polluted, but now the problem is simply transferred. All that debris is now in the blood. How do we keep the blood from becoming polluted?

How does the blood avoid unusual depletion of raw materials and oxygen when it passes through muscle tissue during periods of unusually high activity?

When several tissues are using fuel and producing wastes at different rates, what mechanisms are used to manipulate the vessels and adjust circulation so that each separate problem receives its own, personal solution?

What principles are used to vary flow and adjust pressures locally without changing them elsewhere?

How are oxygen release and waste collection adjusted so that areas of extreme activity will get all they need without depleting supplies earmarked for tissues a little farther down the line?

Detours and Freeways

Optimally, there should be several routes that the blood can take, and a subsequent division of labor. The route the blood follows out to the tissues should be separate from the one running through the purifying chambers. Other pathways should be available to route blood into the nutrient warehouses. The mammalian circulatory system has affected such a separation, yet in actual fact there is only one bloodstream . . . one continuous river. The body has found a way to keep short streams of blood, each one different from its predecessor or neighbor, *functionally* separated while maintaining physical continuity. It seems terribly complicated, but it is not really so hard—not in concept. All that it really requires is careful planning and a few "traffic cops" in the circulation to direct the flow along the freeways and down the various off-ramps.

Separations in a Single Stream

Probably the biggest supply problem involves oxygen and carbon dioxide. Both of these gases are involved in energy production, which means consumption of one and evolution of the other is both critical and nonstop. Once the blood has relinquished its oxygen and has loaded up with carbon dioxide, it *must* undergo treatment before returning to the tissues. The easiest way to handle such a problem is to sweep it clean and replenish its oxygen immediately. The importance the body attaches to doing this is evidenced by noting that, of all the cleaning and supplying operations the blood is subjected to, respiratory exchange is the only one that involves all of the blood every cycle. The bloodstream shoots off tributaries to pick up nutrients from the gut—so one arterial branch does this as it passes the intestinal tract and the other branch does not. The system forks again so the kidneys can scrub the blood clean—but again, only part of it is treated by the kidneys each cycle. Where the respiratory system is involved, no tributary branches lead to the respiratory surfaces. The route to the lungs is part of the mainstream, and none of the fluid can bypass it.

Figure 13.1 Schematic diagram of the human circulatory plan. Please note that 100 percent of the blood goes through the lungs on each circuit. (*1*) Pulmonary pump (right heart chambers); (*2*) systemic pump (left heart chambers); (*3*) lungs; (*4*) cerebral circulation; (*5*) forelimbs; (*6*) digestive tract; (*7*) liver; (*8*) kidneys; (*9*) lower extremities.

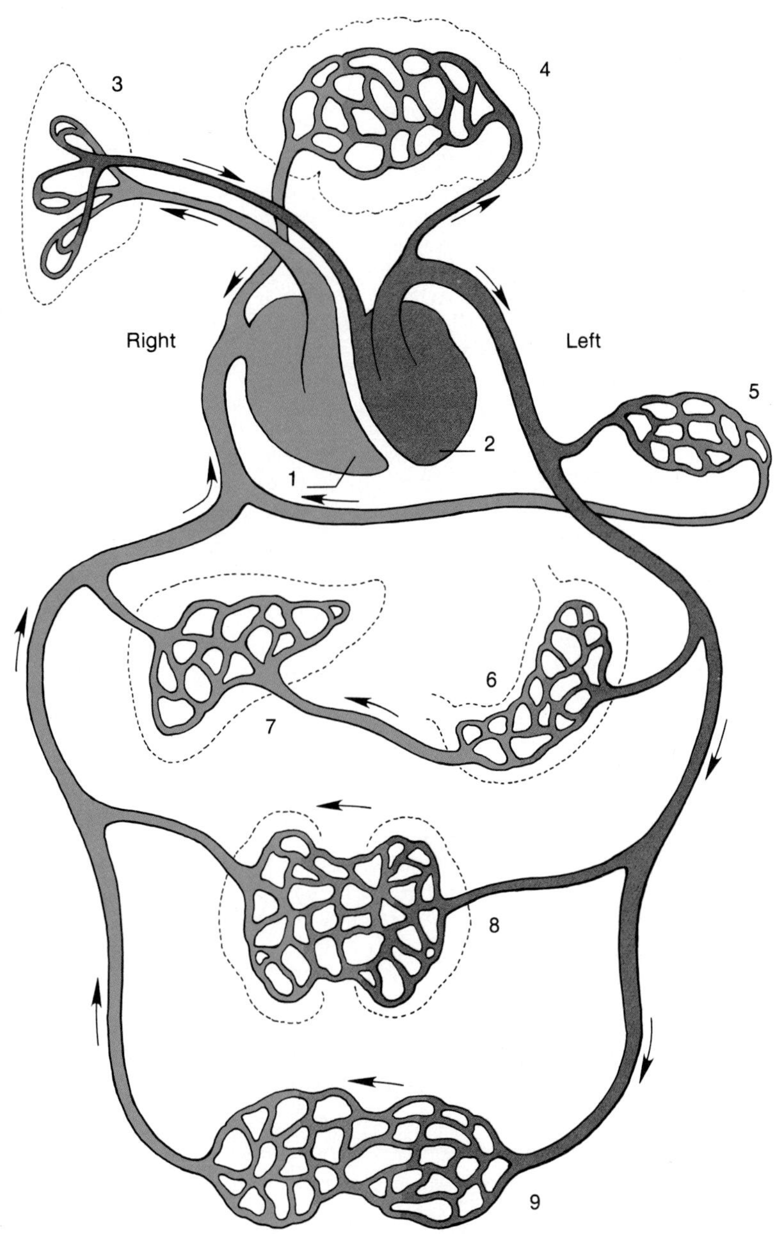

Tributaries and Turnpikes

There are, nevertheless, lots of branches throughout the circulatory system, and each serves to separate the river of blood. None of them is as complete as the pulmonary separation, but they do their job nonetheless.

As you can see in figure 13.1, each of these separations deflects a certain percentage of the blood away from the main "highway." As the aorta courses through the body, tributaries spring from it continuously, and bifurcations divide the stream, rerouting some of the blood into warehouses or cleansing stations while the other branch continues its journey to the systemic capillaries. Following this pattern, a predetermined fraction of the blood goes into a supply area or a scrubbing station every circuit, so part of the blood is always getting cleaned or restocked.

An Early Pit Stop

In one of the earliest separations, one branch off the aorta dives down to the gut, where digested nutrients are picked up. These nutrients are ultimately destined to provide fuels and raw materials for the body's cellular machinery. A little further refining is usually necessary, but that is done in the cells. The digestive system refines it sufficiently to be transported, and the blood picks it up and carries it as it is.

When it leaves the absorptive areas of the gut, that part of the bloodstream is actually overloaded with

Panel 13.1

The Reason for a Two-Pump Plan

The complex circulatory plan in humans is an evolutionary refinement of previous plans, and all of its parts, including the two separate pumps, are necessary.

Fishes have devised the simplest method of handling the problem of exposing all of their blood to oxygen-replenishing surfaces each circuit. As you can see in figure 13.A, the blood goes straight to the heart after leaving the systemic capillaries. It has completed its route through the fish's body, and by the time it enters the heart, it is loaded with wastes of all kinds and is depleted of provisions. It is clearly venous blood, so before it can be reused, it has to be processed. In any orderly operation, the most critical parameter should be adjusted first, and it is. The fish's blood is first recharged with oxygen and the plasma swept clean of excess carbon dioxide. This means a trip through the capillaries of the respiratory organ, and in fishes, this organ is the gills. It is during this sojourn that we encounter a critical weakness in the fish's circulatory plan.

A Low-Pressure Systemic Circulation

Blood enters the gills at the highest pressure available in the fish's circulatory system. But when it pushes through the tiny vessels in the gills, nearly all the pressure disappears. The enormous surface area of the respiratory capillaries results in tremendous frictional losses, and that steals the pressure head provided by the heart. As a result, when the blood leaves the gills and heads out to the tissues, it does so slowly and at a very low pressure.

Figure 13.A Schematic of the fish circulatory plan: (*1*) Venous blood entering the heart; (*2*) the two-chambered heart; (*3*) gill capillaries; (*4*) cerebral arteries; (*5*) systemic arteries. Numbers 4 and 5 are low-pressure systems.

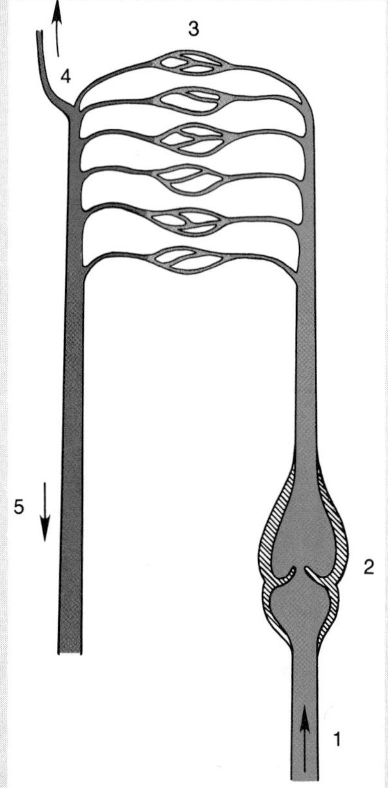

Obviously this circulatory plan works if you are a fish, because after all, there are lots of fishes around. It is not,

nutrients, and this has to be adjusted fairly quickly. This is no casual operation—it is quite possible to have too much of a good thing. Glucose, for instance, is too abundant in the post-absorptive blood to be circulated through the entire system. It could conceivably do some damage if it remained for any length of time in high concentrations in the tissues, so instead of heading out to the body cells after loading up in the intestinal capillary beds, the nutrient-laden blood first homes in on the liver.

The Liver: A Processing Plant and Warehouse

The liver is a remarkable organ. It seems to be involved somehow in almost everything going on in the body. In this case, it has to remove some of the excess nutrient materials from the blood and "put them in mothballs" until they are needed. Blood glucose is carefully checked; any excess is converted to storage molecules (glycogen) and stowed away. Amino acids, lipids—all the foodstuffs—get the same consideration. Amino acids are incorporated into proteins or become part of the body's free amino acid pool. Excess fats are converted to their particular storage form. By the time the blood leaves the liver, much of the extra nutrient that it carried has been adjusted or stored, and nutrient concentrations are either at, or close to, correct levels.

For the time being, the excess nutrient molecules have been packaged and stored—but they are ready to undergo rapid activation and utilization whenever necessary.

Figure 13.B Schematic of the dual circulation of humans. Please note that while the two systems are functionally separate, there is no morphological separation. There is only one bloodstream.

The right heart and the pulmonary circulation make up an essentially low-pressure system, and neither the pump nor the arteries is very thick-walled. The left system, however, is high pressure, and both arteries and heart have walls of thick muscle. (Since passage through capillaries always steals pressure, there is very little muscle required in the veins.)

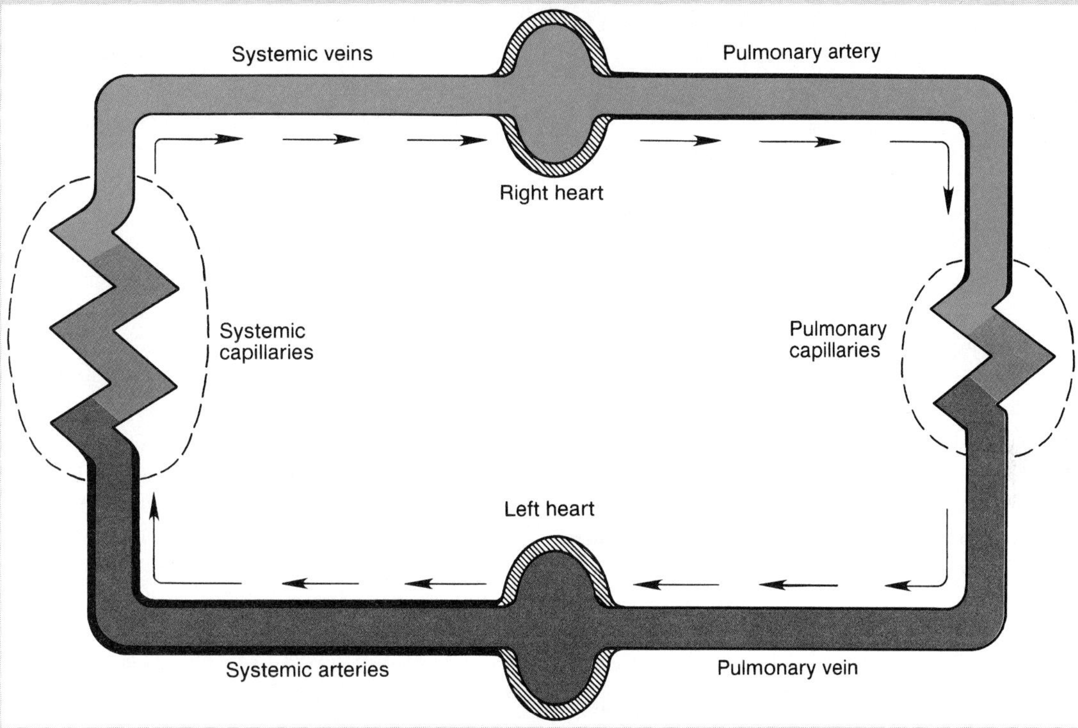

however, good enough for a warm-blooded mammal. Energy consumption in mammals is much too high, and resupplying it is too important to settle for anything but peak efficiency. Just imagine the pressures required to get blood from the heart up into the head of a human, let alone a giraffe or some of the long-necked dinosaurs. No low-pressure system could begin to do the job. Somehow, somewhere, that blood pressure has got to be restored after it leaves the respiratory surfaces. The simplest way, naturally, would be to install *another pump* on the other side of the respiratory surfaces (figure 13.B). Such a pump would provide the additional hydrostatic pressure head so essential to a really efficient systemic circulation. That is precisely how it is handled in the human circulatory plan.

The Renal Branch

Shortly after the first separation breaks a vessel free to flow through the gut, another tributary separates from the aorta, dividing the arterial stream again. This time, the turnoff diverts the blood to the kidneys, where it undergoes processing to adjust its loads of minerals, nitrogenous wastes, and water. The kidney is one of the most important organs in the entire body for maintaining fluid homeostasis. It does produce the waste known as urine, and for that reason it is considered the primary organ in our excretory system, but excretion is not its most important job.

A Mainline Processing Plant

All of these forks in the circulation are important or they would not exist. The blood must not be allowed to get choked up with either wastes or nutrients, and constant, careful monitoring and adjustment is necessary to avoid this. Flushing blood through the kidneys is a constant process in a normally functioning person, but important as it is, it is not necessary to flush all of the blood each time around. It is not a disaster if the liver fails to adjust nutrient levels in all of the blood all of the time, nor is it necessary for the gut to be injecting processed nutrients constantly.

Of all the treatments the blood is subjected to, it appears that only one must never be partial or neglected—not even for a few minutes. *Delivery of oxygen* to the body's cells must be a constant, never-ending process, and both the blood and the circulatory system have been designed with this in mind. The most abundant elements in the blood are involved in the transport of oxygen, and of all the organs that process blood, only the lungs process all of it every circuit.

The Dual Circulation of Humans

One of the most important modifications in the vertebrate circulation has been the adoption of a two-pump system. It eliminates the problem of having to deal with a low-pressure systemic circulation.

Since the heart actually features two separated pumps, the mammalian circulatory system is often referred to as a **dual system,** but this designation is not strictly accurate. It's inaccurate because there is not really any separation between the **pulmonary circulation** and the **systemic circulation.** True, each has its own heart chamber to provide the necessary pumping action; each runs through its own exchange zones and then returns to the heart to be pumped out again—but there is only *one stream of fluid,* and it is continuous (figure 13.B).

The bloodstream *is* separate in that the vessels of the two "systems" trade their loads every circuit. Once it is passed through the systemic exchange surfaces, all of the blood must go through the pulmonary vessels. After treatment in the lungs, it comes back to the heart and can then return to the systemic circulation for another pass through the body. There is no break in blood flow anywhere. It flows in a continuous stream from the pulmonary to the systemic circulation and back again, yet by putting them "in series" (in a straight, continuous line), the body achieves a *functional separation* of the two systems. (Obviously, then, the respiratory organs must never fail, and that makes them very important to us. We'll investigate the details of their function presently, but for now, let's continue our consideration of circulatory design.)

Some Hydrodynamics

Circulation of the blood is a much more complex process than most of us realize. It has been likened to the flow of fluid through the pipes in our homes, and in some ways, that's not a bad analogy. There are some important differences, however. For instance:

Pressure

1. The water pressure in our homes is constant, whereas the pressure developed by our hearts is stop-and-go.
2. In our homes, the pressure head probably does not significantly vary 70 or 80 times in a week. In our bodies, arterial pressure varies 70 to 80 times *a minute* . . . when we are resting. If we exercise, it varies through a broader range and more often.
3. In our homes, mechanisms designed to compensate for a sudden change in water pressure are not necessary, and we do not have any. Our circulatory system is loaded with them, and when the occasion demands, both *pressure* and *flow rate* can be adjusted across an extremely broad range.

Plumbing

1. The pipes through which water flows in our cities and homes are rigid. Our blood vessels, on the other hand, are pliable—they *stretch.* The veins in particular are flimsy, easily distorted tubes with an elasticity that is surprising. Our arterial "pipes" do not have the plasticity the veins have, but they are far from rigid.
2. Because the plumbing in our homes is rigid, any pressures that develop at the source will exist everywhere in the system the instant they are produced. If our arteries were rigid, as pressures developed in the heart, they would be felt everywhere in our arterial circulation, and they would drop to zero as soon as the heart stopped contracting. As it is, however, the peak pressure produced in the heart is never present in the arterial system, because the arteries stretch and thereby absorb some of the heart's energy. This "stored" energy is returned to the system when the heart relaxes, providing enough pressure to keep the blood moving through the smaller vessels in a steady stream.

System Design

1. The water delivery system that supplies our homes is an open system. Once it delivers its load to the exchange zones, there is an enormous delay before the fluid is recycled if, indeed, it ever is. The closed circulatory system that operates in our bodies has an extremely short recycling period, so any delays or demands for increased flow anywhere will affect the velocity and pressure everywhere.
2. To minimize systemic variations due to local demands in the circulatory system, precision regulatory systems operate continuously—systems that continually adjust flow volume and pressure in individual blood vessels everywhere.

Figure 13.2 A view of the heart with its protective membranes removed. The great central mass is all muscle (myocardium), and the surface grooves (sulci) indicate the dividing lines between chambers.

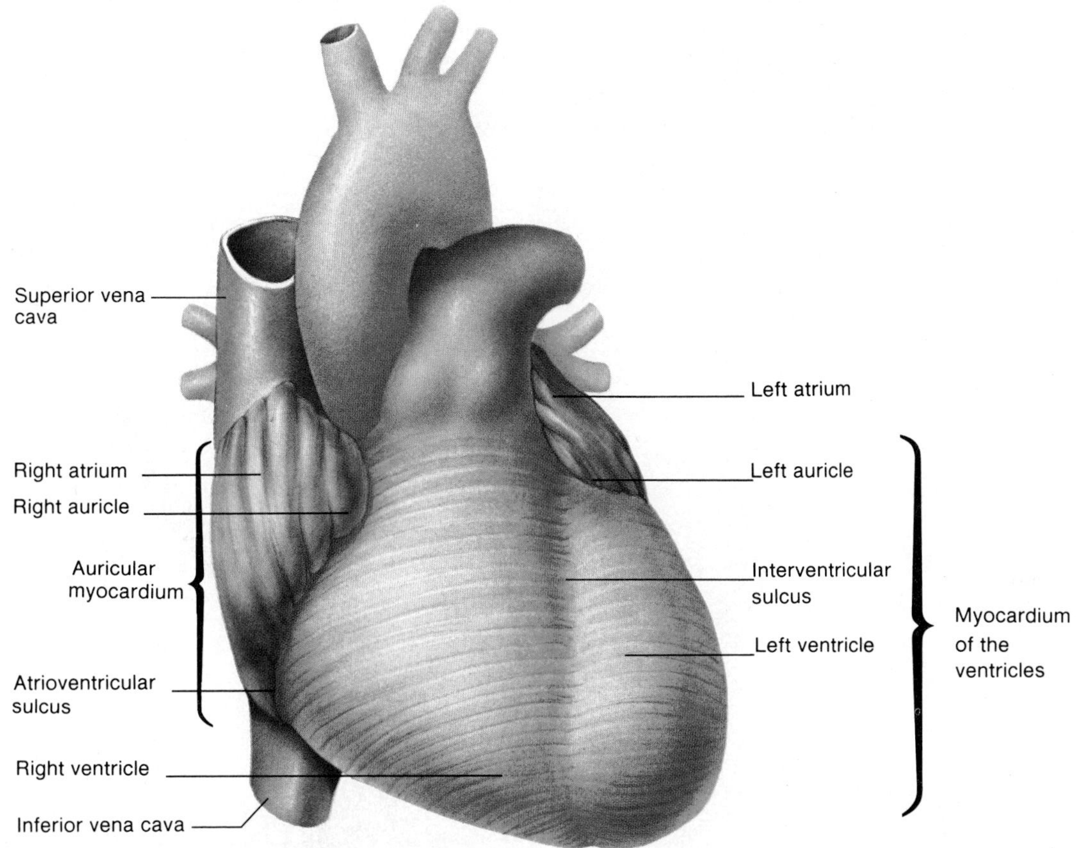

To understand how all these things are accomplished, we must take a look at how our bodies produce the blood pressure and then investigate some of the things that battle against it. The pressure head supplied by the heart, as it turns out, is the only force that works to thrust the blood out into the arterial circulation. Since this is where it all starts, the heart is the logical place for us to begin also.

The Human Heart

The human heart is a typical mammalian heart. As such, it is a solid lump of muscle, and compared with the other muscles in our bodies, it is unique. Chemically, it is much like skeletal muscle. The basic mechanisms that provide it with contractile ability are similar to the ones that move your limbs or propel food through your gut. There are a few functional differences, subtle ones. Morphologically, as we know, it is quite different.

The Cardiac Blueprint

The mammalian heart is designed so that there are two pumps in a single structure. Instead of having one heart to pump blood through our lungs and a separate one to pump it through our bodies, we have both pumps packed in a single unit. What is more, these pumps have been assembled with such ingenuity that even though they are both parts of the same structure and pump synchronously, they do not produce anywhere near equal pressures. We will discuss this shortly, but first of all, let us look at the overall design.

The human heart weighs about 350 grams—that is a little over three-quarters of a pound—which makes it a pretty fair-sized lump of muscle (figure 13.2). This is the **myocardium.** It is not actually *solid* muscle, inasmuch as it is hollowed out inside, but where it *is* solid, it's muscle. The surfaces both inside and out are covered with a thin sheet of connective tissue (figure 13.3). On the inner surfaces, lining the

Figure 13.3 An external view of the heart, showing the external membranes and their arrangement.

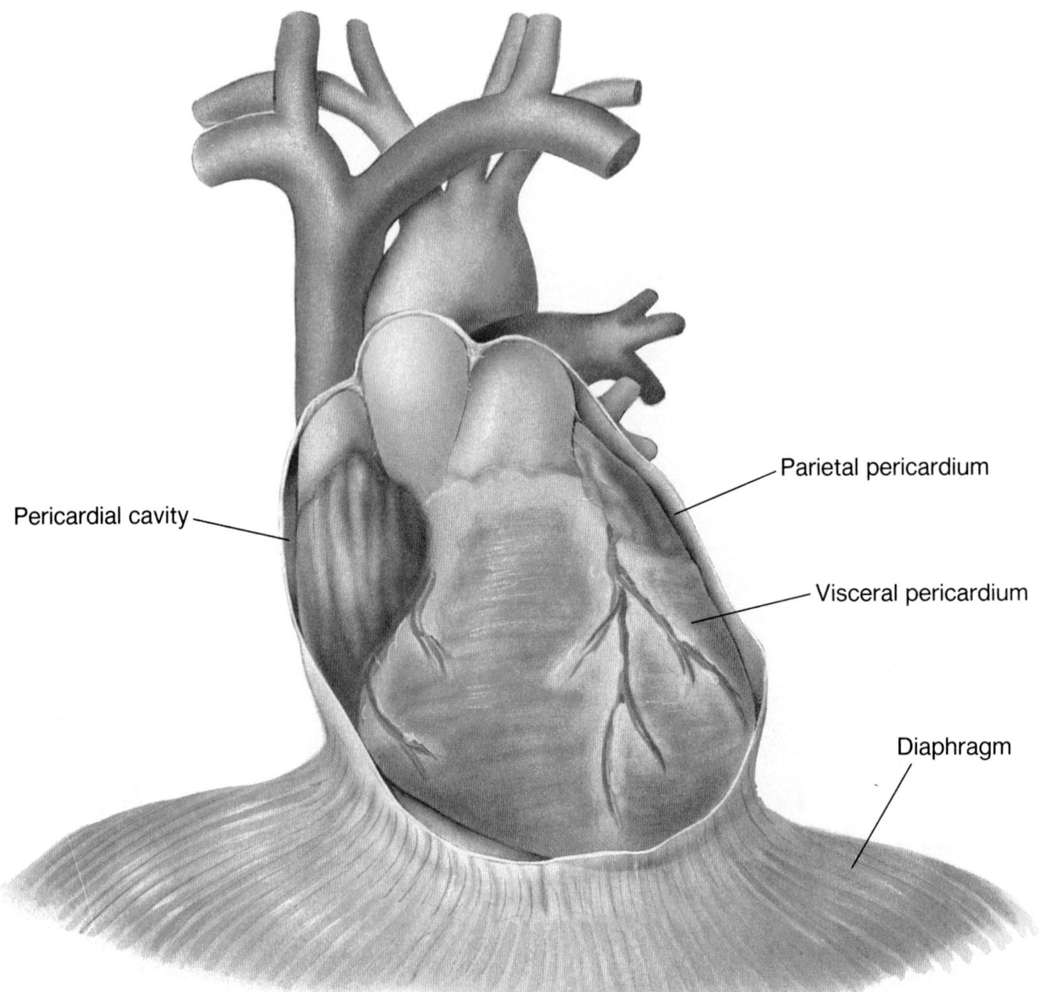

chambers of the heart, this connective tissue is called the **endocardium** (figure 13.4), while the sheet wrapped around the outside of the heart is known as **epicardium.** As you can see from figure 13.3, the epicardium has two parts. The inner part—the **visceral pericardium**—adheres tightly to the outer surface of the heart, covering it completely. Then it splays upward and fans out in a broad, tough sheet that forms a sack. This is the **parietal pericardium,** and the sack it forms is known as the **pericardial sack.** Inside this pericardial sack the heart reposes, immersed in a serous fluid rich in proteins.

Avoiding Wear

These sheets of connective tissue, plus the serous fluid inside the sack, have an extremely important function. The heart, you see, while it is fixed firmly in the middle of the chest, is nevertheless suspended from the great blood vessels and hangs down into the pericardial sack like a bunch of grapes dangling from several thick stems. This means that when you lie down on your back, the posterior surface of your heart muscle lies down, too, touching the posterior surface of the pericardial sack. When you flip over onto your front, the heart lies against the anterior surface. In other words, it responds to your body movements and the demands of gravity.

It also means that your heart is rubbing against something almost constantly. As it continually contracts and relaxes, contracts and relaxes, it moves against the tissue it touches, creating friction. This situation represents a potential problem. The heart muscle is probably the single most important muscle in the human body, and because of the way it works, the operation of each part of it depends intimately on every other part being present and working right. For this reason, damage to any part of that muscle could represent a problem of considerable proportions. To avoid any such damage, there must be no frictional losses, and that is, at least in part, what the connective tissue sheets surrounding the heart are for. That is one reason, too, for the pericardial fluid. The epicardium

Figure 13.4 A diagrammatic section of the apex of the heart showing the myocardium and the protective sheaths that cover it inside and out.

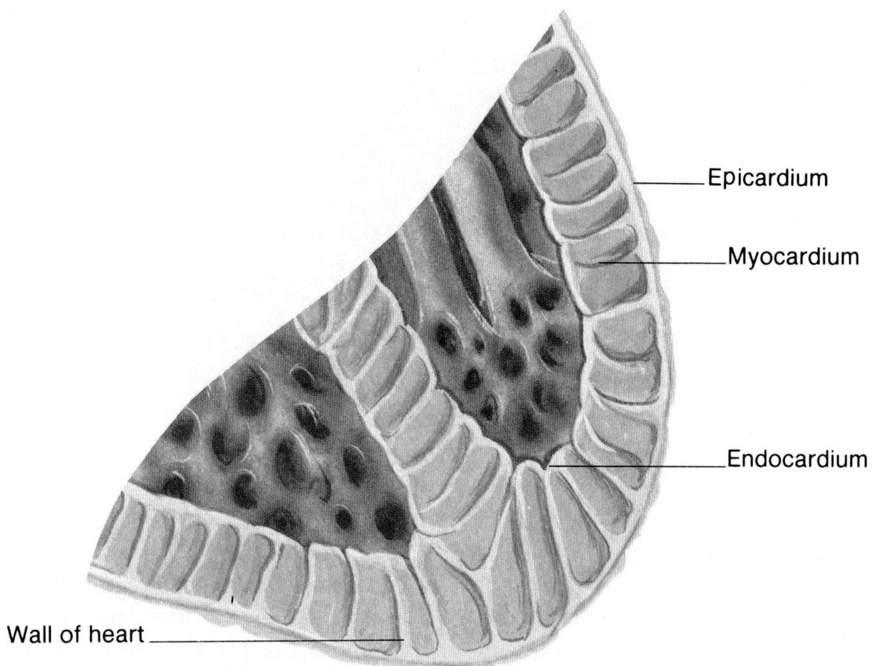

and pericardium are highly polished veneers. When they are wet—which they always are—they have the sheen of a frozen pond. Such glistening, smooth surfaces rubbing against each other would produce almost no friction due to their very nature, but just in case, the serous fluid is there. This fluid is quite thin—much thinner than the lubricants most of us have used to oil our household appliances—but thin or not, it is an excellent lubricant. The proteins that it contains act like millions of tiny ball bearings, so that when the smooth surfaces of connective tissue move against each other, they never quite make contact. In between them, these tiny "ball bearings" roll back and forth with each beat, preventing even slight frictional wear from occurring.

Despite all these precautions, something could still go wrong. Maybe friction *could* wear off some slight bits of tissue. This possibility has been anticipated, and thanks to careful design, any slight loss will be connective tissue, not muscle. And except in the most extreme circumstances, it never amounts to more than a few cells every hour or so.

Chambers

There are four separate chambers in the human heart, two for each pump. The **atria,** the uppermost chambers, receive blood from veins, and figure 13.2 shows the ear-shaped appendages called **auricles** that project from the atrial wall. Blood is pumped from the atria into the largest of the heart chambers—the **ventricles.** Both the atria and the ventricles have muscular walls and are able to contract, but the atrial musculature is rather weak; in fact, the walls of the atria are actually more elastic than muscular. They are designed not only to contract and squirt blood into the ventricles, but also to stretch without offering much resistance to the incoming blood. The venous blood entering the heart from the systemic circulation moves under a very low pressure head, and any significant resistance would almost certainly stop it. The rebound elasticity of the atrial walls probably contributes to the suction the heart is able to apply to the entering venous blood.

There is often confusion about the terms *atrium* and *auricle* when applied to the heart. The term *auricle* was once used to designate the entire atrium of the heart. However, the word *atrium* refers to a chamber that ultimately leads into a second chamber, and this is such a perfect description of these upper heart structures that the term *atrium* gradually came into favor. For a while, *auricle* and *atrium* were considered synonymous. Then gradually *auricle* was accepted as referring to the muscular wall, while *atrium* was reserved for the open chamber itself.

Both ventricles are fairly heavily muscled, but the right one is less so. It has merely to pump the blood about a foot, into and through the lungs, while the left ventricle must propel its contents a much greater distance. And that is not the only resistance—all the blood going into the chest, shoulders, arms, and head must be thrust against the force of gravity. The left ventricle is easily the most heavily muscled of all the heart's chambers.

Figure 13.5 A cross-section through the human heart, showing the coronary skeleton of fibrous rings and the heart valves attached to them.

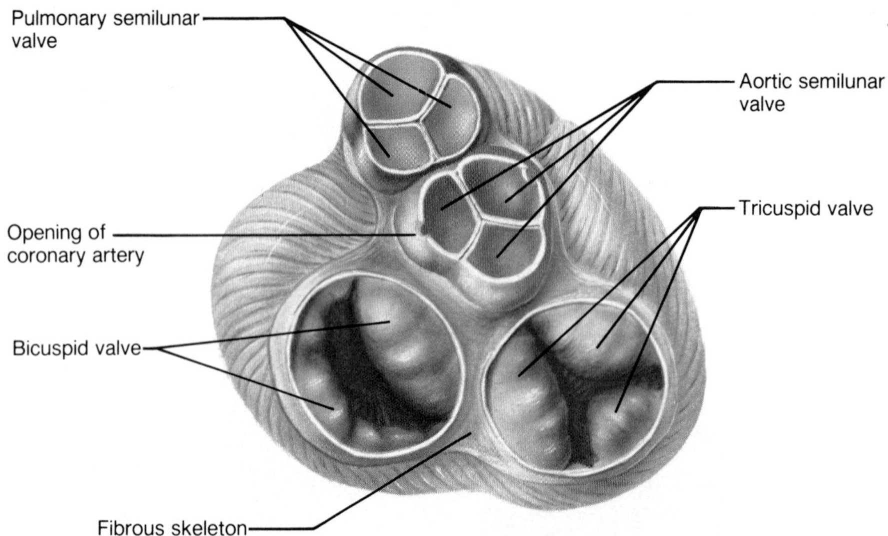

The Coronary Skeleton

Imbedded deep within the heart is a thick mass of fibrous connective tissue that forms a stiff barrier separating the atria from the ventricles. This dense, fibrous tissue forms a series of thick rings around the base of both the pulmonary artery and the aorta. These rings are continuous with the heavy masses of similar tissue along the upper half of the septum that separates the two ventricles. This stiff, dense tissue is known as the **skeleton of the heart** (figure 13.5).

The Heart Valves

The heart chambers are structurally separated from each other, and that, of course, is functionally essential. However, there must also be access routes between certain chambers so that blood can flow from one to the other. Simple holes will not suffice, because continuity between chambers must be intermittent; hence it must be possible to close off the access route when necessary. This is accomplished through the use of strategically placed *valves,* and there are four of them in the heart. Two of them guard the openings between the atria and the ventricles; hence they are known collectively as **atrioventricular** or **A-V valves.** The A-V valve between the left chambers of the heart is the **mitral** or **bicuspid valve;** the one between the right chambers is the **tricuspid valve.** Two other valves guard the exits from the ventricles; they are at the base of the aorta and the base of the pulmonary trunk. These are the **semilunar valves.** The one in the aorta is known specifically as the **aortic valve,** while the one in the pulmonary trunk is the **pulmonic valve.**

All four valves are imbedded solidly within the coronary skeleton, which provides not only a firm attachment, but also prevents them from dilating or collapsing during the vigorous movements produced repeatedly by the heart (figure 13.5).

Both the pulmonary artery and the aorta are, at their origin in the heart, surrounded by these dense rings of fibrous tissue, and these rings are continuous with other, similar rings that surround the valves.

Heart Movement

Some principles of cardiac activity have become pretty firmly entrenched in physiology. One of them states that *the strength of the heart's contraction depends on how much the heart muscle is stretched before the contraction begins.* These changes in stretch do not require any hormonal or neural control. The ability is built right into the myocardium and it explains to some extent how the heart can change the power of its beat immediately when it needs to. The more the heart is filled, the more powerful its contractions will be. This is known as the **Frank-Starling Heart Law,** and there is an abundance of support for it.

Not every conclusion that Frank and Starling reached about cardiac phenomena is correct, however. In writing of their heart research, they went on to say that once the contraction is completed, the heart simply relaxes and is stretched out as blood from the veins pours into it. The energy is supplied by venous pressure, and the heart simply lies there, completely relaxed, and lets itself be filled. As it turns out, this conclusion is unlikely. There are several reasons to question it.

The most obvious one can be seen easily in an experiment that is often conducted in undergraduate biology laboratories. Excised hearts (hearts that have been cut out of a living animal) will, when placed in a nutrient solution in a beaker, continue to beat rhythmically, contracting and then *expanding as they*

Figure 13.6 Threads or struts of connective tissue are strong between individual muscle cells, and these are stretched when the heart contracts, thus storing some of the available energy (*a*). This stored energy may help to expand the heart during diastole (*b*). (*c*) This image, taken with a scanning electron microscope, shows the thin threads of connective tissue linking the lateral surfaces of muscle cells in the heart. (From "The Heart as a Suction Pump" by Thomas F. Robinson, et al. Copyright © 1986 by Scientific American, Inc. All rights reserved.)

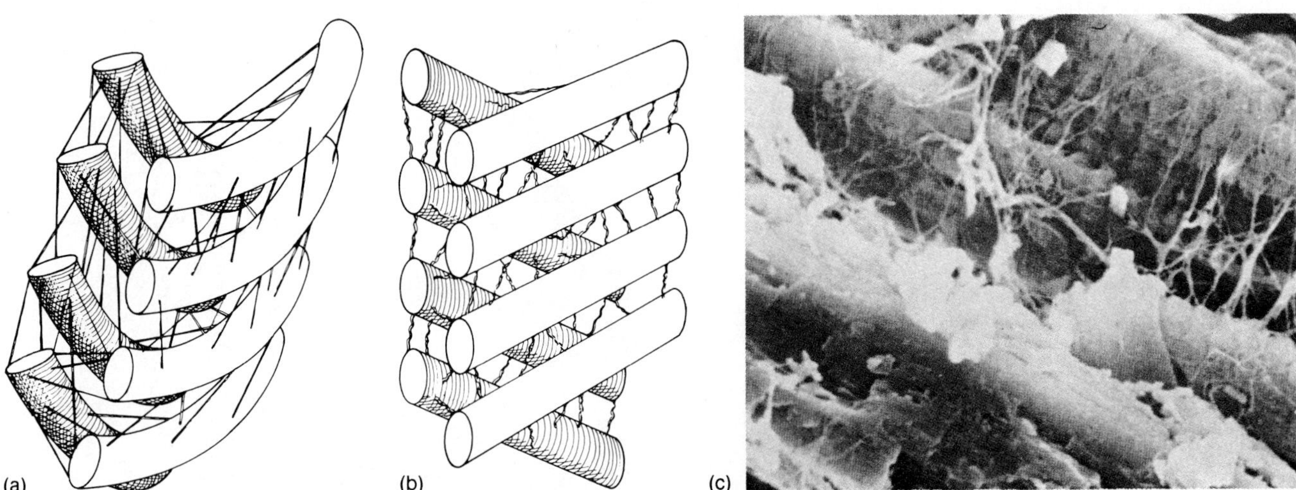

fill for another contraction. There are no veins, hence no venous pressure, in a glass beaker. Obviously, the heart is filling itself, and to do that, it must be producing some kind of suction.

Current theory suggests that the heart can not only contract with power, but it can also use energy to expand. The electron microscope shows that heart muscle fibers are connected to each other by strands of connective tissue, woven along the outside of the individual cells and holding them in place much as a venetian blind holds its individual slats in place (figure 13.6). The contractile proteins in cardiac muscle, like those in other types of muscle, exert their tension and produce their motion during contraction, but in the process, they stretch this elastic connective tissue, thus storing some of the contractile energy. It is also suggested that the contractile process forces an expansion of individual myocardial cells, increasing their diameter and storing additional elastic rebound energy. During the relaxation period that follows, this stored energy from the shortening process is used to lengthen the muscle fibers and thus expand the atrial and ventricular chambers without waiting for inrushing blood to stretch their walls.

This is an important capability. The venous blood in the great veins near the heart has almost no pressure. It has passed through myriad capillary beds in the systemic circulation, has fought gravity to make its way up legs and trunk, and by the time it reaches the upper chest, it needs every bit of help it can get to finish its circuit of the body. The expansion of the heart supplies that help by providing a negative pressure or suction to draw it into the right atrium. It aids similarly in the movement of blood into all the heart chambers, providing help that the moving fluid evidently needs.

This newly discovered ability of the heart has made quite a stir in physiological circles, because it indicates that under the right set of circumstances, muscles can use energy to *lengthen*, which was thought never to occur. Apparently the phenomenon is restricted to cardiac muscle, and a great deal of work remains to be done to completely explain the mechanisms. Nevertheless, all available experimental evidence suggests it is real enough and thus strongly supports its existence.

The idea of storing energy for future use is a lot older than most people realize. We, as humans, have been using the principle for millenia. The bow and arrow, one of the oldest weapons known, is a prime example of this. Consider what happens when an arrow is shot from a bow. The bow bends as you strain on it with your muscles. Then, when you release the string, it hurls the arrow forward with tremendous force, sometimes enough to slam it inches deep into solid wood. Now obviously the bow is not alive, and therefore the energy that hurled the arrow through the air cannot have originated with the bow. Where did it come from?

It came from you! Your muscles provided the energy when you drew back on the string. You forced energy into the wood of the bow as you caused it to bend, and the energy was stored in the wood in the same way potential energy is stored in a box that is picked up off the floor and placed on a table. When the bow is released, the potential energy you provided with your muscles changes, all at once, into kinetic, and thrusts the arrow away, while the wood returns to its original shape.

Figure 13.7 The heart's two pumps are enclosed within a single organ, and the blood flows in an unbroken stream through both. The right ventricle forces blood to the lungs, while the left ventricle forces blood to all other body parts. How does the composition of the blood in these two chambers differ?

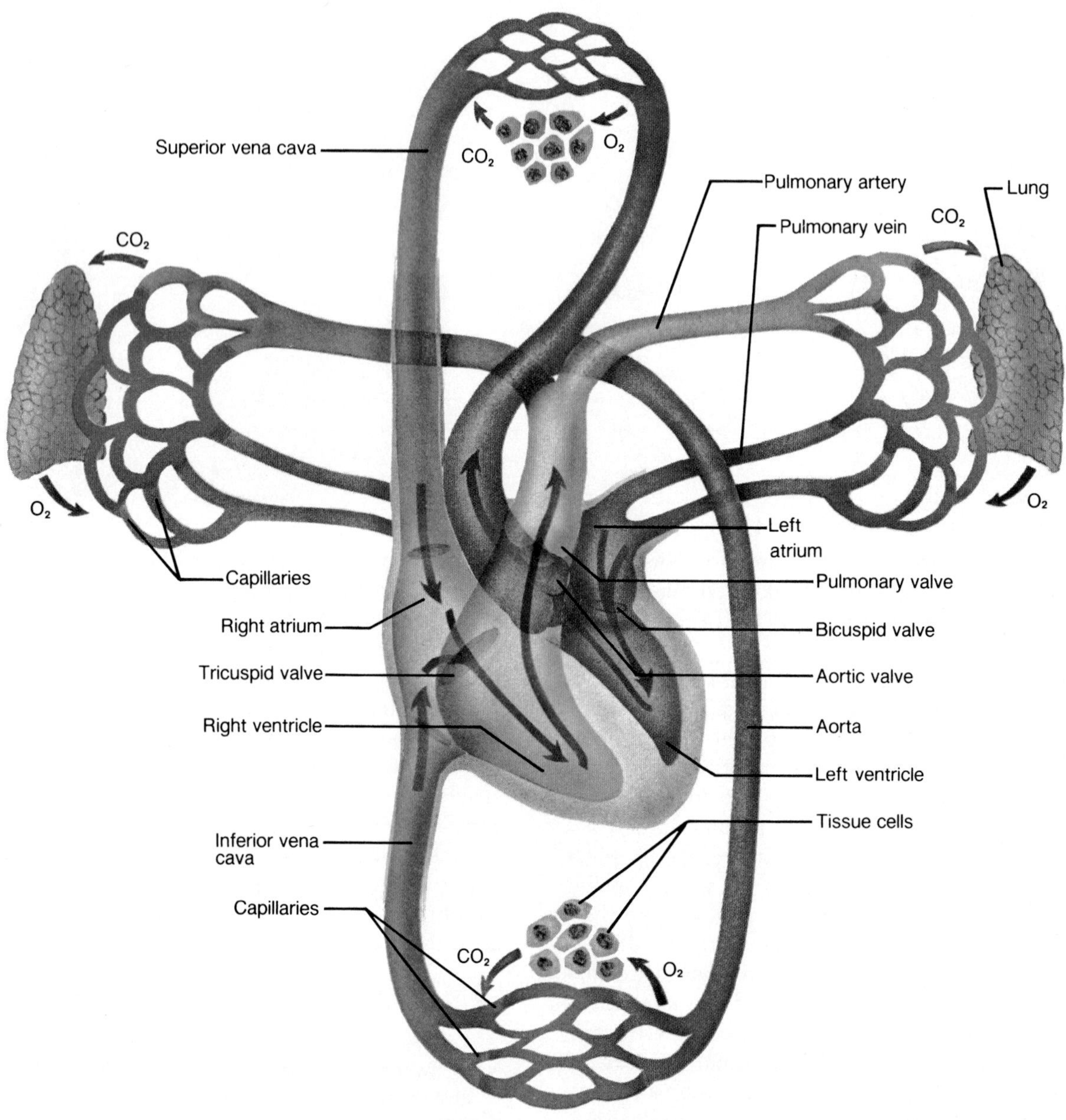

Systole

The contractile period, when the heart muscle is active, is known as **cardiac systole** (pronounced "*siss*-toll-ee"), which is a Greek way of saying it is "getting smaller." During this period, the heart muscle is clamping down on the blood it contains and forcing it out into the arteries. When it is finished squirting out its contents, when most of the blood is gone and the heart chambers are relatively empty, contractile tension must be relieved so it can fill up again.

Diastole

The period of relaxation is called **cardiac diastole** (*diastole*, "standing apart"; hence, "separating contractions"). During diastole (pronounced "dye-*ass*-toll-ee"), the heart is rebounding, muscles are flaccid, and the chambers can fill with blood.

The Path Through the Heart

The four chambers in the heart form the two separate pump-sets that are designed to keep the blood moving. Because of their unique design, they can vary pressures as needed and speed up or slow down according to demand (figure 13.7).

The Right Heart

Blood from the systemic circulation enters the right atrium from the **superior vena cava** and **inferior vena cava,** the two great veins that feed the heart blood

Figure 13.8 Cutaway view of a human heart. Arrows indicate blood flow through the heart. Note the relative thicknesses of myocardium in the right and left ventricles. The right ventricle feeds a low-pressure system, while the left ventricle's is high pressure.

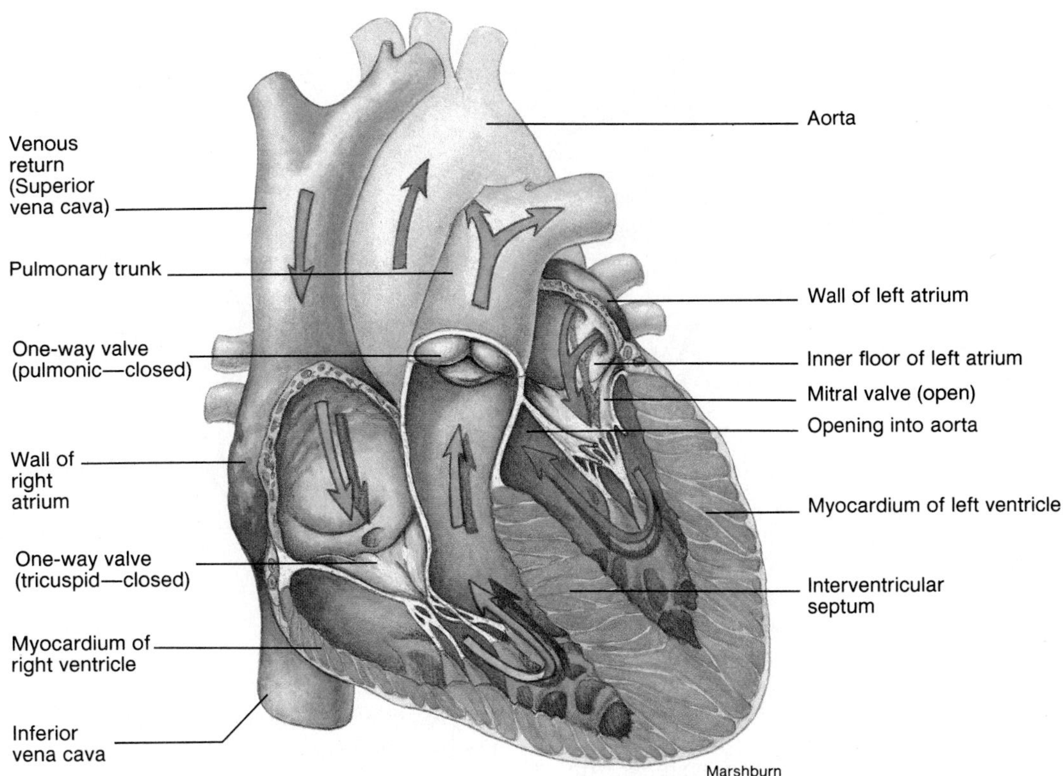

from the systemic circulation (figure 13.8). This blood has just run its route through the systemic capillary beds, dispensing O_2 and nutrients as needed and accepting all the CO_2 and other wastes dumped by the laboring cells. From the right atrium it is pumped through the tricuspid valve into the right ventricles and then into the pulmonary artery through the **pulmonic semilunar valve,** heading for the lungs. This is the beginning of the pulmonary circulation.

Arteries are commonly viewed as being the vessels that carry "pure" blood, while the veins have a reputation for carrying "impure" blood. This is not the way professionals view these groups of vessels. It is true that most veins carry deoxygenated blood and that most arteries carry freshly oxygenated blood, but that has no bearing on how they are named. It is not what the vessel *contains* that determines whether it is a vein or an artery, but rather *which direction* the blood it contains is going. Arteries carry blood away from the heart; veins carry blood toward the heart. In the pulmonary circulation, veins carry the "purest" blood and arteries carry the "impure." As you can see in figure 13.7, the pulmonary artery carries blood that has just returned from the systemic circulation and has been dumped in the heart by the great veins. It is the only artery in the body that carries deoxygenated blood.

In the thoracic cavity, near the lungs, the pulmonary artery splits into two vessels, one going to the right lung, the other to the left. Each of these arteries further divides and subdivides until capillary beds form against the respiratory surfaces of the lungs. Here the hemoglobin is recharged with O_2, and the level of CO_2 is adjusted to conform with the body's requirements. Then the blood heads back to the heart through four **pulmonary veins,** this time entering the left atrium.

The Left Heart

Blood is forced into the left ventricle through the mitral valve, and although both ventricles have to pump the same volume of blood so as to avoid traffic jams, the blood leaving the left ventricle has roughly six times the force of the blood pumped into the pulmonary circulation. With this enormous pressure head behind it, blood leaves the left ventricle through the **aortic semilunar valve** and enters the **aorta,** heading for capillary beds throughout the body. This is the beginning of the systemic circulation.

Figure 13.9 The cardiac conduction system.

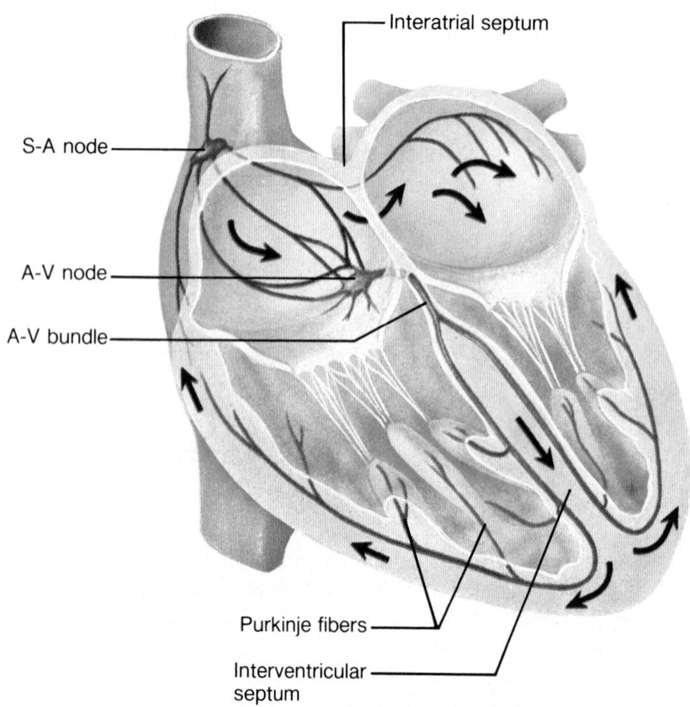

Origin of the Heartbeat

As with every other muscle in living systems, the heart's contraction is preceded by electrical activity. As we have already seen, in skeletal muscles, this electrical activity is triggered by the consciously controlled activity of motor nerves. In the muscles around our intestinal tract and blood vessels, nerves can also stimulate a flow of electricity in the muscles. But in cardiac muscle, nervous input—although it exists—is not necessary for continued, rhythmic, and adjustable cardiac operation. The basic rhythm of the heart is **myogenic,** meaning it has its genesis in the muscle, and as it turns out, much of its ability to respond to changing demands is built into its muscle cells.

An Inherent Basic Rhythm

Mammalian hearts can be removed from experimental animals rather easily, and if reasonable care is taken, it can be done without killing the heart. If the heart is kept at the proper temperature and in a nutrient solution well supplied with oxygen, it is possible to dissect the excised heart into tiny chunks and tease these chunks apart until individual muscle cells are isolated. Such cells, viewed under a microscope, can be seen beating independently, each at its own established rate. If the cells are then gently pushed together so that they are touching one another, they will all contract together, at the same rate, accepting the basic rate of whichever cell among them is beating fastest. That is apparently the way they work when the heart is intact.

The Pacemaker

There is a small cluster of unusual muscle cells on the outer surface of the heart muscle (figure 13.9). This group of modified cells is located just beneath the epicardium at the point where the great veins carrying blood back to the heart push their way into the right atrium. Because of its location and its nodular appearance, this cellular aggregation is known as the **sinoatrial** or **S-A node.** It is a specialized company of cells. They are unquestionably cardiac muscle, but they *look* a little different from the cells around them, and their inherent contractile rhythm is faster than any other cells in the heart. They are, therefore, the instigators of electrical activity in the heart, and they establish the basic rate for the contraction of heart musculature. For that reason, this group of cells has been given the alternate name the **pacemaker.**

Depolarization begins in cells of the S-A node and radiates out from the pacemaker region, spreading across the atria from cell to cell like splash ripples on the smooth surface of a pond. Since muscle contraction follows the flow of electricity, the muscle cells closest to the S-A node will contract first, and the rest will follow as the depolarization wave passes over them. The pattern will move from the point of origin outwardly, in concentric circles. The motion resembles a smooth, unhurried wave rolling gently across the whole upper segment of the heart. That is exactly what atrial contractions are like: gentle, wavelike, and relatively slow-moving. They squeeze the top of the heart first and progress toward the atrial base, directing the flow of blood down toward the two A-V valves through which the blood must pass to enter the ventricles. Contractile power is not very great, because the atria of the heart need not do much work to move the blood into the two lower chambers. The flow is all downhill and the distance is short. Furthermore, as noted previously, the larger, more heavily muscled ventricles provide considerable suction to aid the atria in their endeavors; hence powerful contractions, even if they were possible, would be excessive.

The depolarizing wave is able to flow completely over the surface of the atria, but it cannot cross over to the ventricular muscle mass because of an obstruction: the fibrous connective tissue of which the coronary skeleton is constructed. The coronary skeleton lies between the atria and the ventricles, and because of its permeability characteristics, it functions as an insulator; hence, it electrically isolates the upper heart chambers from the two ventricles, preventing the electrical signal from crossing.

The insulating characteristics of this *septum* are tremendously important, although it may not be immediately obvious. On the surface, it seems like it just gets in the way. It seems to impair the flow of electricity into the ventricles, and superficial reasoning hints that this is not good. Obviously the electrical impulse *must* be able to pass from the atria to the ventricular muscle if the heart is going to coordinate its activity.

However, a more circumspect look at the location of the valves within the heart chambers shows us that there is a very good reason for electrically separating the atria and the ventricles. As we have seen, all the heart valves are imbedded in the connective tissue septum between the upper and lower heart chambers (see figure 13.5). In order to get out of the heart, blood must pass through the semilunar valves, and as you can see, they are not at the *bottom* of the ventricles, but rather right at the *top*. That arrangement would present an almost insurmountable problem if the depolarization simply flowed across the septum into the ventricles.

Remember the sequence of events that occurs when a muscle contracts? The electrical depolarization comes first. That operates like a trigger finger, releasing calcium into the sarcoplasm. Contraction then follows along the same path as the electrical activity and right on its heels. If the depolarization simply crossed over to the ventricles as soon as it reached them, the top of the ventricles would contract first, and if you think about it, you will realize that's bad. It would initiate a rhythmic contraction that would squeeze first at the top and progress in a wave toward the bottom. That would force the blood down toward the bottom of each chamber, and since the ways out are at the top, down is not the direction it needs to go. To wring the blood out of the ventricles properly, the depolarizations should obviously begin at the bottom or *apex* of the ventricles. That way, the ventricles will start squeezing at the bottom of the heart and squeeze progressively upward. Nature has, therefore, ingeniously insulated the ventricles from the atria so that the flow of electricity can be directed instead of just letting it happen.

The A-V Node

On the right atrium, at the point indicated on figure 13.9, there is a second cluster of specialized cardiac muscle cells known as the **atrioventricular** or **A-V node.** The cells in this node are myocardial cells, and they penetrate the A-V septum. Thus the electrical activity in the atria can cross over to ventricular cells at this point. It does not, however, snap across the septum like a spark jumping a small gap. It must pass through the cells and the cells of the A-V node conduct more slowly than those of the atria. This delays the impulse about 100 ms before passing it through. Once through the septum, the electrical signal does not simply spray out like water from a shower head. Taking the path of least resistance, it enters a series of high-conductance modified cells that carry it down to the apex. These are bunched into a narrow bundle of specialized muscle fibers called the **ventricular bundle,** the **A-V bundle,** or the **bundle of His** (pronounced "hiss"). As figure 13.9 shows, this bundle splits apart just across the septum, forming two strips like the tines on a tuning fork. They, in turn, plunge down into the ventricular musculature, heading for the bottom tip of the heart. At the bottom are highly specialized cardiac muscle fibers that form tiny conducting "wires" called **Purkinje fibers.** These fibers separate from the bundles and carry the impulses out into the ventricular musculature.

When the electrical signals cross the septum into the ventricle, they go directly to the bundle of His and are then conducted rapidly through the bundle and into the Purkinje fibers without stimulating any of the myocardial cells. Only after they fan out in the Purkinje fibers do these impulses begin stimulating myocardial cells to contract. Because these fibers originate near the bottom of the heart, the bottom muscle cells are depolarized first. Ventricular contraction

Figure 13.10 Comparison of action potentials in nerve fibers, skeletal muscle fibers, and ventricular myocardial cells.

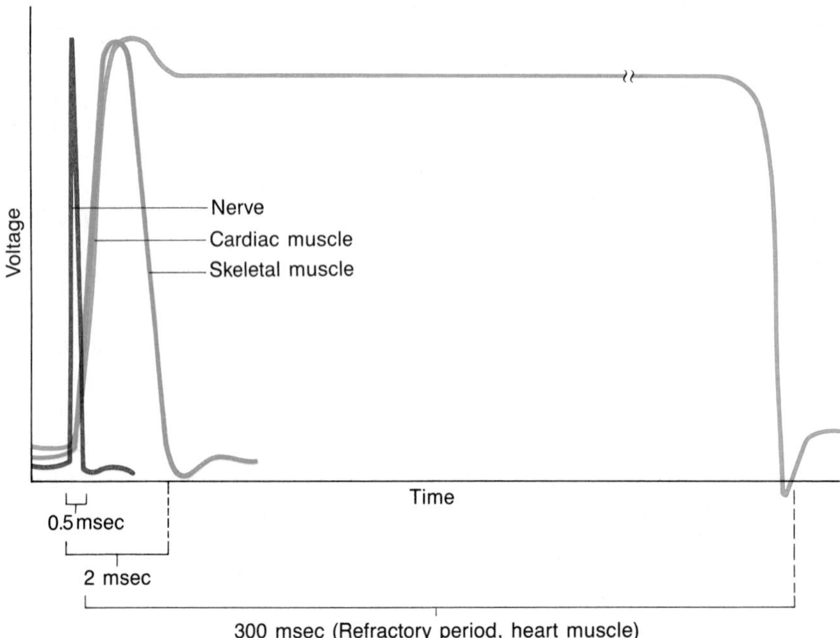

therefore begins at the bottom of the heart and squeezes progressively upward toward the valve openings. Like squeezing toothpaste out of a tube, the contraction pushes the blood from the bottom up, finally squirting it into the valves at the top. Because of the relative size of the muscle walls, the ventricular muscles contract with more force than the atria do, and that is as it should be. Both the left and right ventricles have a much harder job to do than the atria have; the left ventricle in particular must develop a good deal of pressure if it is going to force the blood through the entire peripheral circulation. With all its fibers contracting very close together in time, pressure is maximized.

The Action Potential in Myocardial Cells

The pattern of electrical activity in individual ventricular muscle cells is just as unique as the pattern of electrical activity through the heart as a whole. To appreciate the significance of the variation, perhaps we should compare the action potentials that appear in nerve and skeletal muscle cells with those that appear in ventricular myocardial cells (figure 13.10).

When an action potential is propagated on a nerve fiber, its appearance and disappearance is extremely rapid. Its duration at any given point on the fiber is on the order of a half millisecond.

Skeletal muscle passes the action potential a little more deliberately than a nerve fiber does, but it is still pretty fast. When an action potential appears on the sarcolemma, it can last for as long as two milliseconds—and that is four times as long as it lasts on the nerve innervating the muscle. As is the case with all muscles, the action potential is the electrical switch that turns on the contractile system and permits the muscle to begin doing its job.

Cardiac muscle is unique. As you can see from the figure, when a ventricular muscle cell fires, the action potential lasts a long time—as long as 300 ms before the muscle lets it go. It is followed by a perfectly normal recovery period.

No Tetanic Contractions

There is an important reason for this unusual electrical characteristic. Holding onto the action potential for 300 ms means that during that period of time, no other stimulating impulse can affect either the cell membranes or the contractile mechanisms inside. In other words, throughout that entire period—and the extended sodium inactivation period that follows—the heart muscle is refractory, and during refractory periods, the muscle cannot fire again. Recalling what we learned of muscle contractility (chapter 11), we can see that with a refractory period that long, *cardiac muscle cannot be tetanized.* No abnormal bombardment by neural or endocrine activity will ever paralyze the heart by freezing it in a contractile state.

A Diaphragmatic Anchor

As figure 13.3 shows, the pericardial membrane that surrounds the heart is attached at the bottom to the **diaphragm.** As we might expect, this articulation is functionally important. The diaphragm is a sheet of fairly heavy skeletal muscle and serves as both a lower border and a hermetic seal for the thoracic cavity. When the ventricles contract, the individual cells become shorter, and as a result the whole heart becomes shorter and fatter. This might reasonably be expected to pull the entire heart upward toward the great vessels attached near the top, since after all, these vessels are pretty rigid. But because of its connection to the diaphragm, that does not happen. Instead of the heart being pulled up toward the big vessels, it is pulled down toward the heavier and stronger diaphragm. This anchor at the bottom of the heart pulls the relaxing atrial musculature down, stretching the flaccid atrial walls, increasing their internal volume. This, it is theorized, stores potential energy in the relaxed muscle cells, producing suction when the ventricles relax and thus speeding the filling process.

Cardiac Innervation

As I have already pointed out, the S-A node is the primary pacemaker of the heart muscle. It is part of the heart; hence the heart's basic contractile rhythm is said to be *intrinsic,* meaning it is built-in. The heart does not need any neural or endocrine stimulus in order to beat regularly. As the Frank-Starling law points out, it can also, within certain limits, regulate intrinsically its rate and strength to conform to varying needs of the body. This is known as **automaticity,** because a reflex-like control is adjusted without any conscious volition. However, the intrinsic regulatory mechanisms of the heart are like the *coarse adjust* knob on a microscope or a radio. It can do a good job of helping you find what you are looking for, but to obtain a clear focus with minimum hassle, you need the *fine adjust* knob. The autonomic nerves that wrap around and penetrate the heart muscle serve that fine-adjust function.

Nervous Inhibition

Fibers of the tenth cranial nerve (the vagus) innervate the heart, and most of them terminate on the S-A node. When they are active, they have an inhibitory influence. When slightly active, they will slow the heart and reduce the strength of the beat, while a powerful burst of vagal activity can actually stop the heart and keep it stopped for as long as a half-minute. As usual, the vagus nerve serves a parasympathetic function.

Nervous Stimulation

Sympathetic fibers from the **accelerator nerve** speed up or strengthen heart movements. Some of these nerves *may* attach to the S-A node, but the latest investigations seem to indicate that most of them swirl around the ventricular muscles and terminate on bundle fibers. As with the vagus, these neural controls seem to concentrate largely on conductive tissue rather than on the contractile cells.

Nerves from both branches of the autonomic nervous system can respond to many things that the heart muscle itself is not very sensitive to (figure 13.11). Stretch receptors in arteries near the heart monitor blood volume, and baroreceptors in similar vessels keep a close watch on systemic blood pressure. Both neural and endocrine control systems keep abreast of isolated pressure changes in peripheral and central body areas, and they can recommend an adjustment or two when necessary. Nerve fibers and endocrine centers respond to emotional experiences of the conscious portion of the brain and can produce some eloquent changes in rate, as anyone knows who has ever walked along a dark, lonely road late at night. An unexpected crashing in nearby bushes or the sudden, unannounced appearance of a cat, darting across the road in front of you, can set the heart to pounding hard enough to hear.

Electrocardiography

With electrical impulses playing the major governing role in muscle contraction, it is logical to conclude that a check of the heart's electrical characteristics can give us considerable information about its condition. Heart rate, strength, and contractile synchrony are all controlled by voltage fluctuations across the muscle, and if there is something wrong, it can often be detected electrically. Things like heart arrhythmias, conduction abnormalities, a weaker beat—even the condition of the heart cells—can be spotted without actually seeing the heart itself. This information is gathered by using a standard **polygraph** and producing what is known as an **electrocardiogram (ECG).**

Electrodes placed in carefully selected spots on a subject's body can provide precise records of the electrical activity that precedes and controls heart contractions. As long as the record is obtained across the heart, it does not matter too much how far from the heart the electrodes are placed. Medical personnel

Figure 13.11 Heart rate can be affected by the central and autonomic nervous systems and the endocrine glands. Parasympathetic neurons end mainly on the nodes, whereas large numbers of sympathetic fibers terminate on the bundle of His.

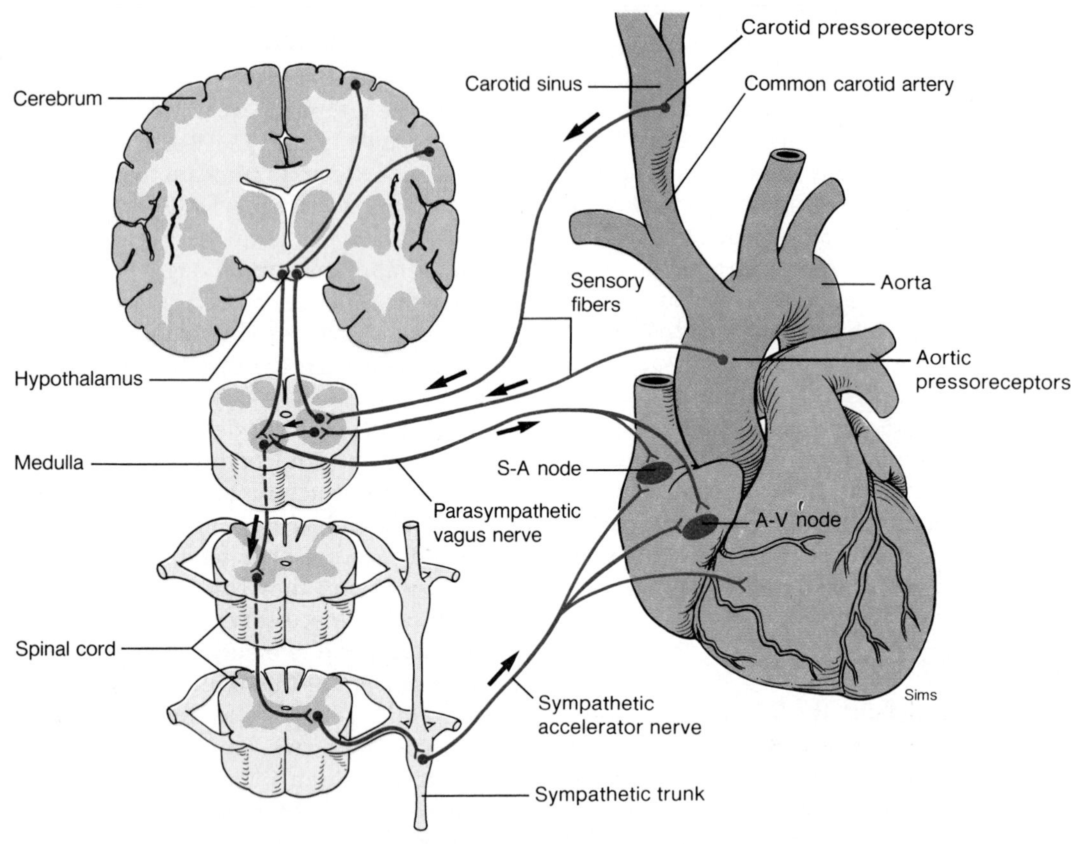

Figure 13.12 An ECG recorder. The electrodes attached to the chest correspond electrically to the "standard" leads positioned on arms and legs.

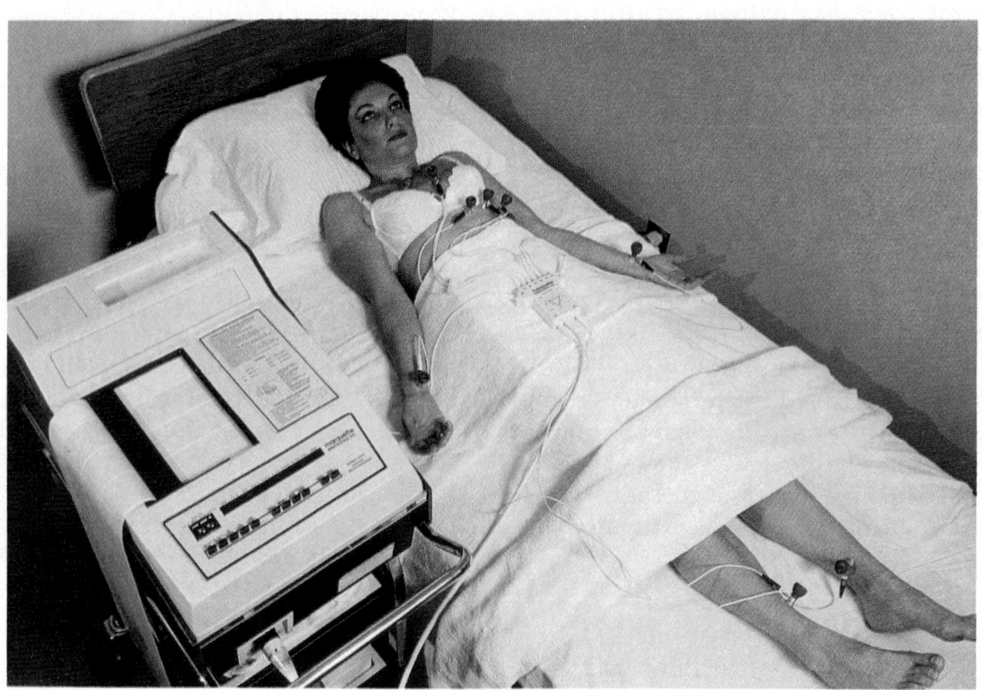

Figure 13.13 The "standard" leads and their relative ECG patterns. These are bipolar leads. Exploratory electrodes for unipolar chest leads are placed as indicated by the numbers in the upper right portion of the figure.

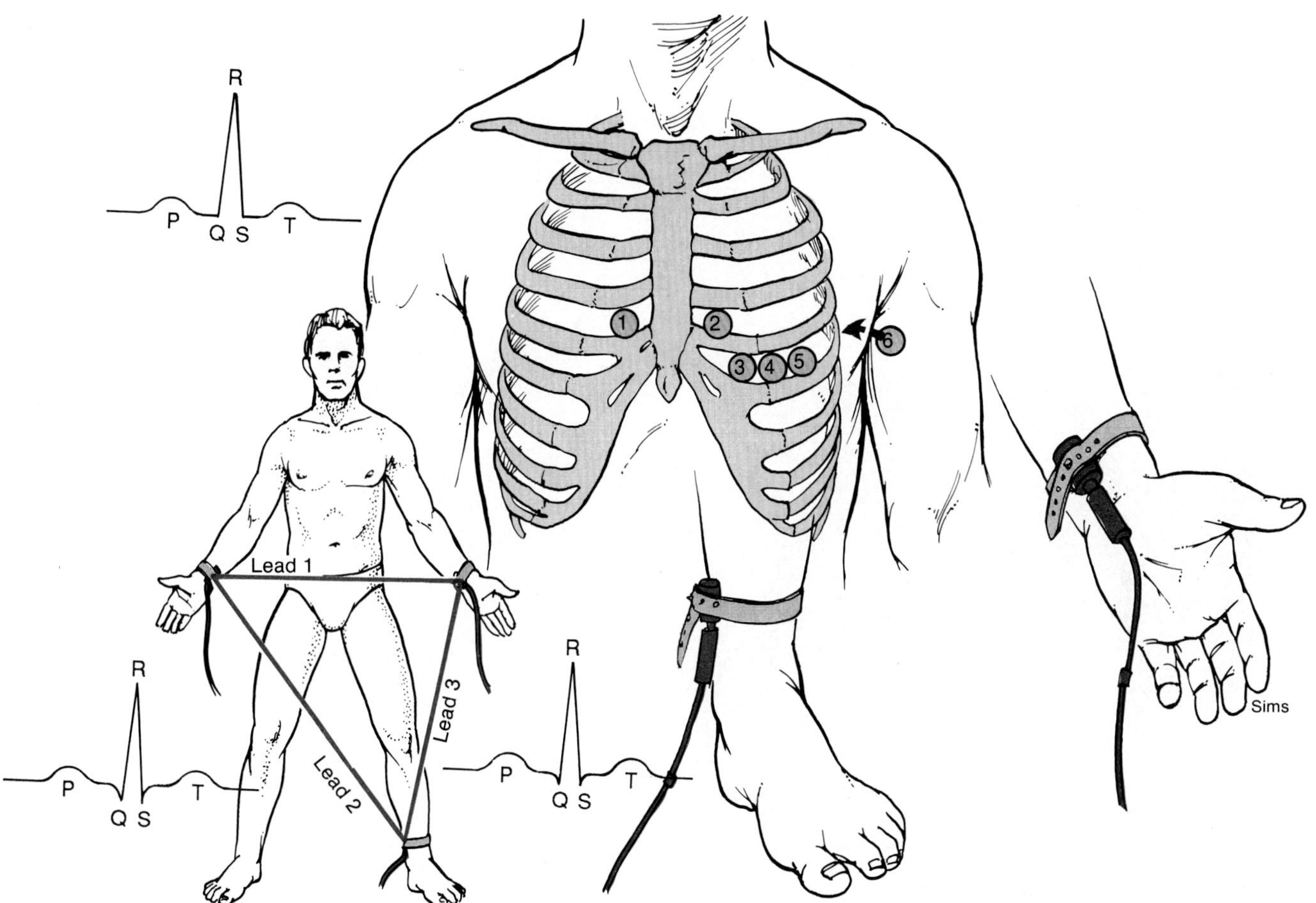

functioning in a professional capacity usually place the recording electrodes right on the individual's chest (figure 13.12). This eliminates the likelihood of picking up stray action potentials from skeletal muscle activity in a subject's limbs because, as you can see, the limbs are bypassed. However, as long as the subject is kept quiet, satisfactory records can be obtained by spotting the electrodes on the limbs and recording from there.

The shape of the ECG pattern depends, of course, on the condition of the heart, but it also depends to some extent on where the recording electrodes are placed (see figure 13.13). Placing the electrodes in different spots on the body can substantially change the configuration of the record, so it is important to establish formal placement sites so that results can be standardized and meaningful comparisons made.

The Standard Leads

Years ago, therefore, it was internationally agreed that three electrodes would be used to make standard recordings, and that the *Standard Limb Leads* would involve both arms and the left leg (see figure 13.13). The record obtained between the two arms—or across the heart horizontally—was, by general agreement, given the designation **lead 1.** A recording made between the right arm and left leg is known as **lead 2,** while a record between the left arm and left leg is **lead 3.**

These are **bipolar leads,** meaning that the recordings represent a potential difference between two active leads on the body. **Unipolar** recording uses only a single active electrode, which is placed on the chest (figure 13.13), with the other electrode serving as a reference, retained at zero (ground) potential within the ECG recorder. These unipolar leads have designations like AVR, AVL, and AVF (the A stands for *augmented).* They, too, have become standardized leads. Still other leads were added later, and designated standard (today, there are 12) and they are often used in medical practice. But leads 1, 2, and 3 were the first, and they are still used more often than any others in routine checking.

There is simply no way that we can include in this text any comprehensive discussion of the electrocardiogram. However, every potential nursing or paramedical student should certainly know what an

Figure 13.14 Electrocardiogram record typical of lead 2. (*a*) The ECG measures electrical activity through the heart. The colored portions of the wave represent activity in the correspondingly colored parts of the cardiac conducting system. (*b*) The time intervals involved can be calculated easily from properly marked paper.

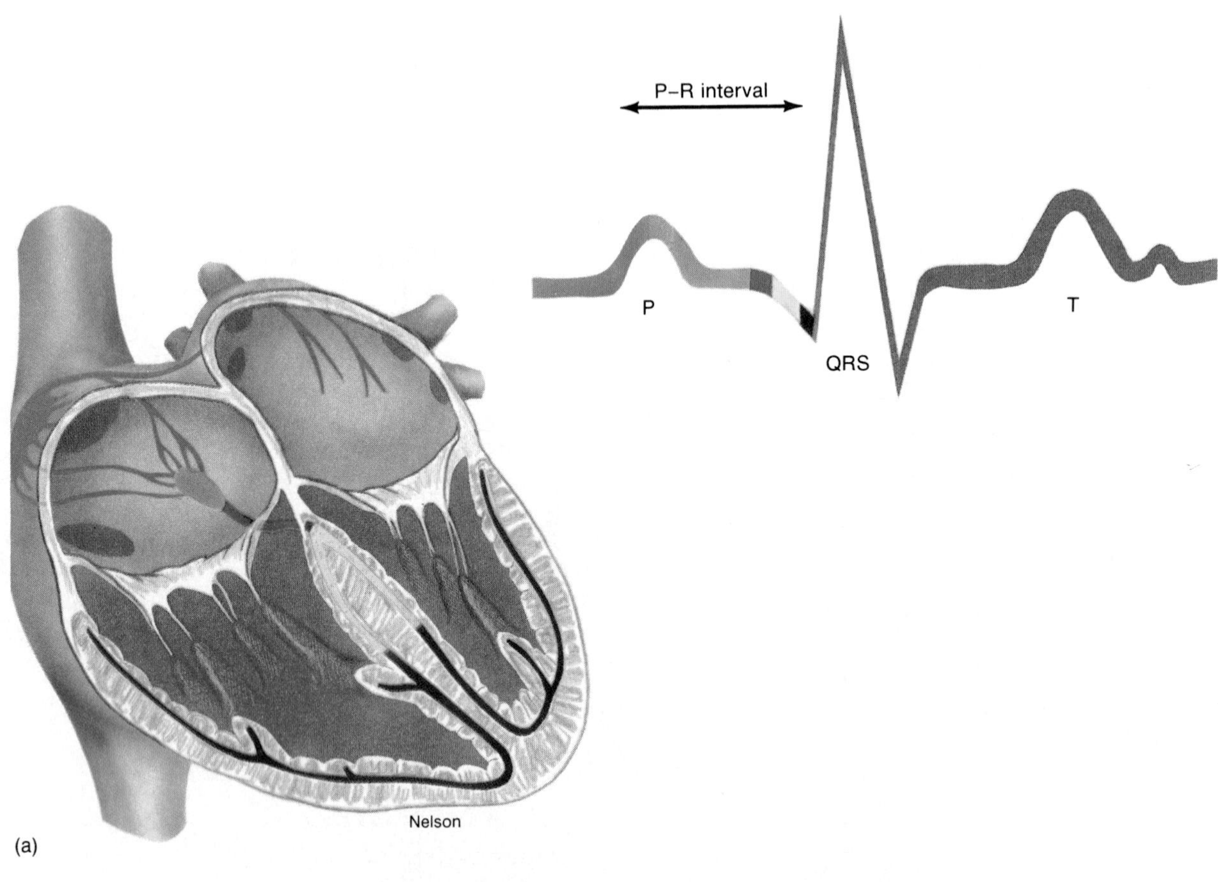

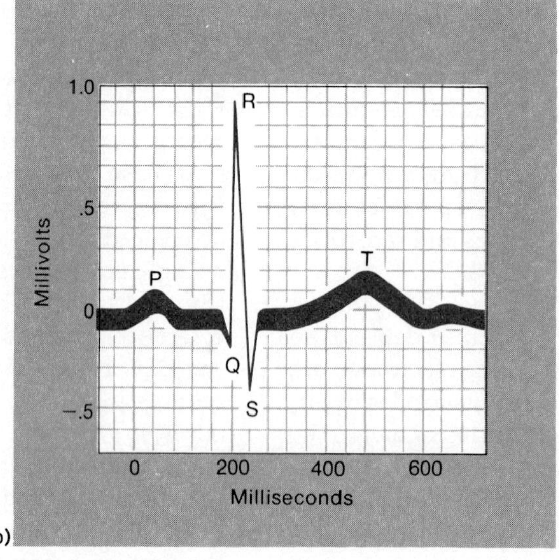

Figure 13.15 The depolarizing waves that sweep over the heart ventricles are actually fairly long (300 msecs) and are of opposing polarity. The trace we see on the ECG diagram is an algebraic summation of the two (*red line*).

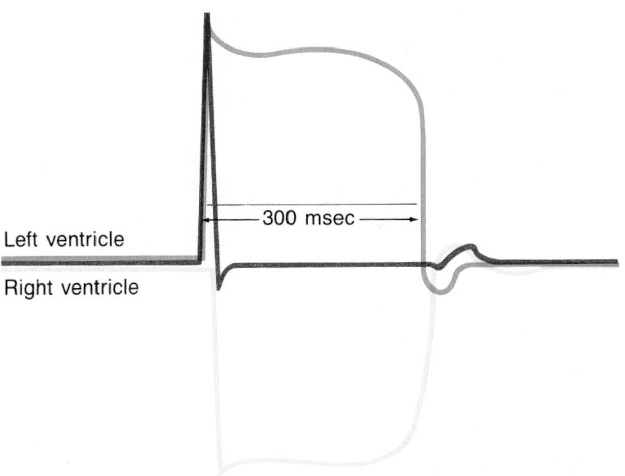

electrocardiogram looks like and what the major deflections are caused by. Let us concern ourselves with a trace from *lead 2.* This is the reading between the right arm and the left leg, and in a normal, healthy heart looks like figure 13.14*a.*

Note, if you will, that each of the major deflections has been assigned a letter, and from this letter sequence we obtain the name of the ECG wave. It is known as a **P-Q-R-S-T wave.** The wave marked with a *P* represents the beginning of the process. When the S-A node initiates the electrical activity in the atria, the **P wave** is the result. The depolarization spreads over the atrial musculature and is rapidly followed by atrial systole. For this reason, it is often stated that the P wave represents atrial systole, although, to be perfectly accurate, it actually represents the electrical activity of the atrium, which precedes physical activity by a hundred milliseconds or so. You should pay particular attention to the gentle nature of the P wave, since it reflects the smooth, gentle contractions of the auricles very nicely. The depolarization is not very large; it rises slowly and falls off just as delicately.

The QRS complex, as this next wave is known, rises and falls with a suddenness that belies the extended refractory period of the heart. This is because it is actually the algebraic sum of two waves. Electrical signals transmitted through the bundle and Purkinje fibers depolarize the two ventricles almost, but not quite, simultaneously. The polarity of the wave passing through the left ventricle is opposite the one moving across the right. This means that when one is plus, the other is minus, and vice versa. Therefore, much of the QRS wave that we see on the electrocardiogram readout has been cancelled out by the algebraic summation of these two separate electrical signals. The voltage change that passes over each individual ventricle is shown in figure 13.15. As you can see, the two patterns superimpose on one another, and the resultant QRS wave (broken line) is the summation.

The **T wave** corresponds to the onset of ventricular diastole, and it has been suggested that it represents the electrical recharging of the ventricles. It represents the last of this summation as shown in figure 13.15.

Irregularities in Electrical Patterns

Irregularities can occur in the conductance of the electrical signals through the heart muscle. It is not unusual for disease or physical damage to injure the S-A node. When that occurs, the result can be debilitating at best and deadly at worst, because the heart will beat more slowly and may not be fast enough to sustain life. It is almost as common for damage to impair the A-V node. When this occurs, obviously there will be no problem with the *initiation* of the heartbeat, and the impulse will spread across the atria in a perfectly normal manner with an equally normal contraction following. But when the impulse tries to cross from the atria to the ventricles, the damaged node blocks it. These and other irregular conditions are covered in more detail at the end of the chapter.

The P-R Interval

The time span between the beginning of the P wave on the ECG tracing and the beginning of the R wave is known as the **P-R interval** (see figure 13.14). It represents the length of time required for the depolarizing impulse to cross the A-V node and get into the bundle of His. (It is not called the P-Q interval because the Q component is not always present, even in a perfectly normal wave.) Normally, this process takes between 150 and 200 ms (less than two-tenths of a second), but sometimes, if something is wrong with the A-V node, it can take longer. Any increase in the P-R interval suggests that something is interfering with conduction through the A-V node and a potentially dangerous situation could be developing. Often, such delays in transmission are forerunners of what is known as a *heart block.*

It is important for us to remember that while each of these ECG events precedes a mechanical activity that takes place in the heart (figure 13.16), the electrical and mechanical events are nevertheless separate. The QRS complex represents the electrical phenomena passing through the ventricles. These phenomena signal the beginning of mechanical activity—indeed, are all that make it possible—but they

Figure 13.16 The conduction of electrical impulses in the heart, as indicated by the electrocardiogram (ECG). The direction of the arrows in *e* in indicates that depolarization of the ventricles occurs from the inside (endocardium) out (to the epicardium), whereas the arrows in *g* indicate that repolarization of the ventricles occurs in the opposite direction. (Source: *Emergency Medicine,* Volume II, Issue #2, February 15, 1979, Fisher Medical Publications, Inc.)

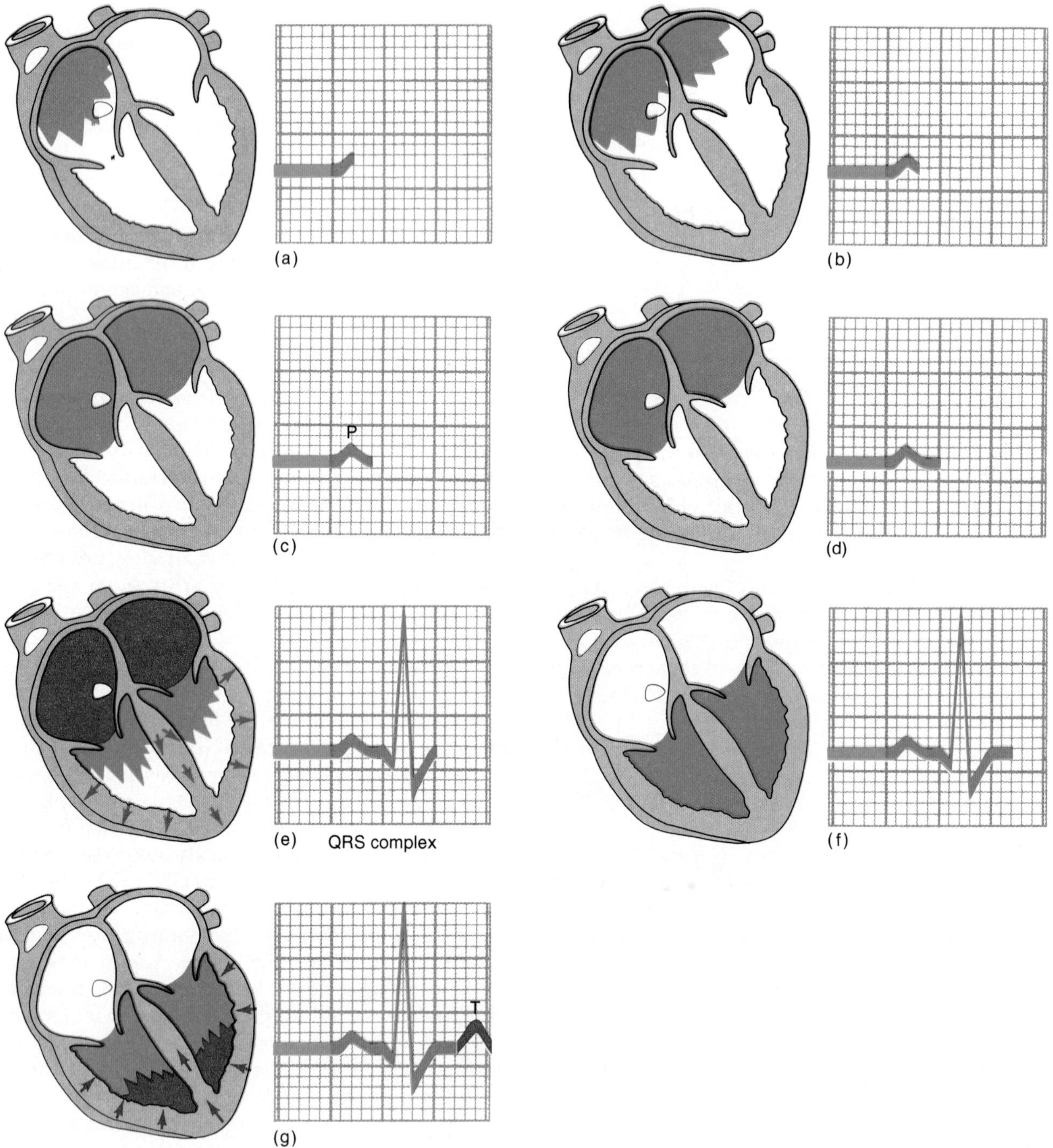

are *not* the mechanical events themselves. It is not correct to state that the QRS complex represents ventricular systole. It *is* correct to state that the QRS complex represents the electrical activity that initiates ventricular systole.

The Cardiac Cycle

As we have said many times, the heart is a pump. Its movements provide the necessary pressure to force fluid through the blood vessels and into the capillary beds of our bodies. In this sense, it is like the high water towers we can see in our cities that provide us with water pressure in our homes. But as we have already seen, there are some important differences.

The biggest difference is that the pressure head supplied by our heart is intermittent. The blood is fired into the arterial circulation at specific intervals with long pauses in between. The heart fills, then it contracts to squirt out the blood that is inside of it, then the muscles relax so it can fill again. This is a cyclic process; hence the movement of fluid through the heart and from it is pulsating, like the flow of bullets through the barrel of a machine gun. Yet the flow of blood through the body's capillary beds, the venous system, and a substantial portion of the arterial system is not intermittent, but steady. The two conditions seem to be incompatible, and one could consider the possibility of having encountered a paradox, but that is not the case this time. What makes it possible is a modification in fluid transport—one totally unlike anything engineers have designed or built.

Pressure

Before we continue with our discussion of this cyclic activity, it might be well to briefly discuss what we know of *pressure.* Now this is an interesting word. We all use it day after day, and most of us are pretty sure that we have a reasonable handle on what the word means. So right now, without reading any further, define pressure.

Were you able to describe to your own satisfaction what it is? Most probably couldn't, because while you understand the properties of pressure, you really do not think very much about the phenomenon itself. So before we go any further in our discussion of the cardiac cycle, let us be sure we know exactly what we mean when we use the term *pressure.*

In a physical sense, *pressure represents a ratio between a given container and the amount of fluid that is put into that container.* If one were to place 2 liters of water in a vessel designed to hold 2 liters, there would be no pressure, positive or negative, and the ratio is would be 1 : 1 (one-to-one). The way to produce what we commonly think of as pressure inside a container would be to attempt to overfill it. By trying to cram 5 liters into a 3-liter jar (making the ratio 5:3), we would produce considerable positive pressure inside the jar merely by trying. If the walls of the vessel were rigid, as glass or metal is, we would never get more than 3 liters into that 3-liter jar (liquids cannot be compressed), but we would produce considerable pressure inside the jar as long as we tried. On the other hand, if the walls of the jar were elastic, we might get more than 3 liters into it. As to the pressure involved, the jar's elasticity would have a lot to say about that.

If the sides of the vessel stretched and did not resist the change in size, there would be no pressure within the vessel. This is important, so I'll say it again in a slightly different way. *If the walls of the vessel are not rigid or semi-rigid, overfilling will produce no pressure increases inside the vessel.* Container walls that have no resistance to distortion, hence no tendency to return to their original size, are known as *ideally elastic,* and ideal elasticity exists, as far as I know, only in theory.

But there are lots of containers with *partially* elastic walls. The one we encounter most often is the balloon. Its walls are quite elastic, but as I am sure we all know, they do resist overfilling a little bit. Also, their walls have a tendency to return to their original size, as anyone knows who has blown one up then released it. Balloons that have been overfilled with air (blown up) have considerable pressure inside them . . . a pressure we view as *positive* with respect to the atmosphere.

Vacuum cleaner hoses and hoses attached to certain portable hair dryers often tend to be elastic also, which is why many are reinforced by steel rings every inch or so. They're not as elastic as a balloon, but they are more elastic than a garden hose. We all know that when we crimp a garden hose, it does not blow up like a balloon. It actually does stretch a little, however, and if you have a weak spot anywhere between the faucet and the crimp, the hose might demonstrate its elasticity at that weak point by expanding there and bursting. Keep a picture of that phenomenon in your mind, because we will be reminded of it later and the picture will be useful.

The pots and pans we keep in our homes are generally rigid, and our household plumbing is not elastic at all. The walls are solid—*inelastic,* a physicist would say. Any pressure applied to the contents of a metal or glass jar would be felt immediately throughout the entire jar.

In living systems, none of the containers are rigid. The heart is often quite flaccid and capable of stretching—particularly the atria. In fact, as I said, one of the reasons that blood flows so freely into the atria when they are relaxed is that their walls are so beautifully elastic and stretch easily. And it is the elastic property of our arterial vessels that produces some interesting alterations in a blood-flow pattern that would otherwise be stop-and-go. As we will see, this is functionally important.

Figure 13.17 Pressure changes in the heart. Solidly colored areas indicate the outflow of blood from a heart chamber. Stars mark the points at which heart sounds occur.

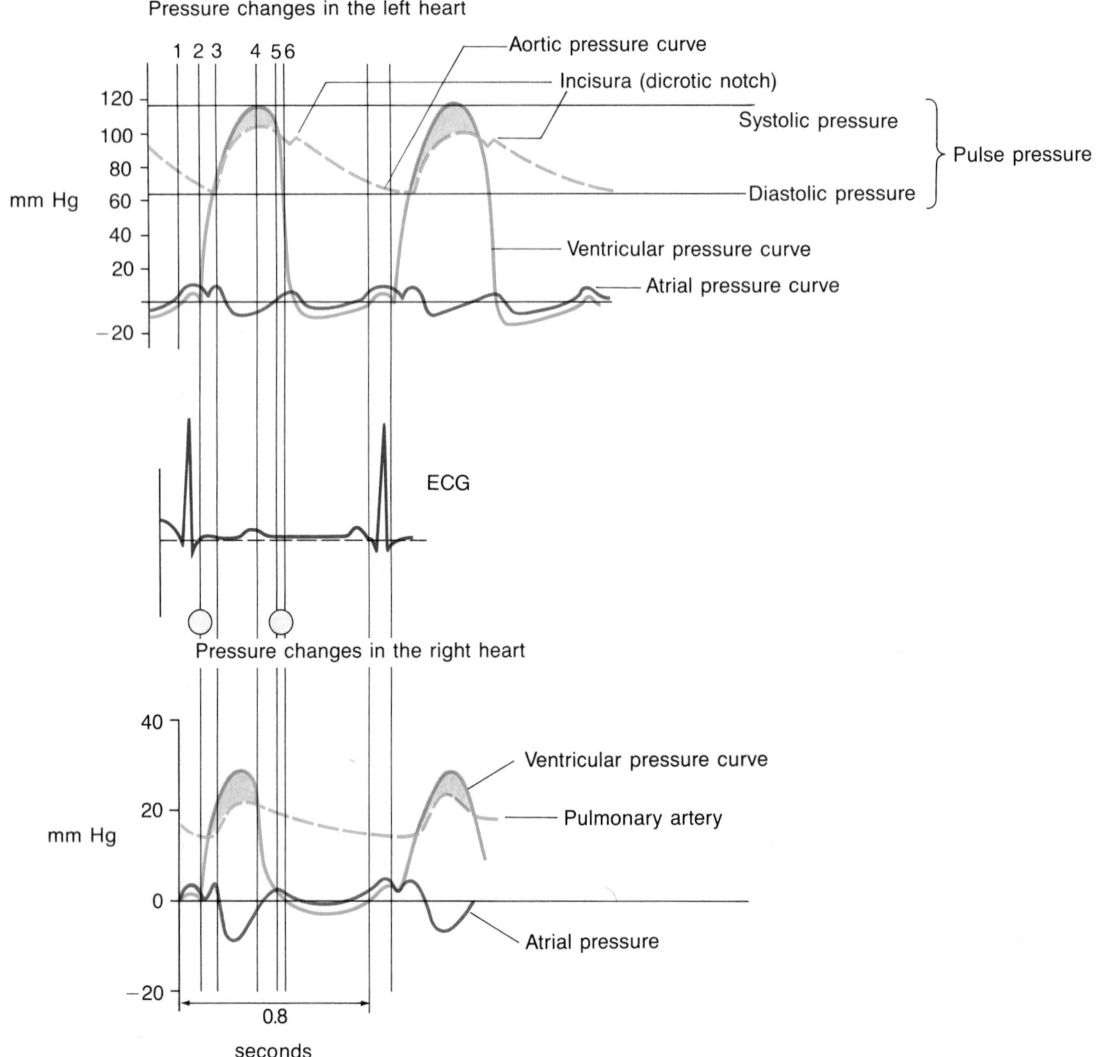

Our bodies also take advantage of the fact that there are two ways one can increase pressure inside a fluid-filled container. One need not try to overfill the container. One could just fill it up, then make it smaller . . . that would certainly increase the pressure. That is what the heart does. After it fills up, contraction of the muscle makes it smaller. So by altering the size of the container, our bodies can produce pressure changes within the heart, and that, in turn, permits blood to be pumped through the body. Nature is a remarkable physicist, as we will see.

Starting at the left side of figure 13.17, let us investigate, one line at a time, the section marked "Pressure Changes in the Left Heart."

The Atrial Pressure Curve

Begin at the extreme left of the diagram and follow the pressure changes (red line) that occur in the left atrium through a single cycle. At the beginning, both the atrium and the ventricle are relaxed. Pressure in the atrium at this point is quite close to zero (it can even drop below zero if the subject is drawing air into his lungs), but regardless of its real value, it is important to note that it is greater than the pressure in the ventricle. During this period, blood is flowing without significant interference into the atrium and through the atrium into the ventricle. There is some resistance to its flow through the mitral valve, because the opening is not very large, but the valve is as open as it can get, and because the heart muscle is being stretched a little, the resultant suction is able to fill the ventricle to about 70 percent of capacity before the atrium ever contracts.

Line 1 represents the beginning of atrial systole. Not much pressure exists; remember, with both gravity and ventricular suction helping, the job it has to do is not arduous, and the pressure it produces is adequate to fill the remaining 30 percent of the space in the ventricle.

Line 2 represents the beginning of ventricular systole. The contraction of the ventricle is much more powerful than that of the atrium because of the relative size of the musculature. As soon as the intraventricular pressure exceeds the pressure in the atrium, the mitral valve slams shut. Pressure in the atrium promptly increases, because the cusps of the valve are bent and forced a short distance back into the atrial chamber by the ventricular pressure. The increase is short-lived, because, as ventricular systole continues, the tremendous force exerted by the ventricular muscles hauls the heart down toward its connection with the diaphragm. This stretches the relaxed atrial walls, making the chamber larger and producing a negative pressure inside. This negative pressure prevails throughout the greater part of ventricular systole and helps to "suck" blood into the atrium from the great body veins.

At line 6, pressure in the ventricle drops below the pressure in the atrium. As soon as this occurs, the A-V valve swings open, and the blood that has piled up in the atrium and stretched its walls quickly squirts out into the ventricle, reducing the pressure inside the atrium and shrinking its walls. With the mitral valve once again wide open, the left heart is now effectively just one chamber, and as the various forces involved begin to stretch the myocardium, pressure once again becomes slightly negative throughout. As before, this aids in filling up the heart.

Drawn by internal suction and aided to some degree by venous pressure, the chamber once again starts filling up with blood. Soon there is so much blood surging in that it is filled, and the walls begin to stretch. At this point, pressure in the chamber starts to go up again. It continues to slowly increase as we approach line 1, and the cycle is ready to occur again.

The Ventricular Pressure Curve

As before, we begin at the extreme left of the figure. The pressure in the ventricle (solid black line) is slightly negative. The mitral valve is open, producing one large, relatively empty chamber. Pressure throughout the chamber is slightly negative, creating a suction that draws blood into the heart, filling the atrium and pouring through the open valve into the ventricle. The chamber fills to about 70 percent of its capacity.

At line 1, atrial systole occurs. Blood squirts into the ventricle under about 15 mm Hg pressure as the atrial wall forces its contents out into the ventricle, stretching even the heavily muscled walls of that chamber and increasing the internal pressure. The end of atrial systole reduces the intraventricular pressure slightly, but for only an instant.

Line 2 represents the beginning of ventricular systole. Pressure in the ventricular chamber climbs like a Fourth of July skyrocket as the great muscles clamp down on their contents, banging shut the mitral valve and effectively separating the ventricle from the atrium. Both the A-V valve and the aortic valve are now closed, and suddenly, *the ventricle is a closed chamber.* For a period of about 50 msec, tension in the ventricular muscles increases steadily but the muscles do not get any shorter . . . they cannot get any shorter, because the chamber is filled with blood and the blood has no place to go. This is, therefore, an *isometric contraction,* and it stores power in the myocardium, the tensing muscles accumulating energy like a coiled spring. In a way, it is like running an automobile's engine up to high rpm's before releasing the brakes in a drag race. Movement is suppressed, and so potential energy builds and builds; when it is finally released, the conversion to kinesis can be impressive.

There is nothing unusual about the process of building up a store of energy in a system so that it can be released in a sudden, explosive surge—not to animals, anyhow. We have all employed the principle to improve performance, although it's not likely many of us realize it. When a muscle builds up tension without permitting the fibers to shorten, it is like stretching a rubber band before letting it go. When movement is finally permitted, there is an explosive energy release that could not be attained any other way. If you doubt this, try flicking a piece of paper off a table without letting your finger press against your thumb first (figure 13.18*a*). Pay attention to the distance the paper travelled, and then try the same thing again, this time flexing your thumb against your finger and storing some energy before you let go and flick (figure 13.18*b*). See the difference in the response of your finger, and in the distance the paper will travel? This is what is happening in the heart during this period.

Between lines 2 and 3, then, the ventricle is squeezing down on its contents like a vise tightening up on an unopened can of orange juice. Tension is increasing, pressure is increasing, but the ventricles are not releasing any blood—nothing is moving. This is the period known as the **isometric contraction phase.**

Figure 13.18 The mechanical advantage of isometric contraction. (*a*) A purely isotonic action. (*b*) An action similar to *a*, except for the isometric tightening of the involved muscles prior to movement. Note the difference in the effect.

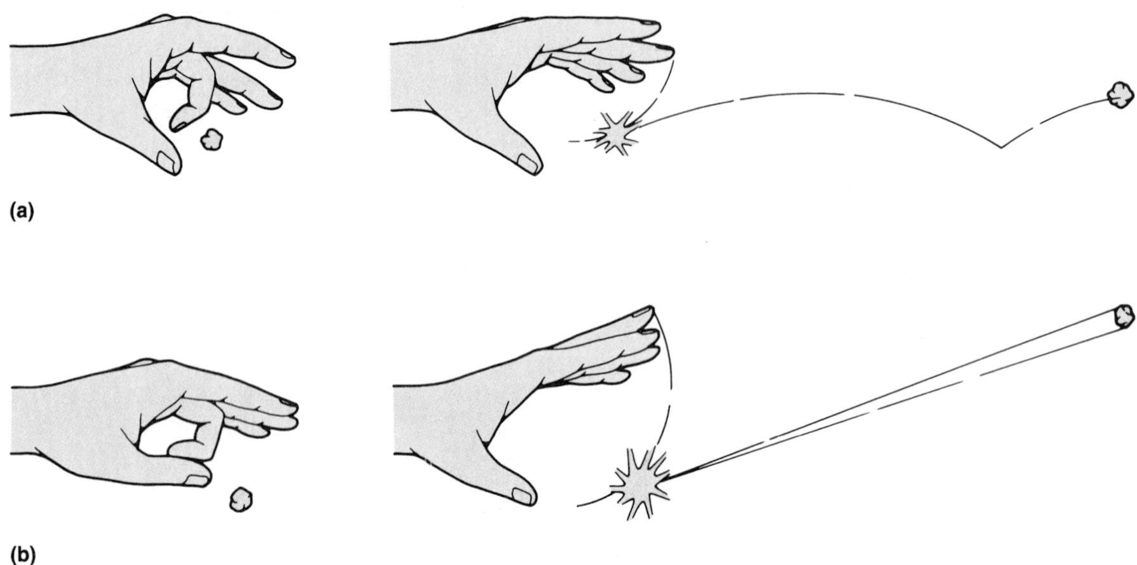

Finally, a point is reached at which the pressure within the ventricle is greater than the pressure within the aorta; hence at line 3, the aortic valve opens. The opening is sudden and explosive; blood bursts out of the ventricle into the aorta. Imagine how orange juice would fly if the top suddenly blew off the compressed can with the vise tight. The blood is enclosed in its tubes, so its movement is more controlled than that of the orange juice would be, but the eruption is just as violent. About 150 ml of blood is instantly in the aorta, forcing the walls to expand to accommodate this great ball of fluid that has suddenly appeared. Pressure inside the ventricle continues to go up because the muscles are still contracting, but as you can see, the *rate* of increase is slowing, because the contents are being squirted out.

The period between lines 3 and 4 is known as the **rapid ejection phase.** At line 4, pressure in the ventricle begins to decrease, slowly at first, then accelerating. The ventricle continues to contract for a few msec longer, but it contains less than half the blood it had when ejection began, and with the semilunar valves wide open, the pressure falls off. This is the **reduced ejection phase.**

Just before line 5, ventricle diastole begins, and at line 5, the aortic valve closes. The ventricle is, once again, a closed chamber—an emptier one this time. As the muscles continue to relax, tension disappears, but lacking any opening to admit more fluid, the muscles cannot elongate and we once again have an isometric situation. This one lasts for about 50 msec (between lines 5 and 6) and is known as the **isometric relaxation phase.**

At line 6, the mitral valve opens and once again blood can flow from the atrium into the ventricle. For about three-tenths of a second (between lines 6 and 1), the pressure in both the atrium and the ventricle is below zero. As we have already seen, when the mitral valve opens, the atrium and ventricle become a single chamber, and the stretching musculature reduces the internal pressure. Blood rushes into the atrium from the veins and subsequently through the mitral valve into the ventricle, and the cycle is ready to begin again.

A Brief Digression

Before we begin our discussion of the aortic pressure curve, we must delve a little more deeply into pressure phenomena so we will understand what's going on.

For purposes of this discussion, let us inspect figure 13.19.

A Rigid System

Consider what would happen if all the tubes in this structure were made of metal like our household plumbing and were absolutely rigid. As you can clearly see in figure 13.19*a*, as soon as the pump applies pressure, all of that pressure is immediately felt throughout the system and is retained as long as the pump continues to apply it. As soon as the pump stops, pressure throughout the entire system drops immediately to zero. At the delivery end of the system, fluid flow reflects the intermittent action of the pump. It squirts out during each pressure application and stops as soon as pressure is no longer applied (figure 13.19*b*). This is typical of a rigid system.

Figure 13.19 (*a*) Fluid flow in a rigid metal system: *A*—pump; *B*—pressure gauge (manometer); V_1, V_2, V_3—one-way valves; *C*—area of flow resistance. (*b*) Pressure changes in a nonelastic, intermittently pumping system.

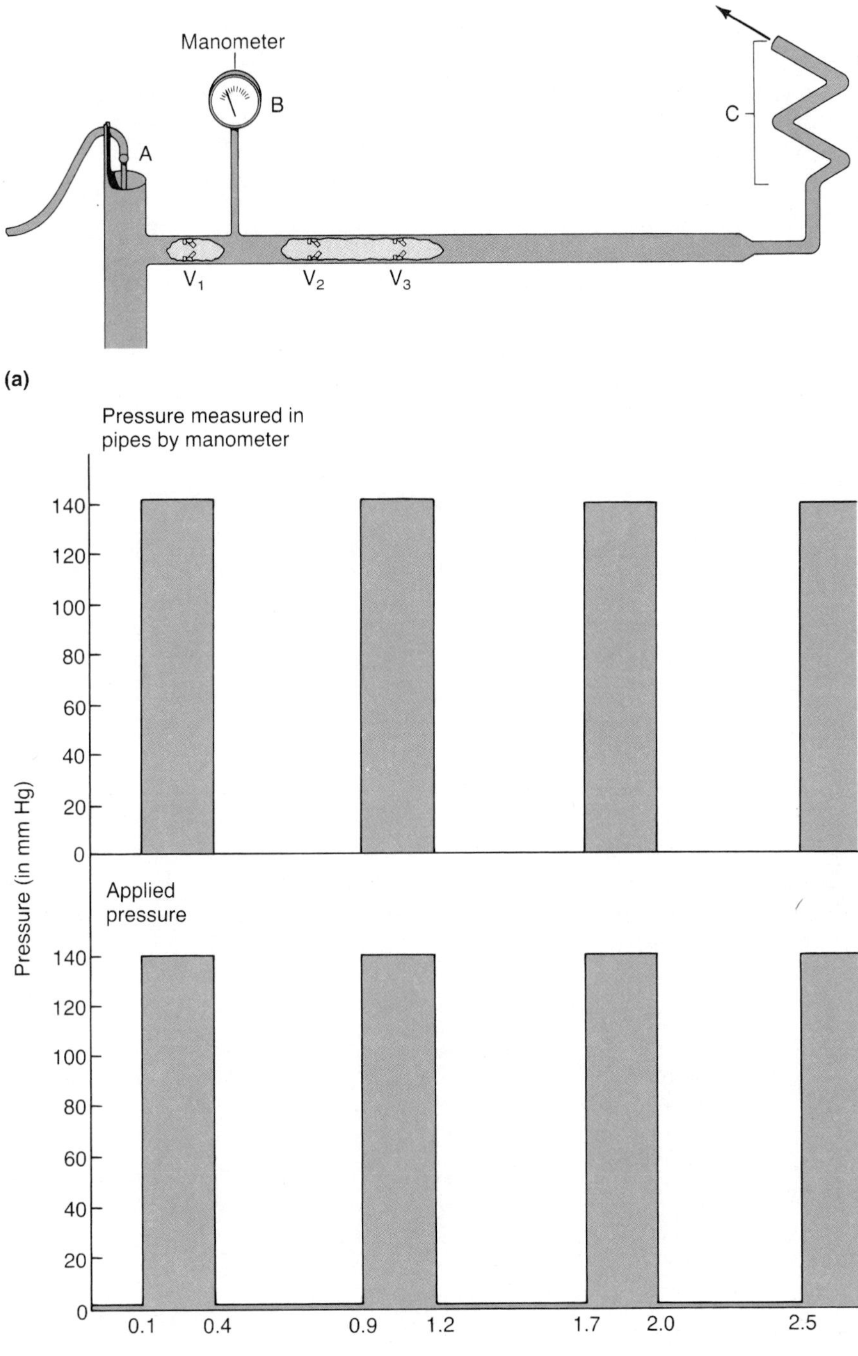

Figure 13.20 (*a*) Fluid flow in an elastic system with an intermittent pump. (*b*) Pressure changes in elastic tubes.

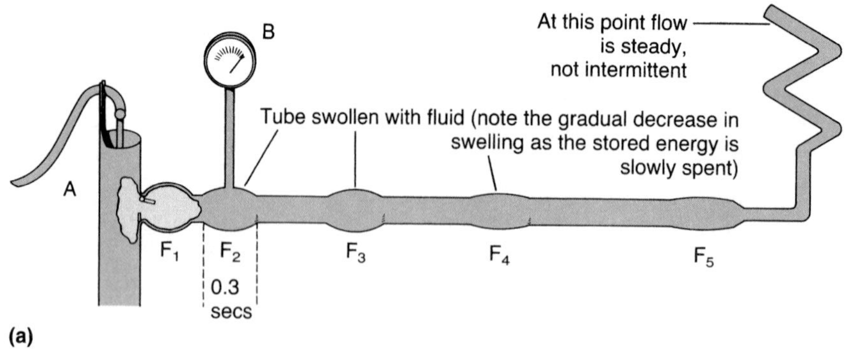

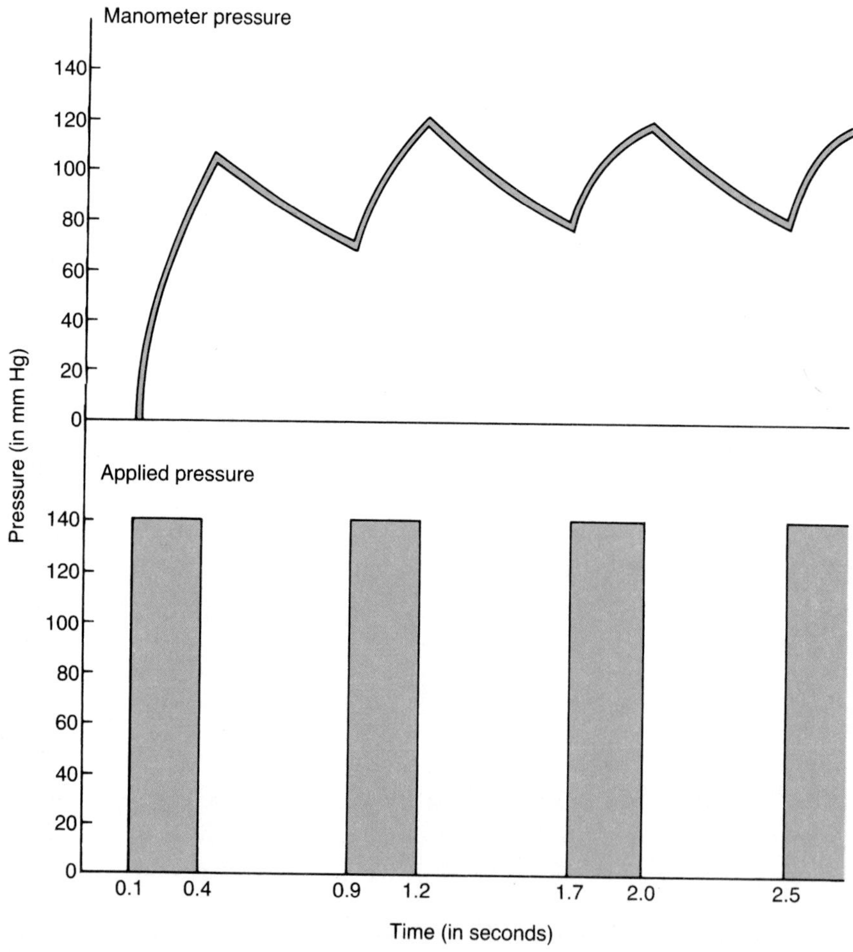

The Elastic System

Now let us investigate the pressure curves in a system in which the tubes are not rigid (figure 13.20*a*). In a system with elastic tubing, if we apply the same amount of pressure (140 mm Hg) for the same length of time (0.3 seconds), we will see a pattern of pressure changes quite different from what we saw in the rigid system. For one thing, the pressure buildup in the delivery system will be a good deal slower when we start pumping. What is more, it never achieves the peak value of the applied pressure, because the tube swells to accommodate the fluid being thrust into it, and some of the pump's energy is thus transferred into the tubes. The containers are, in effect, getting bigger, and the pressure increase is lessened accordingly. When the pump stops, pressure in the system does not disappear the way it did in the rigid system. Instead, it falls off slowly. It does so because the tube is

Figure 13.21 Schematic drawing of an artery (*a*) compared to a vein (*b*). Note the difference between the thickness of the tunica media and that of the tunica adventitia. The tunica media is smooth muscle, while the adventitia is mainly connective tissue containing elastic and collagenous fibers.

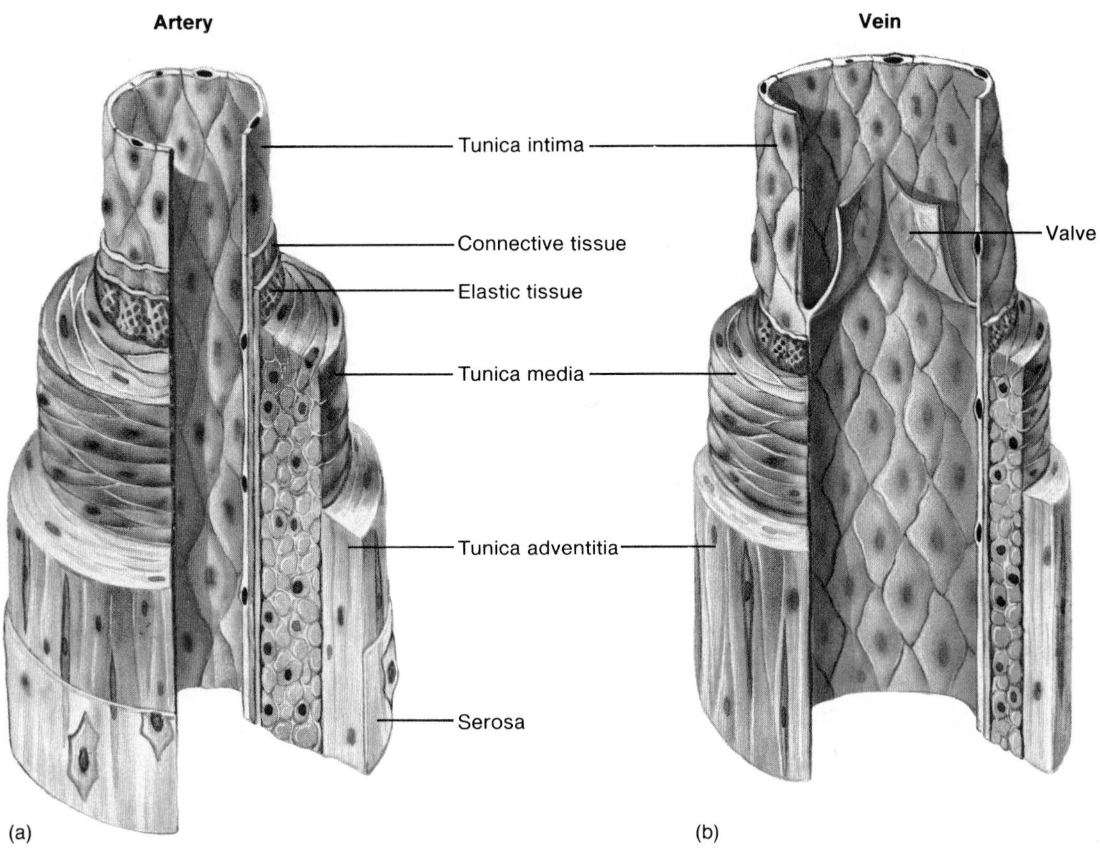

swollen where it was overfilled and is trying to collapse, like a blown-up balloon does, to its original size. The tendency to collapse squeezes the contents, creating a positive pressure inside the tube. The pressure is not aimed in any particular direction. It tries to push the fluid anywhere it will go, but it obviously cannot go through the walls of the tube, and because of the valves that are present, it will only go in one direction—away from the pump. As the fluid is pushed forward through the tube, the pressure in the system starts to fall . . . not precipitously as it did when the tube was rigid, but slowly, as the pressure is gradually applied to the fluid and continues to move it.

If the pump is activated again within a second or so, it will increase pressure in the system before it can drop back down to zero (see figure 13.20*b*). The sudden pressure increase pushes another mass of fluid into the tube, which once again expands to accommodate it. If the pump is activated in this manner, thrusting fluid into this elastic tube every second or so, the pressure never will fall to zero, or even close to zero. The period when the pump is active will have a high positive pressure, and, because the pump stores some of its energy in the elastic walls of the tube, the period when it is not active will still feature a positive pressure within the tube—not as great, but definitely positive.

This is pretty much the way the heart and arterial systems operate.

The Aortic Pressure Curve

The aorta is an enormous blood vessel, and, being immediately adjacent to the powerful left ventricle of the heart, it must be able to absorb considerable pressure and endure a great deal of stretching without bursting. The aorta is constructed with this in mind. Figure 13.21 compares the two major blood vessel types in living systems. Note the extra layers of tissue in the artery and the extra thickness of the arterial walls. The smooth muscle in the large arteries reflects elasticity rather than contractility. The muscle doesn't actively contract or pulse to drive the blood along. Rather, it stretches to accommodate the large volumes of fluid that continually drive into the lumen of its vessel, and this stretching represents a storing of potential energy within the arterial wall.

Starting at the left of figure 13.17*a*, we can see the aortic pressure descending gently as the elastic tissues wrapping this huge artery press against the blood inside as it tries to return to its original shape. Before this "rebound" pressure has decreased very much, the aortic and ventricular pressure curves cross (line 3), and like the flicking finger or the orange juice can that suddenly blew its top, the aortic valve bangs open and a great ball of blood bursts from the ventricle and gushes into the aorta. The aorta promptly swells like a limp-walled rubber hose to accept this fluid, and it continues to swell as long as the heart drives the blood into it (shaded area, figure 13.17*a*).

The pressure in the ventricle levels off and begins to fall after injecting this ball of blood into the aorta. Less than two-tenths of a second after the initial surge, the pressure within the ventricle drops below aortic pressure. By this time, the swollen part of the aorta that contains the newly released ball of blood is several millimeters away from the heart, and the pressure that originally drove it there is suddenly gone. The vessel walls try to spring back to their original size, pressing the blood away in both directions.

The Incisura (Dicrotic Notch)

The one-way valves in the system will not permit the blood to flow back into the ventricle, of course, but it can go back a little way. As far as the aortic valve, to be exact, at which point this sudden backward surge slams the valve shut. Having had the door slammed in its face, the rapidly moving blood bounces back to where it came from, producing a sudden, very short, increase in aortic pressure. This is the **incisura** or **dicrotic notch** that we see in the aortic pressure curve immediately after the aortic valves close (figure 13.17*a*).

Following the incisura, aortic pressure falls slowly as the muscles in the arterial wall compress the bulging blood globules that are stretching its sides out of shape. Before any real progress can be made, however, diastole is over, pressure in the ventricle has shot up again, and another ball of blood is crammed into the aorta.

Throughout most of the arterial system, the intermittent rhythm produced by the heart is perceptible. Zones of high positive pressure interspersed with zones of slightly lower positive pressure are present for a considerable distance through the arterial system, and each can be clearly seen. If we exposed some of these arteries, we would be able to see that they resemble the neck of an ostrich after the bird has swallowed several oranges. Each vessel would feature tiny bulges at regular intervals, the bulges representing masses of blood that the elastic vessel walls are trying to flatten out. While they are trying, the blood is moving through the arterial system toward smaller and smaller vessels, and the bulges are getting progressively smaller.

Should an artery get cut, blood spurts out of the opening in an accelerated rush each time one of these swellings passes through the break. Between each of these spurts, blood flow is slower, but it does not stop (figure 13.22). This is a type of bleeding that is characteristic of arteries, and since the force of each spurt can be quite strong, the body's normal defensive mechanisms may not be able to seal the vessels without a little outside help.

Figure 13.22 Spurting of blood when an artery is cut.

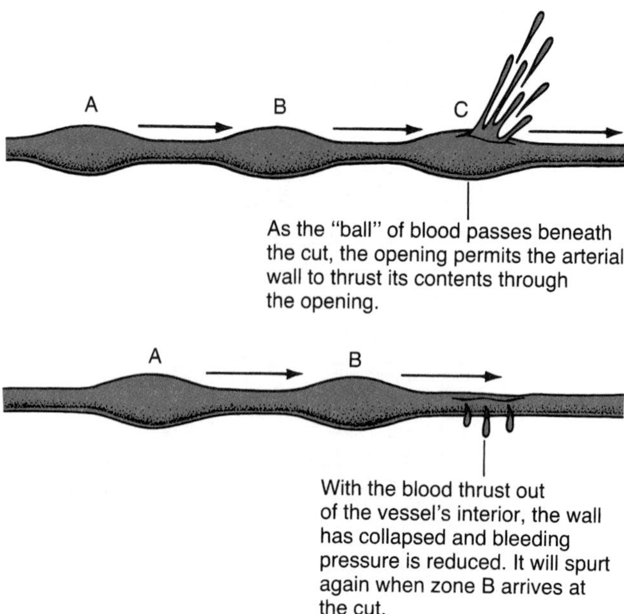

Pressure Changes in the Right Heart

Since the entire heart contracts as a unit, pressure variations in the pulmonary system follow the same time curve. What is more, the right ventricle pumps just as much blood as the left does. The *pressures* involved in the pulmonary circulation, however, are much lower (see figure 13.17*b*). Whereas the left ventricle produces a systolic pressure on the order of 120 mm Hg, that of the right ventricle is more like 25 mm Hg—and in between beats, during diastole, the pressure in the ventricle often drops all the way to zero. Considering these facts, it is reasonable to ask how in the world the right ventricle manages to move as much blood per beat as the left ventricle does.

Pulmonary Vessels

Part of the answer involves the size of the blood vessels. Blood flow through the pulmonary system is abetted by an artery that is even larger than the aorta. In fact, all the pulmonary vessels are larger than their systemic counterparts.

Also, resistance throughout the pulmonary circulation is relatively low, much lower than it is in the systemic circulation. Keep in mind that the heart and lungs are on approximately the same level in the body, so gravity is not much of a problem, and the distance to be traversed is not great. In fact, the heart is so close to the respiratory capillaries that if the right ventricle were to apply a pressure much greater than it does, most of the arterioles in the lungs would probably blow out.

So the job of the right heart is relatively easy. It has only to provide enough pressure to power the blood into our lungs and through a single capillary bed. The arterioles in the pulmonary circulation are quite short, and blood is only in the capillaries for about a second. Since these vessels have no smooth muscle wrappings, they are easily expandable, and their resistance is very low. The blood makes just one pass through the lungs, then heads back to the heart.

The Myocardium

The heart is one of the hardest-working muscles in our body. It is true that it functions in a stop-and-go pattern. It is also true that it has an adequate rest period after each contraction. But keep in mind that its job never ends. One thing the heart muscle can depend on is being required, every minute of the day, to contract and relax, contract and relax, over and over again without pause. Our skeletal muscles can sustain bursts of activity, sometimes for a couple of hours if we are in good enough condition, but sooner or later, the activity has to stop for hours-long rest periods. Visceral muscle can maintain activity for even longer periods of time than skeletal muscle, but its efforts are seldom maximal, and the energy consumption over any given period of time is pretty small.

The heart does not work like either of them. Its contractile pattern is so regular that it is monotonous. A period of contraction is followed by a rest period that is roughly twice as long. This pattern continues, day after day, year after year, as long as the person lives. This stop-and-go pattern is functionally critical. The heart contracts in order to pump the blood. We recognize that, certainly. What most of us do not realize until the fact is brought to our attention is that relaxation is just as important. The heart *must* relax, or it will not be able to fill, and if there were nothing inside of it, then its contractions would be wasted. So cardiac diastole is not important merely to rest the muscle. It is just as indispensable to moving the blood as the contractions are.

Heart Sounds

Because of this intermittent, stop-and-go activity, the flow of blood through the heart causes the valves to open and close rhythmically like doors between rooms, and their movements are correlated with the contraction-relaxation patterns of the heart. Since the relaxation period is longer than the period of contraction, the "doors" responsible for each opening and closing noise can be identified. Consequently, if the cardiac cycle is kept in mind, any unusual sounds can have great diagnostic value.

Figure 13.23 The origin of the coronary arteries.

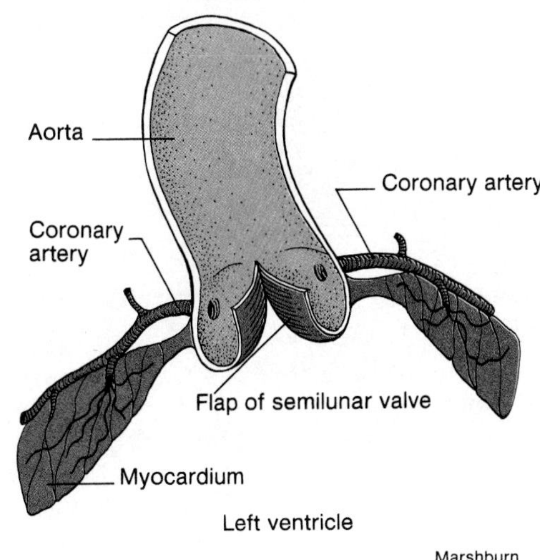

The regular beatings of the heart are called the **common heart sounds,** and they begin with ventricular systole. Systole increases pressure in the ventricles so much that the A-V valves slam shut and the aortic and pulmonic valves burst open, producing considerable noise and making what is called the **first heart sound.** The **second heart sound** follows about a quarter of a second later when the ventricles relax; it is the result of the pulmonic and aortic valves banging shut while the A-V valves swing open. Then, there is a relatively long pause, which identifies the phase of the cardiac cycle. The result is the "bump, bump, *pause* . . . bump, bump, *pause* . . ." (or as it is often written in textbooks, "lub-dub . . . *pause* . . . lub-dub . . . *pause* . . .") of a typical cardiac cycle.

The Coronary Circulation

More than any other muscle—indeed, more than any other organ in the body— the heart muscle requires oxygen. Even when the body is at rest and the heart is beating gently, it gobbles up all the oxygen it can get. All of the blood in the body passes through the heart many times a day. But only a tiny fraction of that huge volume actually flows through and nourishes the heart muscle itself. The vessels that "feed" the heart consist of two tiny arteries that branch off the aorta just above the point where that vessel leaves the heart (figure 13.23).

These **coronary arteries** enter the myocardium and promptly break into hundreds of capillaries, spreading out and sweeping through the muscle, carrying oxygen to every cell (figure 13.24). By the time it finishes its trip, the blood is drained of almost all of the oxygen it was carrying, and this hardly ever happens to blood. In most body tissues, hemoglobin releases somewhere around 30 percent of its oxygen load, which means when it returns to the lungs it is

Figure 13.24 (*a*) The heart's arterial blood supply. (*b*) The venous drainage of the heart muscle.

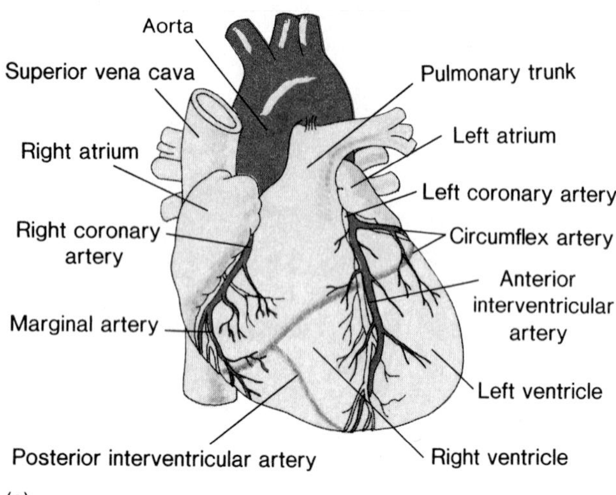

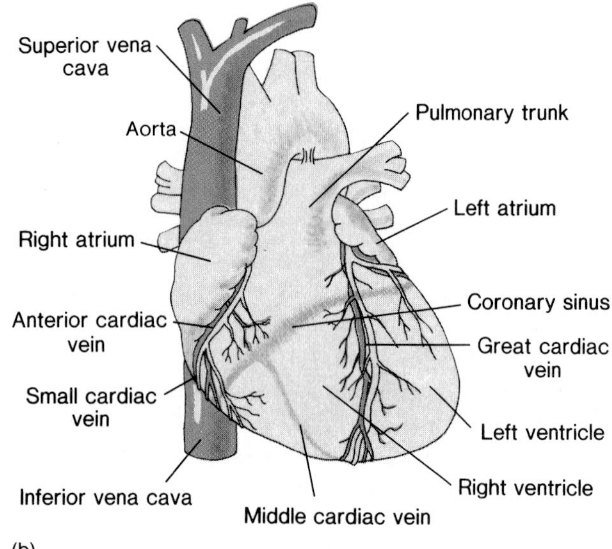

still about 70 percent saturated. In the heart, however, the oxygen is gobbled up at an exceptional rate—so furiously, in fact, that the interstitial fluid in the myocardium contains only about half the oxygen present in interstitial fluid elsewhere, and the venous blood is concomitantly depleted.

Some Unusual Features of the Coronary Circulation

The blood flow through coronary capillaries is unusual in that it is intermittent, and the rhythm of its intermittent flow coincides with the heartbeat. Not only that, but the coronary vessels develop their greatest blood flow, not during ventricular systole, as one might expect, but rather during ventricular diastole. This may seem illogical, but there is a good reason. Blood flow through muscles is nearly always restricted when muscles tighten up, because they compress the vessels that run through them. The myocardium is no exception. When the ventricular musculature is contracting and squirting blood into the aorta, the muscles clamp down so hard that the coronary arteries are squeezed quite flat, and fluid cannot move through them. So despite the fact that hydrostatic pressure is highest during systole, the coronary blood flow is often lowest then. When the ventricles relax, the entire coronary circulation is able to open up, and blood from the aorta, which has just left the ventricle and is nearly at ventricular systolic pressure, is able to rush into the coronary arteries.

After providing oxygen and other nutrients, the blood infusing the myocardium collects cardiac wastes, then drains through **coronary veins** into the **coronary sinus.** From this sinus, it is routed into the right atrium.

Adjustment in Coronary Blood Supply

When the heart suddenly speeds up or increases the strength of its contractions, it quite naturally needs more oxygen to fuel the increased activity. Yet, as we have noted, the blood in the coronary circulation has virtually no extra oxygen to release. Thus the only way to meet the increased demands would seem to be to increase the volume of blood flowing through the coronary circulation. On the surface, this would appear to be an almost impossible task. The coronary arteries, you will recall, achieve maximum blood flow during diastole. During periods when the body is relatively inactive, this diastolic rest period is obviously sufficient. But when the person exercises vigorously, when the heart is pounding rapidly, it would not be unreasonable to expect the much shorter rest periods to be inadequate. In addition, the heart muscle is also exerting much more effort with each contraction. All this is true, yet the heart seems to be able to handle itself just beautifully during exercise.

The heart uses several methods to obtain adequate energy. For one thing, the coronary arterioles can dilate, when necessary, to really impressive sizes, admitting an increased volume of blood during each diastolic period. This dilation is apparently intrinsically controlled, and very small drops in oxygen concentration in the coronary blood supply can stimulate it. Because the volume of blood in the coronary circulation is relatively small, demands for extra blood do not detract significantly from the main systemic supply, and the coronary vessels can remain dilated for extended periods without producing problems elsewhere.

Other compensatory mechanisms involve the energy sources utilized by the heart muscle. It seems that only about 18 percent of the oxygen consumed by the cardiac musculature is devoted to oxidizing glucose, while nearly 70 percent is utilized to metabolize fatty acids. This represents a considerable deviation from the fuel priorities of other tissues. Skeletal muscle and the brain gobble up much of the fuel that is present in the blood, and these systems use glucose as their primary energy source . . . in fact, for the brain, glucose is the only energy source. Since the myocardium prefers fatty acids over glucose, it has an almost untapped fuel reserve, which it can use freely without depleting the fuel supply for other important tissues. In addition, the heart can remove lactic acid from the blood and oxidize it rapidly as a primary energy source. During an exercise period, skeletal muscles produce lactic acid at a furious rate and dump it into the blood in large amounts, thus giving the body a large oxygen debt to repay. Instead of making things more difficult for the heart to obtain energy, this by-product of skeletal muscle activity provides the heart with still another source of fuel.

A Major Weakness

The coronary blood vessels route blood from the aorta almost as soon as it is pumped out of the left ventricle. The dispersion of coronary capillaries into the myocardium is thorough, and the dissemination of nutrients is profound—in fact, no cardiac muscle cell is more than two or three micrometers away from a capillary. But there is one rather surprising weakness in the coronary circulation, and this weakness is the source of much trouble. Many of the coronary arterioles and their smaller cousins, the **metarterioles,** are "blind."

Generally speaking, the pattern of vessels in the arterial circulation is as follows: Arteries accept the blood pumped out of the heart and proceed to break into smaller and smaller vessels. Eventually they get so tiny in size that they are not considered arteries any more. They have been given the diminutive name **arterioles.** These arterioles carry blood deep into the tissues before they separate into metarterioles and finally into the tiniest vessels—the **capillaries.** As we know, these latter are the exchange vessels, and all nutrients and wastes are moved between blood and interstitial fluids through capillary walls.

Arterioles precede capillaries in the overall scheme of things, which means that they function, in a way, as guards for these capillary beds. One way they guard is by providing what is known as **collateral circulation** for the tissues in their care. Collateral circulation refers, essentially, to a detour, an alternate route into a given capillary bed (figure 13.25).

The number of collateral arterioles in the coronary circulation is limited. This means that many parts of the heart muscle are fed by capillary beds that have only a single source with no alternate vessels. If something plugs up an arteriole supplying part of the heart muscle, there may be no detour that the blood

Figure 13.25 Arterial flow patterns showing the importance of providing alternate routes into a capillary bed. (*a*) A normal, unplugged entrance to a capillary bed. (*b*) An arteriosclerotic plug in a mainline vessel can be bypassed and blood will still feed the capillary bed.

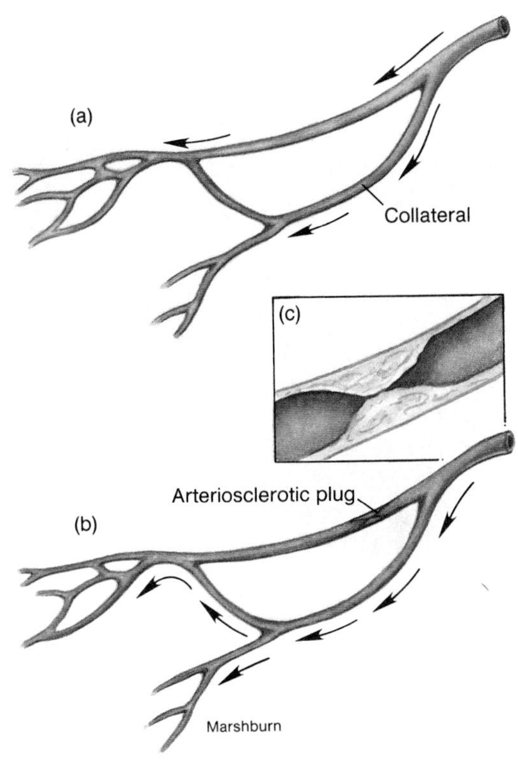

can take to bypass the stopped-up vessel. With no alternate route available, sections of heart muscle may experience an inadequate blood supply—a condition known as **ischemia.** The result is considerable pain in the pectoral region of the chest. Usually this is restricted to the thoracic cavity in the vicinity of the heart, and often it comes on when the victim is experiencing physical exercise or unusual emotional shock. Victims relate that the pain feels like someone has reached into their chest and is squeezing their heart—*hard.* This is **angina pectoris,** and while its source is the chest region, it can often be felt by nerves in the left arm so that the whole upper left side of the body hurts, a phenomenon known as **referred pain.**

If the arterial blockage is severe, and sections of myocardium are completely deprived of blood for more than a few moments, large sections of myocardium may die of inanition (the lack of a blood supply). Such attacks are known as **myocardial infarctions** (*infarct,* "filled in" or "stuffed"), and they are extremely dangerous. The care taken by the body to avoid frictional damage to the myocardium suggests how important it is that no heart muscle cells be lost, yet an infarction can kill cells in fairly large areas, throwing a tremendous load on the other myocardial cells. If the rest of the heart cannot take up the slack, the victim dies.

Figure 13.26 The layered walls of an artery.

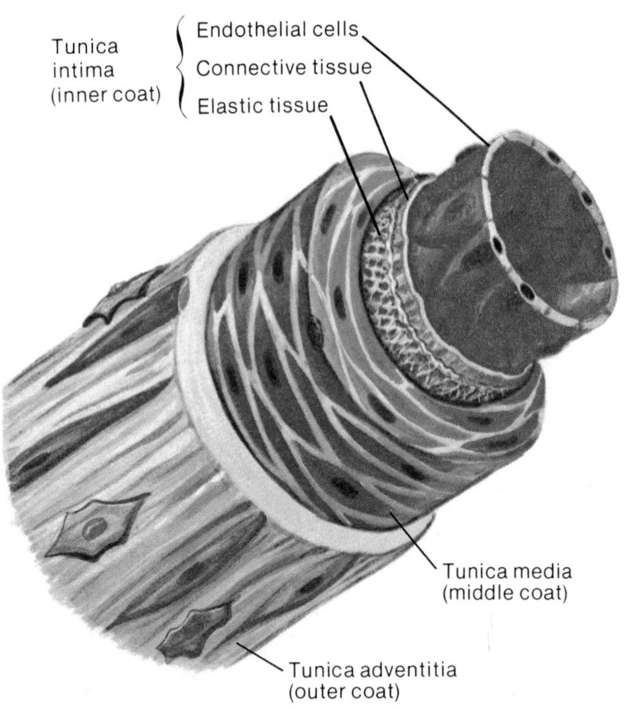

Figure 13.27 Intravascular pressures in the human circulatory system. (*a*) The systemic circulation. (*b*) The pulmonary circulation.

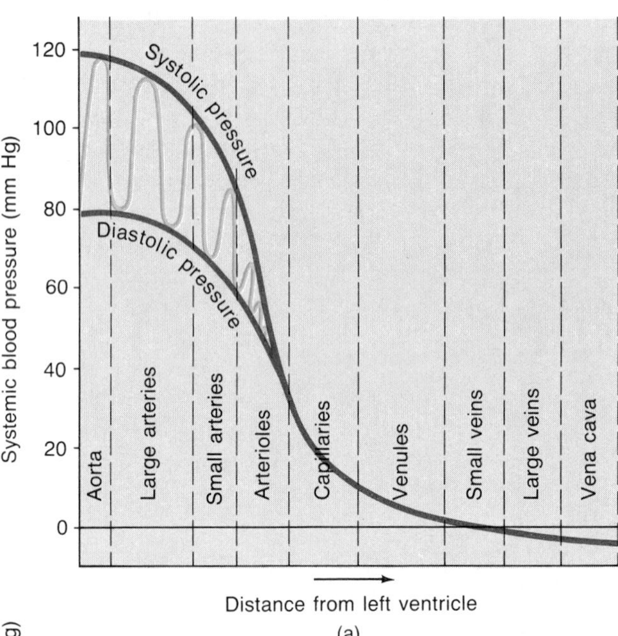

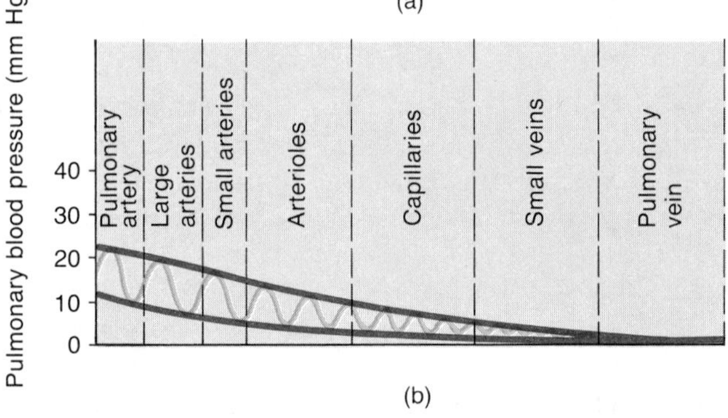

The Blood Vessels

I have referred to several different kinds of blood vessels on a few occasions, and while most of us probably think we have a pretty good idea what each of these vessels is, it would not hurt to discuss them briefly just once more.

Arteries

The fundamental structure of all large arteries is the same. They consist of three tissue layers (see figure 13.26). The layer lining the lumen is epithelial tissue, and it provides the lumen with a smooth, glossy surface. Frictional losses against an ice-slick surface like this are minimal.

The **tunica media** consists of several sheets of smooth muscle. This is the layer that is mainly responsible for the strength and elasticity of arterial walls.

The outer layer, the **tunica externa,** is fibrous connective tissue. This is most abundant on large arteries and is probably responsible for providing the vessel with the tensile strength it needs to resist bursting when the huge balls of blood gush into the lumen and expand the walls.

The blood leaving the heart is carried by arteries. In the systemic circulation, these are the vessels that handle the oxygenated blood. In the pulmonary circulation, they transport the nonoxygenated blood toward the lungs to be recharged. In both cases they are carrying blood under high, intermittent pressure, and they all need considerable strength and elasticity, especially those closest to the heart.

Arterioles

As the arteries thrust outward from the heart, they begin to divide into smaller and smaller vessels. Finally they achieve the status of arterioles. Arterioles are generally considered to have a lumen of less than 170 micrometers diameter, although this tends to be a bit subjective. The blood flowing through arterioles experiences considerable frictional loss because the vessels are so small and the surface-area-to-volume ratio is so high. As a result, pressure drops rapidly after leaving the larger arteries, and most is lost in the arterioles, the most resistant of all our blood vessels (see figure 13.27).

One of the most important features of the arterioles is their ability to constrict or dilate and thereby administer precision adjustments to alter fluid flow

Figure 13.28 (*a*) Lumen diameter of a vessel with normal tone; (*b*) diameter as a result of vasoconstriction; (*c*) diameter as a result of vasodilation.

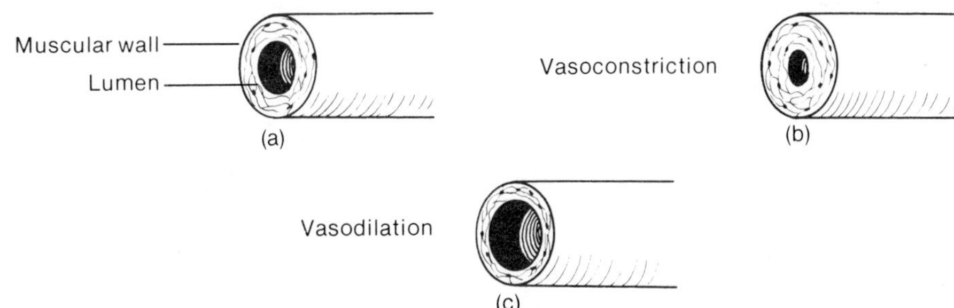

Figure 13.29 Small arterioles have some smooth muscle fibers in their walls; capillaries lack these fibers.

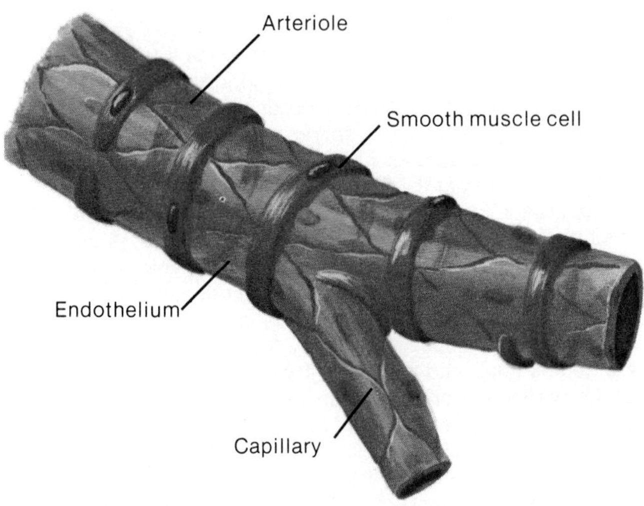

and blood pressure on command (figure 13.28). Neurons of the autonomic nervous system and hormones from various endocrine glands, by exerting their influence on the smooth muscle cells wrapping the arterioles, can produce constriction and/or dilation in these blood vessels.

Arterioles ultimately branch into even smaller vessels, the metarterioles, which communicate directly with capillaries. The walls of even these tiny vessels still show the three basic layers common to all arteries, but they are tremendously reduced. Often the tunica media and endothelial layers are only a single cell thick. Metarterioles, like arterioles, can exert a fine control over the volume and pressure of the blood that passes through them through minute adjustments of their smooth muscle layer. They are the smallest vessels that can do this (figure 13.29).

The Arterial Circulation Summarized

Arteries have been likened to the various aerial routes around the world travelled by our major airlines. Like jet airliners, their job is transportation between the major countries, carrying large quantities and covering vast distances at high speed. The arterioles are smaller, like railroads or bus routes along major freeways. Still fairly broad and certainly able to handle large numbers, they still do not move things as quickly or nearly as far as those that the major airlines handle. Metarterioles are the main thoroughfares leading around the cities and towns, and as the capillaries branch off, they take travellers in single file down the narrow streets into the business districts of the various towns they want to visit.

Capillaries

So the business section of the circulatory system is the capillary bed. All the rest of the blood vessels operate, like freeways or highways, to carry the blood back and forth through the body. They can make certain adjustments to the system and can vary the volume of blood they carry, but there is no exchange with any of the fluids around them. Exchange is what capillaries are for. Just as the businesses and stores lining the streets exchange ideas, money, goods, and services with the inhabitants, the capillaries exchange materials with the cells and interstitial fluids.

The number of capillaries in the body is almost beyond belief. Someone with an obvious love for numbers once calculated that there were more than fifty billion of them in an average human. With that many around, it comes as no surprise to learn that no cell in the body is ever more than fifty micrometers from a capillary.

Another fact of extreme importance emerged from this same observation. Capillaries are microscopic in size. Their lumen is seldom more than nine micrometers in diameter, so individually their capacity is minuscule. But considering the fact that there are fifty billion of these tiny vessels, it does not take much mathematical talent to calculate that their combined volume is on the order of 400 ml. That is pretty close to a half-liter, a remarkable volume for such small vessels.

Any structure that small cannot be composed of many layers of cells. It follows therefore that capillaries are extremely fragile vessels. Microscopically, their structure makes one think that the inner layer of endothelial cells slipped out of the metarterioles like the inner lining of a coat sleeve pulled inside out, and continued all alone into the tissues, leaving the two outer layers behind. That's just about right. The capillary wall is only a single layer of cells thick, and it is this very fragility that renders it so effective. Because the total volume of capillaries is so great, when blood enters the capillary systems it is as if water flowing swiftly along a narrow river bed had suddenly entered a lake and slowed down, a phenomenon known as, logically enough, the **lake effect.** Blood, therefore, travels slowly through the capillaries. The rate is only about 0.5 mm per second, and that is a lot more slowly than it moves in any of our other tubes. Since the average capillary is about a half-mm long, blood is in the exchange area for about one second. That's not long, but it's more than enough time to do its job.

The Forces of Exchange

Many of the forces discussed in chapter 3 are involved in these exchanges. Diffusion, filtration, and osmosis play very definite roles, and it is possible that active transport is also involved, although it isn't likely. Diffusion and osmosis take a great deal of time to finish their work when only moderate distances are involved, but when the distances are minute, these forces can complete their jobs in milliseconds. As we know, distances are really small in capillary beds. If the capillary will let the molecule through, it can zoom across the tiny membrane almost instantly. Water, for example, can flow back and forth *across* the capillary membrane some two to three thousand times faster than it moves *through* the capillary when it is travelling with the blood. With that kind of speed available, one second is plenty of time for all kinds of exchange.

Intrinsic Controls

Filtration The capillary membrane quite naturally plays the role of a sieve or a piece of filter paper. As was pointed out in chapter 12, it is an ultrafilter. The hydrostatic pressure head provided by the heart represents a considerable force in these tiny vessels, especially if there is any resistance on the distal end of the vessel—and there almost always is. With blood pressure working the filter, water can squeeze through it easily, along with many of the things dissolved in it, and the things that will pass through the capillary pores are delineated from things that are held back solely on the basis of size. This appears to be adjustable over a fairly broad range, and it depends on many variables, including the type of tissue they are operating in. In brain tissue, for example, the capillary pores are quite fine, and there is very little movement of molecules larger than glucose. On the other hand, capillaries in the liver often permit passage of proteins as large as 62,000 daltons.

The fineness of the capillary filter in the brain is one of the things that has contributed to the concept of what is called the **blood-brain barrier.** This barrier has been the subject of considerable debate ever since it was first hypothesized in the 19th century. The idea, as originally offered, stated that there is a profound barrier between the brain and the blood and that many molecules that cross with ease into tissues like the liver or the kidney simply will not enter the brain.

While there is little doubt that such a barrier exists, it perhaps requires a little explanation to place it in its proper perspective. Naturally, the brain has special requirements regarding its interstitial fluids. Inorganic ions and hormones, as well as some amino acids, cannot be permitted to fluctuate as widely in the brain as they do in many other parts of the body. The potassium concentration in the fluid around a neuron can influence the threshold voltage, so it must remain constant. When compared with tremendously active tissues like the liver, there certainly are many things that are rejected by the brain, and the barrier appears profound indeed. However, there are other tissues in the body that have barriers that are quite strong, and it appears that the effectiveness of all the barriers is variable. Much depends on the material that is trying to pass. Phospholipids, for instance, do not cross into the brain as quickly as they do into the liver, but they go even more slowly from the blood into skeletal muscle. Glycine is picked up by the brain more rapidly than it is picked up by cardiac muscle. So is glycerol. And glucose and sulfur are readily accepted by the brain, much more rapidly than the spleen or the lungs will take them. Yet we never hear of a blood-spleen barrier or a blood-lung barrier.

The current view of cerebral exchange is that the filter pores in brain capillaries are not as permissive as they are in most other tissues. Movement out of the capillary is further restricted by certain glial cells (astrocytes), whose endings form a complete covering around most brain capillaries. Such structural variations help maintain the restrictive nature of the blood-brain barrier with minimum energy expenditure. Nevertheless, the brain as a whole accepts things in much the same way a single cell would do it: selectively, as its metabolic demands dictate. While it does reject many things the liver will take, we must not forget that the liver is an extremely active tissue and will often accept things in volumes that no other tissue will. Substances that the brain can use are apparently not impeded in any way.

Colloid Osmotic Pressure The net movement of materials into and out of a capillary represents a balance between the filtration pressure provided by the heart and the osmotic pressure of the body fluids. The pressure provided by the heart is not so hard to understand, but the existence of the blood's *colloid osmotic pressure* requires a little explanation.

When blood enters the exchange areas, a firm continuity exists between the water in the interstitial fluid and the water in the blood. Lots of other things start whizzing back and forth across the capillary membrane as well. Fat-soluble materials, of course, do not have to wait in line to get through the pores, as they can simply dissolve in the membrane and go through it. Small organic molecules like amino acids, glucose, and the like may take a little bit longer, but not much—their movement is relatively free and easy. These small particles are capable of exerting tremendous osmotic influence on any system, but in this particular case there is really nothing to impede their movement, so they quickly equilibrate on both sides of the capillary membrane. With equal concentrations both inside and out, these particles play no part in the development of an osmotic gradient across the membrane. The formed elements (the cells) cannot leave the capillaries, and so they remain in the blood. They have the potential, therefore, to establish an osmotic gradient, and they do, but they are so large and relatively so few in number that what little osmotic influence they might have is too small to measure.

Proteins, primarily albumin, provide the real osmotic differential. Albumin is unable to pass through any of the filters present in the capillary membranes and so is restricted to the blood. At the same time, it is small enough to be quite abundant, and therefore it can have an osmotic influence on the system. And it does.

Because this osmotic pressure is being exerted by colloidal-sized particles, it is known as the **colloid osmotic pressure (COP)**. In the blood plasma of an average human being it has been calculated that COP can amount to about 28 mm Hg. By contrast, the osmotic pressure exerted by the few proteins present in interstitial fluids is only about 5 mm Hg, meaning that there is an osmotic gradient of 23 mm Hg across the capillary membrane. This represents a continuous force trying to draw water from the interstitial fluids into the blood. We have, therefore, in the capillary beds, a collision of opposing forces. The colloid osmotic pressure and the hydrostatic pressure head provided by the heart meet head-on in these tiny vessels, and their antagonistic efforts keep fluids moving vigorously in both directions. The disparity between the two is not as great as one might think. The heart provided the blood with 120 mm Hg of pressure in the beginning, but much of that was stolen as it moved through the smaller arteries, arterioles, and metarterioles. By the time it enters the capillaries, most is gone. The pressure thrusting blood through the capillaries has an average value of about 23.5 mm Hg.

Figure 13.30 Albumin and other plasma proteins produce a colloid osmotic pressure of 28.0 mm Hg. Interstitial proteins have a COP of 5 mm Hg. 28.0 minus 5 equals a net absorptive COP of 23.0 mm Hg. Heart pressure equals 23.5 mm Hg. The COP represents a negative force to the blood; heart pressure represents a positive force to the blood. 23.5 minus 23.0 equals +0.5 mm Hg.

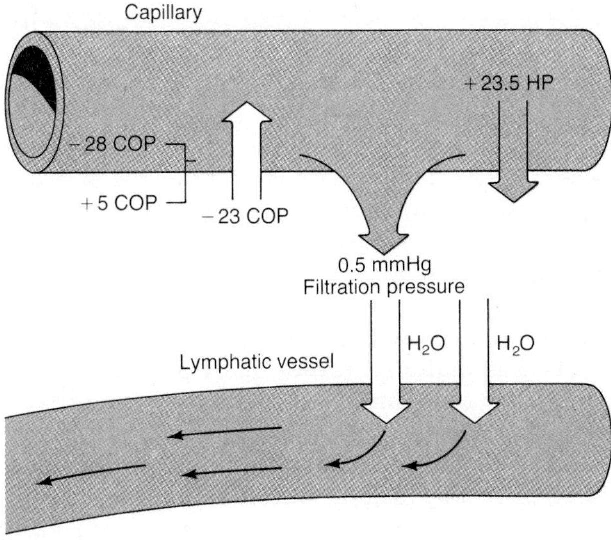

These figures apparently apply along the entire length of the vessel, and they indicate that there is a constant tendency for water to leave the blood and enter the interstitial fluid. (Algebraically add −23 mm Hg COP to +23.5 mm Hg filtration pressure = 0.5 mm Hg effective filtration pressure.)

It is important for us to remember that this 0.5 mm Hg pressure differential does *not* represent the force governing the movement of fluids across the capillary bed. In actuality, there is a pressure of 23.5 mm Hg driving material through the filter into the tissues, and 23 mm Hg pressure driving fluids back into the blood. The 0.5 mm figure is the difference between the two forces . . . it represents a nonequilibrium. Yet despite its miniscule value, it has an important job to do. It is the only driving force the lymph has outside of the lymphatic vessels. Small though it is, it is steady, and it produces a constant pressure that results in a net flow of water into the interstitial fluids. The flow is just enough to account for the steady trickle of lymph into the lymphatic vessels so it can ultimately return to the blood. It is a slow process, of course, but then, 0.5 mm Hg is not really a great deal of pressure. Figure 13.30 illustrates the process.

The Veins and Venules

When the blood leaves the capillaries, it enters a series of vessels called **venules.** Venules can produce some frictional resistance to the flow of blood; hence, like arteries and arterioles, they are considered **resistance vessels.** They are fundamentally similar to the arterioles in structural plan, but flimsier (see figure 13.21). Their design is consistent with their job. By the time blood enters venules there is not much pressure left. The intermittent pressures provided by the heart are long gone, and flow is smooth. Since they lack the necessity of containing sudden bursts of blood backed by the power of the heart muscle, venous vessels with a thick layer of muscle would be a waste of protein; hence the tunica media is quite thin in both venules and veins.

Pressure in the venous system can get so low that, were it not for the presence of the skeletal muscles, blood collected in veins of the feet and legs might never make it back to the heart. Fortunately for our survival, the muscles are there, and they aid in venous return by giving some of their energy to the return flow each time they contract (figure 13.31).

As was indicated earlier, most of the pressure supplied by the heart is lost in the bed of the arterioles, and what little remains usually vanishes as the blood makes its way through the capillaries. As a result, there is virtually no pressure head available to drive blood through the venous circulation. Hence there is a powerful tendency for blood to flow backwards, especially in legs and arms. To avoid this, the venous vessels are supplied with an abundance of one-way valves. Blood flowing in the wrong direction is not much of a problem in the arterial vessels, so they have relatively few valves. In veins, however, large or small, we can usually find a valve every inch or so.

The low pressure in our venous system and its dependence on skeletal muscle contraction, especially in vessels of the lower zones, is apparent when people are forced to stand for long periods of time in one position. This typically happens in military formations during reviews or when a political figure stops by a military base to deliver an impassioned oration. During these times, soldiers are often required to maintain a motionless, upright posture, sometimes for hours, and it is not unusual for a percentage of them to fall, unconscious, to the ground. Without the energy that is normally supplied by the contraction of leg muscles, and lacking the intrinsic pressure necessary to overcome gravity, the venous blood tends to pool in the legs and feet. If this continues for any significant length of time, the volume of blood available for the brain and the upper body organs is depleted, and the homeostatic mechanisms of our body take the only reliable means they have of restoring normal blood distribution—they lay the individual down.

Figure 13.31 Action of the one-way venous valves. The contraction of skeletal muscles helps to pump blood toward the heart, but it is prevented from pushing blood away from the heart by the closure of the venous valves.

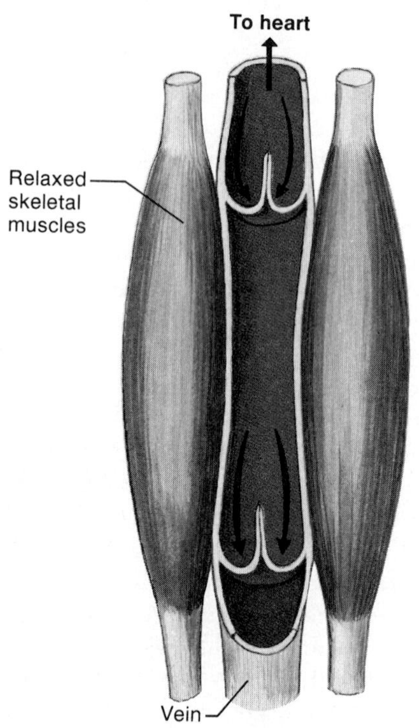

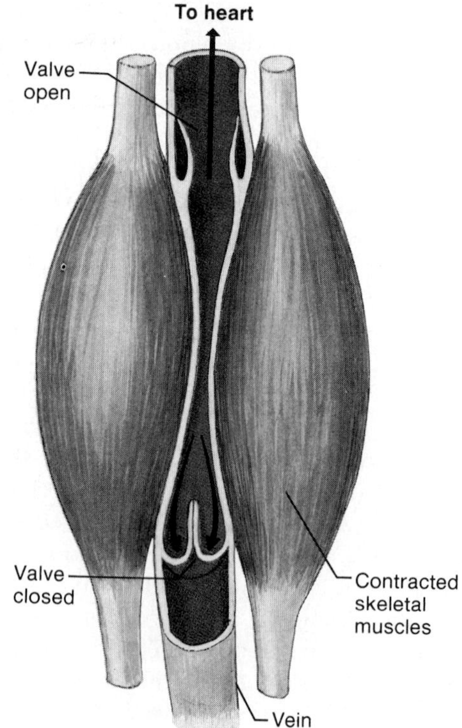

Cardiac Volumes

For the sake of convenience and consistency, researchers decided years ago on some standard terms that could be used to define certain cardiovascular parameters. Since these terms will be used from now on, it is time to become familiar with them.

Stroke Volume

The first is **stroke volume.** Stroke volume is defined as the volume of blood (in ml) pumped into the aorta during any given heartbeat. Such a volume would obviously be proportional to the strength of the heartbeat. Since, according to the Frank-Starling heart law, the strength of the heartbeat depends on the volume of venous return, the *stroke volume is proportional to the amount of venous blood that enters the heart.*

Cardiac Output

The **cardiac output,** or **minute volume** as it is sometimes called, is the volume of blood pumped into the aorta by the left ventricle in one minute. It is not a difficult determination to make. One need merely count the number of times the heart beats in a minute and multiply that figure by the stroke volume. In an average, healthy adult at rest, the stroke volume is about 70 ml. An average human heart rate is between 70 and 75 per minute, hence the cardiac output of this person at rest would be:

CA = stroke volume × number of beats per minute
= 70 ml/beat × 73 beats/min
= 5110 ml

The average human being has a total blood volume of between five and six liters. Hence, from the above figures, you can see that all of the blood in a person's body passes through the heart of the average human being, at rest, each minute.

End Volumes

End Diastolic Volume (EDV)

As was pointed out earlier, the relaxation of the heart muscle is just as important as its contraction, because during diastole, the heart chambers fill up. As blood pours into the atria from the great veins, it is drawn through the wide-open A-V valve into the ventricle. About 70 percent of the blood that is going to enter the ventricle is sucked in due to the negative pressure produced by cardiac "stretching," and the remaining 30 percent is forced in by atrial contraction. The total volume of blood in the ventricle just before ventricular systole occurs is known as the **end diastolic volume** (EDV). In an average resting person this runs between 120 and 130 ml. The EDV magnitude obviously depends on two things: (1) the heart rate and (2) the volume of venous return. Clearly, a long diastolic pause will permit more blood to enter the heart, so the faster the heart beats, the smaller the EDV will be. Equally obviously, a large venous return (VR) will increase the EDV. We would say, therefore, that the EDV is directly proportional to the VR and inversely proportional to the heart rate.

End Systolic Volume (ESV)

The chambers of the heart are never totally emptied of blood, even at the end of the most powerful contractions. The volume of blood still remaining in the ventricles after they have finished contracting is known as the **end systolic volume** (ESV). Since the average EDV amounts to about 125 ml, and since the average stroke volume is about 70 ml, the average ESV in a resting human will be 125 − 70 = 55 ml.

Regulation of the Heart

The beat of the heart is, as we have seen, of cardiac origin. If the heart were to be removed from the body and kept in a nutrient solution with all the glucose and oxygen it needed, it would continue to beat steadily, paced by the S-A node. This rate would not vary, as long as the S-A node remained healthy.

Obviously, this kind of invariance is not what is required in a living system. The needs of the body change from moment to moment, and the heart must change accordingly if it is to do its job properly. When in place within a living body, the heart has a built-in variability, one that is independent of neural or hormonal control, that can increase or decrease its beat strength. When venous return is high, the extra blood pouring into the heart chambers stretches the myocardium, and the heart responds, as we have already seen, by producing a more powerful beat (the Frank-Starling law). This is an important cardioregulatory mechanism, and it works nicely, but it is not enough for the constantly shifting circulatory priorities of highly active organisms like humans. Humans, like all mammals, are always "on the go." One moment a man may be on his back pounding a nail into an overhead board, and a moment later, he has turned over on his stomach and is leaning down to get another nail. Humans can go from resting positions to full, running activity in a second or two, and the cardiovascular requirements change each time a move is made. The person at rest has very different demands from a running person, and the heart must be able to adjust to meet these demands. This is where the autonomic nerves and the endocrine system come into play.

As has already been noted, there are terminals from both parasympathetic and sympathetic neurons on the heart, and they serve as a sort of "fine adjust" mechanism to tune the heart to the best rate and power for the job it has to do. To handle these kinds of adjustments, the control systems must receive input from various sites throughout the body.

Cardiac Inhibition

The cardioregulatory parasympathetic neurons originate in the **cardioinhibitory center** of the medulla. Along with other fibers of the vagus nerve, they emerge from the CNS at the brain stem and travel down the neck into the thoracic region, where they branch off and home in on the heart. These preganglionic parasympathetic neurons synapse near the right atrium, almost on the surface of the heart, and the short postganglionic neurons continue on from the ganglion to various sites on the heart's surface. Most terminate on the S-A or the A-V nodes, but there are some parasympathetic terminals on the muscle of the atria and ventricles.

Stimulating any of these vagal fibers will change the beat of the heart in one of two ways. It may reduce the heart rate, an adjustment known as a **negative chronotropic effect** (*chrono,* "time"; *tropic,* "a change"); or it may reduce the power of the beat, an adjustment known as a **negative inotropic effect** (*ino,* "a muscle").

Cardiac Stimulation

The sympathetic neurons that innervate the heart also originate in the medulla, in a zone known as the **cardioaccelerator center.** Unlike the inhibitory fibers of the vagus nerve, however, they remain within the CNS and travel down the spinal cord to the thoracic region. Here they emerge from the CNS and promptly synapse in one of the sympathetic chain ganglia with their postganglionic fibers. The postganglionic fibers that emerge from the ganglion form the **cardioaccelerator nerve,** which joins the vagal neurons on their way to the heart. As we have already seen, a few sympathetic fibers terminate on the S-A node, but most seem to synapse on the A-V node and the bundle of His. Stimulation of these neurons produces both chronotropic and inotropic effects—in this case, positive ones. Sympathetic activity increases both the rate and the power of the heartbeat.

Figure 13.32 The cardiac reflex loops. Afferent fibers between the major receptors and the cardiac control centers are shown by broken lines. Solid lines indicate the efferent pathways from the medullary centers to the effector sites.

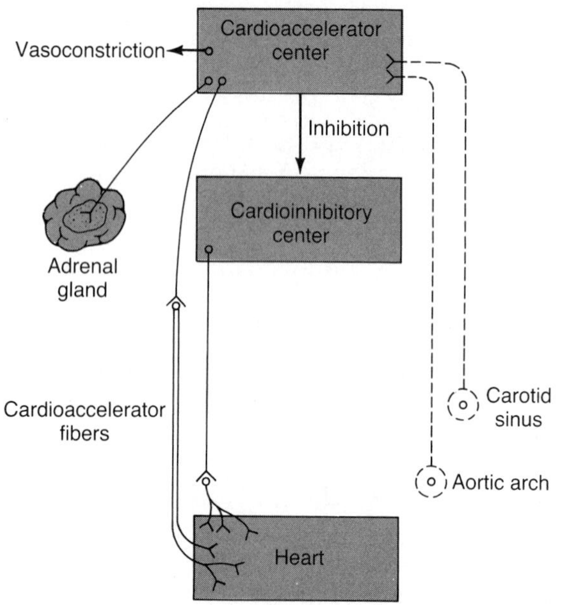

The Cardiac Reflexes

Autonomically induced changes in cardiac activity are mediated by two important receptor zones in the arterial circulation—the **carotid sinus** and the **aortic arch.** The carotid sinus is a slight enlargement of the carotid artery at the point where it divides into the internal and external carotid arteries, just at the entrance to the brain. This fork in the arterial circulation is heavily endowed with stretch receptors and **baroreceptors** (*baro,* "pressure"), which are designed to monitor the volume and the pressure of the blood about to enter the head. Similar receptors are present in the wall of the aortic arch, just above the point where the aorta leaves the heart.

Cardioinhibitory Nerves

When pressure and volume are high, the walls of the carotid artery are distended and the receptors are stretched. They, in turn, stimulate neurons of the **sinus nerve** and/or the **aortic nerve** (also called the **cardiodepressor nerve**) into increased activity, which is carried to the *cardioinhibitory center* in the medulla (see figure 13.32). Integration occurs within the medulla, and if the impulses are numerous enough to warrant immediate action, answering impulses are sent from the medulla, down vagal fibers to the heart. These impulses then inhibit both the rate of beat and the power of the heart muscle.

Cardioaccelerator Nerves

On the other hand, should these stretch receptors detect inadequate blood volume and pressure, they reduce the firing rate of the neurons of the sinus and aortic nerves. This information is picked up by the *cardioaccelerator center.* This center does several things, all intended to increase blood flow. First of all, it acts to inhibit the cardioinhibitory center. This removes any depressing vagal effects that might be present and permits the heart to beat more rapidly. Secondly, the cardioaccelerator center sends messages out along sympathetic neurons, stimulating arteriolar constriction and thus increasing arterial blood pressure. Thirdly, the cardioaccelerator center stimulates the adrenal medulla via the sympathetic fibers innervating that organ. The subsequent release of epinephrine (adrenalin) stimulates the heart muscle to still greater efforts and further increases arteriolar blood pressure (figure 13.32).

Blood Pressure Measurements

Blood pressure is the force supplied by the heart that thrusts the blood through the circulatory system. It is pressure potential; thus it is the hydraulic equivalent of voltage, and it acts on the blood, pushing against every particle of water and material dispersed in it.

Blood pressure is an extremely important indicator of a person's health. If it is too low, there is a possibility that the capillary filter systems will not operate correctly; too great, and the more delicate arterioles might blow out like a weak hose. Clinically, blood pressure readings are always given as two figures, the systolic and the diastolic pressure that exists in the arterial system at any given time. The systolic pressure is, as you know, a measurement of the force applied to the blood when the heart contracts. During diastole, the energy that exists in the system is what was stored when the arteries were forced to expand to accommodate the blood pouring in. Therefore, the diastolic pressure represents the elastic-rebound pressure present in the arteries when the heart is relaxed.

Measurements are generally made by a nurse or medical technician using an instrument known as a **sphygmomanometer.** The receptor portion of these instruments is wrapped around the biceps and triceps of the upper arm and blown up to constrict all the blood vessels beneath it. Then the pressure is slowly released. As the band constricting the arm slowly loosens, the first movement of blood through the **brachial artery** (the main artery in the arm) will occur when the highest pressure is present in the artery. The artery will open up just enough to let a spurt of blood move through it, and in between these high-pressure nodes, the artery will be squeezed shut. These spurtings make a noise (called **Korotkoff sounds**) as they pass through the vessel, and they can be heard clearly with a stethoscope. In the absence of a stethoscope, they can be detected as transient pressure increases on the sphygmomanometer pressure dial. As cuff pressure continues to drop, the spurts of blood getting through will get bigger and bigger and the sounds commensurately louder, until finally cuff pressure equals the rebound pressure of the arterial system. At this point the arteries will open and stay open, and the intermittent "heartbeat sounds" will disappear (figure 13.33). The first pressure reading is taken from the sphygmomanometer dial when the first sounds are heard, and the second reading is taken when the sounds disappear.

In an average, healthy person at rest, these readings should be in the neighborhood of 120 to 125 for the first (the systolic) and 65 to 80 for the second (the diastolic), and they are written as 125/80 or "one twenty-five over eighty." A person having such pressure readings would have a **pulse pressure** of $125 - 80 = 45$ mm Hg.

When a person's "pulse" is felt, the fingers of the nurse's or physician's hand are placed over the artery in the wrist, and as the periodic spurts of blood pass beneath the finger tips, they can be clearly felt. Recall the analogy involving the ostrich swallowing the oranges; what the clinician is feeling are the swellings in the artery as the "balls" of blood make their way through. They reflect the heart rate very efficiently, and their strength and regularity can often provide alert medical personnel with considerable information about a patient's overall health.

The Extrinsic Controls

Considerable manipulation of blood vessels occurs all the time, everywhere in the body. In a given zone, neural impulses may stimulate an arteriolar dilation and a drop in blood pressure, while simultaneously, in an immediately adjacent capillary bed, the endocrine system has instigated a general vasoconstriction and a pressure increase. These neural and endocrine controls are quite versatile. They can unilaterally instigate changes in extremely isolated zones, or they can cooperatively produce a change in blood pressure and flow volume that affects the entire body. In both cases, they represent the fine controls that respond to outside or internal stimuli and adjust to blood flow accordingly.

Figure 13.33 Blood pressure measurement. (*a*) Armband is tight, artery is totally compressed. No blood flows under the armband. (*b*) Armband is loosened enough to permit blood under systolic pressure to move. The artery is still collapsed between beats. (*c*) Armband is loose enough to permit free flow of blood through artery beneath, and Korotkoff sounds can no longer be heard.

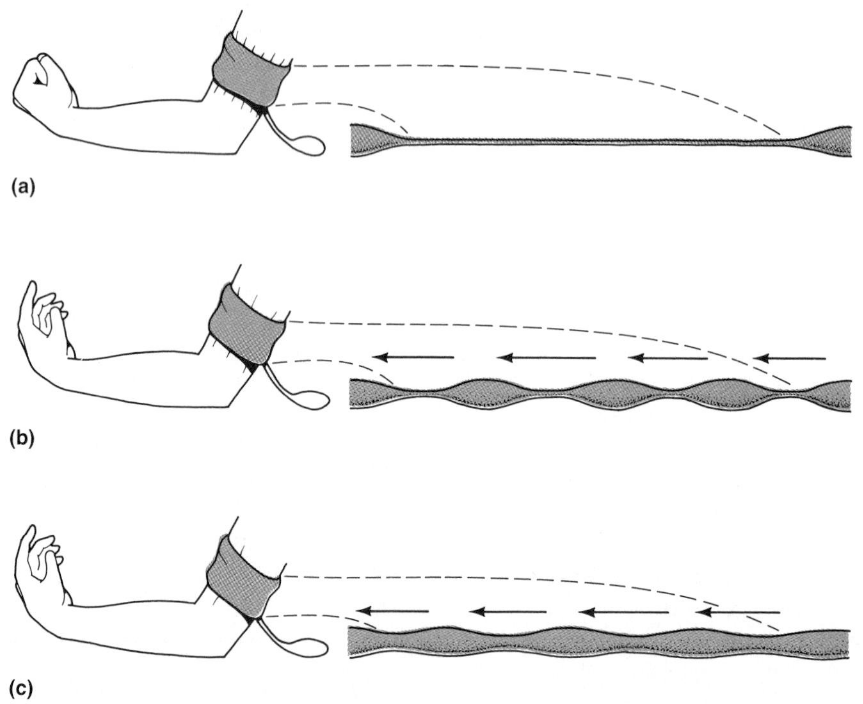

Factors Affecting Flow

Many things can influence the flow of blood through our arteries and veins. The pressure supplied by the heart is lost gradually as blood moves through the various tubes, and it is reduced by many things. For example, the longer the tubes that the fluid must go through, the greater the resistance that will be encountered and the more pressure lost. Resistance also increases when the **viscosity** of the fluid increases, which means that the thicker the blood gets, the harder it is to push through a tube. And finally, the narrower the tube is, the greater the resistance will be. Hydraulic engineers have learned that these factors all fit into an equation called Poiseuille's law, which looks like this:

$$\text{Resistance to flow} = \frac{\text{Fluid viscosity} \times \text{Tube length}}{\text{Radius of tube}^4}$$

In an adult human, the length of the various arteries and veins is not going to change substantially, certainly not on a moment-to-moment basis. Likewise, blood viscosity, since it is one of the things that is closely controlled by homeostatic mechanisms, should be pretty constant, too. Both of these observations being true, a quick look at the equation suggests that the only way left is to change resistance to flow by altering the diameter of the tubes the fluid is flowing through. The result would be an immediate change in pressure upstream from the point where the resistance changed.

As it turns out, varying vessel diameter is a particularly effective way of altering resistance to flow. You can see from Poiseuille's equation that any alteration in tube radius produces an exponential effect. It has been reliably calculated that a 33 percent reduction in the radius of the arterioles will produce a 400 percent increase in resistance to flow. The result is an enormous increase in pressure upstream from the constriction. Living systems therefore utilize this fact freely to selectively alter flow characteristics whenever it becomes necessary.

Thus, when it becomes necessary to change blood flow quickly in a given group of peripheral arteries without altering flow anywhere else, the quickest and easiest way is to change the diameter of the arterioles in that system. If we can accept that, the only question we then need to consider seems to be whether to constrict or dilate the vessel. Do you make a vessel larger or smaller to increase the pressure? Don't answer too quickly—it may surprise you.

Let us consider a simple analogy. If you were to take a hose through which water was flowing and you bent it, you would be, in effect, decreasing the diameter of the tube. Now ask yourself what will happen to the pressure in the hose on both sides of that crimp. Take the side closest to the faucet first; does pressure go up or down? If this gives you difficulty, think about what would happen if the hose were made of rather soft, elastic rubber and could easily blow up

Figure 13.34 Fluid flow through a hose. The pressure applied to the water by the pumps or water tower can force water through the hose very rapidly and blow it out of the end for a considerable distance (*a*). There is some pressure loss in the hose due to its length. The longer it is, the less pressure is available to push out water (*b*). If the water were syrupy, there would be more resistance, and pressure could be lost that way, too. This would be the viscosity factor. But the most effective way by far to increase resistance to flow is to reduce the bore of the tube. An extreme example of this is to crimp the hose (*c*). As you can see, there is almost no pressure available to push water out of the hose, so it must all be trapped between the crimp and the spigot. In fact, if the hose were made of weak rubber, it might even show you where the pressure is (*d*).

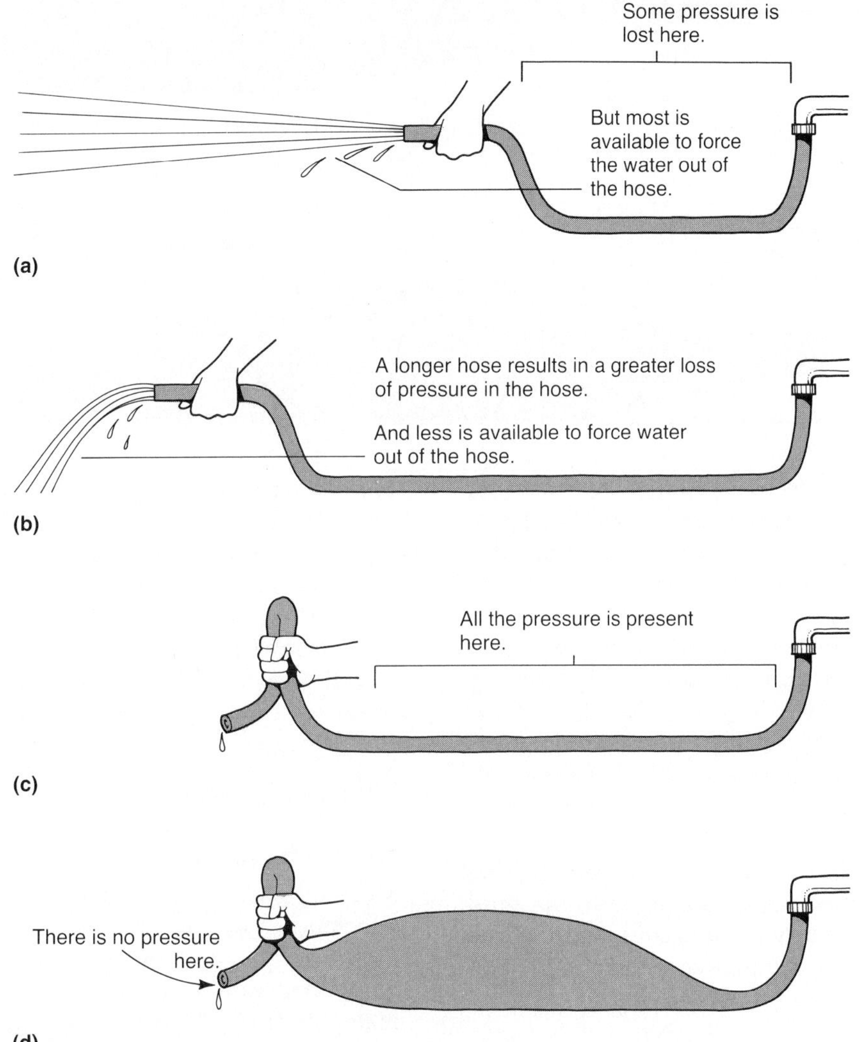

like a balloon (figure 13.34). Would you expect there to be any swelling in the hose when you crimped it? If so, where would that swelling be?

As figure 13.34 shows, there will be a substantial pressure increase on the side of the hose between the spigot and the crimp. The pressure on the other side—between the crimp and the end of the hose—will be very low; in fact, if you crimp it hard enough, there will be no pressure available at all to force water out of the hose. Clearly, then, if you wish to increase the arterial pressure and flow, you *constrict* the arterioles downstream.

That is exactly how pressure changes are accomplished in the body. Speaking generally, arterial blood pressure is increased by arteriolar constriction and is reduced by dilation, and these changes are under the control of both nerves and endocrine secretions. It is also worth noting that *only* arterioles and small arteries are involved in this kind of regulation. The smooth muscle layers in arteries reflect their elasticity, not their contractile power, while venules do not have enough muscle tissue to constrict, and capillaries have none at all.

Fluid Flow in Tubes

When fluid is forced into an already-filled tube, it must overcome several forces to proceed. It must first of all push against the fluid that is already in the tube and thrust it ahead to make room to enter. Once within, it encounters resistance from the walls of the

Figure 13.35 The laminar flow of fluid through a tube. (*a*) The movement proceeds as if the fluid were a series of cylinders, one inside the other. (*b*) In cross section, the flow pattern looks like this.

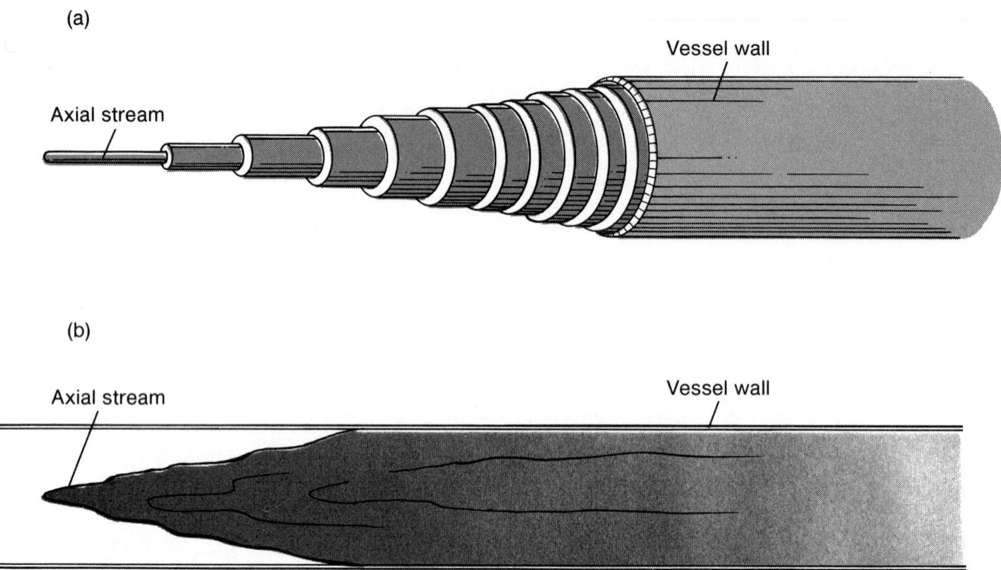

tube in the form of friction. Naturally, the smoother the tube walls, the lower that resistance will be. There is no way, however, to make the walls friction-free; hence the fluid along the outer edges, in contact with the tube walls, will flow very slowly. The layer of fluid next to the outer layer will be able to move a little faster because the frictional losses will be slightly lower, and the same will be true of the fluid layer inside of that one. As a result, when fluid moves through tubes, it moves as if it consisted of a series of cylinders or sleeves enclosed within one another (see figure 13.35).

As long as the flow is not too rapid and as long as the vessel's inner walls remain smooth, the fluid moving through the tube will retain this laminar flow pattern. However, this is not always the case.

Velocity

The speed at which fluid moves through a given tube is determined by two things: (1) the volume of fluid that must move in a given time and (2) the size (cross-sectional area) of the tube involved. If a pipe one inch in diameter carries a liter of fluid in ten seconds, the velocity at which that fluid flows will be slower than it would be if a half-inch pipe were carrying the same volume in the same time period. As the diameter of the pipe gets smaller, the velocity at which the fluid flows must speed up accordingly, and eventually a point is reached where the velocity is too great for the flow to remain laminar. The result is **turbulence,** and it is an unusual occurrence within the confines of the human circulatory system, although certain circumstances can occasionally produce turbulence in the blood vessels. During vigorous exercise, for example, with the heart pumping at a high rate of speed, the velocity of blood flow within the smaller arteries and arterioles achieves such heights that turbulence will occur. In a person of normal health, such turbulence means very little. There are occasions, however, when it indicates potential problems, and knowledge of its existence can be very important.

Clinical Considerations

Heart Murmurs

Morphologically, the heart is nothing more than an enormously expanded artery with some functional modifications, and many of the problems that develop in an artery can also develop in the heart. Fatty materials can be deposited along the walls of the heart just as they can in an artery or vein, and these deposits can partially occlude valves, making an already-small opening still smaller. This is a potential disaster, because the valvular opening may become too small to permit adequate blood flow through it. Fortunately, problems of this sort can often be detected in their early stages, and one of the most reliable and simplest ways is through the use of the stethoscope and a knowledge of what causes the normal heart sounds.

When blood flows at normal velocity through a healthy heart, the regular heart sounds are all that can be heard. Under unusual circumstances, however, the blood will make some extra noises—noises known in the medical profession as *murmurs.*

As you may have guessed from our earlier discussion, not all heart murmurs have an unpleasant connotation. A perfectly healthy person produces a heart murmur during vigorous exercise simply because exercise requires a rapidly beating heart and high-velocity blood flow. Such murmurs are known as *functional heart murmurs* and denote no problems. However, should a fatty deposit develop in one of the A-V valves or at one of the exits from the heart, it produces a **stenosis** (narrowing) of the valve. To maintain normal heart operations, blood will have to flow through the narrowed opening at a higher-than-normal rate, which produces turbulence and sound. Sounds such as these are *valvular heart murmurs* and are considered quite serious. A practiced clinician can usually pinpoint which of the heart valves is narrowed by noting when, during the normal heart sounds, the murmur is heard. If, for instance, one hears "bump (swish) bump, pause, bump (swish) bump, pause" the murmur is occurring as the blood is rushing through opened aortic or pulmonic valves, so one of them must be stenosed. Similarly, if the murmur is heard during the second heart sound, one or both of the A-V valves must be stenosed.

Cardiovascular Disease: Truth and Fiction

Probably no affliction in the last century has drawn greater publicity and public interest than cardiovascular disease, particularly heart problems. We are constantly reminded how important it is to keep active and to avoid certain foods if we wish to maintain healthy hearts. Unfortunately, most of these reminders are offered, not for *our* good, but for the good of some manufacturer of salad oil or special margarine or almost any "polyunsaturated" edible that can be conjured up. We are informed that a certain cooking oil is superb because of its lack of saturated fats; another may be even better because it contains no cholesterol, and a third may be superior to all because it lacks both. We are warned about dietary ingredients that may increase the risk of heart attacks, and the number of substances involved seems to increase daily. Fats of any kind, we are warned, should be shunned, as should almost all meats. At the same time, we are told that a total vegetable diet is not safe either, especially if one lives in tropical or subtropical zones. Coconuts, palm leaves, and avocados, vegetables though they may be, contain the "wrong" kind of oils. Shellfish and crustacea are quivering masses of cholesterol, a highly dangerous fatty substance; caffeine and steroid hormones have been linked to cardiovascular problems. Recent research has suggested that under certain circumstances our own immune systems may be surreptitiously trying to kill us. Even our ancestors are implicated in our heart problems by virtue of genetic inheritance.

How much of this miscellaneous information is accurate, how much is statistical error, and how much is advertisers' propaganda, accepted for so long that it is assumed to be true even without scientific support? These are questions that many of you are going to be asked someday, and as potential authority figures, you should at least familiarize yourselves with the various claims and learn what we *do* know about them.

Cholesterol, Again

As was pointed out in chapter 12, one thing that we find repeatedly throughout the literature is a link between blood cholesterol and cardiovascular disease. Coffee is thought to contribute to circulatory problems because it increases the levels of cholesterol in the blood (although this research is being seriously questioned), eggs are slandered as dietary items because their yolks are rich in cholesterol, and shellfish are castigated for the same reason. Red meat, although not particularly high in cholesterol content, is considered unhealthy because it contains saturated fats, and it is thought that this may contribute in an indirect way to increased cholesterol levels. As to cholesterol itself—that is probably the most slandered and ballyhooed edible substance that ever existed.

Atherosclerosis

Most of the deaths attributed to atherosclerosis seem to result from disruption of heart function, and perhaps we should mention some of the major factors that almost everyone agrees are implicated in the development of arteriosclerotic heart problems. Not all of them can be controlled, of course. Some, like our ancestry, we can do nothing about, but we should at least be familiar with them all.

According to the American Medical Association, the major *controllable* risk factors are, in order of importance:

1. Hypertension
2. Elevated serum low-density lipoproteins (LDL)
3. Smoking
4. Diabetes
5. Obesity

Among the *uncontrollable* risk factors, the most important of all may turn out to be heredity, although no one is really sure just how it exerts its effects. In any case, there is nothing anyone can do about it aside from paying special attention to an individual who has a family history of heart trouble. So we have to leave it alone—yet it would be surprising indeed if it had no role in cardiovascular disease.

A second uncontrollable factor is age. Risk of cardiovascular disease sharply elevates as a person ages—particularly white males. During the period between ages 25 and 34, white American males have a 1 in 10,000 incidence of heart attack, whereas by age 60 the incidence has increased to 1 in 10.

A third uncontrollable factor is sex—gender, not the act. American males of European extraction have more than six times as many heart attacks as their female counterparts, a sexual bifurcation that is not as apparent among other ethnic groups and one that has medical science baffled.

Obviously, then, a 60-year-old, fat, caucasoid American male smoker with diabetes would be considered to have "one foot in the grave," as the saying goes. And often, that's true—but it is not always—and that is where heredity rears its puzzling head. Some men in their early 40s, nonsmokers, lean, fit, athletic, and seemingly destined to live another forty or fifty years will suddenly keel over dead from cardiac infarction, while an individual like the smoking diabetic just mentioned will live to be 90. Since we all live in the same general atmosphere and overall environment, it is hard to ascribe these differences to anything but our genetic background, and researchers wish, fervently, that they knew where and how these effects are applied.

Heart "Attacks"

Despite its firm link to cardiac infarction, high blood cholesterol nevertheless does most of its damage to the vessels that carry the blood throughout the body. The deadly effects produced on the heart are due mainly to occlusions of the coronary arteries, and similar occlusions can be just as disastrous when they afflict arterioles in the brain, kidneys, or other critical organs.

Cholesterol plaques are not the total cause of arterial occlusion, however. Usually they are just one-half of the cause. Most heart attacks are the result of a clot, loose in the circulation, getting jammed in a plaque-narrowed artery and plugging it up. The zone of cardiac muscle nourished by this artery is thus deprived of blood, and that portion of heart muscle dies. This is the familiar **coronary thrombosis** that is so painful and so rapidly fatal.

The tremendous pain that accompanies an infarction is a practical indicator of the importance the living body places on the heart muscle, and it serves to reinforce other indicators mentioned earlier. Every bit of heart muscle is critical to its continued function, and if part of it is damaged or killed, the individual is less perfect because of it. Patients who have had an infarction and survived it usually show a scarred left ventricle, and the result is an abnormal contraction of that side of the heart. If more than 25 percent of the left ventricular musculature is scarred, most physicians feel that the heart must work extra hard to continue normal operations, thus placing a wearying load on an already understaffed system.

The heart is forced to work harder because some cardiac muscle has died, and the problem is exacerbated by one of the heart's most important self-adjusting mechanisms—the relationship between heart dilation and stroke strength. The damaged muscle in the ventricle has been replaced with scar tissue, and scar tissue is stiff and inelastic. Part of the ventricle, therefore, is stiff and will not expand the way the undamaged muscle tissue does, so the chamber does not hold quite as much blood as it used to. This means that if the heart is to retain normal output, the undamaged muscle must expand a bit more than it normally would—in other words, *ventricular dilatation* must take place.

You will recall that the strength of the heartbeat is determined to some extent by how much the myocardial fibers are stretched when the ventricle is filling. Since the ventricle of the damaged heart must dilate abnormally in order to fill normally, the intact muscle fibers must stretch more than they usually do, and thus they wind up doing extra work each time they contract. When extra stress is applied to a muscle, the fibers grow, and myocardial fibers are no exception, so the heart enlarges. Once this abnormal enlargement occurs, the capacity of the heart to adjust to further demands is lost. In other words, if it is called upon to work harder than normal, it cannot do it, and so it simply gives up. In most such cases, almost any unusual physical stress will produce this kind of reaction. Hence patients whose hearts are more than 25 percent scarred by cardiac infarction are considered to be ideal candidates for sudden death due to heart failure.

Encouraging, but Puzzling, Recent Facts

Despite the uncontested observation that heart attacks are the major cause of death in this country, it is also a fact that such deaths appear to be declining. Death due to acute heart attack crested nationally in the early 1960s and has progressed rapidly downward since that time. No one is quite sure why this is true, but several theories have been offered by way of explanation. Some workers have suggested that people are eating less animal fat, are exercising more, and are generally getting thinner, and all these things are true. But if reducing body weight and decreasing intake of beef and pork are really involved in the decline, one should certainly be able to see that a drop in heart-attack deaths occurred in the 1930s, during the Great Depression. In those years, half the country was on a bare subsistence diet. Very few people could afford to buy meat, and very little was consumed. White bread was expensive, so most people ate cheaper, coarser, high-fiber breads and other cheap

Figure 13.36 Some abnormal ECG tracings. (*a*) Tachycardia: unusually rapid beat. (*b*) Bradycardia: unusually slow beat. (*c*) Ectopic (extra) beats. (*d*) Atrial flutter: synchronized, very rapid atrial contractions. (*e*) Atrial fibrillation: desynchronous, rapid contraction of atrial cells. (*f*) ECG of heartbeat controlled by the A-V node. In such tracings, the P wave is often inverted or absent.

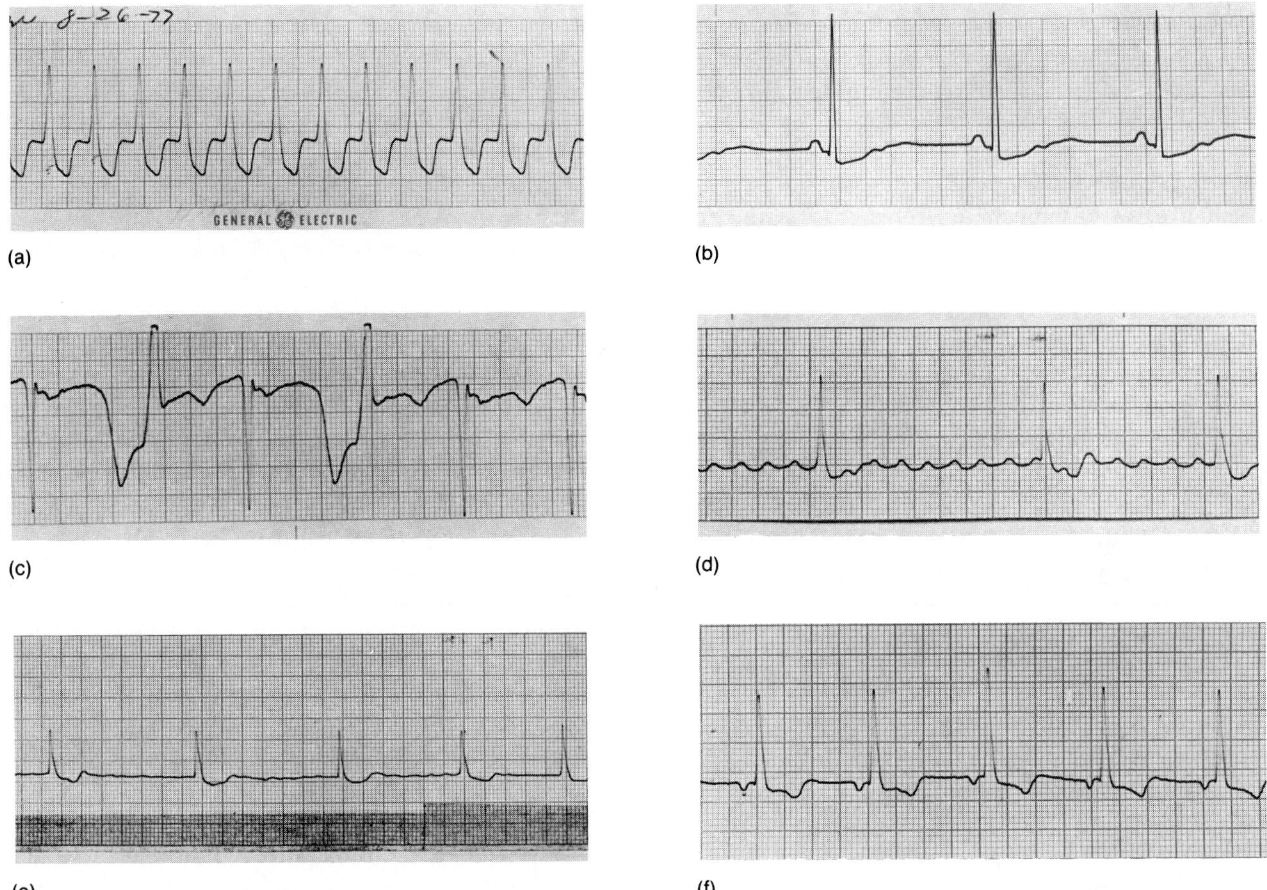

foods . . . in other words, most diets consisted mainly of the cheapest vegetables and fruit and the population was generally skinny. Part of this was due to food lack, but part was due to the amount of exercise they were getting marching through the streets and countryside looking for work. All these things suggest that heart attacks should have dropped like a rock in the Depression years, but that is not what we see. During those years heart attack deaths went up, not down.

Has a drop in smoking been the cause? There is a huge library of evidence tying smoking to cardiovascular problems, so if people are not smoking as much, it should certainly reduce the risk of heart attack. While no one doubts that it does, it does not seem to be responsible for the current drop in heart attack fatalities. Why do I say that? Statistics provide most of the reason. It has been repeatedly demonstrated that the risk of heart attack in men over 60 does not increase when they smoke. If a reduction in smoking is responsible for the current drop in such deaths, men over 60 should not be affected at all, yet they show the same decrease in heart-attack deaths that the overall population does. That suggests that something else is responsible.

Are any of the controllable risk factors involved? Can any of the things we fondly believe are contributing factors to heart attacks be correlated with this decrease in deaths?

It doesn't look like it! Hypertension does not seem to be occurring any less frequently. Admittedly, our ability to control its effects has increased considerably since 1940, but not enough to fit the curves. Nor is there any apparent correlation between the reduction in deaths and increased exercise, reduced weight, or lower serum LDL.

The problem remains unanswered. Something is responsible for the dramatic drop in deaths from acute heart attack, but no one seems to know what it is.

The Cardiac Conduction System

Tachycardia

Tachycardia (figure 13.36*a*) is an abnormally rapid heart rate (>100/min.) and has many causes, the most common of which is vigorous exercise.

Bradycardia

Bradycardia (figure 13.36*b*) is an abnormally slow heart rate which, in an average person, would be anything slower than about 60/min. Such lowered heart rates are quite common during sleep, although there are other causes that are more sinister, such as certain "recreational" drugs and hypothermia. It is not unusual for highly conditioned athletes to have "normal" heart rates of 50 to 60/min.

Ectopic Heartbeats

Unusual, extra heartbeats are referred to as **ectopic beats** (figure 13.36*c*) and are not unusual in perfectly normal hearts. They frequently occur after a person has been hyperventilating prior to performing some athletic feat, such as a prolonged underwater exploration. However, ectopic beats can have a serious underlying cause. Unusual electrical activity is often a result of overindulgence in drugs such as cocaine; sometimes it is caused by ischemic (debilitated or damaged) heart tissues. Such beats almost invariably arise outside of the S-A node, in a part of the heart that seldom initiates a cardiac contraction. As a result, the contraction is often nonproductive and sometimes damaging.

Flutter

Flutters (figure 13.36*d*) are a physician's way of saying that one or more cardiac chambers is contracting at a very high rate. Atrial flutter usually averages between 250 and 350 beats per minute, which is extremely fast—too fast to permit much movement of blood. While this can sometimes happen in a perfectly normal heart, it usually indicates severe damage somewhere on the myocardium.

Fibrillation

Fibrillation (figure 13.36*e*) is also a very high conduction rate in a cardiac chamber, but it differs from flutter. Flutter contractions are regular and well-coordinated, whereas fibrillar contractions are irregular and uncoordinated. Atrial fibrillations are serious, but they are not necessarily fatal. In an otherwise healthy heart, atrial fibrillation will reduce cardiac output usually by less than 30 percent; hence as long as the ventricles are contracting regularly, blood will continue to move properly through the heart. Ventricular fibrillation, however, is nearly always fatal if not corrected quickly.

Both flutter and fibrillation are common during myocardial infarction and are often present during thyroid storms (see chapter 10).

Defibrillation

Fibrillation can be stopped and the heart's proper conducting pathways reestablished through the use of an instrument known as a **defibrillator.** The instrument consists of a pair of metallic paddles that are placed on the patient's chest across the heart muscle; when stimulated, they send out a high-voltage pulse. This pulse, if things go well, depolarizes the whole heart muscle, and all the electrical and contractile activity promptly stops. The hope is that with everything stopped, the S-A node will be able restart things and establish control over the conduction system.

Pacemaker Problems

The S-A node is remarkably durable, but nevertheless, it can be damaged by disease or accident, and sometimes it can fail. Should this occur, the A-V node can pick up the beat and carry on. Its rhythm is not as rapid as that of the S-A node, but under nonstressful circumstances it is capable of maintaining life in most mammals (see figure 13.36*f*). Generally, it runs about 47 percent slower than the pacemaker, which means that if the S-A node produces 70 beats per minute, the A-V node will produce about 40. This would certainly be uncomfortable and probably dangerous in a human being. Chest pains would be common, particularly in the very early morning when the body's rhythms are at their lowest ebb. Such individuals would be worn out physically and tired all the time . . . likely they would be unable to handle any kind of stressful situation, but they might be able to survive—for a while.

Artificial Pacemakers

To relieve such unpleasant and dangerous conditions, biomedical researchers have developed **artificial pacemakers.** These devices consist of self-contained power packs that provide an electrical stimulus to the heart muscle through electrodes that have been surgically implanted in the approximate region of the S-A node. Because there is no way to monitor the varying oxygen demands that the body might make, such pacemakers cannot be set to respond to changing physiological demands. But they need not beat at a constant rate. A heart's natural pacemaker is seldom damaged to a point of nonfunction. Generally, it can operate correctly most of the time. Usually its malfunctions occur sporadically, especially in the early morning, so pacemakers have been designed that can sense cardiac bioelectrical activity, and if the heart produces an impulse before the artificial pacemaker does, it will block the instrument's. This lets the artificial pacemaker temporarily shut down and have the heart's own pacemaker take over when conditions are right, but leaves it free to swing into action when the biological pacemaker slows down too much or briefly fails. This allows the heart to increase its rate all by itself if circumstances warrant it and if it can, yet the patient is assured that it will never beat too slowly. Having one's heart beating at least 75 or 80 times a minute has proven to be an enormous boon to heart patients who would otherwise be forced to live like near-cripples.

Heart Block

Heart blocks occur when something interferes with the movement of the stimulating impulse from the atria into the ventricles. There are various degrees of heart block, some more serious than others, but a complete heart block means that electrical continuity between the atria and the ventricles no longer exists and the ventricles are electrically isolated. They may still contract on their own, due to the intrinsic rhythm of the A-V node or the bundle, but there will be no synchrony between them and the atria. Instead of contracting after the atria have begun to relax, they may contract at the same time, in which case the more powerful ventricles will force the A-V valves to remain closed and render atrial contractions ineffective. The condition can be extremely dangerous, and if corrective action is not undertaken quickly it can be life-threatening.

The easiest way to correct such a problem is to install a small conductor extending from the atrial musculature, through the tricuspid valve into the ventricles. Usually the distal end is imbedded in the muscle of the right ventricle at the origin of the bundle of His. This bypasses the damaged A-V node and permits the S-A node and atrial musculature to once again regulate the pumping of the entire heart.

Sometimes the depolarizing signal can pass the A-V node smoothly but is scattered by a damaged bundle of His. The impulse has gotten into the ventricular area smoothly, but because its transmission through the bundle is garbled, there is no synchrony in the beating of the two ventricles. Such blockage is known as a **bundle branch block,** and it means that impulses must be conducted by muscle-to-muscle spread of the action potential. As a result, contraction of the affected ventricle will be delayed and will not be synchronized with the beat of the other ventricle, nor will it coincide with atrial systole.

A Thought-Provoking Observation The electrical activity of the heart, since it precedes all contractile activity, must be considered just as important as the muscular activity, and indeed it is. Recently, however, some biomedical engineers have suggested that much of our knowledge of the heart's electrical activity may be built on obsolete ECG analytical techniques. Many clinical analyses rely on instruments that provide information that, we are told, is little different from that which was provided by instruments used in the 1940s, despite the rapid advancement of modern electronics. They are convinced that we are obtaining only a tiny fraction of the information we could be using, and they suggest that the wave patterns that are classically analyzed represent less than 10 percent of the information actually available to modern instruments. This, if true, suggests that a complete overhaul of instrumentation and wave analysis is desperately needed and should be done.

Stroke

Stroke is a neurological malfunction—in fact, it is the primary cause of most neurological problems in this country—yet it is a result of vascular disorder. Anything that prevents an adequate supply of blood from getting to a given portion of the brain can correctly be termed a stroke. The word *stroke,* therefore, is actually a very general term that embraces several quite different problems. For instance, strokes can be the result of a blockage in an artery (infarction) or the sudden bursting of a small artery and subsequent cerebral hemorrhage. These are quite different disorders, but they have several things in common. Both are almost always the result of either atherosclerotic disease or high blood pressure, both strike suddenly, usually without any warning, and both have catastrophic results.

Cerebral Hemorrhage This is by far the deadliest form of stroke in its acute form, but if the victim is able to survive the initial impact, the damage is often reparable. Rupture of a cerebral artery is usually the result of a long-standing "hardening" of the artery by atherosclerotic plaque plus high blood pressure in the area. Apparently the most severe hemorrhages result from damage to the large, central artery supplying most of the sub-cortical structures in the brain. Major damage often is caused by the mass of loose blood compressing the sensitive neural tissue, sometimes actually pushing it away from where it is supposed to be. Large hemorrhages are fatal in more than 50 percent of the cases, usually in one or two days. Those who survive will have a long convalescence, but often they can recover many of their consciously controlled body functions.

Cerebral Infarction Because there is a really profound collateral circulation throughout the brain, infarction seldom results from the blockage of a small vessel. Most infarctions are the result of occlusion in a large extracranial vessel, or in one of the smaller, intracranial ones accompanied by an atherosclerotic blockage in the collateral circulation. If the blood supply into the region can be restored quickly enough, the affected brain areas will survive and recovery can be complete. If the blockage dams up the blood supply for more than about four minutes, however, the damage to the neural tissue is permanent,

Table 13.1 Normal Arterial Blood Pressure at Different Ages*

Age	Systolic		Diastolic		Age	Systolic		Diastolic	
	Men	Women	Men	Women		Men	Women	Men	Women
1 day	70†				16 years	118	116	73	72
3 days	72†				17 years	121	116	74	72
9 days	73†				18 years	120	116	74	72
3 weeks	77†				19 years	122	115	75	71
3 months	86†				20–24 years	123	116	76	72
6–12 months	89	93	60	62	25–29 years	125	117	78	74
1 year	96	95	66	65	30–34 years	126	120	79	75
2 years	99	92	64	60	35–39 years	127	124	80	78
3 years	100	100	67	64	40–44 years	129	127	81	80
4 years	99	99	65	66	45–49 years	130	131	82	82
5 years	92	92	62	62	50–54 years	135	137	83	84
6 years	94	94	64	64	55–59 years	138	139	84	84
7 years	97	97	65	66	60–64 years	142	144	85	85
8 years	100	100	67	68	65–69 years	143	154	83	85
9 years	101	101	68	69	70–74 years	145	159	82	85
10 years	103	103	69	70	75–79 years	146	158	81	84
11 years	104	104	70	71	80–84 years	145	157	82	83
12 years	106	106	71	72	85–89 years	145	154	79	82
13 years	108	108	72	73	90–94 years	145	150	78	79
14 years	110	110	73	74	95–106 years	145	149	78	81
15 years	112	112	75	76					

*Mean arterial blood pressure; derived from various studies.
†Value for both males and females.
K. Diem, C. Lentner, (eds.), *Geigy Scientific Tables,* 7th ed., Ciba-Geigy, Basle, 1970, p. 553.

and its extent will determine the degree of recovery. Massage and movement of affected limbs should be started as soon as possible, and when the patient becomes conscious, breathing exercises should be encouraged.

Recovery from a cerebral infarction is seldom 100 percent, although most patients ultimately recover sufficiently to care for themselves and to communicate clearly with others. It is a general rule in neurology that any impairments still remaining six months after the stroke are probably permanent.

Systemic Hypertension (High Blood Pressure)

Persistently high arterial blood pressure is rampant in countries of the western world and it has been estimated that there may be as many as thirty-five million cases of people suffering this problem in the United States alone. That represents as much as 15 percent of the population of this country, and of that group maybe a quarter of them are unaware that they have it. For some strange reason, high blood pressure occurs much more often in black Americans than it does in white Americans, and the mortality rate in our black population is concomitantly higher. Also, it is much more likely to occur in people over the age of 50 than in those who are younger. Records indicate that about 25 percent of white Americans over age 65 have high blood pressure, while in blacks the incidence may be as high as 50 percent.

Distribution seems to vary among white Americans according to sex. Prior to age 50, it is much more common in males than it is in females, but after age 50 it reverses itself and attacks women more often. In blacks, there is no such sexual disparity at any age. It assaults both men and women with equal fervor.

Hypertension may appear in a person without warning and with no apparent cause, in which case it is considered *idiopathic* or *primary* hypertension. On the other hand, it may be associated with some disease, in which case it is known as *secondary* hypertension. Nearly all the cases that appear in this country are primary, which means they never have any single, clearly discernable cause. There is pretty clear evidence that high blood pressure throughout the population is linked to heredity, but parents with high blood pressure do not necessarily doom their offspring to it also. There are many other factors that may be involved, such as diet, general environment, blood chemistry, and neural conditions.

There are so many different kinds of primary hypertension that it is well beyond the scope of this textbook to attempt to cover them all. It is worthwhile, however, to note that while a cure for primary hypertension doesn't exist, it is possible to reduce the risk of serious complications, and alleviating the symptoms is possible in nearly all of the cases. A person suffering from high blood pressure who is not on sustained treatment is taking a tremendous risk. The possibility of the heart simply stopping is an ever-present specter hanging over his or her head, along with such deadly afflictions as stroke, myocardial infarction, or renal failure. And neglecting to obtain treatment or to stay on medication is foolish when statistics demonstrate that proper care can control nearly all of these problems.

One of the biggest difficulties involved with high blood pressure is that an enormous number of hypertensives aren't aware that they have a problem. There are seldom any significant signs or symptoms in the early stages of primary hypertension, and by the time symptoms do appear it may be too late for effective treatment. Things like dizziness, flushing, fatigue, and headache usually accompany the complications of hypertension, and they usually involve critical organs. High blood pressure is the biggest single cause of heart attack and strokes, and a general arteriosclerosis is inevitable in chronic cases. This is so silly when all that is required is a little care with the diet plus adequate drug therapy. There are many, many antihypertensive drugs available, and one of them is almost certain to work on even the most stubborn case.

Table 13.1 shows normal arterial blood pressures at different ages.

Summary

Development of a Circulatory System

Why is a circulatory system necessary? To provide the living cells within the organism with nutrients and a waste-dumping ground.

I. The Simplest Solution. If the organisms are small enough, diffusion will take care of all their requirements. All they must do is find a nutrient-rich medium in which to live. Unfortunately, this won't work when the animal achieves any significant size.

II. The Problem of Growing—A Few Solutions
   - A. A larger organism can exist with no specialized system if it:
     1. is the right shape—flat and very thin, like tissue paper.
     2. lives in a nutrient-rich medium.
     3. can discover a way to move lots of nutrient rapidly past its feeding areas.
   - B. None of these alternatives are really practical for organisms as large as humans.

III. An Alternative Modified. One could slightly modify the arrangement described above. If the whole organism were encased in a shell, the nutrient medium could be concentrated inside. That would leave the organism free to move about and still be able to provide all necessary nutrients for its parts.

IV. The Medium. This would have to be a thin fluid and would have to be directed in such a way as to wash all body parts. It must be able to dissolve all necessary nutrients.

V. A Pump. Movement cannot be left to chance. Energy must be provided to move the nutrients, and a pump is the most practical answer.

VI. Blood Vessels
   - A. A pump would have to have an entrance and exit and tubes to carry the medium in and out.
   - B. Tubes would also be able to separate used medium from new medium and could carry used medium to certain areas for reprovisioning.

VII. Recycling. Such a fluid would be too valuable to discard after having used it once. Provision should be made to recycle it.

VIII. A Terse Summary of the Situation. Cells apparently were designed to take what they need whenever they need it and to indiscriminately dump wastes. The medium must be able to handle this kind of situation.

IX. The System as a Whole. Blood is a transportation system. It picks up provisions from supply areas and takes them to where they are needed. It picks up wastes whenever they are discarded and takes them to where they can be properly handled.

The Circulatory Plan

I. Blood depleted of supplies and filled with wastes must be separated from fresh, nutrient-laden blood.

II. Detours and Freeways
   - A. For the blood flow to be effective, it must have a means of replenishing supplies and clearing away debris from metabolic operations. This requires separation of the bloodstream into various tributaries.
   - B. The primary nutrient carried by the blood is oxygen; hence, once it has released its load of oxygen, it must be recharged before it can return to the tissues.
   - C. The branch leading to the respiratory surfaces is the only branch that carries all of the blood every cycle.

Separations in a Single Stream

I. Tributaries and Turnpikes. On its course through the body, the circulatory river branches repeatedly. Branches run through supply areas and cleansing stations so that part of the blood is restocked with fuel and spare parts and scrubbed clean every circuit.

II. An Early Pit Stop. One of its earliest branches runs into the absorptive areas of the gut. Fuel and raw construction materials are loaded into the blood so quickly that the concentration becomes higher than is optimal.

III. The Liver: A Processing Plant and Warehouse. The liver removes much of the excess nutrient, converts it to storage molecules, and stores it.
IV. The Renal Branch. Another branch of the circulatory river goes into the kidney circulation, where the blood is scrubbed clean of nitrogenous wastes and its pH and mineral content are adjusted.
V. A Mainline Processing Plant. The pulmonary circulation represents a processing area that must operate on a constant basis.

The Dual Circulation of Humans

I. The pulmonary circulation and the systemic circulation are functionally separate. Each has its own pump and its own unique route to follow, yet all of the blood in humans is present in a single, continuous stream.
II. Some Hydrodynamics
   A. Pressure
      1. Unlike the water that flows into our homes, the pressure driving our blood through its system of tubes can be varied. It can be varied throughout the system or merely within a small portion of the area through which it flows.
      2. The pressure in our arterial systems is a stop-and-go system.
   B. Plumbing. Unlike the pipes in our homes, the tubes that carry our blood are flexible. This enables them to store some of the heart's energy.
   C. System Design. City plumbing is an open system. The water we use in our homes may never be recycled. Our body's plumbing (circulatory system) is a closed system, and everything is recycled.

The Human Heart

The mammalian heart is a solid lump of muscle, yet is able to provide separation of pulmonary and systemic streams.

The Cardiac Blueprint

I. Both the pulmonary pump and the systemic pump are in a single heart, and they pump synchronously, yet they produce widely divergent pressures.
II. Avoiding Wear. The heart is wrapped in thin, polished sheets of connective tissue to minimize friction. The polished connective tissue is intended to limit wear should the heart rub against various body structures while working.
III. Chambers. There are two pairs of chambers in the heart. Each pump (pulmonary and systemic) has one atrium and one ventricle.
   A. The Coronary Skeleton. Thick rings of connective tissue provide the heart with rigidity and contain the heart's valves.
   B. The Heart Valves. There are four heart valves, one pair between the atria and ventricles, and a second pair guarding the exits from the ventricles.
IV. Heart Movement
   A. The Frank-Starling heart law states that the more the heart muscle is stretched, the more powerful its subsequent contraction will be.
   B. The heart is able to store energy in its tissues, and when its contraction is over, this energy is used to stretch the heart muscle. This provides suction, permitting the heart to inhale blood.
   C. Systole. This is the medical term that refers to contraction of the heart muscle.
   D. Diastole. This is the medical term that refers to relaxation of the heart muscle.

The Path Through the Heart

I. The Right Heart. Blood from the system enters the right atrium, flows through the tricuspid valve into the right ventricle, and is pumped into the lungs (the pulmonary circulation).
II. The Left Heart. Blood from the pulmonary circulation enters the left atrium, flows through the mitral valve into the left ventricle, and is pumped into the systemic circulation.

Origin of the Heartbeat

I. An Inherent Basic Rhythm. The basic rate of the heart is built into the myocardium. Unlike skeletal muscle, the cardiac musculature does not require neural stimulation in order to contract.
II. Each cell in the mammalian heart has a basic contractile rhythm, and left on its own it will contract rhythmically.

The Pacemaker

There is a mass of modified muscle tissue on the surface of the right atrium that has a basic contractile rhythm that is faster than any other heart muscle cells. This tissue mass is known as the sinoatrial (S-A) node, and it provides the basic heart rate.

I. The A-V Node. Depolarization begins in the S-A node, spreads across the atrial surface, and crosses to the ventricles at the atrioventricular (A-V) node. It is transferred from the A-V node to the bundle of His and is conducted through the ventricular muscle mass by modified bundles of muscle tissue.
II. The Action Potential in Myocardial Cells
   A. The heart has an extremely long refractory period.
   B. No Tetanic Contractions. Because of the long refractory period, the heart cannot be tetanized.
   C. A Diaphragmatic Anchor. The apex (lower tip) of the heart is firmly fixed to the diaphragm muscle.

Cardiac Innervation

Both branches of the autonomic nervous system provide neural controls for the heart.

I. Nervous Inhibition. The vagus nerve (cranial nerve X) supplies parasympathetic innervation.
II. Nervous Stimulation. The accelerator nerve (a spinal nerve) supplies sympathetic innervation.

Electrocardiography

The electrical activity of the heart can be monitored by the use of a special type of voltmeter known as a polygraph.

I. The Standard Leads
   A. Electrocardiographic (ECG) recordings are standardized. Dipolar recordings are made between the two arms, between the right arm and left leg, and between the left arm and left leg.

B. Monopolar recordings are made between various points on the patient's chest and a reference electrode, which is maintained at ground (zero) potential.
C. A typical ECG recording produces what is known as a P-Q-R-S-T wave.

II. Irregularities in Electrical Patterns
A. Any unusual electrical activity that alters the standard wave form can identify potential problems.
B. The P-R Interval. Unusually long P-R intervals can indicate a heart block.

The Cardiac Cycle

I. Pressure
A. Pressure is defined as the ratio between a container and the fluid being put into it. To produce pressure, the container must be overfilled.
B. Vessels with elastic walls will produce less pressure than those with rigid walls.
C. In living systems, none of the vessels are rigid.

II. The Atrial Pressure Curve. At the beginning of the cycle, blood flows through the atrium and into the ventricle, filling it to 70 percent of capacity. Atrial systole fills it the remaining 30 percent.

III. The Ventricular Pressure Curve. Pressure in the ventricle skyrockets as atrial systole ends and ventricular systole begins. The contraction is isometric until the aortic valve opens and the blood bursts into the aorta at high pressure.

IV. A Brief Digression
A. A Rigid System. Pressure changes that occur in a system of rigid tubes are sharp and intermittent.
B. The Elastic System. Pressure changes within a system of elastic tubes are smooth and tend not to be intermittent.

V. The Aortic Pressure Curve. The aorta absorbs considerable pressure from the powerful activity of the left ventricle. The incisura is a brief increase in aortic pressure that occurs when the aortic valve closes.

VI. Pressure Changes in the Right Heart
A. The pulmonary circulation, unlike the systemic, is a low-pressure system.
B. Pulmonary Vessels. Pulmonary vessels are larger than their systemic counterparts.

The Myocardium

I. Heart Sounds. As the heart pumps, it makes a series of distinct sounds that can indicate whether it is operating normally.

II. The Coronary Circulation. The coronary arteries enter the heart muscle from the aortic arch. The myocardium removes about 65 percent of the oxygen from the hemoglobin.

III. Adjustment in Coronary Blood Supply. The coronary arteries can dilate prodigiously and thus increase total blood flow through the myocardium.

IV. A Major Weakness. The coronary blood vessels are often blind, meaning there is frequently no alternate route into parts of the myocardium should something plug the main channel.

The Blood Vessels

I. Arteries. Arteries are thick vessels with much smooth muscle in their walls.

II. Arterioles. Arterioles are small arteries (lumen generally $< 170\ \mu m$ diameter). Most of the blood's pressure is lost in these vessels.

III. Capillaries. Capillaries are the smallest of vessels, most less than 1 mm long and $\leq 9\ \mu m$ internal diameter. Their walls are one cell thick, and they are the most fragile of blood vessels.
A. The Forces of Exchange
1. The capillaries are the "business end" of the circulatory system. All exchange is accomplished through them.
2. Exchange is extremely rapid. Water moves back and forth across the capillary wall two to three thousand times faster than it flows through the tube.
3. Various forces are responsible for movement of materials into and out of the blood.
B. Intrinsic Controls
1. Filtration. The capillary wall is an ultrafilter, and the interstitial fluid is therefore an ultrafiltrate of the blood. The heart provides the necessary pressure to accomplish the filtration.
2. Colloid Osmotic Pressure. The osmotic pressure of the blood is greater than that of the interstitial fluid due to the presence of colloidal-sized particles, most of which are protein. The COP is responsible for enabling materials to cross the capillary wall and enter the blood.

IV. The Veins and Venules. The blood is carried from capillary beds back to the heart by veins and venules. These vessels are much like arteries in structure, but have less smooth muscle in their walls. Skeletal muscles provide the necessary pressure for venous return.

Cardiac Volumes

I. Stroke Volume. This is the volume of blood ejected through the aorta during a single heartbeat.

II. Cardiac Output. This volume is also known as minute volume. It is the volume of blood ejected by the heart in one minute.

III. End Volumes
A. End Diastolic Volume. EDV is the total volume of blood in the ventricle just before ventricular systole occurs.
B. End Systolic Volume. ESV is the volume of blood remaining in the ventricle after it has finished contracting.

Regulation of the Heart

I. Cardiac Inhibition. The heart is slowed through the action of parasympathetic (vagal) fibers.

II. Cardiac Stimulation. The heart is accelerated and the beat strengthened through the action of sympathetic nerves and hormones of the adrenal medulla.

III. The Cardiac Reflexes
   A. Cardioinhibitory Nerves. Impulses from these nerves slow the heartbeat and reduce the heart's power.
   B. Cardioaccelerator Nerves. Impulses from these nerves increase blood pressure and permit the heart to beat faster.
IV. Blood Pressure Measurements. Blood pressure in humans is routinely measured with an instrument called a sphygmomanometer. It is a device that wraps around the arm and is able to accurately measure arterial blood pressure.
V. The Extrinsic Controls
   A. These are control mechanisms that sense external or internal stimuli and alter blood flow accordingly.
   B. Factors Affecting Flow
      1. Resistance to movement of fluid through a tube is directly proportional to tube length and fluid viscosity and is inversely proportional to tube radius to the fourth power.
      2. Since the length of the vessels in a living person is not going to change and since blood viscosity isn't likely to change significantly all of a sudden, the diameter of the tube is altered to increase blood flow into a given area.
VI. Fluid Flow in Tubes
   A. Fluid moves through a tube as if it were a series of sleeves within one another.
   B. Velocity. Velocity of flow depends on fluid volume, the cross-sectional area of the tube's lumen, and the time alloted to move the blood through the tube.

Clinical Considerations

I. Heart Murmurs
II. Cardiovascular Disease: Truth and Fiction
III. Cholesterol, Again
IV. Atherosclerosis
V. Heart "Attacks"
   Encouraging, but Puzzling, Recent Facts
VI. The Cardiac Conduction System
   A. Tachycardia
   B. Bradycardia
   C. Ectopic Heartbeats
   D. Flutter
   E. Fibrillation
   F. Defibrillation
   G. Pacemaker Problems
   H. Artificial Pacemakers
   I. Heart Block
      A Thought-Provoking Observation
   J. Stroke
      1. Cerebral Hemorrhage
      2. Cerebral Infarction
VII. Systemic Hypertension

Review Questions

1. What is the primary goal of the mammalian circulatory system?
2. Why is it necessary for the human circulatory system to have two pumps to pump the blood?
3. Where are these pumps located, anatomically?
4. Describe the overall circulatory plan. Be sure to mention the only operation that treats all of the blood every circuit.
5. Outline some of the differences between the pulmonary circulation and the systemic circulation.
6. How does pressure control in the human body differ from similar controls in our homes?
7. Draw a cutaway of the human heart. Locate and name all the valves and chambers.
8. Locate and name the connective tissue membranes that enclose the heart. What is their function?
9. Describe the coronary skeleton.
10. What does the Frank-Starling heart law state?
11. What is the meaning of the words *diastole* and *systole?* Know the source of pressure in both cases.
12. Trace the route blood follows through the right and left chambers of the heart.
13. On your drawing of the heart, show the location of the sinoatrial node, the atrioventricular node, the bundle of His, and the Purkinje fibers.
14. Identify the pacemaker.
15. Describe the origin and progress of the electrical signal that stimulates a heartbeat.
16. Describe the major electrocardiographic "leads" that have been standardized over the years.
17. Draw and label a typical P-Q-R-S-T wave. Be sure you know what each portion of the wave represents in the cardiac cycle.
18. Define *pressure*.
19. Describe the events that take place in the atria during a single cardiac cycle.
20. Repeat 19 (above), substituting *ventricle* for *atria*.
21. Describe the aortic pressure curve. Be sure you can describe in clear terms how some of the heart's energy is stored in the walls of the arteries and the effect this has on blood flow.
22. How is the heart muscle nourished? Describe any unusual characteristics of the myocardial circulation (there are two).
23. Name the various kinds of blood vessels. Which of these is responsible for material exchange?
24. Describe the exchange process, mentioning the forces involved and their effect on overall material movement.
25. How is the heart rate regulated? Be sure you can trace both acceleratory and inhibitory loops completely through.
26. A friend has been told that her blood pressure is 125/75. What, precisely, does each number mean? What would be the pulse pressure of an individual with such a blood pressure?
27. Describe the factors affecting resistance to blood flow. Which would most profoundly affect the resistance?

Chapter 14

The Respiratory System: Mechanisms of Gas Exchange

Study Hints

This chapter deals with the collecting and processing of oxygen for presentation to the body's cells and the removal of any excess carbon dioxide that evolves during cell metabolism. There are a few things that will definitely help you to absorb this information.

1. We all are familiar with oxygen in its gaseous state. However, it is important to realize that it is not present in its gaseous state inside the body.
2. It is also important to realize that the interior of the lungs is continuous with the atmosphere. The interior chambers open to the surrounding air through a system of tubes that extend through the nasal passages and the mouth.
3. Gaseous oxygen *must not* exist inside the body. Hence, in order to cross the necessary membranes and get into the body's interior, the gases that appear in the lungs must first dissolve in our body's watery matrix. Once the gas is dissolved, it can be absorbed by the blood.
4. Oxygen is a gas, and gases exert pressures even when they are in solution. These pressures can be used in much the same way we use concentration gradients to determine which direction the gases will diffuse when in solution. This is important, because all movement of oxygen in the body is governed by diffusion.

Objectives

When you have finished reading this chapter, you should:

1. be able to describe the anatomy of the respiratory tree.
2. understand why air moves into and out of the lungs.
3. know the various standard air volumes and capacities.
4. understand, at least in general, the gas laws and be able to explain the relationship between partial pressures and percentage of gas in a given mixture.
5. know the importance of respiratory pigments and be able to explain why they are necessary.
6. be able to draw and discuss the critical aspects of the oxygen dissociation curves that are peculiar to hemoglobin.
7. understand the Bohr effect and its importance.
8. be able to explain how most of the body's content of CO_2 is carried in the blood.
9. be able to explain the primary mechanisms that alter normal respiratory rate and depth and know which stimuli are most effective in changing these controls.
10. comprehend the reasons for needing secondary respiratory controls and be able to explain how they work.

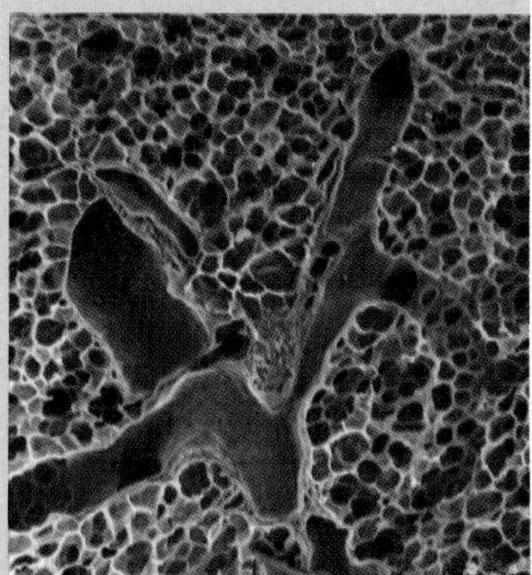

A scanning electron micrograph of a lung, showing alveoli and bronchioles.

Introduction

As I have already stated, energy is critical to life. Without energy, body cells die within seconds, and as we know from chapter 5, oxygen is absolutely essential for sustained energy production. Without oxygen, mammals cannot produce enough energy to keep the body cells alive for more than a few minutes, so the collection, accumulation, and dissemination of oxygen throughout the body may be the premier task of all of our homeostatic mechanisms. We have a rather impressive library of information that tends to support this conclusion, and possibly the most impressive evidence is the body's own blueprint. The design of the circulatory system and the proportional distribution of its contents suggests that carrying oxygen is its most important job. Red cells outnumber white cells by nearly one thousand to one, and the red cells carry oxygen. Of all the many physiological "treatment centers" for processing blood, only one of them deals with all of the blood each circuit, and that is the one that recharges the red cells with oxygen.

The structures through which the air moves as it progresses from the atmosphere into the body are termed the *respiratory system*, although physiologically this is a misnomer. To a physiologist, *respiration* is an enormously broad term. It includes not just the movement of air into and out of the lungs, but also all of the things that happen to the oxygen after it leaves the lungs and enters the deep body tissues. So in addition to breathing, it entails the transport of oxygen throughout the body as well as all the processes of food oxidation within the cellular interior—up to and including the formation of metabolic water (see chapter 5).

This means, obviously, that the mechanisms involved in the process of breathing are only a small part of the respiratory system and that when we study them we are only working on one aspect of respiration. This phase of the respiratory process is generally referred to as **ventilation.** It embraces the process of moving oxygen from the atmosphere into and out of the lungs and the tissues and structures involved in these operations.

Figure 14.1 The bony encasement that protects the lungs and lower respiratory tree.

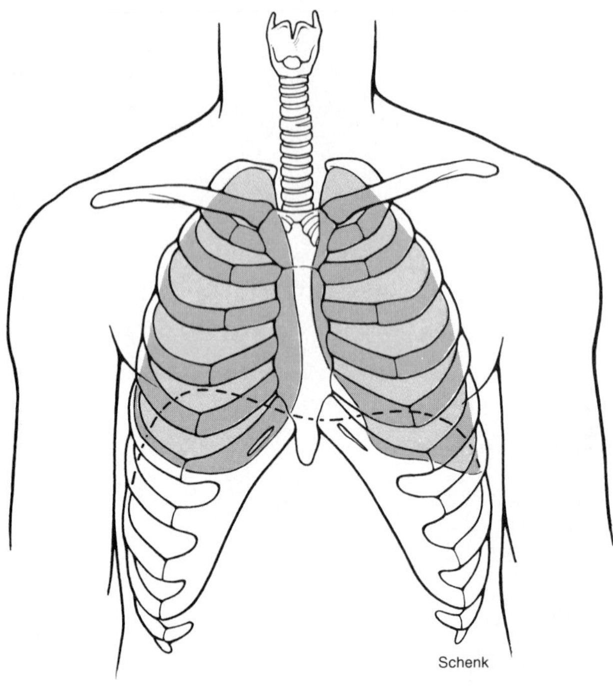

The importance of oxygen is indirectly supported by noting the methods of killing utilized by most of the actively predaceous carnivores. Although it is commonly believed that the big cats and the dog-like carnivores tear at their victims' throats in order to rip open their jugular vein and make them bleed to death, actual observation suggests that this is not the goal. The throat is grabbed, yes, but it is seldom torn away in the carnivore's jaws, and when it is, it's usually an accident. Apparently the grip on the throat is achieved in order to crush the windpipe and cut off the oxygen supply, an observation partially confirmed by noting that the end of the prey's nose is a target as often as the throat—either one can be closed off and the prey smothered. The big constrictor snakes kill their prey, not by crushing, as is popularly believed, but by clamping down on the chest each time the animal exhales until finally it can exhale no more and simply smothers.

Anatomy of the Respiratory Organs

Obviously, the structures responsible for presenting oxygen to the blood are extremely important and so must be well-protected. They are bundled deep inside the thoracic cavity, suspended in a hermetically sealed chamber, surrounded at the top by the bones and heavy muscles of the pectoral girdle and below by the rib cage. Only the brain and the heart enjoy the degree of protection that the body provides for the lungs (figure 14.1). Above the chest, the respiratory tree reaches up through the throat into the bones of the skull. About the only part that is not very well protected is in the throat.

Figure 14.2 The lungs and respiratory tree.

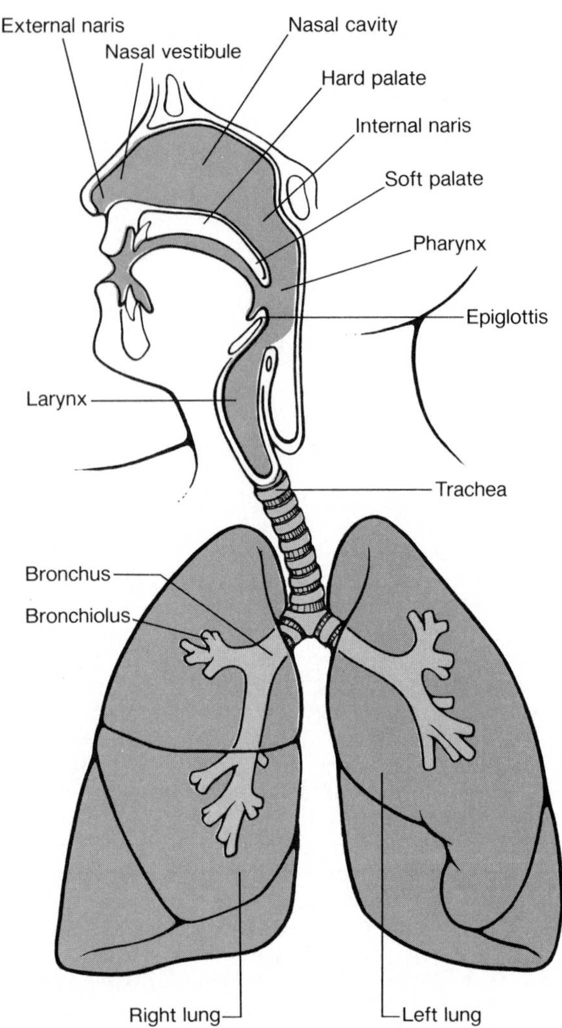

In the skull, the tree begins (or terminates, depending on your point of view) in the nostrils or **external nares.** With the exception of the first centimeter or so, these tubes are encased in bone. After leaving the external nares, they open into a rather large cavity in the skull just above the palate called the **nasal cavity.** From there, they extend back into the throat and open into the **pharynx** at the **internal nares.** Once in the pharynx, the two tubes merge into a single passageway known as the **trachea,** which dives into the throat and continues down into the thorax to about the middle of the nipple line, where it splits once again into two tubes, the **bronchi,** each of which enters a lung. The bronchi, in turn, bifurcate into smaller and smaller air tubes, eventually terminating in the blind sacs called **alveoli** where gas exchange actually takes place. See figure 14.2.

Figure 14.3 Major features of the upper respiratory tract.

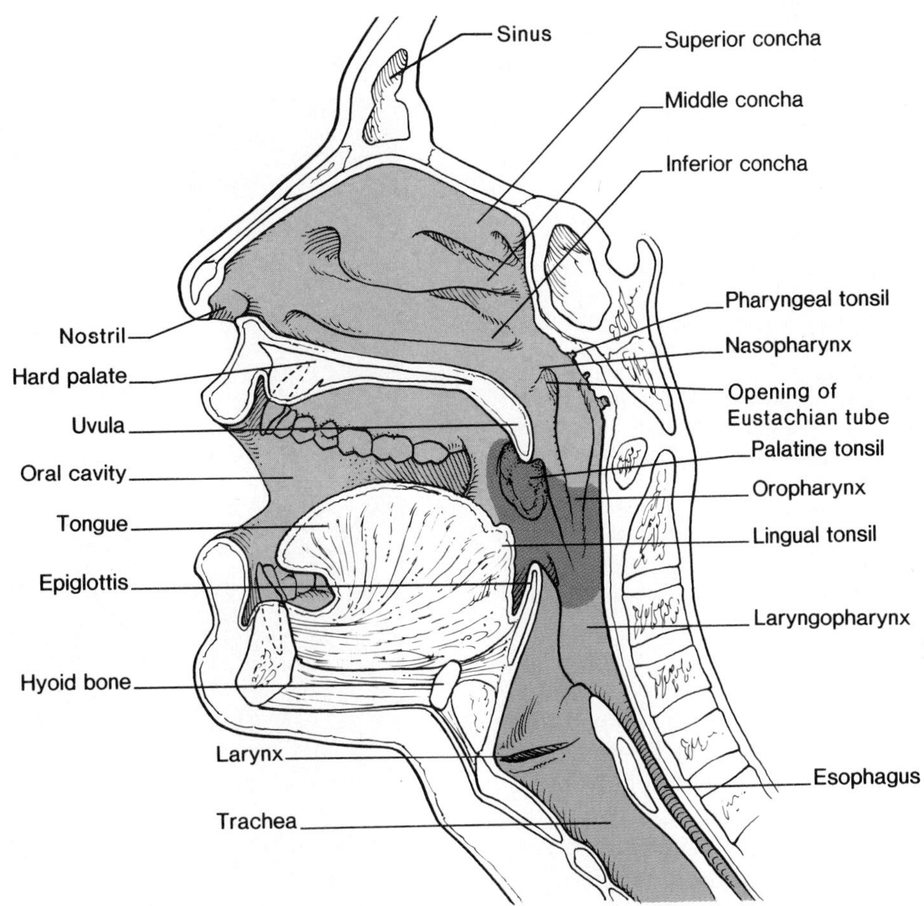

Figure 14.4 Particles trapped by the mucus are moved by beating cilia from the nasal passages into the pharynx, where they can be coughed up and swallowed.

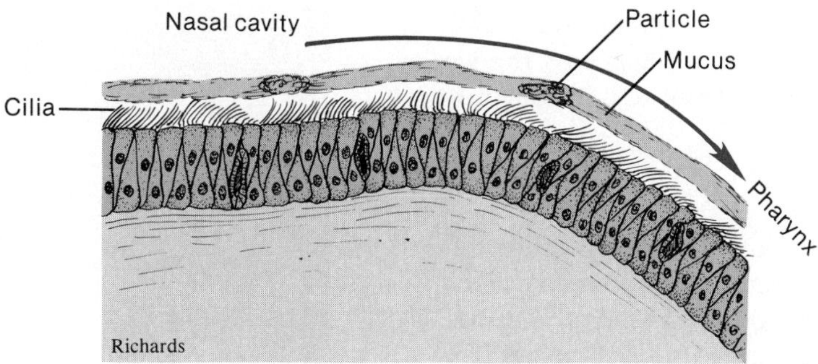

The Nasal Cavity

The nasal cavity is not the collection of nasal sinuses that television advertising talks about so often. Rather, it is a sort of anteroom just past the nostril entrance, and it is lined with nasal **conchae** that project into its interior on three levels (figure 14.3). The uppermost of these—the **superior nasal concha**—is lined with the olfactory receptors that provide us with our sense of smell. The **middle** and **inferior nasal conchae,** which are ventral to the superior, have no such sensory receptors. But they are not inert, functionally.

Collectively, the conchae increase the surface area of the air-carrying tubes, an accomplishment that amplifies several functions. The first is protective. The concha surfaces are covered with epithelial cells (figure 14.4). These cells in turn are covered with mucous secretions intended to trap and remove particles of dust and debris that enter the system with the incoming air.

This is something of a labyrinth through which entering air must pass before it can enter the trachea. It is sometimes referred to as the **turbinate baffle**

system, and when it is working properly, it can trap any particles larger than 4 μm, thus preventing them from entering the lungs. In addition, the large surfaces in the system initiate the process of warming and humidifying the air that is to be carried down into the lungs, an extremely important function.

The importance of the concha's role in humidifying incoming air is emphasized in medical literature by the number of precautionary notes involving patients having had tracheostomies. A tracheostomy is fairly common when a person has an obstruction in the upper tracheal area that cannot be promptly and easily removed. It consists of inserting a breathing tube into the trachea below the level of the obstruction. Paramedical instruction manuals repeatedly underscore the importance of haste in getting such patients into quarters where the air can be properly humidified. Patients who have had a tracheostomy and are provided with cool, dry air instead of warm, humid air can suffer severe lung infections if the alveolar surfaces dry out.

The Nasal Sinuses

The nasal sinuses really play no role in ventilation and are mentioned here merely for the sake of thoroughness. Everyone has heard about them, hence I would be remiss not to mention them (figure 14.5).

They do act somewhat as resonating chambers that modify and perhaps slightly amplify our vocal sounds, but as far as we can tell, their primary function is to reduce the weight of the skull. Unfortunately, they also present the world of microorganisms with an ideal oasis for growth and breeding, and since they open into the nasal cavity, they pick up a great many. When they swell or become infected or inflamed, they can produce mucus in enormous quantities. This mucus drains into the back of the nasal cavity, thence into the throat, producing the unpleasant and terribly inconvenient *post-nasal drip.*

The Trachea

The trachea is, as far as we can tell, merely a tube designed to carry the air back and forth between the internal nares and the lungs (figure 14.6). At the upper end of the trachea is the **larynx** or "voice box" which, when properly tuned, produces audible vibrations as the outgoing air passes through it (figure 14.7). The trachea itself is really nothing more than a hose supported by a series of cartilaginous rings arranged like the steel loops in a vacuum cleaner hose. As you might guess, these rings are intended to prevent the trachea from collapsing when internal pressure is reduced in order to suck air into it.

Figure 14.5 An X ray of a human skull, showing the air-filled nasal sinuses (*arrows*). (*a*) Frontal view. (*b*) Side view. These cavities often provide happy breeding grounds for infectious organisms.

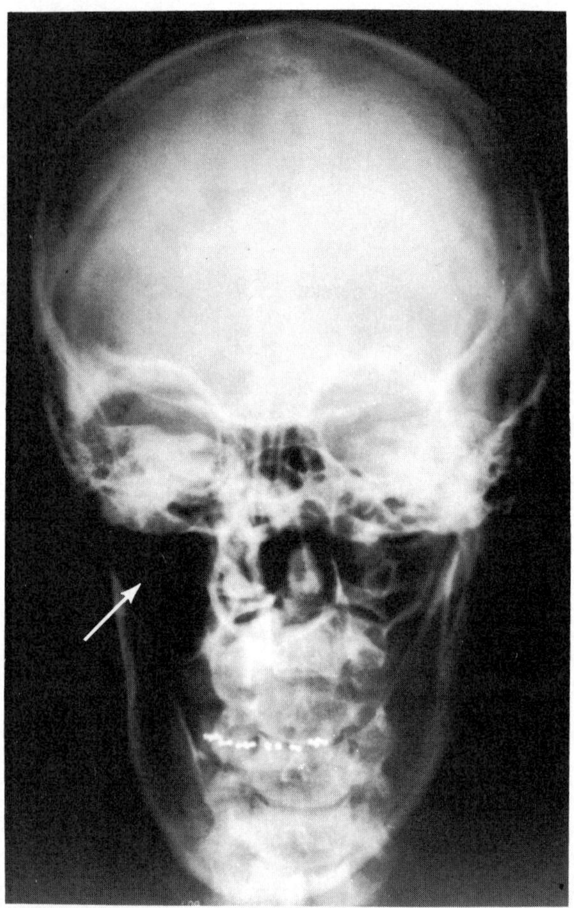

(a)

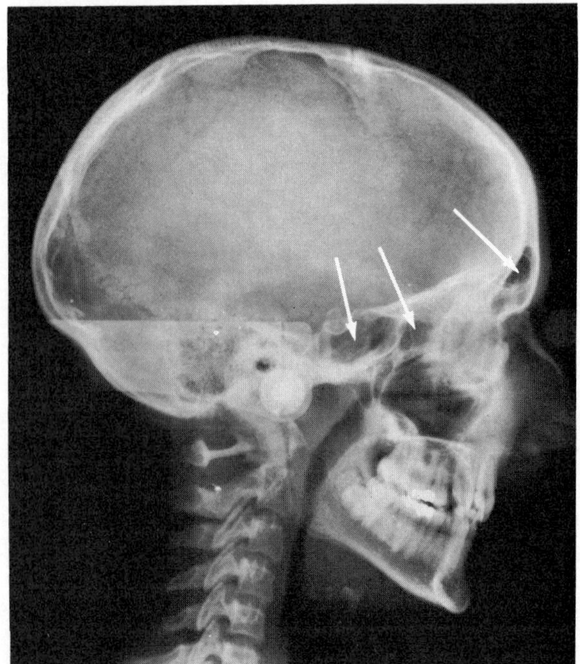

(b)

Figure 14.6 The human trachea, showing the location of the larynx and the branching of the bronchi.

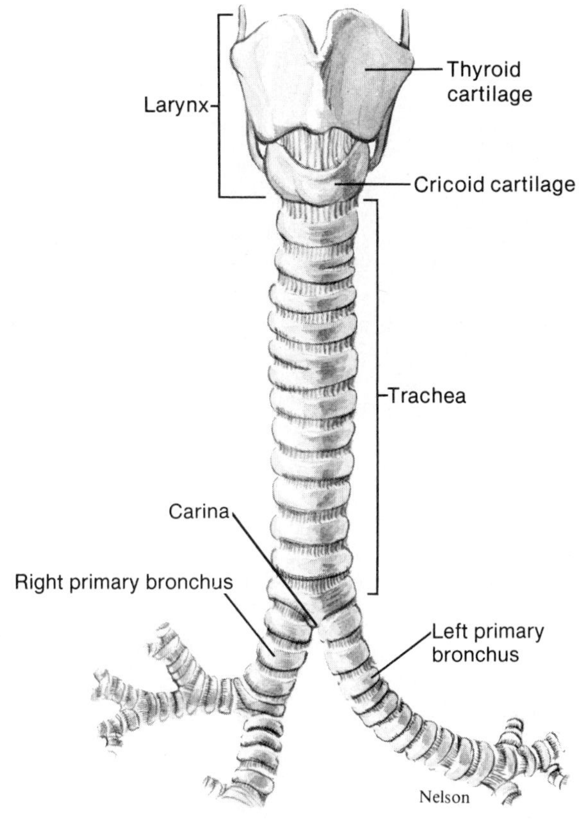

Figure 14.7 A cross section through the larynx, showing the vocal cords (*a*) with the glottis closed and (*b*) with the glottis open. Sound is produced when the glottis is closed.

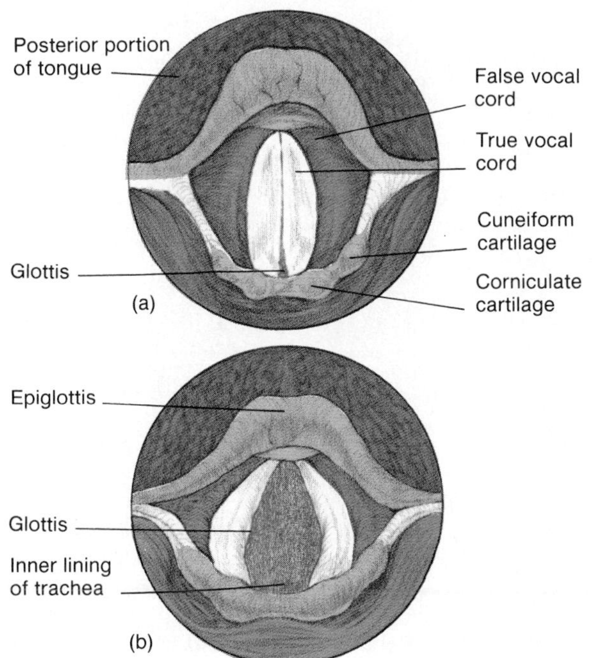

Figure 14.8 A plastic cast of the respiratory tree, showing the tremendous degree of bronchiolar branching.

The Bronchi and Bronchioles

The bronchi actually represent nothing more than a bifurcation in the trachea that splits the incoming air into two streams, one going to each lung (figure 14.6). As was noted, the bronchi enter the lungs and split again and again into progressively smaller tubes. As the tubes decrease in diameter, the cartilaginous rings get correspondingly scarcer. Finally the cartilage disappears, replaced by smooth muscle cells that wrap the air tubes in much the same way that arterioles in the circulatory system are wrapped. By this time, the tubes are on the order of a single millimeter in diameter and have become bronchioles (figure 14.8).

The bronchioles terminate in the masses of blind sacs known as alveoli (figure 14.9). It is in these sacs that gaseous exchange actually takes place. The number of alveoli in an adult human's lungs is not known, but it is estimated to be in the tens of millions, each one resembling a tiny, round berry wrapped by masses of blood capillaries. The total area of contact surface between the capillaries and the alveoli is thought to be on the order of two hundred square meters. This is where gaseous exchange occurs between the alveolar air and the blood, and to facilitate this, the endothelial walls of the alveoli consist of just one cell layer.

Figure 14.9 The raspberry-like alveoli that terminate each bronchiole. Each alveolus features its own capillary bed through which gaseous exchange occurs.

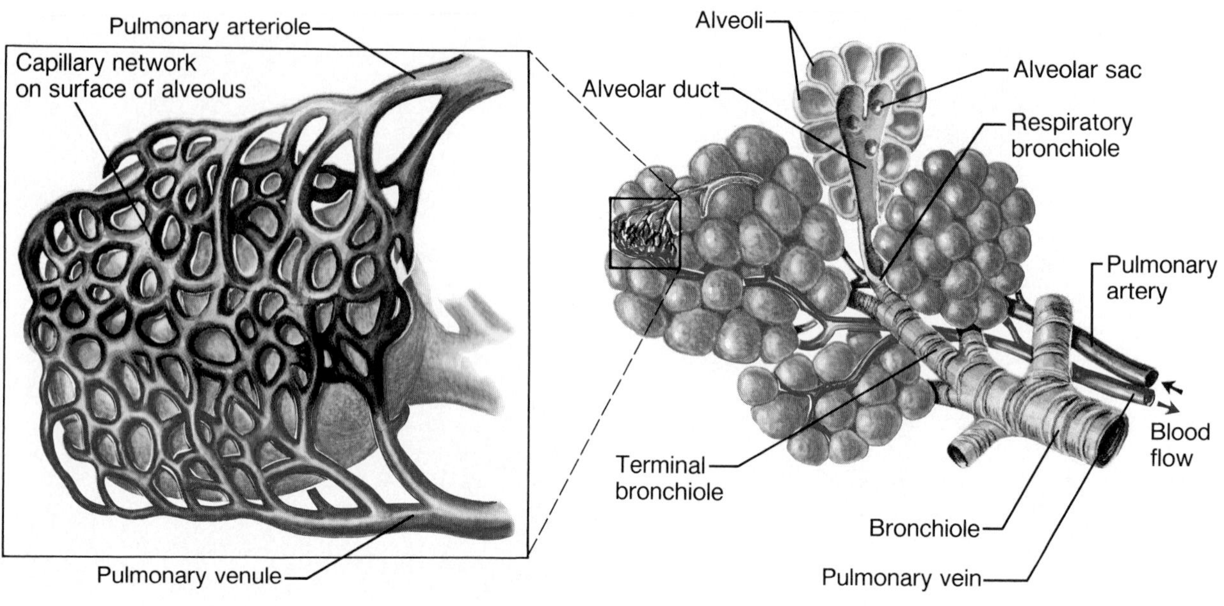

Figure 14.10 A line drawing of an inflated pair of lungs, showing the bronchiolar tree and its association with the lungs.

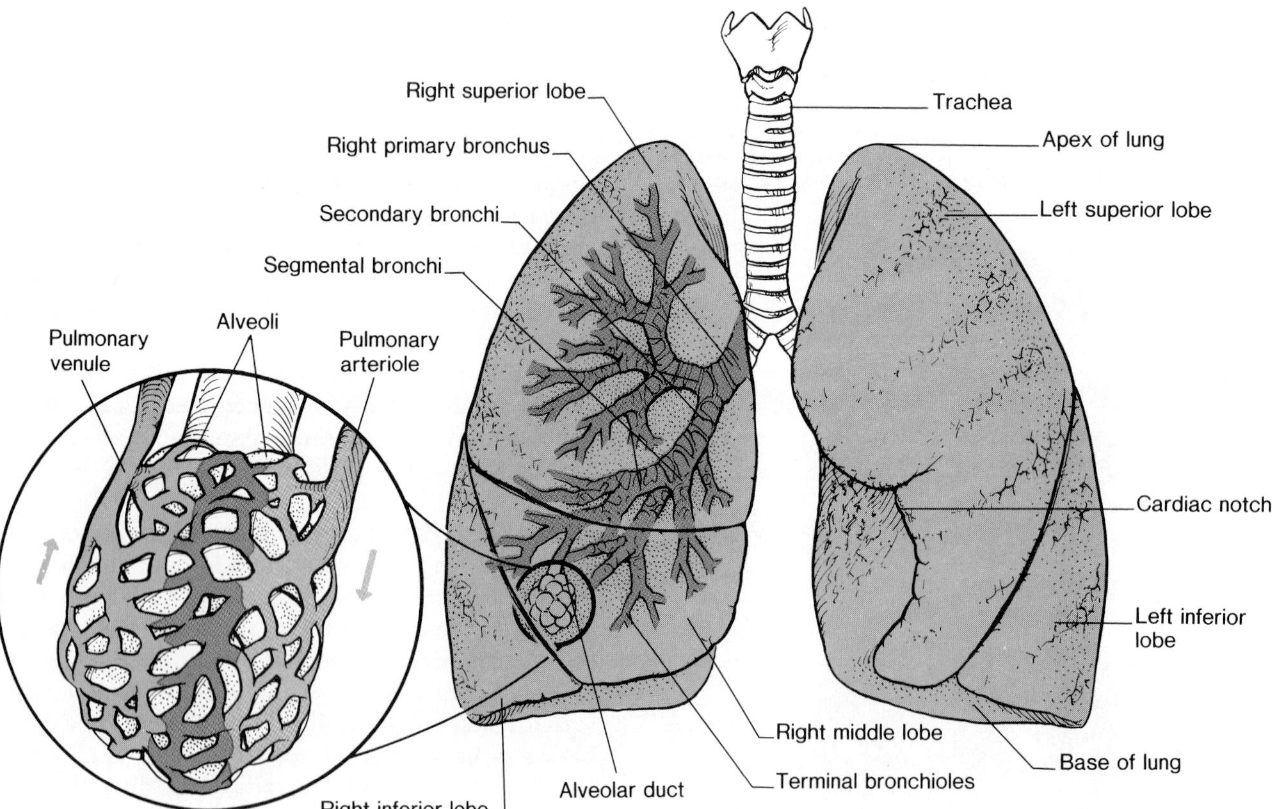

Figure 14.11 A scanning electron micrograph of alveolar casts, showing the associated capillaries.

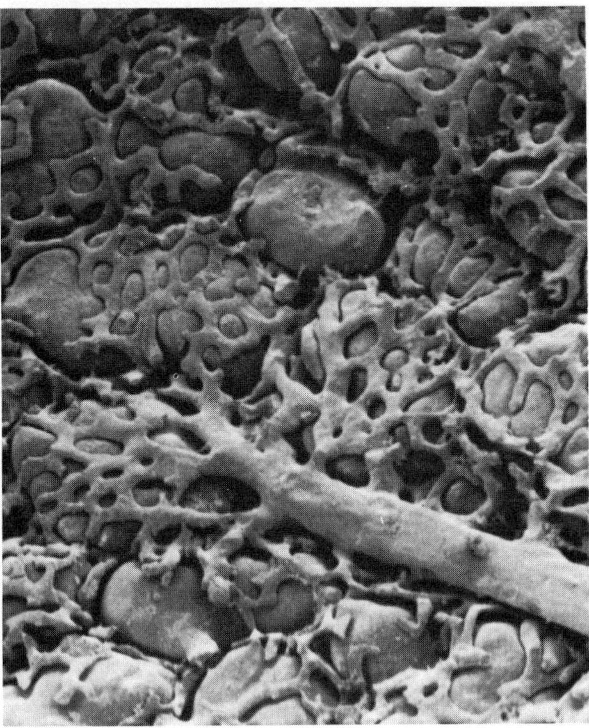

The Lungs

The alveoli and the bronchioles, plus a little connective tissue, make up the lungs. Dissected out, the lungs appear grossly to be rather diffuse, mushy tissue masses, but when they are blown up, these characteristics vanish. When they are inflated, the lungs become rigid with turgor pressure and resemble large, pink balloons (figure 14.10). Obviously, there is a lot of elasticity in the membranes that comprise the tissues and cells of the lungs; otherwise, they could not expand so freely and so easily return to their original size and state without damage. In humans, the right lung is a three-lobed structure, featuring a **superior lobe,** a **middle lobe,** and an **inferior lobe.** (The names *superior* and *inferior* refer to their position in the body, not to their quality.) The left lung has only two lobes, thus making room in the thoracic cavity for the heart.

Both inflating and deflating the lungs requires energy, but in humans, only inflation is an active process. As they blow up and expand in size, the lung tissues store energy in the same way that a balloon does, and when inspiration is finished, elastic recoil uses that stored potential energy to expel the air.

Within the tissue mass, the bronchioles and capillaries travel in close proximity to each other. When the air sacs are reached, the capillaries wrap around them, pressing their walls together (figure 14.11), forming a zone of contact known as the **respiratory**

Figure 14.12 A line drawing of a longitudinal section through the thoracic cavity, showing the pleural membranes.

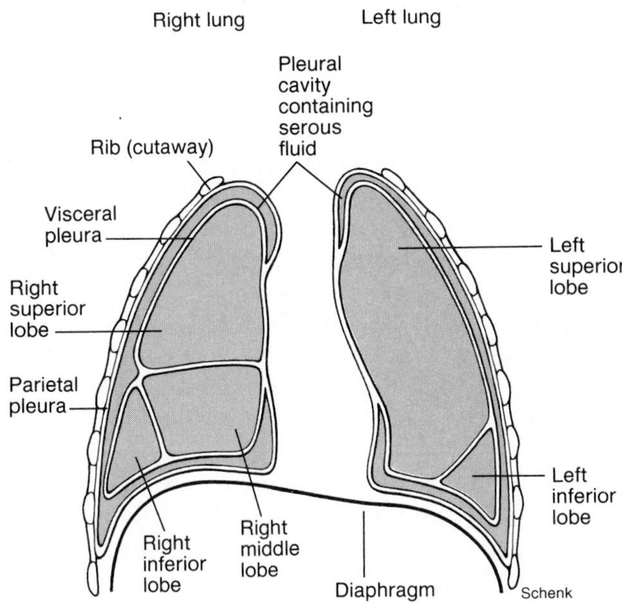

membrane. The entire alveolar surface of this membrane is covered with a sheet of specialized liquid called surfactant, and the membrane itself consists of at least four cell layers, including the alveolar endothelium and the capillary wall, and is between 0.2 and 0.4 μm thick.

Pleural Membranes

Each lung is carefully wrapped by a double layer of slick, permanently moist connective tissue called a **pleural membrane** (figure 14.12). The inner membrane, called the **visceral pleura,** is in contact with the tissues that form the lung surface, and it slips into the gaps between the lung lobes, forming a boundary layer. The outer membrane is called the **parietal pleura,** it is in contact with the tissues of the rib cage and diaphragm, and it covers the outer surfaces of the other organs in the chest cavity. The space between the two pleural membranes is known as the **pleural space,** and it is filled with a layer of serous fluid. As with the heart membranes, it is assumed that the slick-surfaced pleural membranes and the serous fluid in the pleural space are designed to minimize frictional wear on the moving organs that they coat.

Ventilation: The Mechanics of Breathing

The process of getting the air from the surrounding environment into the interior of the lungs is accomplished by altering pressures in our thoracic cavities and letting atmospheric pressure do the rest of the work. You will recall from chapter 13 that pressure is actually a ratio between the container size and the volume of fluid one puts in that container, and that by altering either one, pressures can be made to go up or down. These principles are put into practice by the muscles of our thorax and abdomen.

The main one involved in respiration is the **diaphragm,** which forms the bottom boundary of the thoracic chamber and effects the seal in this area. When relaxed, this is a bell-shaped sheet of muscle that projects well up into the thoracic cavity (figure 14.13). When the diaphragm contracts, it tends to flatten out, increasing the internal volume of the thorax and reducing the pressure therein.

The muscles between the ribs, the **intercostal muscles,** are also involved in the process of breathing. As figure 14.14 shows, each of these muscle-sets lies between a pair of ribs, inserting into both and thus connecting them to each other through a layer of muscle. There are two sets of these muscles, and they are angled in opposite directions. The **internal intercostals** angle obliquely upward and toward the front of the rib cage, while the **external intercostals** angle upward and toward the rear of the rib cage. When the external intercostals are stimulated, their contractions pull the ribs upward and away from the center line (figure 14.15) so that the thoracic cavity expands laterally and anteroposteriorly (from front to back). The internal intercostals are associated with expiration rather than inspiration.

The lungs, of course, are suspended in the thoracic cavity, so naturally they will be affected by any pressure changes that occur around them. However, it is important for us to clearly understand what is taking place here. The most drastic pressure changes occur in the thoracic cavity outside the lungs, and these changes not only are the greatest, but they also last the longest.

Pressures

Within the lungs, during normal, quiet breathing, the pressure changes are quite small. Almost no significant pressure changes take place inside the alveoli, and only very minor ones occur in the respiratory tubes leading to and from the lungs. So while the quiet pumping movements of the chest and the concomitant pressure changes affect the lungs, the changes inside are very small indeed. The relaxed pattern is as follows:

Just prior to the initiation of inspiration (breathing in), the pressure in the **intrapulmonary space** (within the lungs) is essentially the same as atmospheric, which is 760 mm Hg at sea level. Outside the lungs, in the **intrapleural chamber** (within the thoracic cavity, but outside the lungs), there is a very small negative pressure of about −4 mm Hg, which keeps the outer surface of the lungs against the thoracic wall. This holds the visceral pleura tightly against the parietal pleura, thus providing the lungs with the stiffening influence of the inner surface of the rib cage and preventing lung collapse.

Figure 14.13 (*a*) The diaphragm relaxed. The shaded area represents the interior of the thoracic chamber, not the lungs. (*b*) The diaphragm contracted. Note that the internal volume of the thorax has increased (*shaded area*), thereby increasing the fluid/container ratio and lowering the internal pressure.

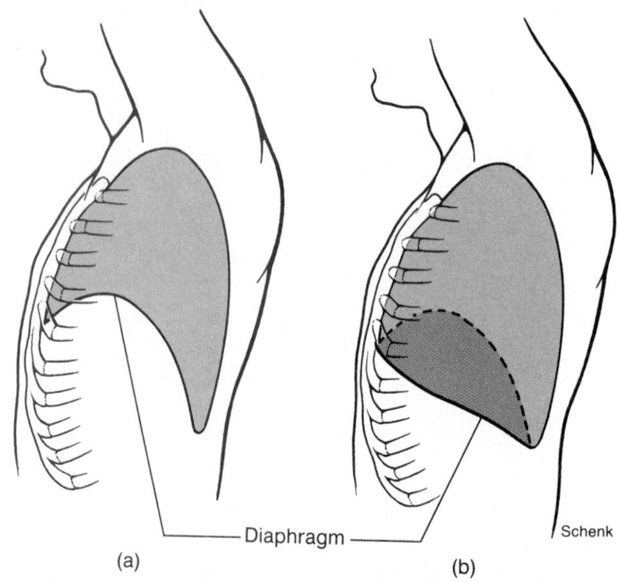

At the beginning of a normal, resting inspiration, the intercostal muscles and the muscles of the diaphragm contract, the chest expands, and pressures within change. In the intrapleural chamber, the pressure drops to somewhere between 757 and 758 mm Hg. Since the visceral pleura is held tightly against the parietal pleura, the lungs tend to expand also—not as quickly, nor as much, but they expand, nevertheless. This increases the internal volume of the lungs, and the pressure in the air spaces inside the lungs falls to about 759.5 mm Hg. This is not much, but it is enough. Remember that the air spaces inside the lungs are in direct contact with the air all around us, a condition maintained by the respiratory tree, which is wide open to the atmosphere. As the intrapulmonary pressure drops, air is pushed into the respiratory tubes and through them into the alveoli, forced there by the higher atmospheric pressure outside. The magnitude of the negative pressure that develops within the alveoli is very tiny and lasts only a very short time—no longer than it takes atmospheric air to rush through the respiratory tubes and equalize the pressures within and without, thus filling the alveolar chambers with fresh atmospheric air (figure 14.16).

Figure 14.14 The arrangement of the intercostal muscles.

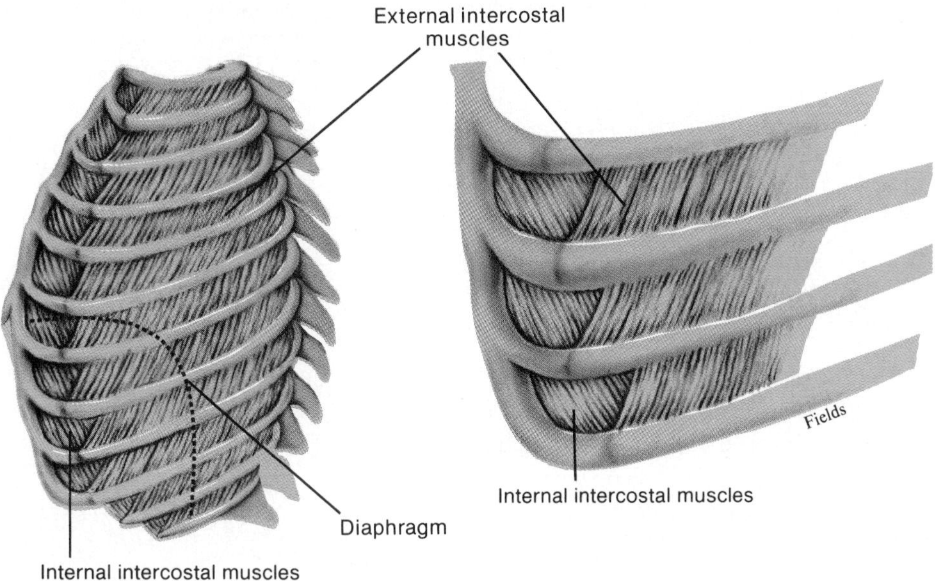

Figure 14.15 Chest expansion when both intercostals and diaphragm are stimulated. (*a*) Shape of the thorax prior to inspiration. (*b*) Shape of the thorax at end of inspiration. Arrows indicate the directions of expansion.

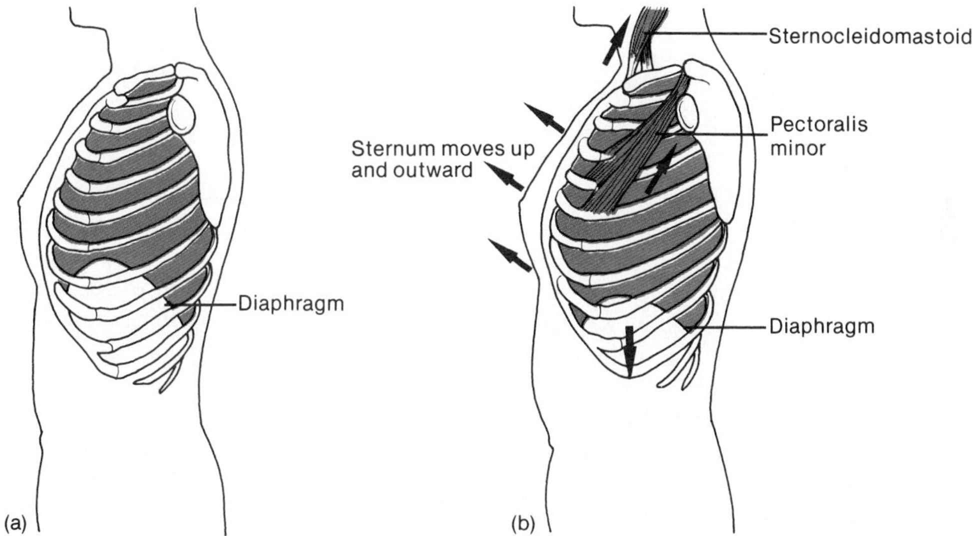

Expansion of the Alveoli

The alveoli represent the ultimate destination of the incoming air. Within these blind sacs are the capillaries that are exposed to the various gases that are breathed into the lungs. It is here that the blood is able to dump its excess carbon dioxide and recharge its erythrocytes with fresh oxygen. Normal alveoli and the blood vessels that perfuse them are incredibly **compliant,** which means they stretch easily. Very little energy is required to inflate them, because the walls of the alveoli are replete with elastic fibers, which elongate easily as the air flows in from the bronchial tree. The elasticity of these fibers is high. They offer very little resistance to stretching, and alveolar compliance is further aided by the presence of the compound known as surfactant.

Figure 14.16 (*a*) The thoracic cavity prior to inspiration. The pressure of gases inside the alveoli is exactly the same as the pressure of the atmosphere, which is 760 mm Hg. Pressure outside the lungs, but within the thoracic cavity, is usually slightly less, due to the elastic tendency of the lungs to collapse. (*b*) At the instant of inspiratory activity, the chest expands, reducing intrapleural pressure. The lungs promptly expand to fill the empty space (*shaded area*), thus lowering the intraalveolar pressure to less than atmospheric. Atmospheric air promptly rushes through the respiratory tubes, following the pressure gradient.

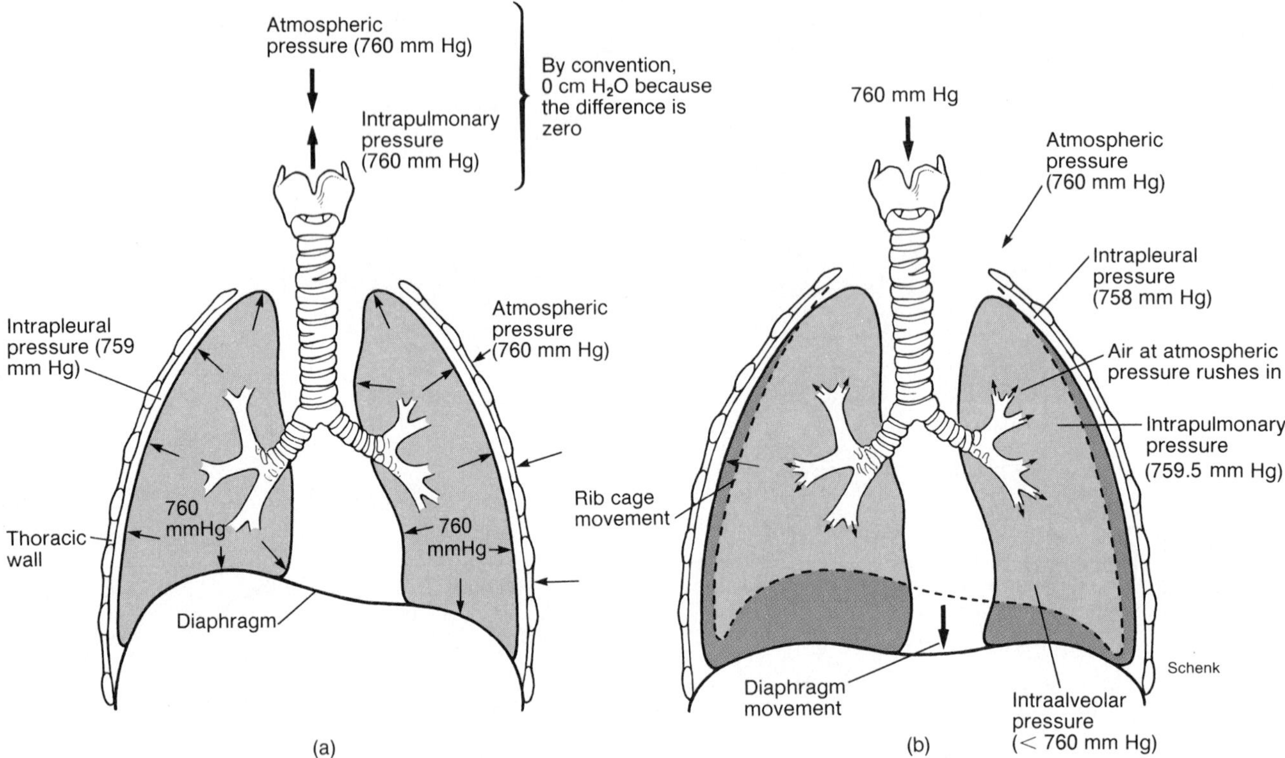

Surfactant

Surfactant was discovered relatively recently, and its chemical makeup has not been completely elaborated. A portion of it is a phospholipid called **dipalmitoyl lecithin,** and this, in turn, is linked to a protein. The entire compound is secreted by a special type of cell in the lung alveolus that is known as the **type II cell** (figure 14.17). Surfactant is synthesized rapidly and is always present in the thin film of water that coats the inner surface of each alveolus. Its presence is critically important, a fact that was nicely illustrated by a simple experiment performed recently in a research laboratory in California.

Any good detergent will produce piles of suds when introduced into water, especially if the water is stirred or agitated vigorously. People often use this feature to enjoy what has become known as a "bubble bath." The bubbles, advocates say, smell nice and aid relaxation. Unfortunately, they don't last very long, usually disappearing in less than an hour. Add surfactant to the detergent, however, and the bubbles you produce will not disappear in an hour . . . or two hours, or ten hours. Twenty hours after the bubbles were first produced in the experimental tub, most were still present, and they were showing no signs of vanishing.

Surface Tension

Their persistence involves the phenomenon known as **surface tension.** Surface tension is an interesting and powerful force, and the surface tension of water is normally quite high (see chapter 3). As the name implies, it is generated on a liquid surface by the tendency of individual water molecules to grip other water molecules rather than associate with air molecules in the atmosphere. The result is a force projected laterally along the surface and slightly downward, and it produces a relentless tendency to reduce the area of water in contact with the air. The sphere is the shape that exposes the smallest possible surface area, so exposed water surfaces assume a spherical shape if they can.

Surface tension thus makes droplets of water on a table top assume a rounded configuration on the upper surface, and it also makes bubbles spherical in shape rather than rhomboid or square. Bubbles, however, are different, because bubbles have two surfaces exposed to air instead of just one. The surface tension of the water on the bubble's inner surface produces forces that tend to make the bubble collapse or burst.

There is a similar tendency for the alveoli in our lungs to collapse, and it is due to the presence, on the inner surface of each alveolus, of a fine film of water.

Figure 14.17 The respiratory surface of an alveolus, showing the surfactant-secreting type II cell at the top.

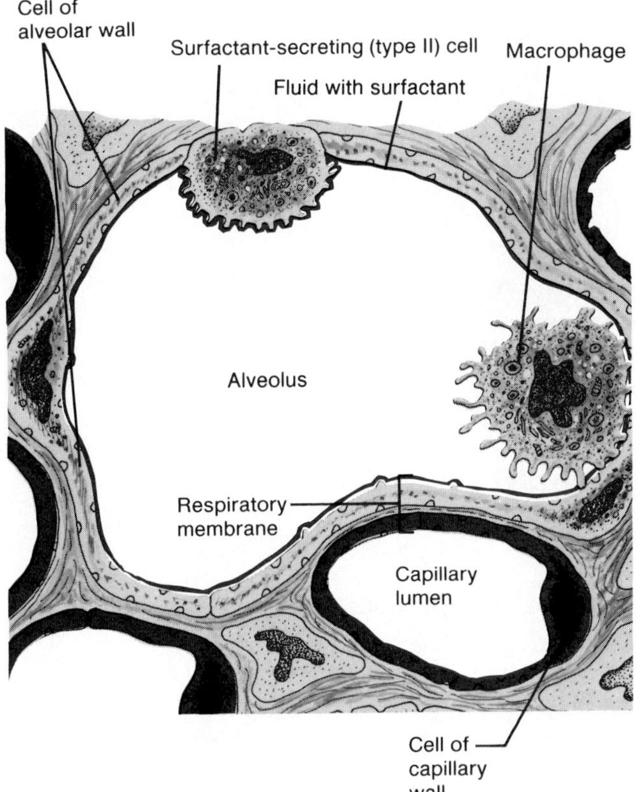

The water is essential to the diffusion of gases across the respiratory surfaces, but its presence presents a difficulty. Since it is on the *inner* surface of the spherical alveolus, it is analogous to the water film on the inner surface of a soap bubble, and as is the case with the bubble, the forces its surface tension generates tend to invite the collapse of the sphere.

In a manner that we do not yet understand, surfactant reduces the surface tension within this water film and so reduces the tendency of the alveoli to collapse. Thus it keeps individual alveoli blown up like healthy bubbles, even when air is expelled from the lungs.

Alveolar Collapse

In the absence of surfactant, the alveoli collapse. This is no small problem. Anyone who has ever played with balloons knows it is harder to blow up an empty balloon than it is to blow up one that is partially inflated. The same is true of alveoli. It takes a much greater inspiratory effort to inflate collapsed alveoli than to inflate those that have not collapsed, and when air is expelled from the lungs, there is a powerful tendency for the alveoli to collapse.

Alveolar collapse is dangerous any time, but it is particularly dangerous in newborn, premature infants. It has, in fact, been a principal cause of their death. Premature babies more often than not have no alveolar surfactant; hence their alveoli collapse each time they expire, and as a result, they must blow up collapsed alveoli with each breath. Such infants are tiny and weak, and many are not capable of such continued effort, so they simply give up and die. Surfactant, added to baby's inhaled air, promptly solves the problem, and normal respiratory efforts will provide adequate oxygen.

Adjustable Resistance in the Respiratory Tree

There is some resistance to the free flow of air through the respiratory tubes into the alveolar chambers, and most of this is encountered within the intermediate-sized bronchioles. The very tiny bronchioles, of which there are thousands, contribute some resistance, naturally, but not very much. Less than 20 percent of the total resistance to air flow within the respiratory tubes is contributed by the small bronchioles.

As is the case with the arterial blood vessels, the body can control the magnitude of this resistance by manipulating the diameter of the tubes. The smaller bronchi lack cartilaginous support, and these, as well as the larger bronchioles, are wrapped in smooth muscle that can contract and reduce their diameter. Parasympathetic nerves innervating the smooth muscles can, when stimulated, produce some profound bronchoconstriction, and when some harmful material enters the passageways, that is exactly what happens. Things like smoke and noxious gases produce an immediate constrictor response, as well as a good deal of coughing. On the other hand, the sympathetic neurons that innervate the smooth muscles of the bronchi and large bronchioles produce a relaxation of the tubes and a general bronchodilation.

Passive Expiration

Once the lungs have been filled, the active participation of the respiratory muscles is over. Deflation requires only that the person relax and the energy that was stored in the lungs and the thoracic wall will force the air out . . . there need be no active contribution by the muscles of the thoracic wall or the diaphragm (figure 14.18).

Forced Respiratory Movements

While a person is breathing in a normal, relaxed manner and oxygen requirements are relatively low, gas pressure within the lungs is, for all practical purposes, fairly constant. As we have seen, the difference between inspiration and expiration pressures is normally so small that intrapulmonary pressures are considered almost constant most of the time. However, during unusual respiratory movements, this is not necessarily the case. When, for example, the thoracic musculature produces a sudden, maximal inspiratory gasp, there are profound pressure changes in both the

Figure 14.18 (*a*) Normal expiration is due to elastic recoil of the thoracic wall and abdominal organs. (*b*) Maximal expiration is aided by the contraction of the abdominal wall and posterior internal intercostal muscles.

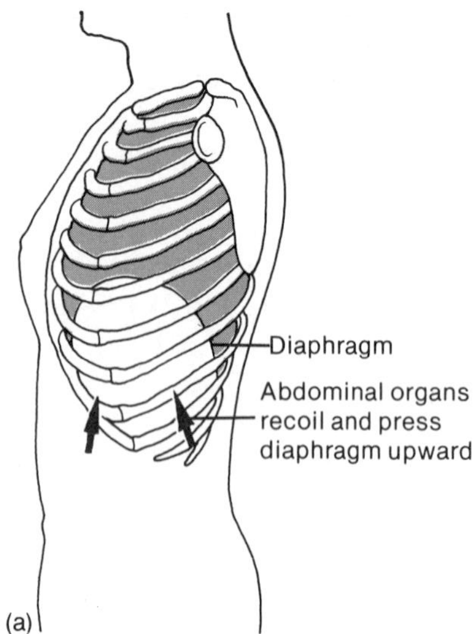

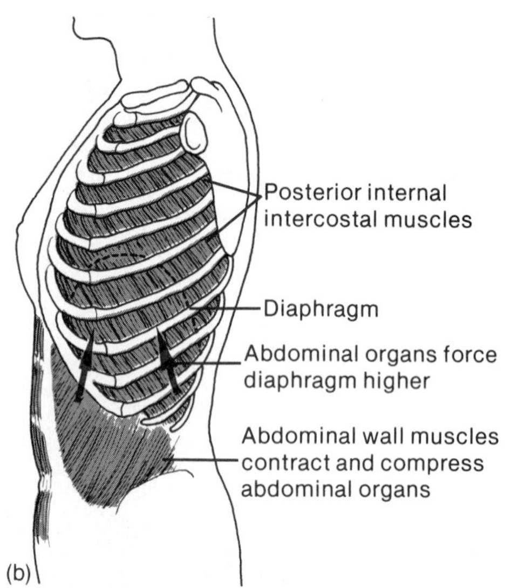

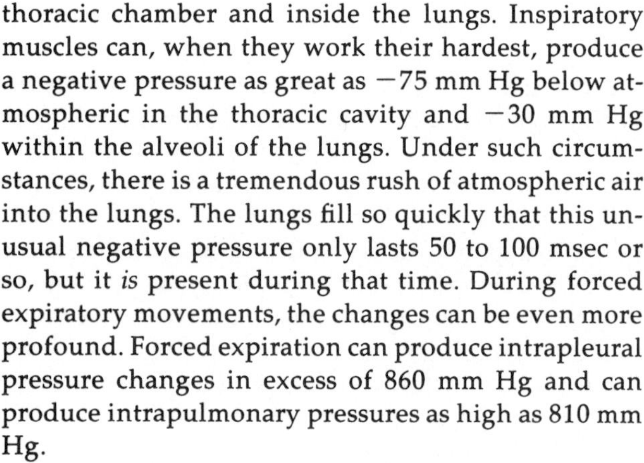

thoracic chamber and inside the lungs. Inspiratory muscles can, when they work their hardest, produce a negative pressure as great as −75 mm Hg below atmospheric in the thoracic cavity and −30 mm Hg within the alveoli of the lungs. Under such circumstances, there is a tremendous rush of atmospheric air into the lungs. The lungs fill so quickly that this unusual negative pressure only lasts 50 to 100 msec or so, but it *is* present during that time. During forced expiratory movements, the changes can be even more profound. Forced expiration can produce intrapleural pressure changes in excess of 860 mm Hg and can produce intrapulmonary pressures as high as 810 mm Hg.

The interior of the lungs—more specifically, within the alveoli—is the zone where the gaseous oxygen and carbon dioxide are dissolved in water and prepared for transfer into the blood. There is a lot of gas in the lungs, however, that never is taken up by the blood, and because of the nature of the lungs, there are also certain volumes that never disappear.

Many factors that are involved in respiratory movements are beyond the scope of this book, but one complicating factor does need to be mentioned, for the sake of clarity. Normal lungs want to collapse to a much smaller volume than the one they occupy in the thoracic cavity. This means that they are always slightly inflated, and elastic recoil is always trying to reduce their size. They are prevented from deflating by the hermetically sealed thoracic cavity. The lung cannot deflate completely because the slightly negative intrapleural pressure prevents it from doing so. But, if the thoracic chamber is punctured, there is no longer any such pressure seal, and the lungs are free to deflate completely. Such deflation is known as a **collapsed lung** and can be extremely dangerous.

Respiratory Air Volumes

Spirometry

As I have already mentioned, the word *respiration* has a number of quite different meanings. To a cell physiologist, it refers strictly to the reactions of intermediary metabolism (chapter 5). To the man on the street it refers to breathing. And to a practicing clinician, it means, specifically, *one inspiration plus one expiration.* The average human respiratory rate is on the order of thirteen to eighteen respirations per minute during relaxation. This means that the air within the lung chambers is being refreshed between thirteen and eighteen times every minute, but it is not being completely replaced. The volume of air within a person's lungs can vary over an enormous range, as can the volume that is moved in and out with each respiration. These volumes vary according to a person's state of activity and health. Hence it was reasoned that by measuring respiratory volumes, doctors could identify and treat systemic difficulties. Having recognized this potential, medical scientists standardized a number of specific lung volumes to help them discover respiratory problems and diseases.

The instrument commonly used to measure these volumes is known as a **spirometer** (figure 14.19). The common student type, as figure 14.19 shows, is a cylinder, open at the bottom and sealed at the top. It is placed in a second, slightly larger, cylinder filled with water; hence the term "wet" spirometer. The patient places the mouthpiece in his mouth and, holding his nose to avoid leakage, he blows into the tube. The air that is expired exits the tube from an opening underneath the innermost cylinder and fills it with air, floating it higher and higher, depending on the

Figure 14.19 (*a*) A Collins type 9L "wet" spirometer. This is a type routinely used in undergraduate laboratories to demonstrate lung volumes to students. (*b*) A highly sophisticated medical laboratory spirometer. This instrument is computer programed and controlled. Results are provided on a permanent hardcopy printout.

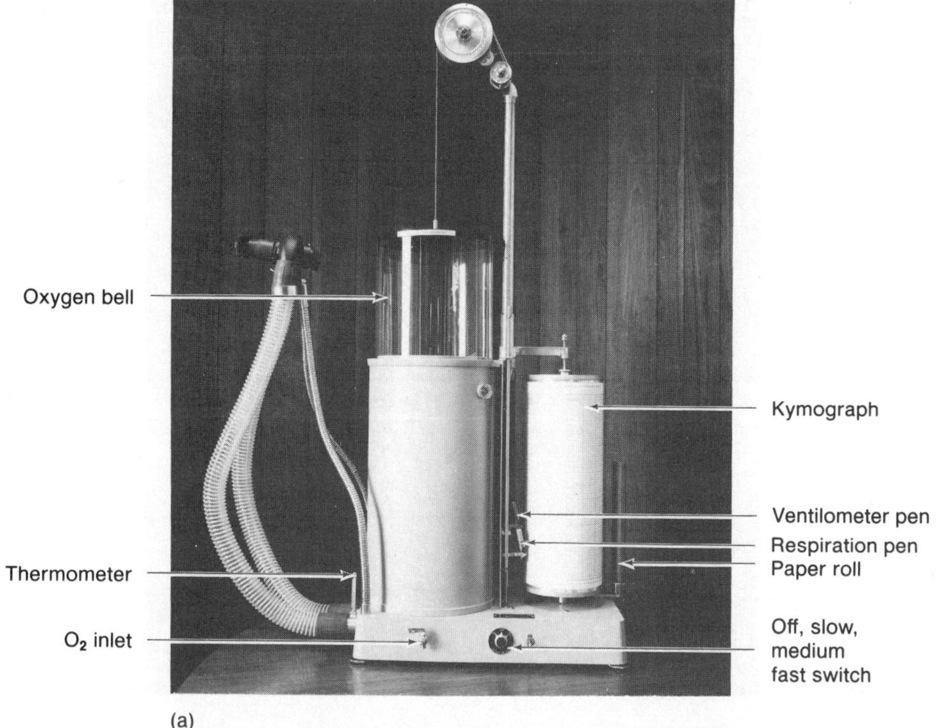

(a)

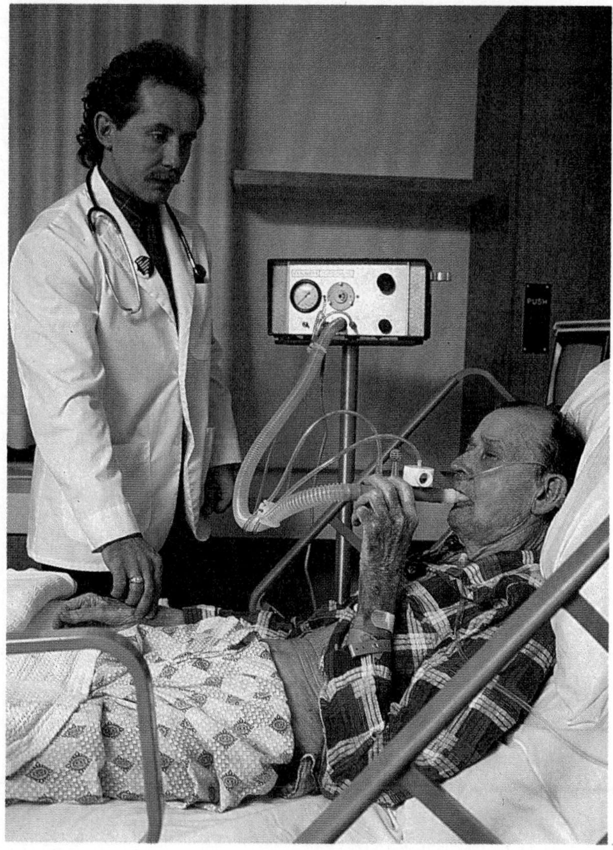

(b)

Table 14.1 Respiratory Air Volumes

Volume	Quantity of Air	Description	Volume	Quantity of Air	Description
Tidal volume (TV)	500 cc	Volume moved in or out of the lungs during quiet breathing	Vital capacity (VC)	4,600 cc	Maximum volume of air that can be exhaled after taking the deepest breath possible: VC = TV + IRV + ERV
Inspiratory reserve volume (IRV)	3,000 cc	Volume that can be inhaled during forced breathing in addition to tidal volume	Residual volume (RV)	1,200 cc	Volume that remains in the lungs at all times
Expiratory reserve volume (ERV)	1,100 cc	Volume that can be exhaled during forced breathing in addition to tidal volume	Total lung capacity (TLC)	5,800 cc*	Total volume of air that the lungs can hold: TLC = VC + RV

*These volumes represent those of the average man. Similar volumes in women tend to be smaller.

Figure 14.20 Respiratory air volumes.

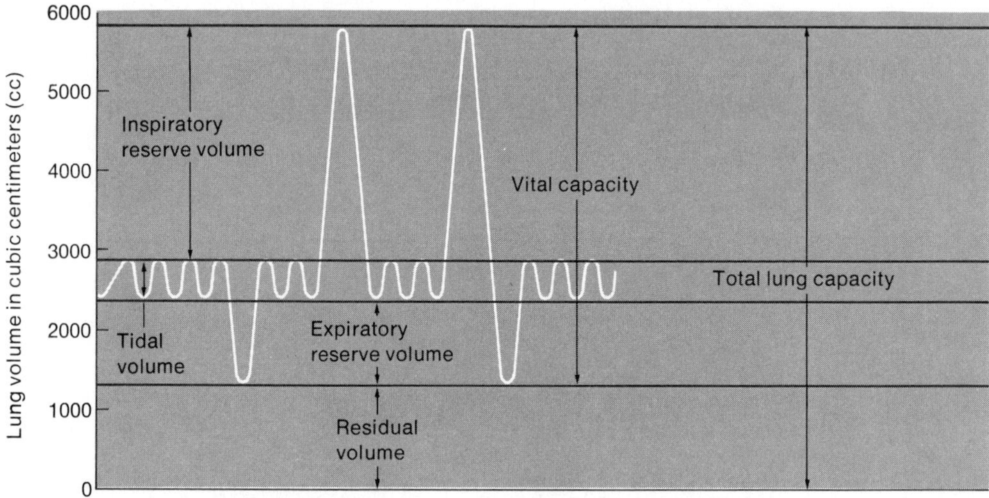

volume of air introduced. The displacement of the cylinder is noted by a pen and is recorded on a paper roll (see figure).

Total Lung Capacity

The lungs contain their greatest possible volume at the end of a forced inspiration. This is known as the **total lung capacity,** and in humans, for the sake of convenience, this has been further broken down into subordinate volumes and capacities by researchers (figure 14.20, table 14.1).

Tidal Volume

The **tidal volume** is the amount of air that is inspired in a single breath. This, of course, can vary quite broadly. During heavy exercise or at the end of a vigorous race, obviously the tidal volume will be considerably greater than it is when one has been sitting at home in an easy chair for a couple of hours, but both are considered tidal volume. That being the case, the most convenient definition of tidal volume might be *the volume of air required by the body's physiological processes at any given moment.* Whether it is a resting 450 ml or a vigorous 2,000 ml, there is always air remaining in the lungs after expiration, and it is almost always possible to inspire more than a tidal lungful.

Expiratory Reserve Volume

The **expiratory reserve volume** is the amount of air that can be forced out of the lungs after a normal expiratory movement. Like tidal volume, this will vary depending on the condition of the individual being examined at a given time, but it is almost always more than the tidal volume. In a resting individual whose tidal volume is about 450 ml, it should be on the order of a liter or two.

Inspiratory Reserve Volume

The **inspiratory reserve volume** is extra air, like the expiratory reserve, but it is on the other end of tidal volume. It is the amount of air that can be forcefully inspired after a normal inspiration. In a resting individual, it is usually between two and three liters.

Vital Capacity

These three volumes—tidal, expiratory reserve, and inspiratory reserve—added together constitute a person's **vital capacity.** The average vital capacity for humans in general has been calculated and is quoted as being on the order of four liters, but that figure is not very meaningful because of a huge difference between men and women. In women it usually ranges between about 2 and 3 liters. Men normally have much larger lungs, and hence their average vital capacity is often twice that of a woman, ranging usually between 3.5 and 6 liters. This is not a sexist assertion. The increased lung volume is necessary, since males have a relatively larger skeletal muscle mass, hence a greater oxygen requirement at any given time.

Residual Volume

No matter how hard you blow, it is not possible—short of collapsing a lung—to force all of the air out of your lungs. Even at the end of the most forceful expiration, there is always some left, and this remainder is known as **residual volume.** Obviously, since it cannot be blown out of a healthy human's lungs, residual volume cannot be measured directly, but it can be measured indirectly through the use of diffusion-dilution techniques. One such method is to have a subject breathe a specific volume of a colored gas in and out until the residual gas and the moving gases reach equilibrium. The amount of dilution of the colored gas can then be easily and accurately measured with the proper instruments. From this information, the total residual volume can be calculated.

Dead Space

There is another important volume to be considered. It is called the **dead space,** and it is not really what you would call a physiological space, since it is never involved in any gaseous exchange. Nevertheless, it is too large to be ignored. The dead space is the internal volume of the respiratory tree. It represents air that has been removed from the atmosphere and pulled into the respiratory system but never comes into contact with the blood. In an average human, it amounts to about 150 ml. If a person with such a dead space were to have a tidal volume of 150 ml, she would simply draw air down into the bottom of the respiratory tree without ever letting it get into the alveolar spaces, while the same air would move back and forth between the lungs and the top of the trachea.

The dead space does not have a great deal of significance in humans, but in many other mammals it is very important, particularly in thermoregulation. Everyone has seen a panting dog trying to keep himself cool in hot weather by evaporating water from his respiratory tract, rapidly puffing away. This high-speed breathing would produce what is known as **respiratory alkalosis** if it were, indeed, full ventilation. High respiratory rates tend to remove a great deal of carbon dioxide from the body fluids, and this has the unfortunate effect of increasing the blood pH to levels above the normal tolerance range, hence the name *alkalosis.* Dogs avoid this problem by moving only the dead-space air for thermal cooling. When only the dead-space volume moves, evaporative cooling can occur without gas exchange, so during hot weather dogs can have two different breathing rates, but only one ventilation rate. In passing, it is also worth mentioning that dogs pant through the mouth, whereas air destined for oxygen and carbon dioxide exchange is run through the nasal passages. This avoids drying out the conchae in the nasal cavity and helps to reduce body water loss.

Not all breathing movements made by humans actually involve ventilation. Movements like sneezing or coughing take place in order to clear certain areas of the respiratory tree. Despite their intermittent nature and the fact that polite society considers them unsavory, they are extremely important to good health.

Coughing and Sneezing

Probably the more important of these maneuvers is the cough. This is almost always a reflex activity and is nearly impossible to resist. The stimulus is usually some liquid or solid that has managed to slip past the glottis (the entrance to the trachea) and enter the trachea. This immediately stimulates the epiglottis (see figure 14.3) to fold back over the glottis and close it off. A second burst of nervous activity stimulates a sudden, forceful expiratory movement against this closed glottis. The result is a buildup of considerable pressure, just as an isometrically contracting finger can build up a lot of force when contracting against your thumb (see figure 13.A). A sudden, clearing movement of the epiglottis opens the glottis and releases a burst of high-pressure air that usually succeeds in blowing the offending material out of the trachea and into the back of the throat, where it can either be swallowed or spat out.

Sneezing is also a reflex action, and like the cough it is almost impossible to resist when the urge arises. It is intended to blow offending material out of the nasal cavity and can be quite messy if not carefully attended.

Table 14.2 Nonrespiratory Air Movements

Air Movement	Mechanism	Function
Coughing	Deep breath is taken, glottis is closed, and air is forced against the closure; suddenly the glottis is opened and a blast of air passes upward	Clears lower respiratory passages
Sneezing	Same as coughing, except air moving upward is directed into the nasal cavity by depressing the uvula	Clears upper respiratory pasages
Laughing	Deep breath is released in a series of short expirations	Expresses emotional happiness
Crying	Same as laughing	Expresses emotional sadness
Hiccuping	Diaphragm contracts spasmodically while the glottis is closed	No useful function
Yawning	Deep breath taken	Ventilates a large proportion of the alveoli and may aid oxygenation of the blood
Speech	Air is forced through the larynx, causing vocal cords to vibrate; words are formed by lips, tongue, and soft palate	Communication

Because coughing is so common, most of us tend to consider it mainly in a casual way, even sometimes as a terrible nuisance, without realizing its importance. Nevertheless, the very frequency of its occurrence should tell us that it is a critical maneuver, without which we would be in big trouble indeed. The trouble is greater than we could ever imagine. Coughing does not merely remove errant foreign material from the lower respiratory areas; it also removes perfectly normal respiratory secretions from alveolar and bronchiolar zones where it periodically tends to accumulate. One of the deadliest aspects of thoracic paralysis is the loss of the ability to cough—it is, in fact, a major cause of death in such patients. Despite the presence of artificial respirators, these people frequently develop what is called "aspiratory pneumonia" and die mainly because they are unable to cough. Respirators in use in most hospitals today contain built-in cough mechanisms so they can periodically "cough" a few times and clear the victims' lungs.

Yawning

One of the most mysterious—and probably the most contagious—of all respiratory reflexes is the yawn. When one person begins to yawn in a roomful of people, those who witness the activity feel obliged to yawn themselves. The result is usually a collection of people who succumb to the contagion and yawn in succession as the action makes its way relentlessly around the room. Exactly what a yawn is supposed to do is not certain, but it is so common, so communicable, and so inexorable once it begins, that it must serve some pretty important purpose. Some contend that it serves to increase oxygenation of the blood during periods of relaxation when minute volume (volume of air moved into and out of the lungs in one minute) tends to be quite low. Others suggest that maybe it serves to clear the eustachian tubes, eliminate growing pressure differentials, and establish a new pressure equilibrium throughout the entire respiratory tree and associated structures. Still others, noting that yawns almost never occur without stretching of muscles and a holding of the breath against a closed glottis, insist that its function is much more than merely a respiratory reflex. Whatever their purpose, yawns seem to be common in every vertebrate ever investigated. Even bony fishes and sharks yawn, and when a big shark does so, its Cheshire Cat gapes display enough dental artillery to thoroughly impress everything around it—and maybe *that* is one of its functions.

There are other nonrespiratory phenomena that involve unusual movements of the respiratory muscles and organs. They are listed in table 14.2.

Some Gas Laws

Before we explore the process of getting oxygen from the alveolar spaces into the blood, there are some fundamental principles governing gases and their movements that we must review. These are basic, physical facts that apply to all gases, and they aid in the understanding of gaseous exchange.

First of all, as we know from chapter 1, the gas phase is the high-energy phase, meaning we are dealing with a very fluid entity when we are dealing with a gas. A gas will expand to completely fill any container it is put into, and the pressure everywhere will be the same. At unequal pressures, there is a prompt movement of gas from high to low.

Secondly, in a gas mixture, the individual gases involved produce pressures equal to their contribution to the whole mixture. For example, if a gas is 20 percent oxygen and the total pressure of the mixture is 1,000 mm Hg, then the pressure of oxygen in the mixture will be 20 percent of 1,000 mm Hg = 200 mm Hg. This partial contribution to the whole is known as the **partial pressure** of the involved gas, and in the case of oxygen, it would be abbreviated **pO_2**. At sea level on a normal day, the atmospheric pressure is 760 mm Hg (30.4 inches), and by merely knowing the percent composition of each gas in the atmosphere, we can calculate the partial pressure of each. Oxygen, for instance, represents almost 21 percent of the atmosphere, hence pO_2 would be $.21 \times 760 \approx 160$ mm Hg. By far the most abundant atmospheric gas is nitrogen (78.6 percent), so the pN_2 in the atmosphere at sea level would be $.786 \times 760 \approx 597$ mm Hg. Carbon dioxide, which normally comprises about 0.04 percent of the atmosphere, has a pCO_2 of just 0.3 mm Hg.

Another principle of great concern involves just how much gas will dissolve in water. Naturally this depends to a great extent on the characteristics of the gas involved. In this regard, gases are like anything else—some dissolve easily while others do not. Salt, for instance, dissolves in water quite easily, while corn starch or flour is hard to get into solution. Similarly, carbon dioxide and nitrogen are both quite soluble in water; oxygen is not.

The type of gas is not the only thing that determines solubility, however. A lot depends on the pressures and the temperatures involved. High atmospheric pressures can force more gases into solution, and you should be aware that even when it is dissolved, a gas still features a pressure. If you were to leave a pan of water on a table top until it achieved equilibrium with the atmospheric gases, the pressure of each gas in the water would be exactly the same as its pressure in the atmosphere above.

The amount of gas that can be forced into solution by increasing atmospheric pressures is impressive. For years, it was suspected that the primary reason an air-breathing animal could not live underwater was that there was simply not enough dissolved oxygen to satisfy an air-breather's high demands. In the late 1960s a series of experiments was conducted to see if this contention was correct, and it was found that when water was placed under an oxygen pressure of 500 atmospheres (500×760 mm Hg), rats, mice, and dogs could be submerged and could breathe water without any ill effects. The water used was a carefully buffered solution that was osmotically and thermally neutral, and the animals had to suffer some horrid emotional trauma to induce them to inhale a liquid, but when they finally did, they appeared perfectly all right. Moving the viscous water in and out of their lungs did not appear to present any particular difficulty, and they were able to adjust their respiratory rates to conform to body demands.

The Significance of Water Vapor

Air that enters the respiratory tree is saturated with water vapor almost as soon as it enters, and water vapor, like any other gas, produces a pressure. Since it always completely saturates the incoming air, the only thing that will affect its partial pressure is temperature, and since temperature in a healthy human is always within a degree or so of 37° C, the pH_2O of alveolar air won't ever change. At 37° C, water vapor has a partial pressure of 47 mm Hg, and at sea level pressures, that represents a little less than 10 percent of the total gases in the lungs. At sea level, then, the pressure of water vapor is negligible and need not concern us. However, if the atmospheric pressures go down, as they will with increases in altitude, the water vapor pressure becomes more and more important. Its unchanging pressure represents a progressively larger percentage of the total alveolar gases. This phenomenon reduces drastically the partial pressures of all other gases in the alveolar air—oxygen, for example, drops from 159 mm Hg to 104 mm Hg, due mainly to the presence of the water vapor. ($159 - 47 = 112$. The extra 8 mm Hg drop in oxygen pressure is due to its mixing with the residual air, which contains a high concentration of carbon dioxide.) If the altitude is great enough, the pressure of water vapor can produce disastrous results.

The presence of water vapor in alveolar air can have profound—even deadly—effects on mountain hikers or even airplane pilots who might be attempting to climb over mountain ranges without proper oxygen equipment. A magazine printed in the 1940s featured an article concerning high-altitude flying, and in it was the statement:

"when flying at 50,000 feet, pilots die even when breathing 100% oxygen. . . ."

This statement bothered me for years, because it did not appear to make any sense. A person's lungs held a certain quantity of air, and if that person were breathing pure oxygen, *all* of the gas in his (or her) lungs would be oxygen. How could that possibly fail to satisfy all requirements for oxygenating the blood? The answer lies mainly in the behavior of water vapor. At an altitude of 50,000 feet, the total atmospheric pressure is 120 mm Hg. That includes all the gases—nitrogen, oxygen, carbon dioxide, and whatever else is present. Naturally, then, the total alveolar pressure will also be 120 mm Hg.

The composition of alveolar gas, however, will be quite different from that of the atmosphere. In the process of passing through the respiratory tree, the incoming air is saturated with water vapor, and at 37° C that is a constant 47mm Hg. That is 40 percent of the total gas pressure, meaning that only 60 percent of the alveolar air will not be water vapor. In addition, carbon dioxide is constantly entering the alveolar spaces from the blood, contributing its own effects. Normally, pCO_2 in the lungs is negligible, but at such low atmospheric pressures it will occupy a significant fraction of the total. Taking these two gases into account, the total pressure of the remainder cannot be higher than 60 mm Hg, and even if it were 100 percent oxygen, that would not be enough to saturate the blood to more than about 85 percent, and that will not sustain life for very long.

Gas Movement

The movement of all gases is determined by pressure gradients, and oxygen is no exception. Its movement from the atmosphere to its final destination within the cell is determined by pressure differences in various body compartments. The bottom of the hill—the zone where the pO_2 is lowest of all—is within the confines of the mitochondria. That is where oxygen is linked onto the protons and electrons pouring out of the respiratory chain, a process that results in the production of metabolic water. Similarly, the high point—the top of the hill—is the atmosphere, which is the ultimate source of all our oxygen. In between these two extremes is a series of steps, each one representing a pressure drop, as the oxygen makes its way doggedly toward its mitochondrial rendezvous with hydrogen.

Alveolar Air

In the atmosphere near sea level, as we have already noted, pO_2 is usually about 159 to 160 mm Hg. Within the alveoli, however, the percent composition of gases is different from atmospheric. Several things are responsible. The saturation of incoming air with water vapor plays a role. Also, oxygen is constantly being removed from alveolar air while carbon dioxide is continually entering. Ultimately, these additions and depletions have their effect so that, despite the fact that the entering air has a pO_2 of 159 mm Hg, pO_2 within the alveoli is on the order of 100 mm Hg, and it generally tends not to vary significantly from that figure. In fact, all pressures within the alveoli remain remarkably constant. Even during the heaviest, most demanding physical activities, when the blood is drawing oxygen in great gulps from the lungs, alveolar pO_2 never drifts below 90 mm Hg. This suggests that there is some very sensitive regulatory activity taking place, activity that involves several homeostatic mechanisms.

Adjustment begins with the gases themselves and some simple dilution factors. Let us examine what happens to a volume of air when it is drawn into the lungs. Assume, for instance, that at the beginning of a normal, resting inspiration, a person's lungs contain about three liters of air (residual + expiratory reserve). An average, resting tidal volume would draw in maybe 500 ml of air. From that 500 ml, we will have to subtract the dead space, so the total volume of fresh, atmospheric air entering the lungs is about 350 ml. That is a volume increase of just a little more than 10 percent, so about 10 percent of the air inside the lungs has a pO_2 of about 159 mm Hg. Since the pO_2 elsewhere is 100 mm Hg, the oxygen in the new air rushes to eliminate the pressure gradient and diffuses quickly, equalizing pressures throughout the lung.

Figure 14.21 The relationship between the alveolar capillaries and the gas-filled alveolus.

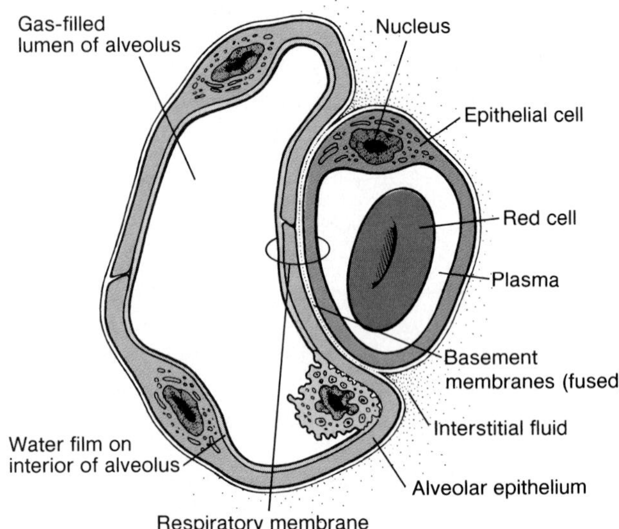

While this new, oxygen-rich gas is spreading through the airspaces, blood coursing through the lungs in an unending stream steadily removes it.

Alveolar Exchange

Blood in the pulmonary capillaries is separated from the gas-filled alveolar lumen by at least two layers of endothelial cells and a pair of basement membranes. Taken altogether, they form a structure about 0.2 μm thick that is known as the *respiratory membrane* (figure 14.21). It is not a great distance to traverse, and early suggestions that lung surfaces might actively secrete the gas into the blood have been shown to be incorrect. Diffusion can provide the necessary energy and can accomplish the crossing in a fraction of a second. But first, the oxygen has to undergo a change in physical state—it cannot enter the blood in gaseous form. To get from the lungs into the circulation, therefore, it must first dissolve in the water film that lines the inside of the alveolus.

Now we can understand why it is so important for the nasal cavity and other respiratory surfaces to saturate incoming atmospheric air with water vapor before permitting it to come into contact with the interior of the lungs. Unsaturated air entering the lungs would dry out that water film in a flash, removing it from the surface of the alveoli and rendering the air sacs incapable of passing oxygen to the blood. As long as the incoming air is completely saturated with water, there is no such danger, and the lungs can continue to operate properly.

Figure 14.22 (*a*) A flat table surface holds very little water. Most simply runs off and is lost. (*b*) A sponge absorbs the water and stores it. The beaker can be emptied and none spills onto the floor.

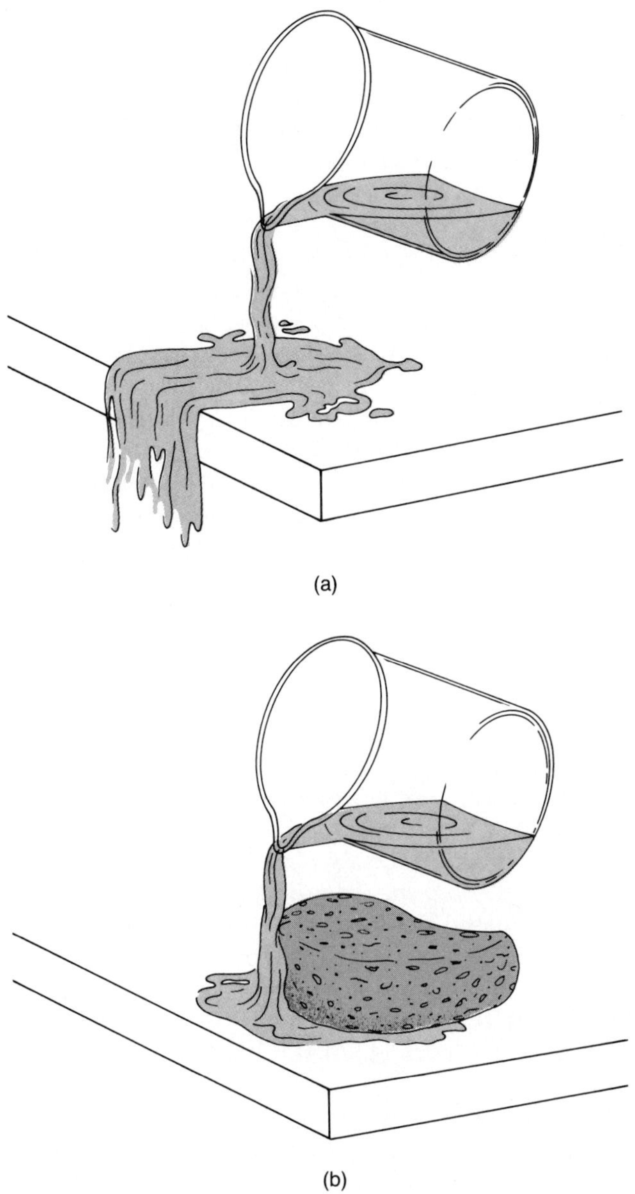

The gaseous oxygen in the alveolus of the lung and the oxygen dissolved in the water film are in equilibrium, so the partial pressure in both compartments will be the same, 100 mm Hg. Since the pO_2 in the venous blood entering the lungs is only about 40 mm Hg, there will be a steep gradient between it and the dissolved O_2 in the water film—a gradient steep enough to force a very rapid diffusion and establishment of a second equilibrium. Within the lungs, therefore, a whole series of equilibria is established (see page 508), and it all happens in about 0.007 seconds (7 msec). Since blood requires about 10 msec to move through a pulmonary capillary, there is plenty of time for complete exchange to occur and for an equilibrium to become established.

There is a bit more to this equilibrium than simple diffusion of dissolved gases from one liquid medium to another, however. Within the blood, another equilibrium establishes itself, and this one is extremely important.

A Problem of Solubility

As we have already seen, oxygen enters the body in the form of a gas, but it quickly dissolves in the thin film of water that lines the interior of the lungs. In a way, that simplifies things. Since it is presented to the blood already in solution, getting it into the plasma is relatively easy and requires no energy—it simply diffuses. There is a problem, however. Neither the water film in the alveoli nor the plasma can hold very much because, as I am sure you will recall, oxygen is not very soluble in water. Considering this, and considering the rate at which our bodies use oxygen—even at rest—researchers realized early that the plasma could not possibly carry enough oxygen to keep us alive. In fact, if we had to depend on the amount of oxygen that the plasma can carry in solution, we would need at least 150 liters of blood to keep us alive. One hundred and fifty liters of blood weighs 330 pounds! We'd have to "pump iron" for five straight years just to get strong enough to lift our own blood. Fortunately, we have hemoglobin; hence we can get by with about six liters of blood instead.

Respiratory Pigment

As we all know, pouring water onto a flat table top can create an interesting mess on the floor; very little water stays on the table. But a great deal of water can be poured onto that same table without *any* running off onto the floor if we simply put a sponge there to suck it up (figure 14.22).

This is much the same way that hemoglobin behaves with respect to the oxygen dissolved in the plasma. Hemoglobin sucks oxygen from the plasma like a high-quality sponge lifts water from a table top. The plasma, like the table top, cannot hold very much, but as soon as dissolved oxygen shows up, the hemoglobin "sponges" suck it out of solution and stash it away inside their own mass (figure 14.23).

Ultimately, of course, hemoglobin, like the sponge, will become saturated and unable to hold any more, but the saturation point of hemoglobin is high— far higher than that of plasma, or the table top. How much difference does that actually make?

Much of the calculating has already been done for us. We know, for instance, that the average human has five million RBCs per mm^3, which works out to

Figure 14.23 As with water poured on a table top, as long as there is a hemoglobin "sponge" available to absorb the oxygen, the alveolar "beaker" can continue to pour oxygen into the plasma.

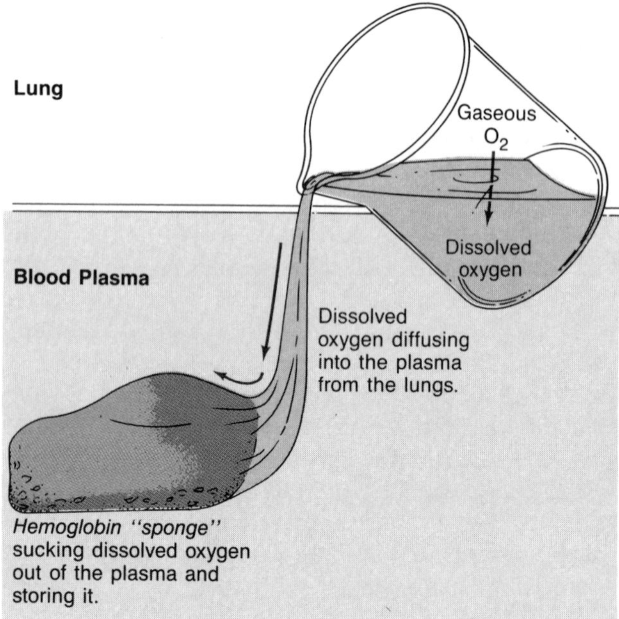

about 14.5 grams of hemoglobin per deciliter of whole blood. The saturation point of hemoglobin has also been calculated, so we know that every gram of hemoglobin is able to combine with 1.34 ml of oxygen. From this information we can calculate (145 X 1.34) that every liter of blood can bind to and transport about 200 ml of oxygen. (In medical jargon, that's a concentration of 20 ml percent or 20 ml per deciliter.) Since average humans have about six liters of blood, they can hold, at normal capacity, more than a liter of oxygen in their red blood cells.

Without the hemoglobin, six liters of plasma would dissolve only about eighteen ml of oxygen—that is less than two-tenths of a liter—and that would not *begin* to satisfy the demands of our body for that precious gas (figure 14.24).

Within the lungs, therefore, we have a series of equilibria that are constantly, and simultaneously, shifting back and forth. There is one involving the maintenance of alveolar partial pressures; there is a second one between the gaseous oxygen and dissolved oxygen in the alveolus; a third between the alveolar oxygen and plasma oxygen; and a fourth between dissolved oxygen in the plasma and the oxygen that is bound to the hemoglobin. As the blood leaves the lungs, however, these equilibria have been reduced to just one—the equilibrium between the dissolved oxygen in the plasma and the oxygen bound to hemoglobin.

Hemoglobin

Hemoglobin is an enormously complex molecule, most of which is protein (figure 14.25, figure 12.14). Within each molecule, there are four prosthetic (nonprotein) groups, each containing one molecule of ferrous (or iron two) iron, and each of these iron molecules can hold a single molecule of oxygen. If, therefore, a hemoglobin molecule combines with a single molecule of O_2, the hemoglobin is 25 percent saturated; if two of the iron molecules bind to oxygen, the hemoglobin will be 50 percent saturated; with three, 75 percent saturated, and with all four irons holding O_2 molecules, saturation is, naturally, 100 percent. As has already been noted, hemoglobin saturates with tremendous speed. When exposed to oxygen in the lungs it will load up in 7 msecs, and it can unload in the tissues almost as fast.

When water is exposed to oxygen gas, the amount of O_2 that will dissolve in the water is directly proportional to the pO_2 of the gas, meaning when one goes up, the other will go up proportionally. If the pO_2 in the air is 160 mm Hg, at equilibrium the pO_2 in the water will be the same, 160 mm Hg. If the pO_2 in the air goes up to 180 mm Hg, it will go up to 180 mm Hg in the water as well, and the amount of dissolved O_2 will increase proportionally. Similarly, if pO_2 goes down in the air, it will go down equally far in the water, and the amount dissolved will decrease proportionally. Thus we say that the relationship between the two is a "straight-line" or "linear" relationship. It is given this name because if we graph gaseous pO_2 against the amount of dissolved O_2 at equilibrium (figure 14.26), the result will be a straight line.

If we expose human blood plasma to gaseous oxygen, we can observe a similar, linear relationship, and that is reasonable, because plasma is mostly water, and the gas is simply dissolving in the watery matrix of the plasma. However, if we expose whole blood to gaseous oxygen, the relationship we observe when pressures are changed is *not* linear. The amount of oxygen taken up by the blood is still tuned to oxygen pressure—it will still increase when pO_2 goes up, but it does not do so proportionally. The curve is curved somewhat like a rather irregular letter *S*, and it is known as a **sigmoid** type of curve (figure 14.27).

Figure 14.24 Plasma and whole blood that are brought into equilibrium with the same gas mixture have the same pO_2 and thus the same amount of dissolved oxygen molecules (shown with black dots). The oxygen content of whole blood, however, is much higher than that of plasma because of the binding of oxygen to hemoglobin.

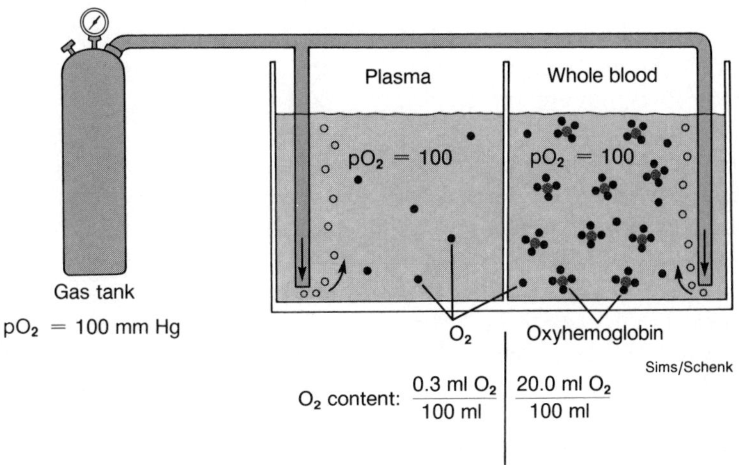

Figure 14.25 The chemical structure of heme.

```
          CH3   CH =CH2
           |     |
           C=====C
           |     |
      HC---C     C=CH
       ||    \\N/    |
CH3---C---C   :     C=C-CH3
      ||    \  :   /   |
      ||     N---Fe---N    |
      ||   //   |    \   |
CH2---C---C     |     C=C-CH=CH2
|         |     N     |
CH2      HC=C/    \C=CH
|           |      |
COOH        C======C
            |      |
           CH2    CH3
            |
           CH2
            |
           COOH
```

Figure 14.26 Graph showing the straight-line relationship between gaseous O_2 and dissolved oxygen as the gaseous pO_2 is changed.

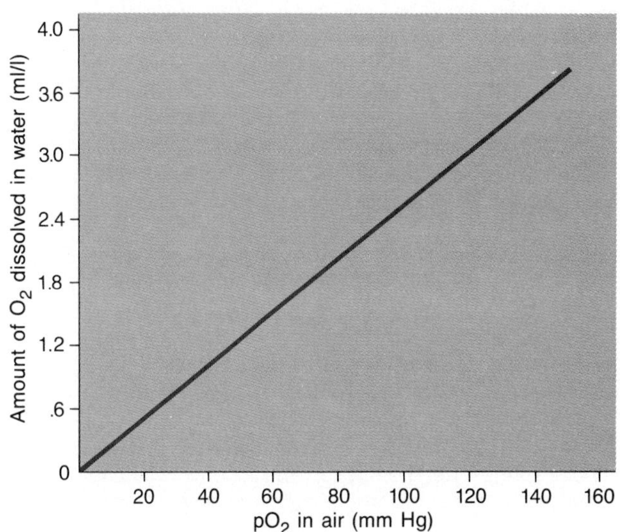

The Hemoglobin-Oxygen Dissociation Curve

Almost all of the oxygen carried in the blood is carried in combination with hemoglobin, so the relationship between pO_2 and the amount of O_2 in whole blood actually represents the relationship between hemoglobin saturation and pO_2. And biochemists have worked out just how it gets such a peculiar relationship with oxygen pressure. In each hemoglobin molecule, as we have said, there are four iron molecules. Each of these ferrous molecules is capable of uniting with a molecule of oxygen, and when one does this, it evidently alters the affinity of its brothers for O_2. As soon as one iron molecule links up with an oxygen, it increases the attraction between the other three and oxygen . . . in other words, the *affinity* of the remaining iron molecules for oxygen is increased. When a second iron/oxygen bond forms, the affinity of the remaining two increases even more, and so on. So the more oxygen in a hemoglobin molecule, the easier it is for still more to hook on. Yet despite this, all of the molecules of hemoglobin in a given volume of blood cannot saturate 100 percent with oxygen unless the pO_2 is somewhere between 160 and 170 mm Hg, which it never is *in vivo*. The pO_2 in the alveoli is usually on the order of 100 mm Hg, which means blood leaving the lungs is never 100 percent saturated with oxygen. As you can see from figure 14.27, at a pO_2 of 100 mm Hg, the blood leaving the lungs is between 97 and 98 percent saturated, and that is its normal saturation level when it enters the left heart. Obviously, most of the hemoglobin molecules have taken up four O_2 molecules, but apparently not all of them are able to at that low a pO_2.

While the blood is inside the arteries and arterioles, things stay about the same (figure 14.28). The established equilibrium between the dissolved oxygen in the plasma and the oxygen that is bound to the blood's hemoglobin stays static because there is really no place for it to go. But when it breaks out into the capillaries, deep in the body tissues, it is suddenly exposed to the pO_2 of the interstitial fluids. Since oxygen is continuously being poured into the cells to stoke the mitochondrial furnaces, its pressure in the interstitial fluids is going to reflect these losses. At the same time, a good deal of CO_2 will have been generated by the same mitochondrial reactions, and its level in the interstitial fluid will certainly be higher than its level in the blood.

In a healthy, resting person, tissue pO_2 is on the order of 40 mm Hg. As the blood flows from the arterial end of the capillary toward the venous end, there is a steady exchange of gases, so the pO_2 of the plasma steadily decreases while the pCO_2 constantly goes up. The distance travelled is always very small, but the pO_2 gradient is so steep ($\approx$60 mm Hg) that the outflow of oxygen is extremely rapid. The movement of dissolved O_2 from the plasma promptly establishes a new equilibrium, and as dissolved oxygen leaves the plasma, the existing equilibrium between it and the hemoglobin shifts, and oxygen begins to break away from the hemoglobin. As you can see for yourself if you look at figure 14.29, the hemoglobin will unload O_2 until it retains only about 76 percent of its original capacity, which means that at a pO_2 of 40 mm Hg, whole blood gives up about 22 percent of the O_2 it normally carries.

The CO_2 gradient is not as steep as the O_2 gradient, but carbon dioxide makes up for it by being so soluble in water. Thanks to this solubility, it can equilibrate almost as quickly as the oxygen can. In fact, capillary exchange of both oxygen and CO_2 is nearly instantaneous, usually requiring less than seven msec.

Figure 14.27 The oxyhemoglobin dissociation curve under "normal" or "resting" conditions in an average person.

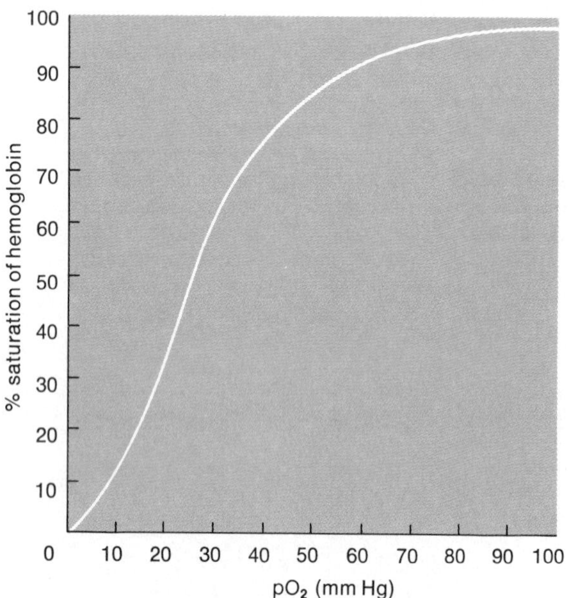

Figure 14.28 Oxygen equilibria at various metabolic levels. (*a*) The oxygen equilibrium in the lungs. (*b*) The oxygen equilibrium in the arteries. (*c*) The oxygen equilibrium in the capillaries. (*d*) Dissolved oxygen movement in the tissues. Since O_2 actually changes to water in *d*, there is never really an established equilibrium.

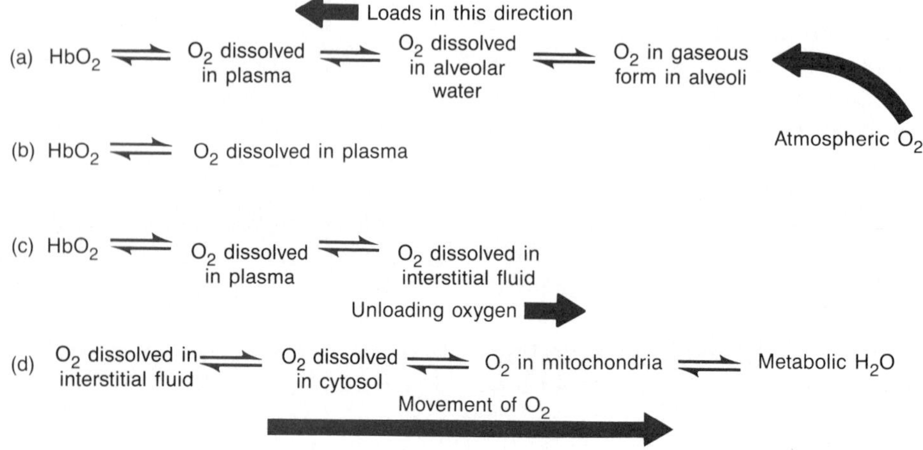

Intrinsic Homeostatic Mechanisms

The unusual relationship between hemoglobin and oxygen has some very definite physiological advantages. In order to understand them, you need to study the dissociation curves a little more carefully. As you can see, the curve levels off at the upper end. At a pO_2 of 80 mm Hg, the curve flattens out, and from that point on, it is very nearly horizontal (see figure 14.30).

What this means physiologically is that should some emergency occur that might deprive the alveolar air of significant amounts of oxygen, it would not necessarily be disastrous. As figure 14.30 shows, even if something like heavy exercise under anaerobic conditions should reduce the alveolar pO_2 to 80 mm Hg, the hemoglobin in the blood would still be able to saturate to nearly 96 percent of total capacity. A drop of this magnitude in alveolar air is unheard-of in human physiological patterns. However, as has been mentioned earlier, people running very hard, as they do in the final sprint of a race, tend to hold their breath until they cross the finish line, and during that period, the pO_2 in the lungs can slip pretty low. In times of such extreme stress, the alveolar pO_2 has been known to fall as low as 89 mm Hg—a condition that, at worst, lasts for only a few seconds and then only during very heavy exercise. At that pO_2, hemoglobin saturation is well above 95 percent. In fact, it is very near the saturation levels it maintains when the pO_2 is its normal 100 mm Hg.

At the other end of the curve—between pO_2s of 60 and 20 mm Hg—a slight alteration in pO_2 can have quite the opposite effect (see figure 14.31). When the circulating blood enters a zone of unusually low pO_2 (20 mm Hg), where there has been vigorous metabolic activity and O_2 has been depleted, hemoglobin is able to unload considerable oxygen. As figure 14.31 shows, even if the blood has previously run through a capillary bed where oxygen demand has been normal (pO_2 = 40 mm Hg), it can still unload an additional 43 percent of its total carrying capacity, and that is a lot of oxygen.

Figure 14.30 The hemoglobin/oxygen dissociation curve above 80 mm Hg pO_2. Note that this part of the curve is nearly horizontal and that a pO_2 change of 20 mm Hg changes Hb saturation by only 2 percent.

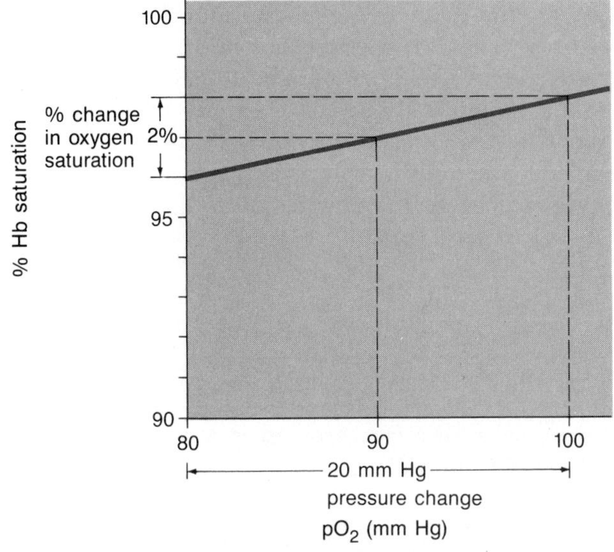

Figure 14.31 The hemoglobin/oxygen dissociation curve below 60 mm Hg. Note that between 40 and 20 mm Hg—a change of only 20 mm Hg pO_2—there is a drop of 43 percent in Hb saturation, more than twenty times the response to a 20 mm Hg pO_2 change above 60 mm Hg.

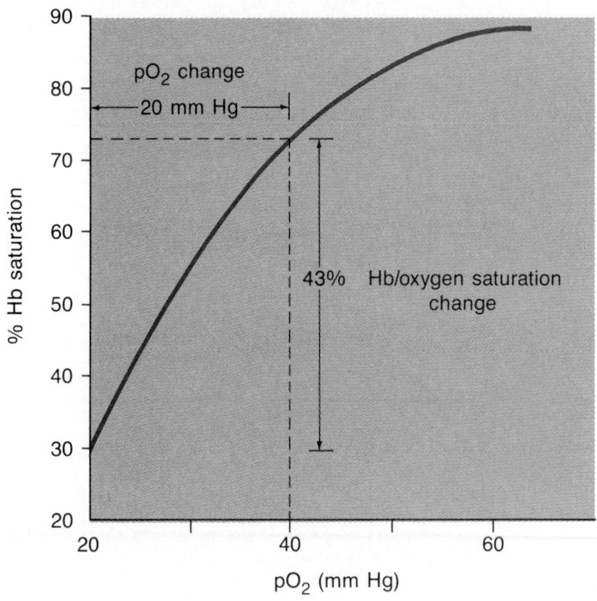

Figure 14.29 Normal oxygen/hemoglobin dissociation curve comparing Hb saturation before and after entering an average capillary bed.

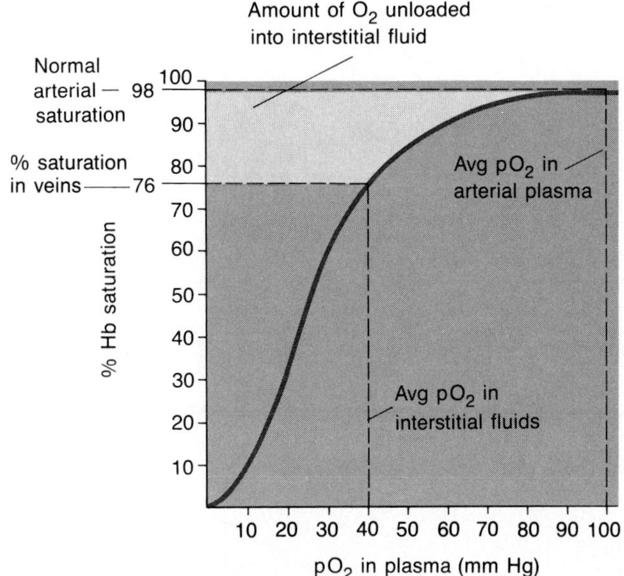

The unusual sigmoid pattern of the oxyhemoglobin dissociation curve,.therefore, represents a respiratory safety factor—a mechanism, built right into the oxygen-carrying molecules, that produces an automatic adjustment to varying demands of different but sequential capillary beds through which the blood may flow. Without this mechanism, adjustments to a sudden changing oxygen demand would have to be accomplished through utilization of one of the major control systems. That would require time . . . time for a receptor to analyze the blood going through a given area, time to pass that information to an integrator, and even more time for an effector response to occur. The intrinsic mechanism, built right into the hemoglobin itself, can bypass all this hassle. Thanks to hemoglobin's unusual chemical properties, the blood is able to respond directly to variable body demands, and on-the-spot adjustments in oxygen delivery can be made with no delays and a minimum of energy expenditure.

When the blood leaves the left heart and enters the arterial circulation it is about 97 to 98 percent saturated with oxygen and is carrying about twenty ml of oxygen per hundred milliliters of blood. Just how much of that gas is unloaded depends on a variety of things, particularly the metabolic activity of the tissues nearby and the blood flow through them.

Altering Hemoglobin's Affinity for Oxygen

There are other dissociation characteristics of hemoglobin that make possible even more sensitive adjustments in response to local demands for oxygen. At least three other factors are involved in modifying the affinity between hemoglobin and oxygen, and they come into play when they are most needed.

First of all, should anything reduce the pH of the fluid around the hemoglobin, *the whole dissociation curve shifts to the right.* This reduces hemoglobin's affinity for oxygen (figure 14.32*a*), a phenomenon known as the **Bohr effect,** and it has important physiological ramifications.

Figure 14.32 Human hemoglobin/oxygen dissociation curves and the Bohr effect. (*a*) The Bohr effect, which results from a lowering of pH. (*b*) The effect of increasing temperature. (*c*) The combined effect: increased temperature and decreased pH. In each case, the horizontal axes represent pO_2 in mm of Hg, and the vertical axes represent the percentage of hemoglobin saturation with oxygen.

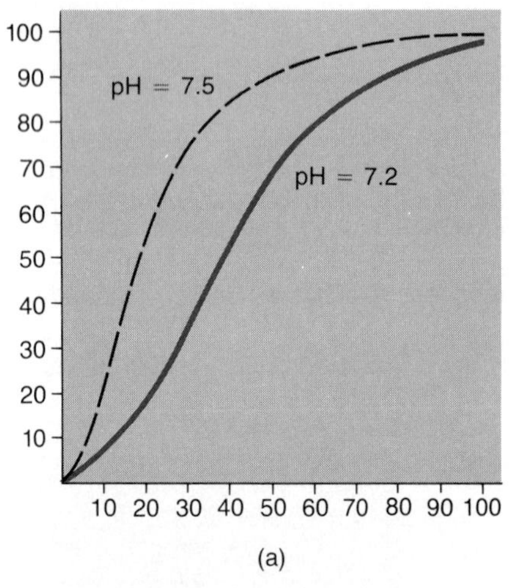

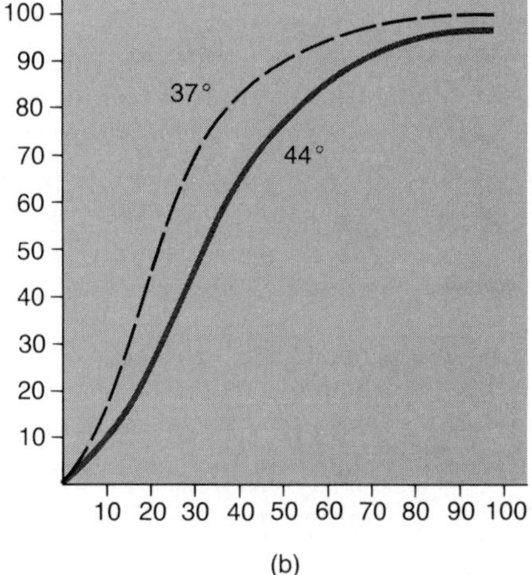

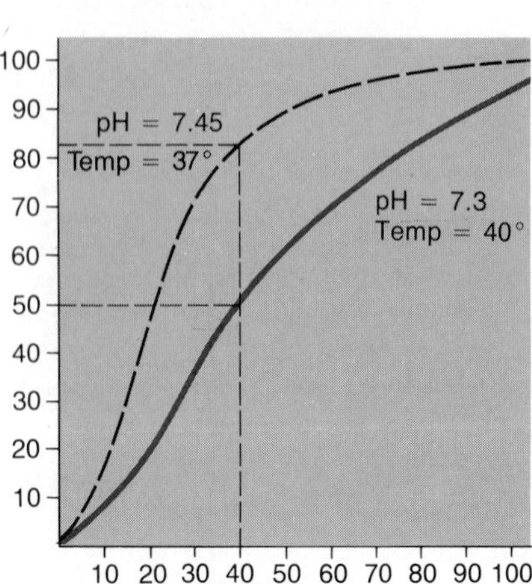

At a pH of 7.45 and temperature of 37°, Hb releases approximately 22% of its oxygen at a pO_2 of 40 mm Hg.

At the same pO_2, but temperature of 40° and a pH of 7.3, the Hb will release nearly 50% of its oxygen.

Secondly, a similar, although slightly smaller, reduction in affinity also takes place when there is an increase in temperature (figure 14.32*b*), and when, as it usually happens *in vivo*, both effects are added together, the shift can be profound (figure 14.32*c*).

It is during periods of really heavy activity that this combined shift is most likely to develop. Hard-working muscles consume a great deal of energy, and in the processing of extra fuel, they produce inordinately large quantities of both CO_2 and heat. Heat all by itself will cause the curve to shift slightly to the right, but that is only a small change when compared to the Bohr effect. It is the reduction in pH that produces the main shift.

Changes in pH anywhere in the body can be dangerous if they get out of hand; consequently this is a phenomenon that requires careful monitoring. A slight change in pH is acceptable if it is localized, but any significant pH alterations that might get out of control cannot be allowed. Careful regulation of local pH changes is therefore a necessity, and control must be precise, yet it must not be overdone. There are two important considerations. The number of hydrogen ions must not be permitted to increase in an uncontrolled manner, but at the same time there have to be enough around to produce the necessary shift in pH. Clearly, then, all the protons that *are* released must be kept in a small area, and after they have produced the pH shift, they must be carefully and quickly gathered up so as to keep the pH change from running wild. Here's how it is done.

Any time a cell is called upon to work hard, it needs lots of energy, and hence it will be grinding out a lot of CO_2. When this CO_2 is released by the hard-working tissue cells, it diffuses quite rapidly into the surrounding interstitial fluids, and from there it slips easily into the blood plasma. Because of its high solubility in water, it starts to spread quickly through the matrix of the plasma, but as it happens, it doesn't go very far. Rushing through the plasma, it brushes against the erythrocytes, and suddenly its rampant spreading slows. Instead of quickly establishing an equilibrium between plasma and RBC interior, then moving on, large numbers of CO_2 molecules begin to enter these cells at a high rate of speed. Lacking any kind of braking effect, they continue to pour in almost as if the RBCs were tiny vacuum cleaners designed to sweep up CO_2 molecules. In a way, that's not too far from right. The erythrocytes can accept large quantities of CO_2 because as soon as the compound gets inside, it is rapidly converted to something else.

Red blood cells contain an enzyme that is not present in the plasma, an enzyme called **carbonic anhydrase.** It is the activity of this enzyme that makes it possible for the RBCs to accept so much CO_2. Carbonic anhydrase speeds up the normally slow reaction between CO_2 and water, and the result is a rapid formation of carbonic acid within the confines of the RBC cytosol (figure 14.33). Since there is no equilibrium forming to put the brakes on the entering CO_2, it continues to rush into the RBCs, and H_2CO_3 begins to pile up.

In aqueous solution, however, H_2CO_3 is not a particularly stable compound, and it begins to quickly dissociate into hydrogen ions and bicarbonate ions. Thus it is here, in the restricted volume of the erythrocyte, right next to the molecules of hemoglobin, where the extra CO_2 generated by working cells produces the Bohr effect.

As the H_2CO_3 dissociates, it releases small, carefully monitored quantities of hydrogen ions (H^+), and these hydrogen ions, in their turn, reduce the pH locally, thus producing the Bohr effect. As the oxyhemoglobin dissociation curves shift to the right, the hemoglobin responds by unloading extra oxygen, and simultaneously, before the hydrogen ions can accumulate or sneak out of the cell into the plasma, they are drawn into chemical combination with the hemoglobin, thus eliminating the possibility of a drastic change in erythrocyte pH.

Nature shows us some wonderful regulatory mechanisms and biochemical techniques when we finally gain enough knowledge to understand them. This is a prime example of her work. The Bohr effect is an important physiological adjustment to increased *local* need for oxygen, but lowering plasma or interstitial pH sufficiently to produce such an effect could be disastrous. Nature solves both problems by restricting the effect to the interior of each erythrocyte. Placing the carbonic anhydrase within the erythrocyte means that hydrogen ions will appear and lower the pH *inside the cell,* right next to the hemoglobin, where the Bohr effect can produce maximal results. The mechanisms adjusting to increased need for oxygen are thus highly sensitive to increased tissue production of CO_2, while the unusual acidity caused by this extra CO_2 is a minor, local event that takes place in a small volume of cellular cytosol.

Simultaneously with the release of the extra oxygen, hemoglobin prevents an accumulation of H^+ ions by combining with, and thus removing, them. The two operations are, in fact, a single process and the fact that hemoglobin itself combines with the hydrogen ions means that each red blood cell, as it passes by an unusually active tissue, is able to accomplish two things. It can respond individually to the need for extra oxygen, and simultaneously it can eliminate the extra hydrogen ions. This means that neither the interstitial fluid around these active tissues nor the plasma that rushes by in the capillaries is affected by a drastic change in pH, and the Bohr effect, which is designed to alter hemoglobin, operates only within the erythrocyte. At the same time, removal of the free hydrogen ions puts a period to the Bohr effect, eliminating the acid condition that might maintain it.

The third modification of the hemoglobin/oxygen affinity is accomplished by a compound known as 2,3-diphosphoglycerate (2,3-DPG). This compound is

Figure 14.33 An example of a localized homeostatic system. CO_2 produced by unusually active cells diffuses into the blood. In the plasma, there is some conversion to carbonic acid (H_2CO_3), but the process is slow, and very little is produced. Much of the CO_2 diffuses into blood cells, where the enzyme *carbonic anhydrase* accelerates H_2CO_3 production and its breakdown into H^+ and HCO_3^-. Inside the cell, the increased H^+ concentration exists long enough to produce the Bohr effect, and then most H^+ is captured by hemoglobin. The HCO_3^- diffuses into the plasma, where it stays until it is removed in the lungs.

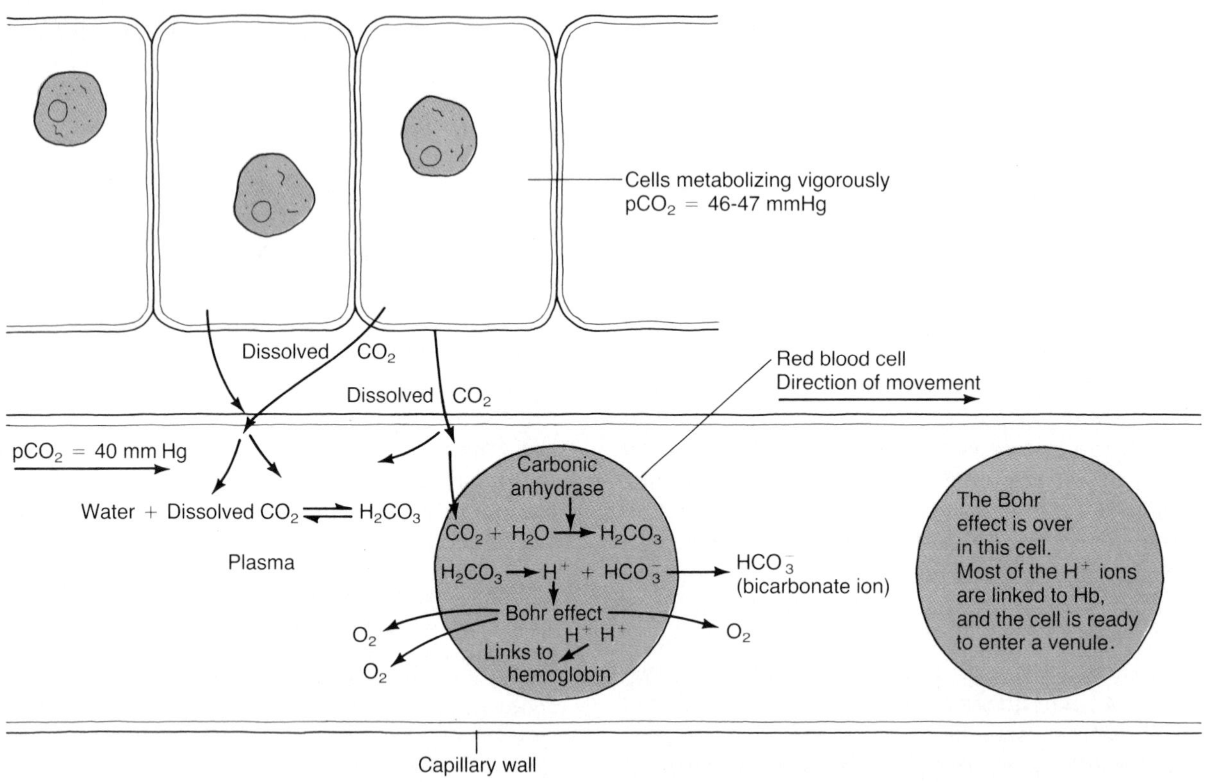

normally present within erythrocytes in high concentrations, and each mole of nonoxygenated hemoglobin (deoxyhemoglobin, Hb) is bound to a mole of 2,3-DPG according to the reaction:

$$HbO_2 + 2,3\text{-DPG} \rightarrow Hb\text{-}2,3\text{-DPG} + O_2$$

When the concentration of 2,3-DPG is reduced, the equilibrium in the above equation shifts to the left; hence the affinity of hemoglobin for oxygen increases as 2,3-DPG disappears. Although the factors involved in changing levels of 2,3-DPG are incompletely known, it *is* clear that the concentration of 2,3-DPG increases when the pH goes up and decreases when the pH goes down. Thus its alterations would tend to support the results of the Bohr effect.

Two, three-DPG is synthesized from 1,3-diphosphoglycerate during normal operations of the anaerobic metabolic pathway present in all body cells (figure 14.34).

Fetal Hemoglobin

There is yet another chapter to the intrinsic homeostatic precautions the respiratory pigment has taken to avoid upsetting body tolerances. In pregnant women, the fetus occupies a unique physiological position for a variety of reasons, many not connected with respiration. However, as far as respiration is concerned, the fetus has the potential to represent a tremendous ventilation problem for the mother. It must be able to obtain enough oxygen for its own metabolic needs, yet it must be able to do so without seriously depleting the maternal supply or placing undue stress on circulatory and respiratory systems. At first glance, the problem seems insoluble, but it is not. The solution consisted of once again manipulating the same hemoglobin dissociation curves . . . this time in a direction opposite to the Bohr effect (figure 14.35).

As figure 14.35 indicates, fetal hemoglobin has a much greater affinity for oxygen than does adult Hb. At a pO_2 of 40 mm Hg (the average resting tissue pO_2), the fetal hemoglobin can be saturated to almost 97 percent capacity, which is as much as adult hemoglobin ever gets. Saturated to a normal level, fetal blood is thus able to deliver all necessary oxygen to its developing tissues, and at the same time, the mother suffers no ill effects. Passing blood through the fetal circulation, instead of being an insurmountable load, is the rough equivalent of passing it through an extra body organ.

Figure 14.34 The biosynthesis of 2,3-diphosphoglycerate.

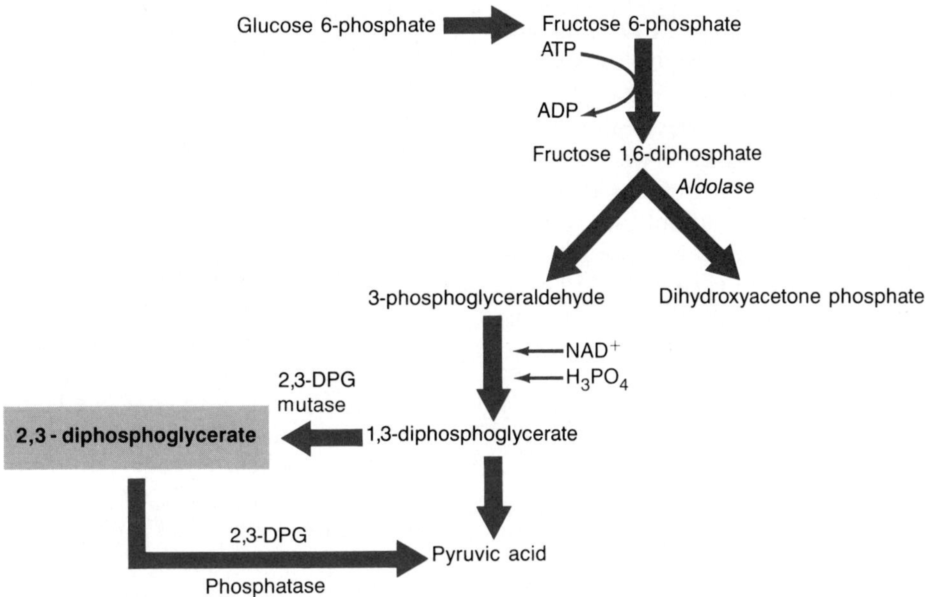

Figure 14.35 The hemoglobin/oxygen dissociation curve of a fetus compared to an adult curve.

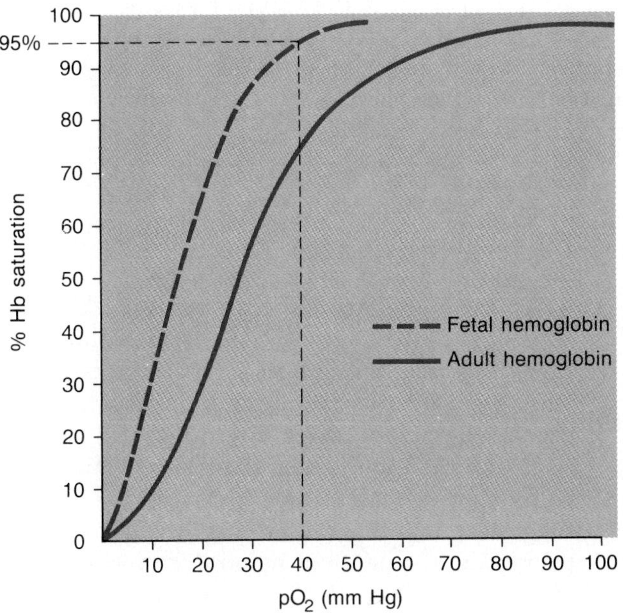

Carbon Dioxide

The hydrogen ions are picked up by the Hb and thus removed from the intracellular fluid, but as figure 14.33 shows, hydrogen ions are not the only ions released when H_2CO_3 dissociates. What about the other ion produced—what happens to the bicarbonate? The bicarbonate ions are produced within the tiny volume of the red blood cells, and since nothing inside the cell combines with them, they rapidly become concentrated there. Following the laws of diffusion, they promptly start to leave the cell in response to the gradient. Each one that leaves, however, means the loss of a negative ion from the cell and so threatens to upset the membrane potential. To prevent this problem from occurring and to retain adequate internal negativity, chloride ions in the plasma around the cell move into the cellular interior—a phenomenon known as the **chloride shift.** The bicarbonate, meanwhile, is in the plasma, where it forms an equilibrium with the carbonic acid that is present and also with the dissolved CO_2 and water. Most of the CO_2 present in our blood and body fluids is in this form—bicarbonate (figure 14.36).

Figure 14.36 As bicarbonate ions (HCO_3^-) diffuse out of the red blood cell, chloride ions (Cl^-) from the plasma diffuse into the cell, thus maintaining the electrical balance between ions. This exchange of ions is called the chloride shift.

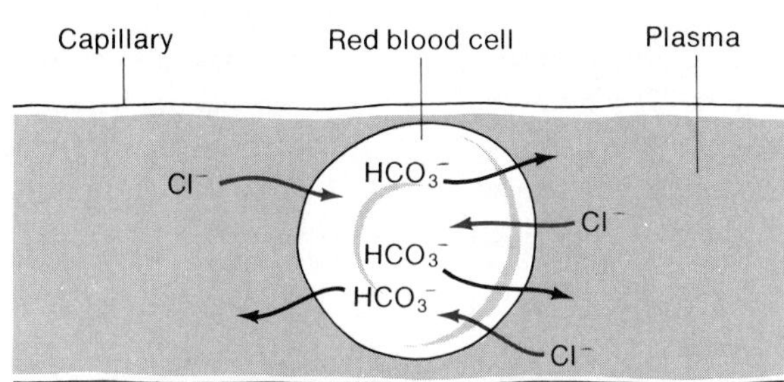

Carbon dioxide is both an essential ion and a waste product. It is a by-product of intracellular respiration; hence as long as our body cells are alive there is going to be a constant production of CO_2. The fact that the pCO_2 inside the cells stays pretty steady is a firm indication of just how quickly it is removed. Despite its constant evolution, the intracellular pCO_2 seldom rises above 46 mm Hg, which is only about 1 mm Hg greater than the pCO_2 of the interstitial fluids. That is not much of a diffusion gradient, but carbon dioxide is so soluble in water that it does not require much of a gradient to diffuse fairly rapidly. In any case, it is obvious that the difference between 46 mm Hg and 45 mm Hg is quite sufficient to remove it quickly from the cytosol.

Once in the interstitial fluid, it promptly enters the blood, again following the concentration gradient. Some combines with hemoglobin to form carboxyhemoglobin, but only about 20 percent of the CO_2 in the blood is carried in this fashion. Most is carried in the form of the bicarbonate ion, which, as we know, is a product of the following equilibria:

$$HCO_3^- + H^+ \leftrightarrow H_2CO_3 \leftrightarrow CO_2 + H_2O$$

In venous blood, when it leaves the tissue spaces, the pCO_2 is on the order of 45 mm Hg. While it is travelling in the veins it stays pretty much the same, but in the lung capillaries, things change. In alveolar gas, pCO_2 is seldom higher than 40 mm Hg, and this provides a new gradient for CO_2 to coast down. Since the pCO_2 in the alveoli is the low end of the grade, there is a general movement of carbon dioxide from the plasma into the alveoli. With CO_2 diffusing out of the plasma, the following equilibrium is upset:

$$H_2CO_3 \leftrightarrow CO_2 + H_2O$$

In order to maintain that equilibrium, some of the H_2CO_3 must break apart into CO_2 and water, and when it does, it upsets the other equilibrium:

$$HCO_3^- + H^+ \leftrightarrow H_2CO_3$$

To replenish the lost H_2CO_3, some of the free hydrogen ions must combine with the bicarbonate ions, and that is what happens. These shifts occur very rapidly, and by the time the blood leaves the lung capillaries and enters the pulmonary venules, the loss of CO_2 to the lungs has reduced the partial pressure of dissolved carbon dioxide in the blood to 40 mm Hg, and a considerable quantity of the bicarbonate has been converted to CO_2 and expelled (figure 14.37).

Control of Ventilation

The Roman physician Galen wrote sometime in the second century A.D. that when he cut the spinal cord of an animal up near its brain, breathing stopped instantly. Since that time it has been clear that the center controlling breathing is located in the brain somewhere near the spinal cord. Subsequent investigation has shown that it is the brain *stem* just above the spinal cord that is most deeply involved in reflex control of breathing. Everything— the sensors and the integrators—is there, in the medulla and pons (figure 14.38).

The **medullary rhythmicity area** (MRA) or **medullary center** features two different types of neurons that apparently fire alternating bursts of action potentials. This suggests that one is involved in stimulating *inspiration* and the other, *expiration*. Like the S-A node of the heart, it seems this center is responsible for establishing a basic rate—although in this case, the rhythm is not what a physician would consider "normal." When the medullary center is controlling breathing all by itself, the result is a kind of exaggerated resting respiration—short inspirations followed by prolonged, relaxed expiration—and that is abnormal. Apparently, in order for respiration to follow what is considered "normal" patterns, neural connections between the medullary center and some of the higher centers in the brain have got to be intact.

The respiratory control areas line up in the brain stem as shown in figure 14.38. Each has been carefully investigated, and the results of the many experiments show clearly:

1. Without an intact medullary center, there is no breathing at all.
2. The medullary center, when isolated, produces the abnormal pattern described above.
3. When the medullary center is connected to the **apneustic center** (figure 14.38), the result is very deep breaths and a slow breathing rate, but correct alveolar pO_2 is maintained.
4. When the **pneumotaxic center** (figure 14.38) is also connected to the medullary center, tidal volume decreases and breathing rate goes up, suggesting that this center is involved in restraining the depth of inspiration and increasing the rate. Again, correct alveolar pO_2 is maintained.

These results stimulated three important conclusions:

1. The adjustments in breathing are being made in response to body demands.
2. The part of the brainstem called the **medulla** is involved in these adjustments.

Figure 14.37 The shifting of equilibria from bicarbonate and hydrogen ions to CO_2 and water permits carbon dioxide to leave the blood and enter the alveolar air.

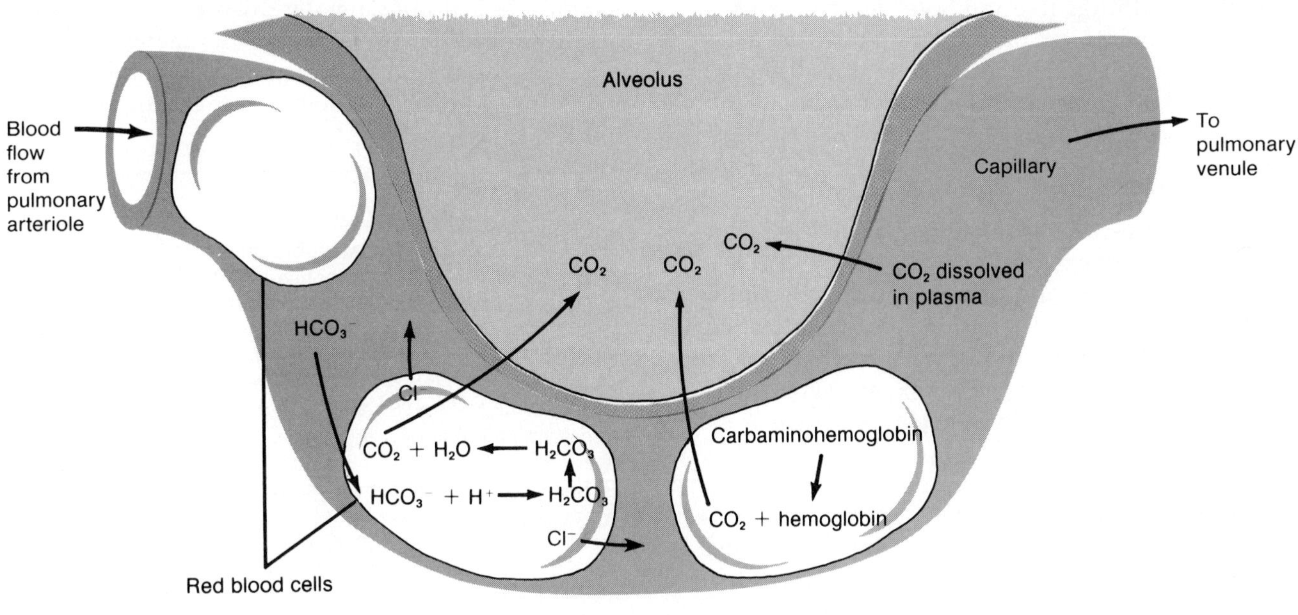

Figure 14.38 The respiratory control centers in the brain stem. (*a*) A longitudinal section through the pons and medulla. (*b*) The approximate location of these centers with respect to the rest of the brain.

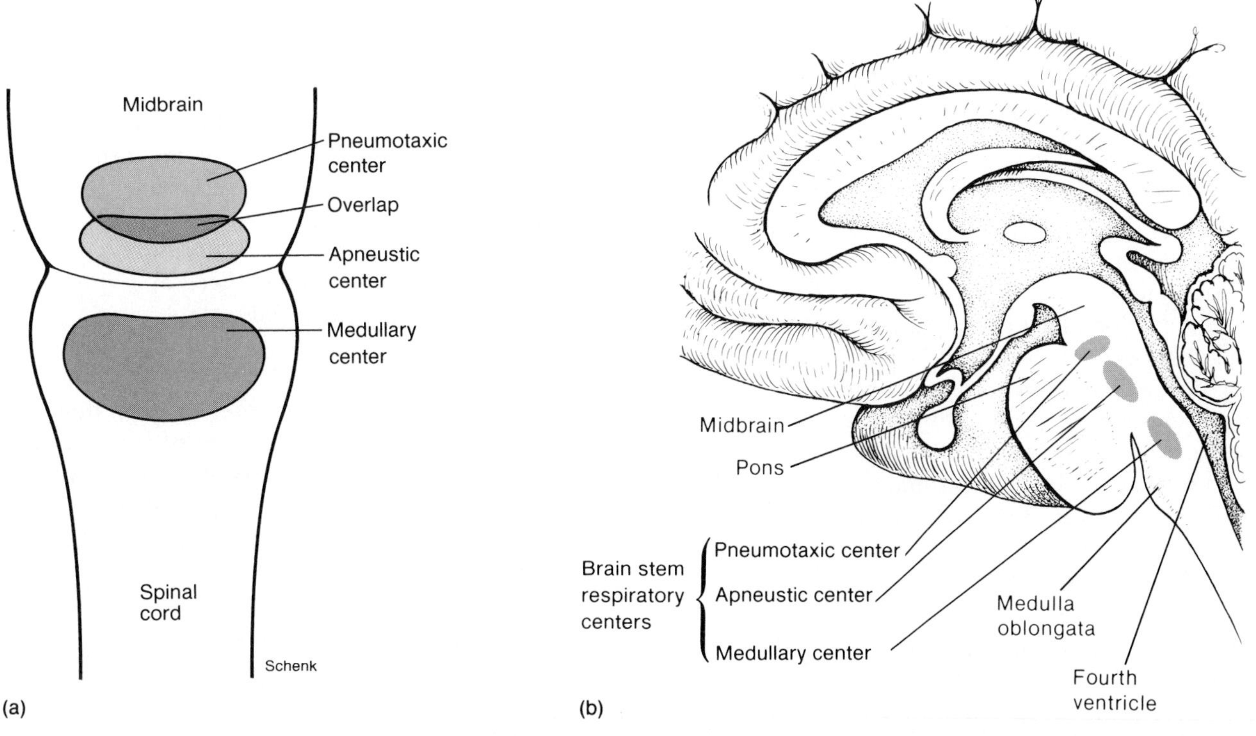

3. Since alveolar pO_2 is maintained in each case despite unusual variations in breathing depth, the controlling stimulus is not likely to be a lung stretch receptor. The centers must be monitoring either alveolar gases or chemical changes in the blood—and of the two, the more likely one is blood chemistry.

This latter hypothesis has turned out to be correct.

Ventilation Adjustments

The homeostatic adjustments accomplished by the hemoglobin—things like the Bohr effect—are small adjustments involving organic molecules in a homeostatic microcosm. These are not profound enough to control whole body responses. Everyone knows that when you exercise vigorously, your body requires extra oxygen, and you respond by breathing faster and more deeply. These responses are gross responses, and they occur because there is an urgent need throughout the body for extra oxygen.

The big question, of course, is why does breathing accelerate? And this big question spawns a cluster of subordinate, related questions: What mechanisms are involved in sensing the need for oxygen? Is the feedback loop a positive one or a negative one? Is it endocrine or neural?

Some answers can be deduced from things we already know. It was confirmed long ago that breathing is a homeostatic response. Along with the blood that pours through lung capillaries, it is one of the things that contributes to the maintenance of pO_2 and pCO_2 in the alveoli of the lungs. As blood removes oxygen, breathing replenishes it, and these two activities strive very hard to strike a balance that keeps things within limits in the alveoli. The fact that alveolar pO_2 hardly ever varies is a clear indication of success; each is regulated with respect to the other. When the blood is removing extra oxygen, breathing must increase—and of course, it must decrease when tissue oxygen demand is reduced. But how does the system know when the pO_2 of alveolar air is dropping or CO_2 is going up?

Hemoglobin's characteristics permit a homeostatic response to things like temperature increase and increased acidity, but these responses are, as we have seen, strictly local changes and are designed to handle small, local oxygen demands. When huge volumes of body tissue require extra oxygen, small adjustments are not enough; total blood flow through the tissues must increase to satisfy the demand. As blood gradually accelerates in the systemic blood vessels, it rushes with increased velocity through the lung capillaries, withdrawing oxygen and dumping off carbon dioxide at an increased rate. To maintain proper alveolar gas pressure, breathing must increase too. But where is the trigger? Is it a lowering of blood oxygen that produces this response?

Considering how crucial the gathering of oxygen is to living systems, that suggestion certainly seems reasonable, but as it turns out, lowered oxygen is *not* the trigger. Instead of oxygen, the body apparently is most sensitive to the concentration of carbon dioxide in the blood.

The Carbon Dioxide Trigger

No one is completely sure why CO_2 instead of oxygen is monitored, although many theories have been advanced. But for us, it really does not matter, because whatever the reason may turn out to be, the fact remains that when CO_2 levels rise, breathing rate and depth increase.

The most logical hypothesis suggests that since oxygen is so abundant in air, it is seldom likely to be lacking in the blood; hence an oxygen response might not be sensitive enough. Carbon dioxide, on the other hand, often takes a long time to disperse in the atmosphere, and if an individual is in a closed environment and in danger of smothering, the fastest and most sensitive indication of danger would be an increase in carbon dioxide, not a depreciation in the oxygen supply. The physiology of water-breathing animals tends to confirm this hypothesis. Fishes live in a medium in which the reverse is true. In water, oxygen is not abundant; as you will undoubtedly recall, it is not very soluble. Carbon dioxide, on the other hand, is very soluble and diffuses very rapidly through aqueous systems. Getting rid of carbon dioxide is not the problem in water that it is in air, and a carbon dioxide mechanism would not be very sensitive. Hence, it would make more sense for fishes to monitor oxygen, and that is exactly what they do. Their respiratory centers are most sensitive to oxygen lack, not carbon dioxide increases.

Experiments have indicated that the sensors are not in any of the respiratory centers of the brain stem, although they are nearby. On the ventral surface of the medulla, exposed directly to the cerebrospinal fluid and not far from the medullary center, several spots have been located that are extremely sensitive to increased levels of dissolved CO_2, and there are rich neural connections between these and the respiratory centers (see figure 14.38*b*).

The Cerebrospinal Fluid

Any elevation of CO_2 in the cerebrospinal fluid (CSF) around these brain stem centers results in an increase in both rate and depth of breathing. As we have seen, elevated CO_2 levels in the blood produce both bicarbonate ions and hydrogen ions, but hydrogen ions cannot cross the blood/brain barrier; hence they cannot produce any direct central response. However, the CO_2 in the blood can enter the CSF. Once there, it lowers the pH of the CSF just as it does in the blood, through the formation of carbonic acid and the subsequent release of H+ ions. But there is no hemoglobin in the CSF, and without hemoglobin present to pick up stray hydrogen ions, the decrease in CSF pH can become far more pronounced than is possible in the blood. The result is a powerful change in the activity of the respiratory centers. Both rate and depth become more profound, and the increased rate

Figure 14.39 The CO_2 and pH feedback loop controlling ventilation. This is a typical negative feedback homeostatic loop. Changes in blood CO_2 are transferred by diffusion to the CSF, and these changes are picked up by sensors on the medullary surface. This information is relayed to the respiratory centers for integration. If action is necessary, instructions are sent to the ventilation controls (effectors). Changes in ventilation alter alveolar pCO_2, which in turn changes blood pCO_2, which is promptly felt in the CSF.

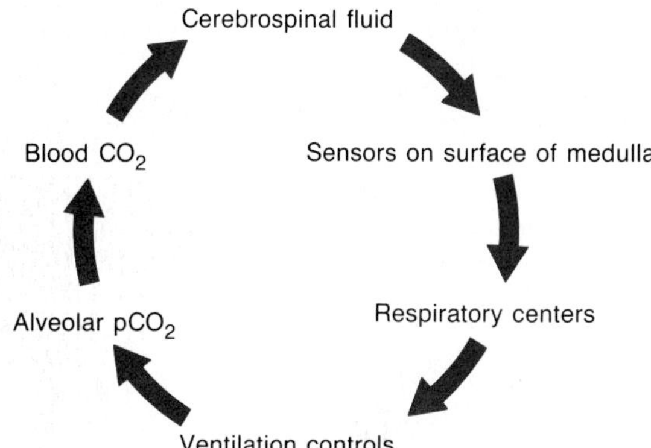

Figure 14.40 A schematic representation of the central nervous respiratory control loops.

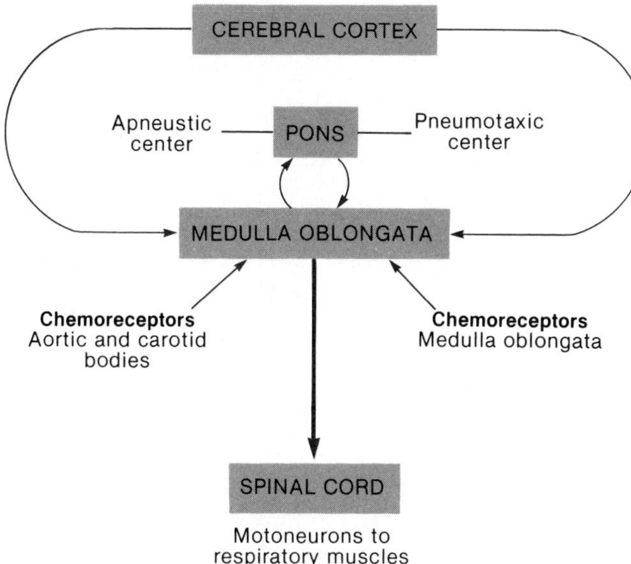

and depth of ventilation blows off CO_2. As the arterial pCO_2 drops, it undergoes depletion in the CSF, and as the pH in the CSF begins to rise, ventilation slowly returns to a rate closer to normal (figures 14.39 and 14.40).

The dominance of the CO_2 sensor response is most prominently exemplified by hikers wandering through mountainous zones in any high mountains, as, for instance, our Sierra Nevada or Rocky Mountain ranges. In altitudes greater than 12,000 feet, people often experience altitude sickness, and when it strikes, there is really nothing one can do except sit down and breathe more deeply and rapidly. After four or five minutes of increased ventilation, one usually feels much better and can continue hiking—until the hiker forgets to maintain the increased ventilation rate and starts to feel sick again. Increasing respiratory rate just a little is enough to offset the illness, and it is reasonable to ask why normal body reflexes do not handle the job so the hiker does not have to keep concentrating on it. At this point, we all should know the answer. Our primary ventilation reflex is controlled by varying levels of CO_2 and in order to produce an increase in ventilation, the blood CO_2 levels must go up. However, at 12,000 feet altitude, the pCO_2 is just as much below normal as is pO_2 and blood levels of CO_2 do not go up as they should. Since our secondary responses to reduced O_2 often do not kick in until we are rendered unconscious, they are of no help in a case like this.

Oxygen Sensors

As I have said, the human body tends to be remarkably indifferent to oxygen levels in the blood. The oxygen content of our inhaled gases could be reduced by half without any significant respiratory response in the average person. Experiments have shown that O_2 in our respired air can drop from 21 percent to less than 10 percent without our breathing rate changing at all. That means a person could pass out from lack of oxygen without eliciting any response from our respiratory control centers. The body does not totally ignore an oxygen dearth, however. Should the oxygen content of respired gases drop to 7 or 8 percent, there is a noticeable increase in both the rate and depth of respiration in the average person, indicating that oxygen is monitored . . . it is just not monitored with a high degree of sensitivity.

There are several receptor groups that are designed to detect changes in levels of blood O_2 and to send this information on to the respiratory centers.

The **carotid bodies** are present in both of the common carotid arteries at the point where they split into the internal and external carotids. A second group of sensors—the **aortic bodies**—is a little closer to the heart, on the inner surface of the aorta (figure 14.41). These peripheral chemoreceptors respond when the pO_2 of the blood inside their parent vessels is lower than normal, and they can produce nervous impulses that result in an increased ventilation rate. Cranial nerves IX and X (the glossopharyngeal and the vagus) carry the information from these bodies into the medulla, where it is monitored and integrated and proper responses are produced (figure 14.40).

Other Ventilation Controls

The importance of respiration is well illustrated by the number of overlapping controls that are present in the body to insure that this particular function works optimally all the time. The miniature controls

Figure 14.41 The peripheral oxygen-monitoring chemoreceptors, the aortic and carotid bodies, regulate the brain stem respiratory centers.

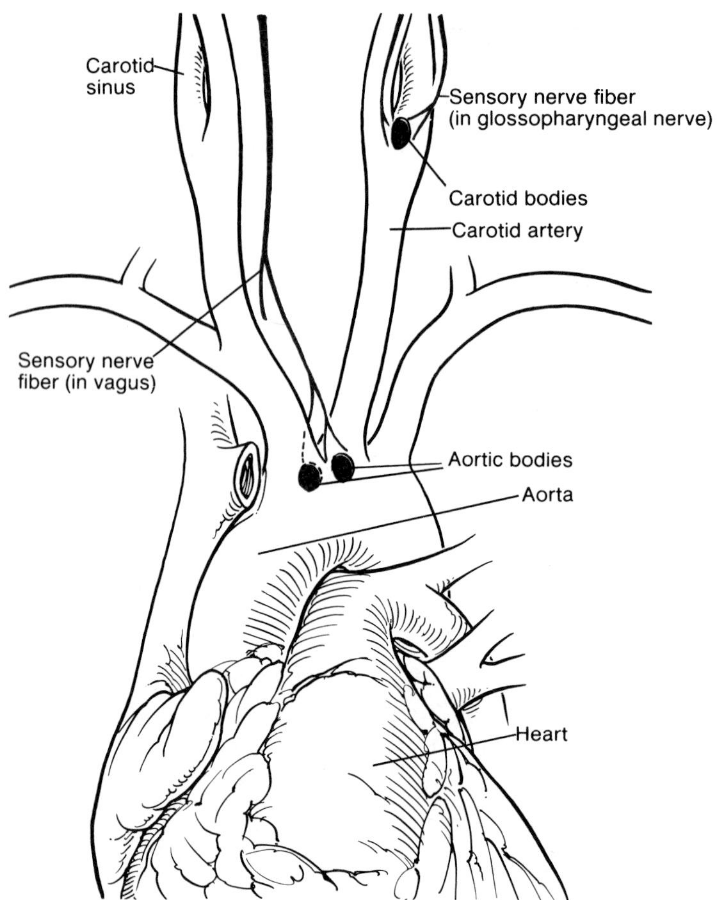

built into the respiratory pigment and the central nervous controls that respond to systemic changes in blood content are sensitive and able to respond to improper gas levels within seconds; yet the body leaves nothing to chance. In addition to these chemoresponsive control loops, there are others within the ventilation system of the thorax. Some of these are chemoreceptors and others monitor mechanical changes in the lungs.

Irritant Receptors

There are various kinds of receptors scattered throughout the respiratory tree, both within the lungs and above them. Most of these are called **irritant receptors.** These are receptors that are designed to detect the presence of unwanted, possibly dangerous, particles and to stimulate respiratory alterations that can get rid of them. Mechano-irritant receptors are most abundant in the upper reaches of the tree, mainly in the nasal passages and the trachea. When a foreign object accidently enters the nasal passages, "tickle" receptors detect its presence and respond with a sneeze reflex. When some foreign object enters the upper portion of the respiratory tract from the mouth (goes down the "wrong way") touch receptors in the trachea and pharynx detect its presence and stimulate a cough reflex to blow the offending particle out. As we descend further down into the respiratory tree, mechanoreceptors become scarcer and chemo-irritant receptors begin to rapidly increase in number. Finally, within the lungs, chemo-irritant receptors are the only kind present. These latter are designed to sense the presence of noxious chemicals in the gases entering the lungs, things like smoke or other irritating gases, and to respond with bronchiolar constriction and cough reflexes.

The Hering-Breuer Reflex

Within the walls of the bronchioles or the smaller bronchi, there are stretch receptors designed to monitor lung inflation. As early as 1868, two pioneer physiologists named Hering and Breuer were able to conclude that human lungs contained sensors that appraise lung expansion and send their information into the brain. The impulses are carried along the vagus nerve, and if the brain's assessment of this information indicates that expansion is becoming excessive, instructions can be sent that will stop inspiration and induce the person to breathe out. The feedback loop is known in medical circles as the **Hering-Breuer reflex,** and its significance in humans is not clear.

It seems that the problem is a relatively new one, and it involves our basic ventilation control centers.

The inspiratory center (figure 14.38) has a basic discharge rhythm that is sent along motor nerves to the muscles of the thorax, producing inspiration. This rhythm continues unabated until it is overwhelmed by inhibitory impulses from the expiratory center, at which point inspiratory impulses stop and passive expiration occurs. The inhibitory impulses arise in the apneustic center and are transmitted to the expiratory center, where they produce gradually increasing activity that finally restrains inspiration. Since the stretch receptors involved in the Hering-Breuer reflex send their impulses into the apneustic center, it was once believed that this reflex was responsible for maintaining normal breathing patterns.

Recent experiments, however, suggest that this is not the case. It seems that the impulses entering the apneustic center from the lung receptors do not achieve any significant degree of intensity until the lungs are stretched to the point where possible damage might occur. Current theory holds that the Hering-Breuer reflex is most likely involved in gauging lung expansion and cutting off inspiratory activity when it appears possible that continued inflation might cause damage.

Clinical Considerations

Some Terminology

Clinicians routinely use a few terms that should probably be introduced in this section because they are often used in describing signs and symptoms of patients with pulmonary problems. They are:

1. **Eupnea:** This is normal breathing.
2. **Apnea:** This is a lack of breathing. A person suffering from apnea is not breathing at all.
3. **Dyspnea:** This refers to a lot of respiratory variations. In addition to breathlessness or shortness of breath, it encompasses things like the heavy breathing that follows a 100-meter dash and also forced or labored breathing such as one might expect from a person who is strangling. Any unusual breathing, any respiratory movements that deviate from normal, fall under the heading of dyspnea.
4. **Orthopnea:** This is a kind of dyspnea that occurs when one is lying down and disappears when one sits up.
5. **Hyperpnea:** This is also a form of dyspnea. It is the kind of heavy breathing one experiences after heavy, prolonged exercise—deeper than normal breaths at a higher frequency than is normal.
6. **Hyperventilation:** This term refers to the same kind of breathing as hyperpnea, but its meaning is rather different. Hyperpnea refers to unusually heavy breathing caused by the body's demands, and hence is a reflex of involuntary origin. Hyperventilation generally refers to a voluntary increase in respiratory rate and depth.

Some Measurements

Ventilation can be measured in several ways. One is known as **respiratory rate,** which is, logically enough, the number of breaths a person takes each minute. Another is **minute volume,** which is the total volume of air moved into and out of the lungs during a single minute. It is calculated by multiplying the respiratory rate by the tidal volume. For instance, a person taking fourteen breaths per minute and having a tidal volume of 500 ml would have a minute volume of $500 \times 14 = 7{,}000$ ml. This person's **ventilation rate**—a third measurement—is the minute volume minus the dead space exchange. Dead space exchange is calculated by multiplying respiratory rate by the dead space volume ($14 \times 150 = 2{,}100$), so a person like the one quoted above, with a minute volume of seven liters, would have an actual ventilation rate of about five liters per minute. All these volumes are utilized in medical practice to calculate how much anesthetic to administer and to diagnose respiratory disorders.

The values quoted in the measurements section are all approximately normal values for an average human while at rest. During vigorous exercise, respiratory rates can increase to astonishing levels. It is not at all unusual for a person having just undertaken a 100-meter dash to breathe at fifty to sixty breaths per minute for a while. In addition, the depth of respiration is almost always significantly increased, sometimes producing tidal volumes as great as five liters. At such a rate and depth, a person's minute volume could be as much as 150 liters and his or her ventilation rate as high as 140 liters per minute.

Respiratory Disease

So many diseases can afflict the body's ventilation mechanisms that respiratory disease constitutes an entire residence specialty in medical practice. Hence any comprehensive treatment is way beyond the scope of this book. There are, however, some afflictions that one hears about constantly—particularly in the advertising media and particularly involving efforts to sell a product or to attract donations. I will attempt to deal with a few of the more familiar ones.

Infectious Diseases

Colds The disease known as the common cold is an acute infection of the upper respiratory tract—specifically, the conchae, pharynx, and upper trachea. The term *cold* originated from the mistaken idea that the disease followed exposure to cold—usually wet cold. It has been fairly well established that this, all by itself, will not cause a cold. Just exactly what does increase a person's susceptibility to the common cold is not clear. It may involve excessive fatigue or some sort of nasopharyngeal allergy . . . even depression has been associated with increased susceptibility. Colds are believed to be caused by a group of viruses known as *rhinoviruses,* of which there are apparently many strains. Immunity is almost impossible to develop when there are so many different kinds of cold viruses, because immunity is highly specific. For the same reason, vaccines against the common cold are generally useless. Young children tend to suffer from more colds than adults, probably because adults have been exposed to many more different cold viruses and have developed resistance to most of them.

The signs and symptoms of the common cold are pretty well known to us all, but one thing that seems to be generally agreed upon is that a real viral cold begins with a sore throat and spreads upward from there. The feelings of malaise and general misery along with an inability to sleep are part of the syndrome.

Unfortunately, there is not much anyone can do to make things easier for the victim. Contrary to popular belief, antibiotics, including penicillin, are worthless against viruses and have no therapeutic value in treating a cold. About the only thing that can be done is to make the patient as comfortable as possible and try to avoid spreading the disease. In this regard, there are lots of patent medicines available that are supposed to relieve the symptoms of the common cold, but they never do a tenth of what they are supposed to. Most of them—products like Dristan, Contac, Nyquil, etc., are about the same. They contain small amounts of very weak and inexpensive vasoconstrictors and a little antihistamine, but their main ingredient is aspirin. The vasoconstrictors and antihistamines are so weak or present in such small concentrations that they are generally of no value, but the aspirin works. In addition to reducing aches and pains that accompany the affliction, aspirin reduces fever and can even, sometimes, help overcome the horrid insomnia that usually accompanies a cold. Unfortunately, aspirin often increases the outpouring of infective virus from the sick person, so unless the cold sufferer is planning to stay home, he certainly does not do friends or associates any favors by taking aspirin.

The Flu Like the cold, the **flu,** or more properly, **influenza,** is primarily an acute infection of the upper respiratory tract, although it often descends into the lower respiratory areas. It is caused by a group of viruses called **myxoviruses.** Myxoviruses belong to an RNA viral group related to those that cause AIDS, and unlike the rhinoviruses, myxoviruses can be killers. It is common for practitioners to refer to nonspecific gastrointestinal or upper-respiratory infections as flu, but in point of fact, the specific disease cannot be clinically diagnosed except during epidemics. Immunity is, of course, specific, which makes production of a general antiflu vaccine almost impossible. Fortunately, however, flu epidemics, including the type of causative virus, can often be predicted and vaccines made available.

Most cases of influenza are mild. Usually they resemble a cold with a relatively high fever, incapacitate the victim for a few days, and then disappear, but this is not always true. The great influenza epidemic of 1918 killed millions of people and incapacitated millions more for months. Fortunately, this is rare. Influenza *per se* seldom kills. Deaths during an influenza epidemic are nearly always the result of complications such as bacterial pneumonia.

In mild cases of the flu, as with colds, there is little that can be done except to try to make the patient comfortable. Patent medicines have no more value than they have for colds. On the advice of a physician, antibiotics can be administered if the disease looks particularly severe, but usually it's prudent to avoid them. When they are administered, they will not help reduce the severity or duration of the influenza attack. They are intended solely to reduce the probability of serious secondary bacterial infections.

Pneumonia This is a very general term. It refers specifically to any acute infection of the tissues of the lung, and usually it refers to the alveolar tissues. There are quite a few different kinds of pneumonia and more than one microorganism that can cause it.

Viral pneumonia is more common in this country than bacterial, and fortunately it is generally milder. Sometimes it is so mild that it passes away without ever being diagnosed. Every once in a while, however, viral pneumonia is caused by a killer virus and fatalities can result, especially if the cause is an influenza virus.

Bacterial pneumonia is usually much more serious than viral, and it is our good fortune that antibiotics, if used early enough, are effective. Sometimes, however, a strain of bacteria will evolve that is resistant to all our efforts. One of the most unusual and deadly of these causes a pneumonia that has been given the picturesque name **Legionnaires' disease.** This affliction is caused by a strain of bacterium known as *Legionella pneumophila* and was not suspected as a pathogen until 1976. It was identified when it broke out among members of the American Legion who were attending a convention in Philadelphia, and it roared through their ranks, devastating members of that convention with unfettered violence. Since that outbreak, more than 1,500 cases of the disease have been reported in this country, and it has been identified in Europe, the Middle East, and even Australia. For some strange reason, it tends to occur in localized bursts that are quite unpredictable.

Legionnaires' disease is a particularly deadly form of pneumonia, and in patients who are not treated quickly and *specifically*, the mortality rate can be as high as 80 percent. Antibiotics are effective, but the right one must be used, and it must be begun early in the infection.

Aspiration Pneumonia This, as the name implies, is a lung infection that is the result of having breathed in and retained some oral, nasal, or bronchial secretion. Its retention may be due to a number of things such as intoxication, coma, anesthesia, or respiratory paralysis. Hospitals report that it can occur as often as 60 percent of the time following abdominal or thoracic surgery and 25 percent of the time after spinal or neck surgery.

Aspiration of vomitus is common in surgical recovery rooms and should be expected. Preliminary therapy in these cases is similar to that given to a drowning victim, up to and including artificial respiration. In comatose patients or patients suffering from paralytic afflictions such as botulism, the cough reflex is inhibited, and they cannot cough up any secretions that may dribble into their trachea or bronchi. Aspiratory pneumonia is particularly lethal during recovery from botulism, because skeletal muscle paralysis is so complete. Botulism is a form of food poisoning that totally incapacitates the skeletal musculature; as a result, the victim cannot move even to breathe. Patients must be maintained on a respirator until the paralysis disappears, which can sometimes take weeks.

Tuberculosis (TB, Consumption, the White Plague) One hundred years ago, this was one of the most prevalent and feared diseases in the world. It was known then as the white plague, and sanatoriums were common in rustic areas of Europe and in the mountain and western states in this country. The disease was so common, and sanatoriums so abundant, that people claimed there was at least one sanatorium outside every city in Europe. At the beginning of this century, there were an estimated 2,500,000 cases in this country, of which as many as 220,000 died every year. Yet by 1950 the number of cases had dropped to 400,000 and fatalities to 33,000 a year. In 1977, case number was down to 30,000, and fatalities to 3,000. This is an impressive record, but if you will look carefully at the figures, you will note that while the incidence of tuberculosis has dramatically decreased, the mortality rate has not . . . a disquieting statistic.

TB is primarily a pulmonary disease in which the disease, after long periods of inactivity, can suddenly flare into acute infections. Its attacks are slow and insidious. It may be present and active for as long as two years, but it progresses so gradually that it often goes unnoticed except for minor periods of respiratory discomfort or unexplained coughing. Cough is, in fact, one of the first signs, and when sputum is brought up it is usually green and loaded with pus. As the disease progresses, pain in the chest begins and episodes of high fever occur, accompanied by dyspnea. The bacteria responsible for the infection actually excavate cavities in the alveolar areas of the lung, and their attacks can harden interstitial lung zones so extensively that whole lobes frequently become rigid and inelastic. This naturally compromises the lungs' function, and the subsequent inability of the patient to achieve adequate ventilation is usually fatal.

Even our best antibiotics have a tough time with tuberculosis, and as the statistics clearly show, the disease is remarkably deadly when it takes hold. Prevention is the obvious key to controlling this killer.

Noninfectious Respiratory Diseases

Asthma A good many things that afflict the human respiratory system do not involve microorganisms of any kind. Probably the most common of these is asthma. Asthma is a chronic affliction that features periodic acute seizures that produce constriction of the smooth muscles around bronchiolar tubes and can narrow them to a point that can threaten life. Some people have only mild attacks at fairly long intervals, while others seem to be wheezing and coughing all the time. In addition to their chronic respiratory problems, these latter have acute seizures too, and when such seizures occur, they are usually severe. Exactly what causes acute attacks is uncertain. It depends on the individual victim, and even then it appears to be quite variable, ranging from exercise to psychological stress.

It is not known what causes asthma. Antihistamines cannot reduce the severity of an attack, so histamines, which are responsible for many allergies, are ruled out as a cause of asthma. Most physicians ascribe asthma to "nonspecific irritant factors" and proceed to treat the symptoms, which is probably the most sensible thing they can do.

Vasoconstrictors are quite effective in relieving much of the discomfort of an acute seizure, as are bronchodilators like isoproterenol. In between attacks, patients are usually cautioned to avoid dusty areas, household pets (especially birds), and open areas when pollen is heavy in the air.

Respiratory Problems Caused by Foreign Particles Most noninfectious pulmonary problems are the result of inhaling dusts and gases of different kinds that are produced by industry. Just how much damage an inhaled particle will do depends on a number of things.

The *physical properties* of the particle are extremely important: things like its size, shape, and how solidly it is jammed into the airways. Large particles like a fish bone usually become wedged in the upper parts of the tract—the trachea or pharynx. Smaller particles go down deeper into the respiratory tree, and those smaller than five micrometers can go all the way into the alveoli. These tiny particles are usually not detected with the explosiveness that the larger particles are; hence, they can linger where they don't belong and cause much more damage. Particles between one and two micrometers in size cause diseases like **black lung** and **silicosis,** both of which used to be, and still are, chronic, debilitating, and often fatal. Small **asbestos** fibers have tremendous penetrability . . . they can get right into the membranes that line the alveoli, and when they do, as often as not, they produce cancerous growths there.

Chemical properties of the particles are also important, of course. Highly acid or alkaline particles are going to do obvious damage. Acids lower the pH in the watery linings of the alveoli, and the lung membranes usually respond by attempting to reduce the acidity by diluting it. This often works if the particles are not too abundant and the condition is not chronic. However, if the particles are numerous, the secretory surfaces will sometimes pour so much fluid into the lungs that victims can drown in their own body fluids.

Even those who work out in the country, well away from the city's atmospheric pollution, are not free of noninfectious pulmonary problems. In the country, organic materials cause most of the problems. Organic particles are much less likely to produce respiratory difficulties than inorganic, industrial pollutants are, but they sometimes do just the same. Things like irritant vapors or water-soluble organic compounds can, if they are inhaled often enough over extended periods of time, produce some pretty nasty pulmonary allergic reactions. It is not at all unusual for people who bale hay, or workers in chicken coops, grain elevators, animal breeding pens, and pet shops to come down sooner or later with a lung inflammation. These inflammations are often precipitated by an allergic response to some organic compound that was repeatedly inhaled while they were working.

Farmer's lung, for example, is caused by inhaling hay dust, and it can produce heavy inflammation of the lung tissue. Woodcutters in redwood forests on the west coast have, on occasion, suffered from an affliction called **sequoiosis,** which is a pulmonary inflammation caused by moldy redwood sawdust. Even nearly total isolation from civilization does not render one invulnerable to this kind of affliction. **Maple bark disease** is a result of merely being near maple trees that contain a mold spore called *Cryptostroma.*

These afflictions are usually mild and transient, but they can be very serious. Antibiotics are of no value, since there is no infection present, although it seems like there should be. The symptoms include such things as dyspnea, fever, chills, and a miserable, hacking cough. To make matters maximally bad, all these symptoms tend to hang on in all their unpleasant ramifications until the cause of the problem is found and discarded. Sometimes the cause is never found, and in cases like that, pulmonary allergies can produce respiratory failure and death.

Smoking Considering the tremendous number of respiratory problems that are just waiting to jump on some unwary lung or bronchiolar tree, you have to ask yourself why anyone would want to increase the chances of catching one. Nevertheless, that is what cigarette smokers are doing.

It has been said that if we encountered a drug that cured the common cold but had the unpleasant side effects possessed by tobacco smoking, it would be banned. Most Americans are well aware of the dangers presented by use of tobacco, yet they persist in using it nevertheless. Smoke from tobacco contains myriad dust particles as well as minute droplets of a lipid called *tar.*

Cigarette smoke is not as strong as the smoke produced by cigars or good pipe tobacco; hence it must be inhaled for the smoker to appreciate the slight euphoria that it produces. This means its harmful components are presented chronically to the absorptive surfaces of the lungs. The tars are known carcinogens, meaning that they can initiate the formation of cancerous growths and can accelerate the growth of those already present. The dry particles in tobacco smoke include dozens of irritants capable of producing racking coughs. In addition, these particles can inhibit the cleansing activity of the mucus and cilia on the cells of the bronchi and bronchioles. They begin by deactivating alveolar cells, then they deactivate whole alveoli, and ultimately, whole clusters of alveoli cease to function. This process often continues until the lungs function at as little as 50 percent of their original capacity. **Nicotine,** which is the main reason for the euphoric feeling offered by tobacco smoke, has less effect on the lungs. It exerts its debilitating efforts mainly on circulatory structures and circulatory accessories, and it has been shown to be a primary cause of arteriosclerotic plaque formation.

The diseases that have been directly related to smoking so far include lung cancer, emphysema, hardening of the arteries, high blood pressure, and cancer of the mouth, pharynx, and trachea. There is no doubt in anyone's mind that these cause-effect conclusions are correct. Smokers do not appear to care, and certainly the tobacco industry will make no effort to reduce addiction to their weed. The attitude of the general public for years had been to leave smokers alone. If they want to reduce life expectancy, it is their lives they are affecting, hence it is their business. That attitude exists no longer. Mounting evidence indicates that passive exposure to tobacco smoke (inhaling "second-hand" smoke) may be able to trigger many of these afflictions; hence it is becoming apparent that smokers may be doing as much harm to those around them as they are doing to themselves. So a smoker becomes everyone's concern.

In the last ten years, the use of tobacco has lost a great deal of its earlier appeal, and many public buildings now forbid its use in any form, while those that permit smoking restrict it to certain areas. Yet, new smokers show up yearly—mostly among the young—junior high school and high school students. After a few years, many of them mature enough to make an effort to stop. Yet one wonders why they started in the first place.

Summary

Anatomy of the Respiratory Organs

I. The Nasal Cavity. The nasal cavity contains three fleshy lobes called conchae that increase the surface area of the cavity and help to warm and humidify the incoming air.

II. The Nasal Sinuses. These cavities serve, in humans, to reduce the weight of the skull.

III. The Trachea. This is commonly known as the windpipe. It extends from the pharynx to the middle of the chest, where it splits into the two bronchi. It is supported by cartilaginous rings to prevent the reduced pressure of inspiration from causing it to collapse.

IV. The Bronchi and Bronchioles
- A. The bronchi carry air into the lungs.
- B. Each bronchial tube is supported, as is the trachea, by cartilaginous rings.
- C. These tubes continually bifurcate, getting smaller and smaller. Finally, they are reduced in size to a point where they no longer require cartilaginous support and become bronchioles.
- D. Bronchioles are wrapped periodically by strips of smooth muscle and are thus able to contract and dilate. They terminate in blind sacs.

V. The Lungs. The blind sacs that represent the end of the respiratory tree are known as alveoli and are the exchange areas between the air and the blood.

VI. Pleural Membranes. Smooth connective tissue membranes enwrap all the respiratory organs within the thoracic cavity.

Ventilation: The Mechanics of Breathing

Skeletal muscles provide the movement necessary for breathing. The diaphragm and the external intercostal muscles, when contracted, increase the volume of the chest cavity and the lungs. Increasing chest volume reduces pressure within, and atmospheric pressure forces air into the lungs. Contraction of the internal intercostal muscles and relaxation of the diaphragm reduce the volume of the thoracic cavity, thus increasing the pressure therein. This forces air out of the lungs.

I. Pressures. Gas pressures are greatest in the atmosphere. When gases enter the lungs, they are adjusted and altered, mostly due to warming and humidifying.

II. Expansion of the Alveoli. The walls of the alveoli are extremely elastic, permitting these tissues to expand to enormous sizes.

III. Surfactant. Surfactant serves to reduce the surface tension on the inner surfaces of the alveoli. This helps avoid collapse of the alveoli after expiration.
- A. Surface Tension. The lowered surface tension on the inner surfaces of the alveoli prevents alveolar collapse.
- B. Alveolar Collapse. Reduction in the amount of surfactant can result in alveolar collapse. Alveolar collapse (called hyaline membrane disease) is the commonest cause of death in prematurely born infants.

IV. Adjustable Resistance in the Respiratory Tree. This is accomplished by contracting or relaxing the muscles surrounding the bronchioles.

V. Passive Expiration. During normal, resting respiration, expiration requires only that the person relax. No muscle contractions are needed to expire.

VI. Forced Respiratory Movements. Normally, respiratory movements are reflexly controlled. It is possible, however, to voluntarily alter reflex breathing patterns. Although gas pressures are usually constant, forced changes in breathing patterns result in changes in gas pressures within the alveolar spaces.

Respiratory Air Volumes

For the sake of convenience, the volume of air that the lungs will accept or hold under varying circumstances and conditions has been categorized.

I. Spirometry. Lung volumes are measured with an instrument known as a spirometer.

A. Total Lung Capacity. This is the total amount that the lungs will hold, including the air volume that remains in the lungs after the most forceful expiration.
B. Tidal Volume. This is the volume of air that moves reflexly into and out of the lungs.
C. Expiratory Reserve Volume. The amount of air that can be forcefully expired after a normal expiration.
D. Inspiratory Reserve Volume. The amount of air that can be forcefully inspired after a normal inspiration.
E. Vital Capacity. The amount of air that can be forcefully expired after a forceful inspiration. It is the total of tidal volume, expiratory reserve, and inspiratory reserve.
F. Residual Volume. The amount of air remaining in the lungs after a forceful expiration.
G. Dead Space. The volume of air in the respiratory tree that is not in contact with the blood.

II. Coughing and Sneezing
A. Both are reflex actions, designed to help clear unwanted materials from the respiratory tract or the lungs.
B. Yawning. The function of the yawn is not known.

III. Some Gas Laws
A. Gas is the high-energy phase of matter.
B. All gases in a mixture exert individual pressures on the whole. The amount of pressure they exert is a function of their percent composition in the gas mixture.
C. Another principle concerns how much gas will dissolve in water. The type of gas is one factor; the other is its pressure.

IV. The Significance of Water Vapor
A. Water vapor always saturates alveolar air.
B. Water vapor always produces a partial pressure of 47 mm Hg in alveolar air.
C. Only temperature changes can alter pH_2O_{vapor} in alveolar air.

Gas Movement

I. Alveolar Air. Oxygen movement in humans is determined by pressure gradients. The highest oxygen pressure is in the surrounding atmosphere; the lowest oxygen pressure is in the intracellular mitochondria. Oxygen flows, therefore, from the atmosphere toward the mitochondria.

II. Alveolar Exchange
A. Gases moving from the lung interior into the blood must first dissolve in water. The interior surface of the lungs is coated with a thin film of water, and the oxygen dissolves in this film.
B. A Problem of Solubility. Oxygen is not very soluble in water. Carbon dioxide is very soluble in water.

III. Respiratory Pigment. Because oxygen is not soluble in water, it would require nearly forty gallons of blood to carry all the oxygen a human normally needs. Since this is clearly not possible, something must be added to the blood that will handle the oxygen. This addition is the respiratory pigment hemoglobin.

IV. Hemoglobin. Hemoglobin is restricted to the interior of the red blood cells. Because hemoglobin is present, 100 ml of whole blood is capable of carrying nearly 15 ml of molecular oxygen. Hemoglobin is therefore responsible for carrying nearly all the oxygen utilized by the body.

The Hemoglobin-Oxygen Dissociation Curve

The relationship between oxygen pressure and dissolved oxygen in whole blood is not a straight line relationship. The oxyhemoglobin curve that describes the relationship is a sigmoid curve. This curve has extremely important physiological significance.

I. Intrinsic Homeostatic Mechanisms
A. Because of this relationship, hemoglobin is able to handle small homeostatic adjustments that would otherwise cause many small problems within the body.
B. Homeostatic spontaneity. All the small, local adjustments in oxygen and carbon dioxide homeostasis can be carried out within a single erythrocyte, which can handle oxygen requirement problems of individual cells, one at a time.

II. Altering Hemoglobin's Affinity for Oxygen
A. First: Lowered pH in the vicinity of hemoglobin reduces its affinity for O_2.
B. Second: Increased temperature in the vicinity of hemoglobin will reduce its affinity for O_2.
C. *A* is known as the Bohr effect.
D. Third: 2,3-diphosphoglycerate, when present, decreases hemoglobin's affinity for O_2.
E. Fetal Hemoglobin. Fetal hemoglobin has a higher affinity for O_2 than does adult hemoglobin. This permits a pregnant woman to saturate fetal hemoglobin without depleting her own systemic oxygen supplies.

III. Carbon Dioxide. Carbon dioxide decreases pH of the blood and can cause hemoglobin's affinity for O_2 to be substantially reduced.

Control of Ventilation

Nervous control of respiration rate and depth is centered in the brain stem. The pons has two of the centers, the medulla has the other.

I. Ventilation Adjustments. The respiratory control centers respond more readily to high CO_2 levels than they do to lower-than-normal O_2 pressures.

II. The Carbon Dioxide Trigger. The central receptors that monitor CO_2 levels respond to lowered pH levels in the cerebrospinal fluid (CSF).

III. Oxygen Sensors. There are chemoreceptors in the circulatory system that can stimulate respiration when oxygen levels slip dangerously low. They are not very sensitive, but they will not permit a person to die from lack of oxygen.

IV. Other Ventilation Controls
A. Irritant Receptors. Particles stuck in the airways cause sneezes or coughs. Smaller particles or irritating gases also cause coughing.
B. The Hering-Breuer Reflex. The Hering-Breuer reflex is thought to be activated when overinflation of the lungs may cause damage.

Clinical Considerations

- I. Some Terminology
- II. Some Measurements
- III. Respiratory Disease
  - A. Infectious Diseases
    1. Colds
    2. The Flu
    3. Pneumonia
    4. Aspiration Pneumonia
    5. Tuberculosis
  - B. Noninfectious Respiratory Disease
    1. Asthma
    2. Respiratory Problems Caused by Foreign Particles
    3. Smoking

Review Questions

1. What is the respiratory tree?
2. Draw a diagram of the respiratory organs and label them in as much detail as you can.
3. What are the nares? Where are they located and into what do they lead?
4. Name two functions of the nasal conchae.
5. Describe the location of the pleural membranes and suggest a function for them.
6. What are the two primary sets of muscles that are involved in breathing? Describe the activity of each and the result.
7. Describe the pressure changes that take place when the respiratory muscles are stimulated. Be sure to differentiate between pressures inside the lungs and those outside.
8. Describe the phenomenon known as surface tension. What is its significance in the process of alveolar expansion and relaxation?
9. Why are cartilaginous rings present in the trachea, bronchi, and larger bronchioles?
10. Define *compliance* and *surfactant.*
11. How is resistance to air flow adjusted in the respiratory tree? What muscles are involved?
12. List the air volumes and capacities that have been accepted as standard by clinicians.
13. What is a spirometer? Explain its function.
14. What is the significance of the residual volume and the dead space?
15. What is the significance of sneezing and coughing?
16. Outline the three major gas laws mentioned in this chapter.
17. Why is the pressure of water vapor in the lungs always constant?
18. Describe the dynamics of airflow. Be sure to list all the pressure gradients involved.
19. How is alveolar exchange effected? Discuss the forces involved and the media through which O_2 must move to arrive at the hemoglobin molecule.
20. Why is it necessary for nearly all animals to possess a respiratory pigment?
21. Outline the three separate oxygen equilibria that exist in the lungs.
22. Describe the process of unloading oxygen in the body tissues.
23. Why must oxygen dissolve in water before it can enter the blood?
24. Draw an oxyhemoglobin dissociation curve.
25. Discuss the physiological significance of the dissociation curves in terms of their ability to respond to varying cellular demands.
26. Describe the result when an increased concentration of carbon dioxide enters the interstitial fluid.
27. Define *Bohr effect.*
28. Outline three ways in which hemoglobin's affinity for oxygen can be reduced.
29. What areas of the nervous system are involved in controlling respiration?
30. Draw a diagram of the control areas in the CNS and label them to the best of your ability.
31. Describe the means by which carbon dioxide exerts its influence over these central nervous respiratory control zones.
32. Diagram the loops involved in respiratory control. Where do reduced oxygen levels add their influence? Where are the oxygen receptors located?
33. Describe the Hering-Breuer reflex. What is its significance?

Section V

Maintaining the Blood

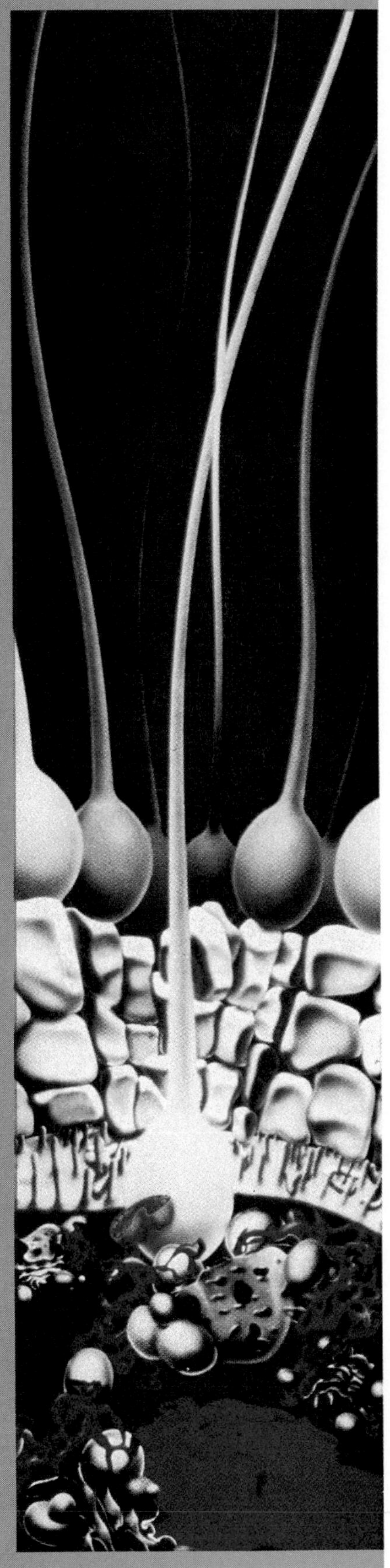

Chapter 15 The Digestive System

Study Hints

Pay particular attention to:

1. the power of the psychological aspect of "hunger" and the ability of the systemic control systems to stimulate digestive activity as a result of thinking about food.
2. the interaction of physical and chemical activities and how each contributes to the digestive process.
3. the families of digestive enzymes that are secreted. Be sure you know their limitations as well as their capabilities.
4. the pH in the various sections of the GI tract.
5. the control systems—both endocrine and neural—involved in the secretion of the various enzymes, and the stimuli that initiate their activity. Be careful about the endocrine controls. Remember that hormones are secreted into the blood and not into the lumen of the gut.
6. the specific contributions of the liver and the pancreas.
7. the specificity of absorption. While diffusion does drive some of the absorptive processes, much of it is active.

Objectives

When you have finished reading this chapter, you should:

1. be able to differentiate between the mechanical and chemical digestive processes.
2. be able to describe the role of the mouth and its secretions.
3. understand how peristalsis works and be able to explain its role in moving foodstuffs through the GI tract.
4. know why the fluid within the stomach is acid.
5. know the various things that contribute to the increased surface area of the interior of the small intestine and be able to explain how these contribute to absorption efficiency.
6. know where (in the digestive tract) the various types of enzymes are secreted.
7. know which cells synthesize the various gastrointestinal secretions and be able to explain how each contributes to digestion.
8. be able to describe the mechanisms that control secretions of the digestive and accessory digestive organs.
9. know which nutrients diffuse across the membranes of the small intestine and which are transported.
10. be able to explain how materials are moved through the lining of the small intestine and into the blood.
11. be able to describe the structure of the large intestine and explain its role in the digestive process.

A scanning electron micrograph of human intestinal mucosa.

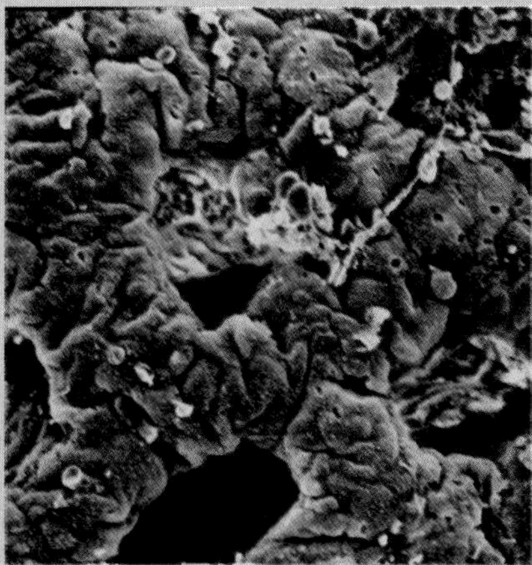

Introduction

Simplistically stated, the human digestive system has only one goal—to maintain nutritional homeostasis throughout the body. As we have seen, our bodies consist of millions of cells, each of which contributes to the good of the whole, and each of which requires care to the point of pampering. The cytosol coddles the organelles, the interstitial fluids provide for the individual cells, and the blood nurtures the interstitial fluids. We know that the blood is not omnipotent—that it must also be cared for. When it fills with debris from cellular activities it must be cleansed, and when its supplies run low, they have to be replaced. We have already seen how some of these problems are handled. In chapter 14, we saw how, when circulatory tributaries are stripped of oxygen and burdened with carbon dioxide, the respiratory system comes to the rescue. In this chapter, we will see what provides the essential fuel molecules and other raw materials when blood supplies run low.

As we have already seen (chapter 3), our body cells require prodigious amounts of energy. Only by continual, judicious expenditure of their precious energy can the body's cells avoid the disruption of their activity, the breakdown of organelles, and eventual death. Hence there must never be any shortage of ATP. Extending this logic, it becomes obvious that there must never be a shortage of fuel molecules needed to produce the ATP. Our body cells bathe constantly in a river of nutrients and will continue to live only as long as the river can provide all that is necessary. It is the job of our digestive system to insure that it always will.

But there are difficulties. In the overall ecology of our world, humans are consumers, not producers. We cannot synthesize our own food from air, water, and sunlight as plants can. But we need food, so we take what others make for us—we feed on other living things—and that, by itself, is a problem. The compounds that we consume are parts of other organisms, and whether they come from plants or animals, they are usually organized into very complex compounds—polymers designed by, and for the use of, other organisms. They have been painstakingly maneuvered into chemical forms that our cells cannot use. We cannot present carbohydrates to our body cells in the form of plant cell walls or offer them amino acids that are polymerized into the contractile proteins of fish muscle—even the blood will not accept them when they are like that. Large, foreign proteins in the blood might be attacked by our body's immune systems and precipitate a conflict that could result in a horrible illness. We cannot afford such a confrontation every time we decide to eat. Therefore, before any foodstuffs can be absorbed by the blood, they must first be processed: broken down to simpler particles and refined to a state where they can avoid immune reactions and be immediately used by cellular machinery. Digestion, then, can be defined as the *mechanical and chemical activities that result in the breakdown of foodstuffs into particles small enough to be absorbed by the body*. That is what the digestive system is for.

Before it can do any of these things, however, the food must be obtained. That means one or both of our body's control systems must be informed that it is time to collect nutrients and offer them to the digestive system. In other words, we have to get hungry.

Hunger

Hunger is a basic drive. It may be the first one that develops in a newly born human, and it certainly is a powerful one. It is not, however, a simple one. Most people feel that the stimuli that produce hunger originate in the stomach, and certainly some of them do. The "growling" stomach, the hunger pangs that people feel when they haven't eaten for several hours and smell something delicious . . . most of these originate in the stomach.

But there is obviously more to hunger than merely stomach contractions and gastric nerve stimulations. People who have had their stomachs removed (gastrectomy) still feel hunger, and if the stomach were the only site of stimulus, this would not be possible. Furthermore, hunger produces behavioral changes; hence it is obviously a central nervous phenomenon. It would be startling indeed if the brain were not deeply involved. Animal studies have shown that it is.

When a certain zone within the hypothalamus is destroyed (the lateral hypothalamic area), the animal will stop eating. Nothing can coax it to consume food again—not its favorite food and not the imminence of death due to starvation. It can be force-fed, and with patience its hunger drive will return, but it never again drinks normally, and its eating patterns are often random. For obvious reasons, this portion of the hypothalamus has been given the name the **feeding center.**

On the other hand, destruction of the ventromedial hypothalamus has the opposite effect. When this zone, known as the **satiety center,** is extirpated, the animal eats around the clock and will eventually resemble a furry football.

Such results suggest that there are neurons within the hypothalamus that are responsible for both the hunger drive and for shutting down the hunger drive. These neuronal centers obviously receive information from outside receptors, some of which must be located in the stomach; personal experience leaves little doubt of that. But the fact that there is also a center that stops the feeding process suggests that there must also be receptors elsewhere, and that these receptors provide information concerning the body's nutritional state.

There seems to be little doubt that these two systems—satiety and feeding— interact to regulate our body weight. A balance must develop between our energy requirements and our food intake, or we could not possibly remain within normal human size limits. If there were nothing to cut off our food intake, we would continue to ingest food and continue to enlarge as the years passed. This is not as far-fetched as it sounds. Some animals, such as the salt-water crocodile and the elasmobranch fishes, are capable of continued growth until they die, and their eating habits reflect this ability.

But humans are not. We have an upper limit to our body size, and most of us have a steady weight condition that makes it pretty clear that these two opposing control systems must balance each other very carefully. It seems obvious also that the information they use to do this must come from sources that can accurately and precisely measure our body's nutritional state. Probably—almost certainly—this information source is the blood. Early workers were convinced that the satiety center's receptors monitored blood glucose, and that may be the case. Recent experiments, however, suggest that the satiety center's information is based on amino acid levels in the blood, not glucose. Clearly, a lot of research still needs to be done.

In any case, it is becoming clear that the hypothalamus is not the only brain area involved in feeding and/or satiety. It processes information from peripheral areas and then turns other centers off or on as the situation warrants. Many of these centers are in the brain stem and are concerned with finding and obtaining, or capturing, food. Outside the central nervous system, the gastrointestinal tract certainly provides different kinds of information and there is little doubt that autonomic nerves monitoring blood constituents in the abdomen are also involved. Control is tight and very accurate indeed (see figure 15.1).

Why, then, are we in this country afflicted with a national epidemic of obesity? When people consume more energy than they spend, the extra energy is stored as fat, and far too many people in this country do just that. A great deal of money awaits the man or woman who comes up with the reason why this is the case.

Some Biological Philosophy

It is perfectly natural to assume that once we have stuck food in our mouths, it has entered our bodies. This concept may be justifiable from a superficial point of view, but it doesn't stand up to strict scrutiny. Structurally, the digestive tract is a tube running through our bodies, and things inside the hollow of the tube are in firmer contact with the environment than with our interstitial fluids. Consider figure 15.2. You will note that tubes can take many different sizes and shapes, but no matter how you compress or stretch them, the hole within is still part of the surroundings, not the interior of the tube. So it is with the digestive tract.

Figure 15.1 The hunger/satiety cycle.

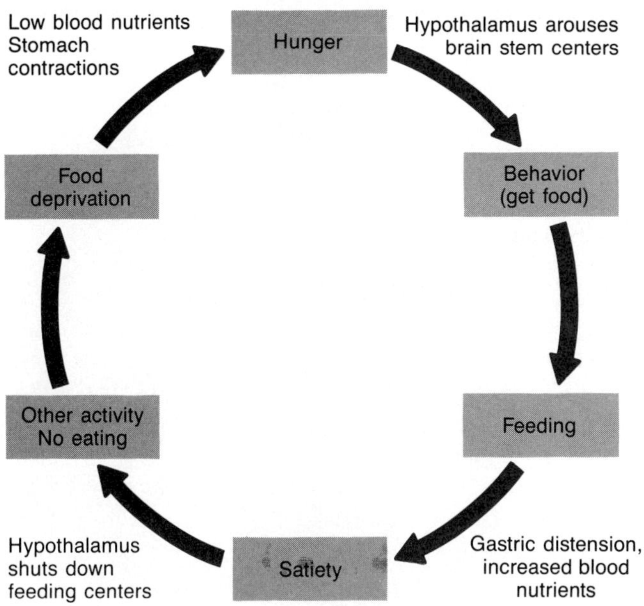

Figure 15.2 When you look at a hose (*a*), it is easy to assume that water running through the hose is inside it. It is almost as easy to consider this to be the case with a pipe (*b*), but it is a good deal harder to accept this outlook when confronted with the hole in a tire (*c*) and almost impossible to believe that the hole in a doughnut (*d*) is *inside* that delicious snack. The point is that we must realize that the hollow within a tube is not part of the tube; hence it cannot be *inside* it.

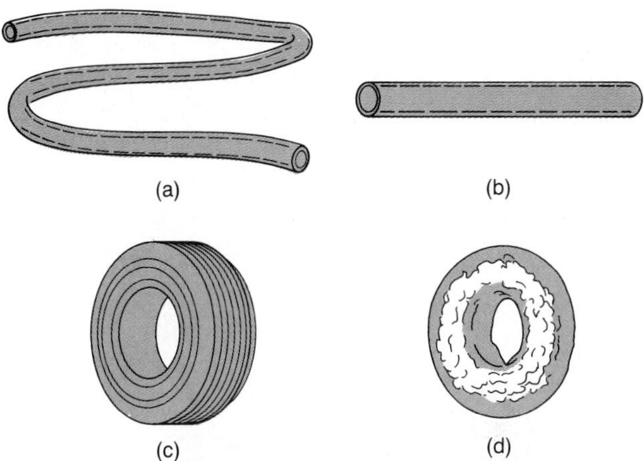

Food within the tract, therefore, is outside the body. This is more than just a philosophical argument. It is an important physiological point, because while food is in the tract, it is subjected to a series of rather drastic treatments. Things take place in this confined hollow that would be lethal within the carefully controlled fluid environment housing the living cells. Consider what goes on in our digestive tracts and you'll see what I mean.

At the entrance, the materials that arrive are torn into chunks. Then they are smashed, rolled around, and smashed some more. Throughout this smashing and grinding process, the chunks of food are thoroughly mixed with buffered water to which enzymes have been added—enzymes powerful enough to shatter some of the food particles. Shortly after being subjected to this rough treatment, the particles are pushed into a long tube that proceeds to dump them into a warm acid bath, where they are exposed to more potent enzymes. Throughout this, the whole mass is vigorously stirred and sloshed back and forth. Each portion of the digestive tract presents the unfortunate food particles with a different type of insult, each designed to continue the destructive activity that the earlier ones began to perpetrate.

The purpose of digestion is to shatter the large food molecules, to break them into smaller and smaller particles until ultimately they reach the point where they are capable of crossing the membranes of the gut and entering the body fluids. Once inside the body proper, some will be built up into larger particles and some will be broken down further, but now the really violent conditions are behind them. There are no more acid baths, no more percolating pools of powerful, destructive enzymes. Conditions that were present in the interior of the digestive tract are not encountered inside the body. If such were permitted to exist in the body proper for even a few moments, the results could be catastrophic.

The digestive tract, however, is more than a simple hollow tube running through our bodies. The acids, the powerful enzymes, and the agitating activity of its walls are not randomly, or even casually, encountered, but rather are carefully orchestrated. The design of the gastrointestinal tract permits regulation and arrangement of interior conditions so that the breakdown of organic molecules, while sometimes extreme, is orderly and takes place in a logical sequence. For the sake of convenience, researchers have divided the digestive tract into several distinct regions. In the first region, food is ingested and mechanical and chemical breakdown begins. It then continues into an enlarged combination storage and treatment zone, where further breakdown takes place. From there it is gradually and selectively fed into an area where digestion continues and absorption begins. In the final zone it is dehydrated, and the remaining waste products and unabsorbable items are formed into fecal material for expulsion from the tract.

Figure 15.3 The organs and accessories of the digestive system.

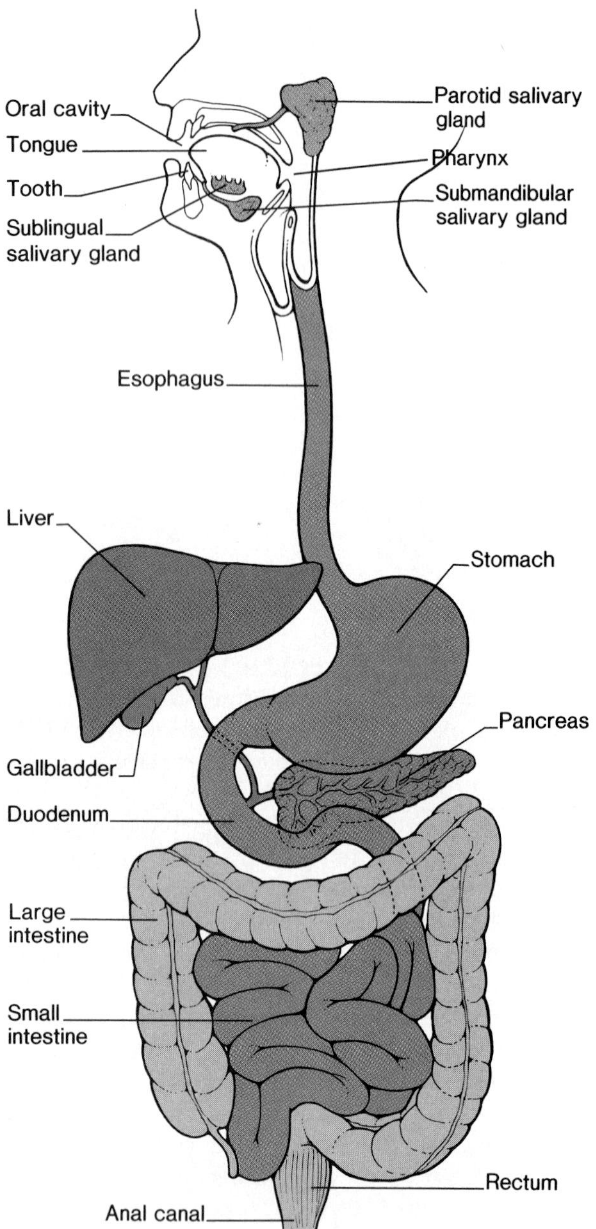

Figure 15.4 This is the entrance to the human digestive system. Mechanical and chemical processing begin when the first mouthful is chewed.

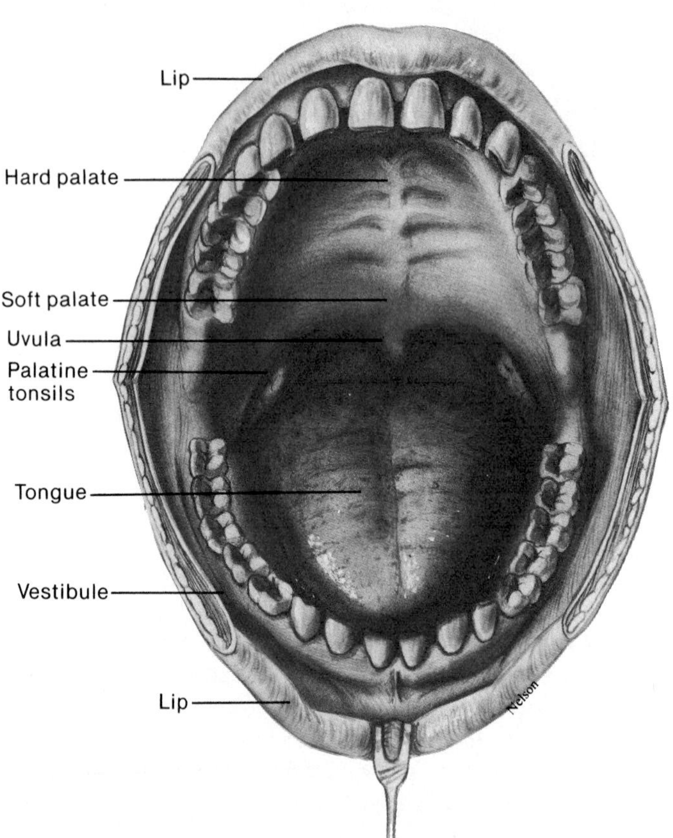

Some Anatomy

The anatomy of the upper part of the digestive tract is fairly well-known to most of us. The **mouth** is, of course, where food begins its journey. From the mouth, it enters the **esophagus,** which is merely a tube connecting the mouth and the **stomach.** The stomach represents both a storage area and a digesting zone. As the stomach finishes with the partially digested food, it is released, a bit at a time, into the **small intestine** and subjected to further breakdown by various chemicals, including some secreted by the **pancreas** and **liver.** Finally, after a journey of about fifteen to eighteen feet, whatever is left unabsorbed is ejected from the small intestine into the caverns of the **large intestine,** where it undergoes final processing and is expelled from the body (figure 15.3).

Digestive Operations

To clearly grasp what goes on in these tubes and caverns, we must delve into some detailed anatomy and microanatomy of each of these divisions and figure out just what it is that each one is capable of doing to the food as it passes through.

The Mouth

The mouth is the portal of entry, and it starts a process that continues throughout the entire tract. Probably it all begins with **mechanical digestion**—activity involving mainly the teeth and the muscles of the jaw. Here, incisors first meet our food and slice it into "bite-sized" chunks, which are then moved to the grinders in the back of the mouth, where flat-surfaced teeth smash it into a paste (figure 15.4).

Figure 15.5 A comparison of jaw articulation: herbivore versus carnivore. (*a*) Humans, like all herbivores, can move the jaw from side to side. This enables us to grind our food on flat-surfaced teeth that all come together simultaneously, much as the surfaces of a pair of pliers meet (*b*). The jaw of the carnivore is hinged very differently. Meat eaters cannot move their lower jaws sideways. Furthermore, the hinging is arranged so that the teeth come together sequentially, as do the cutting edges of scissors (*c*), enabling the animal to slice the tough meat into strips.

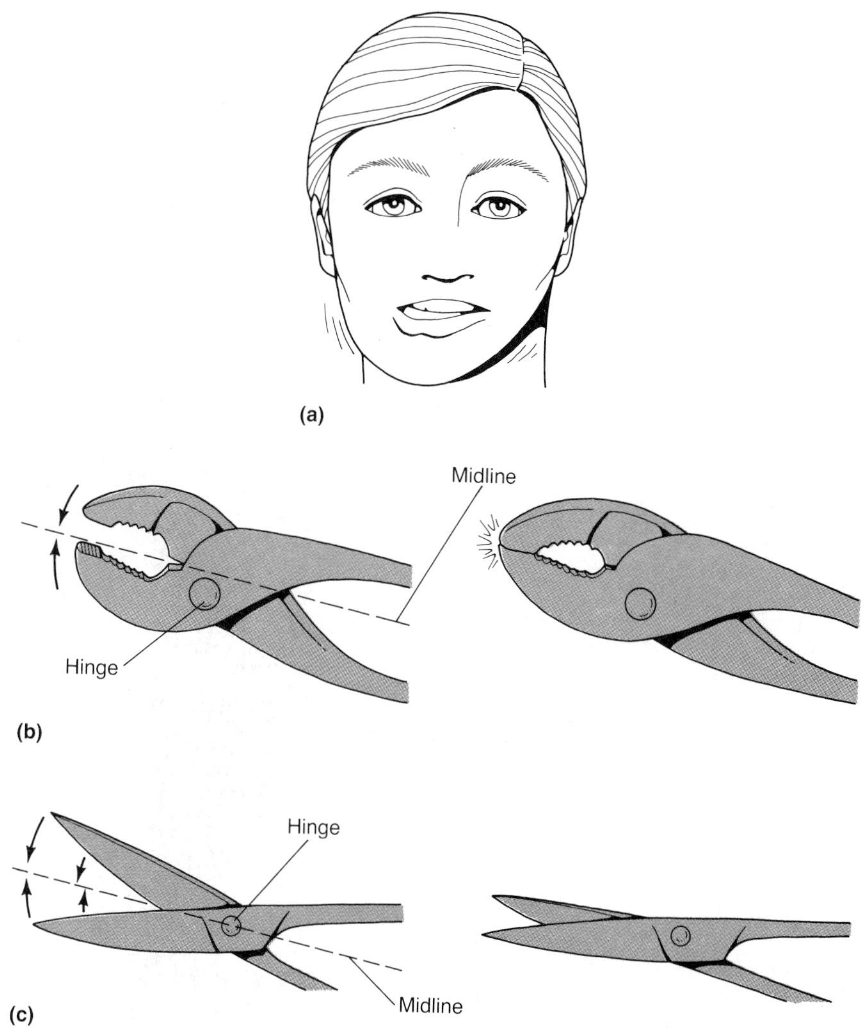

The **tongue** plays an important role in these operations, moving the newly sliced food into the middle of the mouth where the molars and other grinding surfaces can work on it. The tongue also flips the food back and forth, making sure that all of it gets chewed while mixing it thoroughly with the juices that flow from the various secretory glands and cells in the mouth. This treatment is particularly effective when it involves fruits, nuts, and vegetables, since the salivary juices contain a starch-splitting enzyme.

It is probably appropriate at this point to mention that despite what many would like to believe, humans, structurally, are not carnivores; our flat-surfaced teeth and the hinging of our jaws represent a design obviously intended for the consumption of vegetation, not meat (figure 15.5). Our teeth smash and grind food in the way a pair of pliers would smash materials placed between them. Unlike carnivores, we cannot use our teeth like scissors, to slice tough meats.

Finally, the grinding and smashing action of the jaws coupled with the salivary juices have reduced the food to a paste-like consistency that is soft and will follow the contours of the throat as it passes through. The chewing has reduced most of the large chunks of food to smaller chunks with a much higher surface area—a condition ideal for enzyme activity or **chemical digestion**—and has mixed it thoroughly with the secretions provided in such abundance by the salivary glands.

It is apparently considered "manly" in many circles to be an aficionado of half-cooked meats and to dislike vegetables. Possibly there is a feeling of primitive pride—of "machismo"—in assuming the feeding characteristics of a carnivore. It may massage a masculine ego to adopt such an attitude, but in fact it is not an accurate picture at all. Based on our jaw hinges, tooth type, and intestinal length, there is no doubt that humans are designed to be consumers of vegetation. All the teeth in the rear of our mouth, where the serious chewing is done, are flat-surfaced and intended to grind. The jaw hinging also indicates noncarnivorous dietary habits. Our jaws are hinged in such a way that when they close, the teeth all come together at once, like the work surfaces of a pair of pliers, and our mandibles (lower jaws) can move back and forth (figure 15.5) like a cow's or a horse's.

Carnivores are quite different. The rear teeth are not flat-surfaced, but rather have edges like scissors and as is the case with scissors, the jaw hinges will not permit these teeth to come together all at once. Instead, they meet progressively, in such a way as to *slice* rather than *smash.* Carnivores, therefore, can slice the toughest of raw meat into strips that can be swallowed—a trick no human can match. Being vegetarians by design, we are not able to handle raw or tough meats . . . in fact, when we chew on *really* tough meat, we often find it impossible to reduce it to a size that can be swallowed, because we cannot slice the tough fibers apart—all we can do is smash them into a fluid-filled mat that seems to get bigger and bigger the more we chew it. Conversely, meat-eaters have considerable difficulty with vegetables because they cannot smash them but can only slice them. To make things even harder for them, their lower jaws won't move from side to side to aid in the grinding process. How often have you seen your dog or cat chomping away on a single bean or pea trying to satisfy its feelings that its food ought to be sliced at least once?

Exocrine Glands

Salivary secretions are manufactured and released by **exocrine glands** (figure 15.6), and the human digestive system is replete with such glands. The word *exocrine* implies that whatever secretions the gland makes are used outside the body rather than inside, and that is exactly right.

Characteristically, exocrine cells take whatever substrate materials they need from nearby capillaries, put them together to form a special product, then secrete them into the hollow interior of the gland. In the lumen of the gland they are kept isolated from other, possibly contaminating, fluids; eventually they are directed through a duct toward a definite, restricted target area outside the body. Generally, there is a positive pressure forcing the secretions through the duct—pressure provided either by active transport mechanisms that thrust the secretions from the synthesizing cells or by the contraction of smooth muscles around the gland. For safety's sake, digestive enzymes, particularly those capable of splitting proteins, are made and stored in an inactive form and are not activated until they reach their target zones.

Figure 15.6 A typical exocrine gland. Exocrine glands are designed in such a way that their secretions can be segregated within a lumen and directed along a duct to a specific target. Nearby capillaries provide the necessary raw materials, and secretions (often inactive) are collected in the lumen and directed into the duct. Activation of the secretions may occur in the duct, but it usually occurs in the lumen of the target.

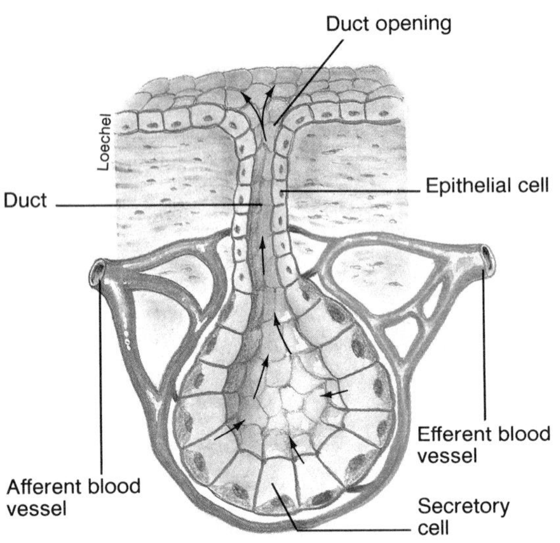

Salivary Secretions

The human mouth is replete with tiny glands called **buccal glands** (the "bu" pronounced as in "bugle"; hence, "byou-cl"). These are able to secrete quantities of saliva. Most saliva, however, is released by three pairs of specialized glands in the oropharyngeal region and by scatterings of secretory cells throughout the mouth. The salivary glands are the **parotids,** which are located across the upper bridge of the mouth near the rear (figure 15.7); the **sublingual glands,** which, as the name implies, are under the tongue; and the **submandibular glands,** which spread along the outer edge of the lower teeth. Each gland has more than one kind of secretory cell, which means it can secrete more than one thing, and saliva contains several compounds.

The average person secretes somewhere between 1,000 and 2,000 ml of saliva over a 24-hour period. Most of this is water—more than 99 percent at times, and always more than 97 percent, which makes it osmotically hypotonic compared to plasma. Much of the solids dissolved in the water are salts—bicarbonates, chlorides, and phosphates of both sodium and potassium. There are some organic compounds as well.

Figure 15.7 The location of the major salivary glands.

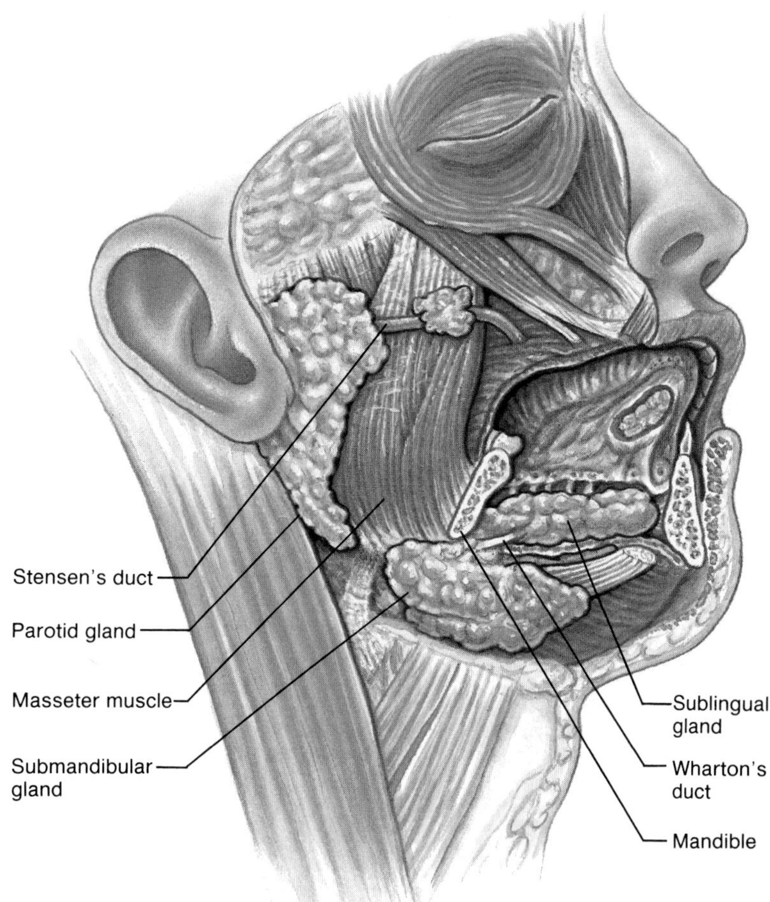

There is some serum globulin, a little albumin, a thick, slippery compound called **mucin,** and a quantity of enzymes. One of the latter is a bacteria-disrupting enzyme called **lysozyme,** which helps rid the food of unwanted microorganisms, and the other is a carbohydrate splitter called **salivary amylase** or **ptyalin.**

The extra water in the saliva dissolves many of the water-soluble materials in the food, which serves two purposes—it permits us to taste what is in our mouths, and it allows the amylase to begin breaking up the soluble carbohydrates. The salivary amylase is actually quite powerful and, given enough time, it can reduce starches to disaccharides, but *in vivo* that seldom, if ever, happens. Usually the food is swallowed before more than 3 to 5 percent of the starches present have been attacked. The salivary minerals also have jobs to do. The chloride ions in the saliva activate the amylase, while the bicarbonate ions function as buffers.

When it is first secreted, saliva is slightly acid, but this state is rapidly challenged by the bicarbonate ions, which immediately begin to regulate our oral environment. When a person is eating and enzymes are flowing lavishly, the bicarbonates are often overwhelmed and the oral pH can dip to 6.8 or 6.5. But between meals, when the flow of saliva slows and buffering action can be effective, the pH of the mouth ranges between 7.0 and 7.5.

Each of the large salivary glands can synthesize both mucin and enzymes and can concentrate and secrete bicarbonate, but they do not do so in the same relative quantities. Parotid secretions, which are released into the mouth through ducts near the upper molars, contain high concentrations of enzymes, as do the secretions of the submandibular glands. But the sublingual secretions contain only a few enzymes. Most sublingual cells synthesize mucin, which serves as a lubricant and a kind of glue to hold the food mass together as it is swallowed.

Like all digestive enzymes, salivary amylase is a **hydrolase,** meaning it catalyzes a reaction called **hydrolysis** (figure 15.8). Hydrolysis accomplishes the opposite of what dehydration synthesis does. Dehydration synthesis, you will recall, assembles polymers from simpler molecules by removing water. Hydrolytic enzymes catalyze reactions that put the water molecules back and thereby break organic polymers apart.

Saliva's Limitations

Like all enzymes, salivary amylase is something of a specialist. Obviously, being an amylase, it does not work on fats, nucleic acids, or proteins. It is designed to attack carbohydrate polymers, but as it turns out, it can only break up certain kinds of carbohydrate polymers, and even then only in certain ways. Salivary amylase is an *alpha*-amylase. This means it can attack and separate the alpha bonds that exist between the glucose molecules in starch and many other polysaccharides, but it cannot break the bonds that hold the cellulose molecule together because these are *beta* linkages (figure 15.9). Further emphasizing its specialization, salivary amylase is restricted to attacking carbohydrate polymers in the *middle* of the molecule. For instance, it can break starch molecules into smaller polysaccharides, but it cannot break molecules off the ends. As a result, digestive operations in the mouth produce lots of **maltose** (a glucose-glucose disaccharide) and plenty of larger glucose polymers, but very little free glucose.

Figure 15.8 An example of enzyme-catalyzed hydrolysis.

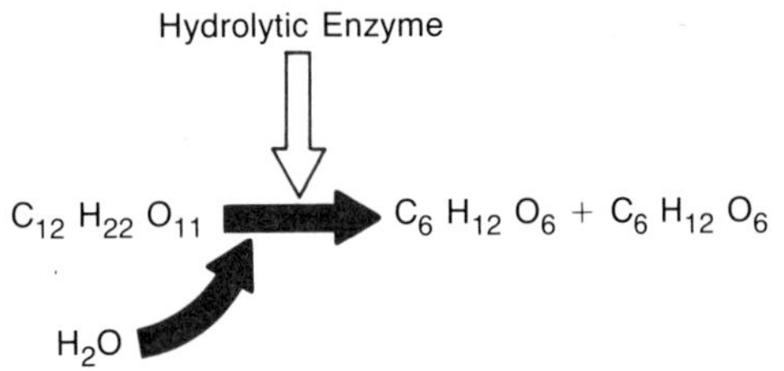

Control Mechanisms

The mechanisms controlling salivary secretion are, as far as we can tell, all nervous and mainly autonomic. It is one of the few instances in which the two branches of the autonomic nervous system do not play antagonistic roles. As it turns out, both autonomic branches can stimulate salivary secretion, although the parasympathetic has a greater overall effect. In addition to the unconscious autonomic reflexes, conscious brain processes also have a powerful influence, although they also exert their effects along autonomic neurons. Thinking about food, smelling food, or seeing food can boost salivary flow significantly.

Figure 15.9 The amylases present in humans can hydrolyze the alpha linkages such as those in starch. The beta linkages of cellulose cannot be attacked by any human enzyme.

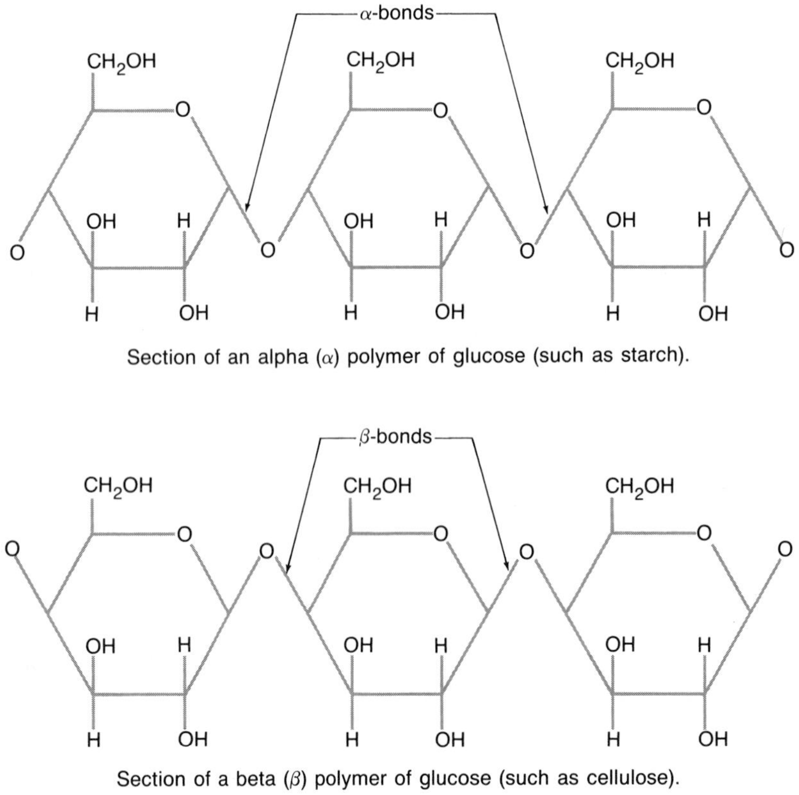

Section of an alpha (α) polymer of glucose (such as starch).

Section of a beta (β) polymer of glucose (such as cellulose).

And of course the actual presence of food in the mouth is the most powerful stimulus of all.

The physical presence of food inside the mouth triggers profound responses. There is a nucleus in the brain stem known as the **salivary center** of the medulla, and impulses travel into it from oral receptors along several cranial nerves (V, VII, IX, and X). The medulla responds by increasing activity in efferent fibers of both sympathetic and parasympathetic neurons entering the mouth. The parasympathetic stimulation is particularly effective. Efferent signals travelling along the vagus nerve:

1. increase glucose and oxygen consumption in the secretory cells of the mouth, indicating that the cells are increasing their efforts to synthesize and secrete their products;
2. cause vasodilation in blood vessels supplying these secretory cells; and
3. stimulate muscle cells around the salivary glands to contract, thus squirting their contents into the mouth.

Generally speaking, the efferent sympathetic neurons tend to augment the activity of the parasympathetic fibers.

The major salivary glands and their secretions are summarized in table 15.1.

Swallowing

Food in the mouth is chewed and rolled around by the tongue and cheek activity. The result is that mucin, bicarbonate, enzymes, food chunks, and the newly released smaller saccharides are mixed together and eventually rolled into a single, semifluid mass. At this point, they slide into the rear of the mouth, pasted together by mucin into what is called a **bolus.** The presence of the bolus at the top of the throat initiates the act of swallowing and ends our conscious control of food processing.

This is a routine enough activity for us and seems ridiculously easy, but it's rather more complicated than one might think. First of all, swallowing is a reflex action. Most of us feel that we can control it thoroughly, swallowing when we want to and not swallowing when we do not want to, but it is not as voluntary as we may think. The early activities are all voluntary. We roll the food, we chomp on it, we manipulate it, and finally we can push it into the back of the mouth and make everything ready for a "swallow" to occur . . . then, suddenly, we lose control. As it happens, when things are in the proper place, the process is almost impossible to stop. You can test this without gagging by simply getting a small amount of water in your mouth and tipping your head back to let it run down your throat. If you try it, you will see how hard it is to avoid swallowing once there is something at the top of your throat.

The mechanical activity of swallowing serves to increase the pressure in the back of the mouth to a point where whatever is back there can be forced into the pharynx. Because of the anatomy of the pharynx, this presents a technical problem. As you can see from figure 15.10, the digestive tract and the respiratory tract both open into that region . . . in fact, they cross over. Therefore, in order for food to get to the esophagus where it has to go, it must first pass through a zone where it could conceivably be detoured into any one of several branches of the respiratory tree—a highly undesirable event. It is the kind of possibility that cannot be ignored. Increased pressure in the pharynx could easily push food or liquid in any direction. It might go right to the esophagus, and that would be good, but it might just as easily go through the internal nares and up into the nasal cavity or maybe down into the trachea. Obviously, steps must be taken to force it into the correct tube and keep it out of the respiratory tract.

Table 15.1 The Major Salivary Glands

Gland	Location	Duct	Type of Secretion
Parotid glands	In front and somewhat below the ears, between the skin of the cheeks and the masseter muscles	Parotid ducts pass through the buccinator muscles and enter the mouth opposite the upper second molars	Clear, watery serous fluid rich in amylase
Submandibular glands	In the floor of the mouth on the inside surface of the mandible	Ducts open beneath the tongue near the frenulum	Primarily serous fluid, but with some mucus; more viscous than parotid secretion
Sublingual glands	In the floor of the mouth beneath the tongue	Many separate ducts	Primarily thick, stringy mucus

Figure 15.10 A view of the digestive and respiratory tracts in the region of the pharynx, showing how they cross over one another.

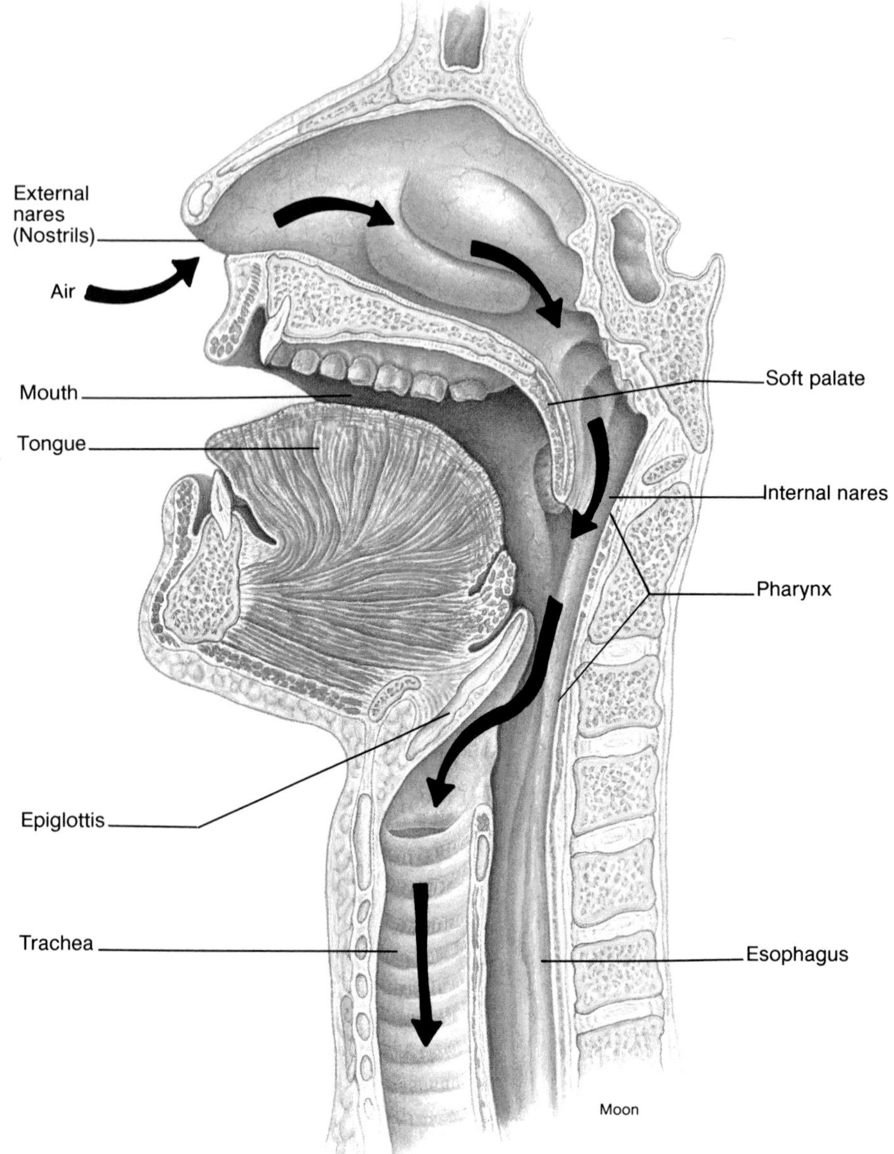

Figure 15.11 shows how this is accomplished. When the tongue pushes the food into the rear of the mouth, it also pushes the **uvula** and the **soft palate** up against the internal nares and closes them off. The **larynx** or voice box is pulled upward to a position just under the tongue. This movement pulls the vocal cords together and forces the epiglottis against the glottis, thus sealing off the respiratory tract as well. This leaves only one opening that the increased pharyngeal pressure can force food into, that is, the esophagus, which is where it belongs. The whole process takes about a second.

The vulnerability of the pharyngeal area is exemplified by the ease with which food particles can be wedged in the trachea, especially by young children. Eating food in large mouthfuls is particularly troublesome, because when food is in the rear of the mouth, a sudden intake of air can drag chunks into the trachea and jam them there. If the air already in the lungs is insufficient to cough it out, people could strangle to death trying to coax air past the food plug and into their lungs in quantities sufficient to work up a good cough. Every desperate intake of breath serves merely to wedge the food particle more firmly, and there is never enough drawn in to blow out the plug. One of the reasons that the Heimlich maneuver (figure 15.12) is

Figure 15.11 The swallowing reflex and peristalsis. (*a*) The tongue forces food into the pharynx; (*b*) the soft palate, hyoid bone, and larynx are raised, the tongue is pressed against the palate, and inferior constrictor muscles relax so that the esophagus opens; (*c*) superior constrictor muscles contract and force food into the esophagus; (*d*) peristaltic waves move food through the esophagus to the stomach.

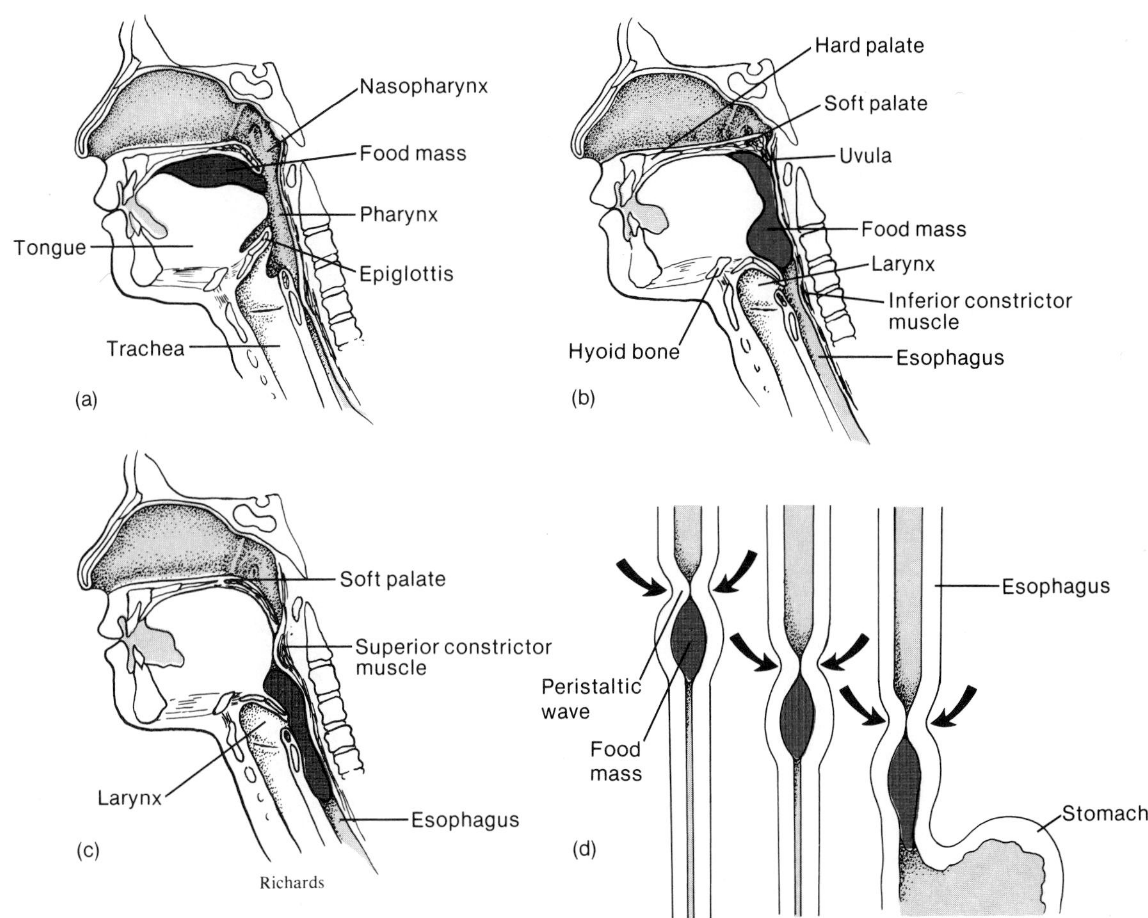

effective is because it utilizes the residual volume of air in the lungs to produce a cough-like response. The residual air, you will recall from chapter 14, cannot be forced out of the lungs by normal respiratory maneuvers, but when a person's thoracic cavity is compressed by an outside force, as much as a half-liter of residual air can be forced out of each lung—more than enough to produce a cough.

Peristalsis

The esophagus is a relatively dull place, not much more than a tube through which food can flow into the stomach and lower parts of the digestive system, but it has a couple of interesting features. It contains lots of mucin-secreting cells, so it is well lubricated, and it is the first part of the digestive system to employ a smooth-muscle feature common throughout the entire tract—**peristalsis.** Peristalsis is a successive series of contractions by bands of smooth visceral muscle that are wrapped around the tubes of the digestive tract. The contractions are controlled by autonomic reflexes, for which the stimulus is food contacting the wall of the esophagus. Each muscle band contracts as an independent unit, but the autonomic controls insure that contraction of each occurs in the proper sequence. When one muscle band contracts, muscles in the zones immediately adjacent to it relax briefly to let the food slide through, then contract in their turn. As the second band contracts, a third band briefly relaxes before it contracts, and so the process continues throughout the length of the tube. It has the effect of producing an apparent wave-like movement along the tube from one end to the other, and thus it can push ahead of it whatever may be within (figure 15.11*d*).

Figure 15.12 The Heimlich maneuver to release food trapped in the trachea. The victim is grasped from behind with the fists clenched just below the rib cage. Pressure is applied suddenly to the hands by bending the elbows (*not* by hugging). The abdominal organs are pushed up against the diaphragm, which forces residual air out of the lungs, thus blowing out the food particle. If the first thrust doesn't do the job, the maneuver can be repeated until it is successful.

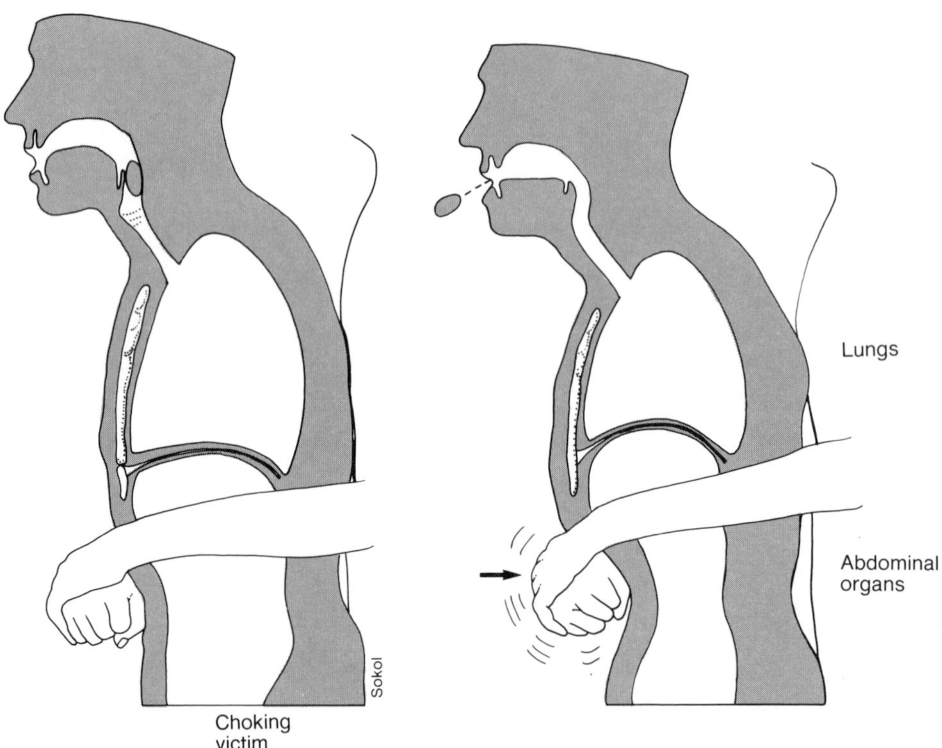

Esophageal peristalsis is a phenomenon that we take for granted, but it was cause for considerable concern by NASA officials in the late 1950s, prior to the first manned orbital flights. People are weightless when in earth orbit, so gravity doesn't exist to hinder or to help them. Researchers knew, of course, that peristalsis occurred in the esophagus, and they were confident that it could handle the swallowing of solid food, but they were not sure how effective it would be in forcing fluids into the stomach when gravity wasn't present to help it along. If you feel particularly adventurous and you want to experiment a little, you might try swallowing water when you are standing on your head. When you have finished coughing and otherwise strangling, you might be able to appreciate the uncertainties that bothered exobiological researchers in those early days.

The esophagus passes through the neck and thorax and exits the latter via a carefully sealed passage through the diaphragm. Just before it penetrates the diaphragm, the esophageal lumen narrows and the walls thicken slightly. This was once called the esophageal hiatus, but it now is believed to be a **sphincter** muscle (figure 15.13). Sphincters are muscles that are designed to narrow or to close openings in tubes, much as drawstrings close the opening into

Figure 15.13 The passageway from the mouth to the stomach. Unlike the trachea, the esophagus is not reinforced with cartilage and hence is collapsible.

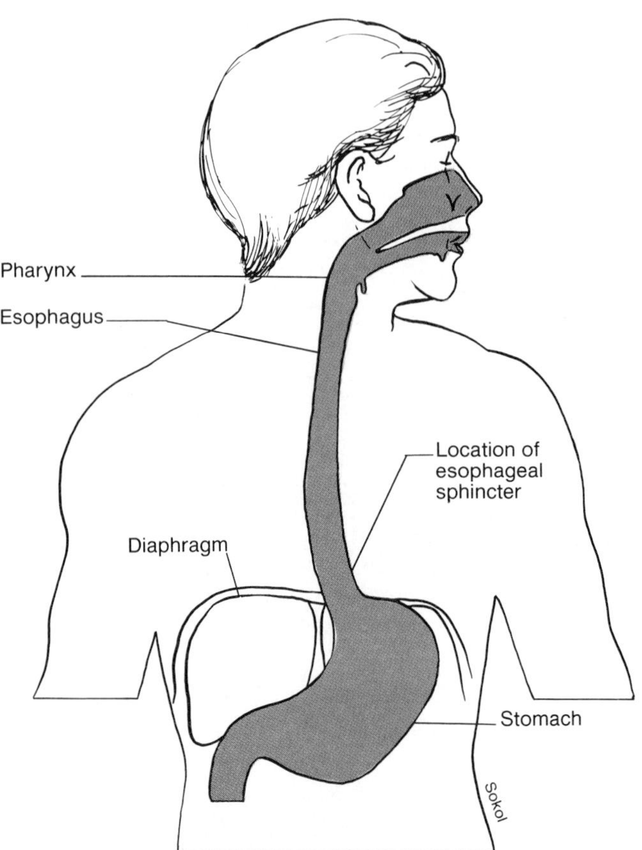

Figure 15.14 The human stomach.

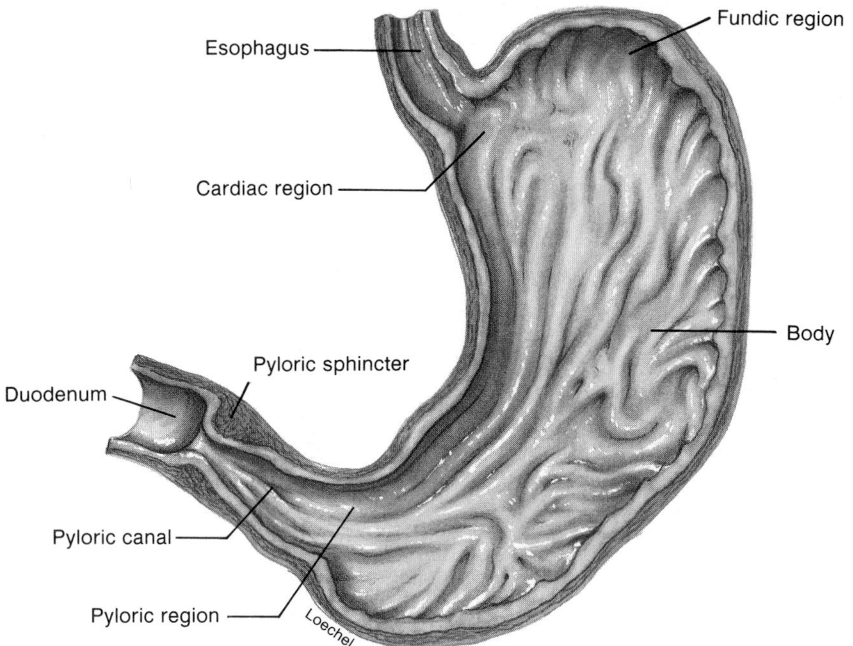

a woman's purse. The esophageal sphincter is normally contracted, but it relaxes when a person swallows, thus permitting food to pass through. Here, in the upper reaches of the abdomen, the esophageal tube suddenly opens into the rather vast expanse of the stomach (figure 15.14).

The Stomach

The stomach is the most extensible part of the digestive tract. Its size varies greatly among individuals, but there are records of some that can hold four full liters of material without significant discomfort to their owners. This is probably not as rare as it should be, but it does represent a minority. Most people have an upper limit somewhere on the order of a liter and a half. It is possible, certainly, for us to swallow more food than our stomachs are designed to hold, but when we do our stomachs let us know by aching or splashing some of their acid contents up into the lower reaches of the esophagus, thus producing the familiar, sizzling sensation typical of "heartburn."

There are four distinct zones in the stomach, and food must pass into and through each in turn. The first one is the **cardia.** This is immediately below the esophageal opening and is very short. Adjacent to the cardia is the **fundus.** As shown in figure 15.14, this is slightly above and sweeps to the right as the stomach forms its J-shaped curve upward. Beneath the fundus is the central portion of the stomach, the **body,** which narrows gradually into the **pyloris** just before it joins the upper end of the small intestine.

The ability of the human stomach to hold a lot is handy for us today, but in our savage past it probably meant a good deal more. Were it not for the stomach's ability to store fairly large quantities of food, humans would not have been able to survive on just two or three feedings a day and may have had to stay in the open to feed—out where giant lions and sabre-toothed tigers might find a meal of their own. Modern records are powerful indicators of how profound is the stomach's ability to store food. Individuals having had gastrectomies (stomach removed) must eat very small meals about every two hours just to maintain normal caloric intake. To a civilized person, that is merely an inconvenience . . . to a savage, having to get up and forage for food every couple of hours, day and night, could have been disastrous.

The Four-Layered Wall

The wall of the stomach consists of four basic layers that continue, with varying emphasis, to form the wall of the digestive tract throughout its entire length (figure 15.15).

The **mucous membrane** is the innermost layer; it is itself, a three-layered structure. The outermost sublayer of the mucous membrane—the **epithelium**—can be protective or absorptive, depending upon which portion of the tract is involved. The middle sublayer is a connective tissue layer called the **lamina propria** and is heavily infiltrated with blood vessels and cells

Figure 15.15 The four basic layers of the gastrointestinal tract: (*a*) The mucous membrane, the submucosa, the muscle layer, and the serous layer are shown. (*b*) A microscopic section showing the microstructure of the same layers.

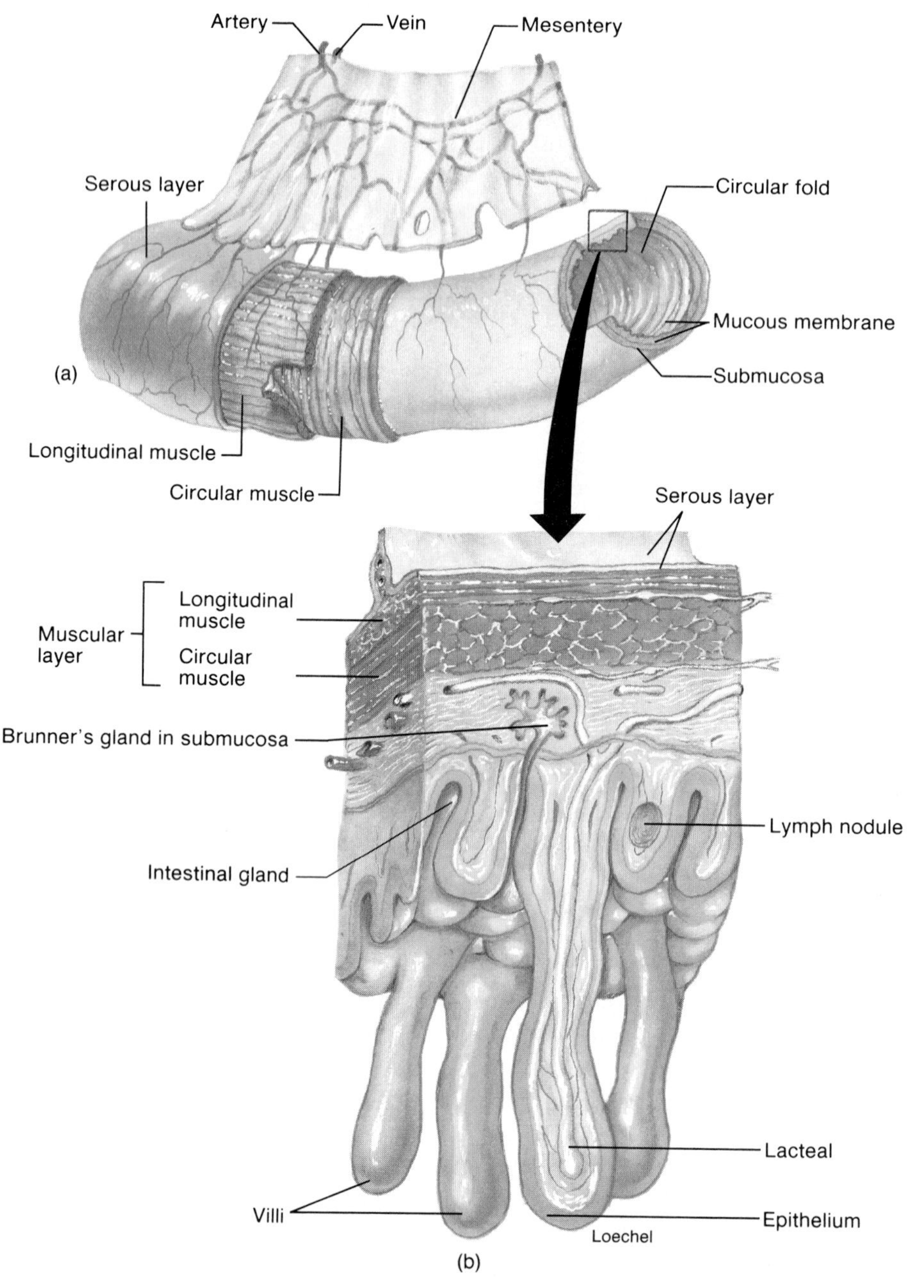

of the immune system. Its function is primarily protective. The innermost sublayer consists of a double layer of smooth muscle heavily infiltrated by fibers of elastic tissue. Bands of muscle fibers extend from the base of each villus up to its tip and are capable of producing independent movement in each villus. Logically enough, this sublayer is known as the **muscularis mucosa.**

The next layer of the stomach wall, the **submucosa,** consists almost entirely of loose connective tissue and large masses of elastic fibers. This is the layer containing **Meissner's plexus,** a large plexus of autonomic nerve fibers both sympathetic and parasympathetic.

The muscle layer or **muscularis externa** is composed of two layers of muscle that vary in thickness according to their location in the GI tract. The outermost muscle layer features cells oriented parallel to the longitudinal axis of the tract, while the inner layer wraps around the tract in circular fashion. These are the muscle layers that are responsible for the peristaltic movements of the tract; hence, as you might

Figure 15.16 The mucosal lining of the stomach. (*a*) Gastric pits are the openings of the gastric glands. (*b*) Three kinds of cells form the secretory areas of the gastric glands. Each cell type synthesizes and secretes a different product.

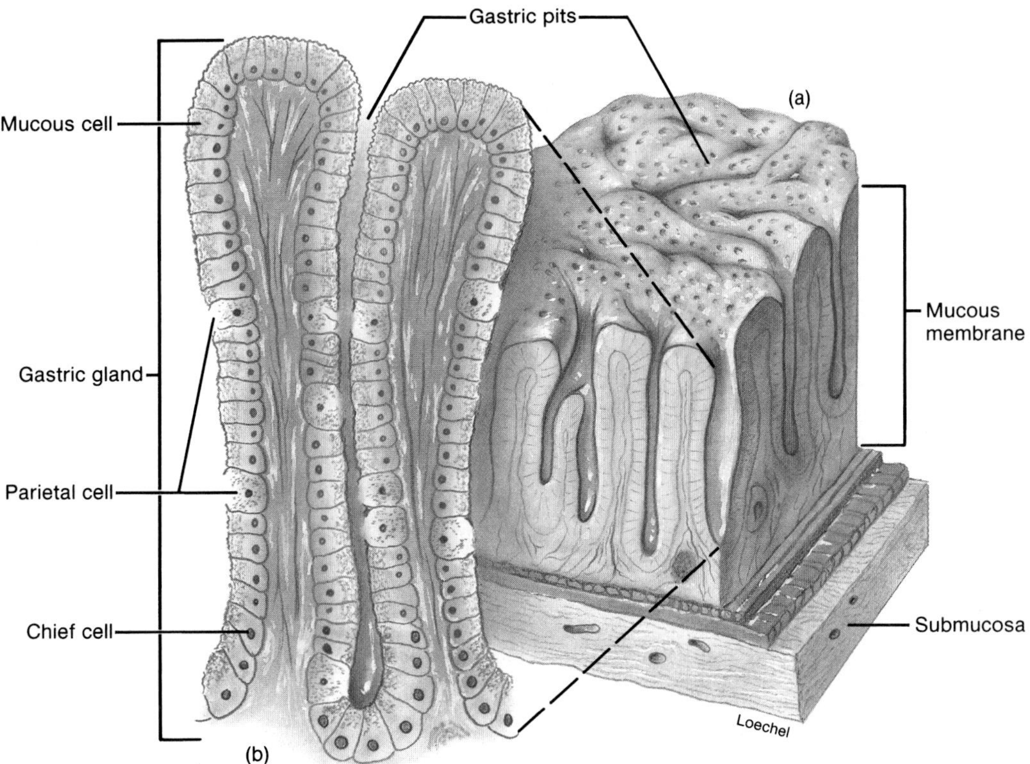

expect, they are richly supplied with autonomic neurons. These neurons originate in a large network of nerve fibers known as the **myenteric plexus,** an extensive nerve plexus that is situated between the two muscle layers. This nerve network has connections with extrinsic nerves as well as fibers innervating the muscle layers, and it is responsible for coordinating the peristaltic and mixing movements of the muscle layers.

Parasympathetic fibers are abundant in this plexus, and the preganglionic fibers that emerge have only a short run to the target, which for most of them is the **ganglionic cells** of the **intramural plexuses.** These ganglion cells terminate on their effectors, usually muscle cells but sometimes secretory glands. Sympathetic fibers that course through these zones are all postganglionic fibers, and they terminate exclusively on smooth muscle cells. As we have seen from chapter 10, sympathetic stimulation produces inhibition of the GI musculature, whereas parasympathetic nerves increase digestive activity.

The **serous layer,** the outmost layer of the stomach wall, consists of loose connective tissue with a covering of epithelial cells. Certain cells of this layer can secrete a thin, serous fluid that covers the outer surface of the entire digestive tract and forms a lubricating sheet that permits the organs in the abdominal cavity to slide freely across each other without producing friction damage.

The mucous membrane of the stomach is rather stiff tissue, and although the stomach can expand to an impressive size, the inner layer does not stretch much—it mainly *unfolds.* When the stomach is empty, the inside resembles the face of an incredibly ancient man (see figure 15.14). The wrinkles and folds, which are known as **rugae,** are large enough to be seen clearly with the naked eye, and these disappear as the stomach gradually fills and pulls them out into an inner surface that has the appearance of pitted percale. Microscopic examination shows that the pits are the openings for the glands that synthesize the gastric secretions (figure 15.16).

Gastric Digestion

While its job as a food storage reservoir is significant, the stomach has other functions to fulfill that are equally important. Protein digestion begins in the stomach, and a great deal of mechanical and chemical activity is associated with gastric operations.

Figure 15.17 (*a*) As the stomach fills, its muscular wall becomes stretched, but the pyloric sphincter remains closed; (*b*) mixing movements mix food and gastric juice, creating chyme; (*c*) peristaltic waves move the chyme toward the pyloric sphincter, which relaxes and allows some chyme to enter the duodenum.

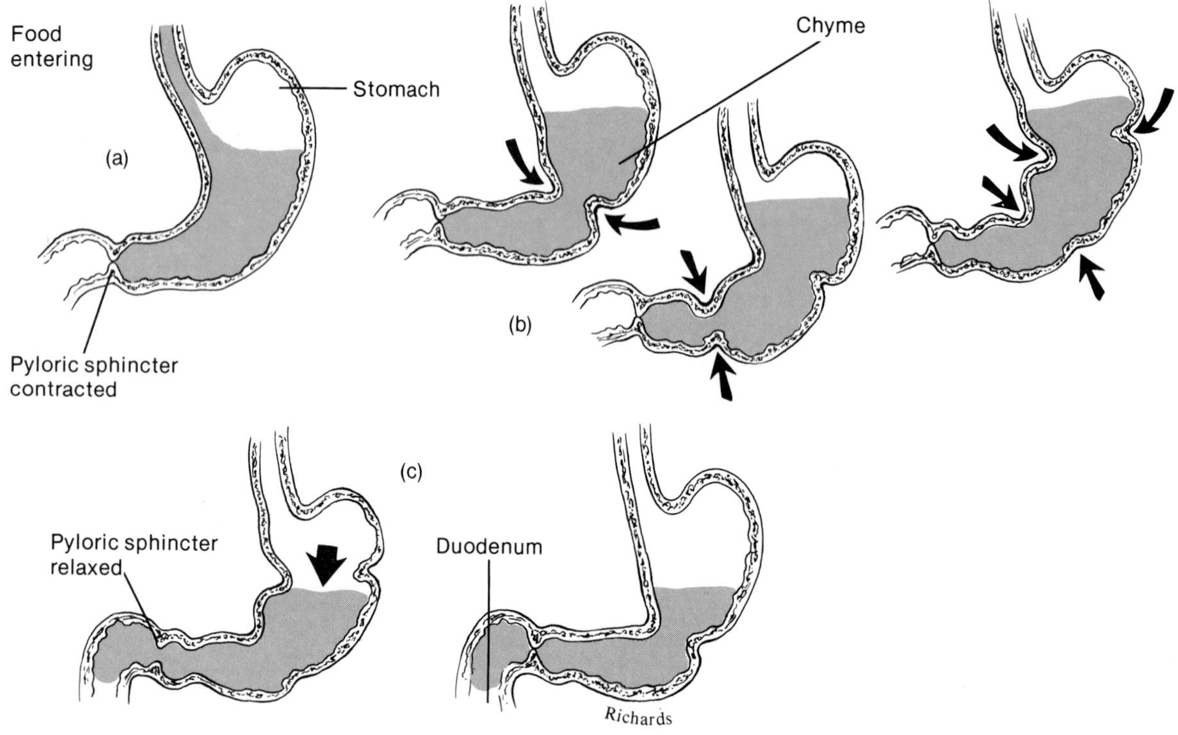

Stomach Movements

There is a lot of smooth muscle wrapped around the stomach, and the activity of this muscle has two important consequences. First of all, it serves to mix the food with all the fluids secreted by the stomach. When food is actually present, activity is brisk, and blending is thorough. This is important, because the bolus of food entering from the esophagus is usually a relatively firm paste presenting a small surface area, it must be agitated and churned to unglue the chewed particles and disperse them so that the enzymes can get at them. Also, the mechanical activity has *directionality*, meaning that it produces peristaltic waves that force the breaking-up material from the front of the stomach toward the rear (figure 15.17). Throughout all this enthusiastic movement, the gastric glands of the stomach are releasing their products to begin the chemical breakdown of the food particles.

Gastric Secretions

The stomach is laden with secretory cells. These cells are clustered in groups called **gastric** or **oxyntic glands,** which are located in the mucosa layer of the stomach wall. They open into the **lumen** (cavity) of the stomach through small apertures called **gastric pits.** There are millions of such pits scattered over the interior surface of the stomach (figure 15.18).

Gastric glands are typical exocrine glands; hence they are structurally quite similar to salivary glands, although their secretions are different. There are four types of cells in the gastric glands:

1. **parietal cells**
2. **mucous** or **neck cells**
3. **peptic** or **chief cells** (figure 15.16*b*)
4. **argentaffin cells**

Each synthesizes a different chemical for secretion.

Parietal Cells

The parietal cells are responsible for synthesizing the most unusual component of gastric secretions, the **hydrochloric acid.** This is not a weakened or special organic kind of hydrochloric acid. It is simple, inorganic hydrochloric acid, and it is powerful. Its actual pH when it is secreted is about 0.8, and if you were fool enough to rub it on, it could burn the skin off the inside of your arm. The most incredible thing about it is that it is made from substrates supplied by the blood. Figuring out just how this was accomplished was a fascinating problem for biochemists, because the blood, as we have seen, is normally slightly alkaline and is very carefully monitored to keep it so. Anything that would tend to change this state is highly undesirable; yet here in the stomach we are confronted by a system that makes a point of doing just

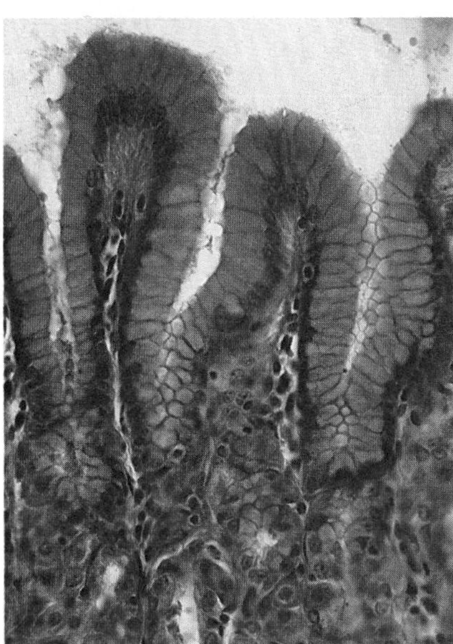

Figure 15.18 A micrograph of the innermost surface of the gastric mucosa, showing the gastric glands.

that. The process of stripping large numbers of H^+ ions from this tightly controlled fluid is bound to leave a great deal of alkaline material behind, and that could upset all the homeostasis so carefully fostered.

Nevertheless, it is done, and the fact that the blood seems none the worse for it is testimony to the magnificence of our body's homeostatic mechanisms.

No one is quite sure how so much acid is isolated from plasma, but it is theorized that the hydrogen ions are stripped from carbonic acid within the parietal cells and the chloride is taken from extracellular sodium chloride and transported into the gut. The complete reaction sequence is outlined in figure 15.19. Pay careful attention to this figure. The production of a high acid medium is extremely important, just as its neutralization is after things leave the stomach. If a normal acid/base balance in the gastrointestinal tract were not maintained, not one of the hundred trillion cells in the human body would receive adequate nourishment.

Having dropped off the necessary substrates for the production of hydrochloric acid, and having accepted large quantities of bicarbonate, the blood flowing away from the parietal cells is now quite alkaline—well above its optimum pH. This condition could be dangerous, and our body's homeostatic mechanisms do not permit it to exist for long. Buffers handle it to some extent, but most of it is taken care of by kidney mechanisms, which simply remove the excess alkaline products and dump them into the urine. As a result, urinary pH rises sharply whenever the parietal cells are active, which always happens during feeding. A highly alkaline urine during, and

Figure 15.19 Lumen of a gastric gland. Carbon dioxide and sodium chloride are nearly everywhere in both interstitial fluids and the blood—CO_2 mainly as carbonic acid and bicarbonate, and salt in its ionic form, Na^+ and Cl^-. Chloride is transported directly through the parietal cell into the lumen of the gland. Within the parietal cells, carbonic anhydrase—an enzyme we have seen before (chapter 12)—produces activity that shifts the equilibrium between carbonic acid and its component ions, thus producing large numbers of free hydrogen ions. Through the expenditure of a little energy, the hydrogen ions are transported into the lumen of the gland, where they associate with the free Cl^- ions, forming hydrochloric acid. Meanwhile the free Na^+ ions, which were left behind when Cl^- was dissociated from the salt molecules in the interstitial fluids, must be dealt with, as must the excess bicarbonate ions (HCO_3^-) inside the cell. As luck would have it, Na^+ and HCO_3^- are perfectly compatible with each other, so as HCO_3^- diffuses back into the interstitial fluids, it associates with the free sodium ions, thus forming sodium bicarbonate and accounting for all the loose ionic particles.

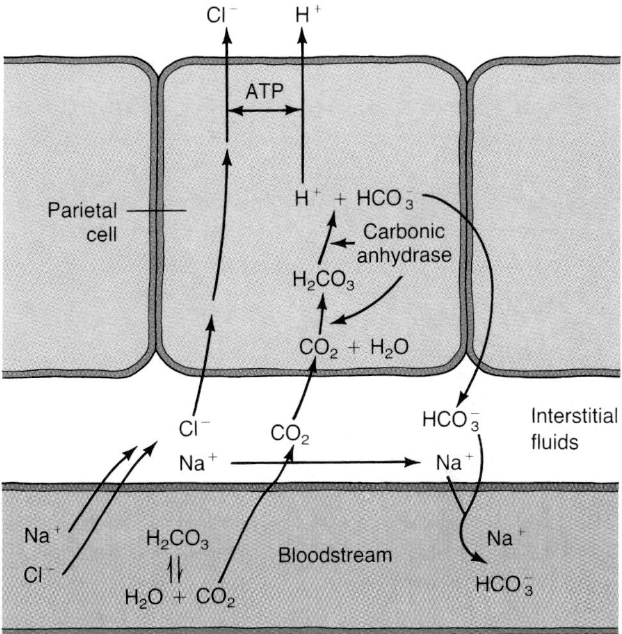

for a short time following, a meal is a normal condition and is referred to as the **urinary alkaline tide.**

Hydrochloric acid as powerful as that which is turned loose in the stomach is obviously dangerous stuff. Not only is it freely capable of burning the inside of a person's arm, it is quite able to do the same to the inner wall of the stomach, and if it ever got loose inside the abdominal cavity, it could be deadly. The gastric *neck cells* see to it that it is not given a chance.

Stomach Protection—the Neck Cells

The neck cells are the cells responsible for the synthesis of mucin, and it is suspected that mucin's function in the stomach is to eliminate, or at least reduce, the possibility of damage to the gastric lining. As figure 15.16 shows, neck cells tend to cluster around the upper surface of the secretory gland, concentrating near the exit duct. That means anything trying to leave the duct will mix with whatever these cells might produce, which in this case is mucin.

Mucin is slightly alkaline and contains a good many buffers; hence the secretions of the parietal cells are buffered slightly and diluted a bit as they drift toward the mouth of the gland before they head out into the stomach. Even so, the acids are powerful, and their pH is still about 1.0 when they enter the stomach lumen. That is awfully acid for living tissues, and it means further protection is necessary. The epithelial cells lining the inside surface of the stomach provide some. They are arranged so that they butt right up against each other along the inner gastric surface, forming solid, tight contacts and leaving no cavities or gaps through which any stomach contents could leak. Mucin adds further protection, flowing over these innermost cells, covering them with an alkaline blanket that forms an almost-impermeable coating anywhere from 1 mm to 1.5 mm thick. Despite all these defensive measures, the acids still are dangerous, and destruction of the gastric epithelium even under normal conditions is rapid. Fortunately, so is replacement. Epithelial cells are generated at an incredibly high rate of speed. It has been estimated that the entire inner lining of the stomach is replaced about every three days.

The Chief Cells

Hydrochloric acid is not the only chemical that can threaten the structural cells lining the stomach. There is also a digestive enzyme present, a powerful protein splitter called **pepsin,** and the *chief cells* are responsible for its creation. Actually, they synthesize a precursor of pepsin called **pepsinogen,** which is an inactive form of pepsin, and they keep it in this inactive form for a very good reason. Pepsin hydrolyses peptide bonds very quickly and could easily shatter the structural proteins of living cells—including those that synthesize it—so it is not given the opportunity. As long as it is stored inside a living cell, it stays in an inert form; the endoplasmic reticulum acts as its reservoir until it is released. Once it is free in the interior of the gut, pepsinogen is activated by contact with hydrochloric acid and by any residual molecules of active pepsin that are still in the stomach (and there are always a few).

Pepsin's Specificity Pepsin's potential for destruction is enormous, but it is nevertheless a highly specific enzyme. First of all, its optimal activity range is between pH 1 and pH 3, which makes it a really unique enzyme. Nowhere in the animal kingdom do such high levels of intestinal acid exist save in the lumen of the vertebrate stomach; hence pepsin is restricted to this locale.

The highly acid vertebrate stomach has presented physiologists with a curious question: why so much acid? No invertebrates have strong acid in their digestive tracts, but every vertebrate does. Hence there must be a special reason, but what could it be? Is it because pepsin works best in an acid medium, or is there some other reason to feature this highly dangerous interior? Nobody *knows* the answer, of course, but science does have a cogent hypothesis.

In view of the fact that there are plenty of protein-splitting enzymes that have optimal pHs in the vicinity of 7.5, it seems unlikely that any living system would create a potentially disastrous cavern within its confines merely to provide one proteolytic enzyme with an ideal working environment. It is assumed, therefore, that pepsin works best in an acid pH because the stomach is acid, not the other way around.

Most researchers feel that the stomach is acid in order to kill bacteria and other potential parasites that enter the digestive tract on, or in, the food we eat. Not very many bacteria can live in pHs as low as that of the vertebrate stomach, and it is assumed that they and most small worms, protozoa, and other tiny life forms are destroyed there—and quickly. Not all are, of course, but most are, and whether or not this is its prime function, such high acidity certainly represents a solid defense against all but the most determined and specialized parasites.

In addition to its predilection for an acid medium, pepsin is also specialized in its manner of attacking proteins. Apparently it is restricted to breaking only certain peptide linkages, and these seldom involve terminal amino acids. As a result, pepsin can break large proteins down to smaller peptide chains, but it produces very few free amino acids or small peptide clusters. Most proteinaceous materials are still fairly large peptides when they leave the stomach.

Gastric Starch Breakdown No starch-splitting (amylolytic) enzymes are released in the stomach, but that does not mean there is no breakdown of starch or other digestible carbohydrate polymers. Salivary amylase is packed into the food bolus during its stay in the mouth, and there is still plenty present when it reaches the stomach. Like all enzymes, this amylase is a protein, and hence is subject to attack by both HCl and pepsin, but at first only the amylase on the surface of the bolus is affected. Even the vigorous activity of the stomach takes ten minutes or so to break a bolus apart, and during that period, all the amylase within the food mass remains active and effective. It has been estimated that as much as 40 percent of the starch we eat is affected by salivary amylase and that most of the activity takes place within the stomach. Many of the complex carbohydrates that entered the stomach are reduced to disaccharides by the time they enter the small intestine.

Table 15.2 The Chemical Constituents of Gastric Secretion

Component	Source	Function
Pepsinogen	Chief cells of the gastric glands	An inactive form of pepsin
Pepsin	Formed from pepsinogen in the presence of hydrochloric acid	A protein-splitting enzyme capable of digesting nearly all types of protein
Hydrochloric acid	Parietal cells of the gastric glands	Provides acid environment, needed for the destruction of bacteria and conversion of pepsinogen into pepsin
Mucin	Goblet cells and mucous glands	Provides viscous, alkaline protective layer on the stomach wall
Intrinsic factor	Parietal cells of the gastric glands	Aids the absorption of vitamin B_{12}
Serotonin	Argentaffin cells	Smooth muscle stimulant

Argentaffin Cells Argentaffin (enterchromaffin) cells are not found in groups or clusters; instead, they sit as individuals in between the chief cells in the gastric glands. They synthesize and release serotonin, a potent initiator of smooth muscle contraction. Recent work indicates that as much as 90 percent of the body's serotonin is produced and stored within these cells. The precise function of the argentaffin cells is not clear, but they are found throughout the gastrointestinal tract, and it has been suggested that they may represent an endocrine gland whose cells are dispersed throughout the entire digestive system.

Intrinsic Factor There is one other chemical synthesized and secreted by the gastric mucosa. It is known as **intrinsic factor,** and it is synthesized in the same cells that isolate the HCl—the parietal cells. Intrinsic factor is secreted into the stomach and is involved in the absorption of vitamin B_{12} by the small intestine. As you know from chapter 11, vitamin B_{12} is the anti-pernicious anemia factor and is critical to the continued production of erythrocytes.

Table 15.2 summarizes the gastric secretions' sources and functions.

Control Mechanisms

Control of stomach secretions is complex. Neural mechanisms, including the thought of food, can influence both muscular activity in the stomach and the outpourings of gastric juice, but even these controls involve the autonomic nervous system and endocrine secretions. As was indicated in chapter 8, it is the parasympathetic branch of the autonomic nervous system that handles day-to-day body operations; hence much of our digestive activity is stimulated by parasympathetic neurons.

Cephalic Phase

Stimulating abdominal fibers of the vagus nerve increases the output of gastric juices, and gastric branches of the vagus can be activated by just *thinking* about food. The vagus is a cranial nerve, and hence it has contacts with higher brain centers, so it is not surprising that stimuli produced by conscious thought can initiate activity along vagal fibers. We all know that the mere thought of food can produce **borborygmus** (stomach growling), and it is the vagus nerve that sets it off. Increased vagal activity, produced when there is no food in or entering the stomach, is known as the **cephalic** or **head phase** of gastric activity.

Gastric Phase

Once food enters the stomach, its walls begin to stretch, and these distensions alone can produce local reflexes that are able to increase the flow of hydrochloric acid and pepsin. Stretching also increases vagal activity, which adds to the outpouring of gastric juices. Each of the body's control systems has its own special control techniques and goals. Vagal activity aims primarily at the chief cells; hence it mainly enhances secretion of pepsin, although it can also slightly increase the production of hydrochloric acid. Endocrine activity, on the other hand, aims primarily at the parietal cells, boosting levels of hydrochloric acid significantly. It involves, naturally, the release of a hormone . . . a hormone called **gastrin,** which is elaborated by a specific type of cell present in a group of glands know as **pyloric glands.** These glands are present in the lower portion of the stomach, concentrated in a zone known as the **pyloric antrum,** and they differ from other gastric glands in that they have only a few parietal cells and chief cells. The cells responsible for synthesizing gastrin—called **G cells**—are thus relatively abundant in the pyloric glands.

Gastrin release is inhibited by pHs below 3.0; thus, when the stomach is empty, the G cells are inactive. When food begins entering the stomach, the total volume of acid is usually low, and the food tends to neutralize whatever is present. This raises the pH above 3.0, and gastrin secretion begins. Its volume is influenced by both stretching of the stomach wall and the presence of certain types of food in the stomach. Protein-containing foods like meat, fish, or meat broths have a powerful effect on the G cells, and when any of these is present, large quantities of gastrin are liberated.

Remember, gastrin is a hormone, not an enzyme. It is not released into the stomach. It is picked up and dispersed by the blood. Travelling in the plasma, gastrin quickly arrives back at the stomach wall, where it stimulates both parietal and chief cells, but mainly the former. Hence, while gastrin can slightly increase the secretory rate of digestive enzymes, its primary efforts enhance the secretion of hydrochloric acid. Under its influence, in fact, the rate of HCl production can increase to a level eight times higher than resting rate, which rapidly converts the stomach interior into a fuming acid bath.

Fortunately, there are built-in safeguards—I say fortunately, because continued production of such quantities of hydrochloric acid could produce an acidity so great that even the mucin lining would be unable to provide a satisfactory defense. As it turns out, the amount of acid released is limited by its own secretory success. As the acid concentration increases, the gastric pH begins to dip below 3.0, which, as we know, reduces the secretory activity of the G cells. At pH 2.0, gastrin secretion stops completely. The low pH also tends to have a suppressing effect on the activity of the parietal cells. Thus, high levels of hydrochloric acid serve as a negative stimulus in this endocrine feedback loop and can reduce the amount of gastrin secreted, even when meat products are present in the stomach.

Vigorous, churning motions of the stomach are interspersed with coordinated peristaltic waves that eventually channel all of the stomach's contents toward the pylorus. This mechanical activity is orchestrated by nerve loops originating within both Meissner's and the myenteric plexuses.

Eructation

During the process of eating, and particularly drinking, it is inevitable that some air will be swallowed. If this air is trapped solidly enough in the food, it may be passed into the small intestine, but chances are that it will be released while the food is in the stomach. As the stomach churns and mixes, these bubbles of gas usually remain small and dispersed, but eventually, particularly as stomach movement slows, they will merge into one or two large bubbles. These large bubbles produce considerable pressure, which eventually forces them into the cardiac region of the stomach, immediately beneath the opening into the esophagus. Swallowing causes relaxation of the esophageal sphincter, permitting these bubbles to erupt into the esophagus and make their way up into the pharynx, from which they are expelled, often with considerable velocity and noise. This, of course, is the process known as eructation or "burping," and in some cultures it is viewed as the ultimate compliment for having been served an excellent meal.

Intestinal Phase

When food leaves the stomach and enters the **duodenum** (the uppermost portions of the small intestine), the *intestinal phase* of gastric activity begins. The presence of the acid-laden food touching the walls of the duodenum evidently causes the release of another hormone capable of stimulating gastric secretion in the stomach. Not a great deal is known about this hormone, but its activity is so similar to that of gastrin that it is thought to be very similar, if not identical. It is known, for convenience, as **intestinal gastrin.** Intestinal gastrin increases the amount of acid produced by the stomach, but its efforts are not as highly rewarded as either the cephalic or the gastric phase of digestion. As we have seen, the gastric phase of digestion usually triggers the release of so much acid that its release actually requires inhibition.

Suppression of Stomach Activity

As far as is known, intestinal gastrin is the only intestinal reflex that *stimulates* the stomach. All the rest try to slow it down, at least partly to reduce the amount of acid that will enter the small intestine. As we know, both branches of the autonomic nervous system are represented in the walls of the gut. Generally speaking, the sympathetic tends to inhibit, while the parasympathetic stimulates digestive activity, and we must remember that their goal is homeostasis. The reason both are present is to preserve balance and smooth control, and hence their relative activity is reciprocal—when the activity of one is increased, the other is suppressed. In addition, there are endocrine factors that play their part. The suppression of gastric activity is a result of the collective activity of all these systems; each plays a role in stimulating gastric activity, and each is involved in inhibition.

Enterogastric Reflex

As might be expected, therefore, the **enterogastric reflex** (*entero,* "the intestine"; *gastric,* "stomach") involves both systems. When it is invoked, the enterogastric reflex slows stomach activity both secretory and mechanical, but it especially slows the peristaltic contractions that thrust the semifluid food mass into the small intestine. As the name implies, the receptors for the reflex are in the small intestine (entero), while the effect is exerted on the stomach (gastric). It is kindled by several things—the presence of large quantities of food in the small intestine, irritants in the food, and high levels of acidity and/or breakdown products of protein digestion. Any or all of these factors can reduce the number of impulses travelling along efferent branches of the vagus nerve. In accord with the reduced parasympathetic activity, sympathetic activity gradually increases, and the net result is a progressive slowing of stomach activity.

Endocrine Suppression

There is considerable evidence to suggest that there are also a few endocrine-controlled reflexes that will both reduce acid secretion and calm muscle activity. The presence of fats, acids, or hyperosmotic fluids in the small intestine stimulates endocrine loops that have a calming effect on the stomach. Collectively, these hormones are known as **enterogastrones,** and while workers feel that they have not isolated all of them, several are known. **Gastric inhibitory peptide (GIP)** is a potent enterogastrone, the release of which is stimulated by the presence of fat or glucose. **Cholecystokinin (CCK)** also works to inhibit stomach activity. The enterogastrones are released by cells in the intestinal mucosa, and when they are working in concert with the inhibitory branches of the vagus nerve, they are collectively able to reduce stomach secretions even when the stomach is loaded with food and its activity is peaking.

Absorption

Absorption in the stomach itself is close to nonexistent. The action of protective mechanisms is so profound that there is very little opportunity for food materials to get *to* the cells of the stomach wall, much less *through* them. Even so, some materials can pass through the gastric mucosa into the blood. These include things like alcohol and aspirin, both of which can temporarily push aside the mucin coat to form a valley through which they can reach the gastric epithelium.

The Stomach Exit

The swirling, cement-mixer activity of the stomach, along with the high quantities of fluid released into the interior, eventually convert a doughy but firm bolus into a semi-fluid pulp known as **chyme.** The peristaltic waves of the stomach drive this chyme toward the bottom or **pyloric** portion of the stomach, where it begins to pile up, increasing the pressure in that region steadily. This slow, steady increase in pressure adds its influence to other factors that will eventually stimulate a sphincter at the base of the stomach to open and, if conditions are right, the chyme exits, a little at a time, with each wave of peristaltic activity.

Factors Affecting Movement into the Intestine

Chyme leaves the stomach when a muscle known as the **pyloric sphincter** relaxes. Three factors are involved in the movement of chyme through the zone controlled by that sphincter muscle, and one of them involves the muscle itself.

1. The first factor is the state of the pyloric muscle. It must be relaxed, because if it is not opened wide enough to clear a passageway between the stomach and small intestine, obviously, nothing is going to move across.
2. A second factor is pressure. Even if the pyloric muscle is wide open, there is no way food can leave the stomach unless the pressure in the stomach is greater than it is in the small intestine.
3. The third factor is the viscosity of the stomach contents. The more fluid the chyme, the more easily it will flow through the narrow opening of the pylorus. Generally speaking, fluids leave the stomach very rapidly—usually within five minutes, and always in less than twenty minutes. This is why soups are such good appetizers . . . they stimulate the appetite, then leave the stomach quickly to make room for the entrée. Solid foods tend to remain for longer periods of time, but as they gradually mix with the rapidly flowing gastric juices, they get more and more liquid until finally, they are fluid enough to leave.

The *type* of food plays a role also. Carbohydrates do not stay in the stomach very long, probably because they dissolve easily in watery juices and things become liquid quite rapidly. For the same reason, proteins tend to move fairly quickly, too, although not as swiftly as the carbohydrates. Fats, as one might expect, can remain in the stomach for hours. There is almost no breakdown of fatty materials in the stomach, and since they are not water soluble, it takes one to two hours of constant mechanical activity to batter chunks of fat into pastes fluid enough to slide through the pylorus. Eventually, even that is accomplished, however, and as the food moves through the pylorus, it enters the small intestine.

The stomach's rate of emptying also changes with age. As the years pass, our stomachs gradually stretch, and the older one gets, the more likely it is to remain large. For young people, living tissue is quite elastic and capable of returning to its original size with little trouble. But as age asserts itself, this elasticity is gradually lost. Its demise is clearly visible as wrinkles in the skin of aged people and, while not as obvious to observers, elasticity also disappears in the tissues inside the body. In addition, there is considerable loss of muscle tone as aging sets in, so the *vigor* of the stomach's contractile activity is less than it was in youth. Furthermore, during the years when a person is growing, large quantities of construction materials are required, and physical activity is more boisterous, which uses up energy at a fantastic rate of speed. With all these raw materials being used up more rapidly, rapid replacement is necessary, and all control systems are turned up to compensate. As a result, the entire digestive system operates with greater vitality and the ingested food is processed faster.

The Interdigestive Phase

When the stomach is empty it is in the **interdigestive phase.** This period is marked by the secretion of small quantities of gastric juices that contain both acid and an alkaline buffering material released by the surface epithelial cells of the stomach. These alkaline secretions contain inorganic materials in roughly the same concentration as they are found in the plasma.

Vomiting

At one time or another, each of us has vomited. This is a reflex activity designed to empty the upper part of the gastrointestinal tract, particularly the stomach, when irritating and possibly dangerous materials are present. It results from stimulation of a nerve nucleus located in the medulla of the brain stem. Both branches of the autonomic nervous system are involved in the process, and in this case their activities are supportive rather than antagonistic. Efferent impulses arise in receptors in the gut and are transmitted to the vomiting center along both vagal and sympathetic fibers. Usually the initial impulses are subthreshold, and they initiate a series of events that end in vomiting.

First of all there is a deep inspiration, which elevates the larynx and closes off the glottis. The soft palate reflexly pushes against the internal nares to shut off the nostrils just before the diaphragm and abdominal muscles contract with considerable force. The sudden decrease in the size of the abdominal cavity compresses the stomach and hurls its contents through the esophagus and into the mouth. Usually there are several waves of abdominal contraction, but the first one or two are the strongest. They gradually weaken as the stimulus to vomit is reduced.

Vomiting doesn't always result from the presence of an irritating substance. Hyperexcitement can cause it, as can deadly fear or the sight of something shocking and nauseating. Usually, however, these urges spend themselves in a single episode. Much more dangerous is vomiting as a result of some disease, such as cholera, which can cause continual vomiting, even when there is almost nothing in the stomach.

What makes such vomiting dangerous is the constant loss of water and important mineral salts, including potassium, sodium, and hydrogen ions. The heavy loss of hydrogen leads to alkalosis, while excessive vomiting of potassium can produce a rare but very unpleasant condition known as **hypokalemia** (reduced potassium). Hypokalemia can result in slowed breathing, convulsions, and in prolonged cases, severe cardiac problems.

The Small Intestine

There are some interesting suppositions about the small intestine that are apparently well-known and are generally considered facts, but are, unfortunately, not true. One of them is that the small intestine is nearly thirty-five feet long, folded neatly back and forth and bundled into a compact mass tucked away inside our abdomens. Another is that virtually all food digestion takes place within the lumen of the small intestine, and once the food is broken down into small enough molecules, it simply diffuses across the lining into the bloodstream.

During life, the GI tract tends to range in the neighborhood of fifteen to eighteen feet (about five meters) in length, and with careful packing it folds neatly in place. That is a lot of tubing to cram into a cavity as small as the human abdomen, but the body manages. Only after death, when muscle tone vanishes, does it stretch out to lengths of thirty or more feet.

While considerable digestion does take place in the small intestine, a great deal of chemical breakdown has already occurred in the stomach. As we have already seen, most mechanical digestion occurs in the mouth and stomach. The great chunks of solid food that enter the mouth are a rough paste when they enter the stomach, and they are a semiliquid when they leave it. Furthermore, there is a considerable amount of chemical activity in both these regions. Starches and other polysaccharides are reduced to much smaller polymers by salivary amylases, and gastric pepsin has split most of the proteins into much smaller polypeptides.

Finally, and this is of great importance to us, absorption is not a passive process. It was assumed for many years to be passive, because the intestinal tract contains very high concentrations of proteins, fats, and carbohydrates when a meal is being digested, and passive absorption seemed to make sense; after all, it would be an energy saver. But energy saver or not, it is not the mechanism responsible for most intestinal absorption.

Before any absorption can take place, however, there is still a lot to do. A great deal of chemical breakdown must occur—much more than either the gastric or salivary enzymes have provided up to this point.

Chemical Digestion

When chyme enters the small intestine, it enters as a partially digested, liquified mass. Carbohydrate digestion has been begun, but it is not complete—protein digestion is about the same, and the lipids are mostly untouched. Fortunately, the small intestine is literally washed in detergents and digestive enzymes that are made to finish the job. Significant quantities of these enzymes are produced by cells lining the lumen of the intestinal tract, but an impressive volume comes from the pancreas.

The Pancreas

We have already investigated the endocrine functions of the pancreas and have seen that those operations alone render it an organ of critical importance. However, like a good many large body organs, the pancreas has more than one job to do. In addition to secreting insulin, glucagon, somatostatin, and pancreatic polypeptide, it plays a critical role in the chemical breakdown of foodstuffs in the small intestine.

Figure 15.20 The pancreas, an organ that is both exocrine and endocrine in function. The acinar cells are responsible for the secretion of digestive enzymes. The islet cells synthesize hormones.

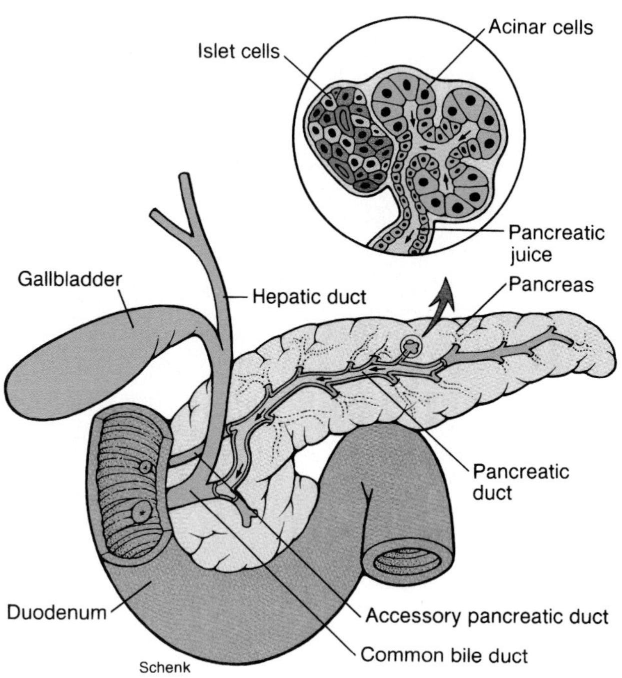

If one were to judge relative value on the basis of how much of an organ is devoted to a given task, we would have to believe that this digestive activity is the most important thing the pancreas does. Most of the pancreatic structure is involved in the synthesis and transport of digestive enzymes into the small intestine. The *islets of Langerhans*, which govern the organ's endocrine activity, are merely small patches of cells that dot the intervals between the large enzyme-producing centers with their batteries of **acinar cells** (figure 15.20). Each day, these cell clusters produce between 1,100 and 1,500 ml of an isotonic, protein-rich fluid loaded with bicarbonates and secreted into strategically located ducts that eventually join the **pancreatic duct** for their trip through the remaining pancreatic tissue and into the intestinal tract (figure 15.21).

Figure 15.21 The pancreas sits on the upper fold of the small intestine. Its ducts open into the duodenum.

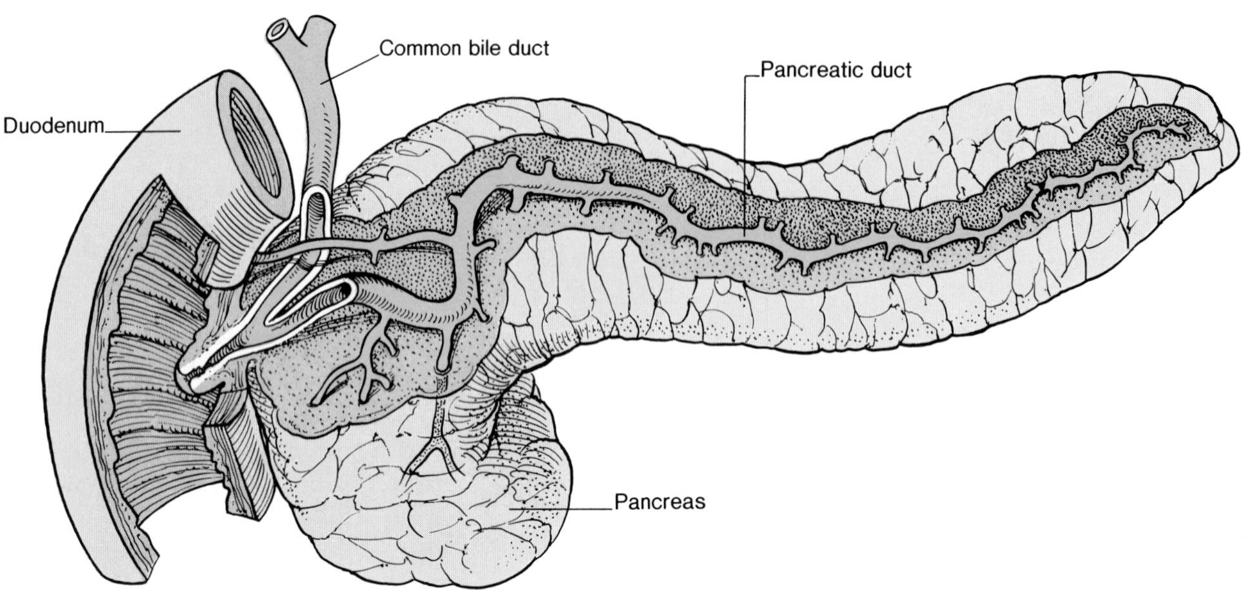

Pancreatic Secretions

Bicarbonates

The pH of the pancreatic fluids is about 8.0 when they are secreted. That is pretty alkaline, and it is mostly because of large quantities of bicarbonates that will neutralize the powerful acids pouring from the stomach with the chyme. The production of these highly alkaline secretions is just as fascinating as the production of the stomach's acid secretions, because chemically, the process is essentially the reverse of that which produced the hydrochloric acid for the stomach (figure 15.22). As you can see from the figure, it is a process that, simply put, takes sodium ions out of the blood and puts hydrogen ions in.

As is the case with acid production in the stomach, the only source of raw materials for bicarbonate production is the blood, and removing sodium bicarbonate while replacing it with hydrogen and chloride ions quite naturally produces a fairly acid blood. Therefore, the blood leaving the pancreatic circulation when food is in the intestine is quite acidic. You will recall from our discussion of gastric digestion that the blood leaving a full stomach is quite alkaline. The alkaline blood from the stomach mixes with the acidic blood leaving the pancreas; thus, as long as there is food in the stomach, the pancreatic *acid tide* continues to associate with the *alkaline tide* from the gastric circulation, and the two neutralize each other, returning the pH of the venous blood to normal.

Pancreatic Enzymes

In addition to the bicarbonate outflow, the pancreas also produces enzymes capable of hydrolyzing all major classes of food compounds. Pancreatic amylases and proteases are abundant, and unlike the gastric enzymes, they operate best in pHs that are slightly alkaline. Pancreatic lipases, finally secreted in large quantities, are able, with the aid of bile, to digest lipid molecules in the intestinal tract. The pancreas also secretes specific nucleases designed to deal with the numerous strands of nucleic acid that are ingested. All of these enzymes enter the small intestine via the main pancreatic duct.

Pancreatic Amylase The carbohydrate splitters produced in the pancreas are secreted in an active form. They promptly assault whatever polysaccharides they can locate. Functionally, pancreatic amylases are similar to the salivary amylases, meaning they are quite capable of breaking the links between individual sugars as long as they do not involve molecules on either end of the chain. So, as is the case with ptyalin, a lot of di- and trisaccharides and small polysaccharides are produced, but very little free glucose.

Proteolytic Enzymes The pancreas is able to synthesize several precursors of proteolytic enzymes. **Chymotrypsinogen, trypsinogen,** and some **carboxypeptidases** are all produced by the pancreas, and each is designed to break specific peptide linkages. Trypsin is the most abundant, and hence is probably the hardest working of them all, but neither it nor chymotrypsin can break terminal amino acids away from the peptide chains. Only carboxypeptidase is adept at doing this. It attacks proteins at their terminus, thus cleaving single amino acids from them. Carboxypeptidase is not, however, produced in very large quantities, so very few single amino acids are liberated by the proteolytic activity of pancreatic enzymes.

Figure 15.22 Starting at the left of the figure, sodium ions associated with chloride are removed from the blood. The sodium is transferred through the pancreatic secretory cells and actively pumped from there into the lumen of the duct. Carbon dioxide diffuses into the secretory cells, where its conversion to carbonic acid, then to carbonate and H^+ ions is accelerated by the intracellular enzyme *carbonic anhydrase.* The bicarbonate ion, through the judicious use of cellular energy, is then pumped into the lumen of the duct, where it associates with the sodium already there, producing the alkaline buffer. The hydrogen ions from the dissociated carbonic acid are removed from the secretory cells and returned to the blood in association with the chloride that was once part of the sodium salt. Essentially, the blood has exchanged sodium for hydrogen ions, and part of its content of sodium chloride has become hydrochloric acid.

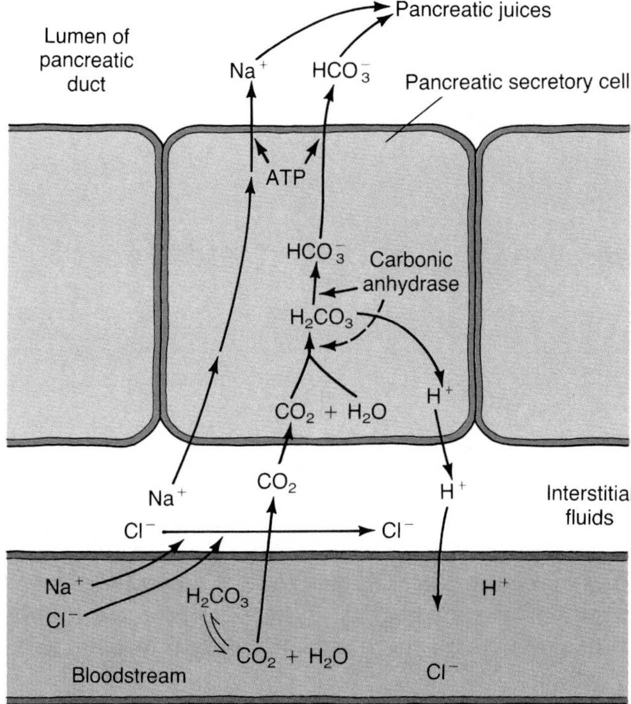

Pancreatic Lipase The lipid-digesting enzymes are known collectively as **lipases.** As is the case with the other groups, the pancreas secretes several. They are similar in chemistry to the proteolytic enzymes, so it is not surprising to discover that both they and certain of the proteolytic enzymes can hydrolyze fatty molecules.

Nucleases The pancreatic secretions also contain enzymes specifically designed to attack RNA and DNA strands and free their monomers. **Pancreatic nucleases** are restricted to separating the nitrogen-containing bases from their sugar-phosphate strands, leaving the latter to be broken up by other, less specific, enzymes.

Self-Protection Like the stomach's pepsin and hydrochloric acid, the pancreatic enzymes are potentially dangerous. Turning a fat or protein-shattering enzyme loose inside a living cell would be disastrous for the cell and all its close neighbors. Hence the pancreas is careful to protect itself. As is the case with the stomach, pancreatic protein splitters are not active when they are synthesized. Trypsin, for example, is synthesized and stored as **trypsinogen,** an inactive compound, and until it is released into the interior of the gut, it is kept that way. Producing inactive enzymes is a most reliable protection, but apparently it is not reliable enough. It is reinforced by packaging inactive enzymes in granules surrounded by thick membranes of protein and lipid, isolating them most effectively from other parts of the cell. As a still further precaution, the pancreatic juices contain an inhibiting chemical that is capable of neutralizing any enzymes that might break out of their sacks and become prematurely activated. Obviously these precautions are necessary, because despite all of them, pancreatic enzymes do occasionally become active while still in the cells of the pancreas, and when they do, a potentially lethal condition known as **pancreatitis** can develop.

Enzyme Activation The enzymes are obviously going to be of no value if they remain in an inactive state; sooner or later, they must be activated. Usually this is accomplished when they are released into the lumen of the intestine or the pancreatic duct, and usually by a chemical already there. The greatest activator of all the proteolytic enzymes, including trypsinogen, is its active form, trypsin. Obviously, however, before newly released trypsinogen can activate anything, it must first be activated itself. This initial activation is accomplished by an enzyme known as **enterokinase,** which is produced in small amounts by intestinal cells. As trypsinogen enters the duodenum, enterokinase manages to attack a few molecules, and their conversion into trypsin sets off a chain reaction that gets faster and faster as more and more trypsin accumulates. Chymotrypsinogen is an enzyme made up of 246 amino acids, and it is activated when trypsin removes 15 amino acids from its terminus. The inactive form of carboxypeptidase is **procarboxypeptidase,** and it, too, is activated by trypsin's enzymatic removal of certain of its amino acids.

Like the proteases, pancreatic lipases require activation when they reach the pancreatic ducts. Unlike the proteases, however, the fat splitters require more than simple activation before they can do their work properly. In the absence of certain liver secretions, they are generally ineffective even in their active form. We will have more to say about this shortly.

Figure 15.23 The liver's location in the body. It is in the upper right zone of the gut, partially surrounded by ribs. This figure is a view from above.

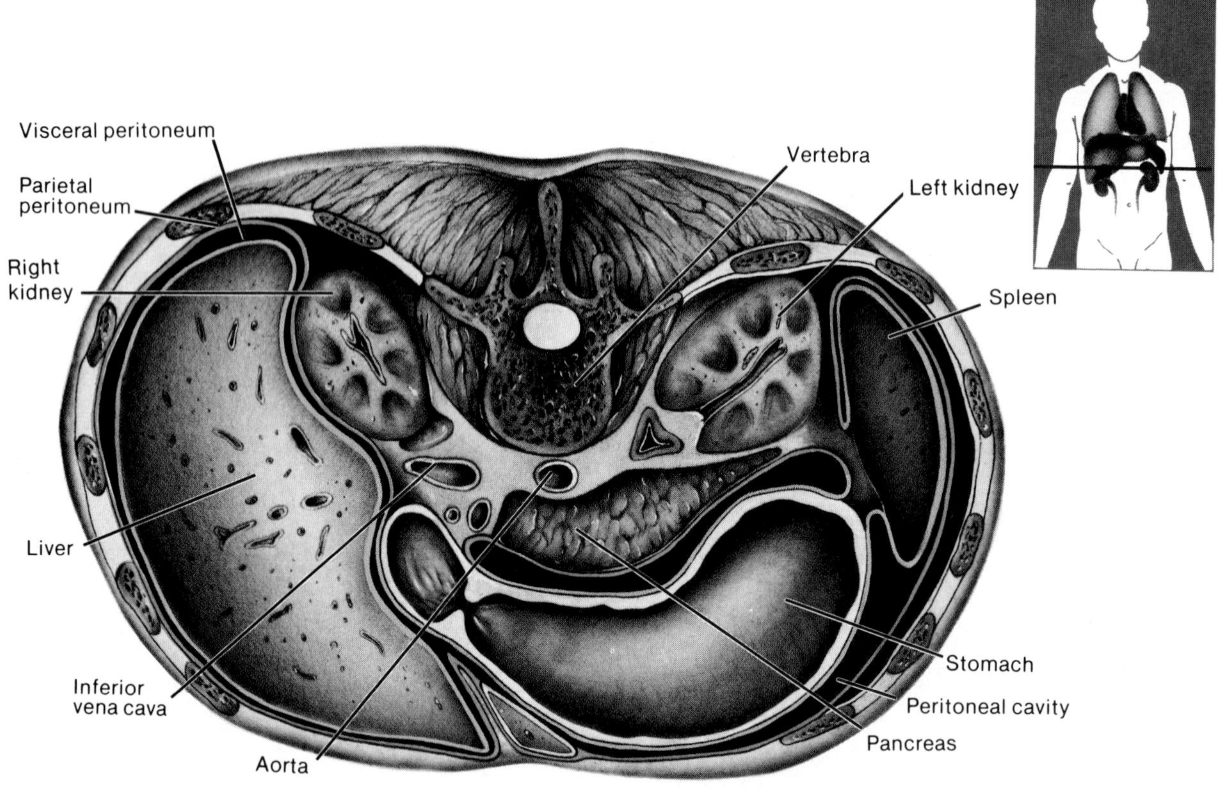

Secretory Control

As is common throughout the digestive tract, the control of pancreatic outflow is both nervous and endocrine. Branches of the vagus nerve can stimulate some sparse pancreatic secretion when food is smelled or seen, thus adding pancreatic activity to the cephalic phase of digestion. The secretions increase slightly in volume as soon as food enters the mouth and again when the bolus drops into the stomach, but without endocrine stimulus, the total amount remains small.

The endocrine system swings into action as soon as food reaches the interior of the small intestine. The hormone **secretin** is synthesized by cells in the intestinal tract and is released as soon as the acidic contents of the stomach contact the walls of the duodenum. Apparently, the main stimulus is the acid; hence it seems logical that secretin would work mainly to reduce the levels of acidity, thereby avoiding damage to the intestinal lining. This it does, and it has two approaches to the problem. One involves stomach activity. When the stomach is full, producing enzymes and acids at maximum rate and passing them quickly into the intestine, secretin can oppose the effects of gastrin and restrain the stomach's activity somewhat. The second approach involves the cells in the pancreas that are responsible for releasing bicarbonates, because these are the chemicals that will reduce the strength of the acid and eventually buffer it to neutrality. Thus, in the presence of secretin, bicarbonate production escalates, and large volumes of heavily buffered, slightly alkaline fluid pour out of the pancreatic duct into the small intestine.

A second hormone is also involved in the control of pancreatic secretions. This one was originally given the name *pancreozymin* by early workers, and it was credited with stimulating the acinar cells of the pancreas. Recent work indicates that pancreozymin and cholecystokinin are the same compound, and the former name has therefore been dropped. We know now that, in addition to its regulating effects on the stomach, CCK can stimulate the synthesis and release of three types of enzymes—proteolytic, lipolytic, and amylolytic—from the acinar cells of the pancreas. As was noted, the secretion of CCK is stimulated by the presence of certain amino acids and fats—mostly fats—in the intestinal tract.

Digestive Activity of the Liver

The liver is an organ of tremendous complexity—one of the biggest and most important in the body (figures 15.23 and 15.24). As the body's largest gland, it

Figure 15.24 The excised liver, viewed from the front (*a*) and from below (*b*).

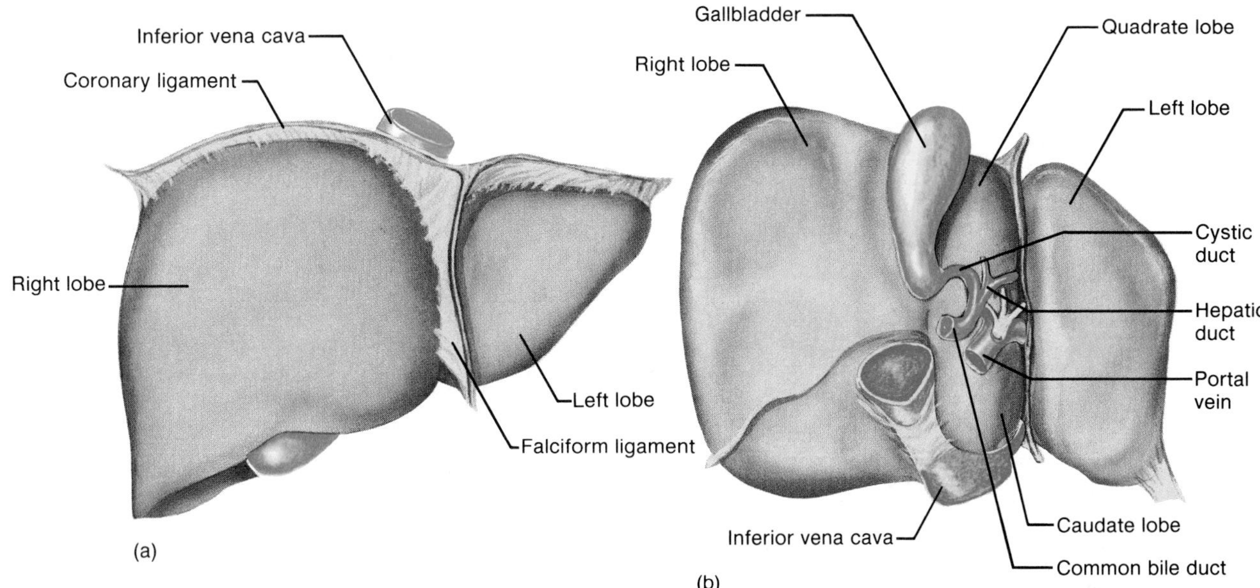

is involved in the metabolism of energy-containing compounds. It is responsible for the disposal of waste products such as bilirubin. It synthesizes dozens of essential body compounds like cholesterol and prothrombin. In addition, it is responsible for much of the fat digestion that takes place in the small intestine.

Not that it secretes digestive enzymes—that, as far as we know, is one thing the liver does not do. Yet without its secretions, more than half of the fat eaten by humans would pass untouched through the digestive tract and be dumped in the feces. When its secretions are present, water-soluble lipolytic enzymes come into contact with the chunks of fat and oils that pass into the small intestine and are able, at least partially, to break up and emulsify the larger molecules before absorption.

Bile

In a normal twenty-four-hour day, the human liver will secrete between 600 and 900 ml of **bile,** a thick, greenish-yellow fluid, most of which is water and salts. The color is provided by a fraction known simply as **bile pigment.** Bile pigment represents the discarded fraction of hemoglobin from dismantled red blood cells that the liver has metabolized (chapter 12) and is dumping into the GI tract for disposal, but it has no digestive significance. The **bile salts** are the chemicals that are involved in the liver's digestive operations, and they, like so many of the body's important compounds, are derivatives of cholesterol (figure 15.25). After synthesis, they are actively transported from the cells, making their way down the hepatic duct and up into the gallbladder, where they are stored until they are needed.

Bile salts have several roles to play:

1. They are detergents; hence they are able to disperse fatty globules in water and keep them dispersed. This increases their surface area and renders them more susceptible to attack by the lipases secreted into the intestinal lumen.
2. They can increase the activity of the pancreatic lipases, enzymes that are synthesized and secreted in a relatively inactive form. For example, bile salts transform pancreatic lipase from a relatively weak enzyme into a powerful one, and they may be the only agent capable of accomplishing this.
3. They have a powerful **choleretic** action, meaning they are the primary stimulus for the synthesis of greater amounts of bile salts by the liver.
4. They keep cholesterol in solution.

Also, while this is not a function of bile salts, it should be noted that in the absence of bile, fat absorption takes place very slowly, and the uptake of fat-soluble vitamins like A and K often falls to subminimal levels.

Not all of the functions of bile are tied to bile salts. Bile also contains considerable bicarbonate, which neutralizes the acid chyme and helps adjust pH levels

Figure 15.25 Cholesterol (*top*) and two of its liver-synthesized derivatives, glycocholic acid and chenodeoxycholic acid. Salts of these two biliary acids are the major components of human bile salts.

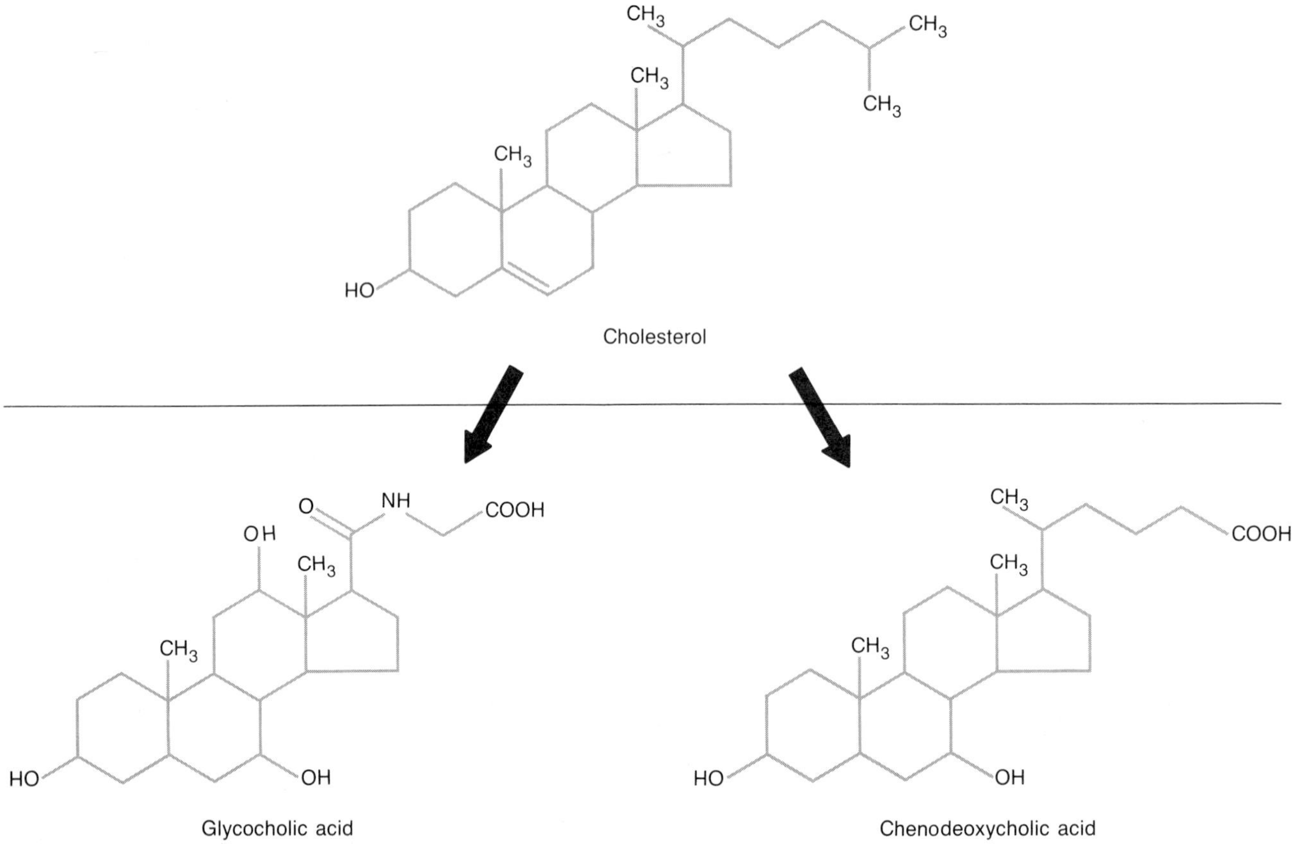

Cholesterol

Glycocholic acid

Chenodeoxycholic acid

to those more favorable to pancreatic enzyme activity. It also serves as an excretory channel for some of the body's metabolic waste products. Bilirubin, cholesterol, metabolized drugs, and excess metal atoms are all excreted into the GI tract in the bile.

The Liver and Cholesterol

Excess cholesterol is excreted primarily in the bile, and the amounts that are dumped depend on many things, including diet. There are several sources of such cholesterol. Whenever cells are broken up, cholesterol will be released (remember, all cell membranes contain cholesterol), and the erythrocyte breakdown rate is incredible. In addition, the liver itself synthesizes cholesterol for use by cellular synthetic machinery.

Without bile, fat digestion is truly crippled. When bile is absent from the small intestine, human feces become clay colored, voluminous, greasy, and have an exceedingly vile odor, all of which is due to the presence of large quantities of undigested and rancid fats and oils (a condition known medically as **steatorrhea**). Experimental animals chronically deprived of bile eventually develop bone abnormalities and mineral imbalances, and none survive long. This suggests that bile is involved in other, even more vital, functions that have not yet been elucidated.

Cholesterol sometimes accumulates in large quantities in the liver and gallbladder. Cholesterol is concentrated during its stay in the gallbladder, and this, when coupled with minor biliary infections, can sometimes cause serious problems. Normally, cholesterol remains in the gallbladder unchanged. As cholesterol, its quantities seldom become excessive, simply because if they get too great, some can be reabsorbed. Infectious bacteria can change all that. Once a population of bacteria gets established in the biliary transport areas, it can grow in numbers very quickly, because bile is not self-sterilizing. These large pockets of bacteria can reduce the cholesterol to a compound called **coprosterol,** which the system cannot reabsorb. As more and more coprosterol is produced, it begins to plug up the gallbladder and other secretory areas of the liver. The result is the painful and debilitating lumps of extremely hard lipid called **gallstones,** which usually must be surgically removed.

Figure 15.26 The flow of bile during periods when the upper digestive tract is empty. Bile produced by the liver flows into the hepatic duct and down the common bile duct, but with Oddi's sphincter closed, it has nowhere to go but into the gallbladder, where it is stored and partially concentrated.

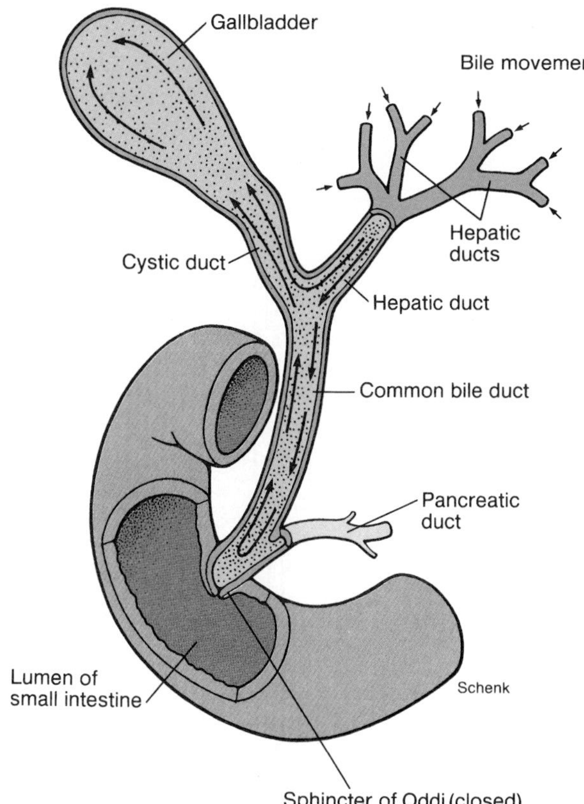

Storage of Bile

Bile salts are synthesized and secreted constantly, but the flow rate varies depending on conditions in the small intestine. Between meals, bile flows very slowly—which is just as well, since the sphincter of Oddi (figure 15.26) is closed. As figure 15.26 shows, Oddi's sphincter guards the opening from the common bile duct into the small intestine. With this opening closed, the bile flowing from the liver has no place to go but up the cystic duct into the gallbladder. Bile is stored in the gallbladder when the gut is empty, and since the between-meals period can sometimes be pretty long, it is well that the gallbladder is elastic and stretches easily to accommodate its steadily increasing contents. Its elasticity has limitations, however. Even at its maximum stretch, its total capacity is seldom more than 70 ml, and the liver can secrete that much bile in just one hour. Nevertheless, observations indicate that the gallbladder can easily store twelve hours' worth of bile. That being true, it is obvious that something besides elasticity is involved. It turns out that the gallbladder's storage capacity is enormously augmented by its ability to reduce the volume of the bile almost as soon as it enters. Bile flowing into the gallbladder contains lots of mineral ions and a great deal of water. These minerals are actively pumped out of the bladder, and water follows the osmotic gradient, thus concentrating the bile. In humans, bile stored in the gallbladder is routinely concentrated about five-fold, but it is not unusual for long-stored bile to be twelve times its original concentration.

Regulation of Bile

So when the gut is empty and the sphincter of Oddi is closed, the gallbladder gradually becomes filled with highly concentrated bile. This makes sense, since it is always nice to have a stockpile of necessary materials. Obviously, however, bile serves no purpose locked up in the gallbladder. For it to be of value, there must be a way to mobilize it when the proper time arrives, and that means some sort of control is necessary to (1) relax the sphincter of Oddi so that bile can leave the hepatic duct, and (2) get the hoard of concentrated bile out of the gallbladder and into the intestine.

This time, there are three different types of controls. The endocrine and nervous systems are involved, naturally, and in addition, there is a feedback control loop that does not involve either system. The stimulus that turns everything on is, apparently, the presence of fats or proteins— especially fats—in the small intestine.

Hormonal Control

Hormonal control is affected by cholecystokinin. CCK is synthesized and secreted by special cells imbedded in the walls of the intestinal tract. As with gastrin, it's important to remember that cholecystokinin is a hormone. It is not secreted into the intestinal tract but rather into the interstitial fluid, whence it is picked up by the blood (figure 15.27). Travelling in the blood, it makes its way back to the liver where it stimulates the smooth muscles surrounding the gallbladder. In response, the muscles contract, squeezing the bladder like the bulb of a medicine dropper and squirting the contents into the hepatic duct.

Figure 15.27 Endocrine control of bile release: cholecystokinin. (*1*) The presence of fats and/or amino acids in the duodenum stimulates the production of cholecystokinin (CCK) by the intestinal mucosa. CCK diffuses into the interstitial fluid. (*2*) CCK is picked up by the blood. Carried through the hepatic portal circulation and through the system as well, it gets to blood vessels in the liver, where it diffuses back into interstitial fluids. Here it has at least two effects: (*3*) It aids in inhibiting the muscles of Oddi's sphincter, causing the hepatic duct to open to the intestine, and (*4*) it causes contraction of the smooth muscles around the gallbladder, thus squirting concentrated bile into the intestine.

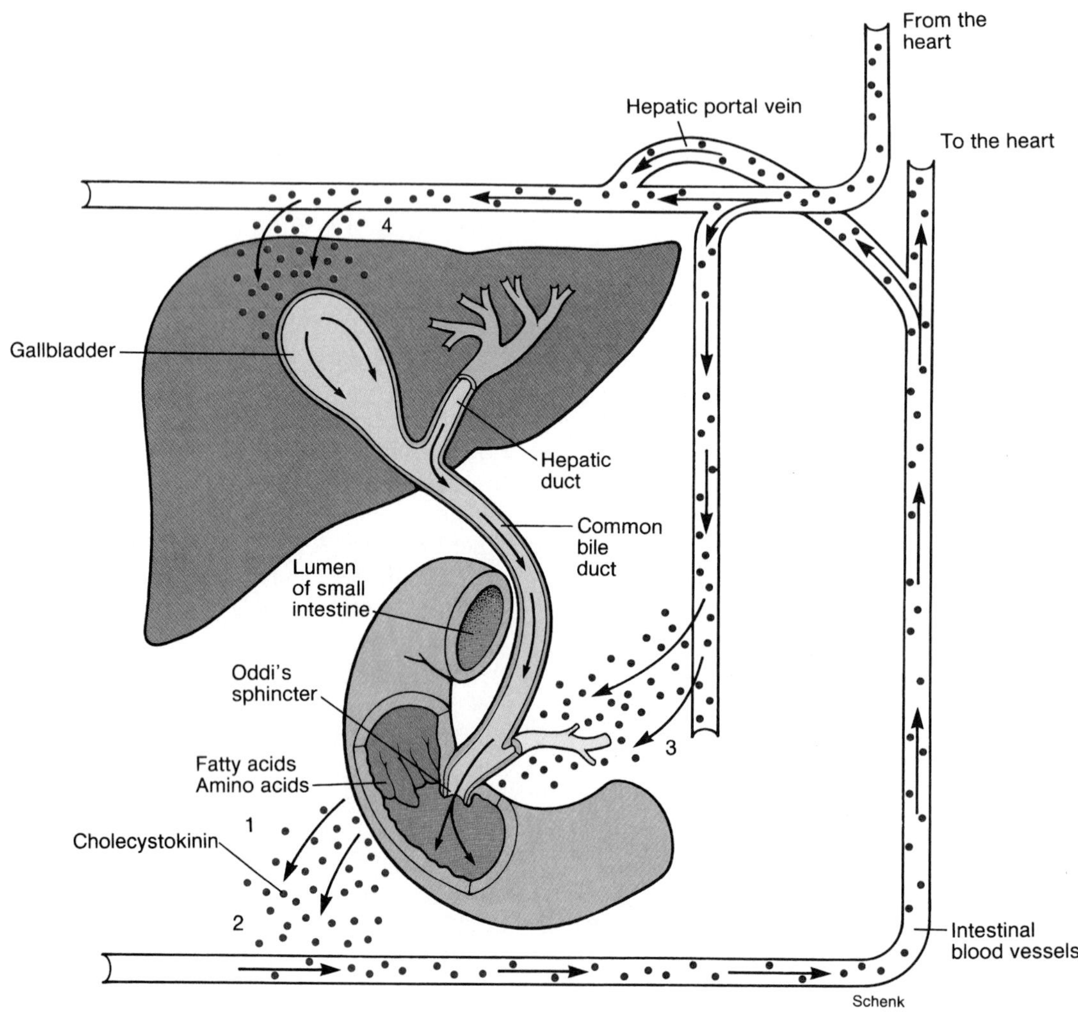

Neural Control

Naturally, the stored bile will go nowhere if the sphincter of Oddi is not relaxed first. Relaxation of the sphincter of Oddi seems to be mainly a reflex—probably a nervous one—although there is evidence that cholecystokinin is at least partly responsible. In any case, the process of relaxation occurs either just prior to, or simultaneously with, the contraction of the muscles surrounding the gallbladder. With the door to the intestinal tract open, the concentrated bile flows through.

Chemical Control

More than 90 percent of the bile salts that are thrust into the duodenum are promptly absorbed through the walls of the intestine and enter the blood. Here, they serve as a chemical stimulus to increase the liver's rate of bile production (figure 15.28). Thus they become an intricate part of one of the few *positive* feedback loops in biological systems (figure 15.29).

As figure 15.29 shows, each time the synthesis of bile salts increases, it increases their volume in the intestine, which in turn increases the blood content of bile salts and stimulates the liver to even greater efforts. Obviously, it is legitimate to ask where all this ends, since, like all positive feedback loops, it is the kind of self-perpetuating process that could escalate out of control if not governed by some kind of restraining or braking mechanism.

Figure 15.28 The cyclic control of bile salt production during feeding. (*1*) Bile salts entering the intestine are absorbed by the blood and carried to the liver. (*2*) Diffusing into the liver, they increase the synthesis and release of additional bile salts, which are released into the hepatic ducts. (*3*) Entering the lumen of the intestine, the additional bile salts are absorbed by the blood, increasing the circulatory content, which further increases the synthesis and release of bile salts. This is a positive feedback mechanism that could run amok were it not for the "interrupter" capability of cholecystokinin.

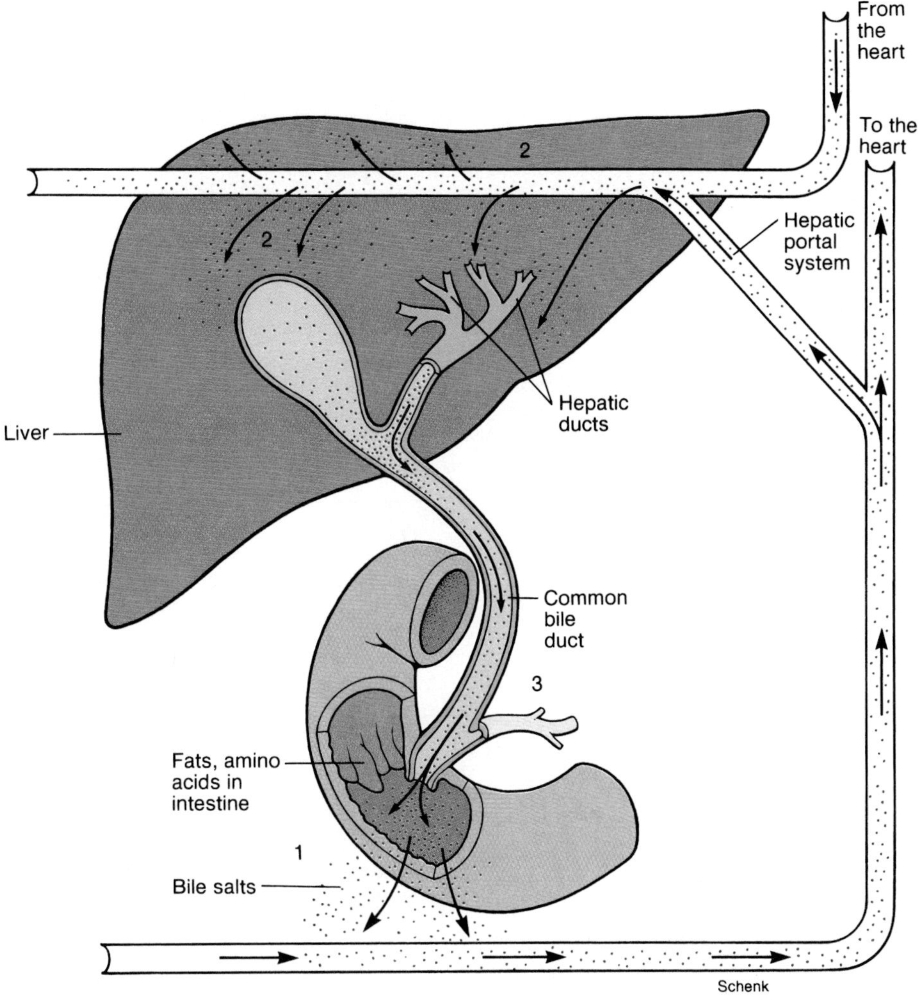

The brake is provided by the contents of the intestine. When fats and proteins are absent—as naturally they would be, once they were broken up and absorbed—the secretion of cholecystokinin stops. Without cholecystokinin, the muscles around the gallbladder relax, and the reflex inhibition of Oddi's sphincter is removed. Thus, the exit from the common bile duct is closed, and with no way of getting into the intestine, the newly made bile backs up into the gallbladder. As the blood is gradually depleted of its bile-salt content, the furiously working liver cells slow to their normal, between-meal production rate.

The actions of the gastric and intestinal hormones are summarized in table 15.3.

Figure 15.29 The positive feedback loop that invigorates the synthesis of bile salts by the liver.

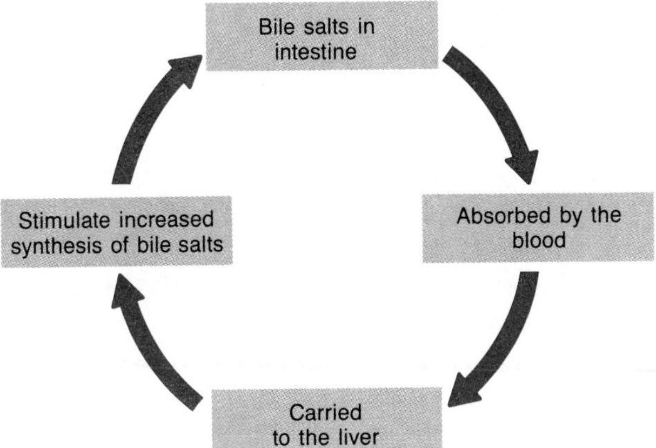

Table 15.3 Gastric and Intestinal Hormones

	Hormone Source	Activity	Stimulus
Gastrin	Stomach lining	1. Stimulates activity of the gastric glands in the stomach—particularly the synthesis of HCl by the parietal cells 2. May mildly stimulate secretion of bile and pancreatic juices	Protein in stomach
Secretin	Duodenal mucosa	1. Stimulates production of bicarbonate from pancreas 2. Inhibits secretion of HCl from gastric parietal cells 3. Reduces gastric motility 4. Stimulates bile secretion slightly	Acid in duodenum
Cholecystokinin (pancreozymin)	Intestinal mucosa	1. Stimulates contraction of smooth muscles around gallbladder 2. Relaxes Oddi's sphincter 3. Stimulates pancreatic acinar cells 4. Inhibits gastric parietal cell activity	Fat in duodenum
Gastric inhibitory peptide (enterogastrone)	Upper intestine	1. Inhibits gastric parietal cell activity 2. Reduces gastric motility	Carbohydrate or fat in intestine

Intestinal Digestion

It was assumed for decades that all food breakdown that was accomplished in the small intestine took place within the lumen—the space inside—and that the lining served only as a passive, permeable coating. It was likewise believed that the process of absorption depended on the diffusion gradient. If the concentration of the various organic molecules was greater inside the intestine than it was in the interstitial fluids, then it diffused across the lining and entered the blood—otherwise it did not.

Recent work indicates that none of these suppositions is correct—not completely. Certainly some food breakdown takes place within the intestinal lumen. The potentials of the pancreatic enzymes and the biliary secretions are all realized there. But not all food digestion takes place within the lumen, and the intestinal lining is definitely not just a passive veneer facing a hollow interior.

The cells comprising the inner lining of the small intestine are active in both food breakdown and in the absorption of digested materials. There are myriad enzymes within the structural cells of the small intestine. Many of them are firmly imbedded in the outer half of the membrane, and as a result, a great deal of fuel breakdown takes place right on the cellular surfaces—a convenient arrangement. With the large particles broken down to absorbable size right on the surface of the cell through which they are going to be reabsorbed, there need be no waste of energy transporting them to an absorptive surface. Each absorptive cell has an assortment of transport mechanisms, all designed to help nutrient particles get from the interior of the gut into the interior of the body.

The idea that food absorption is strictly passive has persisted to the present day in the curriculum of many high schools and even some junior college classes. Yet we have known for decades that this idea is false. It was demonstrated as early as 1870 that both water and proteins could be absorbed from blood serum placed in the stomach of experimental animals. This would clearly be impossible if diffusion were the only mechanism at work, because water and protein concentrations are the same on both sides of the gut. Only a few years later, it was noticed that the gut seemed to selectively absorb things that it needed and to ignore those that were metabolically less important. For example, the six-carbon sugars fructose and glucose—essential in human metabolism—were absorbed at a much higher rate of speed than were sugars like trehalose and sorbose, which are relatively useless to human metabolism.

Some Intestinal Anatomy

The small intestine is a tubular organ that extends from the pylorus all the way to the entrance into the large intestine, a total length of about three meters (figure 15.30). It consists of three regions: the duodenum, which is immediately adjacent to the stomach, is about 25 cm (10 inches) long and about 5 cm in diameter; the **jejunum,** which is approximately 65 cm long; and the **ileum,** which comprises the remaining two meters or so. The entire mass is suspended from the upper wall of the peritoneal (abdominal) cavity by a thick fold of connective tissue called **mesentery.** Through this mesentery course all the blood and lymphatic vessels that nourish and drain the intestinal walls.

The small intestinal wall is a classic example of how structural design can optimize function. Its

Figure 15.30 The small intestine as it is positioned in the abdominal cavity.

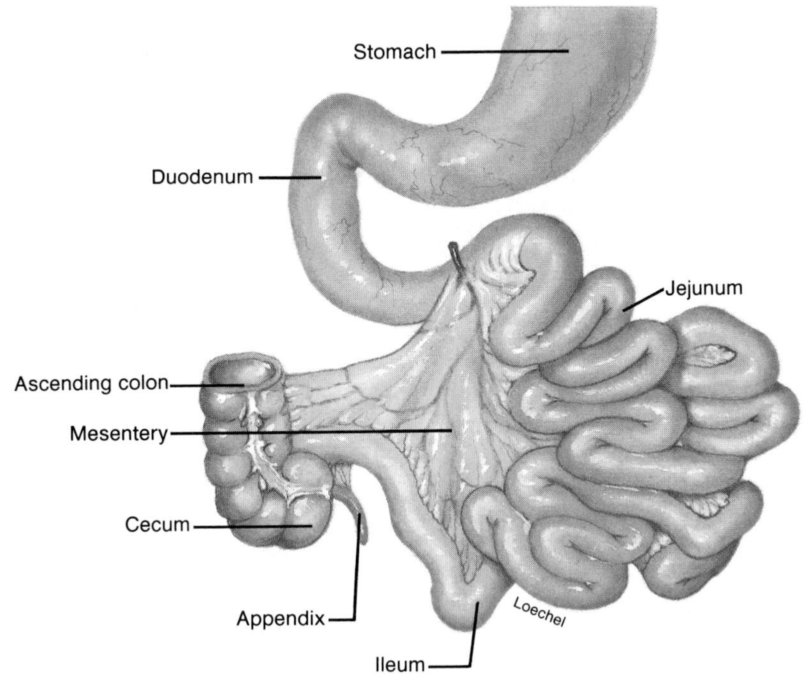

overall design is typical of the four-layered arrangement throughout the GI tract, but there are some significant modifications that maximize function. The **mucosa** lines the inside of the intestinal tube (figure 15.31*a*), wrapped by the **submucosa.** As is the case throughout the tract, the mucosa contains the secretory cells and glands and the absorptive cells of the small intestine, while the submucosa contains the blood and lymphatic vessels that will ultimately carry away the nutrients absorbed by the mucosa. These two layers, in their turn, are wrapped by two layers of smooth muscle. The cells of the innermost muscle layer are oriented so that their long axes are perpendicular to the longitudinal axis of the intestine. As a consequence, when individual cells of this layer contract, the tube elongates and its diameter decreases (figure 15.32*a*). This is the **circular muscle layer.** The outermost muscle sheet is arranged with its cells lying *across* those of the circular layer (figure 15.31*a*). Its individual cells are parallel to the long axis of the gut, so when they contract, the intestinal tube shortens and its diameter increases (figure 15.32*b*). This is the **longitudinal muscle layer.** The **serosa,** as we know, surrounds the entire tube (figure 15.31*a*).

Functional Significance

Intestinal Movement

The two layers of muscle are, as one might expect, somewhat antagonistic to one another, and we should have little difficulty understanding why. As was stated in chapter 11, muscles cannot push, they can only pull. After a muscle cell has done its job and shortened with power, there must be some external agency to stretch it out so it can do its job again, and antagonistic muscles usually handle that. But the muscle sheets that wrap the intestine are stretched out as much by the bulging mass of food inside as by the antagonistic action of another muscle. When the gut is full, these two sheets of smooth muscle sometimes coordinate their activities into peristaltic activity, and sometimes they do not. When they work cooperatively to produce peristalsis, the wavelike contractions provide the propulsive force that moves the chyme through the gut. Their non-peristaltic squeezings are designed to aid in the process of mixing and churning the food to expose every surface to enzyme activity.

The Topography of the Mucosa

The mucosal layers of the intestine are of most interest to the physiologist, because the innermost layer contains the cells that are designed to finish the job of breaking down the organic polymers and then absorb them. They are aided in their task by some unusual morphological features obviously intended to augment absorption.

The most obvious of these are the **circular folds** (figure 15.31*a*) that cover the internal surface like the Himalaya mountain range covers Tibet. This buckling of the mucosal layer serves, all by itself, to increase the internal surface area by a factor of nearly three. Then there are the **villi** (figure 15.31*b*). The entire luminal surface of the mucosa is covered with villi. These are tiny surface projections that reach into the lumen of the intestine. Individually, they are hard to see without assistance, but collectively their pres-

Figure 15.31 (*a*) The layers and inner surface of the small intestine. (*b*) A cross section through one circular fold. (*c*) An intestinal villus.

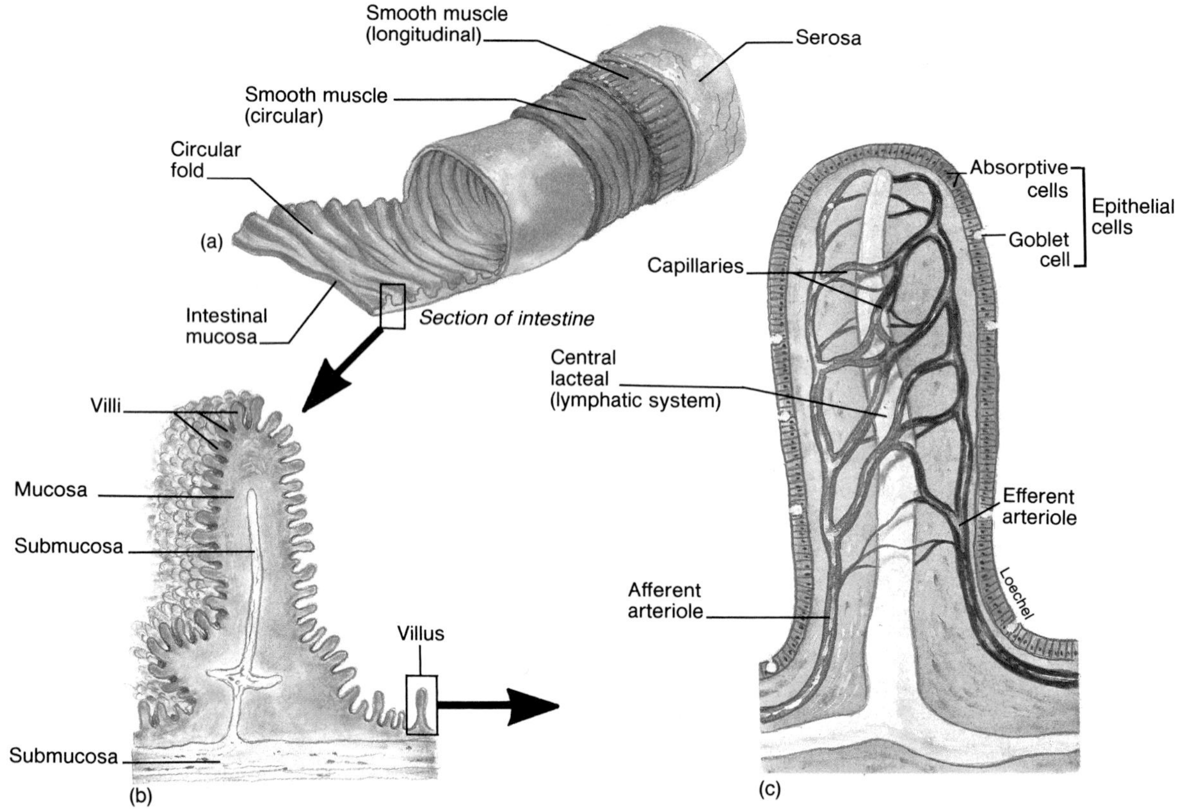

Figure 15.32 Smooth muscle in the intestine. (*a*) Circular muscle contraction decreases tube diameter and increases length (makes it longer and thinner). (*b*) Longitudinal muscle contraction shortens the tube and increases the diameter (makes it short and fat). Both of these diagrams exaggerate the actual processed involved. The exaggerations are deliberate.

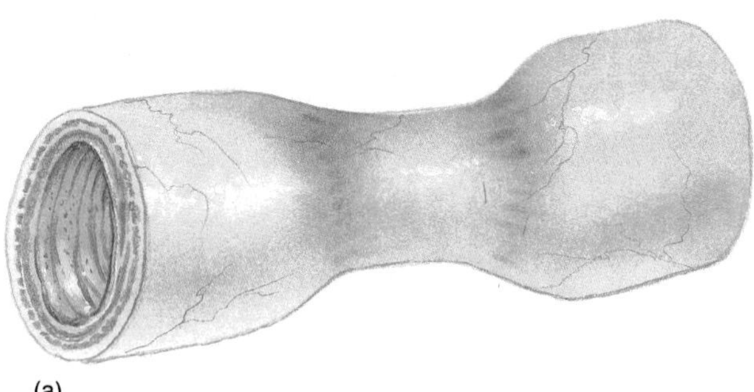

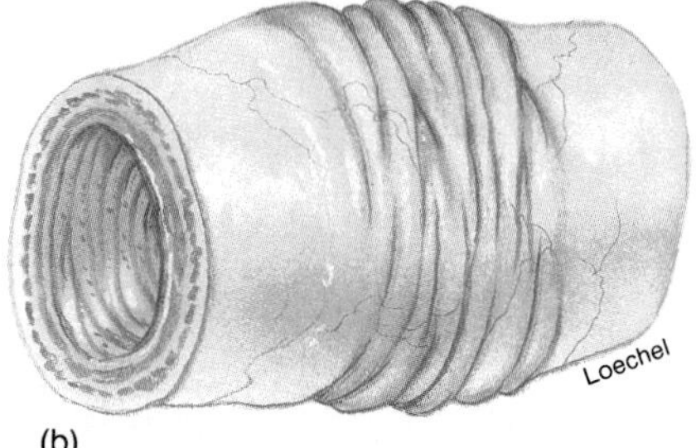

ence is easy to confirm—they make the entire internal surface of the intestinal tract look like a sheet of velvet. They increase the internal surface area of the small intestine by a further factor of about five, and that is not the end. The luminal surface of each villus is covered with epithelial cells—most of which are absorptive—and each absorptive cell has on its luminal surface a series of tiny projections, each one shaped like a villus, but much, much, smaller. Logically enough, these tiny projections are termed **microvilli,** and their presence further increases the internal surface area of the small intestine by a factor of at least twenty.

These morphological features have accomplished an incredible feat. A simple tube the same length and diameter as the small intestine would have an internal surface area of one or two square meters at the most. Yet these special structural characteristics provide the human small intestine with an internal surface area that ranges between 250 and 300 square meters, which is the approximate surface area of two full-sized tennis courts. Besides providing an enormous absorptive surface, this also makes room for a tremendous number of epithelial cells that make up the mucosal surface—cells that synthesize both enzymes and hormones and also transport digested food into the interior of the body.

Figure 15.33 (*a*) The villi of the small intestine. (*b*) An individual villus, showing the cells lining its surface.

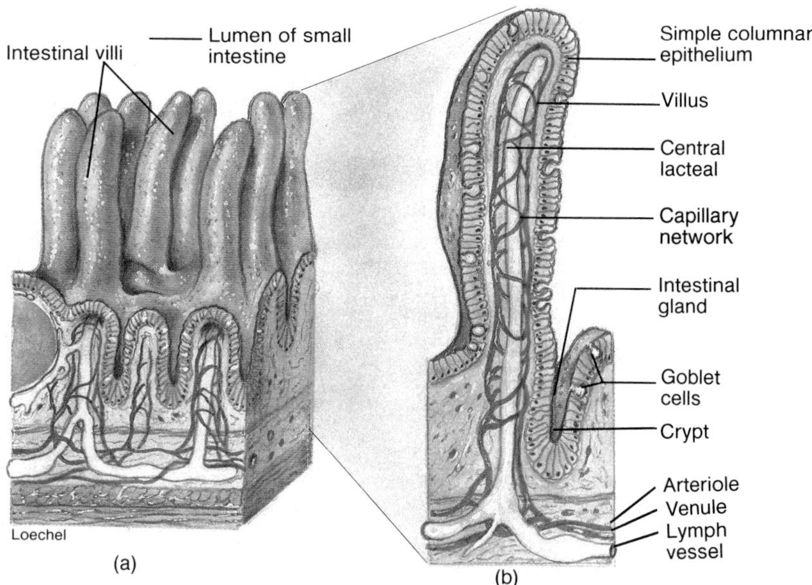

The Mucosal Epithelium

There are two kinds of epithelial cells on the shaft of each villus. There are the **goblet cells,** which synthesize and secrete mucin to lubricate and protect the internal surface of the intestine, and there are the **absorptive cells,** which take care of digestive breakdown and absorption of nutrients. Both are present in the single layer of epithelium that comprises the luminal layer of each villus, although as you can see from figure 15.33, the goblet cells are vastly outnumbered.

These cells form tight junctions with each other, and their arrangement makes it plain that any food passing from the inside of the gut to the interior of the body cannot go *between* the epithelial cells of the mucosa, but must instead pass *through* them (figure 15.33). Below the shaft of each villus—in the **crypt** between them—the epithelial cells are shaped differently from their colleagues higher up, but they still butt close against one another, so there are no breaks in the internal surface. Cells up on the villial shaft do not reproduce, but a lot of cell division takes place in the crypt, and this has a functional significance. Both the absorptive cells and the goblet cells of the small intestine are born, in the crypt, of sister cells undergoing vigorous mitosis. After their production, they migrate up the shaft of the villus toward the tip, maturing as they go. Their progress is rapid—a cell can migrate from the depths of the crypt to the tip of the villus in less than forty-eight hours—and when they arrive at the apex, they are shed into the lumen. The number of cells cast from the intestinal epithelium in this manner boggles the mind. It is estimated that as many as twenty billion cells are sloughed off and extruded into the lumen of the gut every twenty-four-hour period. And each of these cells contains all the things necessary to continue living and to do its job. The total life span of a typical epithelial cell is a short forty-eight to seventy-two hours, but during that lifetime, they can accomplish a great deal.

Intestinal Secretions

Mucin

Not all of the cells of the intestinal mucosa are enzyme producers and absorptive cells. Mucin-secreting **Brunner's glands** are snuggled down in the submucosa between intestinal villi in the uppermost part of the duodenum, and when stomach acid is pouring into the small intestine, they can produce mucus at a rather astonishing rate. Further along in the intestinal tract, well away from the stomach and its hydrochloric acid, goblet cells of the intestinal villi can provide all the mucin that is required. Apparently, mucin from intestinal sources is similar to gastric mucin in both composition and function. Like the latter, it is heavily endowed with bicarbonate. Hence it can function as an alkaline buffer, and in addition it lies thickly on the luminal surface of the intestinal wall, providing protection from both gastric acids and the powerful digestive enzymes loose inside the small intestine.

The Succus Entericus

As you have undoubtedly determined by now, the enzymes of the pancreas, stomach, and mouth serve mainly to break down the food we eat in a relatively rough way. Enzymes like ptyalin, pepsin, and pancreatic lipase are designed to break the huge nutritional ores into smaller polymers, but none of them can peel monomers off the ends—they cannot break the large molecules down completely. The final

Figure 15.34 A micrograph of the luminar surface of one of the columnar epithelial cells that line the surface of the villi. The microvilli are clearly visible (*arrow*).

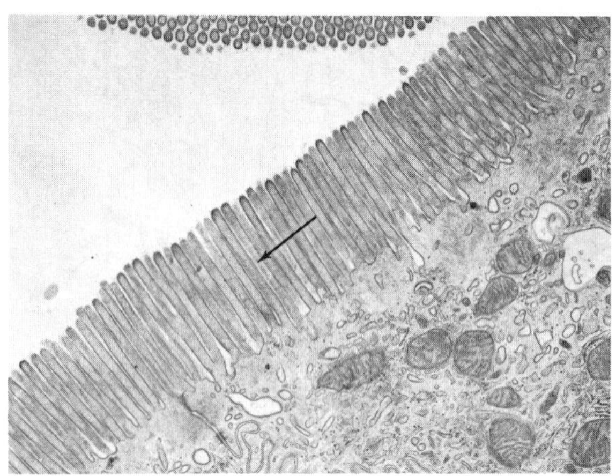

Figure 15.35 Absorptive epithelial cells. Note the absence of any space between cells at the luminal surface.

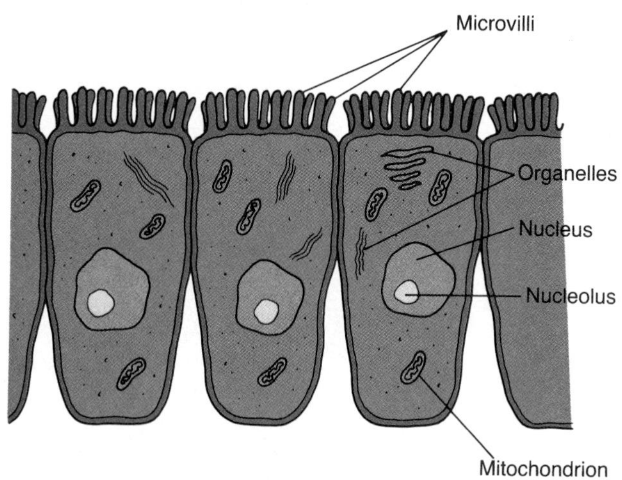

breakdown, therefore, must be accomplished by enzymes of the intestinal tract—enzymes collectively termed **succus entericus** (literally, the "sap of the intestines").

All necessary enzyme types are gathered together in this "sap." Proteases, lipases, and specific amylases are all present in abundance, and they are quite different from the pancreatic, salivary, and gastric enzymes. Intestinal enzymes are designed to break off terminal molecules. They can therefore release large numbers of free amino acids and monosaccharides from their parent compounds.

A Different Mode of Operation

Intestinal enzymes do their jobs in a manner that is quite different from that used by all the digestive enzymes we have considered up to now. Unlike pancreatic and gastric enzymes, they are not secreted into the lumen of the gut but instead remain firmly attached to the surface membranes of the cell that synthesized them. They perform their functions while still anchored to a mother cell that is part of the intestinal epithelium. Even after they have completed their work and are ready to be disposed of, these epithelial cells do not secrete their enzymatic products. When the time comes to enter the lumen of the intestine, the whole cell goes, carrying its enzymes with it. Enzymes of the succus entericus, therefore, are not found floating around freely in the fluids of the intestine, but are still firmly attached to the surface of their cellular parent.

The Microvilli

The fact that digestive enzymes remain firmly attached to the cells that synthesize them is unusual, and the epithelial absorptive cells are unusual structures in other ways as well (figures 15.34, 15.35). Their microvilli that project into the lumen and contribute so much to the internal surface area have an unusual internal ultrastructure themselves. The contractile protein **actin** is present, its parallel strands extending from the top of each villus down into the interior of the cell proper. Myosin filaments are present too, but there are none going up into the microvillus itself. They stay down below, in the cell body beneath the microvillial shafts, where they run perpendicular to the actin strands. Secondly—and this is most peculiar—the membrane surrounding each of these cellular projections has a heavy coating of carbohydrate. This all by itself is unusual in an animal cell, but it is made even more unlikely by its thickness. It adds an outer layer to the microvilli membranes that is thicker than the lipid of the plasma membrane—indeed, is thicker than the membranes of most body cells. From this carbohydrate veneer, myriad filaments project out into the intestinal lumen, forming a mesh or network around each microvillus—a network that has been given the name **glycocalyx** (figure 15.36).

This unusual coating apparently is not pure carbohydrate. There are enzymes present, enzymes made up of protein stalks with carbohydrate side chains projecting out from them like the branches of a tiny oak tree. All three types of digestive enzymes are present, and most are able to finish the work that earlier ones began. For example, **sucrase** and **maltase,** both of which split twelve-carbon disaccharides into their six-carbon monomers, are abundant. So are **aminopeptidases** (enzymes that will cleave terminal amino acids from a polypeptide). The protein fractions of the sucrase and maltase enzymes are peripheral membrane proteins, floating on the surface of the cell membranes without penetrating into the fatty acid interior. On the other hand, the proteins of the aminopeptidases are firmly bonded to *transmembranal proteins* (see chapter 4) imbedded within the cell membrane and projecting into the interior of the cell;

Figure 15.36 Microvilli on an intestinal epithelial cell.

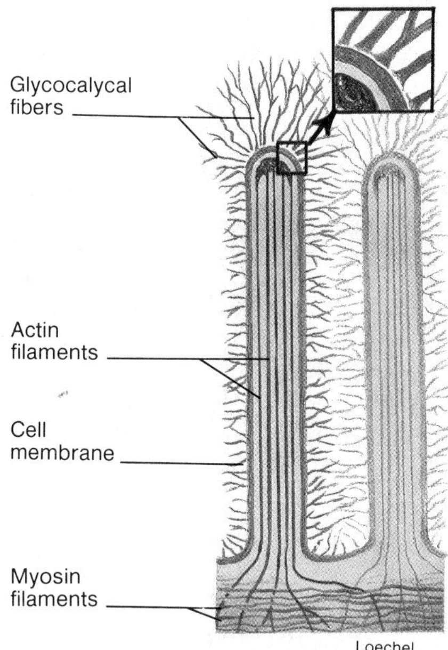

hence they are locked solidly to the outer surface of the cells that synthesized them. In both cases, these arrangements indicate that any digestive efforts produced by these enzymes will take place on the surface of the epithelial absorptive cells.

During the two full days it takes for a cell to work its way up to the apex of a villus, it is constantly digesting and absorbing food particles as they present themselves. When the cells are finally released at the tip of the villus and drift off into the lumen, they continue to perform their digestive functions—no absorption, of course, since they are no longer part of the intestine—but they still synthesize enzymes of all kinds and are still able to break up any food molecules they contact.

A tremendous amount of digestion occurs while they are still anchored in place, and this is a perfectly logical arrangement. It is utterly reasonable to assume that the splitting of a substance like maltose or sucrose into monosaccharides would occur almost simultaneously with absorption— obviously, it makes sense to transport them into the cell immediately, while they're right there. The same conditions apply to amino acids. It's all perfectly practical and of course, it happens . . . but evidently less often than early workers suspected. Apparently only a small percentage of the available monosaccharides are absorbed as soon as they are freed from their polymers. The enzymes on the epithelial cells are present in enormous abundance and evidently are able—particularly when the gut is full—to release unbelievable numbers of monosaccharides and amino acids. So frenzied is their activity that when the intestine is accepting food from the stomach at a high rate of speed, the absorptive surfaces of the intestine get as crowded as New York subways, and like subway passengers, the monomers have to wait their turn to enter. As a consequence, most of them float free in the intestinal lumen for a time. But sooner or later—especially as the gut begins to empty and digestive operations slow a little—nearly all of these monosaccharides and amino acids will encounter an absorptive cell that has a "hand free" and is able to transport them.

Absorption—an Active and a Passive Process

As has already been mentioned, many of the mechanisms designed to absorb food molecules from the intestine are active. Just how they work is not clearly understood, but there is no doubt that they exist and that they use a lot of energy to do their jobs. And even here, in the transporting of food molecules across the gut, we find high levels of specialization. There are separate mechanisms available to transport each tiny particle from the intestinal lumen into the interstitial fluid surrounding the GI tract. At least two are involved in absorbing monosaccharides. They are completely separate from each other and also from the mechanisms that handle the absorption of protein residues and lipid transport.

Sugars

Sugar molecules are usually accepted with considerable alacrity by the absorptive cells, and their uptake is quite rapid—most have a high absorption priority and so are absorbed in the upper portions of the small intestine, even when the gut is full. Reasonably enough, those sugars with the greatest utility are absorbed with greatest vigor. Glucose, for instance, which is in constant demand, is taken up very quickly; galactose is, too, and in nursing mothers it may actually be absorbed more rapidly than glucose. Fructose, on the other hand, is absorbed much more slowly, and there is evidence to suggest that except in unusual circumstances, this particular monosaccharide is not actively transported at all, but must rely on diffusion to cross the intestine.

Amino Acids

A few years ago, workers felt that the combined efforts of trypsin and pepsin hydrolyzed proteins completely, leaving only free amino acids that could easily be absorbed. As we have seen, neither of those enzymes is capable of that. But they get things started, and once intestinal proteases begin breaking off single amino acid residues, absorption is rapid. Little is left to the vagaries of diffusion. Workers have identified four separate mechanisms that are available to transport individual amino acids across the epithelium into the interstitial fluids. Current evidence seems to suggest that they absorb a great deal of protein. Until recently, in fact, it was assumed that it was the way

Figure 15.37 Fat digestion and absorption.

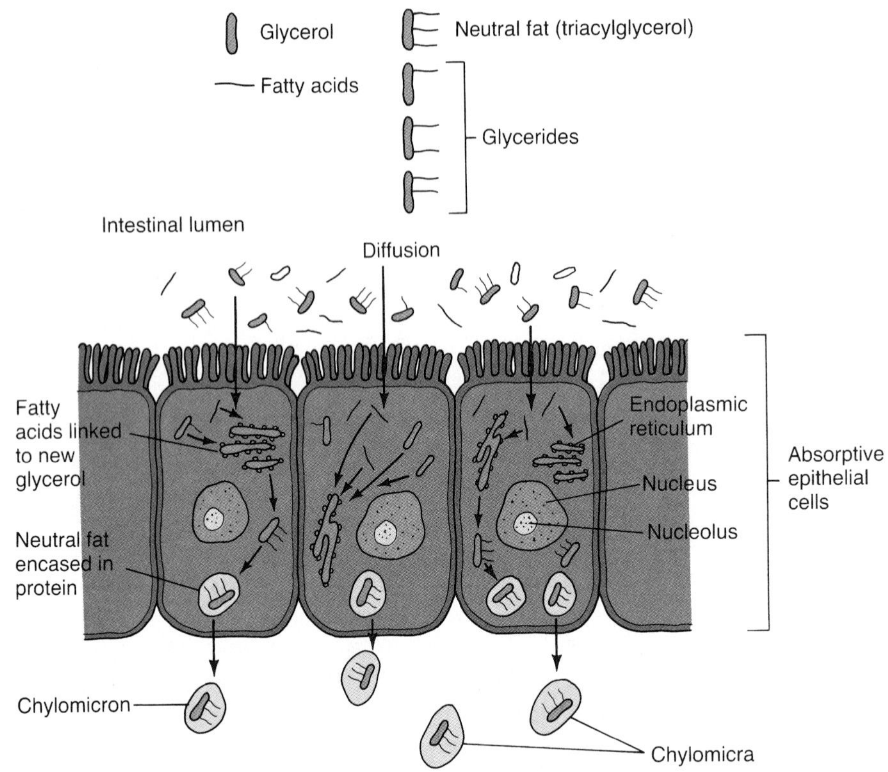

proteins *had* to be absorbed—that only as amino acids was it possible to get this important food into the blood.

As it turns out, this is not the case. Not all protein is completely broken down, nor does it have to be. It is possible for both dipeptides (two linked amino acids) and tripeptides (three linked amino acids) to be transported across the intestinal mucosa into the interstitial fluids, and there are separate mechanisms in our absorptive cells to transport each. Once they are inside the cells, other enzymes break them apart, and they leave the cells and enter the blood as separate amino acids (figure 15.37).

Lipids

Fats are present in the intestinal lumen as large globules of neutral fat or **triacylglycerols** (a glycerol backbone with three fatty acids attached). These large globules are emulsified by bile salts and then are attacked by the pancreatic and intestinal lipases, which strip fatty acids away from the glycerol backbone. As far as we know, no active mechanisms are involved in the movement of fats into the absorptive cells—simple diffusion is responsible. This does not mean, however, that absorption is slow or that it is difficult. Remember that because of the lipid nature of all cell membranes, fatty materials have no difficulty penetrating them, and cells of the intestinal epithelium are no exception. They move so easily, in fact, that if any kind of concentration gradient is available, absorption will be rapid. And the absorptive cells maintain the concentration by changing fatty acids, as soon as they enter the cell, into something else. As soon as they cross the membrane, fatty acids are rushed to the endoplasmic reticulum, where they are reconstituted into triacylglycerols, lined up with newly synthesized molecules of phospholipid, and attached to protein carriers. These tiny particles—now known as **chylomicra**—were once called **blood dust,** and they leave the absorptive cell in this form. Once in the interstitial fluid, they are picked up, not by the blood as are proteins and carbohydrates, but instead by the **central lacteal** (figures 15.31, 15.33), which is a lymphatic vessel within the villus (see figure 15.38).

(Chylomicra normally consist of about 90 percent neutral fat, 5 percent phospholipid, and 1 percent cholesterol surrounded by a protein coating that functions as a carrier molecule.)

Cholesterol is ingested in two forms; either as free cholesterol molecules or as cholesterol esters, hooked to fatty acids. As it turns out, the cholesterol must be absorbed in the free state, and there is a special enzyme in the intestinal tract that is intended to deal with this and nothing else. Called **cholesterol esterase,** it separates cholesterol molecules from any fatty acids they are linked to, after which both molecules are absorbed by the intestinal epithelium.

Figure 15.38 The absorption of nutrients in the intestine. Water-soluble nutrients such as proteins and sugars enter the blood and are carried away. Fats, in the form of glycerol, fatty acids, and/or glycerides, bypass the capillaries and enter the central lacteal, an element of the lymphatic circulatory system.

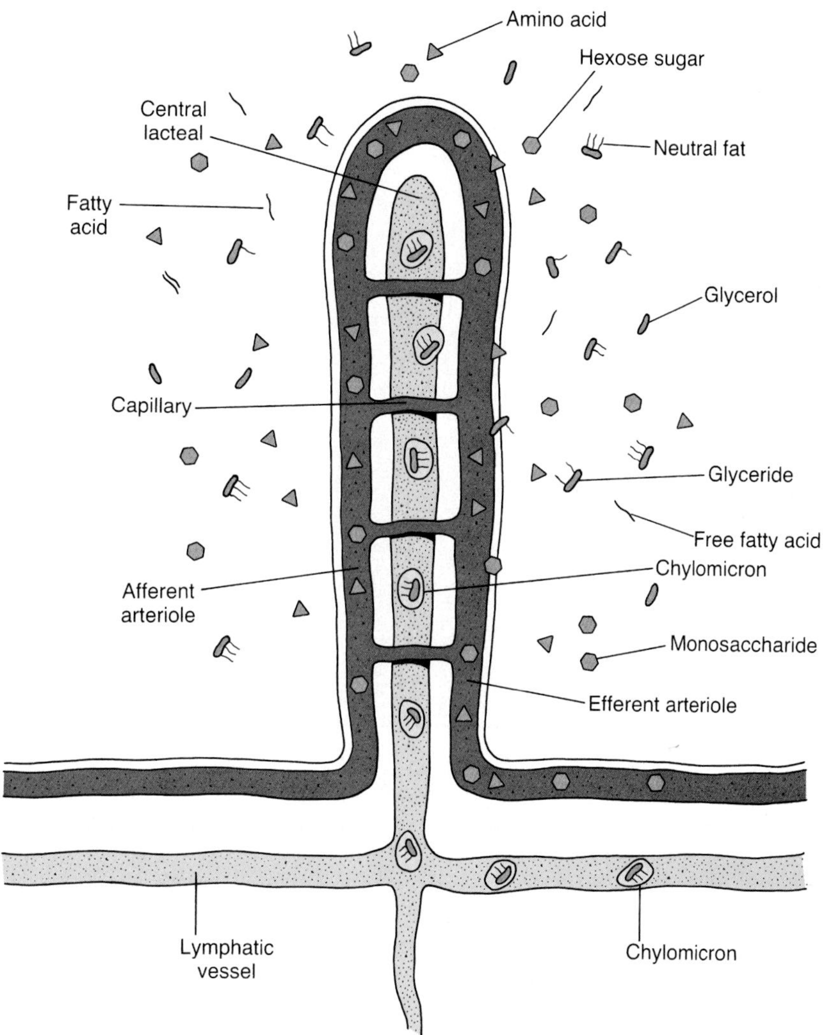

Nucleotidase

Like all the hydrolytic enzymes produced outside the small intestine, the nucleotidases produced by the pancreas are restricted in their capabilities. They can only break the nitrogen-containing bases away from the pentose sugars. To split the phosphates and riboses apart, intestinal nucleotidases are necessary. The end products of their efforts are free phosphates and pentose sugars, both of which are easily absorbed by the intestinal mucosa.

Vitamins

By definition, vitamins are organic compounds that the body must have, but which it cannot synthesize itself. They do not provide us with energy, nor are they used as building materials, yet they are critical for continued, healthy life. Vitamins are involved in the biochemical reactions of metabolism. Some are enzymes, some are coenzymes and a few serve as building blocks for more complicated enzymes into which they will be assembled.

As to their source, the human body is capable of synthesizing a very few of these necessary compounds if we are provided with the proper precursors. Vitamin A, for example, can be built up from a compound called **carotene,** which is present in raw carrots and a few other vegetables. One or two vitamins are synthesized for us by bacteria (see "The Large Intestine," p. 570), but most must be ingested as part of the foods we eat. A normal, healthy diet contains all the vitamins necessary for an average person's daily needs, but it should be noted that no single food or single group of foods contains all of them. Balanced diets are therefore important , and people do not always consume balanced diets. For those who do not, vitamin supplements are available. See table 15.4 for recommended daily vitamin allowances.

During the process of digestion, obviously vitamins must obtain special treatment. Unlike the proteins, carbohydrates, and lipids mentioned previously,

Table 15.4 Recommended Daily Allowances for Vitamins and Minerals

	Infants	Children	Adolescents (15–18 yrs)		Adults (23–50 yrs)	
	0–6 mos	*4–6 yrs*	*Males*	*Females*	*Males*	*Females*
Weight, kg (lb)	6 (13)	20 (44)	66 (145)	55 (120)	70 (154)	55 (120)
Height, cm (in)	60 (24)	112 (44)	176 (69)	163 (64)	178 (70)	163 (64)
Protein, g	kg × 2.2	30	56	46	56	44
Fat-soluble vitamins						
Vitamin A, μg†	420	500	1000	800	1000	800
Vitamin D, μg	10	10	10	10	5	5
Vitamin E activity, mg	3	6	10	8	10	8
Water-soluble vitamins						
Ascorbic acid, mg	35	45	60	60	60	60
Folacin, μg	30	200	400	400	400	400
Niacin, mg	6	11	18	14	18	13
Riboflavin, mg	0.4	1.0	1.7	1.3	1.6	1.2
Thiamine, mg	0.3	0.9	1.4	1.1	1.4	1.0
Vitamin B_6, mg	0.3	1.3	2.0	2.0	2.2	2.0
Vitamin B_{12}, μg	0.5	2.5	3.0	3.0	3.0	3.0
Minerals						
Calcium, mg	360	800	1200	1200	800	800
Phosphorus, mg	240	800	1200	1200	800	800
Iodine, μg	40	90	150	150	150	150
Iron, mg	10	10	18	18	10	18
Magnesium, mg	50	200	400	300	350	300
Zinc, mg	3	10	15	15	15	15

Source: Food and Nutrition Board, *Recommended Dietary Allowances*, 9th ed., National Academy of Sciences, Washington, DC, 1980.
† Microgram

vitamins must not be broken down or in any way disrupted. We require vitamins intact. The whole molecule is essential to our biosynthetic machinery, so if they are to be of any value, the gut must treat them with care. Except for vitamin B_{12}, they are all small molecules, and all are apparently immune to the action of both gastric enzymes and the high levels of acidity encountered in the stomach. Current evidence indicates that as soon as they enter the upper portions of the small intestine they are absorbed, thus eliminating the possibility of their being attacked by intestinal enzymes.

Despite their importance and the speed at which they are absorbed, the process is evidently passive, and the vitamins rely on diffusion to carry them across the intestinal epithelium. The fat-soluble vitamins (A, D, E, and K) slip across the membrane along with other fatty particles and enter the central lacteal, while the water-soluble vitamins follow other dissolved particles into the blood.

Vitamin B_{12} is a special case. For a water-soluble vitamin, B_{12} is a huge molecule, and probably because of its size, it is susceptible to the digestive action of both gastric and intestinal secretions. In order to survive in the gut, therefore, it needs a little protection. This protection is provided by several mechanisms.

As is the case with most vitamins, B_{12} enters the body as part of a larger food molecule, and it remains so until it encounters the acid and the pepsin of the stomach. These compounds free the vitamin molecules, which are then rapidly linked to one of two types of carriers. One type is the **R proteins,** which are both salivary and gastric components, while the second is a glycoprotein known as **intrinsic factor,** which is secreted by the stomach's parietal cells.

Generally speaking, vitamin B_{12} is more attracted to the R proteins than to intrinsic factor. Hence, when the materials leave the stomach, most is bound to R proteins, and only a little is linked to intrinsic factor. In the intestine, however, the R proteins are attacked by proteolytic enzymes, and any vitamin B_{12} attached to them is broken loose. These newly freed molecules are rapidly picked up by intrinsic factor, and as it happens, intrinsic factor vigorously resists catalytic hydrolysis. The complexes are thus able to escape being digested by the proteases in the gut, and so protected, they proceed through the small intestine almost to its end. Here, near the large intestine, there are brush-border cells with specialized receptors that are designed specifically to recognize intrinsic factor/vitamin B_{12} complexes and bind to them. Once bound, the vitamin is slowly absorbed, and it gradually enters the blood as free vitamin B_{12}.

There is a great deal that is not known about the absorptive process. For instance, it has been noted that even after vitamin B_{12} has been bound to the ileal cells, a period of six to eight hours passes before it shows up in the blood, and no one has yet suggested a reason for this delay. Also, no one knows whether B_{12} is absorbed as a free molecule or is transported into the cells while still attached to intrinsic factor.

Whatever the case, there is no doubt that intrinsic factor is essential if sufficient vitamin B_{12} is ever to make it into the bloodstream. In its absence, less than 2 percent of the vitamin entering the gut is ever absorbed.

Water and Inorganic Materials (Minerals)

As is the case throughout the body, there is no mechanism in the gut that will actively move water. The movement of water is passive, and this crucial fluid moves into and out of the gut following osmotic gradients that may exist at any given moment. These gradients are nearly always established and controlled by the epithelial cells of the intestinal mucosa. The epithelial cells possess active pumping mechanisms capable of moving sodium, potassium, phosphates, and calcium from the lumen into the bloodstream, and when these minerals are moved, water passively follows the shifting osmotic inclines. The activity of the pumps varies according to the section of the intestinal tract that is involved and the body's requirements at any given time. Sodium and potassium, for instance, are absorbed mainly in the upper part of the intestine, and in this part of the gut, chloride passively follows their movement. In the lower section of the small intestine, however, sodium absorption begins to tail off a little, while pumps designed to move chloride suddenly swing into action, actively absorbing that anion. Water, naturally, conforms to the movements of both.

All this activity, we must repeat, depends on body requirements. When water is needed, there is a profound movement of minerals from the gut into the blood, and when its ion pumps are working at maximum capacity, the small intestine can absorb water at a rate of nearly half a liter per hour. On the other hand, when the body has an adequate water load, active pumping of minerals is reduced, and water absorption consequently slows. Throughout all this activity, nutrient dispersions within the gut remain isotonic with the body's plasma, a condition that persists, even if water must be moved from the blood into the intestine to maintain it.

Control of Intestinal Enzymes

Since mucin is secreted primarily to protect the wall of the small intestine from the powerful acids secreted by the stomach, it is reasonable to assume that the trigger for mucin secretion would involve these acids somehow, and so it does. However, it turns out that the presence in the duodenum of almost any irritant will stimulate mucin secretion.

Enzyme synthesis is also stimulated by food (chyme) in the intestine. Most of the enzymatic secretions of the small intestine are under the control of neural reflexes that tend to be localized in the myenteric (Auerbach's) and Meissner's plexuses. These plexuses are densely packed masses of nerve cells which, together with other vagal fibers of the gastrointestinal tract, constitute the **enteric nervous system.** This system is designed to integrate the activities of muscles and secretory glands within the intestine and is autonomous, requiring no CNS input. If the sympathetic and parasympathetic nerve trunks entering the intestinal tract were cut, most of the activities of the gut would continue to function normally. Since this is the case, it seems obvious that the major stimulus would be physical distension of the mucosa caused by the presence of food within the lumen of the small intestine. Lighter tactile stimulus and the presence of certain chemicals in the contents can also produce an increase in activity within the cells of the crypt. Since the stimuli are localized, and since the chyme inside the intestine is the prime stimulus for intestinal secretion, the volume of fluid secreted is determined by the volume of food present at any given place within the intestine. The reflexes do not result in a release of enzymes into the lumen of the gut. Instead, they increase mitosis in the cells in the villial crypts. This has the effect of thrusting new cells out and up, forcing older cells near the top of the villi to break free and make way for their younger sisters. The result is an immediate increase in the number of enzyme-covered cells that are shed into the intestinal lumen and a subsequent increased breakdown of the susceptible foods there.

The control that the chyme can exert is impressive. Intestinal distension is monitored by parasympathetic activity, and the involved reflexes can sometimes triple the normal volume of digestive enzymes secreted during a meal.

It has been suggested that there is some hormonal control of intestinal secretion, and a little evidence is available to support this suggestion. Some hormones, which were once known collectively as **enterocrinin,** are secreted by the intestinal mucosa when chyme is present inside the gut. It is possible that these hormones may play a small role in the regulation of the digestive process in the intestine.

Table 15.5 lists the enzymes of the GI tract and their functions.

Table 15.5 Enzymes of the GI Tract

Enzyme	Source	Function	Control
Salivary amylase	Mouth	Breaks up polysaccharides. Cannot remove terminal sugars.	Neural
Pancreatic amylase	Pancreas	Breaks large polysaccharides into smaller polysaccharides. Cannot remove terminal sugars.	Neural
Pepsin	Gastric mucosa	Breaks up proteins. Cannot remove terminal amino acids from protein chains.	Neural and endocrine (gastrin)
Trypsin	Pancreas	Attacks polypeptides. Cannot remove terminal amino acids from chains.	Primarily neural
Chymotrypsin	Pancreas	Functions much the same way as trypsin.	Primarily neural
Carboxypeptidase	Pancreas	Splits terminal amino acids from peptide chains.	Neural and endocrine
Pancreatic lipase	Pancreas	Splits neutral fats into glycerol and fatty acid chains.	Primarily neural
Pancreatic nucleotidase	Pancreas	Cleaves purine and pyrimidine bases from the sugar/phosphate chains.	Endocrine
Intestinal nucleotidase	Intestinal epithelium	Separates the sugar from the phosphates.	Neural
Intestinal amylases	Present on cells of the intestinal mucosa	Split polysaccharides and disaccharides into monosaccharides.	Neural reflex
Intestinal proteases	Present on cells of the intestinal mucosa	Split peptides into single amino acids.	Neural reflex
Intestinal lipases	Intestinal epithelium	Split fats into fatty acids and glycerol.	Neural reflex
Cholesterol lipase	Intestinal epithelium	Frees cholesterol from fatty acids.	Neural reflex

The Large Intestine

The small intestine opens into the large intestine almost at the bottom of the abdomen, just above the vermiform appendix (figure 15.39). Just as the pylorus guards the exit from the stomach, the **ileocecal valve** stands watch at the entrance to the large intestine. The same three forces that control the movement of materials from the stomach into the duodenum are involved with the ileocecal valve, and their influence is about the same.

1. *Condition of the muscle (valve) itself.* If the muscle is not relaxed, the state of the other factors is immaterial. When the valve is closed no movement is possible.
2. *The pressure gradient across the valve.* As is always the case, there must be a force available to move the materials from place to place. The pressure must be higher in the small intestine than it is in the large intestine for anything to move into the latter. Even if the valve is wide open, no movement will occur if the proper pressure gradient doesn't exist.
3. *The viscosity of the intestinal contents.* The more watery the intestinal contents are, the more easily they will flow across the valve. In fact, anything that contributes to increased fluidity of the contents of the gut will enhance their ability to flow through the tract and across all its valves.

The large intestine differs quite a bit from the small intestine in ways that include both the morphology and the abilities of the epithelial cells that line its interior. The name *large intestine* must derive from the fact that its *diameter* is greater than the small intestine's, because in every other respect, it is the smaller of the two. It is, for example, only about five feet long (1.5 meters) compared with the sixteen-foot length of the small intestine. It has an internal surface area of less than 20 square meters compared to the 250 m^2 of the small intestine. It differs also in that there are no villi on the mucosal surface of the large intestine. There are a few similarities, however. For instance, the epithelial cells do possess microvilli on their luminal surfaces, and lots of goblet cells and other mucus-secreting glands are present. Although large quantities of mucin are produced, no digestive enzymes are produced by the epithelium.

Figure 15.39 The large intestine, shown as it is arranged *in vivo*.

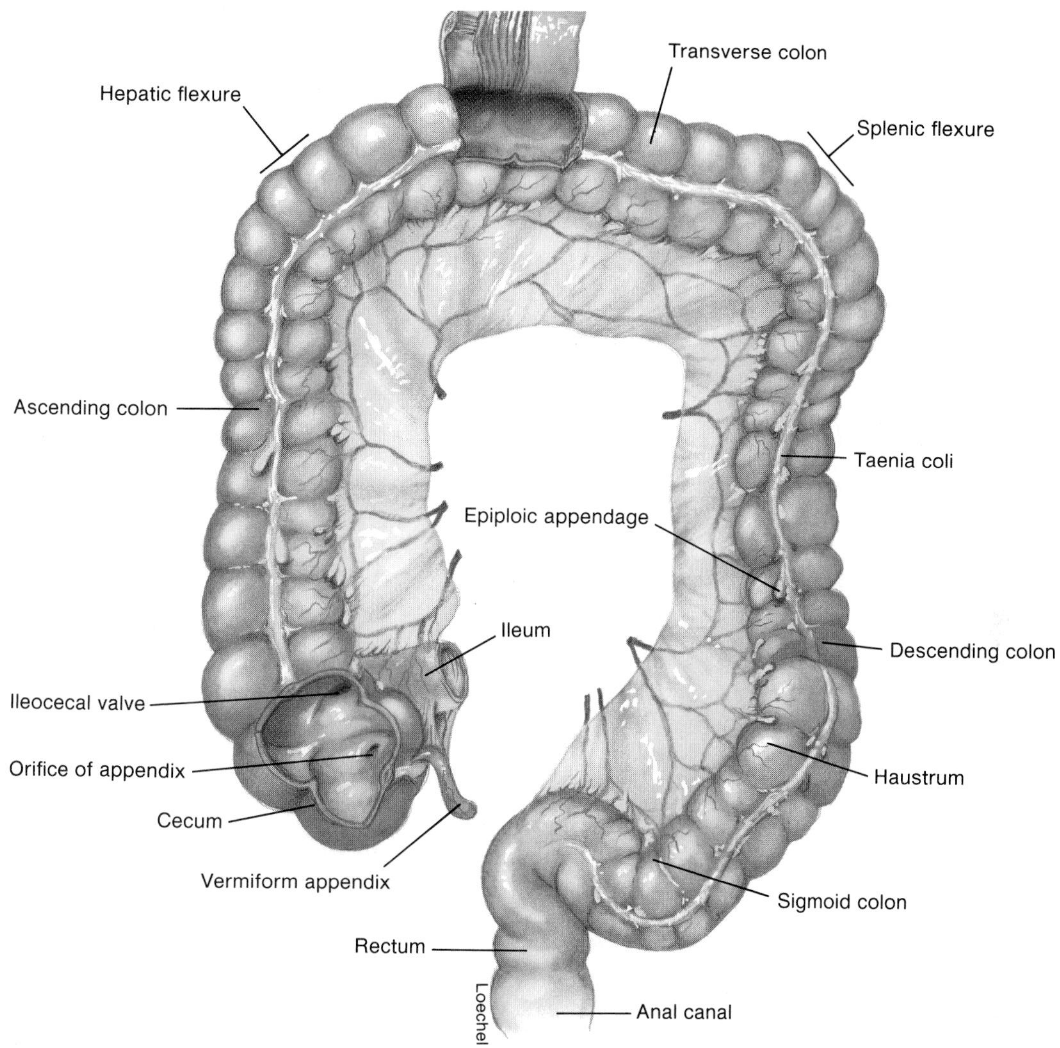

The ileocecal valve releases materials into a large, blind pouch called the **cecum** (figure 15.40), from which dangles a tiny coiled tube about 8 cm long. This is the **vermiform appendix,** a structure better known for its malfunctions than for anything else. When infected or swollen and inflamed, it results in the painful and sometimes fatal affliction known as **appendicitis.**

The cecum opens into a tube known as the **colon.** This structure is divided into the ascending portion, the transverse portion, and the descending portion, based on its position in a living person (figure 15.39). The bottom portion of the descending colon is thoroughly modified. The last 25 cm or so is a heavily muscled tube called the **rectum,** which terminates in an opening to the outside called the **anal canal** (figures 15.41, 15.42).

Function of the Large Intestine

The primary roles of the large intestine seem to be to:

1. reabsorb water
2. produce formed feces
3. reabsorb minerals and any other nutrients that remain

Water Reabsorption

The chyme that enters the large intestine is, as we have seen, quite fluid, and since water is usually at a premium in air-breathing mammals, it is not a good idea to lose any more than is absolutely necessary. As we know, water cannot be actively absorbed, but energy is expended moving large quantities of both sodium and chloride from the lumen into the blood, and as always, the water passively follows them. The

Figure 15.40 The cecum represents the first portion of the large intestine.

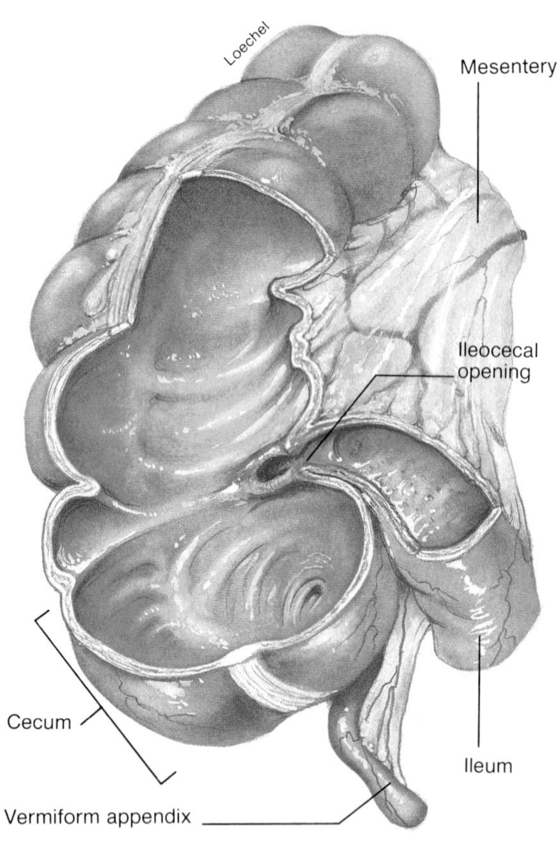

Figure 15.41 The terminus of the intestinal tract, showing the rectum and the anal canal.

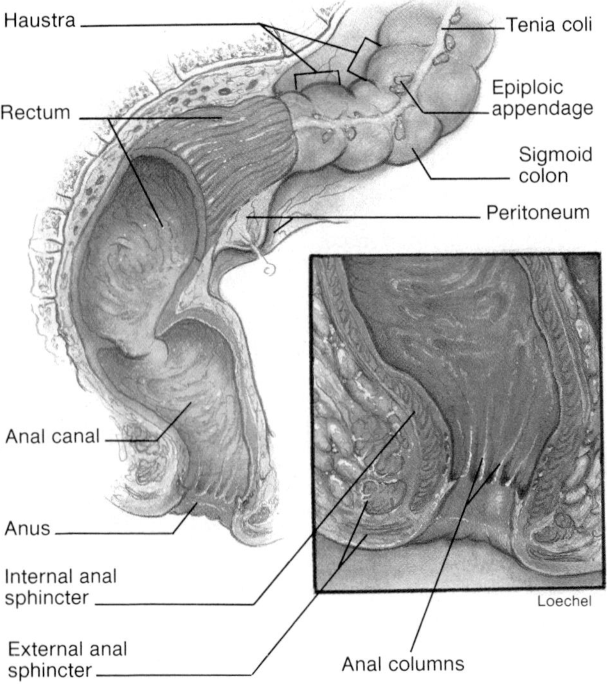

Figure 15.42 A longitudinal section of the human rectum.

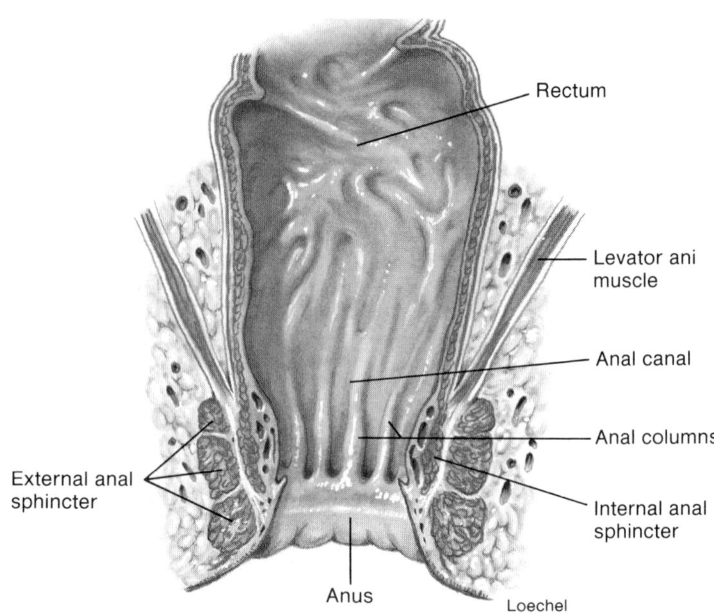

ability of the large intestine to absorb water is impressive. When the mineral pumps are working at maximum capacity, as much as half a liter of water can be returned to the blood each day.

Production of Formed Feces

It is extremely important that the materials entering the large intestine be molded into formed feces so that the digestive and metabolic wastes can be disposed of with a minimum of mess and hassle. The reabsorption of water by the intestinal epithelium contributes mightily to this goal. Also contributing is the large volume of mucin that is secreted by the myriad glands and goblet cells that line the epithelium. The mucus serves both as a paste to stick the waste products together and as a lubricant. The high bicarbonate content of the mucus aids in the control of intestinal pH.

Absorption of Minerals and Other Nutrients

Digestion and absorption in the small intestine is so efficient that there is not much of either for the large intestine to do. As a result, no digestion and very little nutrient absorption takes place there. What little does occur, however, is important. Much of it involves the bacterial population of the large intestine.

Both the beginning and the end of the digestive system is open to the environment. But unlike the beginning, there is no acid bath in the large intestine to block the migration of any organisms that want to get in. Nevertheless, the opportunity to enter is limited. The lower opening is not designed to take materials in, but rather to let them flow out, and that helps. Nevertheless, some manage to sneak past the anal sphincter, and once inside they find an attractive home. The interior of the large intestine is warm, moist, and for the right kind of organisms, there is plenty of nutrient available. As a result, the large intestine features large, established populations of bacteria—normal flora—mostly putrefactive and fermentative, nonpathogenic types. One of the residents is a bacterium known as *Escherichia coli*, a familiar microorganism to students of microbiology. The total number of bacteria that reside in the human colon would astonish most people. For instance, do you realize that 50 percent of the dry weight of normal human feces is due to the presence of bacteria?

These permanent residents feed on the food residue and the newly forming feces as long as either is present. Nitrogenous wastes are broken down and digested by bacterial enzymes, a process known as putrefaction, and carbohydrates are fermented, providing both energy and necessary raw materials for the bacteria. There are by-products, naturally. Vitamins, for instance, particularly the fat-soluble vitamin K, are synthesized by the bacteria of the large intestine and quickly absorbed. Other by-products are taken up less eagerly—things like acid residues, which the alkaline mucin helps to neutralize.

Once all digestive operations have been completed and the proper amount of water has been reabsorbed, the digestive tract releases all the remaining material in the form of feces back into the environment for final disposition.

Another by-product of bacterial activity in the large intestine is gas—**flatus**—which is primarily a product of carbohydrate fermentation. Gases produced by fermentation usually have powerful odors, but not particularly unpleasant ones. However, protein breakdown (putrefaction) produces compounds like hydrogen sulfide and other mercaptans (sulfur-containing compounds that are known for their foul odors) and large quantities of methane (CH_4). This latter can, and will, burn if exposed to a flame.

It is an unpleasant fact that foods that leave much undigested carbohydrate in the gut will produce flatus. As we have already seen, plant fiber is primarily cellulose, indigestible by mammalian enzymes but easily broken up by the exoenzymes produced by many bacteria, including some present in the human large intestine. Foods rich in plant fiber, like beans, for example, are justifiably noted for their ability to produce large volumes of flatus, and individuals who are susceptible to the production of "gas" should avoid them.

Feces

The elimination of waste products from the intestinal tract is much more than a simple, casual dumping. From a purely practical standpoint, it would be a profound disadvantage for an animal to be constantly dribbling waste products from the anus. In addition to being a waste of water, it would be inconvenient and messy—and in the wild, it could be dangerous, because it would mark an animal's trail. Clearly, the formation of feces is one of the most important duties of the large intestine.

Human feces consist mainly of water (about 70 percent), plus indigestible or waste materials. Most undigested nutrients are plant fiber, but there are always large numbers of epithelial cells that are shed during the intestinal digestion process and a few metabolic waste products that the body disposes of by dumping them into the gut. The characteristic color of fecal material is due to the presence of bilirubin (see chapter 12), which turns dark brown when oxidized by the putrefactive bacteria in the large intestine.

Movements of the Large Intestine

Although little digestive activity occurs in the large intestine, considerable mechanical mixing goes on. Slow, deliberate movements separate the pre-fecal semiliquid pastes into smaller chunks and exposes their inner surfaces, permitting the water-absorbing operations of the colon to dehydrate them more completely. The large intestine undertakes peristalsis, too, but unlike the small intestine, restricts peristaltic activity to only two or three periods each day. When it comes, it is coordinated throughout the entire length of the large intestine, and, surprisingly, it is quite powerful. The result is the simultaneous movement of large units of fecal material toward the rectum.

Elimination

In humans, the peristaltic activity of the large intestine can be partially programed. Usually the ingestion of a meal stimulates it to occur, but this is not always the case. Most people, whether they realize it or not, train themselves unconsciously to empty their digestive tract at the most convenient times each day, and external stimuli that typically occur at these particular times will more often than not trigger these intestinal movements.

Inevitably, intestinal peristalsis will thrust the contents of the colon into the rectal zone of the large intestine (see figure 15.41) and will stimulate the **defecation reflex.** Once material enters the rectum, complex reflex activity stimulates further peristaltic movement in the large intestine, thrusting more and more material into the rectum. If it is not emptied, this activity can produce considerable cramp-like pain.

Two anal sphincters guard the exit from the large intestine (figure 15.41). There is an internal sphincter composed of smooth muscle and an external sphincter of skeletal, voluntarily controlled muscle. As is the case with both the pyloric and ileocecal valves, movement across these sphincters depends on the pressure gradient, the muscle's condition, and the viscosity of the rectal contents. It is unlike the pyloric and ileocecal valves in that the external sphincter is innervated by consciously controlled somatic nerves, which permit voluntary inhibition of the defecation reflex, thus forcing the retention of fecal material in the rectum. As this intestinal segment fills, pressoreceptors in the rectal area bombard the nearby autonomic plexes with impulses, and the urge to empty it becomes well-nigh irresistible. The internal sphincter by now is wide open, and the external sphincter is bombarded with autonomic instructions to relax. It can be kept closed through conscious impulses, but only at the cost of considerable effort and some pain.

Clinical Considerations

Diseases of the mouth are usually the province of the dental profession, and that leads to specialization that is beyond the scope of this book. However, there are some oral afflictions that are general enough to mention.

Foul Breath

Despite the admonitions of purveyors of perfumed mouthwash, bad breath is not a major health problem in the United States and should not be a chronic problem with any healthy person. When examining physicians consistently smell strong mouthwash on a patient's breath, they might wonder if there is not a deep-rooted problem. Usually the cause of chronic bad breath is bad teeth, but it is also indicative of things like sinus infections or tonsillitis.

Herpes Simplex

Probably the most common oral infection in the U.S. is the ordinary "cold sore." The cause is the opportunistic virus *Herpes simplex* (not the same as genital herpes). It usually affects the interior of the mouth—especially the palate—but it is more easily noticed when it infects the lips. Since it seems to prefer moist zones, it is amazing that most anti-cold sore medications are ointments, which must serve to maintain ideal conditions for the virus. A much more reliable remedy would be an antibiotic powder that would at least dry out the site of the sore.

TMJ (Temporomandibular Joint) Problems

In recent years, a new and unpleasantly ubiquitous problem involving the uppermost part of the digestive system has surfaced. It involves the joint between the lower jaw (the mandible) and the temporal bone of the skull. When something interferes with free movement of this joint, abrasive friction can occur that destroys the correct articulation of these two bones and results in all kinds of nasty, chronic discomfort, including things like headaches, gastrointestinal upset, and sinus problems. The root of the problem can be—and often is—congenital, but simpler things like loss of a cheek tooth or insertion of a new dental bridge can sometimes create or aggravate an already-existing problem.

Esophageal Afflictions

Simple Sore Throat

Undoubtedly the most common problem with the upper digestive tract involves the pharynx and the lymphoid tissue there, and this is known generally as **sore throat.** Usually it is caused by a bacterial infection—more specifically, streptococcus bacteria. In children, the so-called strep throat can be dangerous, since the high fevers that result often produce convulsions. More often, however, the affliction is more uncomfortable than dangerous, thanks to the numerous antibiotics that are effective against streptococcus.

Scarlet Fever

There was a time when a child's sore throat often heralded the disease known as scarlet fever, an acute streptococcal infection that often was pandemic on this continent. Scarlet fever is usually caused by several different strains of streptococci, all of which produce a similar type of toxin. When the disease was permitted to run its course, bacteria often left the throat where they were concentrated and invaded the ears and kidney, sometimes producing nephridial infections that were fatal. Today the disease is considered to be nothing more than another mild sore throat, easily brushed aside by modern antibiotics.

Gastric Problems

The most common complaint involving the stomach is known clinically as **functional dyspepsia**—a catchall that embraces all the nonspecific gastrointestinal complaints that are usually localized in the abdomen just below the diaphragm. The main cause is poor eating habits, as evidenced by the fact that "bellyaches" most often arise during "feast" days such as Thanksgiving and Christmas when Americans tend to overindulge in traditional foods. In the absence of a problem attributable to some specific disease, treatment is symptomatic, usually involving relaxation and/or antacid therapy.

Gastritis

Overindulgence, particularly in alcoholic beverages, can produce acute inflammation of the stomach lining, a problem generally diagnosed as simple gastritis. Gastritis can be the result of some infectious disease such as influenza, but more often is due to one of three things: corticosteroid therapy, too many aspirins, or alcohol.

Ulcers

Often gastrointestinal distress produces no significant diagnostic signs. Sometimes, however, more general symptoms like **anorexia** (lack of appetite), nausea, and frequent vomiting can quickly pin down a specific problem. More often than not, it indicates the presence of an open sore—a break in the lining of the stomach or upper part of the small intestine. When medical personnel are confronted with a severe but undiagnosed chronic gastrointestinal problem, they immediately worry about such ulcerations, because if one is present, there is always the possibility of sudden gastric hemorrhage, which can be enormous. When it is spotted in time, proper care can usually head off a serious problem, and that care may consist of something as simple as discontinuing the use of an offending agent. Antacids are often recommended to relieve pain.

Peptic Ulcer

Peptic ulcers are holes or tears in the lining of the upper part of the GI tract. By classical definition, any break in the gastric mucosa that extends below the epithelial layer of cells constitutes a peptic ulcer. In practice, however, physicians tend to ignore the classical definition. They consider any intestinal ulceration that is due to the combined activity of pepsin and stomach acid a peptic ulcer (figure 15.43), regardless of where it may be in the GI tract.

It is therefore not surprising to discover that most peptic ulcers are located in the first few inches of the duodenum (small intestine). A good many do occur in the stomach, but most are in the upper part of the small intestine, in the zone where the lining is exposed to the powerful acids pouring from the stomach. Some people can head off any such problems by producing enough mucin and buffering agents to neutralize these stomach secretions before any damage is done. Others cannot. They apparently produce the mucin and buffers, but not soon enough to avoid damage. Why there are two such different groups of people is not clear.

Figure 15.43 A line drawing of a peptic ulcer near the pyloric antrum.

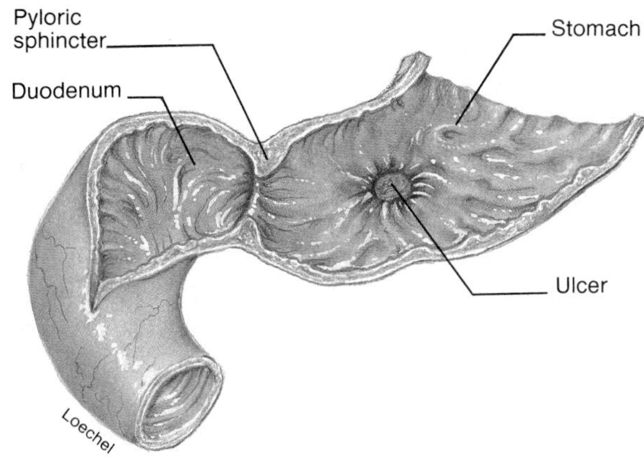

Sometimes drugs are responsible. Aspirin and other anti-inflammatory drugs have been firmly linked to the development of some ulcers, and when their use was discontinued, the ulcers vanished. Unfortunately, such simple cause-effect relationships are rare where ulcers are concerned. The simple truth is that no one really understands why most ulcers occur. Medical literature repeatedly states that they can happen only if the stomach secretes acid, but it nearly always does, so that tells us nothing. In any case, it is inconsistent. It is true that duodenal ulcers are generally associated with high acid production, but gastric ulcers are not, and this suggests that there is more to their development than just high acid levels. Furthermore, there have been repeated observations that abnormally high acid production does not always produce an ulcer.

As an alternative, it has been suggested that there is a balance between pepsin, acid, and mucin secretion that must be maintained, and if that balance breaks down, an ulcer shows up. There is not much evidence to support this, but it is hard to believe that ulcers could develop were it not for some secretory malfunction. If this idea is correct, however, then ulcers could be caused as easily by *hypo*secretion of mucin as by *hyper*secretion of acid or pepsin, a fact that complicates an already too-complex situation.

One thing that always appears to be involved is some form of neural stress. Gastrointestinal researchers have been consistently unable to produce ulcers experimentally unless their animals were subjected to nervous trauma. Frustration, coupled with an appropriate gastric insult, produced ulcers in monkeys, but as soon as the mental stress was removed, the ulcers promptly vanished. It is not hard to interpret the meaning of that kind of experimental result, but it is extremely difficult to generalize it meaningfully to humans, because in people, stress takes so many forms.

Treatment Initially, antacids are the best treatment. Magnesium hydroxide, aluminum hydroxide, bicarbonates—almost anything that will increase the gastric pH will relieve the immediate problem. If the stomach pH can be kept relatively high for just a few days, the mucosa will often repair itself. Cell division is extremely rapid in the epithelial cells of the GI tract. As we have seen, absorptive cells in the small intestine are born and shed in forty-eight hours, and this kind of reproductive activity is generally true throughout the gut. It doesn't take long to replace damaged or worn-out areas. Even the worst damage will heal completely in two or three weeks.

Not all antacid preparations are necessarily good. The most powerful are the bicarbonates—both sodium and calcium—and because of their strength, they must be utilized with caution. Using them intermittently to relieve acute symptoms is fine, but they can present a serious problem if used for extended periods. Unlike the metallic hydroxides, both calcium and sodium bicarbonates are absorbable, and herein lies the problem. Continual uptake of bicarbonates by the blood can raise the pH of body fluids, resulting in systemic alkalosis. In a normal person, alkalosis would probably be spotted fairly quickly and just as rapidly remedied, but in a person already sick and miserable from an active ulcer, symptoms like nausea or headaches might not be noticed and that could be disastrous. If systemic alkalosis persists, severe kidney damage can result, and that may be worse than a bleeding ulcer.

Whether bicarbonate, carbonate, or in some other compound, calcium salts are never a good idea as an antacid. Apparently calcium can reflexly stimulate production of acid by the gastric mucosa, which could make an already-existing problem worse by boosting an acid production that is already too high.

The biggest difficulty facing patient and physician is not so much getting rid of an existing ulcer as it is avoiding the development of a new one. Most physicians try to head this off by recommending bland diets. They eliminate fats, spices, and acidic fruits or fruit juices, and while this certainly cannot do any harm, it doesn't appear to do any good, either. With the exception of pepper, none of the foods mentioned above seem to play a role in the development of ulcers, and there is no evidence to suggest that elimination of any of them is of benefit. On the other hand, reduction of anxiety or mental depression has been consistently effective, and apparently anything that lessens mental stress will work. Physicians say their patients often report significant relief from anxiety following a relaxed talk with anyone who will listen carefully to their problems and offer supportive suggestions.

Problems of the Digestive Accessory Organs

Viral Hepatitis

Hepatitis is an acute inflammation of the liver and is becoming more and more common every year in this country. There are three major causes—viruses, alcohol, and drugs. Of these, only the viral type is a genuine infection. It may also be the most common, with type B the best known. Viral hepatitis is an acute systemic disease which, for some reason, seems to exert most of its efforts on the liver.

The reader is referred to any good pathophysiology textbook for more complete discussion of this disease, since the symptoms and signs are myriad and variable.

Liver Cirrhosis

Of all the horrors that afflict mankind, only cardiovascular disease and cancer outstrip liver cirrhosis as a killer of humans between the ages of 45 and 65. The affliction is characterized by the appearance of connective tissue bands and/or nodules that are produced by the liver but do not belong there. They are stiff clumps of tissue and can interfere seriously with proper liver function by crowding out normally functioning liver cells and/or by disrupting blood flow through the organ.

The incidence of liver cirrhosis has increased tremendously in the last few years. Its occurrence parallels the incidence of alcoholism in this country. More than 50 percent of the cases of liver cirrhosis are alcohol-related; hence alcoholism is considered the primary cause.

The earliest signs are vague. Victims appear well-nourished and seem healthy enough. They may have an unusual complaint every once in a while, but nothing to excite them unduly. During routine physical examinations they may mention periodic weakness or some nonspecific malaise, but often the diagnosis comes as a surprise to both physician and patient. In the early stages it is not particularly serious. But if drinking persists (and it often does), connective tissue invasions become heavy, and scarring starts to occur. Both of these things seriously damage the liver. As the problem progresses, blood pressure steadily increases and finally will skyrocket (**portal hypertension**), hair will be lost, testicles will atrophy, and there will be a general wasting away of skeletal muscle tissue. If the patient chronically abuses alcohol, more often than not alcoholic hepatitis will occur simultaneously.

Treatment There is not much that medicine can offer in the way of therapy. There are no drugs known that will either arrest or reverse the progress of the disease, and what few corrective procedures are available depend mainly on the patient. Nevertheless, alcoholic liver cirrhosis has many stages, and usually some recovery is possible. It must be clearly understood, however, that halfway measures will not work at all; the victim must stop drinking. If the condition is attacked before full-blown cirrhosis has occurred, merely removing the offending chemical and concentrating on eating nutritious foods will arrest—maybe even reverse—its progress. If, however, the patient has reached the stage where alcoholic hepatitis has occurred and **jaundice** (a yellowing of the skin and the white of the eyes) is clearly evident, there is little hope of recovery. In fact, chances of surviving for more than a year are less than 50 percent.

Gallstones

The number of people who succumb to the formation of "stones" in the gallbladder is rather surprising. Medical records indicate that roughly 10 percent of the people in this country have them, and the percentage may be twice that high in middle-aged Americans. The condition is at least partly due to the fact that in some people the liver produces an unusually high level of cholesterol. When the cholesterol is accompanied by a concomitant reduction in the production of bile salts and some form of gallbladder problem—like a bacterial infection—the appearance of stones is almost inevitable. The stones themselves are composed of pure cholesterol, pure bilirubin, or a combination of both, and usually they precipitate in the gallbladder (figure 15.44).

Symptoms are seldom clear cut, although most victims experience profound nausea accompanied by pain in their right side just below the diaphragm—pain that is often agonizing and sometimes radiates up their back to the right shoulder. Should the hardened material obstruct the flow of bile through the biliary system, jaundice may occur.

Surgery is the most common treatment; it usually results in the removal of both the offending stones and the entire gallbladder.

Pancreatitis

The most common pancreatic affliction is diabetes mellitus (see chapter 10), which has already been discussed. However, inflammation of the pancreas (pancreatitis) is not uncommon, and this is seldom an endocrine problem, since it usually involves the acinar cells and the digestive abilities of the pancreas.

No one really knows exactly what precipitates an acute attack of pancreatitis, but one very important factor is the inappropriate activation of powerful digestive enzymes while they are still inside the pancreatic cells that produced them. Trypsin and pancreatic lipases are capable of causing tremendous damage to living cells, but they are not the most common culprits. The two enzymes that are thought to do most of the damage are **phospholipidase,** which

Figure 15.44 (*a*) An X ray of a gallbladder that contains gallstones. (*b*) A posterior view of a gallbladder that has been removed (cholecystectomy) and cut open to reveal its gallstones (bilary calculi). A dime is placed in the photo to show relative size.

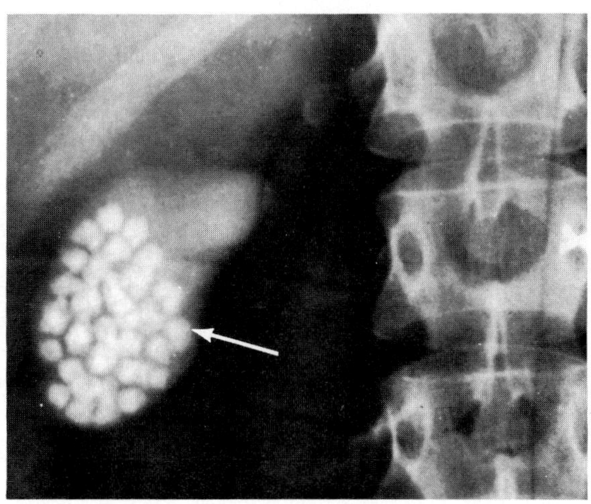

(a)

(b)

is one of the pancreatic lipases, and **elastase,** a relatively sparse pancreatic enzyme that hydrolyzes the protein **elastin.** We do not know much about elastin, except that it is, as the name implies, very elastic and is abundant in the walls of arterial vessels, where its pliability is an advantage. Since elastase attacks this protein, it can break down and harden the walls of pancreatic blood vessels. If enough of that type of damage is done, serious hemorrhage can result.

Abdominal Pain

As common as headaches—as common as the common cold—is abdominal pain, often referred to as a "bellyache" or a "stomachache." Despite the euphemism, the pain center is seldom actually in the stomach. Most abdominal complaints involve the intestines or accessory organs like the liver and pancreas, and it is usually the intestine. Large bubbles of flatus (gas), particularly if they are present in an inflamed intestine, can cause excruciating pain that sometimes lasts for hours. Intestinal blockage occurs more often than most people think, and in such cases, vomiting usually accompanies the pain. Inflammation of the membrane that wraps the abdominal organs (peritonitis) can be as agonizing as appendicitis, which is still another possibility . . . there is no end to the list.

Most common bellyaches are a result of overindulgence of one kind or another at the dinner table and will pass shortly. For those that do not, there are so many possible causes that we will make no attempt to list them here.

Appendicitis

The vermiform appendix is a small accessory that is attached to the large intestine (figure 15.40). Its function is utterly unknown, and it may be that it has none in humans. It can become heavily inflamed (appendicitis), and the accompanying pain, nausea, and malaise can be ghastly. Several things can cause the initial inflammation, but it is usually the result of a hardened bit of fecal material (called a **fecalith**) sneaking in and obstructing the opening, thus preventing the normal secretion of mucin and other materials from escaping into the main intestine. This results in swelling, inflammation, and ultimately bacterial infection. If left untreated, the organ may expand, become gangrenous, and finally burst, spreading its infectious, deadly contents throughout the peritoneal cavity. People still die of it, although in this country, such endings are rare. Its cure is a simple operation.

Diseases of the Colorectal Region

The most common diseases known involve the colorectal region of the gastrointestinal tract. Of these, the most common and most numerous complaints relate to the process of defecation. More things can happen to interfere with this process, and the organs and reflexes involved, than any other body function. We will discuss the most common, not necessarily the most dangerous.

Constipation

Constipation is, according to definition, a difficult defecation. Common usage has stretched this to mean an *infrequent* defecation, and in this context it has been exploited by hawkers of patent medicines since civilization began.

Some of the earliest medical notes ever discovered suggest that retaining fecal material in the intestinal tract can poison a person's body, and all such waste products should be removed as quickly as possible. Illness that was unexplained (and until the last one hundred years or so, that was nearly all illness) was often treated with heavy doses of laxatives on the assumption that the problems were due to poisons in the GI tract. Records obtained from Egyptian tombs that date back to 2,500 B.C. mention the healthful results of vigorous enemas and laxative doses. One Greek physician of circa 300 to 250 B.C. mentions a statistical connection he observed between constipation and a person's susceptibility to episodes of "falling sickness" (epileptic seizures).

We are not free of these myths even today. It is still common for advertisers to suggest that daytime sleepiness, general listlessness, or lack of energy are due to "irregularity." Irregularity is never defined, and no one, least of all the medicine peddlers, knows what it means, but that does not really matter. People are warned against this terrible, vague entity, and convincing them that they need laxatives isn't very hard.

The term "irregularity" is, in fact, not a bona fide medical term at all. It is the invention of an advertising agency, as are a lot of other pseudo-official terms like "tired blood," "B.O." and "ring around the collar." Currently it is considered reprehensible not to defecate at least once a day; if they do not, people worry about being "irregular." Others become concerned about their health if the appearance of their stools is not what they consider optimal, or if they do not feel "satisfied" about having defecated . . . the list of hypothetical problems seems endless. All of them lead people to patent medicine counters to stoke themselves with laxatives.

The truth is that daily bowel movements are not essential, and not everyone's physiology requires it. Most people do establish a rhythm after a while. For some people it may be two or three times a day—for others, it may be once every two or three days. Both cases are perfectly normal. Each individual has his or her own internal standards, and once established, they are usually adhered to—but there is nothing inviolable about this rhythm. Changing dietary habits slightly can alter the rhythm. So can moving to a new home, going camping, or spending a day or two climbing around in the mountains—all can shift the rhythms, and health is not endangered.

Speaking generally, it's a mistake to assume that because this rhythm has been shifted or interrupted, laxatives are needed. Most physicians suggest that people leave laxatives strictly alone unless they are professionally prescribed.

Cathartics

The original name for laxatives was *cathartics,* meaning "to purify," which underscores the ancient attitude toward defecation and anything that promoted it. There are dozens of kinds on the market, but they all fall into three or four categories.

Bulk or Fiber The average diet should contain enough indigestible material to insure that the large intestine will be able to form feces of sufficient bulk to stimulate the defecation reflex. Fiber, a natural laxative, is abundant in vegetables like beans, lettuce, cabbage, and corn, and this is the only kind of laxative that should ever be taken on a regular basis. Unlike most laxatives, high-fiber foods do not tend to "sweep the bowel clean" as so many artificial ones claim to do. Instead, they tend to increase bowel activity slowly and to stimulate defecation only when feces are present.

Irritants Manufacturers of these types of laxatives would prefer the designation "stimulant," but "irritant" is more accurate. These include such chemicals as phenolphthalein, cascara, and castor oil, and they stimulate defecation by irritating nerve endings in the gastric and intestinal mucosa. So intense is the irritation that the intestinal mucosa cannot tolerate their presence, and they are rushed through the GI tract. Peristalsis sometimes is so violent that cramping results, and fluids are often hustled into the intestinal lumen to dilute the irritating chemicals. The whole process is so violent and nasty that it is hard to believe people would voluntarily put themselves through it, but they do.

Liquifying Agents Chemicals like magnesium sulfate (epsom salts) fall into this category. The idea is to fill the lumen of the gut with unabsorbable or poorly absorbable salts like magnesium and sulfate, which will produce an osmotic gradient that will draw water into the intestinal lumen. As we have seen, anything that will liquify the chyme will facilitate the movement of material through the gut and especially across the various valves in the GI tract. These medications are not as violent as the irritants, but they work pretty fast and can produce some serious side effects—like unusual fluid loss or serious electrolyte imbalance—if used indiscriminately.

Softening or Wetting Agents These are available in over-the-counter preparations, but because they tend to be relatively gentle cathartics, not many people buy them. They are designed to soften fecal matter by entering the fecal mass and wetting it down. For this reason they are often referred to as "detergent" cathartics.

Hemorrhoids

Medicine has classified hemorrhoids into two basic groups—internal and external. As you can probably figure out from the names, the external type is outside the anal sphincter, while internal hemorrhoids are not. Both are very common in the U.S., and it has been estimated that about 35 to 38 percent of the adult population is or has been afflicted with them.

The fundamental cause is interference with blood flow through the hemorrhoidal veins, which produces **varicosities** (permanent weak spots or distensions). In essence, hemorrhoids are varicose veins in the anal and rectal area. They can be the result of many things—liver disorders, prostate problems, and, of course, congestion of the blood vessels of the pelvic region due to pregnancy.

There are three degrees of internal hemorrhoids, and the third degree is the worst. First-degree internal hemorrhoids are totally invisible and generally undetectable without the use of a proctoscope. They are seldom a problem, although if their original cause is not attended to, they frequently become second degree. Second-degree hemorrhoids are usually more distended than first-degree and are sometimes pushed through the anal opening to the body exterior during defecation—a process known as **prolapsing.** The less severe of the second-degree hemorrhoids will recede back into the rectum spontaneously when defecation is over. If the condition is permitted to persist, however, the swollen tissue stretches more and more until it will no longer recede by itself but must be pushed back where it belongs manually after each visit to the toilet. If still not attended to, the day will come when such manipulation no longer works. They can be pushed back inside the rectum, but they pop right back out. At this point, they have become permanent external structures and have reached the third stage.

Treatment depends on their severity. First-degree hemorrhoids are treated successfully by merely removing the cause, if it can be found. Second- and third-degree are usually removed surgically.

The affliction known as **thrombosed external hemorrhoids** is not a true hemorrhoidal condition. Actually, it is a bruise on the external surface of the anal sphincter, and it can be extremely painful—so painful, in fact, that it is sometimes necessary to remove the bruise-clot under local anesthesia to provide relief. Most of the time, however, this isn't necessary. Warm baths (*sitz baths* are good), mild analgesics (painkillers), and bed rest for a couple of days will generally alleviate the problem.

There are some unusual methods of surgically handling prolapsed hemorrhoids that may be of interest because they sound like some kid's imaginative dream. There is a technique known as the *rubber band method* that involves, as the name states, a rubber band. Simply put, a rubber band is placed tightly around the base of the hemorrhoidal tissue. It has the same effect as a rubber band would have if placed around your finger—the tissue distal to the band turns purple because proper blood flow is prevented. Naturally, you would remove the rubber band around your finger before any permanent damage could be done, but in the case of the hemorrhoid, the band is left there until the tissue dies of inanition. Another treatment method involves the use of super-cold liquid gases such as nitrogen. The super-cold liquid is applied to the base of the hemorrhoid, thus freezing and killing the stalk. The procedure is known as **cryosurgery** (*cryo,* "cold") and has the advantage of not requiring a hospital stay.

Summary

Hunger

I. Hunger is a basic drive. It can be produced by many things. An empty stomach will produce hunger pangs, and there is a feeding center in the hypothalamus that responds to blood nutrient levels.

II. Some Biological Philosophy. The interior of the GI tract is *not* inside the body. This is an important point. The presence of strong acids and powerful enzymes could not be tolerated within the body tissues.

Some Anatomy

The anatomy of the gastrointestinal tract begins with the mouth, proceeds through the stomach, thence to the small intestine and large intestine, into the rectum, and finally to the anus.

Digestive Operations

I. The Mouth
   A. Both mechanical digestion and chemical digestion begin in the mouth.
   B. Chewing initiates mechanical digestion.
   C. The saliva contains a starch-splitting enzyme that initiates chemical digestion.

II. Exocrine Glands. The glands that produce enzymes in the mouth are exocrine glands. Exocrine glands synthesize materials from blood and secrete them through ducts into their target zones, usually a nearby structure.

III. Salivary Secretions. There are three pairs of specialized exocrine glands within the mouth. Enzymes, lubricants, and buffers are produced by these glands.
   A. The enzyme is called ptyalin.
   B. The lubricant is mucin.
   C. The buffers are primarily bicarbonates.
   D. Saliva's Limitations. Saliva's enzymes can break starch into smaller molecules, but they cannot remove monomers from the ends of the molecules.
   E. The lubricant serves also as a glue to hold the chewed food mass together.
   F. Bicarbonate flow can be overwhelmed during eating, and the oral pH can become quite low.

IV. Control Mechanisms
   A. Both autonomic branches stimulate salivary secretion.
   B. The thought of food can also stimulate these secretions.
   C. The physical presence of food stimulates a center in the medulla known as the salivary center.

V. Swallowing
   A. Swallowing is reflexly controlled.
   B. Food or liquid at the rear of the mouth stimulates the reflex, and once it is initiated, voluntary controls cannot slow it or prevent it from occurring.
   C. The nasopharynx is closed off and the epiglottis shuts the glottal opening at the top of the trachea when swallowing occurs. Thus, food is prevented from entering the respiratory system. The only opening available for it to enter is the esophagus.

VI. Peristalsis. The rhythmic contractions that propel food from the back of the mouth to the anus are known as peristalsis. It is controlled mainly by neural impulses.

VII. The Stomach
   A. The stomach is an enormously extensible portion of the gastrointestinal tract. It serves as a storage reservoir.
   B. There are four distinct zones within the stomach, each featuring its own characteristics.

VIII. The Four-Layered Wall. The plan of the wall of the entire digestive tract is a standardized, four-layer foundation that is modified here and there according to the job that needs to be done.
   A. The Mucous Membrane (Mucosa)
      1. This is the innermost layer. It contains nearly all of the secretory glands and cells.

2. Any cells designed to absorb the hydrolyzed nutrients are also present in the mucosa.
3. Because of many wrinkles and structural components, the mucous membrane has an enormous internal surface area.

B. The Submucosa. The layer is immediately outside the mucosa. It contains, among other things, the blood and lymphatic vessels which will carry absorbed nutrients into the interior of the body.

C. The Muscle Layer
1. Two layers of smooth muscle wrap the two innermost layers.
2. Cells of the innermost muscle lie parallel to the axis of the gut. When this layer is contracted, the gut becomes shorter and fatter.
3. The outer muscle layer wraps around the gut. When these cells contract, the gut becomes long and thin.

D. The Serous Layer. This is the outermost layer. It consists of loose connective tissue covered with epithelial cells.

Gastric Digestion

I. Stomach Movements. The rolling and twisting movements of the stomach serve to break up the food bolus and expose it to the action of gastric fluids. These movements also propel stomach contents toward the opening into the small intestine.

II. Gastric Secretions. Four types of secretory cells provide a variety of chemicals to the interior of the stomach.

A. Parietal Cells
1. These cells secrete hydrochloric acid and intrinsic factor.
2. Intrinsic Factor. This is a protective chemical designed to transport vitamin B_{12} through the gut without its being broken down.

B. Stomach Protection—the Neck Cells. These cells secrete mucin. Mucin is a viscous chemical that coats cells on the stomach interior and helps prevent direct contact with the stomach acid. It also contains bicarbonate, which can buffer any acids that succeed in penetrating the coating.

C. The Chief Cells
1. These are the cells that secrete the enzyme pepsin. Pepsin is secreted as an inactive protein, pepsinogen, which is activated by chemicals within the stomach lumen.
2. Pepsin's Specificity. Pepsin is a protein splitter. It cannot, however, break amino acids away from the ends of a protein molecule.
3. Gastric Starch Breakdown
a) The stomach secretes no starch-splitting enzymes.
b) Starch digestion occurs in the stomach nonetheless, due to the presence of the salivary amylase that has not been destroyed.
c) Fully 40 percent of all starch digestion takes place in the stomach as a result of this salivary amylase activity.
4. Argentaffin Cells. These cells synthesize and secrete serotonin, a neurotransmitter. Its purpose is unclear.

III. Control Mechanisms.

A. There are two aspects to the initiation of digestion in the stomach, the cephalic phase and the gastric phase.

B. Cephalic Phase. Smelling or seeing food when one is hungry can cause salivary and gastric secretions and gastric movement to begin.

C. Gastric Phase
1. This phase begins when food actually enters the stomach. Once food enters the stomach, both hormonal and neural control mechanisms increase the secretory rate of its glands and the activity of its smooth muscles.
2. Gastrin. Gastrin is a hormone secreted by special cells in the gastric mucosa. Like all hormones, it is secreted into the blood. Release of this hormone increases the output of HCl by the stomach.

D. Eructation. Euphemistically, this is known as burping, and it is important in reducing the distension of the stomach.

E. Intestinal Phase. This phase of digestion begins when food leaves the stomach and enters the small intestine.

IV. Suppression of Stomach Activity

A. One aspect of the intestinal phase of digestion is the suppression of stomach activity, particularly the secretion of hydrochloric acid. This suppression is easily overridden when the stomach contains food, but it shuts down gastric activity when the stomach is empty.

B. Enterogastric Reflex. This neural reflex slows stomach secretion and movement. It is initiated by the presence of food or acid in the small intestine.

C. Endocrine Suppression. Several duodenal hormones are involved in suppressing gastric activity. Collectively, these hormones are known as enterogastrones. They are secreted by cells of the intestinal mucosa in response to the presence of fat or acid.

D. Absorption. Little absorption takes place in the stomach.

V. The Stomach Exit. Factors Affecting Movement into the Intestine.

A. The muscle guarding the entrance must be relaxed.

B. There must be more pressure in the stomach than in the intestine.

C. The food in the stomach must be semiliquid.

VI. The Interdigestive Phase

A. This phase exists when the stomach is empty. It is marked by the secretion of very small quantities of both acids and buffering materials.

B. Vomiting.
1. This is a reflex designed to empty the stomach when harmful or irritating materials are present.
2. It is a neural reflex involving both branches of the ANS, working in support of each other.

The Small Intestine

I. Most digestion occurs in the small intestine. It is assisted by two organs that are not part of the digestive tract *per se* but serve powerful supportive roles.
II. Chemical Digestion. Chemical digestion begins when food enters the duodenum. Entering food is highly acid and semiliquid. Carbohydrates and proteins are partially digested. Lipids are essentially untouched.

The Pancreas

I. The pancreas is a critical endocrine organ. It also plays a very important role in chemical digestion within the small intestine.
II. Pancreatic Secretions
   A. Bicarbonates. Bicarbonates neutralize the acids as they pour from the stomach.
   B. Pancreatic Enzymes
      1. Pancreatic Amylase. These carbohydrate splitters produce very few monomers. They split complex saccharides into smaller sugars, often into disaccharides, but they cannot remove terminal saccharides from a molecule.
      2. Proteolytic Enzymes. Protein-splitting enzymes have the same limitations as the amylases. They can break proteins into smaller peptides, but they cannot remove terminal amino acids from polypeptide chains.
      3. Pancreatic Lipase. These enzymes can break fatty acids away from glycerol.
      4. Nucleases. These enzymes are designed to break up strands of RNA and DNA. The pancreatic nucleases are restricted to separating the nitrogenous bases from the rest of the strand.
      5. Self-protection. The lipolytic and proteolytic enzymes secreted by the pancreas are synthesized in an inactive form.
      6. Enzyme Activation. The enzymes are activated only when they are released into the lumen of the intestine.
   C. Secretory Control
      1. Both hormones and neural control are exerted over pancreatic secretions. Some of these controls also suppress the activity of the stomach.
      2. Secretin is stimulated by the presence of acid in the duodenum. It stimulates the secretion of bicarbonates from the pancreas and reduces stomach activity.
      3. Cholecystokinin is stimulated by the presence of fats or acids in the duodenum. It increases enzyme-secreting activity in the pancreas.

Digestive Activity of the Liver

I. The liver produces no digestive enzymes for intestinal hydrolysis. Its chief contribution to the digestion of nutrients in the gut is bile.
II. Bile
   A. Bile contains two major fractions, bile salts and bile pigments.
   B. Bile pigments do not take part in digestion. They are primarily waste products of erythrocyte metabolism.
   C. Bile salts are surface-active agents. They permit lipases to interact with fats and break them down.
III. The Liver and Cholesterol. The liver also synthesizes and secretes cholesterol. Most is utilized for cellular anabolism, but some is secreted with the bile.
IV. Storage of Bile. Bile is stored in the gallbladder between meals. It is also concentrated there.
V. Regulation of Bile
   A. Hormonal Control. Cholecystokinin exerts the main hormonal control. It is stimulated by fats in the duodenum. When it is present, the smooth muscles of the gallbladder contract, squeezing out all contents.
   B. Neural Control
      1. Neural control is mainly reflex and occurs in conjunction with the contraction of the gallbladder. It serves to open the bile duct.
      2. Oddi's Sphincter. This sphincter muscle wraps around the bile duct and when closed, it prevents bile from flowing into the small intestine. It is relaxed by the neural reflex just described.
   C. Chemical Control
      1. There is another control mechanism present. This is a positive feedback loop.
      2. Bile Salts
         a) Bile salts present in the blood are the greatest stimulus for the production of more bile salts. This situation could run out of control were it not for a cutoff system.
         b) This cutoff system is present in the neural reflex that controls the sphincter of Oddi. When fats are no longer present in the gut, the sphincter closes, preventing the movement of bile into the intestine. This shuts off further production of bile salts and interrupts the feedback loop.

Intestinal Digestion

I. Most digestion and nearly all absorption take place in the small intestine.
II. Some Intestinal Anatomy. The small intestine has the same four-layered construction as the stomach. It is about five meters long.
III. Functional Significance. The presence of the muscle layers permits intestinal movement to occur.
   A. Intestinal Movement. Intestinal movement is both directional and churning. It is intended to thoroughly mix the contents while propelling them slowly but relentlessly toward the large intestine.
   B. The Topography of the Mucosa. The internal surface of the mucosa, which, if smooth, would probably be no greater than 2 square meters, is actually between 250 and 300 square meters because of its morphology.
IV. The Mucosal Epithelium. This layer is filled with secretory glands, secretory cells, and absorptive cells.
V. Intestinal Secretions

A. Mucin. Mucin protects and lubricates the interior of the intestine.
B. The Succus Entericus. This is a catchall phrase referring to the collective secretions of the small intestine. The intestine produces enzymes to digest compounds of all food groups, but most are not secreted into the interior of the intestine.
C. A Different Mode of Operation
   1. Some enzymes are carried into the interior in epithelial cells that are shed regularly.
   2. Enzymes are retained on the surfaces of epithelial cells and operate on foodstuffs without leaving the mother cell. A great deal of hydrolysis occurs on the surfaces of these cells.
   3. These cells are also responsible for absorbing much of the nutrient they digest. It is taken in immediately after being broken up.
D. The Microvilli. The microvilli are composed of contractile protein and covered with a sheet of glycoprotein.

VI. Absorption: an Active and a Passive Process. The absorption of food of all kinds can be active or passive.
A. Sugars. Glucose and galactose are actively absorbed, and activity is rapid. Fructose is probably absorbed passively.
B. Amino Acids. Proteins do not have to be broken down to single amino acids to be absorbed. Di- and tripeptides are freely transported across the membrane.
C. Lipids
   1. Lipids need not be transported across the cellular membranes because they can penetrate so easily.
   2. They are seldom broken down to fatty acids and glycerol. Most are absorbed as glycerides.
   3. Most lipids are not absorbed into the blood, but rather into the lymph.
D. Nucleotides. Absorption of the phosphates and ribose sugars is active and rapid.
E. Vitamins
   1. Vitamins obtain special treatment because they must not be broken down. With the exception of B_{12}, all are small and are not damaged by enzymes.
   2. Vitamin B_{12}. This is absorbed in the lower part of the small intestine.
F. Water and Inorganic Materials (Minerals). Minerals are actively transported. Water follows the concentration gradient thus produced.

VII. Control of Intestinal Enzymes. Both intestinal motility and secretory activities are controlled by nerves present in the myenteric and Meissner's plexuses. These are autonomous controls, which can function independently of the CNS.

The Large Intestine

I. Movement from the small intestine to the large is dependent on the same factors that govern movement from the stomach to the small intestine.

II. Function. Absorb water, produce formed feces, absorb minerals and nutrients.
A. Water Reabsorption
   1. Water movement is passive and follows osmotic gradients.
   2. The osmotic gradients are actively produced, and when sodium and chloride pumps are operating at a high rate, as much as a half-liter of water can be moved across the mucosa of the large intestine each day.
B. Production of Formed Feces. After water absorption has occurred, the remaining wastes are stuck together with mucin and prepared for elimination.
C. Absorption of Minerals and Other Nutrients
   1. Mineral absorption is mainly active and often provides an osmotic gradient for water to follow.
   2. Nearly all the food nutrients are already absorbed. However, bacteria within the large intestine produce some vitamins, mainly vitamin K, and the large intestine absorbs these.

III. Feces. The formation of feces is important. It saves constant defecation and helps conserve water.

IV. Movements of the Large Intestine. Movements are relatively ponderous in the large intestine, but they eventually serve to propel the contents into the rectum.

V. Elimination. Elimination is both an autonomically controlled reflex and a consciously regulated phenomenon. The controls are all neural.

Clinical Considerations

I. Foul Breath
II. Herpes Simplex
III. TMJ (Temporomandibular Joint) Problems
IV. Esophageal Afflictions
A. Simple Sore Throat
B. Scarlet Fever
V. Gastric Problems. Functional dyspepsia is a catchall term for such problems.
A. Gastritis
B. Ulcers
C. Peptic Ulcer
VI. Problems of the Digestive Accessory Organs
A. Viral Hepatitis
B. Liver Cirrhosis
C. Gallstones
D. Pancreatitis
E. Abdominal Pain
F. Appendicitis
VII. Diseases of the Colorectal Region
A. Constipation
B. Cathartics
   1. Bulk or Fiber
   2. Irritants
   3. Liquifying Agents
   4. Softening or Wetting Agents
C. Hemorrhoids

Review Questions

1. Describe hunger. How is it stimulated in human beings?
2. Name the parts of the hypothalamus that are involved in regulating the eating process.
3. Why does the digestion of food occur outside the body instead of inside?
4. Compare the processes of dehydration synthesis and hydrolytic digestion.
5. Outline the digestive tract, beginning with the mouth and ending with the anus.
6. Describe the process of digestion that begins in the mouth. Be sure to mention:
   a. the effects of mechanical digestion
   b. the effects of chemical digestion
7. What is an exocrine gland? Draw a typical example of one.
8. Where are the salivary glands located? What are buccal glands?
9. Name the components of normal saliva.
10. What do the enzymes in saliva do? How specialized are they?
11. Describe the control mechanisms involved with salivary secretion.
12. Outline the swallowing reflex.
13. Describe the esophagus and its secretions. Where is the esophageal sphincter?
14. Describe the stomach, naming and locating all its zones.
15. Name the four types of cells found in the stomach epithelium.
16. Describe the process by which hydrochloric acid is concentrated from the blood.
17. What is the alkaline tide? Describe its cause.
18. How is the stomach protected from the powerful acids and enzymes that it contains?
19. Does any starch digestion occur in the stomach? Explain.
20. Describe the control of gastric secretion. Be sure to distinguish between release of acid and release of enzymes.
21. When does the intestinal phase of digestion begin?
22. Describe the control systems that suppress stomach activity.
23. Identify the valve guarding the exit from the stomach and outline the conditions necessary before the chyme can pass through it.
24. Describe the structure of the small intestine.
25. Describe peristalsis.
26. Describe the enzyme secretions of the pancreas and the particular function of each.
27. Describe the endocrine and neural controls that regulate secretions of the pancreas.
28. How does the liver aid digestion?
29. Describe bile pigments.
30. What are the components of bile salts? What are their functions?
31. Describe the regulatory mechanisms for bile secretion.
32. What is the function of the gallbladder?
33. Describe the interior surface of the small intestine. Name the different epithelial cells of the small intestine and what each secretes.
34. How do the production and operation of the intestinal enzymes differ from those of the stomach and pancreas?
35. Describe the process of absorption in the small intestine. Be sure you describe how all the different food groups are handled.
36. Describe the regulatory mechanisms involved in the secretion of intestinal enzymes.
37. What are the three primary functions of the large intestine?
38. Describe the process of fecal elimination.

Chapter 16 The Kidney: The Blood's Scrubber

Study Hints

1. Pay particular attention to the main function of the kidney. Most people tend to consider it mainly an organ of excretion, and while it is that, it is much more.
2. Be aware of the unusual nature of the initial filter system. Note how it differs from the filtration limitations of the systemic capillaries.
3. Pay particular attention to the various forces at work within the filters.
4. Be sure you know where most solute reabsorption takes place.
5. Be aware of the tonicity of the filtrate at various points within the nephron.
6. Be sure you understand the workings of the loop of Henle. This is a countercurrent multiplier system, the only one known to exist.
7. Know where the hormones *aldosterone* and *antidiuretic hormone* perform their jobs and what it is that they do. Also make sure you know what percentage of total water reabsorption they affect.

Objectives

When you have finished reading this chapter, you should:

1. be able to draw and label the gross anatomy of a kidney.
2. be able to draw and label a nephron.
3. be familiar with the forces involved in the formation of the initial filtrate that collects in the nephron.
4. know the difference between active reabsorption and tubular secretion.
5. be able to outline the processes that are involved in the formation of urine, beginning in the proximal convoluted tubule, proceeding through the loop of Henle into the distal tubule and finally into the collecting tubules.
6. know why the loop of Henle is called a multiplier system.
7. know where the endocrine system is involved with the kidney's operations, which hormones are involved, and where each exerts its influence.
8. be able to describe the primary function of the kidney.

Introduction

Our mental journey into the functioning of the human body has taken us into cells, our individual living units, and we have investigated the tiny organelles that collectively produce life. We have seen how these units are nourished and kept from polluting their environments, and we have viewed the systems our bodies use to coordinate the efforts of all body mechanisms in this work. Investigations of the various body fluid compartments have shown how nourishment is carried to each cell and how cellular debris is carried off for disposal. We have seen how oxygen is brought into the body to provide for efficient energy production and how food molecules are processed so that the body can use the resulting chemicals for energy and raw building materials. The blood carries all of these things deep into the interior of the body, where they can be moved into the various body zones as they are needed. Provisions that enable body machinery to keep running are thus always available.

The blood, as a transportation system, functions magnificently. Its mechanisms, both gross and tiny, are designed to spot overabundance or deficiencies, large or small, and to deliver or accept materials accordingly. We have seen how the liver processes and stores many excess nutrients, thereby preventing the blood from becoming overburdened with them, and because there is constant monitoring and replenishment, the blood is never depleted of nutrients. Oxygen taken from the blood is replaced in the lungs, and the CO_2 that was dumped in by the cells' metabolic machinery is removed.

Kidney glomerulus in renal corpuscle.

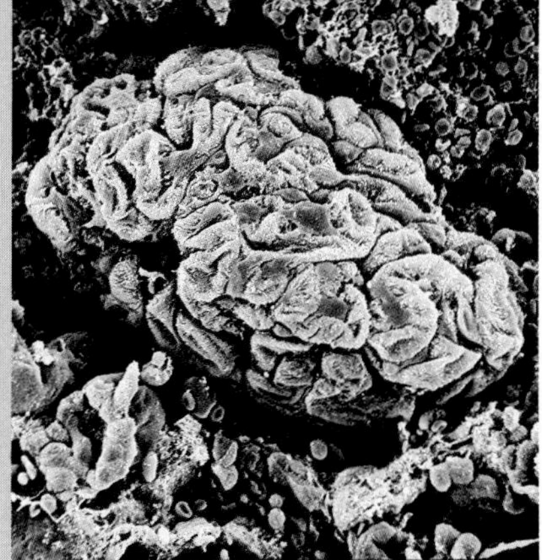

All this activity is crucial to continued living and cannot be permitted to cease. But of course there is a cost. No process, no matter how smooth its operations, is 100 percent efficient. Along with the energy production and the constant building and refurbishing operations, there is a steady production of waste and debris that is shovelled out of the cells on the assumption that the interstitial fluid can deal with it. As we know, the interstitial fluid functions to some extent as a bridge between the blood and the cells' constantly whirring machinery, so the interstitial fluid's method of dealing with it consists of dumping it in the blood, thereby neatly avoiding any further responsibility.

From a totally idealistic point of view, it is not a good idea to dump metabolic sewage into the blood. If it were permitted to accumulate, the debris could poison the entire physiological environment. Because of its intimate and constant contact with the interstitial fluids and body cells, the blood must maintain its own homeostatic tolerance standards. Like a river sweeping past a city, it is a source of water, food—even climate alterations. It also provides a cheap and easy transportation system to bring products and new residents in . . . and it serves, unfortunately in some cases, to sweep the city clean. Dumping raw sewage into rivers was OK when there was no one living downstream and suffering, or upstream doing the same thing. When a polluted river becomes a problem, there is a great foofaraw to stop the polluting. Yet in a city, just as in a living body, by-products of life are always produced and the garbage must be disposed of. How do you stop dumping it without rendering the city uninhabitable?

Our physiological mechanisms learned eons ago that environmental considerations must coexist with economic necessity. Just as the cities in our world must live, our body cells must live—they cannot be allowed to starve. Yet by the same token, the internal environment must not become polluted by the by-products of this intense industry. By way of compromise, our bodies have built "sewage treatment plants" that are designed to handle the debris that continually enters the blood. Our kidneys are our bodies' sewage treatment plants, and considering the job they must do, they are quite small. With dimensions about 12 cm long by 6 cm wide by 3 cm thick, they occupy only a little real estate within the body. Yet their blood supply is prodigious, and judging by the amount of energy they consume, they are expensive. Yet they are indispensible. Poisons can kill as completely as starvation and a great deal more rapidly.

These treatment plants are relentless in their pursuit of purification. There are circulatory tributaries that leave the river of blood at selected points, and they steadily divert a substantial flow away from the mainstream and into the treatment plants. The volume of blood sweeping through these downstream branches is large—fully one-fifth of the cardiac output is diverted to these plants every minute—and the processing is complicated and unbelievably thorough.

Like any good sewage treatment plant, the kidneys identify and remove many kinds of metabolic sweepings by simply thrusting them from the body. But that is only one phase of its many operations. The main idea of a treatment plant, remember, is to *revitalize* as well as *purify*, so dumping the accumulated debris is only one part of its duties.

The kidney's primary function is to maintain homeostasis within the body fluids. It accomplishes this by perpetually monitoring and ceaselessly adjusting the blood.

Our kidneys monitor and adjust:

1. the blood's pH,
2. its solute concentrations,
3. its nutrient content,
4. salt content,
5. total volume,
6. even its osmotic properties.

In addition, kidneys adjust the concentration of various nutrients by disposing of the excess. For instance, when blood volume becomes a little too great, the extra water is often dumped, yet when it is needed, water is conserved by limiting the amount excreted. Systemic blood pressures can be adjusted by kidney mechanisms, hormonal activity can be mediated—even behavioral phenomena can be stimulated to aid in the pursuit of body fluid homeostasis (it is not at all unusual for a kidney secretion to stimulate thirst). Clearly, environmental problems are not minor considerations in the overall plan of living engines.

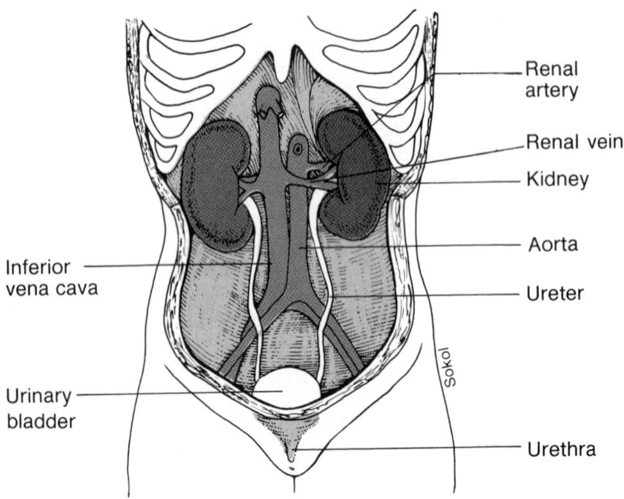

Figure 16.1 The so-called excretory system. This includes the kidneys, ureters, urinary bladder, and urethra. Be sure you realize that the kidney serves as much more than a simple excretory organ.

Kidney Structure

Anatomically, the kidneys resemble enormous beans. They are located a little higher in the body than most people think they are (figure 16.1), and the upper half at least enjoys the partial protection of the rib cage and the heavy muscles of the lower torso. The interior of the kidney consists of a series of **renal pyramids,** roughly triangular-shaped chambers crammed full of tiny tubules known as **collecting tubules.** These clusters of tubules, which open into the **renal calyx,** are separated from each other by **renal columns.** The outermost part—the *rind* or *shell* of the kidney—is known as the **cortex.** The interior is the **medulla** (figure 16.2).

Blood Supply

Taken as a fraction of total body weight, the kidneys represent a little less than 0.5 percent of a human, yet they receive more than 20 percent of the total cardiac output, and even when they are at rest, they consume about 8 percent of the oxygen made available to the systemic circulation. Blood enters the kidneys through the **renal artery,** a tributary of the **abdominal aorta** (figure 16.3).

As figure 16.3 shows, the dorsal aorta is the major arterial vessel in the trunk of the body. It is fed directly by the great aorta; hence the kidney is assured that its blood will be supplied at very high pressure. The renal artery dives into the kidney and splits into several **interlobar arteries,** which pass through the renal columns into the cortical zone of the kidney, where they form tiny, partial arches over the renal pyramids (figure 16.4).

Smaller vessels called **interlobular arteries** branch off these half-arches, some of which head into the cortical surfaces, where they provide nourishment for the cells near the outer surface of the kidney. Other interlobular branches head for individual *nephrons,* where they serve as the **afferent arterioles** feeding into these functional units of the kidney. After passing through a capillary bed within the nephrons, the **efferent arterioles** that emerge run only a short distance before splitting once again into a bed of capillaries called the **peritubular capillaries** (figure 16.5). These capillaries enwrap the nephron tubules, picking up any materials that leave the nephrons. Some branches of the peritubular capillaries plunge down into the depths of the kidney alongside parts of the nephron and form still another capillary bed called the **vasa recta** capillaries. These vasa recta vessels are extremely important. In addition to being crucial to the nephron's multiplier system, they represent nearly 20 percent of the total peritubular capillary makeup. Functioning cooperatively, the thick mass of capillaries surrounding each nephron insures that anything passing from the nephron into the surrounding interstitial fluids will be rapidly assimilated by the blood.

Nerve Supply

Kidney neurons are all sympathetic in origin. Despite considerable effort to do so, no parasympathetic supply has ever been uncovered. The fibers entering the kidney accompany the arterial blood supply, and they terminate in the smooth muscles that encircle the afferent and efferent arterioles entering and leaving the glomeruli. By dilating or constricting these blood vessels, they can manipulate the pressure of the blood within the filtration system and can thus control, to some extent, the amount of filtration that takes place within the kidney at any given instant.

The Nephron

Within the cortex and extending sometimes slightly into the medulla are the functional units—the **nephrons** (figure 16.5). There are roughly a million to a million and a quarter of them in each kidney. It is within these nephrons that the job of processing the body fluids is accomplished, and the volume of work these tiny organs perform is awesome.

Figure 16.2 (*a*) Longitudinal section of a kidney; (*b*) a renal pyramid containing nephrons; (*c*) a single nephron.

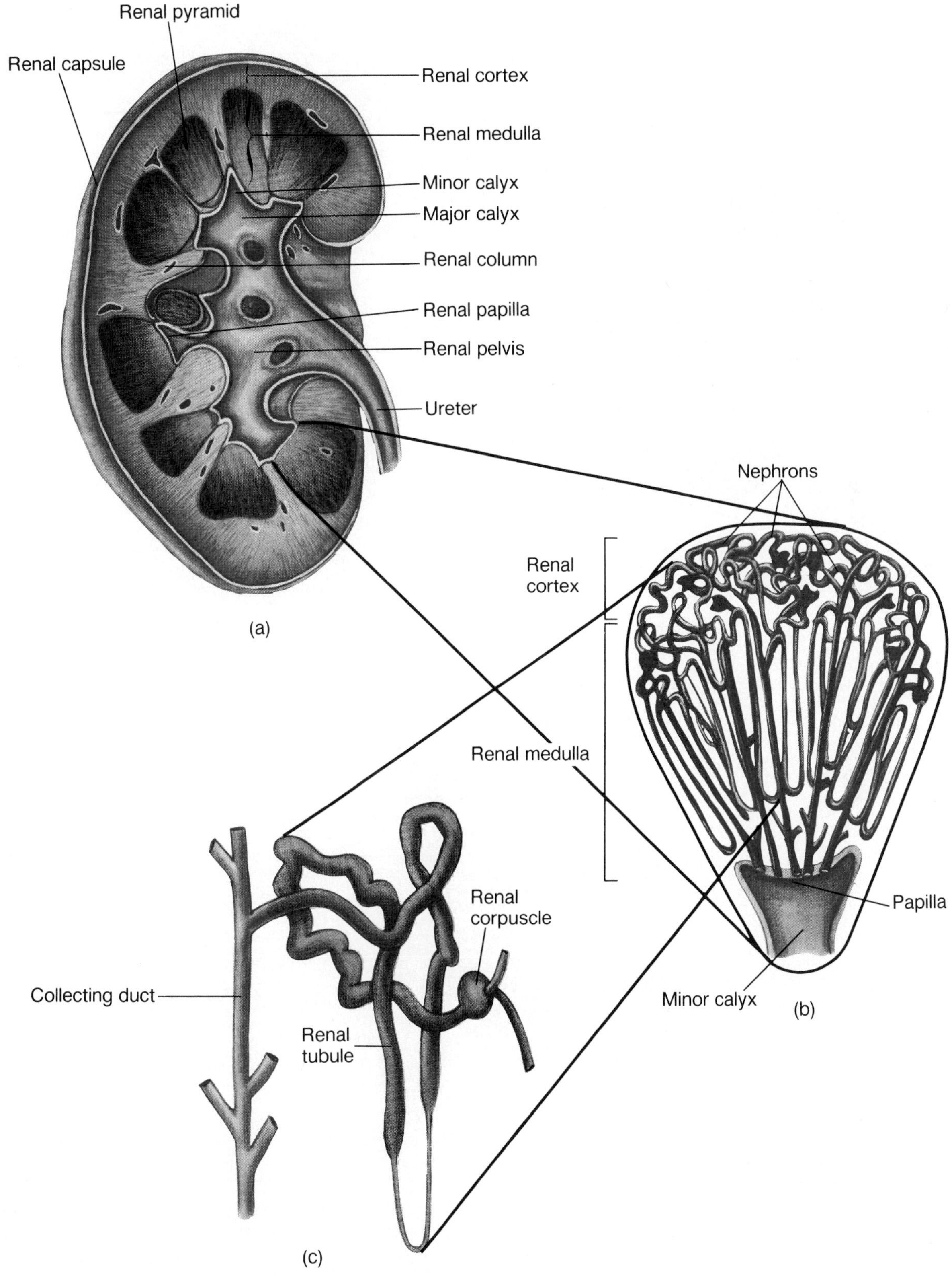

Figure 16.3 The blood supply to the kidneys. Note the position and size of the adrenal glands.

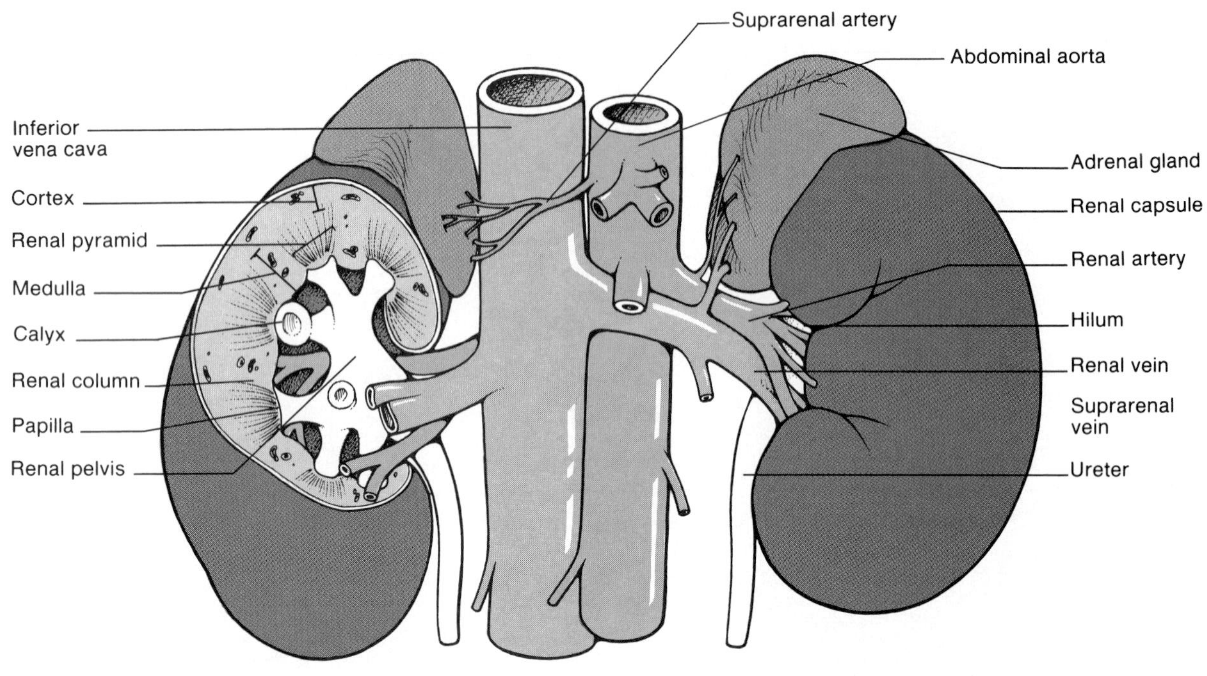

Figure 16.4

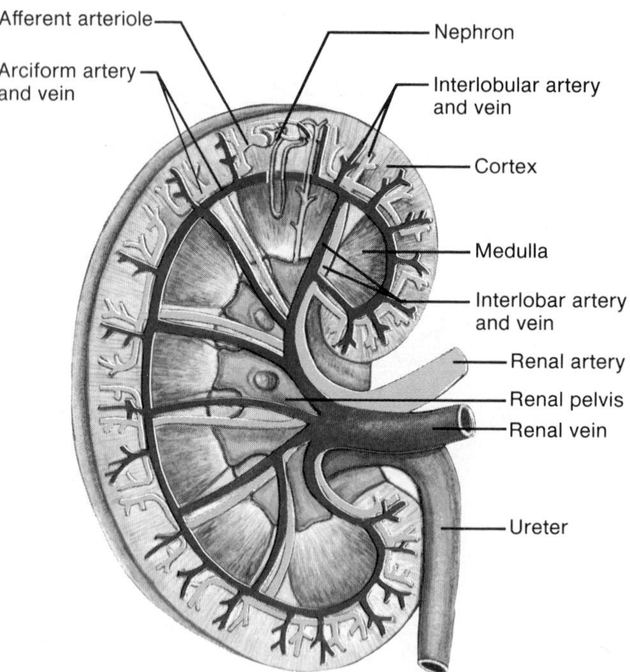

There are two kinds of nephrons in human kidneys. The **cortical nephrons** are, as their name implies, mainly in the kidney cortex. They occupy the outer portion of the cortex, and even the deepest parts of their tubules rarely penetrate into the medulla. In humans, cortical nephrons represent nearly 90 percent of the total number of nephrons in the kidney (figure 16.6).

The remaining 10 percent or so are known as **juxtamedullary nephrons.** The main mass of these nephrons is in the lower portion of the kidney cortex, and their tubules have an unusually long loop that penetrates deep into the kidney medulla. These are the nephrons that confront the kidney environment that is necessary for the concentration of urine.

Figure 16.5 A schematic drawing of a kidney nephron and the associated blood vessels.

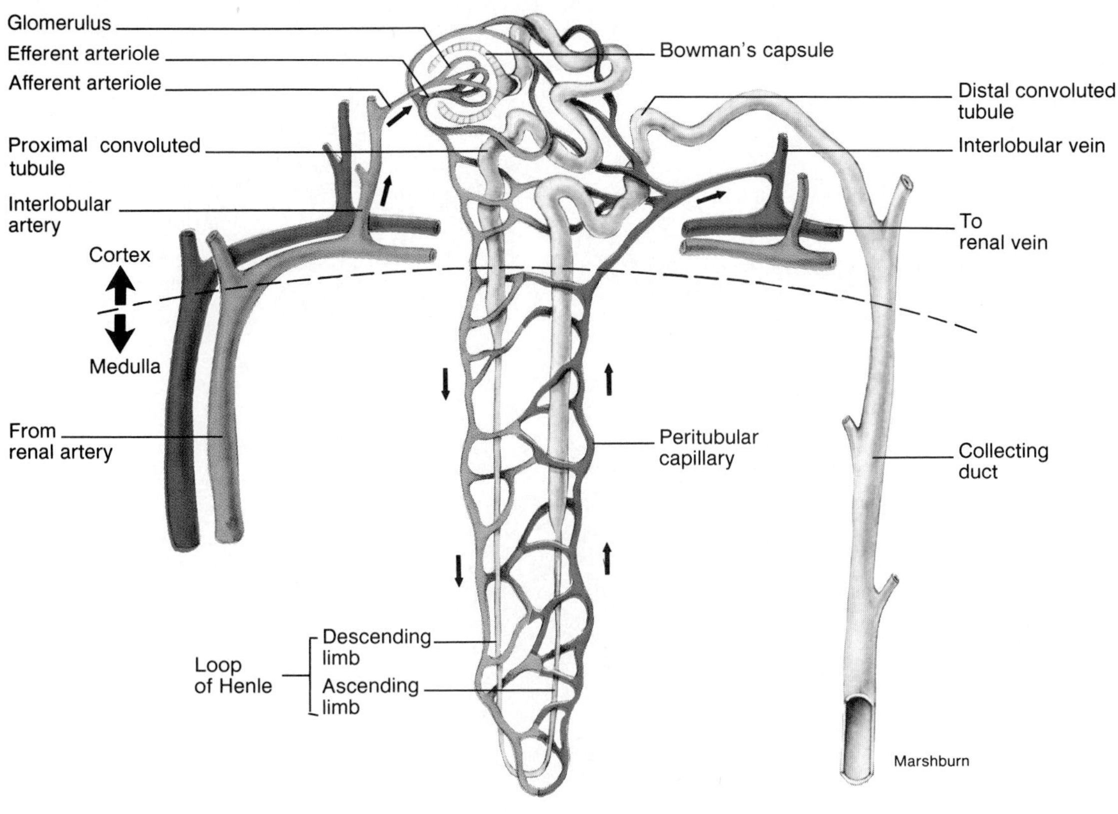

Figure 16.6 The two types of kidney nephrons and their position in the kidney.

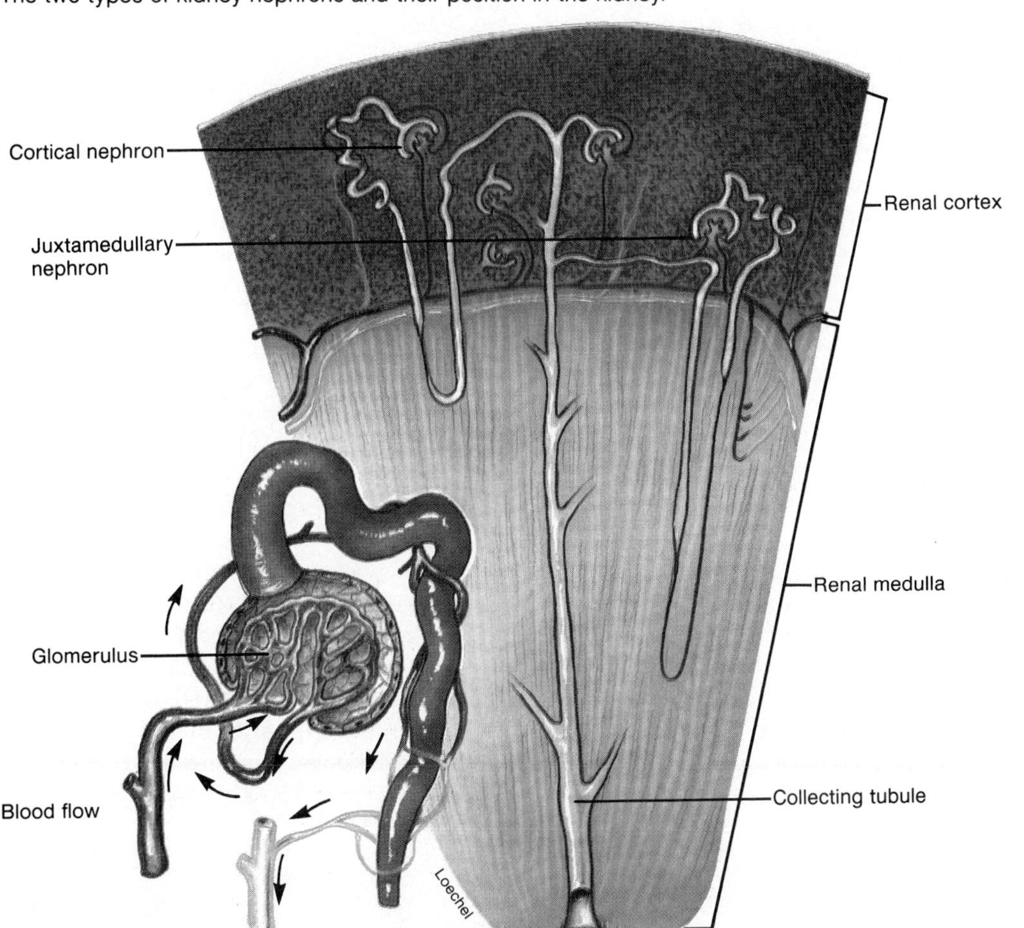

Figure 16.7 (*a*) The renal capsule. (*b*) Partial section of a renal capsule. Note the capillary pores (*lower right*) that permit the filtration of larger molecules than can pass through most systemic capillaries. The glomerulus is a circulatory entity, and blood filtering through the glomeruli is strained by both the capillary walls and the filtration slits before making its initial contact with kidney tissue—the filtration membranes of the podocytes.

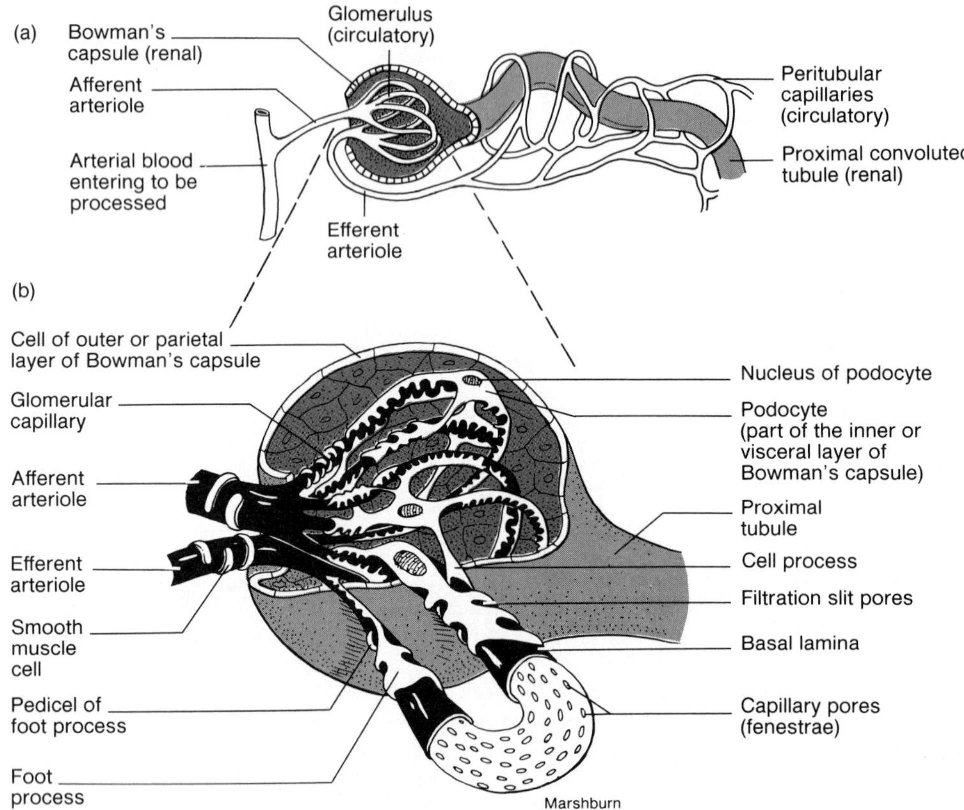

As much as 1,200 ml of blood is processed by the nephrons every minute of every hour. When it enters the kidneys, the blood is only slightly befouled, because purification is a perpetual process, but even so there is always considerable metabolic garbage present, and everything needs adjusting. There are nutrient materials that are too abundant, the pH is upset, and mineral concentration is not what it ought to be. Yet by the time it reenters the general circulation, the blood is scrubbed clean of pollutants and is thoroughly rejuvenated both chemically and physically by the myriad mechanisms of the kidney.

Structure of the Nephron

As is always the case, anatomical arrangement is closely linked with function, and in order to understand how the kidney's nephrons operate, we must have a window-clear picture of what it is made of and how the various components fit together.

Structurally, the nephron does not appear particularly complex. It is a combination of kidney elements and intimately associated nearby blood vessels. Functionally, it all begins with the **renal corpuscle.**

Renal Corpuscle

The renal corpuscle incorporates elements of both the kidney and the circulatory system, **the Bowman's capsule** being renal in origin and the **glomerulus** part of the circulatory system. As you can see from figure 16.7, afferent arterioles from the renal artery enter the renal corpuscle and promptly break into a tangled bed of capillaries that form the glomerulus. Wrapping almost the entire length of each glomerular capillary is the innermost layer of kidney tissue in the form of specialized cells called **podocytes.**

These podocytes resemble a horde of amebas enfolding the capillaries completely, sending out foot processes or **pedicels** that engulf the blood vessels as if they were feeding on them (figures 16.7, 16.8). Each pedicel is arranged so as to *interdigitate* with the pedicels of adjacent podocytes in much the same way as the fingers of two hands can be made to interlock (figure 16.9). The small spaces between them are known as **filter slits** or **slit pores,** and it is through these slit pores that the fluid leaving the circulatory system enters the kidney. These pores are not simply

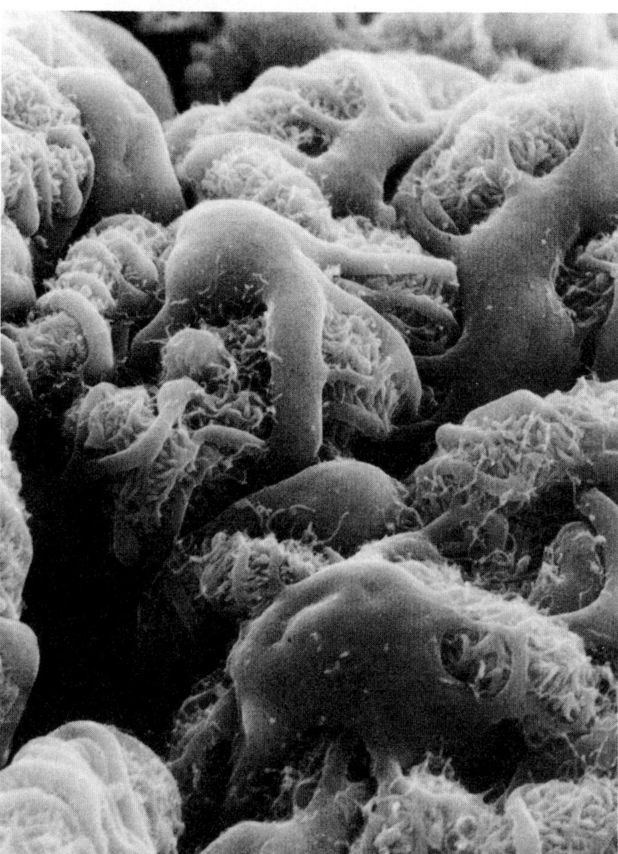

Figure 16.8 Scanning electron micrograph of the capillary ball known as the *glomerulus.* The filtration slit pores are clearly visible between the pedicels.

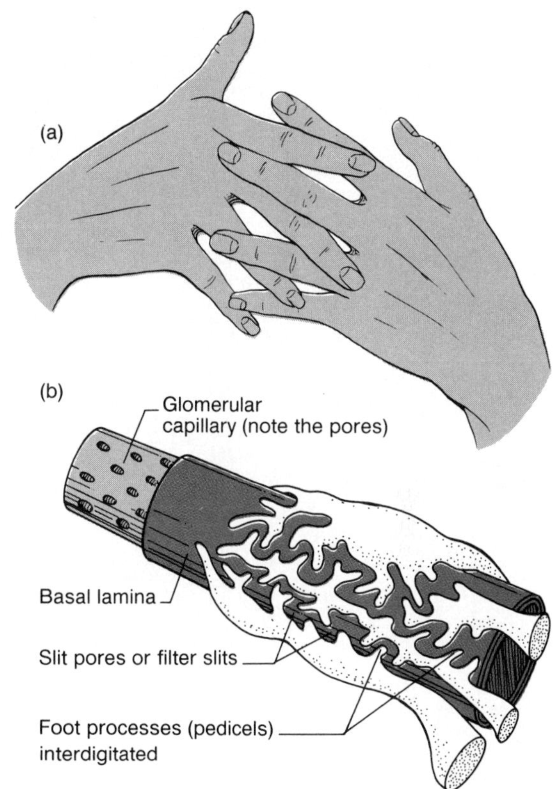

Figure 16.9 (*a*) Fingers locked together or *interdigitated.* (*b*) The interdigitation of the pedicels of Bowman's capsule. The small pedicels of the podocytes are also interdigitated, leaving spaces between called slit pores or filter slits. Each slit pore is covered by a thin membrane that extends out from the pedicel.

naked capillary surfaces, however. Each slit is carefully covered by a diaphanous membrane called a **slit membrane** through which the fluid must pass before it enters the tubule of the nephron.

Proximal Convoluted Tubule

From Bowman's capsule, the filtrate enters the **proximal convoluted tubule** (figure 16.10). This is a sinuously twisting tube that loops back and forth across itself as it serpentines through the cortex of the kidney. It is called the *proximal* tubule because it is proximal (right next) to the renal capsule. Structurally it is pretty simple, consisting of a single layer of cells—but these are not the flattened, squamous epithelial cells of which capillaries are composed. Rather they are broader cells—called **cuboidal**—and they have what is known as a **brush border,** meaning they are equipped with thick clusters of microvilli (figure 16.11) lining their internal or luminal surfaces (the surfaces facing the lumen of the tubule).

Loop of Henle

There is a great deal going on in the proximal tubule, so the fact that it is quite long and highly convoluted seems logical. When the tubule ends, it does so abruptly in the **loop of Henle.** The variation in the length of the loop of Henle depends to a great extent on the species of animal that owns the kidney (see box). In humans, only the loops of the juxtamedullary nephrons actually penetrate into the medulla (figure 16.10*a*). Physiologically, this portion of the nephron is extremely important in the conservation of water by and for the organism.

Regardless of its length, the loop of Henle is divided into two parts—the thin **descending limb,** which plunges down into the medulla then loops at the bottom, and the thick **ascending limb,** which climbs back up into the kidney cortex.

There is a sudden structural transition in the walls of the tubule when it ceases to be the proximal tubule and becomes the thin descending limb of Henle's

Figure 16.10 The morphology of the nephron. There is a point of contact (just below the renal capsule) between the distal tubule and the afferent arteriole. They form two physiologically important structures: the macula densa and the juxtaglomerular apparatus.

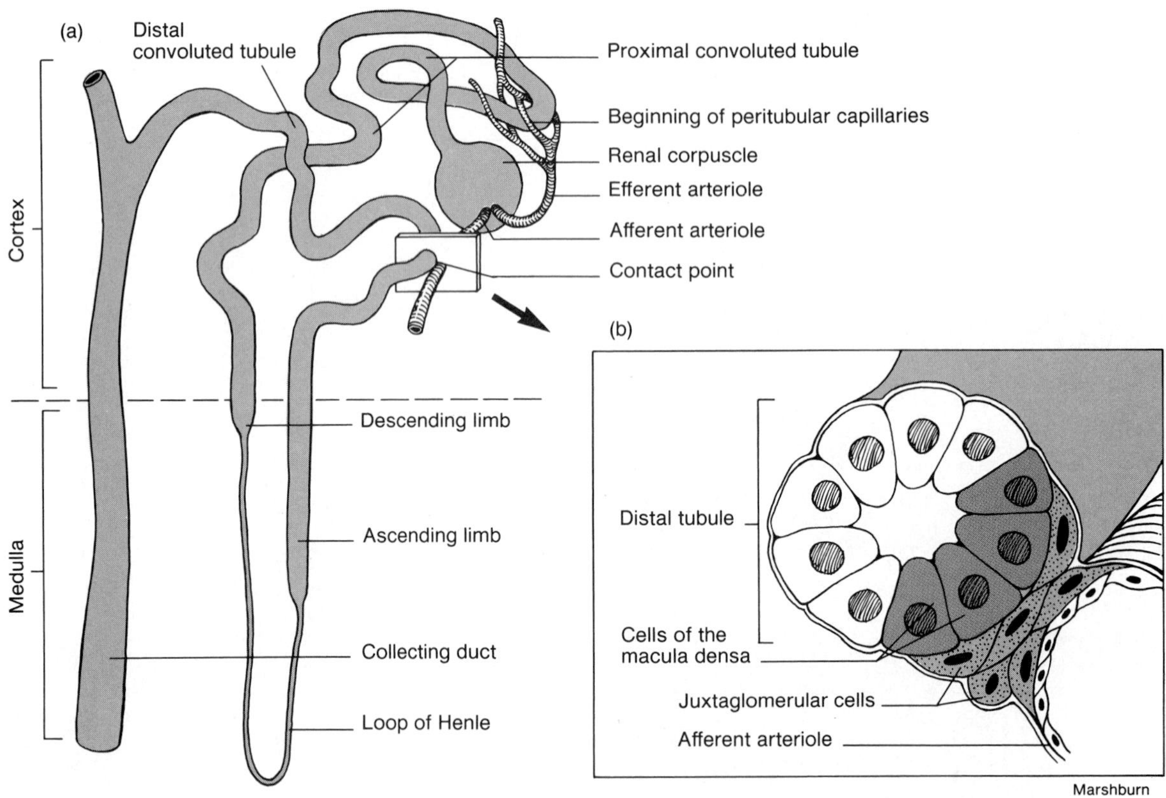

Figure 16.11 Epithelial cells. (*a*) Simple squamous epithelial cells—the type of cell that comprises the peritubular and vasa recti capillaries. (*b*) Cuboidal epithelial cells—the type of cell that comprises the proximal tubule.

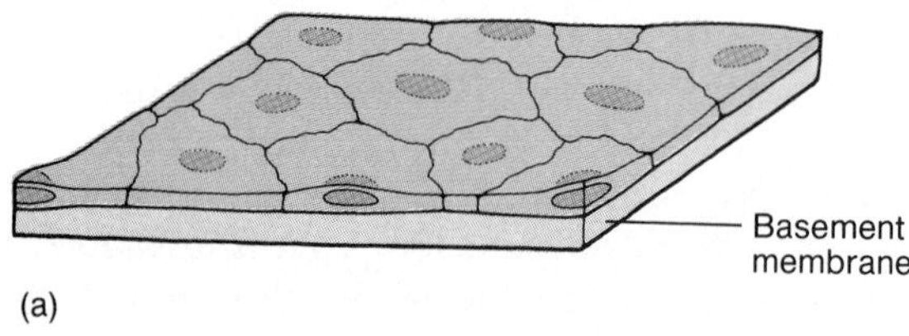

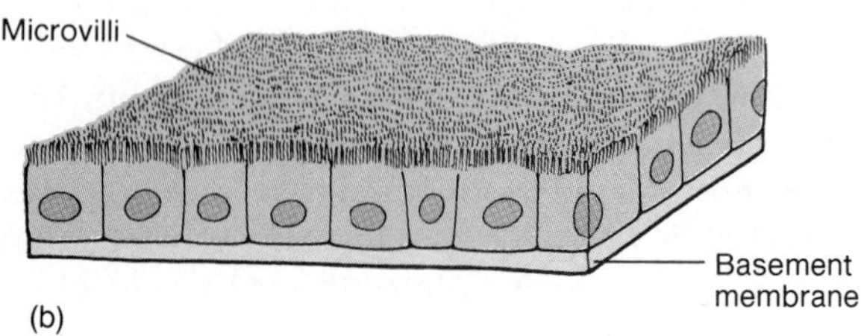

loop. The cuboidal cells of the proximal tubule change suddenly to be flattened, thin squamous cells, and the brush border that was so abundant on the interior surface of the proximal tubule becomes very sparse. The descending limb of Henle's loop thus has structural features similar to those of blood capillaries. In humans, this part of the loop varies from 4.5 mm to 10 mm in length.

The transition to the ascending limb is also abrupt. The squamous cells of the thin limb change suddenly to thicker cuboidal cells with a hint of brush border. This limb climbs upward, enters the cortex of the kidney, and bends back toward its own glomerulus, where it brushes up against its afferent arteriole. At this contact point, some of its cuboidal cells attach to the juxtaglomerular cells of the arteriole, thus forming the **juxtaglomerular apparatus.** The thick ascending limb, whose total length is usually less than 9 mm, has become the **distal convoluted tubule.**

The loops of Henle are fundamental to the ability of the organism to concentrate its urine and thereby avoid water loss. This ability is beautifully correlated with the depth of the kidney medulla and the percentage of Henle's loops that penetrate into it.

The beaver, for instance, lives in fresh water. It seldom leaves its pond, and when it does, it doesn't go far away. Since it spends much of its life swimming, and since fresh water is never a problem for these animals, their kidneys have lost the ability to concentrate their urine significantly. Beaver urine is isotonic with their body fluids, and it is considered significant that the medulla of the beaver kidney is quite narrow and is almost completely devoid of any nephridial structures. The loops of Henle are very nearly straight and are high in the cortex.

The kangaroo rat, on the other hand, lives in the deserts of the American southwest and seldom— possibly never—encounters free water in its lifetime. Such an animal obviously must be equipped with first-class water-conserving mechanisms, and it has the astonishing ability to concentrate its urine to up to three times the concentration of seawater. The kidneys of this animal feature thick medullary zones. More than 90 percent of the loops of Henle penetrate deep into them.

Humans are somewhere between these two extremes. They can concentrate their urine to well above the concentration of plasma and other body fluids but cannot begin to approach the salt concentration of seawater, and as one might expect, our kidney morphology reflects this. Human medullary zones are fairly thick—thicker than the beavers' but not as thick as the kangaroo rats'—and fewer than 15 percent of Henle's loops actually enter those zones.

Distal Convoluted Tubule

As the distal convoluted tubule begins, the nephron once again starts to snake back and forth, twining itself into convolutions as tortuous as those of the proximal tubule (figure 16.10*a*). Like the proximal one, the distal tubule is composed of a single thickness of cuboidal cells, but this time they lack microvilli. The rather broad meanderings take the tubule next to many of the peritubular capillaries, but the most important contact is at the juxtaglomerular apparatus (see figure 16.10*b*). Cells within this complex are richly supplied with cytoplasmic granules that are considered to be the source of **renin.** Thus, the juxtaglomerular apparatus is involved in the manipulation of fluid electrolytes through the sequential release of several compounds and enzymes ultimately involving the adrenal cortical hormone *aldosterone.* This will be considered in more detail later in this chapter.

Collecting Duct

The individual nephron ends with the distal tubule, but there is a final structure involved with the nephrons that is physiologically important and may be significantly affected by their activity. It is the **collecting duct** (figure 16.10*a*), into which several nephrons empty the waste fluid known as urine. This tubule carries the urine through the pyramids of the kidneys to the ureter and thence to the urinary bladder.

Kidney Operations

During a normal twenty-four-hour day, about 1,800 liters of blood enter the human kidneys, meaning that *the average person's entire blood supply runs through the kidneys three hundred times every day.* With each pass about 10 percent of this volume is filtered through the glomerulus and enters the nephrons. Here it is scrubbed clean of any impurities that it might have picked up, its salt and mineral content is checked, pH is carefully adjusted, and everything it is carrying is subjected to intense scrutiny and manipulation. One hundred and eighty liters of blood plasma—about forty-five gallons—are therefore treated each day by our kidneys. Day after day, rain or shine, 180 liters of fluid actually leave the blood and enter the lumina of the nephrons. And this is only for the human body at rest. When the person is active and the blood is pumping vigorously through the system, a good deal more blood is treated in the same length of time. Yet the average person produces only about a liter and a half of urine in that same time period, which means more than 99 percent of that filtered fluid is returned to the blood. Between the glomerular filters and the urinary bladder—somewhere inside our kidneys—a great deal of activity is taking place.

Filtration

As we have already seen, blood entering the glomerular capillaries is forced through a three-layered glomerular filter system, and this is the only way any significant volume of fluid can enter the nephron for treatment. The blood entering these capillary beds is subjected to the same forces as it faces in systemic capillary beds, but there are some important differences. In the main, the differences are quantitative; the filtration pressures in the renal corpuscle are a little more powerful and the filters are more permissive than are those of systemic capillary beds.

The pressure increases are mainly due to the relationship between the afferent and efferent arterioles entering the renal corpuscle. As figure 16.7 shows, the efferent arteriole leaving the glomerulus is much smaller than the afferent one. This, as we know, increases the pressure within vessels of the glomerulus (you will recall that when a hose is crimped, pressure on the proximal side of the crimp increases considerably—see figure 16.12). In addition, the cells that make up the walls of the glomerular capillaries are a little different from those comprising the walls of systemic capillaries. Like capillaries everywhere, glomerular capillaries are just one cell thick, but unlike most, the walls of glomerular vessels are perforated with pores or **fenestrae** (*fenestrae,* "windows"; figures 16.7, 16.9). These larger openings permit the passage

Figure 16.12 A familiar example of pressure change by constricting part of the system. In the kidney, point 1 would be analogous to the small efferent arterioles. Their reduced size increases pressure in the glomerular capillaries (*point 2*).

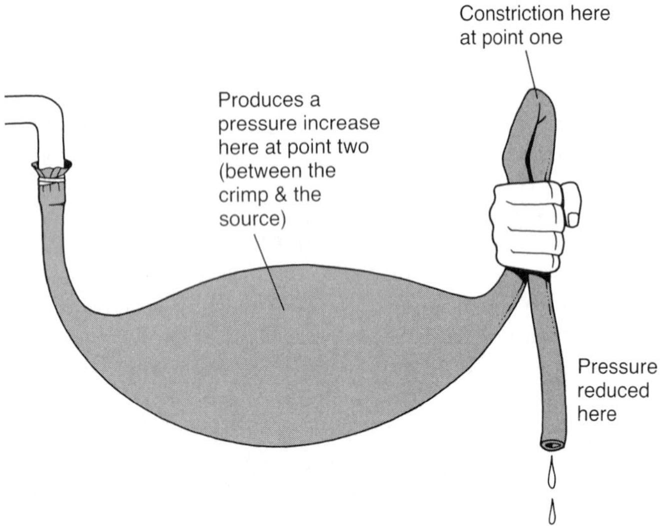

Figure 16.13 Cross section of a glomerular capillary showing the three tissue layers through which fluid is filtered (*see arrows*).

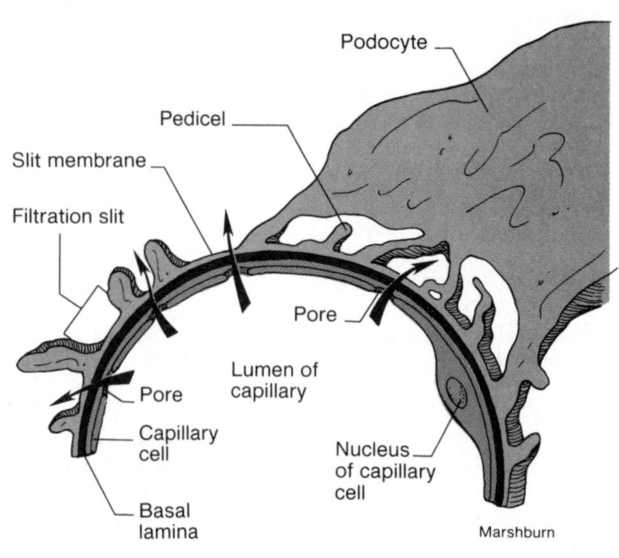

of much larger molecules than can make their way through capillaries elsewhere. Having slipped through the fenestrae, the filtrate must then make its way through the basal lamina and then the filtration membranes between the foot processes of the podocytes (figure 16.13).

The glomerular filter system through which fluid must pass to get into the renal portion of the nephron, therefore, consists of three entities:

1. the capillary wall with its unusually large pores,
2. the basal lamina, and
3. the slit membranes that cover the filtration slits between the pedicels of the podocytes.

Among them, they do not govern the passage of dissolved particles with nearly as much restraint as systemic capillaries do; glomerular capillaries are anywhere from 100 to 1,000 times as indulgent in this respect. There is some uncertainty about this (see box), but it appears to be true.

Most workers today feel reasonably confident that the human fenestrae will permit any molecules smaller than about 160 Å (1,600 nanometers) to pass through and that the basal lamina and filtration membranes scale that down to a little less than 50 Å. Fifty angstroms is roughly the diameter of a small- to medium-sized protein (about 25,000 daltons), so anything smaller should be able to get out of the blood and into the lumina of the kidney nephrons. In actual fact, small proteins do find their way into the nephrons of the kidney, but they are returned to the blood with such vigor by mechanisms in the nephron that they seldom appear in the urine.

It must be remembered that most of what we know of kidney function is derived from experiments performed on dogs, cats, rabbits, rats, and a very few lower primates. We have generalized the physiology of those animals to humans. Broadly speaking, human kidneys probably work in a fashion that is very similar to those of the animals investigated, but chances are that they are not *exactly* the same. For instance, beavers and kangaroo rats represent extremes in water reabsorption abilities in mammals, while humans, like dogs and cats, are somewhere in between. Renal corpuscles in mammals vary quite broadly in the size of their filter systems. We are not exactly sure just what the human filter size is. When we compare the permissiveness of systemic capillaries with those in the glomerulus, things are complicated further by the fact that systemic capillaries vary from person to person and even *within* single individuals, depending on their location in the body. Capillaries in the liver, for example, permit many things to pass that would never get into the interstitial fluids around muscles.

Pressures in the Renal Capsule

As is the case in the systemic capillaries, several forces are involved in the process of filtration, and some of them are at war with each other. The force that drives fluid through the filters and out into the nephrons is the hydrostatic pressure head supplied by the heart. This is the only force thrusting in that direction. Naturally, with certain solutes being held in the blood by the restrictions of the filter, their plasma concentration will increase, thereby boosting the colloid osmotic pressure (COP) of the blood as it flows through

Figure 16.14 The forces supporting and opposing filtration in the renal corpuscle of a kidney nephron.

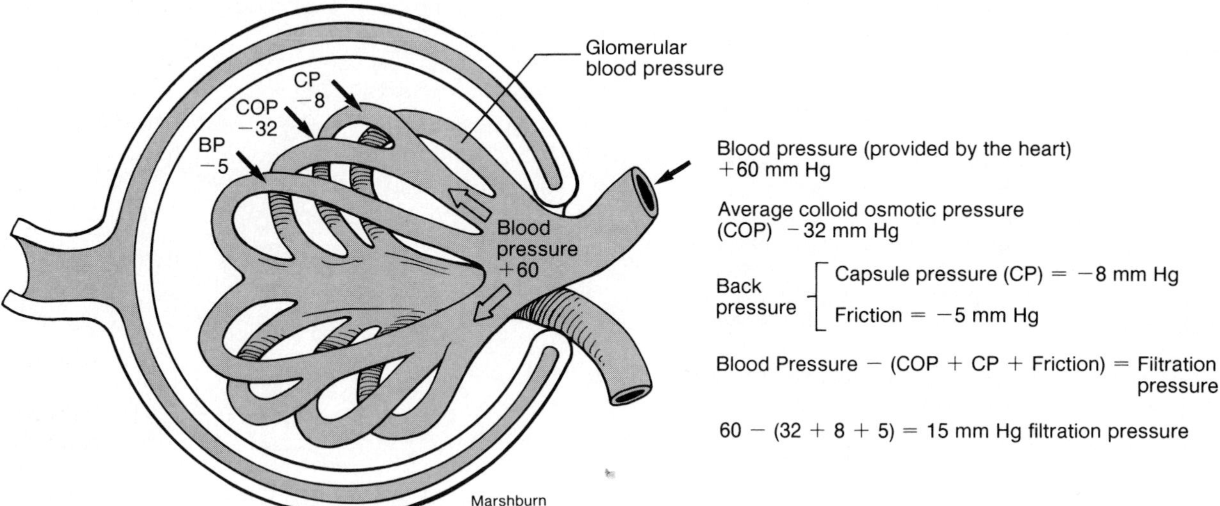

the glomerular capillaries. Consequently, the COP of the blood steadily increases as it progresses through the glomerular capillaries, while the hydrostatic pressure just as steadily drops. Further resistance to filtration is added by the walls of Bowman's capsule, which tend to be rather inelastic. When the glomerulus and capsule are full—which is most of the time—there is a steady opposition to stretching, which translates into a constant backpressure known as **capsule pressure (CP)**. Friction also plays a role in resisting filtration. Although it is negligible at low flow rates, it must be considered a negative factor during periods of rapid blood flow through the kidneys.

The interplay of forces within the renal corpuscle is illustrated in figure 16.14. As you can see, when the various forces are all considered, there is a net tendency for fluids to leave the glomerular circulation and enter the lumen within the kidney nephron. As is true of capillary beds everywhere, this net tendency is called the **effective filtration pressure.** It amounts to about 15 mm Hg, and it creates the filtrate within Bowman's capsule. At that effective filtration pressure, about 104 ml of fluid passes from the blood into Bowman's capsule every minute. The volume of fluid that the kidneys filter in a minute is known as the **glomerular filtration rate (GFR),** and in this case, the GFR would be 104 ml.

You should understand, however, that it is not a constant. Our body's requirements change from moment to moment, and physiological adjustments are quickly made to accommodate changing requirements. Local vasomotor manipulation can instantly change blood pressures in localized kidney zones, and when that happens, the GFR naturally changes in the affected nephrons. System-wide blood pressure changes will also affect the pressure of blood entering the kidney, and when the pressure goes up or down, the GFR is bound to change—but the changes are never really drastic. As is the case with other organ systems, intrinsic mechanisms make quick, effective local compensations. When, for instance, the blood pressure increases to 75 mm Hg, the plasma osmotic pressure won't change much, but with fluid pouring into the capsule at a more rapid rate, both capsule pressure and friction will increase. The approximate values of all the forces involved would be:

Blood pressure = 75 mm Hg
COP = 32 mm Hg
Capsule pressure = 18 mm Hg
Friction = 7 mm Hg
Effective filtration pressure = 75 −
[32 + 13 + 7] = 23 mm Hg

At a pressure of 23 mm Hg, about 120 ml of fluid enters the kidney every minute. Thus when the blood pressure changes from 60 to 75 mm Hg (a 25 percent increase), the GFR changes from 104 to 120 ml (about a 15 percent increase).

The kidney circulation is equipped to operate independently within limits, and it is capable of accomplishing some impressive pressure changes within its own vessels. One of the most effective methods of changing pressure relationships is, as we have seen, alteration of vessel diameter. Both the afferent and the efferent arterioles are capable of constriction that can powerfully influence the effective filtration pressure. In the normal range of blood pressures, the GFR is regulated intrinsically. Changes in renal vascular resistance can limit the total pressure to which the glomeruli will be exposed and, in company with the changing resistances encountered in the nephron, they tend to stabilize the GFR.

The pressure changes that can result from changing afferent or efferent arteriole diameter are often profound. For example, sympathetic activity can produce vasoconstriction in the afferent arterioles. When they are constricted, the hydrostatic pressure within the glomerulus can drop as low as 28 to 36 mm Hg. This, if all other factors were to remain the same, would cause kidney shutdown. But as we know, the body continually fights to maintain homeostasis, and if such a pressure drop were to occur, other mechanisms would swing into action immediately to insure that the other factors would *not* remain the same. For example, a drop in blood pressure would immediately reduce the amount of fluid filtered and thus would reduce the fluid loss and the COP. Similarly, with less filtrate being produced, both the CP and frictional resistances would become negligible. Although in some situations the effective filtration pressure can drop as low as 2 to 3 mm Hg, it is nonetheless retained, and the kidneys continue to function—albeit at a reduced rate.

This does not mean that systemic pressure changes have no effect on the filtration of blood in the kidneys. It just means that there are intrinsic mechanisms that can compensate for a short time for systemic changes that are not too profound. But if even moderate changes persist for too long, they can be a problem. For instance, a moderate increase in systemic blood pressure can be handled without significant problems if it lasts only a short time, but it can have a tremendous influence on urine production if it lasts for a matter of hours. Should a person with normal pressure (120/75) experience a mild hypertension (180/115), his or her urinary output, if that high pressure were sustained, would probably quadruple within a few hours. Obviously a day or so of this sort of fluid loss could be disastrous, especially if no facilities were available to replace the loss.

As the filtrate leaves Bowman's capsule, it comes under the scrutiny of the mechanisms of the proximal convoluted tubule. These mechanisms identify everything, and somehow each is classified as either beneficial or undesirable. If it is considered undesirable, it is left alone to make its way through the nephron, but if it is something of potential value to the organism, it is subjected to further scrutiny and possibly some manipulation. There are always materials in the filtrate that must be returned to the blood, and these are sorted out and handled by the nephron.

Figure 16.15 Reabsorption is the process by which substances are transported from the glomerular filtrate into the blood of the peritubular capillary. (What substances are reabsorbed in this manner?)

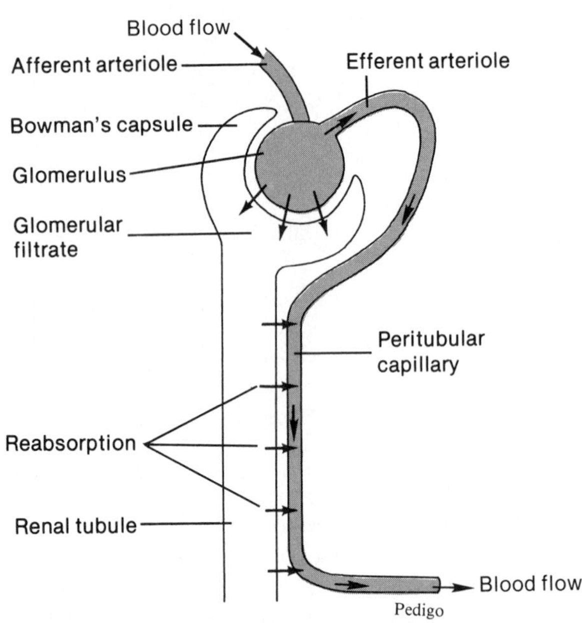

Reabsorption of Materials from the Filtrate

Thanks to the presence of the vast network of peritubular capillaries (figure 16.15), anything that the tubule pumps into the interstitial fluid will promptly equilibrate with the blood, and as its interstitial concentration increases, the blood will absorb it.

Several mechanisms within the proximal tubule are designed to handle the movement of both solutes and water (figure 16.16). Wherever possible, diffusion, with its built-in energy supply, is permitted to handle the movement, but even with the most frugal handling, there is a lot of energy-consuming machinery running all the time. Remember, if it can be used, diffusion is always the desirable method of moving materials from place to place because it is energy-cheap. Active transport, on the other hand, is an energy-expensive process. For this reason, active transport and diffusion often work in concert to transfer necessary materials from the kidney filtrate to the interstitial fluids. Sodium movement utilizes both systems . . . it can diffuse from the filtrate into the tubule cells, but then it must be pumped from the cells into the interstitial fluid. Once the sodium is in the interstitial fluid, diffusion once again takes over and moves it into the blood (figure 16.17).

Protein Reabsorption

The movement of proteins requires energy-gulping mechanisms almost all the way. Proteins are actively taken into the tubule cells by endocytosis, and once

Figure 16.16 Line drawing of the cells of the proximal tubule. The microvilli on the luminar surface provide a huge surface area for reabsorption, and materials must pass *through* the cells; tight junctions preclude passage between cells.

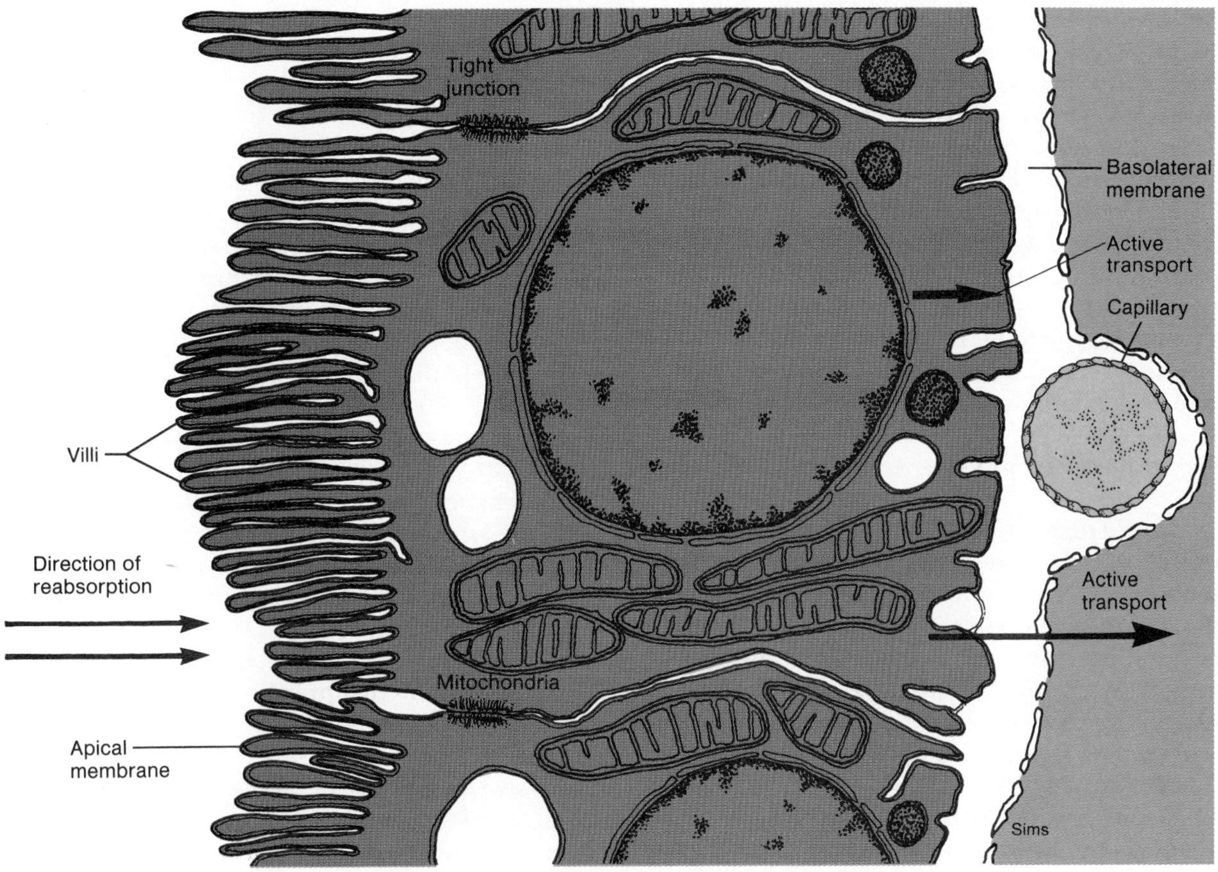

Filtrate side
Tubule cells
Blood side
Tight junction
Basolateral membrane
Active transport
Capillary
Villi
Direction of reabsorption
Active transport
Mitochondria
Apical membrane
Sims

Figure 16.17 Mechanisms of salt and water reabsorption in the proximal tubule. Sodium is actively transported out of the filtrate, and chloride follows passively by electrical attraction. Water follows the osmotic gradient out of the tubular filtrate and into the blood.

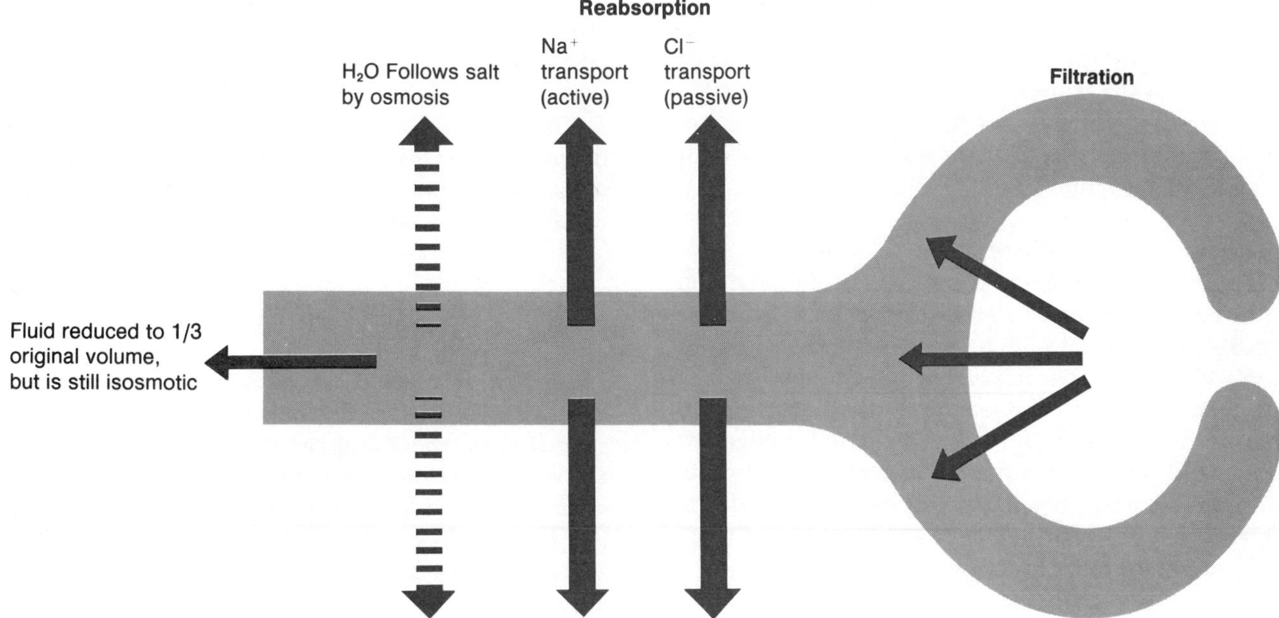

inside they are broken up into their amino acid residues through lysosomal action. Then other energy-requiring mechanisms pump the amino acids into the interstitial fluids, where active mechanisms may or may not transport them into the blood. Peptides, small proteins, hormones, and carbohydrates are all involved in this process of tubular reabsorption, and all require some form of active transport at one point or another. It is all carrier-mediated, so like the endocytotic operations, the carriers can become saturated, and periodically they do. That obviously means that there is a limit to the number of endocytotic vesicles that can form in a given cellular membrane, so each molecule has to wait its turn. Sometimes this takes too long, and the proteins or peptides are swept away from the proximal tubule before they can be transported, a situation that is reflected in the appearance of small to moderate quantities of protein in the excreted urine after a protein-rich meal.

Glucose Reabsorption

Glucose, which, like proteins, requires carrier-mediated transport, can also saturate the tubular reabsorption mechanisms. When glucose is in normal concentration in the blood (about 100 mg/dl), the transport mechanisms can handle it all. When it begins to approach a concentration of 300 mg/dl, however, the transport mechanisms become saturated, and despite the fact that the tubule's transport mechanisms are working at maximum rate, they cannot keep up with the glucose load, and the sugar begins to show up in the urine. This is typical of a diabetic, but a person need not be diabetic to experience some glucose in the urine. Often, following a meal rich in carbohydrates, the blood will load to more than 300 mg of glucose per deciliter, which explains why it will occasionally show up in the urine of a perfectly normal person immediately after eating. Generally speaking, however, glucose hardly ever shows up in the urine. All of the glucose that is filtered from the blood into the kidney filtrate is actively and selectively reabsorbed by mechanisms in the proximal tubule.

Water and Salt Reabsorption

Water, of course, is never actively moved anywhere, so to handle the reabsorption of this precious commodity, osmotic gradients are established for the water to follow. The movement of sodium from the filtrate draws large numbers of anions along with it, thanks to the attraction of positive ions for negative ones. This means a profound movement of chloride, bicarbonate, and phosphate ions as well as sodium. This movement of minerals produces a powerful osmotic gradient that attracts water in enormous quantities as the filtrate moves through the proximal tubule. The reabsorbing machinery in the proximal tubule, both active and passive, operates with such enthusiasm that virtually all of the glucose, proteins, amino acids, and other carbohydrates—as well as 75 percent of the water that was in the original filtrate—are absorbed before the filtrate enters the loop of Henle.

Tubular Secretion

The fluid that forms in Bowman's capsule is the result of the process known as ultrafiltration. And as with all filtration processes, materials are separated purely on the basis of size. Those things that are small enough to slip through the glomerular sieve appear in the filtrate in about the same concentration as they are found in the plasma. Hence the pH, osmotic pressure, and mineral content of the filtrate are just about the same as they are in the blood. Every once in a while, however, things show up in the filtrate in greater concentrations than were present in the blood, indicating clearly that something besides glomerular filtration is involved in putting materials into the nephron.

That something is known as **tubular secretion,** and in many respects, it is essentially tubular reabsorption running in reverse. Tubular secretion moves materials from the interstitial spaces into the interior of the tubule, whereas tubular reabsorption moves things the opposite way. Sometimes the process is passive and sometimes it is active, depending on the materials involved. If small ions like hydrogen and/or potassium are able to, they follow a diffusion gradient into the filtrate from the interstitial fluids outside, with water often following. If, on the other hand, the materials must be moved into the tubule against an electrochemical gradient, active transport mechanisms are needed, and energy must be used. Molecules like creatinine (a breakdown product of skeletal muscle activity), penicillin, and other large molecules destined to be excreted are enzymatically transported across the tubule cells and into the filtrate.

By the time the filtrate leaves the proximal tubule, its volume has been reduced to less than a quarter of what it was, and most of the many solutes have been returned to the blood.

The Loop of Henle—A Countercurrent Multiplier System

The loop of Henle and its nearby blood vessels employ an unusual structural design, along with some highly specialized metabolic apparatus, to produce the entity known as a **countercurrent multiplier.** *Countercurrent* arrangements are actually pretty common in biological systems. They represent a means of maintaining a constant diffusion gradient between vessels involved in any kind of exchange (figure 16.18).

Figure 16.18 A countercurrent heat exchange system. Such circulatory patterns serve two purposes: they avoid high heat loss to the environment from exposed surfaces, and they prevent ice-cold blood from entering the body core. The illustration shows a typical thermal countercurrent exchange system found in the naked portion of a bird's legs—the zone below the feathers. As you can see, blood flowing into the body core is always one degree cooler than that flowing out. The thermal gradient is 1 at every point along the leg. The exchanger is therefore constant but is never very high, because the gradient is kept small. The warm arterial blood entering the limb is cooled by the venous blood returning. In this way, the cold zones in the feet (which must be near 0° C in winter) remain outside the body core. Very little heat is lost to the environment, because the feet are nearly as cold as the air or water. The blood returning to the body is then warmed by the arterial blood.

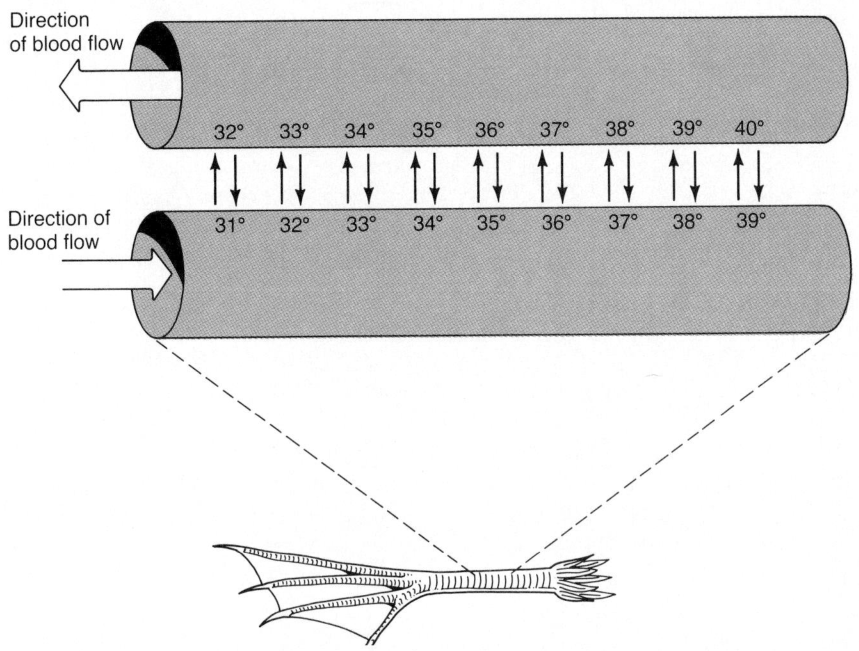

Countercurrent systems serve a triple function. As figure 16.18 shows, they can be designed to prevent unnecessary heat loss and to avoid high thermal shock, but the main feature is that they maintain a constant gradient between the afferent and efferent vessels involved in the exchange process. The exchange, therefore, even though it is passive, can be more easily manipulated, and any necessary adjustments can be accomplished with a minimum of variability. This is a desirable feature when several items are being exchanged and more than one transport mechanism is being used. The countercurrent system employed by the kidney is unique in that it features a closed loop at one end, thereby making it the only known *multiplier* system (figure 16.19).

The loops operate as follows, beginning with the descending limb:

The descending limbs are permeable to water, chloride, and sodium ions. That means they are permeable to much of the solute, because by the time the filtrate enters this limb, it has been denuded of most organic molecules—the only ones left at this point are not going to be returned to the blood. The movement of electrolytes and water has been profound, and considerable volume has been lost, but so many solutes have been removed that the filtrate hasn't been concentrated; the fluid flowing into the loop is approximately isotonic with plasma. As it plunges down into the loop, however, it encounters steadily increasing sodium and chloride concentrations in the interstitial fluid of the medulla, and this means increasing osmotic gradients. Since the wall of the descending limb is permeable to water, sodium, and chloride, they all will move—water leaves the filtrate and both sodium and chloride ions diffuse in. By the time the loop bottoms out, the solutes in the filtrate are as concentrated as they are ever going to get. That does not necessarily mean that a great deal of water has been lost. Obviously there has been some water movement, but the filtrate's increased concentration is due as much to the inward movement of salt as to the egress of water. Actually, despite its concentration, only about half of the water that entered the descending limb has been removed by the time it reaches the bottom of the loop.

Now a strange thing happens—something almost unheard-of in biological systems. Once past the cloverleaf turn in the loop, the walls of the tubule become almost completely impermeable to water. At the same time, the chloride ions within the filtrate are subjected to a vigorous pumping action and begin to

Figure 16.19 The countercurrent multiplier in the kidney. The numbers represent approximate osmolarity in milliosmoles. Note the hypotonic nature of the filtrate entering the distal convoluted tubule. Within such a nephron, if physiological mechanisms were correctly adjusted, urine could be concentrated to more than four times the concentration of plasma.

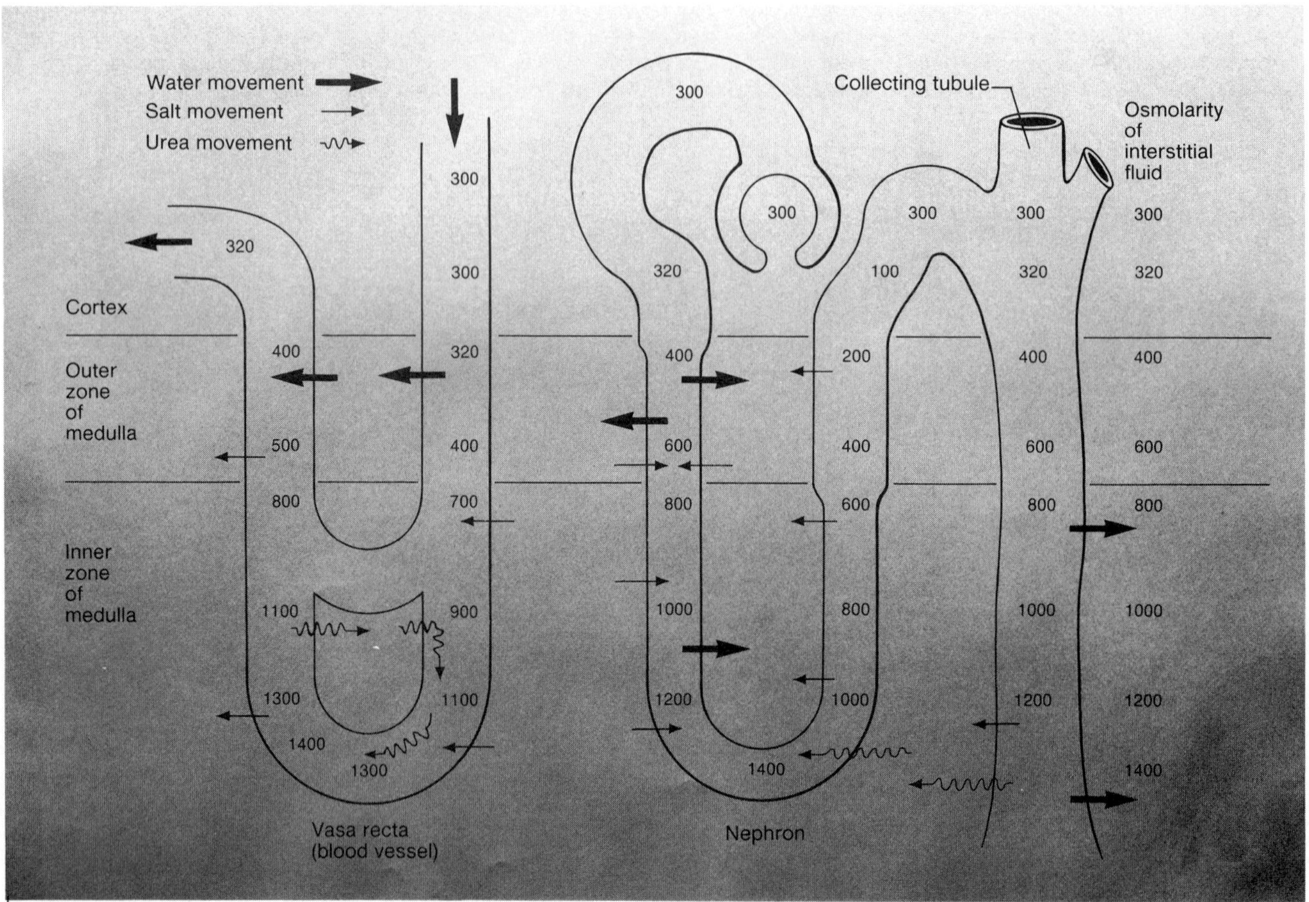

stream into the interstitial fluid that surrounds the ascending limb. Since the tubule walls present no particular barrier to the positive sodium ions, they passively follow the negative chloride ions like chickens follow their mother. The net result is a massive movement of salt into the interstitial fluids of the kidney medulla and a rapid dilution of the filtrate as it climbs the ascending limb of the loop. So much salt is pumped out, in fact, that by the time the filtrate enters the distal convoluted tubule, it is actually only about one-third the concentration of blood plasma in the general circulation.

This removal of salt by the transport mechanisms of the ascending limb is the multiplier action exhibited by the loop. It is called a multiplier because it can concentrate salt in the kidney medulla to such a high degree—much higher than plasma ever gets. It can do this because much of the salt that is pumped from the ascending limb cycles over to the descending limb, goes to the bottom of the loop, then, as it once more enters the ascending loop, it is pumped out again, a process that is repeated over and over. The loop thus continually recycles the same salt through the loop of Henle, and this, coupled with a steady addition of new salts entering from fresh filtrate, enables the kidney to build up the concentration of salt in the medulla to very high levels indeed (figures 16.19, 16.20, 16.21).

The Vasa Recta

Obviously, if the salt and the urea that is pumped so vigorously into the medulla were carried away as soon as it left the nephron, there would be no more salt than there is anywhere else. Yet it is not carried away, and this is partly due to the sluggish movement of blood through the vasa recta vessels. Mainly, however, it is due to the countercurrent association that these vessels have with the loops of Henle. It is the nature of countercurrent relationships to maintain a constant gradient between exchange surfaces at all times. Hence salt diffuses *out* of the vasa recta vessels that are heading up toward the cortex, but it diffuses *into* those that are descending into the medulla. Because there is so much salt entering the tubules, the osmotic gradient between the interstitial fluid and the blood in the vasa recta tends to be fairly small; as a result, only a little water diffuses out of the descending vessels. On the ascending section of the loop, once again the water gradient is small, because salt is

Figure 16.20 (*a*) Fluid in the ascending limb becomes hypotonic as solute is reabsorbed; (*b*) fluid in the descending limb becomes hypertonic as it loses water by osmosis and gains solute by diffusion.

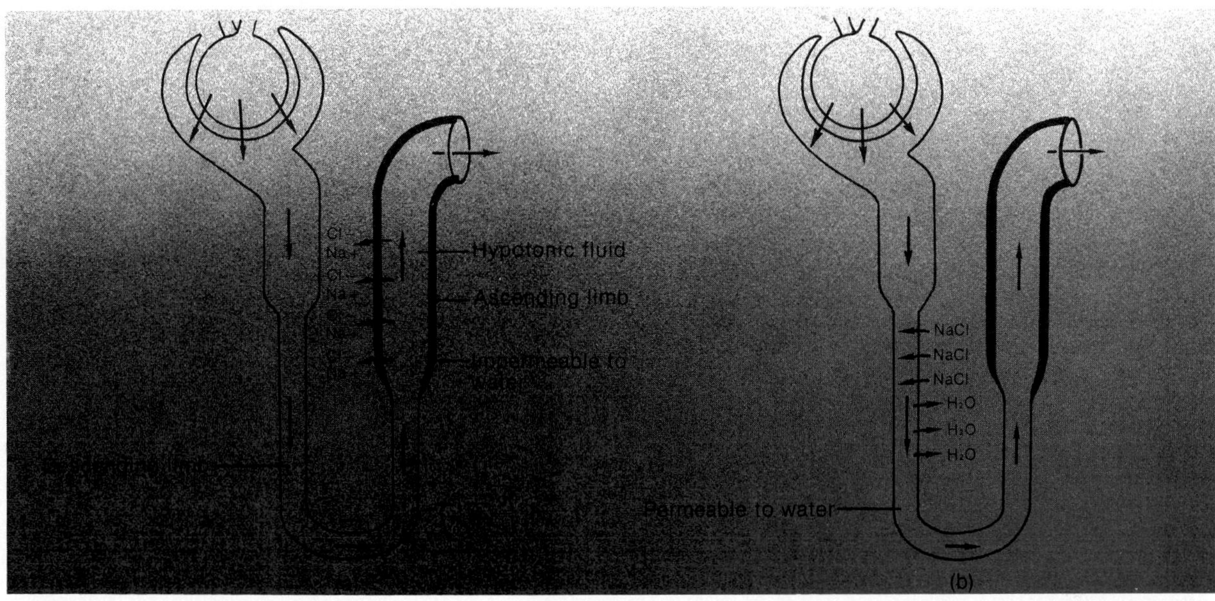

Figure 16.21 The looping "multiplier" action of the loop of Henle. (*a*) Each time the salt completes a circuit through the loop, its concentration increases in the filtrate and in the surrounding kidney tissue. (*b*) This establishes a modifiable salt concentration gradient in the interstitial fluid surrounding the loop.

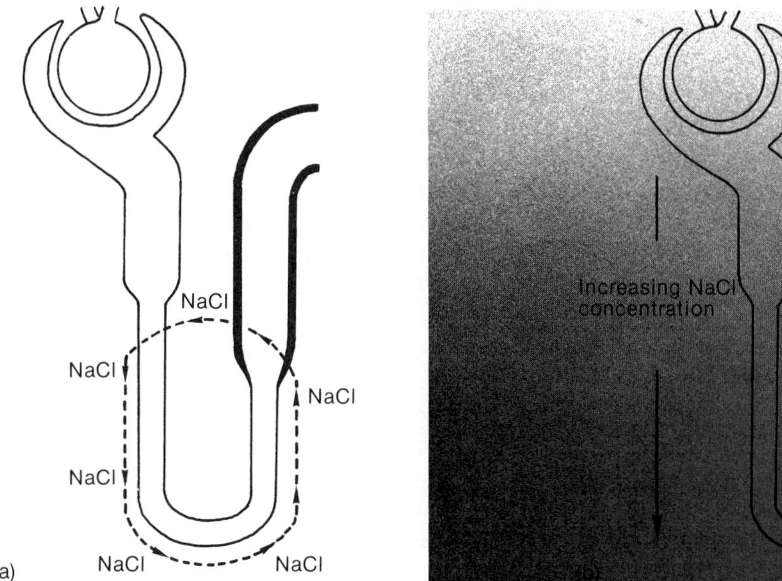

steadily being pumped out of the filtrate into the interstitial fluids, where it is presented to the vasa recta vessels. As a result, only small quantities of water enter the ascending vessels. Thus, as figures 16.19, 16.21, and 16.22 all show, salt tends to recycle within the medulla, while water simply slides past the region.

Quick-Response Regulatory Mechanisms

The salt concentration is apparently not a constant but can be juggled according to the needs of the organism. It is evidently possible to vary the rate at which salt is removed by the vasa recta vessels within the kidney. By increasing or decreasing this rate, the salt concentration of the medulla can be fitted—within limits, of course—to the needs of the moment. It seems that the vigor of the pumping activity in the ascending limb of Henle's loop is also adjustable over a fairly wide range. If there is lots of chloride in the filtrate, the pumps work very hard indeed, whereas if chloride concentration falls off, the pumps decrease their activity accordingly.

Figure 16.22 The countercurrent operations of Henle's loop and the capillaries of the vasa recta are mutually supportive.

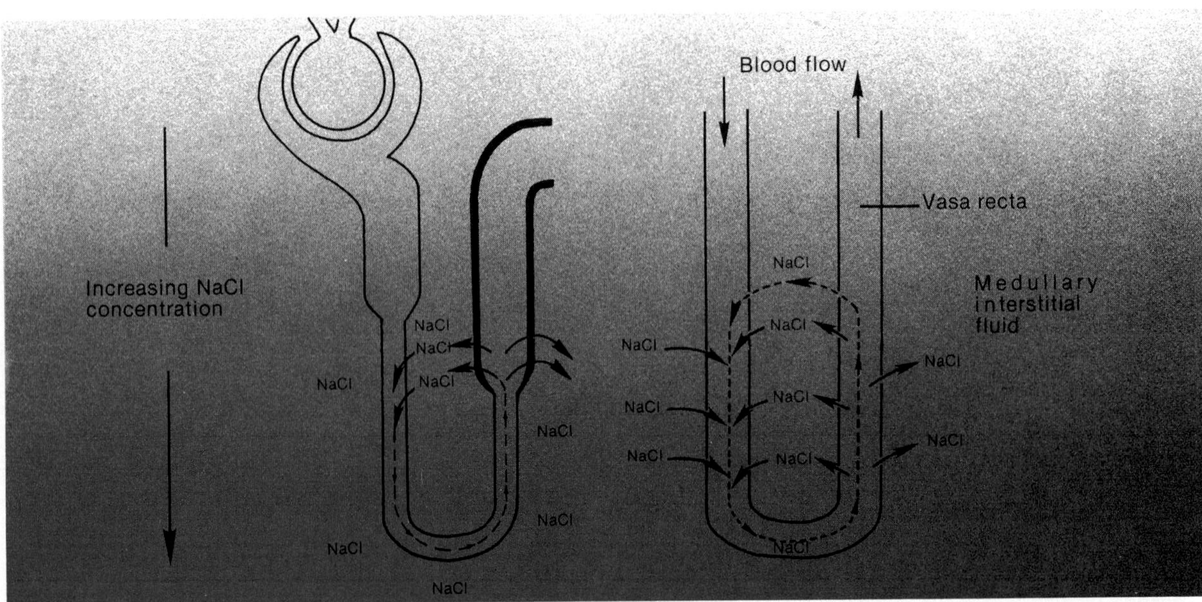

Reabsorption in the Distal Tubule

As I mentioned already, by the time the fluid enters the distal convoluted tubule it is hypotonic to blood plasma. The primate kidney, and presumably the human kidney as well, feature distal tubule walls that are not very permeable to water. Hence, while there is a tendency for water to flow into the interstitial areas in response to the osmotic gradient, it cannot do it. However, considerable electrolyte movement can take place here, and the amount of such movement depends on the adrenal cortical hormone aldosterone. Aldosterone can stimulate the active pumping of sodium across the distal tubule and into the blood, but workers do not know for sure if that directly affects water movement. The kinds of osmotic gradients that water normally follows are not established here, because usually, when a sodium ion moves out of the filtrate, a potassium ion moves in. This maintains not only neutrality but presumably osmotic equilibrium as well, since there is a one-for-one exchange.

The last place where water removal and urinary concentration can occur is therefore within the collecting duct. Thanks to the vigorous ionic movement that takes place in the distal tubule, by the time the filtrate enters the collecting duct it is isotonic with blood plasma. Whether or not there will be any further reduction in its water content depends on just how permeable to water the walls of the duct happen to be. This permeability, it seems, is adjustable and depends on the amount of *antidiuretic hormone (ADH)* that is available at any given time. More will be said about both ADH and aldosterone shortly.

Uric Acid and Urea

One of the primary waste products disposed of by the kidneys is **urea.** In fact, it is the relative abundance of this substance that gave urine its name. Urea is a nitrogenous waste molecule, which means it is mainly a by-product of protein or amino acid metabolism. Also, it is one of the few water-soluble substances that can cross cell membranes with ease. It is filtered into Bowman's capsule along with all the other solutes that can squeeze through the filter, and once in the proximal tubule, it becomes vulnerable to all the diffusion gradients that exist between the filtrate and the interstitial fluid outside. As water passively follows the salts and other solutes leaving the filtrate, the concentration of urea gradually increases, and a steadily mounting gradient begins to develop between the urea in the filtrate and urea in the interstitial fluids. Urea, however, despite its high permeability, can't move as quickly as water, so before it can arrive at equilibrium with the interstitial fluids, it has passed through the proximal tubule and into the loop of Henle. If it is a juxtaglomerular nephron, it will be exposed to the gradients in the medulla, and the medullary zones of the kidney feature a high concentration of urea. Thus, any tendency for urea to migrate out of the filtrate in the loop is much reduced or eliminated, and the ascending loop and distal tubule walls are impermeable to both urea and water. It passes rapidly through this part of the nephron and into the collecting ducts.

The upper portions of the collecting ducts are also impermeable to urea, so despite the high diffusion gradients that exist there between the interstitial fluid and the filtrate, urea cannot respond, and it moves, unchanged, into the lower zones of the duct. The lower parts of the collecting ducts are permeable, and if quantities of water are reabsorbed there, there will be a tendency for urea to move also. But very little of the urea that thus enters the interstitial fluid of the medulla ever finds its way back into the blood. Urea that is lost from the collecting duct becomes part of the high urea concentration in the kidney medulla (figure 16.19). In addition, as was the case in the proximal tubule, water movement is much more rapid than that of urea, so despite the fact that it tries very hard to arrive at equilibrium with the interstitial fluids in the kidney, urea never quite makes it.

When all these factors are considered, we find that, while more than 99 percent of the water filtered through the glomerulus will usually find its way back into the blood, less than half of the urea that is filtered ever does so. Consequently, the urine serves as a fine vehicle to rid the body of urea.

Uric acid is also a nitrogenous waste, but in mammals it is a relatively unimportant one. Chemically, it is a purine, which puts it in the same category of organic compounds as some DNA bases. It is thought to be mainly a by-product of nucleic acid metabolism. Experimental evidence shows that all the uric acid filtered through the glomerulus is reabsorbed in the proximal tubule, yet the same evidence indicates that considerable uric acid is present in the urine. This indicates that it is probably transported into the filtrate via *tubular secretion,* although just where this might take place is unclear.

Just because uric acid is a purine does not *necessarily* mean that it is a by-product of purine metabolism. In birds and reptiles, for example, it is not at all. In these animals, it is the chief means of eliminating all nitrogenous waste products, and it provides these animals with a superior means of eliminating nitrogenous wastes while simultaneously avoiding water loss. Uric acid is excreted by these animals as a white, precipitated paste that contains very little water, and we are all familiar with it whether we know it or not. Much of the excretory debris that one finds on public buildings where pigeons congregate consists of this white paste.

Elimination of Urine

Urine is, of course, a waste product and must ultimately be eliminated from the body. To achieve this, the collecting ducts eventually merge, forming a single tube into which they channel their contents. Each kidney has one of these tubes—called **ureters**—and they carry the urine from the kidney into the **urinary bladder** for storage. As is the case with many goblet-like structures, the walls of the urinary bladder are quite elastic and can stretch to accommodate large volumes of urine, from a maximum of about 500 ml in a small woman to 1,300 ml in a large man, with the average ranging from 700 to 800 (figure 16.23). Distensibility has its limits, however. Eventually the bladder reaches that limit, and when it does, if it is not emptied it can produce so much resistance to the flow of urine from the kidney that it can actually cause the kidneys to shut down. To prevent this, naturally, we empty the bladder regularly.

The difference in urinary bladder capacity between men and women is quite profound and has often stimulated both jocularity and complaints among groups of people—primarily couples—in this country. During intermissions at concerts, movies, or stage plays, the women's restrooms are invariably full, and ladies can be seen standing around in varying stages of desperation waiting for the line to move up or a stall to be vacated. When travelling by automobile across country, stops must be made at a (to a man) disturbing frequency so that female passengers can relieve themselves. This often leads to unpleasantness in the form of thoughtless jokes or vitriolic complaints. To the insensitive male there is no excuse for such behavior . . . it is easy to assume that women are "coddling" themselves or are just being "ornery." For some reason it never occurs to them that there is a solid, anatomical reason why women are unable to hold as much fluid in their bladders as men can. Nevertheless, it is true.

In women, the urinary bladder hasn't very much room to expand. As figure 16.23 shows, it is surrounded by bone or heavily muscled organs on three sides, leaving only the upper anterior section able to expand up into the peritoneal cavity. In men, with no uterus above to stifle the swelling bladder, there is plenty of room for such expansion to occur, and as a consequence their bladders can hold a good deal more without significant discomfort.

Micturition

The urinary bladder is emptied through the **urethra.** This is a single tube running from the bottom of the urinary bladder through the lowest portion of the abdomen and then to the outside—at the tip of the penis of the male or just anterior to the vaginal opening in the female.

Urine elimination is known medically as **micturition,** and although it is easily controllable, it also operates as an unconscious reflex. The autonomic center responsible for operating this reflex is known, logically enough, as the **micturition reflex center,** and it is located in the lower or *sacral* segments of the spinal cord.

The reflex operates as follows: When the bladder is empty, the muscles of the bladder wall are relaxed, and the internal and external sphincter muscles that surround the urethra are contracted. When the

Figure 16.23 The male (*a*) and female (*b*) urinary bladders compared. Note the presence of the heavily muscled uterus in *b*, which restricts inflation of the bladder. As a consequence, women must urinate more often than men.

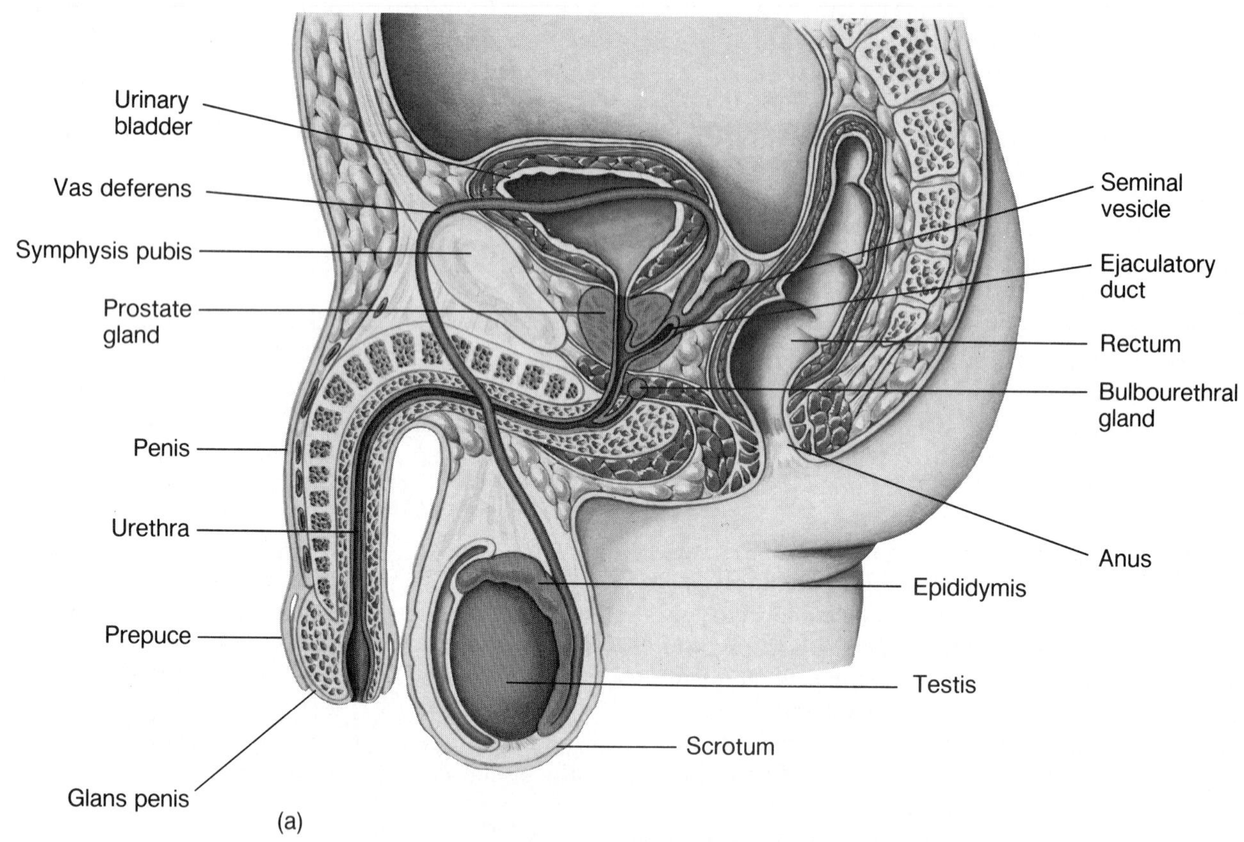

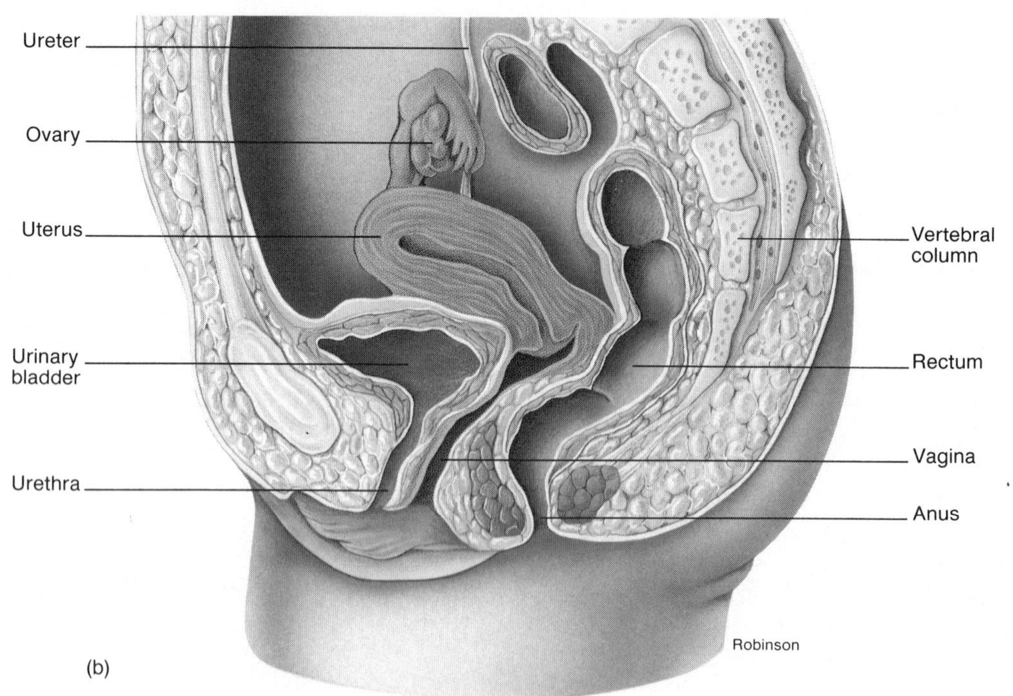

bladder is empty, it is folded back and forth upon itself, and until those folds are opened out there is no resistance to filling. Moderate increases in urine volume, therefore, produce no increases in pressure—the bladder simply unfolds to accommodate the extra fluid—up to about 300 ml. During this time neural messages are also minimal, and there is no conscious stimulus. But when the urine volume is somewhere between 250 and 300 ml, the bladder walls begin to stretch. As the bladder gradually fills, parasympathetic stretch receptors in the bladder wall begin to send messages to the micturition reflex center indicating that increasing volumes of fluid are entering. Once this occurs, if there is no conscious interference, the sphincter muscles around the urethra relax, the muscles around the bladder contract, and the urine is voided.

Where people are concerned, conscious interference is the rule rather than the exception. Obviously, civilized people have to wait until they have made it to a restroom before they can void, and this capability is carefully trained into each of us very early in life—a process euphemistically known as "potty training." This training can be so effective that we seldom have to think very much about it unless the urge to urinate is intense. Even during sleep we can easily control the reflex. To keep each of us aware of the status of our bladders, we are informed constantly of its size by parasympathetic impulses that are relayed past the reflex center to the cerebral cortex. As urine volume reaches between 400 and 500 ml, these impulses begin to convey an increasing sense of urgency, at which point the internal sphincter opens reflexly, leaving only the external sphincter to prevent micturition. If the bladder continues to expand, the messages from stretch receptors become more and more urgent, and the individual has to exert more and more conscious control to keep it contracted. When the decision is finally made to urinate, the external sphincter is relaxed and the reflex takes over, draining the bladder.

Water Balance and Electrolyte Regulation

As we know, water is indispensable to life. Well over half our body weight is just plain water, and this water is distributed throughout the body with great care.

The Fluid Compartments

We have water within our body cells—we all know that by now. To maintain intracellular homeostasis, the cell uses materials in the interstitial fluid. The interstitial fluid, in turn, is nurtured by another, still different solution, the blood. Each of these watery solutions has a homeostasis of its own to maintain, yet in fact none of them is isolated because a perpetual and rapid exchange takes place between them every second. To add to their dynamic nature, the fluids themselves are in constant motion, and an exchange anywhere, no matter how small or isolated, is usually felt throughout the entire system. Nevertheless, each solution is unique (figure 16.24). Acidity can vary from solution to solution, water content and electrolyte composition are very different, and the protein content is likewise different. For convenience of communication, therefore, we describe our body water in terms of separated compartments.

It is probably safe to say that most of us believe that nearly all of the water in our bodies is in the blood, but that is not true. As we learned in chapter 12, between 65 and 67 percent of all the water in our bodies is inside our cells—a volume designated the intracellular compartment. The remaining 33 percent is in the extracellular compartment, and most of that—between 26 and 27 percent—is interstitial fluid. Less than 7 percent is actually in the blood (figure 16.25). An incredible fact emerges when one considers these figures: 93 percent of our body fluids are maintained, cleaned, and regulated by the remaining 7 percent. Think what this means! All the catabolic debris and other by-products of metabolic activity are dumped into a vast internal ocean that must be cleaned and restocked by a single tiny river, with the assistance of a few treatment plants and supply depots. Plainly, any changes that occur in the larger oceans will be exaggerated when they reach the smaller volume of the river, so the river must be able to compensate rapidly. And you would certainly be justified in believing that in order to have a significant effect on two such huge oceans, this little river would have to keep at its job constantly, because if it ever fell behind, it might take a very long time indeed to catch up. That is why the kidneys have to run all the time—to keep that bloodstream scrupulously clean. No wonder they are so important!

Regulating the Internal Environment

Merely cleaning up the fluids is not enough, however, and it is not all that the kidneys do. When people ingest food and drink, they are altering their whole internal environment. A hamburger does not just add nutrients to the blood—it also adds non-nutrients like sodium and sulfur ions. Milk increases the amount of ionic calcium, while soft drinks, in addition to increasing the body's water loading, can alter the pH of the internal environment. All these things have to be considered when the kidney processes its filtrates; one cannot be adjusted without taking all of the others into account.

There is a tendency for all of us to view our body processes simplistically. When the beer is flowing freely, it is easy for us to imagine that the extra fluid being imbibed simply flows through the kidneys to the bladder and is disposed of when we urinate, but there's a lot more to it than that. All that extra water

Figure 16.24 As you can see, extracellular fluid contains much sodium and chloride and is relatively high in bicarbonates and calcium. Intracellular fluid maintains osmotic equilibrium with extremely high concentrations of potassium, magnesium, and phosphates.

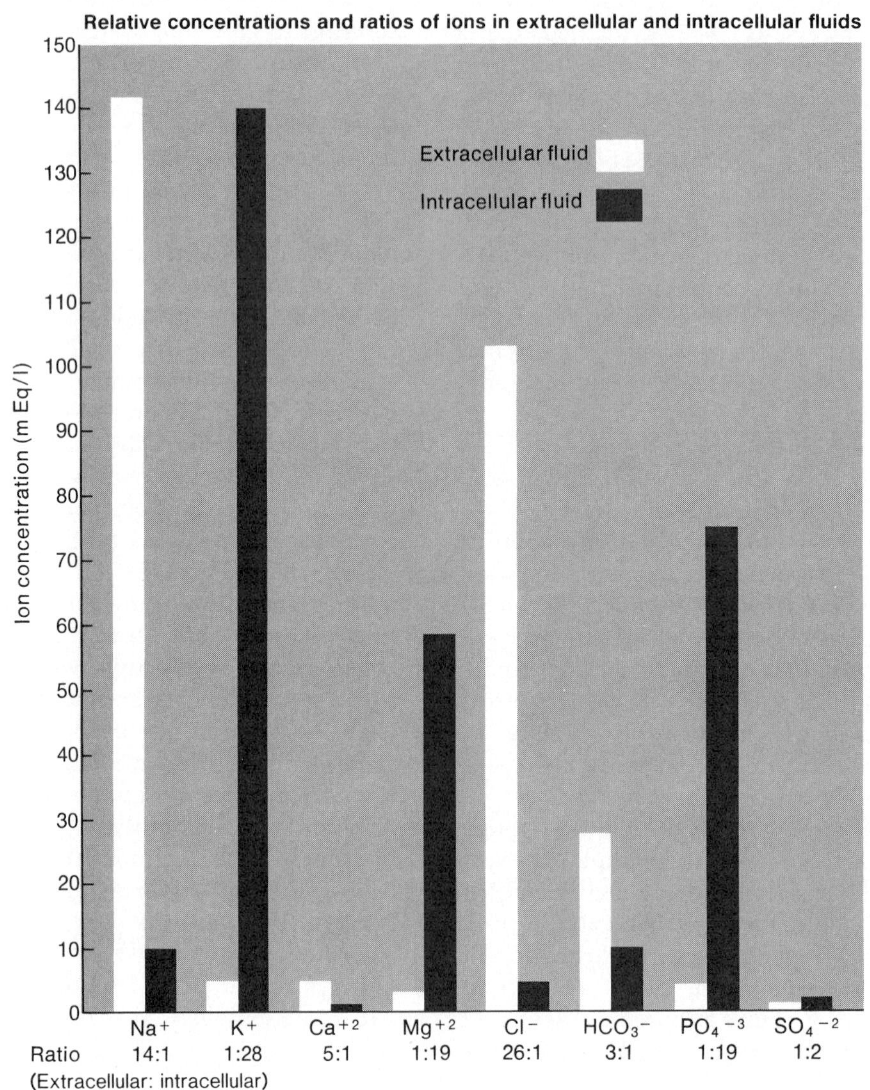

Figure 16.25 More than 60 percent of the water in a human is inside the body cells. Only 6 to 7 percent of our total body water is in the blood.

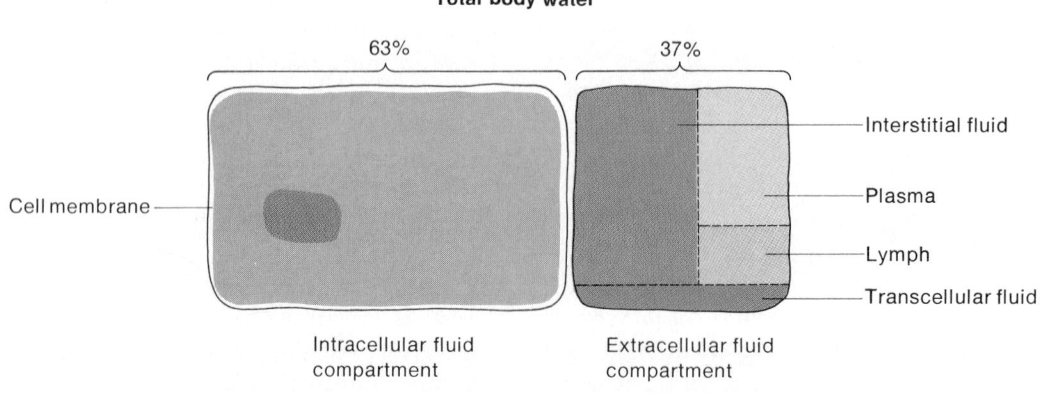

inside our digestive tracts cannot just shift, suddenly, over to the excretory system and then run out. It is removed from the gut by the blood, and when it gets picked up it doesn't remain by itself in a separate mass. It becomes part of the body's water matrix, and a lot of important solutes promptly move into it. Its presence induces immediate osmotic changes and quick solute and water shifts between body compartments. By the time it circulates to the kidneys, it is not just extra water anymore—it has been incorporated into the body fluids. It cannot be simply transported to the urinary bladder and disposed of, because now it contains all sorts of important things, and they would all be lost. The kidneys are thus faced with a homeostatic problem—a problem of the type they face a hundred times each day. They must eliminate the extra fluid quickly but without any loss of essential minerals or nutrients. Each of the solutes must be appraised carefully before the extra water is lost. Any adjustments that are made must be precise.

Fortunately, our kidneys can handle all these considerations, and they do so quite nicely. Whether the individual has indulged in too much water or is beginning to show signs of dessication, the kidneys can smoothly adapt. When socializing beer drinkers eliminate the extra fluids, it isn't difficult to see that all the necessary accommodations have been made. The urine is abundant and it's nearly colorless, which tells us that it is mostly water. On the other hand, individuals who have gone without drinking for some time have the opposite problem. They need to conserve water while still eliminating undesirable wastes, and the urine they produce is dark yellow, often quite aromatic, and obviously pretty concentrated.

As a matter of fact, the difference in solute concentration in the two situations can be startling. The beer drinker's urine is often diluted to less than one-quarter the strength of blood plasma, while solute concentrations in the urine of our water-deprived subject might be four times greater than those of plasma. All of these varying dispositions are accomplished by the machinery in the nephrons, and all follow the demands of systemic homeostasis. As we have seen, the kidneys have certain intrinsic controls that permit them to automatically compensate for sudden hydration anomalies that might change filtration pressure for a few minutes or reduce the total volume of blood passing through. But these are generally short-term adjustments, often secondary to systemic requirements. Highly tuned, long-term adjustments incorporate, as you might expect, the body's major control machinery—the nervous system and our hormones.

The Angiotensin-Aldosterone Response

When a person goes for a long time without drinking, water volume in all compartments falls, and the concentration of solutes naturally goes up. Among the first receptor zones capable of detecting this is the *juxtaglomerular apparatus* in the kidney (see figure 16.10*b*). The cells in this apparatus can respond to several stimuli, all dealing with early signs of dessication—things like decreases in blood pressure or a reduction in blood volume. When such things are detected, the juxtaglomerular cells are stimulated to secrete an enzyme called **renin** (pronounced *reen-in*) into the blood.

Figure 16.26 The renin/angiotensin/aldosterone loop.

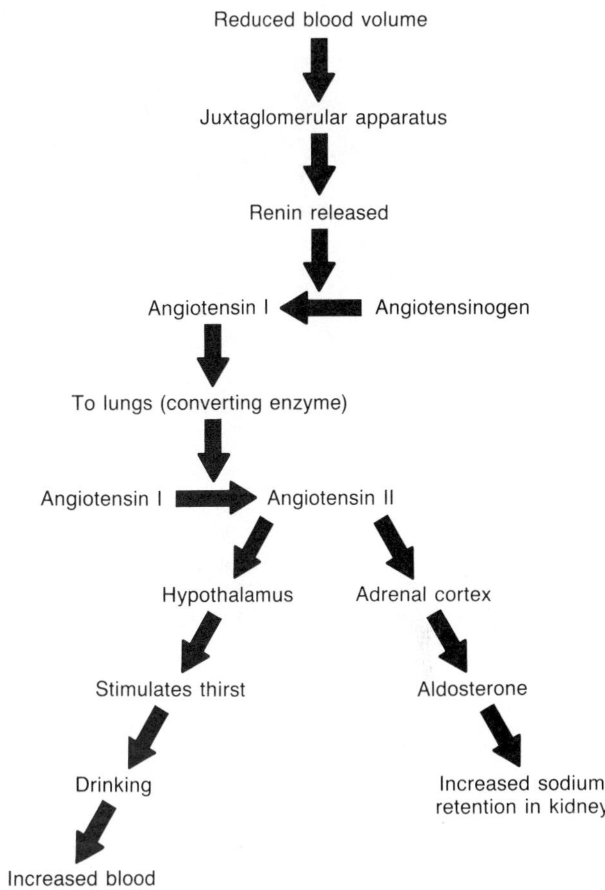

The blood plasma is filled with proteins, and as we know, many of them are enzymes circulating in an inactive form, just waiting for the right signal. Renin provides part of the signal for one such enzyme. Under its influence, the inactive plasma protein **angiotensinogen** is converted into **angiotensin I.** Angiotensin I, however, is still not fully operational and must undergo further catalytic processing, this time in the lungs. In the tissue of the lungs there is a second enzyme known simply as **converting enzyme.** Here, under its influence, angiotensin I is converted to **angiotensin II,** which is the final active form (figure 16.26). With angiotensin II circulating freely in the blood, several things occur.

Figure 16.27 The electrolyte exchange processes that are mediated in the distal tubule by aldosterone.

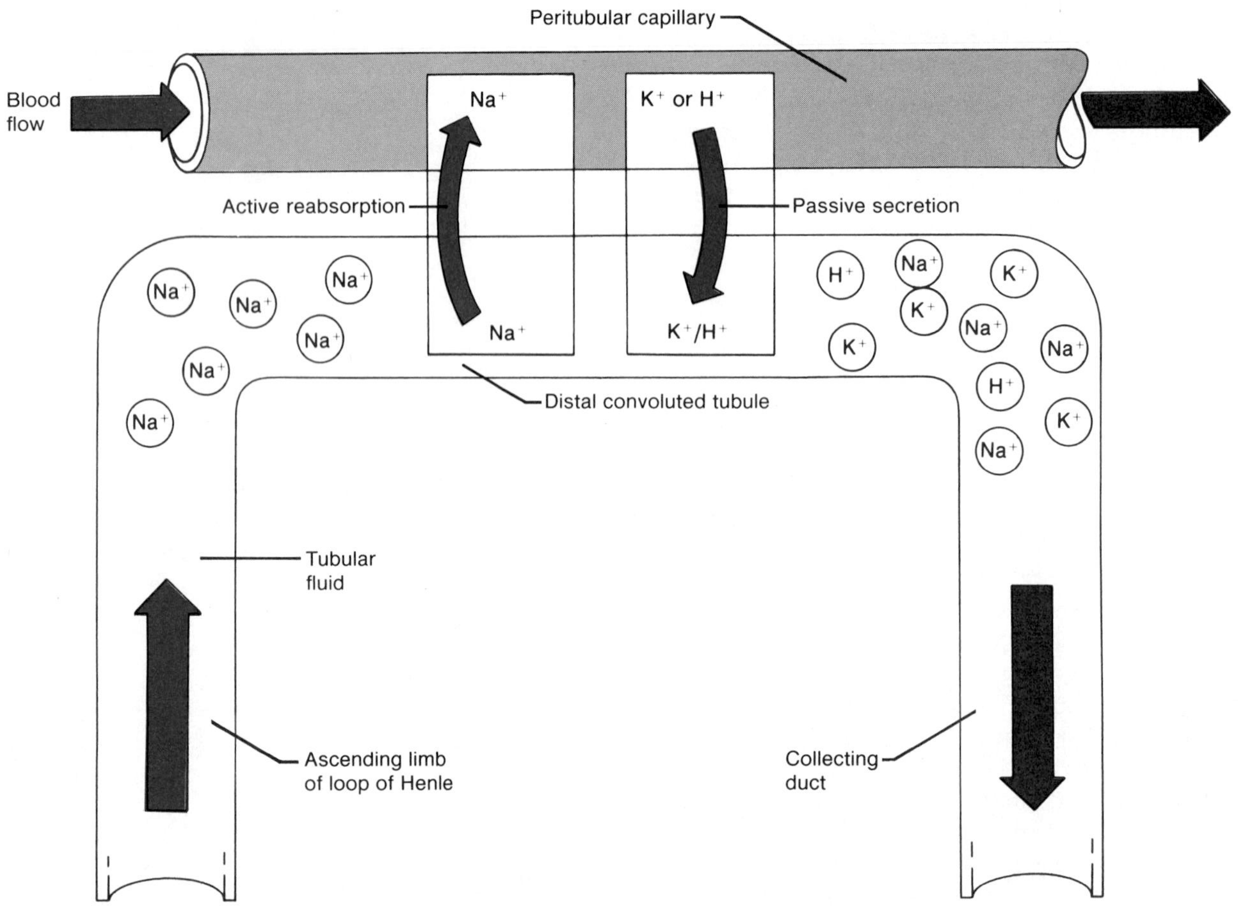

Behavior Alteration

To begin with, angiotensin II is a powerful thirst stimulant. It apparently exerts it effects in the hypothalamus, which in turn relays its messages neurally to conscious control centers. Animals injected intravenously with angiotensin II will promptly head for a water source and gulp water frantically, even if they already are well hydrated. From observations of human subjects, we believe it has much the same effect on people, making them desperately thirsty and stimulating an immediate drinking response.

Endocrine Effect

Secondly, angiotensin II has a powerful effect on the secretory cells of the adrenal cortex—more specifically, those cells that elaborate the mineralocorticoid *aldosterone*. Aldosterone has a profound effect on the distal tubules of the nephrons. In the presence of aldosterone, there is an acceleration of sodium transport out of the filtrate into the interstitial fluid (figure 16.27). Most of this sodium is promptly picked up by the blood, but some of it certainly is involved in increasing the salt concentration in the kidney medulla. This naturally boosts the osmotic strength of the medullary interstitial fluid; thus it can increase the amount of water reabsorbed from the kidney nephrons. In this indirect way, aldosterone may contribute to increased water reabsorption from the kidneys.

The Antidiuretic Hormone (Vasopressin)

Our bodies produce another hormone that is deeply involved with systemic water balance. In fact, with the exception of our behavioral responses, the antidiuretic hormone (ADH) secreted by the neurohypophysis may be the body's most important water-conservation tool.

This hormone operates in the kidney (figure 16.28). It represents the final tuning given the filtrate before it is excreted, so it must be carefully harmonized with the water and solute requirements of the body in order to maximize fluid homeostasis. There are at least two things that this hormone may do to accomplish its goals: (1) it seems able to alter the permeability to water of the walls of the collecting duct and the distal convoluted tubules, and (2) it may be involved in accelerating the activity of the chloride-pumping mechanisms in the ascending limb of the loop of Henle. If this is true, it could at least partly control the osmolarity of the kidney medulla.

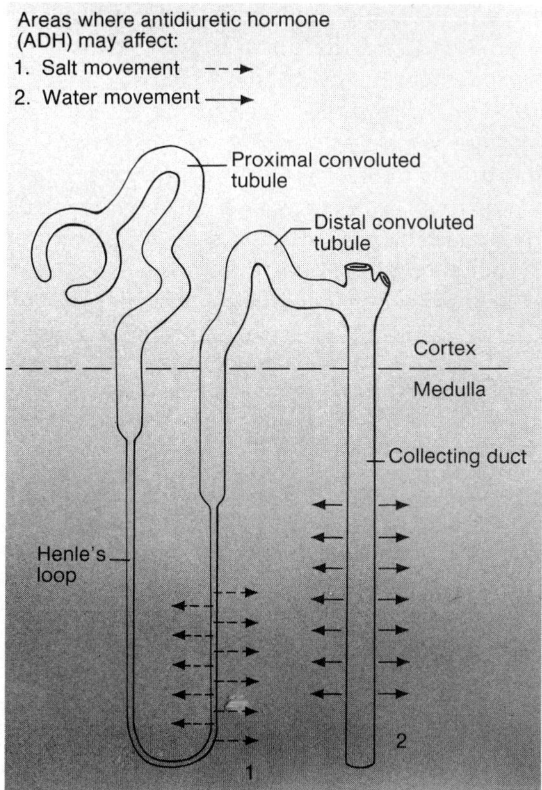

Figure 16.28 Areas implicated in the activity of antidiuretic hormone (vasopressin).

As to the first effect, keep in mind that the fluid entering the distal tubule is hypotonic to plasma. Only the fact that the tubule walls are impermeable to water prevents considerable reabsorption from taking place due to osmosis. Also, remember that the collecting duct must pass through the medulla of the kidney on its way to the ureter. If the walls of the duct are impermeable to water, then all the water it contains will be transported to the urinary bladder and eliminated. But, if the walls of the distal tubule and collecting duct are permeable to water, then, as the filtrate passes through the nephron and is exposed to the strong osmotic gradients around it, water will be osmotically withdrawn and returned to the blood (see figure 16.28).

This method allows for enormous precision in filtrate reabsorption. As long as the hormone can vary the permeability of the collecting duct through a fairly wide range, it obviously will be able to adjust, with considerable delicacy, the amount of water that is reabsorbed.

The second effect attributed to ADH simply adds to its delicacy of control. By increasing or decreasing the activity of the chloride pumps in the loop of Henle, ADH can shape—within limits, of course—the osmolarity of the medium through which the collecting ducts must pass. Between them, these two capabilities would enable ADH to respond to body requirements with tremendous precision.

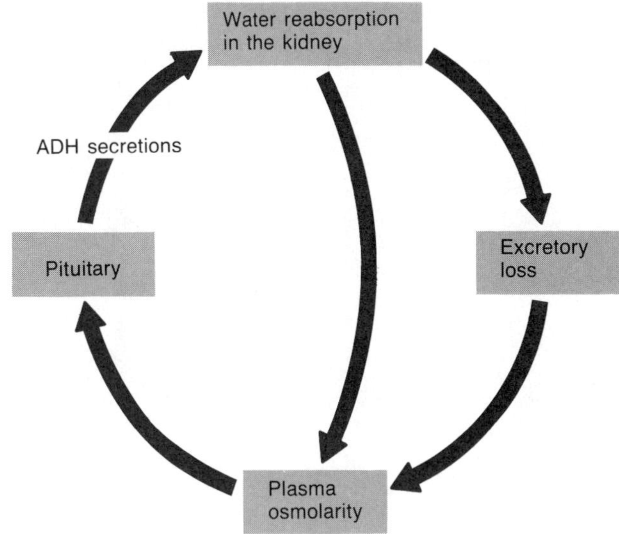

Figure 16.29 The water balance feedback loop involving the antidiuretic hormone.

The Feedback Loop

ADH is evidently not affected by secretions of the adenohypophysis, nor are any hypothalamic releasing factors involved in its release. ADH gets all the information it needs directly from the blood circulating through the brain, and it is primarily responsive to osmotic pressure (figure 16.29).

When there is plenty of water in the system and blood osmolarity is low, ADH is not released. This leaves both distal tubule and collecting duct walls impermeable to water and permits the urinary filtrate to run through them with no reabsorption taking place. But when blood osmolarity increases, this fact is detected by neurosecretory cells in the supraoptic nucleus (SON) of the hypothalamus (see chapter 10), and it is a signal that water loss from the blood is more than is optimal. The cells of the SON then generate neural impulses that travel down their axons into the neurohypophysis at an increasing rate. This results in the secretion of ADH, in large quantities if water levels are low, less if they are not so low. When ADH levels in the kidney are high, there is an increase in the amount of water reabsorbed from the collecting ducts and returned to the blood. This reduces the rate of water loss from the body and consequently slows the rate of the blood's increase in osmolarity.

It is important to note here that ADH is a typical hormone, able merely to speed up or slow certain homeostatic processes. It cannot replace water that is lost, nor can it reverse any increases in blood osmolarity. Thus we must consider ADH less effective than the behavioral response (drinking). But one must be careful not to underestimate its effects. Probably less than 8 percent of the water that filters through the

Figure 16.30 The interaction between the antidiuretic hormone (ADH) and aldosterone.

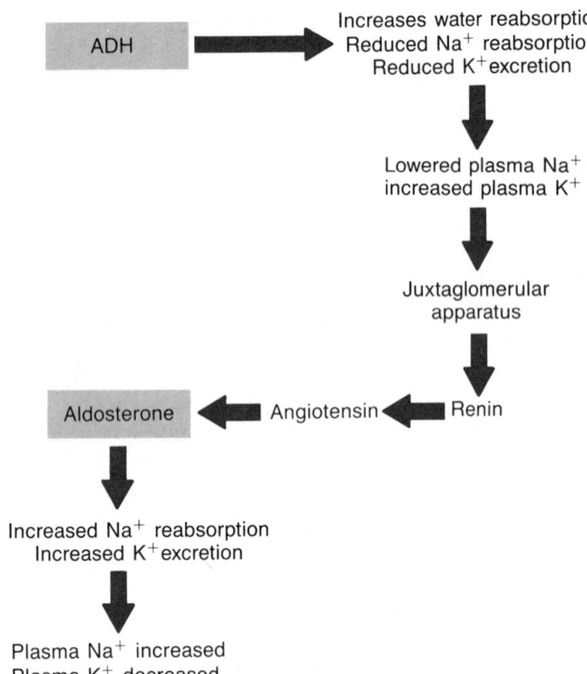

glomerulus into Bowman's capsule is influenced by ADH, but if that were to be consistently lost, it would be more than enough to upset homeostasis enormously. In the absence of ADH, a person may urinate as much as twenty liters of fluid a day—an incredible volume and one that would require immediate and constant replacement.

Electrolyte Balance

ADH is involved in electrolyte balance as well as in water balance. When physiological amounts of ADH are present, three important substances are affected. Water reabsorption is enhanced dramatically; sodium reabsorption is affected too, but only slightly; and potassium excretion is reduced. If ADH were to continue operating at this level with no opposition from other homeostatic mechanisms, an insufficiency of sodium (hyponatremia) or an overabundance of potassium in the body (hyperkalemia) would almost certainly result. Since either condition is extremely dangerous, ADH seldom is unopposed (figure 16.30).

Opposition comes in the form of aldosterone activity. Both hyponatremia and hyperkalemia can stimulate the renin-angiotensin-aldosterone loop into activity. As we have already seen, aldosterone is involved deeply with electrolyte metabolism and also slightly with water balance (figure 16.28). The presence or absence of aldosterone can dramatically alter the movement of ions into and out of the kidney filtrate, and when ADH is running with vigor, some sort of electrolyte adjustment is necessary. As we know, sodium is normally pumped from the filtrate in both the proximal and the distal tubules. Apparently aldosterone does not affect this activity in the proximal tubule, but it certainly does in the distal. When aldosterone is present, sodium pump activity in the distal tubule accelerates significantly, and this normally is able to affect potassium movement also. If body potassium is abundant, it is exchanged for sodium on a one-for-one basis—for every sodium ion that is pumped out, a potassium ion enters the filtrate.

Unlike their behavior in most cell membranes, sodium and potassium do not *have* to be exchanged when they begin moving across the cell membranes of the kidney; aldosterone can apparently operate independently on both ions, and sometimes it does. If, for instance, potassium is present in excess, aldosterone can adjust to the situation and can excrete it in larger quantities, even when there is no sodium movement at all. And sometimes— particularly when it involves people who eat large quantities of meat and very few fruits or vegetables—potassium levels are just too low for the body to let any go, so none is put into the filtrate regardless of the amount of sodium being reabsorbed. When this happens, in order to maintain electrical equilibrium, chloride ions sometimes accompany the sodium. If chloride retention is desirable, hydrogen ions can be substituted for potassium, diffusing into the urine as the sodium moves out (figure 16.27).

Sodium

In recent years the American public has become increasingly aware of some of the problems that have been associated with the ingestion of large quantities of sodium. It may therefore be a good idea to consider how this ubiquitous and important mineral affects water balance in the body.

Sodium is, as we all know, a prime constituent of table salt, and it is mainly in this form that it is ingested. The average diet of most modern Americans includes at least 7 g of sodium per day, and usually closer to 11 to 15 g. Humans ingesting quantities like this often remain perfectly healthy, but their extracellular water compartments are sometimes quite large.

Is this bad? Some medical people feel that it is—highly so—while others say it is not. The latter group suggests that in case of sudden extracellular fluid loss—like hemorrhage or diarrhea—it provides an emergency supply that could prevent serious systemic shock. The former group says these unusually large extracellular compartments are sometimes directly responsible for cases of high blood pressure, and even if they are not directly responsible, they exacerbate the problem.

The popular attitude in the U.S. today seems to be that we would all be better off if we reduced our sodium intake drastically. We are constantly being warned about the presence of sodium in what we eat—particularly in the so-called fast foods—and advertisers try very hard to convince consumers that a given product is superior to all competition because it has very little sodium. Nutritionists tell us to consume no more than 500 mg of sodium per day . . . an amount that most of us surpass by a huge margin.

What makes it all so difficult is that sodium is everywhere. It is present in all seafoods, packaged meals, fast foods, and canned vegetables. Large quantities are used in canning, and things like olives and pickles are cured in salt, hence are loaded with it. Snack items like peanuts, pretzels, popcorn, and soda crackers are liberally sprinkled with salt. In addition, most of us add lots of salt to the fresh vegetables and meats that we eat, so there is really no end to the list. To make matters worse, foods that contain little or no sodium are available, but they taste terrible, so what is one to do? Is the consumption of sodium as disastrous as we are led to believe?

This is an interesting question, and it is difficult to respond to. It is difficult because, frankly, we don't know the answer. We can only cite evidences that have accumulated over the years, and these, like almost everything in science, are inconclusive. A more detailed discussion of this problem appears in the "Clinical Considerations" section at the end of this chapter.

Potassium

Potassium is the major cation in our intracellular compartment. Generally speaking, adults eat about the same amount as they excrete, so the body maintains a constant potassium balance. Many vegetables—especially fruits like bananas and apricots—are rich in potassium, but animals do not appear to have the craving for potassium salt that they do for sodium salt, at least partly because the former has a bitter aftertaste. Potassium salts are not used as preservatives, no one sprinkles their vegetables or meats with them, and few fast foods contain any potassium at all. Since the tendency for humans to overconsume potassium does not exist, nobody seems to say much about it; yet it is important. Unlike sodium, potassium seems to have no difficulty crossing plasma membranes. It tends to concentrate inside cells because of the presence of large numbers of negative organic ions, and there are energy-consuming mechanisms within our cell membranes to see to it that inside the cell is where it stays. As long as it stays inside the cells, it is critically important for many things, including the electrical activity of neurons and muscles and the polarization of all other cells. Outside the cells, however, it's another story. In the central nervous system, extracellular K^+ is a depressant. It has the same effect on the cardiovascular system, depressing both the frequency and the strength of the heartbeat, and it can reduce the power of skeletal and smooth muscle contractions significantly.

Potassium is excreted mainly through the kidney; hence the kidney is the prime regulator. Potassium, like sodium, is filtered through the glomerulus, and much of it is reabsorbed in the tubules. When it is scarce, it is intensely retained; when there is too much of it around, the kidney, in response to efforts of the renin–angiotensin–aldosterone loop plus its own intrinsic sensors and mechanisms, excretes the excess.

Acid–Base Regulation

We should all be aware, at this point in our reading, that as long as a person lives, contaminants that threaten homeostasis flow steadily into the body fluids, most with the potential to change the status quo throughout the entire system. There is a steady influx of debris from cell metabolism and wastes in the form of by-products of nutrient breakdown or synthetic reactions. Occasionally we ingest alkaline metals and bicarbonates. These pollutants can suddenly show up, locally abundant, at any point in the body at any time, and they have to be dealt with instantly, before they can cause damage.

If they take the form of excess acids or alkalines, the *blood buffers* are our first line of defense. It is their job to grab up excess hydrogen or hydroxyl ions as soon as they appear and combine with them immediately, thereby avoiding any marked pH changes in body fluids. Acids are probably the bigger problem. Because of the ceaseless efforts of each cell to produce enough free energy to stay alive, there is a perpetual evolution of carbon dioxide as fuel substrates are broken up in the mitochondria, and in living systems an increase in CO_2 means an increase in acidity. So an unremitting acid stream pours steadily out of our cells and into our body's fluids minute after minute, day after day, as long as we live. Our buffer systems must therefore be both durable and resilient, but we must remember that there is a finite amount of buffer in any living system, so there is a limit to how much it can handle at any given time. If it has to work alone against such an endless source of contamination, sooner or later it will become saturated, and until it can be rejuvenated its effectiveness will end. Obviously, this must never happen, and to prevent it there are several means of "recharging" the buffer systems.

Most organs and tissues help to some extent. The liver helps through its metabolism of certain metabolic wastes and the GI tract gets into the act by providing an avenue of discharge from the body. Sweat glands likewise contribute a little bit, but these systems play only minor roles in overall acid-base regulation. The lead parts are played by the respiratory system (chapter 14) and the kidneys.

The efforts of all body systems are closely related and fully integrated. Buffers are designed to handle *immediate* problems. They can be in action in milliseconds. The respiratory system is only a little bit slower. By increasing respiratory rate, it can eliminate large amounts of carbon dioxide and thus can help us adjust to changing conditions in a matter of minutes. Long-term changes require the efforts of the excretory system. Although its response is not as rapid as that of the blood buffers or the respiratory system, the excretory system's efforts are more smoothly applied, and its effects tend to be more persistent.

Renal Secretion of Hydrogen Ions

The kidney uses several methods to maintain a correct acid-base balance in body fluids, and they involve the direct movement of hydrogen ions. You will recall (chapter 14) that there is a series of equilibria involving carbon dioxide, carbonic acid, and bicarbonate plus hydrogen ions. The relationship is written:

$$H_2O + CO_2 \rightleftarrows H_2CO_3 \rightleftarrows HCO_3 + H^+$$

As you can see, anything that increases the levels of CO_2 in the fluids will result in a shift of everything to the right; levels of carbonic acid will increase, and a small part of it, in turn, will break up, thereby releasing hydrogen ions and increasing acidity. It would be accurate to say, therefore, that an increase in CO_2 tends to lower the pH of the body fluids. The lungs can alleviate sudden systemic increases in CO_2 by boosting the rate and depth of ventilation, thus blowing off large quantities of this gas (chapter 14). The kidneys go about it a little more directly. The reactions involved are shown in figure 16.31, and the key exchanges are highlighted.

You should note the following:

1. For each carbon dioxide molecule that moves into the cell of a tubule from the interstitial fluid, a hydrogen ion moves out of the cell into the urinary filtrate.
2. Each time a hydrogen ion moves out of the cell into the urinary filtrate, a sodium ion moves into the cell. Sodium and hydrogen ions are exchanged between the cellular interior and the urinary filtrate on a one-for-one basis.
3. The sodium ions do not remain in the cell but diffuse quickly into the interstitial fluid.
4. To retain electrical and chemical balance in the interstitial fluid, a bicarbonate ion accompanies the sodium.

All this moving about adds up to the following: for every CO_2 molecule that leaves the interstitial fluid, one sodium bicarbonate molecule is absorbed.

CO_2 Is the Key

You can see, then, that the whole thing starts with carbon dioxide. If carbon dioxide levels in the blood are high, there is a great deal of CO_2 movement into tubule cells. This is followed by a general efflux of H^+ into the urinary filtrate, which in turn triggers the chain of events diagramed in figure 16.30. It's easy to see, then, that carbon dioxide levels control the rate of all these reactions as well as the direction in which they move. Also, if you trace the bicarbonate ions, you will see that their movement tends to support the renal disposal of acid-producing hydrogen ions. As long as CO_2 levels are high enough to stimulate hydrogen ion excretion, large quantities of both bicarbonate and sodium are reabsorbed into the interstitial fluid; ergo, acid leaves the body while alkaline buffers increase.

Eliminating the Concentration Gradient

One other point needs to be made. As you can see from figure 16.31, most of the hydrogen ions are converted into carbonic acid (H_2CO_3) when they leave the tubule cells. As the concentration of this weak acid builds up, it will begin to break down into CO_2 and H_2O, and this is a substantial energy-saver. By becoming part of a water molecule, the erstwhile hydrogen ions are no longer involved in the diffusion forces that exist between the filtrate and the cellular interior. Thus the kidney can shift tremendous numbers of hydrogen ions into the filtrate without having to spend energy fighting a huge concentration gradient.

The Problem of Hydrochloric Acid

The insertion of hydrogen ions into some other compound in the urinary filtrate is equally important for another reason—a reason involving chloride. You see, chloride is the primary negative ion in all body fluids, and the urinary filtrate is no exception. It is always there in fairly large concentrations, usually as part of a potassium or sodium salt. When it is excreted, that is the way it usually leaves—as part of a metallic salt. If it is present in the filtrate as part of a sodium salt and the sodium is selectively reabsorbed, the chloride

Figure 16.31 One mechanism by which renal tubules are able to discard excess hydrogen ions and retain sodium bicarbonate.

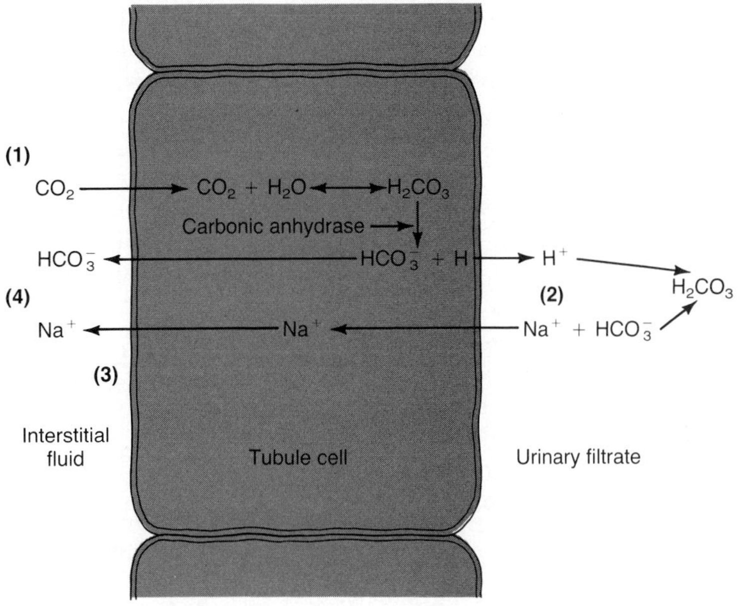

is not disturbed, because potassium usually exchanges quickly for sodium. For every sodium ion that is reabsorbed, a potassium ion is pumped into the filtrate, and the chloride on both sides of the nephron just connects to its new cation (figure 16.32*a*).

This process works nicely and leaves no spare molecules around *unless* the body should need to get rid of excess acid. When body pH is too low, sodium is reabsorbed along with anions like bicarbonate, both of which will aid in increasing the pH of interstitial fluids. Potassium is not exchanged. Instead, as we have already seen, hydrogen ions are excreted from the body fluids. If care were not taken to keep them away from the chloride in the filtrate, there would be a massive production of hydrochloric acid—a potential disaster in the making (figure 16.32*b*). There is sometimes a little acid production within the filtrate, but conditions there are pretty carefully monitored. If the urine were to become too acid it could physically damage the cells, so the pH is carefully controlled and is not permitted to drop below 4.5.

Laboratory experiments with excised kidneys have given us additional information. Forced lowering of the pH, lethal *in vivo,* can be accomplished in the laboratory, and when it is pushed below 4.5 there is a selective inhibition of all hydrogen ion transport. In living systems, such a shutdown would not be a good idea. Inhibiting hydrogen ion transport would certainly prevent the production of a highly acid urine, but if the body fluids were still too acidic, it would substantially reduce the kidney's homeostatic abilities. It would mean the kidney could no longer aid in the disposal of excess acidity. The body handles this the way it handles many potential difficulties—its mechanisms avoid the problem instead

Figure 16.32 (*a*) Chloride compatibility with either Na^+ or K^+ in body fluids. If Na^+ is exchanged across the nephron for K^+, chloride on both sides simply teams up with a new partner. (*b*) The problem of extra chloride. If the body has too much acidity, there is no Na^+/K^+ exchange. Instead, Na^+ and HCO^3 enter the blood to raise the pH while the excess H^+ leaves to reduce acidity. The H^+ ions enter the nephridial cells and stay there, often becoming part of some other molecule. A small number of hydrogen ions leave the tubule cells and pass into the filtrate, where they link to the free chloride, thus forming hydrochloric acid. This route is indicated by broken lines.

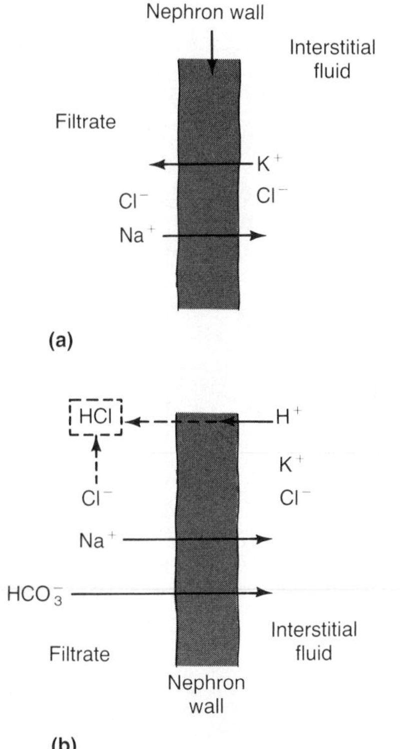

of confronting it. None of the excreted hydrogen ions are permitted to remain free. Instead, each such ion is promptly made part of another compound, thereby eliminating the problem without having to deal with it. With hydrogen ions tied up covalently in water molecules or some other compounds, the body can eliminate large quantities of hydrogen ions without having to worry about too much hydrochloric acid.

Renal Secretion of Ammonia

That takes care of the excess hydrogen, but what about all the extra chloride that is left accumulating in the filtrate? There is a second hydrogen ion–secreting mechanism in the kidney tubules, and this one helps dispose of not only the extra hydrogen, but also the extra chlorine that was left behind when the sodium ions migrated back into the interstitial fluid. It involves the excretion of a few waste nitrogen molecules as well. Nitrogenous wastes are the product of protein breakup, and they are among the most abundant waste products carried by the urine. Most is in the form of urea (figure 16.33), but not all. Sometimes, when the body is fighting extra acid production and hydrogen ions galore are being excreted, the body utilizes these nitrogenous wastes to help solve the problem. These nitrogenous wastes appear as NH_2 molecules, each of which rapidly combines with one hydrogen ion to produce ammonia, NH_3. In their turn, each ammonia molecule adds a fourth hydrogen ion in the kidney tubules and thus is converted to the *ammonium ion* (NH_4). This is the form in which it enters the filtrate. Once in the filtrate, it can link to the excess chloride that is already there, thus forming ammonium chloride and eliminating chloride, hydrogen, and some waste nitrogen in one fell swoop (figure 16.34).

Figure 16.33 Urea, the main excretory vehicle for disposing of nitrogenous waste.

NH_2
$C{=}O$
NH_2

Clinical Considerations

Sodium and High Blood Pressure

Salt was much more important in the past than it is today. Just a few centuries ago, it was so important that wars were sometimes fought over it. The reason for its importance is its ability to preserve foodstuffs over extended periods of time. Until the advent of refrigeration and the invention of canning, almost the only method used to store perishables was to "salt them down." Salt beef and pork were staples on ocean-going ships for centuries, and our ancestors used the technique to store all their perishables. It was so common that they and their children developed a liking for cured foods—"country-style" hams and most bacons are still cured with salt today. Herbivores in general have a passion for the flavor of salt.

Figure 16.34 The process by which chloride, hydrogen, and waste nitrogen are eliminated.

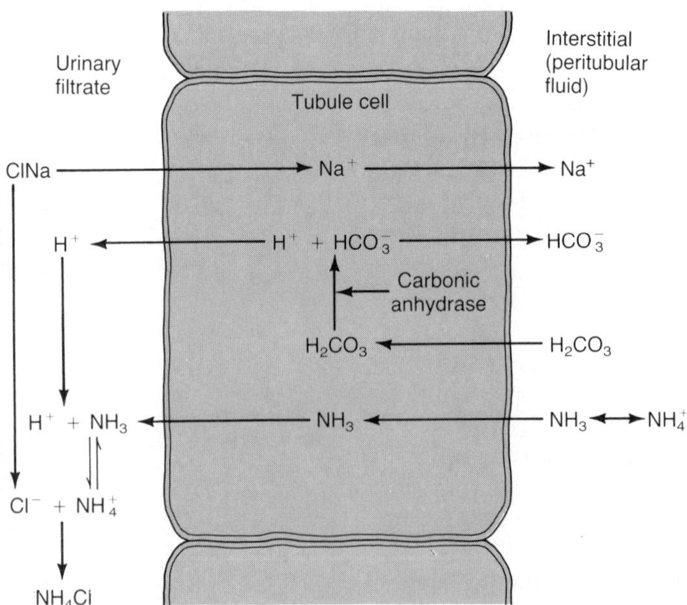

Goats, horses, deer, cattle—all will crowd around exposed sodium chloride deposits (called "salt licks"), and carnivores often focus their hunting activities around such licks. So there is nothing new about the craving most herbivores display for salt . . . and humans are indeed herbivores physiologically and anatomically.

This apparently inherited desire for salt is reflected in our use of it, now that it is abundant and cheap. Some statistical evidence seems to show that in populations where salt intake is high, a large percentage of the people suffer from high blood pressure, whereas few suffer from it where salt intake is low. Medical personnel often add personal experience to this evidence, citing case histories in which restricting the salt intake of hypertensive patients has had considerable benefit. The attitude within the medical profession seems to be universal—sodium is not good and its intake should be severely restricted. Today, that attitude is so deeply ingrained that very few physicians doubt its veracity.

Yet there is a tremendous library of experimental evidence already available that seems to indicate that very little of this is true. For instance:

1. Lots of normal, healthy people consume 12 to 15 g of sodium every day. Furthermore, the high salt-intake societies in which these people live have only an average incidence of hypertension.
2. Obese hypertensives show dramatic reductions in blood pressure when they simply lose weight. Sodium restrictions will not reduce blood pressure without weight loss, but weight loss will reduce pressure whether sodium is restricted or not.
3. Since the majority of the hypertensive patients placed on low-salt diets lost considerable weight, we cannot ascribe any observed reduction in blood pressure to reduced sodium intake.
4. While there seems to be little doubt that increased sodium intake can increase the volume of the extracellular compartment, there is no evidence to correlate these increased volumes with high blood pressure.
5. The kidney's homeostatic abilities include ridding the body of excess electrolytes, a job that they perform admirably.

Furthermore, it can be downright dangerous to reduce sodium intake drastically. Sodium, as we should recall, is the primary cation in the extracellular fluids, and since plasma membranes are relatively impermeable, it is bound to be extremely important in maintaining internal osmotic balance between the body compartments. Considering this, we must realize that too little sodium in the body fluids can be just as disastrous as too much. If levels fall too low, osmotic pressure in the extracellular fluids is reduced, and water moves into the cells. Under such circumstances, body cells become waterlogged, a condition that can be fatal. Also, we know that sodium bicarbonates and carbonic acid must be retained in the correct ratio for proper buffering to take place in the extracellular compartment. If sodium levels get too low, bicarbonate levels drop, the bicarbonate/acid ratio falls off, and body fluids can become dangerously acidic.

The body's homeostatic mechanisms are beautifully tuned to maintain established conditions throughout the body, and sodium balance is no exception. Moderate amounts of sodium are lost daily through sweating and fecal disposal, and it is known that our daily salt intake must be slightly higher than output to maintain normal health. Current evidence indicates that whenever salt intake is a little low, our kidneys can reduce sodium excretion to almost zero. Conversely, when intake is too high, the kidneys get rid of the excess. It is important to remember this. Maintaining correct levels of sodium is one of the prime functions of the kidney.

On the other hand, there is considerable evidence to suggest that certain people are not able to handle sodium excretion very well, and these people do accumulate extra body water. Whether or not this affects blood pressure is unclear, but there is some evidence to suggest that it does. Under such circumstances, it might make cutting back on sodium a good idea if you happen to be one of those individuals who are "salt-sensitive."

Urinary pH and Diet

Urine is usually slightly acid ($pH \approx 6.7$), but it isn't always. On occasion it is quite acid ($pH < 5.0$), and there are other times when it can become quite alkaline. More often than not, these pH variations can be linked to the type of food being consumed. For example, it is interesting to note that the urine of people who consume large quantities of meat and few vegetables tends to be quite acid, ranging in pH from 5.0 to 5.8, whereas those who consume mainly vegetables and fruits almost always produce urine that is quite alkaline. Several things contribute to both these phenomena.

The alkaline urine is at least partly due to the fact that most fruits and vegetables contain large quantities of potassium. This creates a body excess of that alkaline metal, which the kidney handles by excreting it in large amounts, usually in the company of chloride ions but often linked to bicarbonate or phosphates, the latter two contributing profoundly to the higher urinary pH.

Meat eaters not only lack this extra potassium (meat contains very little), but there is also a good deal of sulfur in animal protein. As the protein is broken down in the digestive tract the sulfur ions are released, and they ultimately find themselves becoming part of a sulfuric acid molecule in the urine.

Whether having acid urine is better than alkaline is difficult to say because so many things are involved, but some considerations are worth mentioning. We know, for example, that there are generally quite a few calcium salts in the urinary filtrate. We know also that in acid solutions, calcium salts remain ionized, and when acid solutions become alkaline, these same salts often precipitate out. There is considerable evidence to indicate that chronic production of alkaline urine might exacerbate the formation of calcium-salt kidney stones and may even be part of the cause. Acid solutions will not dissolve calcium stones that have already been formed, but they may prevent them from forming in the first place. Because of this, urine acidification through the manipulation of diet has been used to prevent a recurrence of kidney stones in patients who have already passed one or two.

Considering only these facts, it would seem that production of an acid urine is beneficial and, as long as it doesn't damage the kidneys, the more acid, the better. Unfortunately, the chronic production of a highly acid urine produces a different, yet basically similar, problem. This problem involves *urates*—the nucleic acid metabolites mentioned earlier in this chapter. Urates are usually present in small amounts in the urine; as long as the urinary pH remains above 6, these nucleic acid metabolites are fairly soluble. However, when the pH falls below 6, the solubility of these salts is drastically reduced, and they precipitate out as uric acid. All they need is some kind of nucleus to precipitate onto. If they find one in the kidney or urinary bladder, the result could be the formation of uric acid kidney stones. Obviously, it is as the Ancient Greek philosophers always said: "In nothing, too much," meaning essentially, moderation in all things.

Gout

Normally, urates represent only a tiny fraction of the nitrogenous waste that humans excrete, but if for any reason amounts get a little higher than normal, they can cause difficulty. Normal amounts of sodium urates are generally soluble enough to dissolve in the plasma, but if the amounts increase much above normal, the plasma cannot hold them in solution and they precipitate out as monosodium urate crystals. Usually they do so around joints and tendons, especially in the ankles and wrists, producing the painful and hard-to-treat condition known as gout. If the affliction is not too severe, it can sometimes be corrected and then prevented from recurring by simply drinking lots of fluids daily, but more often professional help is necessary to avoid serious and permanent joint deformation.

One of our most effective drugs for combatting the misery of gout is known as **colchicine,** and the history of this drug is most interesting. It involves one of the most loved figures in American history, Benjamin Franklin.

Franklin suffered from gout, and it has been said that he hated to travel because when he did, he was in constant pain from gouty toes. Nevertheless, for the sake of his country he did travel, and as most of us are aware, he was America's first ambassador to France. It was in France that he became aware of a secret remedy for gout that a French druggist made and sold to wealthy customers. Franklin was in absolute agony from the pain in his toes, so when he got the man's address from his French valet he promptly hobbled down to the pharmacy and purchased some of the secret remedy. It was not without side effects. Franklin writes that he had a terrible, five-hour bout with diarrhea immediately after taking the remedy, but once the GI upset subsided and he felt better, he suddenly became aware that the pain in his toes had almost disappeared.

Franklin was ecstatic, and he immediately asked the druggist what the drug was and where it could be obtained. Poverty in France was rampant at that time, and since this particular druggist had an exclusive franchise on a chemical that cured gout, he was able to live rather well. Naturally enough, therefore, he guarded his remedy very jealously and flatly refused to divulge its secret until he discovered that Franklin was an American. When he realized that Franklin would soon be leaving France and would really have no chance to interfere with business, he gave up his secret. The drug, he said, was **colchium,** and it was extracted from the plant we know today as *Colchium autumnale*, or the *autumn lily*. Franklin made arrangements to obtain both the plant and samples of the drug to bring to his country with him when he returned. The active fraction in that plant was, of course, colchicine.

Renal Failure

This is too broad a subject to delve into in any depth, but in modern times the surgical procedure known as **kidney transplant** has become so well publicized that it deserves some mention here. It is necessitated by total failure of the subject's kidneys.

Chronic kidney failure often goes unnoticed in the beginning, but it gradually increases in severity until the subject cannot help but note that something is seriously wrong. There is a tendency for such a victim to fatigue much too easily, muscle tone is lost, and there is a good deal of intestinal upset, including

Figure 16.35 A typical dialysis cartridge. Note the adherence to the countercurrent principle.

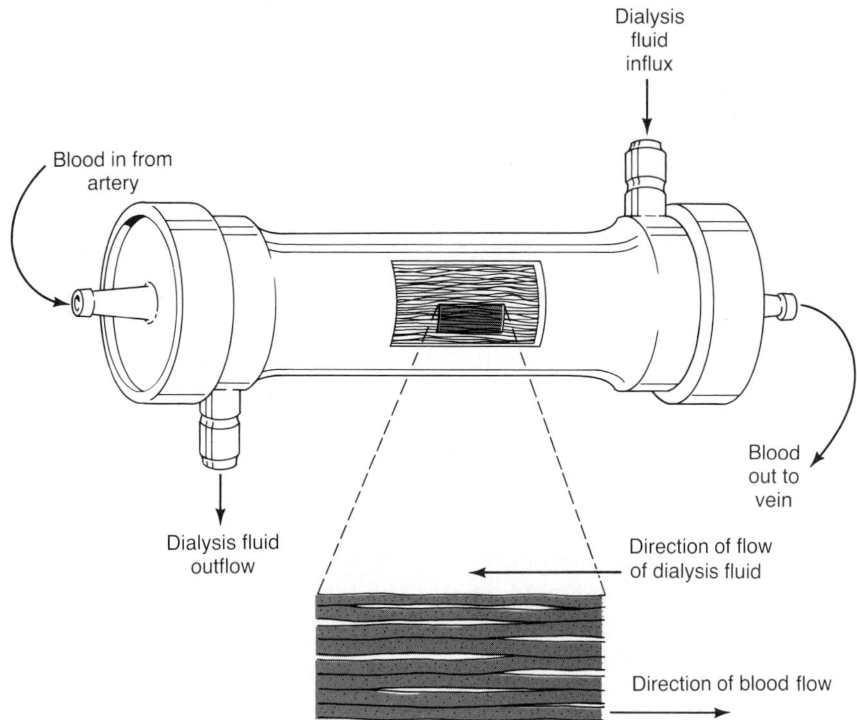

a chronic, horrid taste in the mouth. Medical analysis will show high levels of nitrogen, sodium, and water retention, usually accompanied by systemic acidosis—all (as you should know at this point) indicative of the kidney's failure to do its job. When all efforts to reduce these conditions fail, physicians resort first of all to a procedure called **dialysis.**

Dialysis

Dialysis consists of utilizing a machine to handle the duties normally undertaken by the kidneys. There are actually two different methods of dialyzing patients whose kidneys have failed. Both are terribly inconvenient and disrupt life drastically—but they keep the patient alive.

The better-known of the two techniques is called **hemodialysis** and consists of inserting catheters into the patient's blood vessels—one into an artery and the other into a nearby vein. When the patient is hooked up, his or her blood is shunted from the artery, run through the dialysis machine and then returned through the vein. The pressure provided by the heart is adequate to pump the blood through the machine, and an accessory pump is normally not used.

While in the dialysis machine, the blood circulates through many hundreds of very small, thin-walled tubes (figure 16.35). These tubes are made of a special, semipermeable cellulose with pores that are carefully sized to retain most proteins and all the cellular elements within while permitting relatively free exchange of minerals, acids, and waste products like urea and creatinine. The tubes all are immersed in a circulating dialysis fluid, which features carefully measured concentrations of glucose, sodium, potassium, calcium, and chloride. Exchange is accomplished purely by diffusion. Dialysis sessions clean the patient's blood and permit continued life, but the style of living is enormously restricted—sometimes to the point where it is well-nigh unbearable.

Problems with Dialysis

Normally, a person whose kidneys have completely failed must undergo dialysis two or three times a week and, unless the patient owns a dialysis machine, each session requires an overnight stay in the hospital. Most patients realize that without these treatments, death—a most horrible death—is inevitable, and so can eventually adapt to this regimen. But even when they are settled-in mentally, there are complications. Patients have chronic battles with low blood pressure, fevers due to infections, sodium-potassium imbalances—even seizures on occasion—all due to the fact that the blood must be routed out of the body and cleansed artificially. There is a permanent hole in the circulatory system where the catheters have been placed, and these openings represent routes for infection; the chronically indwelling tubes represent foci where blood clots can form, and no matter how carefully the dialysis fluid is prepared, it is never going to be perfect—hence the osmotic pressure of the patient's body fluids is never exactly right. Small wonder that nearly all such patients hope someday to be able to obtain a live, functioning kidney from some donor.

Transplantation

Obviously, it is beyond the scope of this book to spend much time on transplantation. However, it is probably worth mentioning that at this point in our history, the surgery involved in kidney transplantation seems to have been pretty well perfected. The problem that has not been solved involves efforts by the recipient's immune mechanisms to destroy the foreign tissue that has invaded the body and to cast out the newly introduced intruder. This is a problem of tissue rejection, and it is considered in detail in the next chapter.

Glomerular Problems

There are many things that can afflict the glomerulus. Lesions can be caused by bacteria (**glomerular nephritis**) or a vast number of other, diverse things—like diabetes, Hodgkin's disease, malaria, syphilis, and so on. Any of these things can cause glomerular damage, and what damages the glomerulus can affect the filtration process in the renal corpuscle. There are varying degrees of severity, but all involve capillary permeability. Sometimes the filter system is too permissive, in which case we find things like blood cells and excessive protein in the urine. At other times disease can cause the cells of the glomerular capillaries to swell and shrink up the fenestrations, thus making filtration extremely difficult. In severe cases, the glomerulus may completely collapse and permit little, if anything, to filter through. One of the first indications of this latter kind of trouble is a very low urinary output (**anuria**). This type of anuria is usually accompanied by things like puffiness around the eyes and general edema, large quantities of protein—often blood cells—in the urine, nausea, vomiting, constant fatigue, abdominal pain, and wasting away of muscle tissue. The end result of all this can be complete kidney failure; hence the affliction is extremely dangerous.

Occasionally such signs and symptoms indicate a condition that is reversible. If the problem is caused by bacteria, ridding the body of the invader is usually all that is necessary. By now, however, we should realize that the kidneys are irreplaceable, and the operations that they perform are of such tremendous importance that the possibility of their being damaged should never be viewed lightly.

Internal Pollution

The kidney processes so much blood every minute of every day that it is safe to say that anything that gets into the blood will ultimately affect the kidney one way or another. Materials that are generally toxic are often cleared in the kidney, and often relatively harmless things that are present in the blood in diluted form become so concentrated in the nephridial tubules that they can do tremendous damage very rapidly. Heavy metals like lead and mercury are particularly noticeable these days because of their abundance in certain paints and sometimes in our drinking water, but they are not the only things. Our children, intent on fitting in with their peers, often "snort" things like paint or airplane glue to get "high," thus inhaling solvents like carbon tetrachloride and toluene, both of which can do tremendous renal damage. Nor are adults immune to such self-inflicted damage. Many are addicted to painkillers like aspirin and acetaminophen (Tylenol), and it is not at all unusual for these analgesics to produce acute renal failure. Even certain antibiotics, things as common as streptomycin and neomycin, have been recorded as culprits. In fact, in hospitals, antibiotics are the leading cause of kidney failure.

Can such damage be repaired? Sometimes. In cases of overindulgence in analgesics or an unfortunate choice of antibiotics, the treatment can be as simple as removing the offending toxin and letting the body heal itself. But things are not that simple when dealing with heavy metals or inhaled lipid solvents. Usually, by the time a victim of heavy metal poisoning or a "glue sniffer" is brought to the attention of a physician, the damage is too severe to be repaired.

Kidney Stones

These were mentioned previously. Their cause is not really known, although it has been suggested—particularly in the case of calcium stones—that alkaline urine may contribute. The stones usually form in the renal pelvis, and when they pass into the ureter they often stick in there and plug the delivery system. Obviously, such a stone must be passed, which is a very painful process indeed, and few of those who have undergone it ever want to repeat. If the stones fail to pass, it is possible sometimes to break them up with ultrasound and permit the smaller granules to be flushed out. If that doesn't work—and it doesn't, always—the only resort is surgery, a debilitating and painful experience, but one that is usually successful.

Bladder Infections

Infections of the bladder and urethra are fairly common, particularly in women, and if the causative organism is a fungus it can be particularly annoying and hard to cure. Most people are not aware of it, but urine, freshly voided from a healthy person, is not filled with germs, but tends rather to be sterile. The human urinary bladder and urethra are normally sterile also, and when infectious organisms are found in the urine, it is usually indicative of a urinary tract infection. Women suffer from such infections more than men because the anus is loaded with bacteria and is so close to the urethral opening. Clothing moving back and forth between the two orifices can sometimes infect the otherwise sterile area.

The infections are usually gram-negative bacteria and are extremely hard to destroy. To make matters worse, recurrences are not at all uncommon, and each must be treated as an initial infection.

Summary

Kidney Structure

I. Blood Supply. The kidney receives about 20 percent of the average cardiac output every minute.

II. Nerve Supply. All the renal nerves are sympathetic in origin. They all involve the arterial supply and terminate in the smooth muscles around afferent and efferent arterioles of the glomerulus.

The Nephron

I. The nephron is the functional unit of the kidney. There are more than a million in each kidney.

II. About 90 percent of the nephrons occupy the outer portion of the kidney—the cortex. The remaining 10 percent are juxtaglomerular nephrons, and portions of these penetrate into the depths of the kidney medulla.

III. Structure of the Nephron. The nephron consists of a renal corpuscle, a proximal convoluted tubule, a loop of Henle, and a distal convoluted tubule.

IV. Renal Corpuscle
   - A. The renal corpuscle is composed of a circulatory entity (the glomerulus) and a renal entity (Bowman's capsule).
   - B. The capillaries of the glomerulus have unusually large pores in their walls and are wrapped fairly tightly by podocytes, which are elements of Bowman's capsule. Blood is filtered through the capillary walls and membranes of Bowman's capsule.

V. Proximal Convoluted Tubule. Most materials that are going to be reabsorbed are reabsorbed in the proximal tubule. Amino acids, proteins, glucose, and many other important molecules as well as mineral ions and water are removed from the filtrate and returned to the blood in this structure.

VI. Loop of Henle. The loop of Henle may be the only example of a countercurrent multiplier in biological systems. It is responsible for establishing and maintaining the high salt concentration that exists within the boundaries of the kidney medulla.

VII. Distal Convoluted Tubule. The walls of this tubule are impermeable to water. Aldosterone exerts its effects on this structure.

VIII. Collecting Duct
   - A. The permeability of the walls of this structure is adjustable. In the presence of ADH, they are permeable. In the absence of ADH,they are impermeable.
   - B. Through manipulation of this permeability, ADH is able to affect about 8 percent of the water reabsorption that takes place in the kidney.

Kidney Operations

I. During a twenty-four-hour day, a normal kidney will process 180 liters of blood. Only about a liter of fluid is excreted during that same period. Obviously, then, a tremendous amount of activity must be devoted to reabsorbing most of the materials that are filtered into the kidney.

II. Filtration
   - A. The blood is subjected to ultrafiltration in the renal corpuscle. Particles smaller than about 50 Å (25,000 daltons) can pass through the filter. Anything larger is held back.
   - B. Pressures in the Renal Corpuscle. There are several pressures involved in the filtration process. The pressure provided by the heart tends to filter blood through the glomerular capillaries. The osmotic pressure of the plasma and the backpressure provided by the accumulating fluid in Bowman's capsule oppose the blood pressure.

III. Reabsorption of Materials from the Filtrate. Nearly all reabsorption takes place in the proximal tubule. Some reabsorption is passive (diffusive), and some is active.
   - A. Protein Reabsorption. Reabsorption of proteins requires energy. It is normally 100 percent effective.
   - B. Glucose Reabsorption. Glucose is also actively reabsorbed. It is also 100 percent, usually.
   - C. Water and Salt Reabsorption
     1. Salts are actively transported out of the urinary filtrate, and water passively follows the osmotic gradient.
     2. The amounts of salt and water that are reabsorbed in the proximal tubule are fairly constant.

IV. Tubular Secretion. Tubular secretion is essentially the process of tubular reabsorption running in the opposite direction. Materials are moved from the interstitial fluid and pumped into the lumen of the kidney nephron.

The Loop of Henle – A Countercurrent Multiplier System

I. Countercurrent systems are common in biological systems. They conserve energy and maximize material and energy transfer.

II. Multiplier action permits the loop of Henle to produce, with a minimum of energy, a tremendous concentration of salt in the medulla of the kidney.

III. The Vasa Recta
   - A. These blood vessels surround the loop of Henle and are an intricate part of the multiplier mechanism.
   - B. Thanks to the slow movement of blood through these vessels, the salts pumped into the medulla are not immediately carried away by the blood.

C. The countercurrent relationship between the vasa recta and the loop of Henle also facilitates the concentration of salt.

IV. Quick-Response Regulatory Mechanisms. The concentration of urine can be varied by varying the concentration of salt in the kidney medulla. It can also be varied by changing the collecting tubule walls' permeability to water.

V. Reabsorption in the Distal Tubule
   A. Reabsorption in this portion of the nephron is partially controlled by the steroid hormone aldosterone.
   B. When aldosterone is present, sodium is actively pumped from the filtrate and returned to the blood. Potassium usually replaces sodium in the urine that is forming, although that is adjustable.

VI. Uric Acid and Urea
   A. Urea is the form in which the human kidney disposes of most of the body's nitrogenous wastes, nearly all of which are products of protein metabolism.
   B. Uric Acid. In mammals, uric acid is a relatively unimportant waste product. It *may* be transported into the filtrate by tubular secretion. What little there is, is thought to be a product of nucleic acid metabolism.

Elimination of Urine

Micturition. Micturition is the medical term for urination. It is an autonomic reflex that can be, when desired, consciously controlled.

Water Balance and Electrolyte Regulation

I. The Fluid Compartments
   A. The body has two major water compartments, the intracellular compartment and the extracellular compartment.
   B. Most (about 66 percent) of the body water is in the intracellular compartment.
   C. The extracellular compartment includes the interstitial fluid and the blood.

II. Regulating the Internal Environment
   A. The kidney is responsible for regulating the content and volume of all body fluids.
   B. It also adjusts pH and osmolarity.
   C. It is more than just a waste-disposal system. Nutrients will be discarded along with waste products if the former are present in too high a concentration.

III. The Angiotensin–Aldosterone Response. This response begins with the production and release of renin from the juxtaglomerular cells of the kidney.
   A. Behavioral Alterations. Angiotensin stimulates thirst and drinking behavior.
   B. Endocrine Effect. Angiotensin also stimulates the secretion of aldosterone.

IV. The Antidiuretic Hormone (Vasopressin)
   A. The antidiuretic hormone can alter the permeability of the walls of the collecting duct. It can thus vary the amount of water that is reabsorbed from the urinary filtrate in the collecting duct.
   B. The Feedback Loop
      1. Stimulus/control for ADH is blood osmolarity. Sensors are in the hypothalamus.
      2. Integration of the stimulus occurs in the hypothalamus, and effector impulses are relayed to the neurohypophysis.
      3. The antidiuretic hormone is released from the neurohypophysis.

V. Electrolyte Balance
   A. ADH and aldosterone are both involved in maintaining the proper balance between potassium and sodium in body fluids.
   B. Aldosterone is the major control. It exerts most of its influence on active transport mechanisms in the distal convoluted tubule of the kidney.

VI. Sodium
   A. Sodium is the major extracellular cation in animals. It is usually relatively scarce in the diets of herbivores; hence, it is much sought after.
   B. As a major ingredient in table salt, sodium was once one of the most important minerals on the earth. Its ability to preserve foods without refrigeration is unsurpassed.
   C. It is believed to be overly consumed by Americans today.

VII. Potassium. Potassium is the major intracellular cation in animals. It is abundant in the diets of herbivores, not so abundant in the diets of carnivores.

Acid-Base Regulation

I. Blood buffers are our first response to changes in the pH of body fluids. The lungs play an important role in maintaining fluid pH also. The most prolonged activity in controlling the pH of the fluids is exerted by the kidney.

II. Renal Secretion of Hydrogen Ions
   A. Retention of large quantities of hydrogen ions could disrupt pH balance in the blood. At the same time, eliminating too many at one time could damage delicate kidney tissues.
   B. CO_2 is the Key. Most of the changes in pH that occur in body fluids are due to the entry or exit of carbon dioxide.
   C. Eliminating the Concentration Gradient. By converting many of the hydrogen ions to water, the body avoids severe pH changes and large concentration gradients.

III. The Problem of Hydrochloric Acid. The body takes many steps in the kidney to avoid producing hydrochloric acid in the urine.

IV. Renal Secretion of Ammonia
   A. Much of the nitrogen that is excreted leaves as urea, but not all.
   B. When there are large amounts of hydrogen ions to be excreted, some extra hydrogen ions are incorporated into ammonia as the ammonium ion, which then links to chloride to form a salt, ammonium chloride.
   C. This not only helps dispose of extra hydrogen ions, but it also gets rid of any extra chloride that might be present.

Clinical Considerations

I. Sodium and High Blood Pressure
II. Urinary pH and Diet
III. Gout
IV. Renal Failure
  A. Dialysis
  B. Problems with Dialysis
  C. Transplantation
V. Glomerular Problems
VI. Internal Pollution
VII. Kidney Stones
VIII. Bladder Infections

Review Questions

1. What is the major function of the mammalian kidney?
2. List five items that the human kidneys monitor and adjust.
3. Sketch a longitudinal section of a human kidney and label the principal zones and structures.
4. Describe the blood supply available to the kidney. How much blood flows through this each twenty-four-hour period?
5. Which branch of the nervous system provides the major input to the kidney?
6. Draw and label a nephron.
7. Describe the renal corpuscle.
8. What is meant by glomerular filtration? Describe the process, taking care to name all the structures through which filtered material must pass.
9. Describe the types of cells that form the walls of the various tubules of the kidney.
10. Discuss the pressures involved in the process of glomerular filtration. How do they control each other? What is GFR?
11. Describe the glomerular capillaries. How do they differ from systemic capillaries?
12. What limits the passage of particles through the filter? Name a few substances that are permitted to pass through the filter.
13. What substances are normally reabsorbed by the kidney almost completely?
14. Where does most reabsorption take place?
15. Describe the process of tubular reabsorption of salt and water.
16. What are the peritubular capillaries? What is their function?
17. Describe the process known as tubular secretion. What substances does it normally involve?
18. What is the tonicity of fluid leaving the proximal tubule and entering the loop of Henle?
19. Describe a typical countercurrent exchange system. Draw and label a typical one.
20. How is chloride reabsorption related to the operation of the mechanisms of the loop of Henle?
21. Describe the method by which the loop of Henle succeeds in producing and maintaining a high concentration of salt in the kidney medulla.
22. What abilities do the vessels of the vasa recta possess that makes their continued operation crucial to the proper functioning of the loop of Henle?
23. Describe the movement of water from the proximal convoluted tubule to the collecting duct. Be sure to mention where each movement occurs and how much of the filtrate's water is involved.
24. What portion of the nephron is most affected by the hormone aldosterone?
25. Describe the activity of what is called the "angiotensin–aldosterone loop."
26. Describe urea and its significance in excretion.
27. What is the meaning of the word *micturition?* Describe the reflex in as much detail as you can.
28. Contrast the function of the blood buffers, the respiratory system, and the kidneys as controllers of body pH.
29. How is the urinary bladder adapted to performing its function?
30. What is the chemical composition of normal urine?
31. What two theories are offered to explain the function of antidiuretic hormone?
32. Describe the complete stimulus–integrator/controller–effector loop involved in the regulation of the antidiuretic hormone.
33. Describe the interaction of antidiuretic hormone and aldosterone in the control of electrolyte balance in body fluids.
34. What evidence supports the contention that large amounts of sodium are bad for human health?
35. What evidence contradicts that mentioned in the previous question?
36. What is potassium's role in the body? How, and by what, is it regulated?
37. Describe the kidney process by which excess hydrogen ions are removed from body fluids.
38. How is the formation of hydrochloric acid in the urine avoided?
39. Under what circumstances is ammonium chloride excreted in the urine? How does it form?

Chapter 17 The Vertebrate Immune System

Study Hints

1. Try to fit the immune responses into the general goal of all body functions—homeostasis. That is all it really is: the body's effort to maintain homeostasis in the face of a foreign invasion.
2. Although it may seem melodramatic, you will probably find it easier to understand our immune operations if you will make an effort to equate them to military campaigns.
3. Read the section on immunoglobulins carefully.
4. The chemicals released by the various cells are important. Be sure you remember which is which.
5. Be sure you can figure out what type you are dealing with when, for instance, anti-A antibody causes the agglutination of a subject's blood.
6. Try to separate the allergy types clearly in your mind, and pay particular attention to the most common ones, since they will be the ones you will encounter most often.

Objectives

When you have finished reading this chapter, you should:

1. be able to broadly outline the mechanisms involved in the immune response.
2. be able to describe the differences between nonspecific immunity and specific immunity and know which blood cells are involved in each.
3. understand clearly the relationship between B cells and T cells.
4. know which cell type is involved with each immune system and be able to describe what each normally does.
5. know the difference between the primary immune response and the secondary immune response, and be able to explain which is the more powerful and why.
6. be able to explain, clearly, the responses of both B and T cells to the presence of an antigen.
7. understand how B and T cells cooperate with each other.
8. be able to explain the differences between allergies brought on by the humoral immune response and those brought on by the cellular immune response.

Aggressive macrophage.

Introduction

It should be obvious from the previous chapters that living things remain viable only as long as they can protect themselves from significant changes in their internal environments. Everything we have studied up to this point has underscored that. But until now we have been concerned with homeostatic systems that deal with pollution that we produce ourselves—byproducts of some otherwise-beneficial operations taking place within our bodies. It is time now to consider active aggression, the problem of things in our external or internal environment that launch unwanted invasions and produce materials that damage our bodies.

All organisms have evolved mechanisms to defend against predation. Some animals can run like the wind; others can climb trees or fly or swim at high speeds; still others grow to enormous size and, if they can survive childhood, can ignore the predators they have outgrown. But not all predators are visible. Some of the most dangerous ones, in fact, are not things we can run away from. They do not sneak up on us in the dark because they don't have to. They march up to our bodies in broad daylight, without our even realizing it. Nearly all are so small that they are invisible to every one of our sensory mechanisms. They can slip past our most alert defenses. Once inside our bodies, they have the potential to wreak destruction and chaos. In the past, these invisible attackers killed people and animals literally by the millions, while those destined to survive sat by and watched, baffled and helpless. Even today, millions of people die each year as a result of this infinitesimal predation, and most people are still helpless, for it requires medical professionals to protect us against things that we cannot even see.

Those who study microbiology, parasitology, or any of the medical sciences are invariably stunned by the teeming panorama of potentially harmful organisms. They cannot help but wonder how anybody manages to survive the continual, unremitting onslaught of the hordes of organisms seeking to invade our bodies and share the nutrients and services that are reserved for our cells. Libby Hyman, one of the world's greatest invertebrate biologists, once said that if every organism on the earth, with the exception of roundworms, suddenly died, it would be possible to locate and identify everything that used to be around just by noting the populations of roundworms and where they were concentrated. She could, she claimed, locate trees, cats, alligators, insects—and all would be easily identifiable according to the worms that parasitized them. There is no reason to doubt this woman's hypothesis. The concept is mind-boggling. It suggests that every tree, grass blade, and animal, from earthworms to giant sequoias, is either infested with roundworms or is fighting a perpetual battle to avoid being so. Yet roundworms are not a major problem in this country, or indeed, in the Western world.

There is a host of other such organisms—so many, in fact, that the total number of potential attackers staggers the imagination. Only a few bacteria cause disease, but bacteria of all kinds swarm everywhere, they blanket the earth. When one traces a line with a finger across a table top, he is cutting a swath in a population of bacteria. The soil is alive with them, water is likewise filled—even the air is laden with them, floating back and forth on dust particles often too small to see—yet if they are more abundant than the fungi, they are only marginally so. There are flatworms that are carefully designed by nature to parasitize humans and their relatives; there are protistans that cause horrible diseases, and there are the viruses, most ubiquitous and abundant of all the parasites—things that have no real life of their own and must borrow it from others in order to exist.

Of all the sentient organisms on the earth, humans are the only ones able to recognize such attacks and realize what is responsible. Because of this, we today are capable of using our intelligence to fight these predators. We have managed to devise ways to bring about the deaths of the attackers or, even better, to avoid the attacks entirely. But it was not always like this; in fact, it was hardly ever like this. Out of the hundreds of millennia we have been on the earth, it is only in the last century or so that we have known the identities of these attackers, and only within the last forty years have we been able to produce an arsenal full of truly effective weapons to use against them. What protected us against them in the years before? After all, our ancestors obviously managed to survive and stay healthy long enough to produce families. Is it possible that microscopic armies mobilize inside of people and stand ready to give their tiny lives in defense of the whole organism?

Our Personal Armies

That is an unusually dramatic way of describing the vertebrate immune system, but it is probably the easiest and possibly even the most accurate way of viewing it. We do indeed have personal armies within us, armies consisting of specialized cells and carefully designed chemicals that have only one goal: "to defend (our bodies) against all enemies, both foreign and domestic," but especially foreign.

When we view the job undertaken by this system and the methods utilized, when we observe the mindless but nevertheless skillfully designed techniques utilized by so many of the organisms that attack us, it is nearly impossible to avoid comparisons with military campaigns. Potential invaders surround us everywhere, probing endlessly for weak points in our body's defenses. When one such weak point shows up, they pounce. From rapidly established beachheads, they fan out into every available niche, using our own roads and highways to increase their control, foraging as they go, establishing forts and colonies as they move along.

As soon as they invade, our bodies immediately take steps to mobilize. If the invader is a strange one, we have certain battalions that fight what are essentially "holding actions" and "strategic withdrawals" until special countermeasures are available in sufficient quantities to stage a counterattack. When the counterattack comes, obedience to prescribed military axioms is apparent everywhere. Invader colonies are isolated and enormous assaults are mounted against them. Communication lines are cut, roads are blocked, and the individual pockets of the invaders are wiped out "in detail" before they can "dig in" or consolidate. If the invaders are life-threatening and if they are present in large numbers, cells everywhere are mobilized to fight. Essentially, martial law prevails throughout the body, and every homeostatic mechanism that can be spared from its routine duties joins the fray. Ultimately, the invader is either destroyed or the person dies; there is seldom any halfway result.

This is what happens when an unfamiliar enemy attacks. Days may go by while the body's defenses are recruited and go on a war footing. Weapons devised to kill that specific invader must be produced, and the design and distribution consumes time. On the other hand, if the invader is familiar, if it has attacked before and failed, the weapons are already stockpiled and need only be brought to the fore. Because of this, the battle seems never to be in doubt. The attackers may attain small local toeholds, but once the body becomes aware of their existence and location, they are obliterated very rapidly. Often the person involved is never aware that an invasion was attempted.

A Well-Defended Fortress

Our internal armies are indeed models of efficiency, but they are not our only defensive resource. As it happens, we have other ways of defending ourselves from microscopic assaults and some of the most effective are passive, representing nothing more than obstacles put in the way of an invasion. The human body is a marvelously designed fortress that any prospective attacker must breach if there is to be any possibility of success.

Skin

The first line of defense is the **skin.** Unless an attacker can get through the skin, invasion is not possible, and getting through the skin is not easy. If we consider it only as a simple, passive barrier that covers us completely, it is a nearly impenetrable fortress wall (figure 17.1). Barring damage, it is almost impossible for any but the most specialized parasites to get through it into the interior of the body. Most organisms that land on the skin—including bacteria and viruses—just dry out and die.

Not all of them do, however; specialized parasites can survive. Some hardy bacteria form what is called a **spore**—a covering that they retreat into like a snail pulls into its shell. Thus they can remain in a state of suspended animation, sometimes for years, until food and moisture in abundance coax them out of their shells. Viruses do not have that kind of sophistication, but there are a few that can survive dessication. They simply form crystals and stay crystallized until conditions are more favorable.

Our skin is more than a simple passive barrier, however. Spore-forming bacteria and potentially harmful viruses cannot simply hibernate on it and wait for an opportune moment to break through. Because of the layered construction of the epidermis (figure 17.2), the skin can decontaminate itself to some extent. The outermost epidermal layer, the **stratum corneum,** is composed of dead cells that are continually being added to from beneath. This layer consists of cells that have been invaded by a thick, water-resistant protein called **keratin,** which adds to their ability to resist penetration. These outermost cells are constantly being sloughed off and naturally, spores and viral crystals are sloughed off with them.

And there are still more aggressive defenses available. There are many cutaneous secretions that continually wash the skin surface and undoubtedly carry away a good many potentially harmful organisms. Also, there is a large population of bacteria that live permanently on the skin, doing no harm and taking up space that might otherwise be harboring an aggressor. All in all, as long as it remains intact, the skin represents a remarkably tough nut for a potential invader to crack.

Figure 17.1 Schematic of a skin section. The skin is probably the largest single organ in the human body.

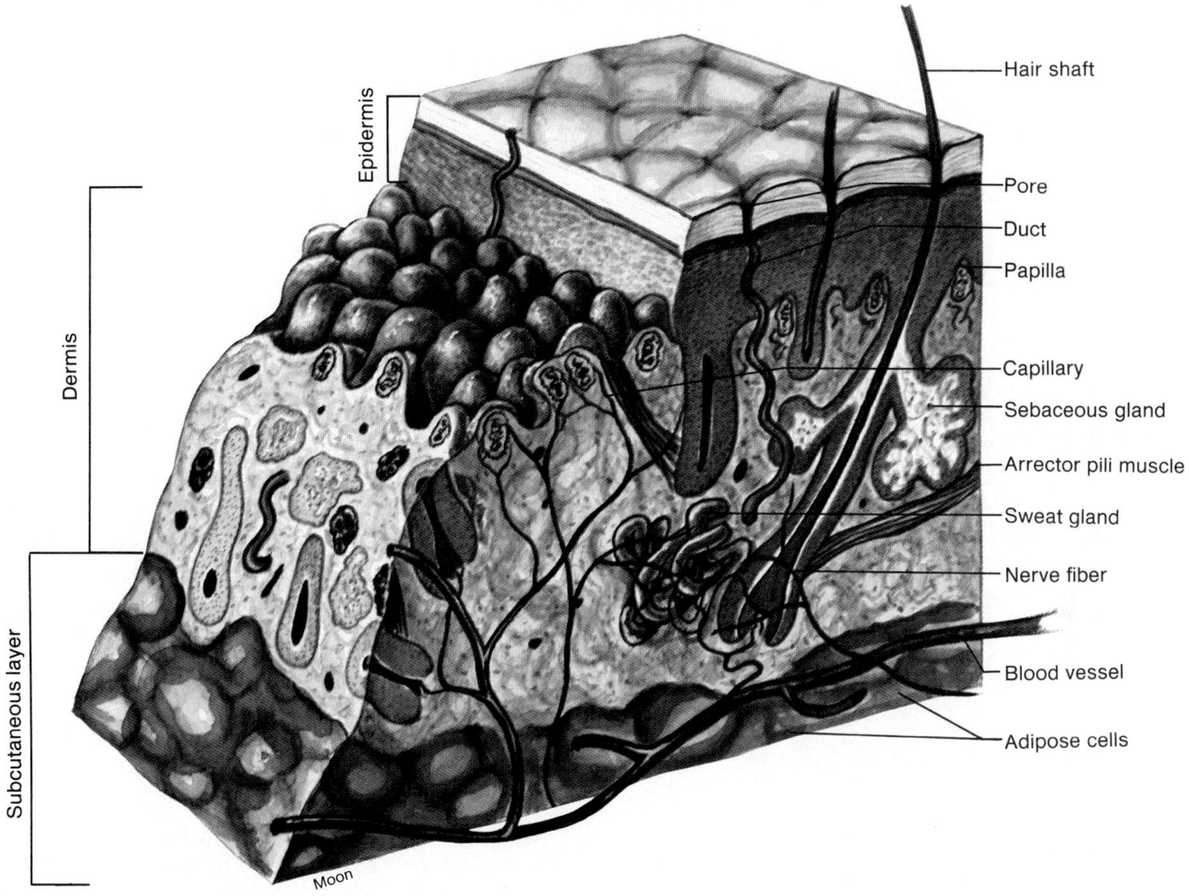

Openings Into the Body

Mucous Membranes

There are, however, gates in the fortress wall. The mouth, anus, nasal, and sexual openings represent potential weak points, since an invader could bypass the skin barrier by entering through one or more of these gates. Even here, however, there are defenses. The first and most obvious are the mechanical barriers in the form of **mucous membranes** that are present in each of these openings.

The Respiratory Tract

The mucous membranes that line the respiratory tract, for instance, are nearly as effective as the skin in resisting bacterial invasion. In addition to the mechanical barrier that they represent, the entire surface is covered with a thick, sticky mucus that traps even the most motile bacteria, while the cilia lining the inner surfaces sweep everything toward the throat where it can be spat out or swallowed.

Defenses in the Gastrointestinal Tract

The Mouth

The membranes inside the mouth are no less formidable. Like the skin surface, they represent a fairly powerful mechanical barrier and can decontaminate by sloughing off the outermost layers. In addition, saliva is constantly washing through the oral regions, picking up all kinds of organisms and getting them out of the mouth. There are a few weak points, such as the zones where the teeth meet the membranes—called the **gingival margins**—and the more delicate tonsil tissue at the entrance to the throat. These are often threatened by invading organisms, and they have special systems to help them avoid constant infection, but by and large, the mouth is a well-defended zone. Often, invading organisms will make no attempt to penetrate the defenses in the mouth and will slide down the throat with the salivary secretions.

Figure 17.2 (*a*) The various layers of the epidermis are characterized by changes that occur in cells as they are pushed toward the surface of the skin. (*b*) Micrograph of a section of skin from a thickness of the stratum corneum. This is typical of skin areas like the hand or the side of the foot where unusual wear occurs.

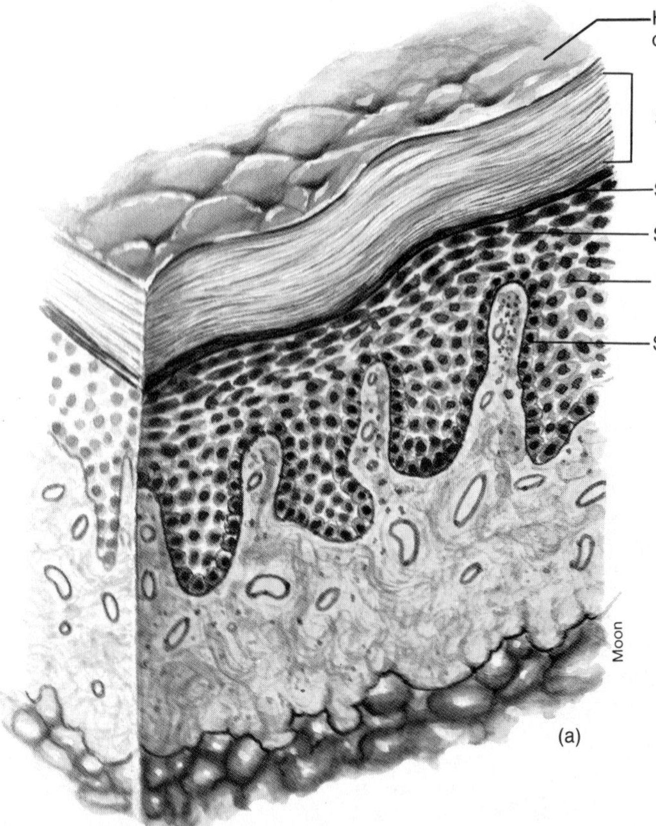

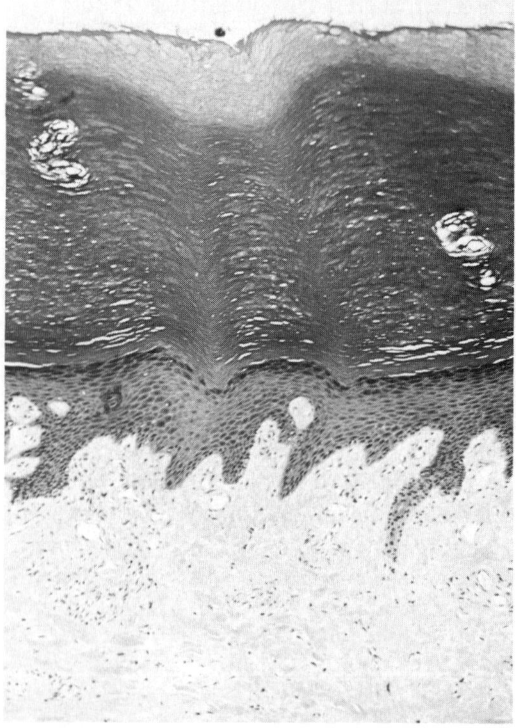

Gastric Defenses

Obtaining ingress to the body by travelling down the throat is seldom a victory, however. The stomach lining is not much of a mechanical barrier, but as we already know from chapter 15, the whole gastric interior represents a most hostile environment for anything that is living. First of all, the stomach is filled with hydrochloric acid. The pH is often as low as 1, and it is nearly always lower than 3, which is very acid indeed and rapidly fatal to most living things. For those organisms that it does not kill, there are other lines of defense. Movement of material in the stomach is quick, and nothing that enters has much time to damage anything before it is thrust summarily into the small intestine.

The Small Intestine

As is the case with the stomach, the lining of the small intestine is fairly tender and does not represent a particularly strong barrier to a determined invader. But things happen fast in the intestinal tract, and peristalsis is so powerful that nothing stays in one place for long. So rapid is the movement of intestinal contents that the population of bacteria in the lumen is not nearly as great as one might expect. Peristalsis is aided in its antibacterial activity by the thick coating of mucus that covers the interior of the tract, trapping bacteria by the millions and carrying them along with the indigestible wastes. For those few bacteria that manage to anchor themselves to the intestinal wall, there are protective antibodies in the intestinal secretions—proteins that are ready to attack and destroy.

The Large Intestine

As is the case throughout the gut, in the large intestine there is not really much of a mechanical barrier. And as we already know, peristalsis in the large intestine is not powerful, either. For the first time, invading bacteria entering the GI tract through the mouth may notice that they have found a warm, moist, nutritious environment wherein to establish a colony.

The interior of the large intestine is indeed such an environment, and its relatively stagnant nature is augmented by a constant influx of food remnants and particles that are waste products to a human but that bacteria may be able to use. Nevertheless, there are ways of keeping out the undesirables. The primary defense here is the endless billions of harmless bacteria that are already present—bacteria that are known as **normal flora** and are able to live in peace with the host. They take up nearly all the available space, which makes things hard enough for newcomers, but there's more. Normal flora are equipped to discourage competition because they have been faced with such problems before—not just from organisms entering the host with food, but also those that may make their way in through the anus. Successful normal flora deal with such vexations constantly, and they could not survive if they were not able to handle them. In their relationship with their host they have discovered how to obtain food a lot more efficiently than the recent arrivals, so they push, they crowd, and they are first in line for nutrient. Often that is enough to discourage or starve out the invaders. If none of that works, many of them have still another means of intimidating interlopers. They can secrete antibacterial materials that discourage any kind of homesteading and can actually destroy squatters that stay in the area too long.

Defenses in the Urinary and Sexual Openings

The vaginal interior is not a particularly pleasant home from a bacterial point of view, so most bacteria make no effort to set up housekeeping there. To begin with, the vaginal lining represents a mechanical barrier that is quite strong—almost as powerful as the skin. And in addition, the vaginal environment tends to be quite acid . . . not as acid as the stomach, but too acidic for many bacteria to accept. There is also a resident population of bacteria that are well-adapted to this environment and tend to make every effort to reject any new settlers. Also, there are secretory cells throughout the vaginal lining, constantly producing fluids, most of which are capable of trapping bacteria and flushing them toward the body exterior. So despite the fact that it represents an opening in the body surface and hence is a possible gateway to the interior, the vagina is not generally viewed as an easy route for bacteria to follow into the body.

The urinary tract is protected at least as well. In both sexes, the lining of the urethra is a powerful mechanical barrier capable of discouraging most potential infiltrators. The best defense here, however, is not the barrier. Rather it is the torrent of urine that periodically surges through the urethra, inundating everything within the lumen and carrying it out of the body. Since it really does not damage or destroy invaders but simply washes them away, this may seem like a casual and uncertain defense mechanism, but it is not. It's not possible to actually count the number of potential disease-causing organisms that are disposed of in this manner, but we can easily see what happens when urine is *not* flowing properly. Anything that interferes with the normal periodicity of urine flow will increase the possibility of infection enormously and urinary tract infections are common during periods of dessication or temporary kidney failure.

External Enzymatic Defenses

Enzymes, in addition to being essential catalytic agents within living systems, are also able to protect the body's interior from interlopers, and not just in the GI tract. The openings made for the eyes represent still another gateway into the interior of the human fortress. The conjunctiva (see chapter 9) is a tough barrier to penetrate, but the edges of the eyes are less so. Here the main protection is the flow of tears. Not only is this flow capable of flushing away unwanted bacteria, but present in human tears is an enzyme called **lysozyme** that is capable of dissolving bacterial cell walls, thus discouraging many bacteria from establishing residence in the vicinity of the orbit.

Inflammation

Any time body cells are injured or destroyed, the nearby tissues immediately take steps to insure that the destruction does not spread. The initial response is known as **inflammation,** and despite its protective nature, few people are thrilled to see it. Inflammation means an unattractive inconvenience at best and a miserable, aching sore at worst. But regardless of the cosmetic difficulties, the unsightly blemish of inflammation is one of our best defenses against bacterial or viral attack.

When we notice a skin area that is swelling, turning red, getting hot, irritating (pain or itching), and accumulating pus, we recognize it and pretty well know what to expect. Inflammation is a phenomenon familiar to all of us. We may not be sure what produced it, because it can be caused by many things: mechanical damage, ultraviolet radiation, cuts, burns, or the presence of a chemical irritant such as poison ivy sap. Inflammation is probably most easily defined as *the body's most immediate reaction to the death of some of its cells.* It is produced by several mechanisms in our body's nonspecific defense arsenal. Whenever cells are damaged anywhere in the body, the first response involves the release of histamine, most of which comes from nearby *mast cells.* Mast cells, you will recall

Figure 17.3 Effect of histamine on capillaries. (*a*) In the absence of histamine, junctions between capillary cells are tight, and particulate movement is restricted to the pores. (*b*) Histamine causes the cells to contract, pulling them away from one another and creating gaps through which larger molecules may filter. This reduces the effective COP in the capillary and increases extracellular fluid in the area.

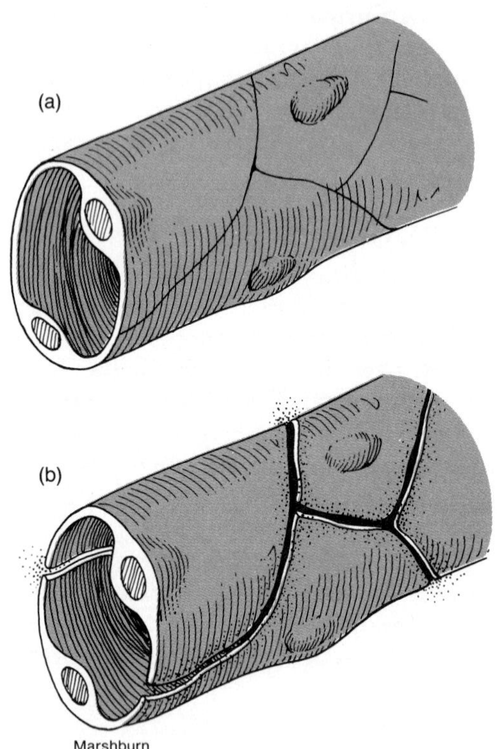

from chapter 12, are always found in close association with arterioles, and they play an important role in the inflammatory response. Damage to body cells causes nearby mast cells and basophils to release the materials stored within, including their histamine. Histamine is apparently able to shrink the cells that form the walls of capillaries, making the capillaries leaky (figure 17.3) and contributing mightily to the accumulation of fluid in the vicinity of the tissue damage.

Leukotrienes

In addition to histamines, the basophils and mast cells near the damage zone release their stores of **leukotrienes.** Leukotrienes are nonsaturated fatty acids whose total effects are still unclear. There is little doubt that they do more than we are aware of, but we know some of the things they can accomplish. They certainly are involved in increasing vascular permeability even beyond that which is caused by histamine. This increases fluid accumulation even more. They also are involved in the development of some allergic skin rashes (hives) and are probably the most important agents implicated in the constriction of bronchial tubes during asthma attacks. In addition, they seem able to attract large numbers of white blood cells to the immediate zone of inflammation.

Prostaglandins

Prostaglandins, which were first discovered in the late 1960s, are chemically similar to leukotrienes and are also deeply involved in the inflammatory process. In fact, the prostaglandins may produce more of the collective inflammatory effects—including the pain—than any other single thing. There is quite a library of information indicating that prostaglandins are involved in the production of pain. Almost everywhere pain exists one can find prostaglandins, and it is an experimental fact that chemicals able to antagonize the effects of prostaglandins will ease or eliminate much of the pain. Inflammatory responses hurt, and most workers believe that most of the pain is caused by the prostaglandins—they certainly have the ability to produce it. In addition, they apparently amplify the effects of both the leukotrienes and the histamines, since they increase capillary permeability and help to attract increased numbers of leucocytes and macrophages. They also seem to be responsible, at least in part, for increased blood flow through the damage area. The increased blood flow produces redness, heat, and swelling in the immediate vicinity. The extra fluids pouring into the area also contain clotting factors from both the damaged cells and the plasma, and a network of fibrin begins to form, sealing off the area. The exchange of materials between the inflamed area and nearby interstitial fluids is thus restricted or stopped, preventing the spread of bacteria or any toxins that may have entered.

The Development of the Inflammatory Response

The extent and speed at which inflammation takes place depends on the damage that has occurred and the danger that threatens. A cut that is teeming with staphylococcus will be attacked almost immediately. The inflammatory response will seal off the area as quickly as possible, because that particular organism is dangerous and can cause tremendous tissue destruction. An invasion by a less dangerous bacterium, on the other hand, might require hours to stimulate a complete inflammatory response, and before it is completed and the area walled off, an invasion of other body zones might already have occurred.

The most commonly observed phenomena that take place during inflammation can be explained as follows:

1. *Redness* is due to the dilation of the arterioles supplying the affected area and both neural and chemical messages are involved. As the capillaries distend with blood, the bright red of their erythrocyte contents lends its blush to the skin surface.
2. *Swelling* is related to the increased blood supply in the area and also to the activity of the chemical messengers present. Since there is lots of histamine around whenever there is tissue damage, the capillaries, in addition to being swollen with extra blood, let more and larger particles through the filter, thus reducing the colloid osmotic pressure in the plasma within. Leukotrienes and prostaglandins add their effects also, and the net result is a surge of larger-than-normal quantities of fluid into the interstitial areas nearby. This results in the puffy softness of tissue edema.
3. *Heat* is due to the increased blood flow through the area. It usually seems like the area is on fire, but in actual fact, the heat never exceeds the temperature of the body core and seldom reaches it. Our skin surfaces are usually several degrees cooler than our body interior, and inflamed areas feel hot mostly because they're warmer than surfaces nearby.
4. *Irritation* refers to both pain and itching and when inflammation is involved, we are not certain of the origin of either since they may be caused by a variety of things. Pain is probably partly due to the prostaglandins in the vicinity and partly to local nerve endings that are informing the CNS that there is damage and/or pressure in the area. The prostaglandins can attach to the free nerve endings, thus increasing the bombardment of afferent information leaving the area and entering the CNS. Much of this afferent information is in the form of pain. The itching that usually follows pain is most likely the result of other chemicals typical of inflammation that contact and stimulate touchy nerve endings.

Inflammation as a Defense Mechanism

If the injury is internal and there is no break in the skin surface, the tissues near the damage site need simply facilitate the movement of extra fluids, dissolved raw materials, nutrients, and clean-up crews to remove the useless or dead cells so they can be replaced. If, however, the inflammation is the result of a cut, the problems become a little more involved. Given a few hours, a scab will begin to form on the skin surface, producing a covering network of insoluble *fibrin* and providing a foundation for repair. But a scab takes time to form, and before it does, there is a substantial period during which the smooth, relatively impenetrable skin surface lays open to the air, and the dust floating in it.

Any such break represents a breach in the mechanical defenses of the body, and bacteria take immediate advantage of gaps in the wall to rush into the nutritious, warm interior. As soon as a cut opens up, foreign organisms begin to pour into the opening and immediately establish "beachheads" from which they can spread out and take advantage of their good fortune. Drawing both moisture and sustenance from the fluids surrounding them, they begin to establish colonies, and their numbers start to increase. The body responds to the emergency just as quickly. The reactions mentioned earlier occur almost immediately, and as fluids pour into the area, pressure naturally goes up in the interstitial fluids, which causes more fluid to enter nearby lymphatic vessels. This, of course, is good, because it tends to offset the torrent of extra fluids cascading into the area and helps to reduce the swelling. Of course, the fact that this fluid is carrying potentially harmful bacteria along with it does present a more sinister possibility. If allowed to continue without interference, it represents a threat to the entire organism. The "beachhead" may expand beyond the ability of the body to control it. Fortunately, the body has anticipated such a problem and has taken steps to handle it.

Those organisms that enter the lymphatic circulation must sooner or later enter a lymph node, where there are highly organized defenses available to prevent their spread and even to continue living. We will deal with that shortly. For now, let us get back to what is happening in the immediate vicinity of the cut and see how the body handles *that* aspect of the invasion.

Leucocyte Defenses

Most of the unusual chemicals released into the damage zone help to increase blood flow and thereby augment delivery of materials into the area by the blood. Both chemical and neural messages stimulate vasodilation in the arterioles that supply the nearby capillary beds, which increases the amount of blood each of the tiny vessels can carry. This, coupled with the leaky capillaries, means that extra fluids are available and are going to pour out into the interstitial spaces. Capillary leakiness never gets out of control—none of the formed elements of the blood can get through the enlarged openings—but much of the water and its solute contents can, and they do. As more and more water is lost, the blood cells begin to crowd

Figure 17.4 The process known as diapedesis. White blood cells, capable of ameboid movement, squeeze through openings in capillary walls in order to enter interstitial spaces.

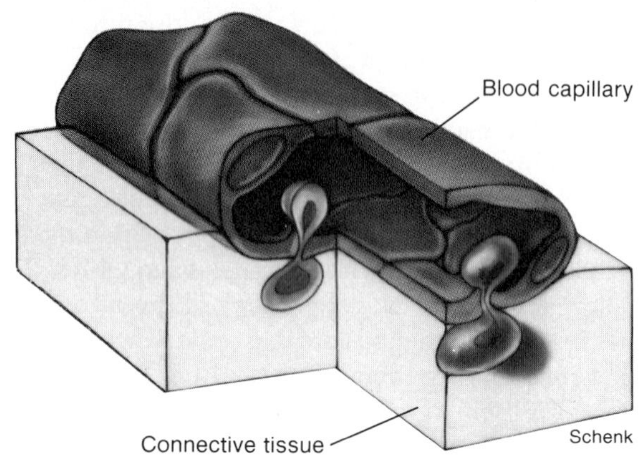

each other abnormally, and the concentration of the larger proteins left behind increases to the point where the blood begins to thicken. This has several effects.

One of them is to slow blood flow through the local microcirculation. As this occurs, the white blood cells—mostly neutrophils—are forced away from the center of the vessels to the outer edges. This is a process known as **margination,** and while its precise cause is unclear, its results are well known. As the white cells roll slowly along, they are spun gently by the passing blood and bump occasionally into the endothelial linings of the arterioles and capillaries. This stimulates a process known as **pavementing.** Sooner or later these white cells, instead of bouncing off the endothelium, will to adhere to it. When one sticks, others begin to do so as well, and the process slowly accelerates. Soon tiny bumps or nodules composed of white cells are deposited along the endothelium, and before long, the entire inner surface of the capillaries and arterioles resembles a cobblestone floor. Some of the leucocytes, possibly utilizing **hyaluronidase,** an enzyme that loosens the "mortar" between the cells that make up the blood vessel wall, are able to squeeze between the cells, a process known as **diapedesis** (figure 17.4). Once in the interstitial fluid, like an army of amebas they pour into the tissue spaces where the bacteria are massing.

Chemotaxis

This migration of white blood cells is not a haphazard or random occurrence—it does not just happen. The margination is a result of the inflammatory response, and the pavementing takes place where the white cells are needed. They are attracted to the invasion scene by a barrage of chemicals that are present in the area—a process known as **chemotaxis.** These chemotaxic compounds have many sources. Some are released unwittingly by infectious bacteria entering through the cut, some are secreted by leucocytes already in the area, others come from the interior of damaged or dying body cells, while still others are activated by the extra plasma proteins that leak out of the blood. In any case, once they are drawn to the area, most are able to sneak through the capillary walls and enter the interstitial fluids.

Now that they are available in large numbers, the phagocytic white cells promptly begin to eat the invaders, stuffing themselves until they can hold no more. At this point they die, crammed full of dead bacteria. As the conflict continues, the casualties on both sides increase and begin to distend tissue in the immediate vicinity with the thick, yellow-white exudate we call *pus.*

Walling Off the Infection Site

Eventually, cells known as **fibroblasts** are brought into the area and begin to deposit layers of fibrous connective tissue around the inflammation, walling it off. This encapsulation serves two purposes—it prevents the attacking bacteria from getting into other parts of the body and it limits the combat to the encapsulated zone.

The sealing-off of an infected area is supposed to be a good thing, and usually it is, but on occasion the process can produce pretty unsightly skin lesions. Sometimes it simply forms a blackhead (a walled-off skin lesion that is not inflamed) or a pimple (a walled-off, inflamed skin lesion containing pus). In either case, the problem is usually more cosmetic than anything else—after all, no one likes to have an unpleasant-looking swollen lump, particularly on one's face. Once in a while, however, serious difficulties develop and it becomes more than an appearance problem. Pimples generally result from an inflammation around the base of a dermal hair. Sometimes, when invaded by the bacterium *Staphylococcus aureus,* they can develop into really painful nodules called **boils.** Such nodules are usually restricted to areas like the neck and buttocks, and they are painful enough there. Every once in a while, however, they occur on the fingers, in the nostrils, or inside the ear (meatus), and when they do, they can do more than just hurt. For example, boils inside the auditory meatus can actually damage the tympanic membrane and affect a person's hearing. Even on the epidermal surface, they can sometimes get pretty serious. Rarely, two or three boils will coalesce to form a single large, very painful mass known as a **carbuncle.** Carbuncles most often form on the back of the neck and are more common in males than females.

Treatment never includes attempting to squeeze the offensive structure. You should not do it even if it is a mere blackhead, since the clumsy efforts of one's fingers usually produce a pit that can become a scar. Unfortunately, it is often difficult to know just what to do. Boils and carbuncles can be effectively handled with systemic antibiotics, but antibiotics have no effect on blackheads and pimples. As most of us already know to our intense discomfort, there really is not any treatment for blackheads and pimples. Antibiotics do not work because pimples are not caused by forces of infection. They seem to be due to the onset of puberty and the rush of adult hormones, although no one really understands why steroids should produce the rashes of blackheads and whiteheads that infest teenaged faces. The blemishes generally disappear in a year or so, after the first hormone surges are past. This does not, however, mean there is nothing a victim can do. Dermatologists insist that the severity of this so-called teenaged acne can be reduced by careful face washing several times a day. But they acknowledge that it can be a discouraging battle. Even the most careful treatment does not remove already-existing pimples, nor will it prevent the formation of new ones. It merely reduces their number and sometimes doesn't even do that. Some physicians have had good results with exposure to ultraviolet radiation, but this is not uniformly dependable.

Our Inner Defenses

But what happens when the outer defenses are breached and the invasion sites cannot be completely walled off? Or what happens if the invaders manage to break out of the interstitial fluid and find their way into the lymphatic circulation?

Defenses in the Lymphatic Circulation

Interstitial fluid drains into the lymphatic circulation. Whatever gets into the interstitial fluid, therefore, has a good chance of entering the lymph, and when inflammations occur the probability increases. The reason is quite simple. The edemas common in inflammatory reactions increase local pressure in the interstitial fluid, which means that more will be forced into the lymphatic vessels. So when there is a war going on between bacteria and our immune systems in a given area, vast numbers of free bacteria can find their way into the lymphatic circulation, where they contentedly travel in the hope of finding a quiet place to settle down and raise a colony. Fortunately for us, this hardly ever occurs. As we know from chapter 12, the lymphatic circulation is laid out in such a way that everything it carries must sooner or later go through at least one lymph node, and the body sets traps for cruising bacteria in these nodes. Ultimately, then, all the bacteria that slip into the lymphatic vessels will be filtered out of solution in the lymph nodes, and this is where some tremendous battles occur. Huge numbers of phagocytic white blood cells—especially neutrophils and monocytes—are involved in these conflicts, and they are snuffed out by the millions.

Defenses in the Blood

The lymphatic circulation is thus protected, but what of the blood? Do all bacteria that enter the blood cause a systemic crisis? The possibility certainly exists. Organisms that enter the bloodstream have by then shattered any attempt to isolate them and destroy them in detail. They can be carried to every corner of the body in a matter of minutes and whenever they find a promising, nutritious corner, they can slip out of the blood and settle down. Or, if they prefer, they can stay in the warm, food-laden blood, eating, metabolizing, producing toxins and depleting food stores intended for the body's cells. What happens then?

These organisms quickly come to the attention of one of the most relentless and vigorous defense forces in nature—the **vertebrate immune system.**

Immunity

In its strictest definition, *immunity* means "freedom from harassment," and it includes governmental harassment as well as that of neighbors. But in the biological sense it refers to the ability of a person to avoid disease by either preventing the invasion of the body by parasites or by killing any that might invade and neutralizing whatever poisons they produce. Immunity features some highly specialized operations.

Nonspecific Immunity

As one might expect, the body seldom leaves much to chance. Any system capable of operating effectively is important, so it usually has a backup— sometimes several backups—in case any part of one should fail. Our immune operations are no exception. Protecting the body from damage by outsiders is no insignificant effort, and should it fail the organism will die quickly. Hence the body has more than one method of dealing with invaders.

The phagocytic leucocytes we have already discussed (chapter 12) represent part of this systemic immunity. Their main job, as we know, is to engulf and destroy any foreign or nonfunctional object—invading bacteria, damaged or worn-out body cells, and other bits of undesirable debris. Often they have subsidiary functions that also can be quite important. **Macrophages** (monocytes), for instance, in addition to operating as phagocytic predators, can process certain foreign or invading materials to make them easier to locate, and they can actually store small amounts of iron for use by our hemoglobin-synthesizing mechanisms. *Eosinophils* can phagocytize bacteria, too, but in addition they provide an important defense against metazoan (multicellular) parasites. Generally speaking, phagocytic cells are not restricted to living within the confines of the blood. When tissue invasions occur, most of them stay there only long enough for the blood to carry them into the tissue where the fighting is going on, and then they leave. They are all part of what we call our **nonspecific immune system.**

The Specific Immune System

But there is one type of white blood cell that probably plays a bigger role in combatting invading organisms than any other. It is the **lymphocyte,** and we have not mentioned it in any detail before. Lymphocytes are the mediators of a truly incredible system within the body. They do not take instructions from the endocrine glands, and they do not worry much about the commands of the nervous system, either . . . in fact, they seem not to need any directions at all. Their objective is homeostasis, and in that, they are the same as all other body parts. It is merely that their methods involve active conflict and often cell destruction. Their efforts are directed at seeing to it that no foreign material can force a significant or prolonged change in the body's internal milieu. But unlike the rest of the body, cells of this system operate with seemingly complete independence, almost as if the entity of which they are a part had a collective mind of its own. They work as individuals, yet they operate as members of a group. The group is independent, yet it works within and for the whole living body. It is as if they represented a second entity with the human body, cooperating when necessary and yet never responsible to any mechanisms except their own.

The parallels that can be drawn between the cells of our immune system and a modern army are many. They mobilize when invaded, they utilize reserve forces to confront second invasions, they always seem to be fighting the last war, and sometimes they kill civilians—they will even wipe out entire local populations in order to save the whole organism. And sometimes they are wrong.

They are cells of the **specific immune system.**

Two Types of Specific Immunity

Most of you have already been introduced to the **humoral immune system,** although you may not realize it. Humoral immunity involves **antibodies,** and most people recognize the name, although they may not know what they are or how they work. For those who do not already know, antibodies are specific, soluble proteins that are intended to attack foreign particles, including bacteria, that might seek to enter the body.

Something else that most of you probably do not know is that humans have more than one specific immune system. In addition to our humoral immunity, we have a second one known as the **cellular immune system.** Although it often works with the humoral system and is necessary for our immunity to work at maximum efficiency, the cellular system deals with different problems and uses different methods to handle those problems. For instance, unlike the humoral system, it does not produce or use antibodies. Instead, it employs several groups of specialized lymphocytes, some of which kill or incapacitate whole cells.

An Indispensable Ability

Despite their differences, these two immune systems share one extremely important and basic ability—an ability that is utterly indispensable to a defensive army. It is one that scientists recognized early, yet one that is still not completely understood. It is *an internal awareness of self.* This is a really incredible ability when you consider that it is being attributed to single cells. Only by being able to recognize "self" can we identify anything as being "foreign," and unless the system were able to spot foreign material, it would be useless as a defender. And we know that these cells *can* spot things that are foreign, and when they do, they usually attack them. I say usually because not everything foreign is attacked, and not everything that is attacked is foreign. Nevertheless, if it is attacked it belongs to a class of substances known as **antigens.**

Antigens

Anything that can elicit an immune response must be considered an antigen. Please be sure that you read the foregoing definition carefully. The key word is *elicit.* Just being foreign does not make something an antigen. Just being attacked by the body's immune system does not mean the material is an antigen, either. To be an antigen, it must be able to stimulate the body's immune system to *initiate* a specific immune reaction. To be antigens, particles generally have to have a molecular weight of 8,000 daltons or more. Anything smaller simply will not turn on the immune system.

This doesn't mean that smaller materials cannot be attacked by our immune system. On the contrary, small particles are often involved in an immune response. But particles of a size too small to be antigenic cannot rouse the immune system all by themselves.

The only way they can become specific targets is by bonding to a larger molecule—usually a protein. The protein will attract the attention of the immune system and motivate it to produce an immune response. These responses usually include attaching an antibody to a certain specific zone on the surface of the antigen, and if the antibody happens to attach to the zone featuring the smaller molecule, the specific immunity that develops will be directed against the small particle, too. Should the small molecule be reintroduced into the body when it is all alone and unbound, it will be attacked and destroyed by the specific antibody (figure 17.5).

Haptens

Smaller molecules against which specific immunities develop are known as **haptens.** There are a lot of them, including, for example, penicillin.

The number of antigens that must exist on the earth is enough to boggle the mind—there may be no limit to the number—and every one of them can elicit an immune response when they enter the body. There is a lot we do not understand about just how the immune mechanisms remember antigens and recognize them when they appear again, but we are reasonably sure that it involves molecular patterns on the surface of the antigen, patterns known as **antigenic determinants** or **epitopes.** Antigenic determinants are the sites on the antigen to which the attacking antibody molecules attach. They are always present on the surfaces of parasites or disease-causing germs, but that is not the only place they are found. Anything that is not produced by a person is foreign to that person, and that means it has the potential to be antigenic. That includes things like animal dandruff, lipids in plant sap, or large carbohydrate structures that may mean us no harm at all—in fact, any large molecule we might encounter in our daily wanderings can be an antigen. When you recall the variations possible in amino acid sequences alone, it is hard to imagine any limit to the number of possible permutations, yet there probably is not a single one that some antibody, somewhere, cannot recognize and attack. Nevertheless, there *is* a limit to the number of antibodies a given individual can make. No one knows what that limit might be, but most workers feel that it is about a million or so. Yet research has shown that nearly all of us can respond to a lot more than a million antigens. If that is true, it can only mean one thing: individual antibody molecules must be able to recognize and combine with more than a single type of antigenic determinant.

Figure 17.5 The designing of a specific anti-hapten weapon in the body's arsenal. (*a*) The hapten "rides into" the body on a protein molecule large enough to stimulate the production of an antibody specifically designed to attack it. (*b*) The proper immune mechanism "reads" the characteristics of the protein plus the hapten. (*c*) The immune system now contains the blueprint for attacking the foreign protein or the hapten or both. Should either show up again, it would be subject to an immune response.

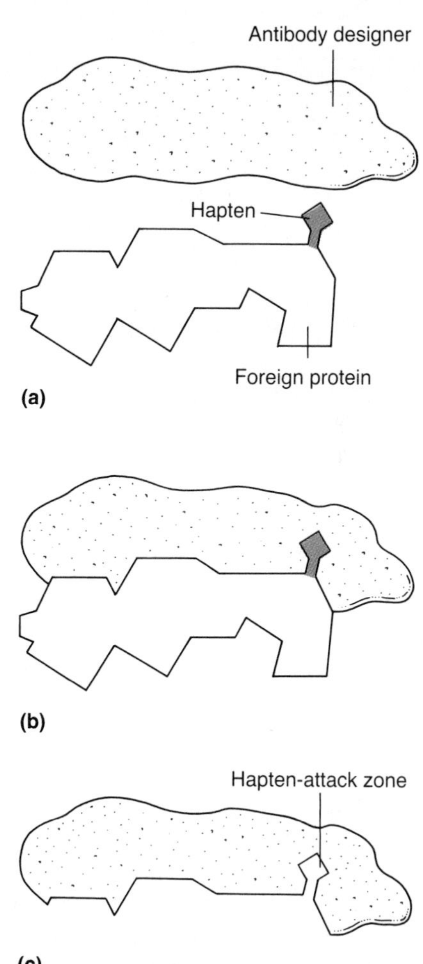

Lymphocytes

As we know, lymphocytes are the cell mediators of both cellular and humoral immunity. Like the other blood cells, they originate in the bone marrow, but somewhere along the production line there is a differentiation into two separate kinds of lymphocyte—types with distinctly different jobs to perform and distinctly different capabilities. Until the cells mature, it is not possible to distinguish between the two types morphologically, but most workers suspect that they are probably different in internal design and chemistry from the moment of their birth (figure 17.6).

Figure 17.6 The source of lymphocytes is the bone marrow. When they leave the bones they are considered "undifferentiated," because scientists are unable to tell whether they will become B or T cells. Differentiation occurs after they leave the marrow.

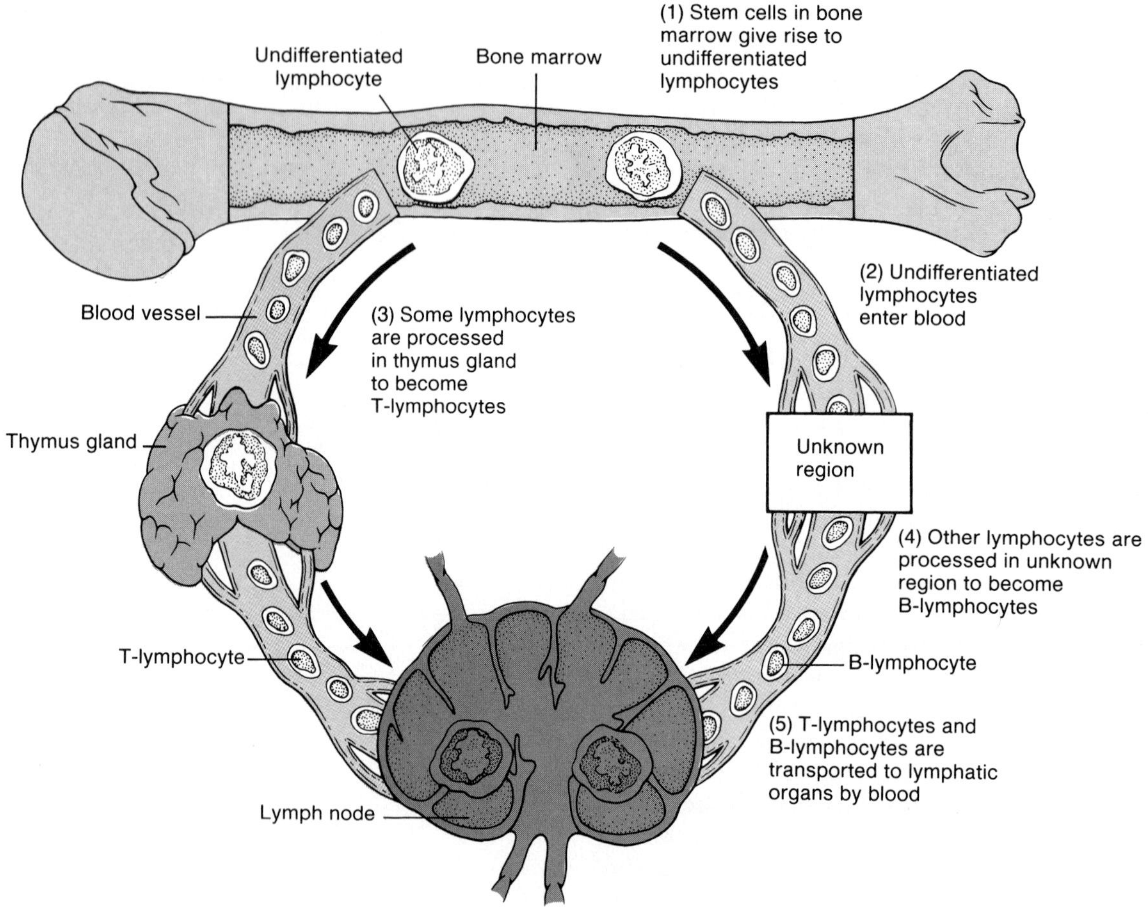

T Cells

One group of cells, after its birth in the bone marrow, migrates to the thymus gland, and there it pauses for a while. Under the influence of the secretions of the thymus gland, these cells begin to proliferate frantically, and with each mitotic division, changes occur that ultimately give rise to the **T cells** (*T* for *thymus*) of the cellular immune system. As fully mature T cells emerge from this thymic factory, they are picked up by the blood and lymph and carried to various body areas—like the lymph nodes and the spleen—where they provide a "seed" population of T cells in case of sudden emergency (figure 17.7).

B Cells

The other population of lymphocytes bypasses the thymus gland and instead heads straight for the secondary lymphoid organs, where they lie in wait for invaders. These are the **B cells** of the humoral immune system. If attacked, they are destined to mutate into the ultra-large **plasma cells** capable of producing the protein antibodies characteristic of the humoral system (figure 17.7).

The designation *B cell* derives from the fact that, in birds, these cells differentiate in a structure called the bursa of Fabricius. The bursa is a small pouch just off the lower part of the intestine in birds; there is a structure that appears functionally analagous to this in shrews and at least one of the marsupials. No such structure is evident in any of the other placental mammals; hence there is no zone in the human body where it is known that lymphocytes destined to become B cells can differentiate. No one really knows just what they do after they leave the marrow, or where they go. They may go straight to the secondary lymphoid tissues as B cells or they may first be treated in some other structure. The liver, the appendix, the tonsils, some part of the intestinal tract—even some mysterious area within the bone marrow—have all been suggested as possible zones of differentiation for newly born B cell lymphocytes.

Neither of these cell types restricts its activities to the secondary lymphoid tissues or organs. Both B and T cells are abundant in the blood, continually circulating throughout the body and looking for trouble. But there are always large populations in the lymph

Figure 17.7 The ontogeny of an immune response. The stimulus could be the entry of any antigen, toxin, virus, bacterium, etc. Once the system detects such a foreign presence, there is a prompt proliferation of the cell types as shown here.

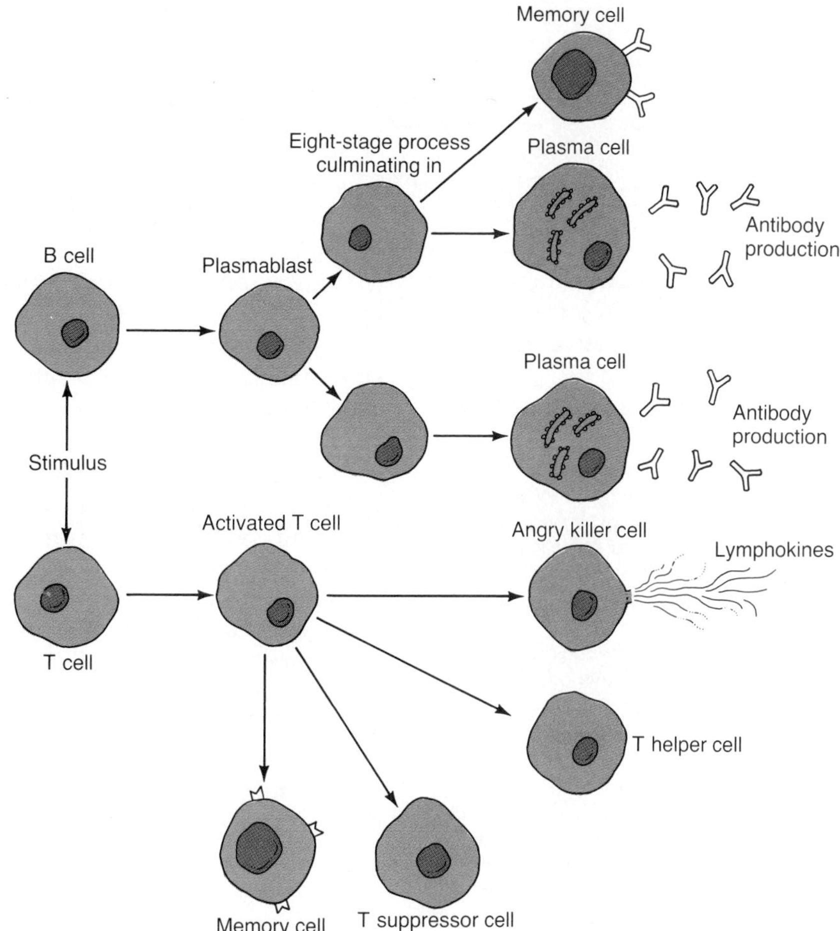

nodes, spleen, and other lymphatic tissues, because, if a systemic invasion is attempted, these are the areas where the invading foreigners will probably congregate first.

Humoral Immunity

Humoral immunity, or the antigen-mediated immune system, is implemented primarily by the B cell lymphocytes with a powerful assist from the T helper cells. The humoral system involves antibodies as aides in administering its response.

Antibodies

Antibodies are formed from a family of plasma proteins called *globulins* (see chapter 12). You will recall from your earlier reading that there are three different types of globulins—the alpha, the beta, and the gamma. Research extending over half a century indicates that the vast majority of human antibodies are synthesized from the gamma globulins, although some are made from the beta group, and once in a while an antibody from alpha will be uncovered. Therefore, in order to avoid confusion without losing accuracy, it has become an accepted convention to refer to all antibodies as **immunoglobulins (Ig)**.

The Immunoglobulins

In all the great apes, including humans, there are five different classes of immunoglobulins, and that is more than there are in any other vertebrates. These have been designated IgG, IgA, IgM, IgD, and IgE. IgG is easily the most abundant. It is the only one of the globulins that can cross the placenta and enter fetal plasma, and it is an effective protector when the body is invaded by bacteria, viruses, parasites, or some kinds of pathogenic fungi.

IgA is the second most abundant, but unlike the others, it does its job mainly in zones outside the deep body tissues. It is secreted from regions like the gastrointestinal tract, urogenital tract, and respiratory tract onto the internal surfaces of many of the tubes passing through or leading to the exterior of the body.

Table 17.1 Immunoglobulins and Their Functions

Class	Lasts in Body (Days)	Main Function
IgG	23	Fixes complement. Crosses placenta. Agglutinating antibody.
IgA	6	Present mainly in external secretions. Able to resist proteolytic activity of intestinal enzymes.
IgM	5	Largest of immunoglobulins. Restricted to bloodstream. First antibody to appear after immunization. Agglutinating antibody.
IgD	7	Unknown
IgE	8	Probably responsible for some allergic reactions.

As you know, these tubes are potential entrances to the interior of the body, and IgA represents an external defense force arrayed against any invasions via these routes.

IgA is a particularly interesting protein because it seems to be immune to the activity of many of the proteolytic enzymes produced by the gastrointestinal tract. As you know, such digestive enzymes are designed specifically to break up all proteins, yet they do not attack IgA at all. Just how IgA manages to defend itself is not clear, but workers think they understand *why* it does so.

Newly born infants have very limited immunological capabilities, and it is normally two or three days before their immune mechanisms are capable of mounting a full-scale immune response to any kind of infection. It seems that their ability to synthesize antibodies is adequate, but they lack the substrate immunoglobulins. Any resistance to bacterial invasion must therefore be provided by the mother, and this includes immunoglobulins—the substrate for the manufacture of antibodies. The immunoglobulin IgG can slip past the placental barrier while the baby is still *in utero;* hence it will be present. That provides the newborn with internal antibodies, but what about its external protection?

The milk offered by a nursing mother to her brand-new baby is particularly rich in a compound called **colostrum** that is secreted by the new mother for the first day or two It is not as nutritious as milk, but it does contain certain ingredients critical for survival that the newborn cannot yet produce in sufficient amounts. Among these ingredients is the immunoglobulin IgA. Because of its ability to avoid destruction by the intestinal enzymes, its presence in colostrum means that the infant will be able to obtain a completely formed immunoglobulin and hence will be able to synthesize antibodies from IgA to protect it against surface infections during its first few days of life.

IgM is the largest of the immunoglobulins. No one knows just why, but whenever an immunization is received, antibodies derived from IgM are the first ones to show up in the patient's blood. Probably because of its size, IgM tends to stay in the bloodstream, where it serves mainly as an agglutinate antibody, although it can activate complement to some extent. We'll have more to say about both agglutinates and complement activation shortly.

IgD is something of a mystery. It was not discovered until the early 1960s, and even today we know very little about it. Hundreds of thousands of molecules of IgD are present on the surfaces of mature B cells; hence it may be involved with antigen binding, but this is uncertain. Also, IgD seems to be involved in some allergic reactions, particularly those involving penicillin, but we know even less about this. All in all, IgD is a mysterious and little-understood immunoglobulin.

IgE is the rarest of the immunoglobulins, and it is probably just as well that it is, because it has been implicated in the development of human allergies. Like IgA, it seems to be mainly involved in reactions that occur outside the deep body tissues, particularly in the respiratory and gastrointestinal tracts. According to modern theory, it is at least partly responsible for things like hay fever and asthma.

Table 17.1 summarizes the immunoglobulins and the way they work when they are doing their jobs.

Antibody Structure

In some respects, all antibodies are the same. They are all protein, and their basic structures are similar, namely, two pairs of amino acid chains, one heavy and one light. Nevertheless, despite these fundamental similarities, there can be considerable variation within each antibody class as well as between classes. As you can see from figure 17.8, each immunoglobulin molecule has a zone referred to as a *constant zone* and a second one known as the *variable zone.* Immunoglobulin molecules that are essentially similar in the constant zones belong to a single class. For instance, all IgG molecules will have the same, or nearly the same, structure throughout the constant areas. Any variation that occurs within the IgG class does so only in the variable zones, and although there can be quite a bit of difference in these areas, as long as the constant zones stay the same, they are all in the same class.

On the other hand, if immunoglobulin molecules differ significantly in the constant zones, they are considered to belong to different classes. Between

Figure 17.8 The basic structural plan of an immunoglobulin molecule. Each unit consists of two identical light chains of amino acids plus two identical heavy chains. Note the location of the antigen binding sites.

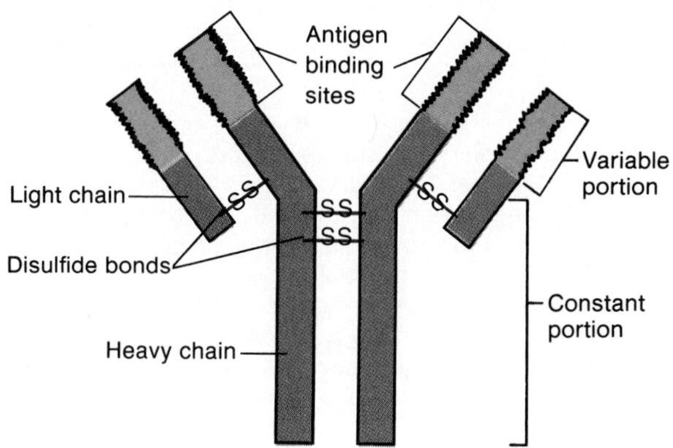

Figure 17.9 Some quantitative immunoglobulin variations. Note: The J chain is a small but dense molecule with many sulfhydryl molecules. It serves, at least partly, to hold both IgA and IgM polymers together. It is not present in IgG.

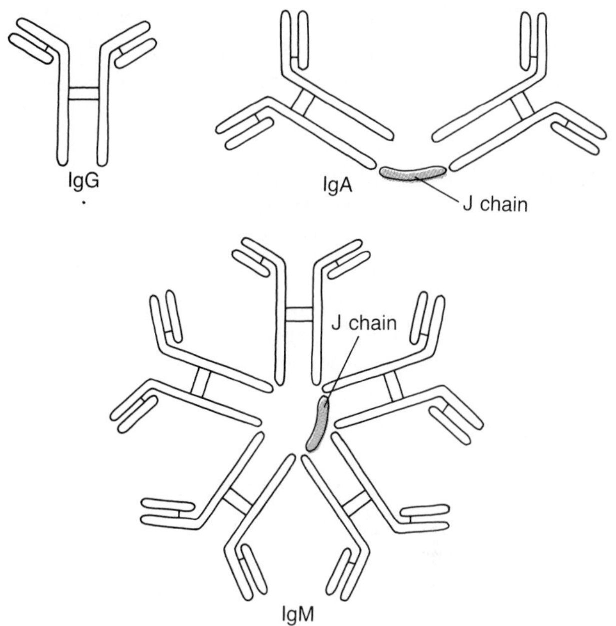

classes, there is considerable variation, both quantitative and qualitative. For example, IgG molecules consist of the basic immunoglobulin structure outlined above, which is to say, two heavy chains and two light chains. IgA molecules, on the other hand, are frequently composed of two such basic structures linked together across a third kind of chain, thus forming a *dimer*. The massive IgM molecule is even more complex. It consists of five unit structures (making it a *pentamer*) arranged in a kind of three-dimensional star shape (figure 17.9).

In addition to these quantitative structural changes, there is qualititative variation in the chemistry of the individual monomers. IgA molecules, for instance, are not simply dimers of IgG, nor are IgM molecules merely five IgG molecules stuck together. The amino acid sequence in both the heavy and light chains is different in all three classes. The constant zones of IgA molecules are quite different from those found in the chains of IgM and IgG and they, in turn, are different from each other. The fact that IgG can traverse the placental barrier and enter the fetal blood is due to some unique characteristics of the constant parts of the heavy chain, characteristics that none of the others share.

The flexibility of the variable zones apparently provides the immunoglobulin chains with their ability to adjust to the many different types of foreign molecules they are designed to attack . . . an attribute they must have, for attacking is their job, and there is no way to predict what the size, shape, or characteristics of an invader might be.

Antibody Function

Antibodies are created to make war on antigens; it is their reason for existing. They are produced in response to a given antigen and are specifically blueprinted to attack and render harmless that particular antigen. This means that each type of antibody must have some morphological characteristics that are unique, completely different from the structure of antibodies designed to handle other antigens. Antibodies that were synthesized to assault the typhoid organism will not affect the organisms responsible for dysentery or cholera, and antibodies designed to assail the latter two cannot resist typhoid. This property, known as **specificity,** is a major characteristic of the whole vertebrate immune system and is quite apparent in the properties of antibodies.

Specificity is evidently determined by the primary structure, the amino acid sequence, of the proteins of which a given antibody is made. Each antibody has zones on its surface called **antigen binding sites** that are shaped to comply with the antigenic determinant on the surface of the antigen. What happens after the antibody binds to the antigen depends on the antibody involved and also, to some extent, on the nature of the antigen.

Antibodies can mount or mediate several different kinds of assaults.

Agglutinates

They can link onto the foreign invaders, sticking to them as if they were covered with glue. Antigens are often covered with antibodies that are in turn stuck onto the surfaces of other antigens that are likewise covered with antibodies stuck onto other antigens. Such masses, called **immune agglutinates,** can, under the right set of circumstances, form globs big enough to see with the naked eye, and they promptly precipitate out of the fluids where they develop. As soon as they appear, they are promptly attacked by the phagocytic macrophages or neutrophils that abound in the vicinity of any such conflict. Such agglutinates are due almost exclusively to efforts of the IgM antibodies and usually involve only a few very large antigens (figure 17.10).

Disrupting Surface Topography

Viruses, in order to enter their target cells, must first bind to a specific zone on the outside of the cell membrane. Once anchored, they can inject their DNA or RNA into the cells' interiors. These viral nucleic acids realign cellular priorities, programing the cell to synthesize new viruses and ultimately destroying the cells involved. Antibodies disrupt this activity by changing the shape of the viral surface, thereby making it impossible for the virus to fit on the cell. By keeping the viruses in solution, antibodies render them harmless, and sooner or later they can be either metabolized or eliminated without wreaking any damage.

Figure 17.10 Formation and disposal of an immune agglutinate. (*a*) Antigens and IgM antibodies confront each other. (*b*) Antibodies stick to antigens, forming a lattice that precipitates out of solution. (*c*) The immune precipitate is engulfed by a phagocyte.

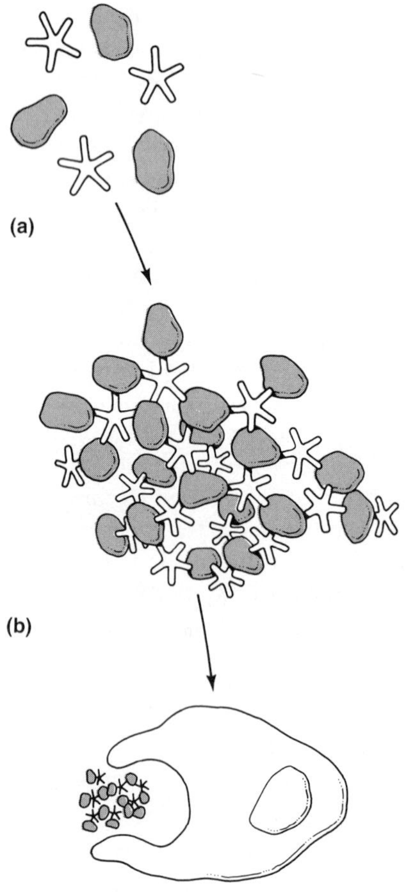

The study of viruses is extremely complicated and is well beyond the scope of this course. Nevertheless, we should be aware of the basic nature of viruses in order to appreciate the problem they present to living systems.

First of all, you should realize that viruses are unusual entities. While it would probably be wrong to state that viruses are not living systems, it would be equally wrong to say that they are alive. They apparently occupy a position somewhere in the twilight zone that exists between things that are clearly alive and those that are clearly not alive. They certainly have little in common with living things; they don't eat, they don't metabolize foods or produce energy, they cannot move or repair damage to themselves, they cannot even reproduce . . . all the operations so critical to living things. But there are some advantages to this sort of existence. Because they don't eat, inanition is no problem; they cannot suffer from lack of water or oxygen or anything else. They can even crystallize, like salt, and remain that way for years without significant changes. After all, if they are not alive, how can they die?

Even so, one should not get the idea that viruses are indestructible. Some are quite flimsy, and if exposed to sunlight or even open air they will dissociate rapidly. Some of the deadliest of all the viruses can persist only for moments outside the human body, and they break up rapidly if exposed. The AIDS virus is one of these.

When viruses mount an attack on a living system, they do so by attaching to the cell membranes and injecting their own DNA inside the living cell. Once within, the viral DNA is able to reprogram the cellular DNA, and the cellular machinery, instead of tending to its own problems, starts to make new viral DNA and new viruses. Eventually the cell fills with viruses and bursts, releasing the newly formed viruses to go and do the same thing to some other cell.

Inactivating Toxins

By combining with poisonous proteins and other toxins, antibodies can inactivate them, thus rendering them harmless.

Opsonization

Some bacteria can encapsulate themselves in a polysaccharide jacket that will resist the onslaught of phagocytic cells and thus protect the bacteria against any nonspecific immune attacks. Specific antibodies are evidently able to **opsonize** this protective layer. They alter the polysaccharide shell by attaching to the surface. For some reason, this renders it useless as a defensive barrier, thus making the cell highly susceptible to phagocytic attack.

Complement Activation

Probably the most effective method antibodies have of dealing with cellular antigens is to lyse (rupture) attacking cells by activating a group of plasma proteins known as **complement.**

At least twenty different proteins are involved in the human complement system, and although they cooperate, not all serve in the same bacteria-destroying pathways. These proteins are always present in the blood, circulating through the system again and again in an inactive form. Under the right set of circumstances they can be activated, and when they are, they can cause the death of any antibody-coated cells they encounter. Sometimes all that is necessary is for the complement to attach itself to the surface of the antigenic cells involved—an attachment which, when done correctly and on the right kind of cell, apparently makes it easier for wandering phagocytes to spot and ingest them. Other times the complemental proteins will take more drastic action, producing enzymes that can actually eat away the wall of the antigenic cell and dump out its contents.

There are apparently two different ways the body can activate complement. One way has been termed the **classical pathway** and the other, the **alternative pathway.** As figure 17.11 shows, they begin with the

Figure 17.11 Simplified model of the two complement-activating systems. As you can see, while they follow different routes, they employ the same enzymes, link to the same proteins, and wind up at the same place.

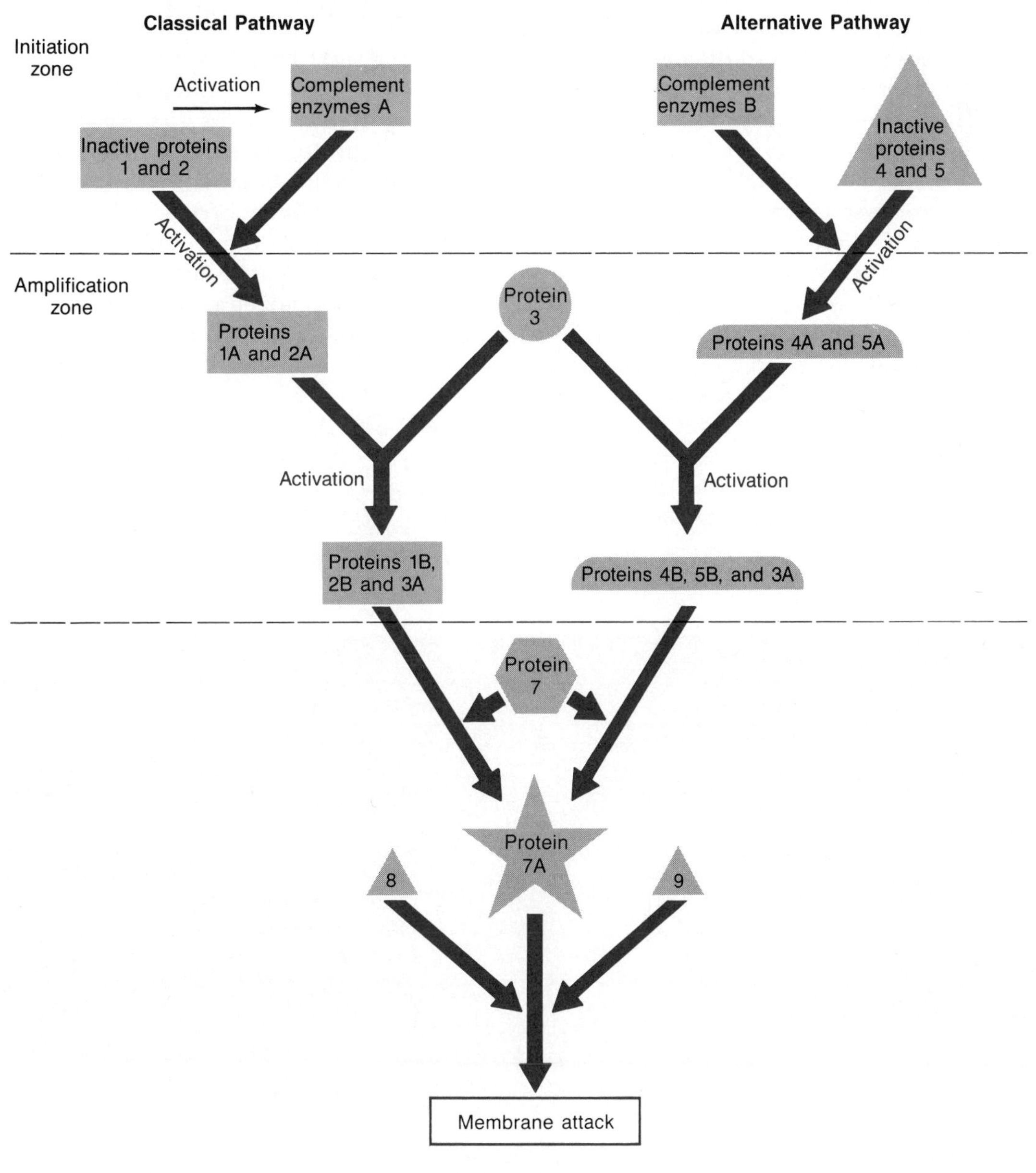

activation of different enzymes and their routes are separate, but ultimately they achieve the same goal. Just the same, they are different, and the differences are interesting.

Let us consider the classical pathway first. The classical pathway cannot operate without antibodies. It begins when an antibody attacks a bacterial cell and an antigen/antibody complex forms on the cell surface. The presence of the complex activates a second protein and the process begins. Four more proteins are sequentially turned on, and each one plays a role in the lysis of antibody-coated cells.

Activating the complement/antibody defense system is an intricate process that is beyond the scope of this book, yet we can make some generalizations to simplify it a little. For instance, once the initial step is accomplished, the subsequent steps run by themselves. The binding of the antibody to the antigen surface sets the whole thing in motion. From then on, newly activated proteins can either function as enzymes, in which case they catalyze the next step, or they can link onto some blood protein and thus produce the next compound in the series. Since each enzyme that is produced is able to catalyze more than a single reaction before being metabolized, there is a chemical amplification system at work also. It has been suggested that the activation of just one enzyme can result in the production of enough end product to lyse several invading cells.

If this process is effective and the invaders can thus be killed, all is well and good, but this does not always happen. Some bacteria and a few other microorganisms release substances that inhibit the attachment of the antibody to their surfaces, and this can slow down—even stop—the antibacterial process. The bacterial cell thus becomes immune to the classical pathway and the subsequent complement-induced lysis. Should this happen, the immune system has another way of achieving the desired ends.

Another pathway is activated by those very substances that inhibit the classical pathway. This pathway, known simply as the alternative pathway, can be triggered even in the absence of an antibody/antigen complex on the cell surface. Although different proteins are involved in this pathway, some of them are nevertheless able to amplify the response, just as some of the classical pathway proteins did. Thus, bacteria that can turn off the classical plan of attack will still succumb to the immune system. The technique they used to save themselves from the first type of attack actually started up a second type.

Table 17.2 summarizes the types of defenses antibodies can use against invaders.

The Humoral Immune Response

When the right kind of antigen gets into the lymph and makes its way to centers like the lymph nodes, some vigorous activity begins. We are not completely clear on how everything is accomplished, but we know quite a bit about what the immune systems do and when each event occurs. We know, for instance, that some antigens can stimulate B cells directly, although we are not sure just how. At other times, the antigen alone is not enough; the B cell requires a mediator—a second signal-producer—before it is able to mature fully and begin production of antibody.

B Cells and Antibody Production

First of all, the antigen must be discovered, identified, and analyzed by a particular type of lymphocyte. Only a few such lymphocytes can synthesize antibodies to a given antigen, and if the antigen failed to

Table 17.2 Antibody Defenses

Type of Action	Result	Details
Independent	Agglutination of antigens	Antibody surfaces become adhesive, sticking to antigens in groups and eventually forming large clumps.
Independent	Precipitation of agglutinates	Immune agglutinates become too large to remain suspended and precipitate out of solution.
Independent	Topographic disruption of antigens	Alters surface configuration of attacking viruses, thereby rendering them incapable of attaching to target cells.
Independent	Inactivation of toxins	Changes chemical patterns on the surfaces of some toxins, rendering them harmless.
Independent	Opsonization	Breaks down surface armor of certain bacteria, rendering them susceptible to attack by phagocytes.
Allied with complement	Lysis	Dissolves the cell wall of bacteria, spilling out the bacterial cytoplasm and killing the cell.

encounter its specific lymphocyte, there might never be any production of antibody. As it happens, however, each person has an astonishing number of lymphocytes, each of which is able to respond to a specific type of antigen.

Probably the most intimidating question that today's researchers have to answer about the development of immunity is: Since each type of lymphocyte is devoted to the production of a particular type of antibody, and since all normal humans can produce antibodies to any antigen, how can any individual have such an enormous population of lymphocytes? It seems that such a mass would inundate all other materials in the blood.

Scientists have offered at least two theories to explain this incredible profusion of leucocytes. One is known as the **somatic mutation theory.** The somatic mutation theory holds that each individual inherits certain immune capabilities from his or her parents. These capabilities represent a basic library of antibody information—a foundation, if you will —which is able to enlarge as the person grows, and thus can adapt to any new antigens that the parents may never have encountered.

The second theory is known as the **germ-line theory.** This proposal carries genetic inheritance even further than the somatic mutation theory. It suggests that each person inherits *everything* from his parents and that the gene pool inherited carries all the information necessary to code for *any* antigen that may be encountered. The biggest clinker in this second theory is, of course, the fact that many people can resist antigens that their parents never encountered and that their ancestors never encountered, all the way back to Cro-Magnon man and beyond. How many pre–20th century people, for instance, ever had to reject a heart or a kidney transplant? Yet when such organs are transplanted into people today, they are routinely attacked by the recipient's immune system.

Primary and Secondary Response

In any case, the immune response begins when the specific lymphocyte encounters the right kind of antigen. If it is a powerful natural antigen, this might be enough to begin B cell proliferation, but often it is not. Frequently a little help is required—another signal must be produced. This second signal is almost certainly a chemical one. We know only a little about this chemical, and although it has not yet been completely analyzed, it has been named. It is known as **interleukin,** and it is apparently produced by a specialized type of T cell known as a *helper cell* (T_4) after it has contacted the same antigen (figure 17.12).

Plasma Cells

Stimulated by the signals, the specific group of B cells designed to respond to that particular antigen begin to undergo rapid proliferation in the lymph nodes, differentiating through a sequence of mitotic divisions that usually ends with plasma cells (figure 17.12). It is the plasma cells that synthesize the antibody, and according to at least one theory, as each plasma cell proceeds to divide again and again, the result is production of a series of **clone groups**—populations of identical cells, all having come from a single plasma cell "parent" (figure 17.13).

All members of a clone group produce the same antibody, and each group's antibody is very slightly different from those of all the other clone groups, although all of them attack the same antigen. By the time the immune reaction has run its course, there are several variations of IgG and IgM antibody in the blood, each having been produced by a separate clone group of plasma cells. These variations differ not in the antigen that they attack, but in their technique of attack, and they provide the vertebrate body with an assault group of enormous variety and effectiveness.

Memory Cells

Not all of the cells produced by an activated B cell become plasma cells. Some of them form a special kind of cell known as a **memory cell.** It is these memory cells that retain both the identity of the antigen and

Figure 17.12 The role of the helper cell in humoral immunity.

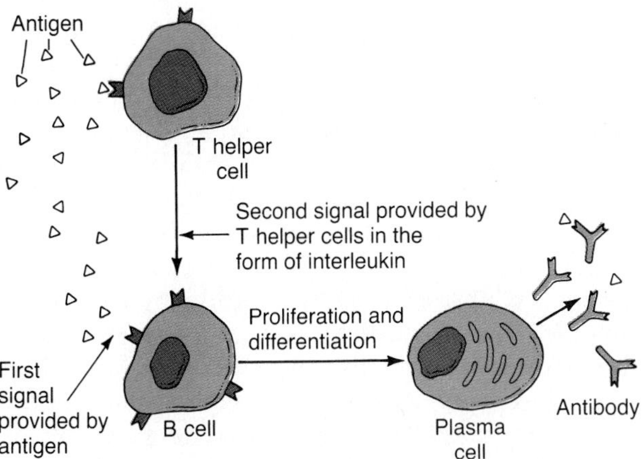

Figure 17.13 Development of a clone group of plasma cells. Because all cells in this group are derived from the same B cell, all will produce the same antibody.

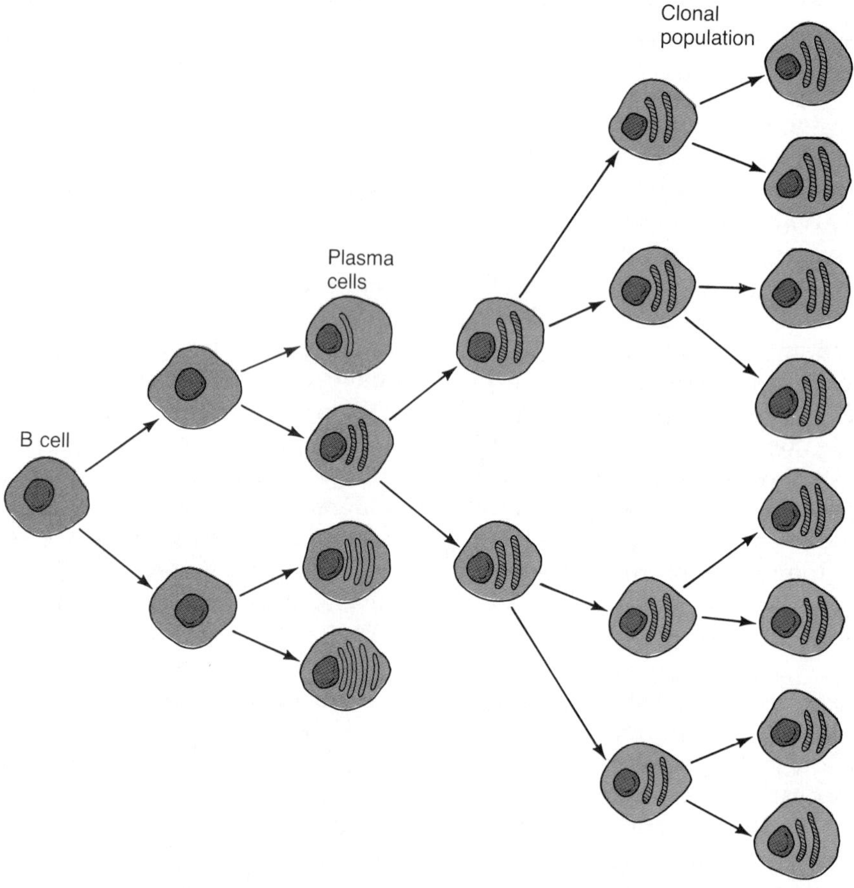

the program for producing the antibody that destroyed it. These are the cells that "remember" a disease we have already had and render us immune to subsequent attacks (figure 17.14).

Primary Response

When people are confronted with a disease they have never had before, they usually have to put up with being quite ill for several days before they begin to throw it off. It takes a little while for our immune systems to locate and identify the organism or chemical that is responsible and then several days more to design and build the materials necessary to attack and destroy the invader. The first antibodies to form are those synthesized from IgM. This may take from a few days to a couple of weeks, depending on the antigen involved, but it is usually less than a week. A short time after IgM antibodies show up, antibodies of IgG begin to appear, and they quickly become the predominant type. The earliest antibodies generally are not as effective in attacking the antigens as those produced later on, but they do provide at least a delaying action while the more effective forces are assembled. Finally, all the defensive forces will be brought together, and as systemic levels of highly effective antibody begin to climb, the disease quickly declines in ferocity and shortly thereafter disappears. With nothing to attack, there is little point in the body's maintaining high antibody levels in the blood, and they proceed to decline fairly rapidly, quickly returning to a pre-illness level. This pattern is known as the **primary immune response** (figure 17.15*a*).

With the disease beaten and the antibody levels back to normal, is a person subject to a second or third attack by the same organism? This is a reasonable question, since most of us are well aware that once a disease has been defeated and the victims have recovered, they usually have nothing more to fear from that particular disease. Generally, that's true. Recovery from a specific disease usually means that the erstwhile victim is henceforth immune to that disease. It does not mean, however, that the organisms that produce the disease will never attempt an invasion again. It merely means that there is a different response pattern the second time around.

Secondary Response

The tremendous effectiveness of the secondary immune response is due to a number of things, and they are all tied to the memory cells produced during the initial attack. The system has already been alerted to that particular antigen; it has fought and defeated

Figure 17.14 After the activation of a B cell by a certain antigen, there is a furious proliferation that gives rise to many antibody-secreting plasma cells and, once in a while, a memory cell.

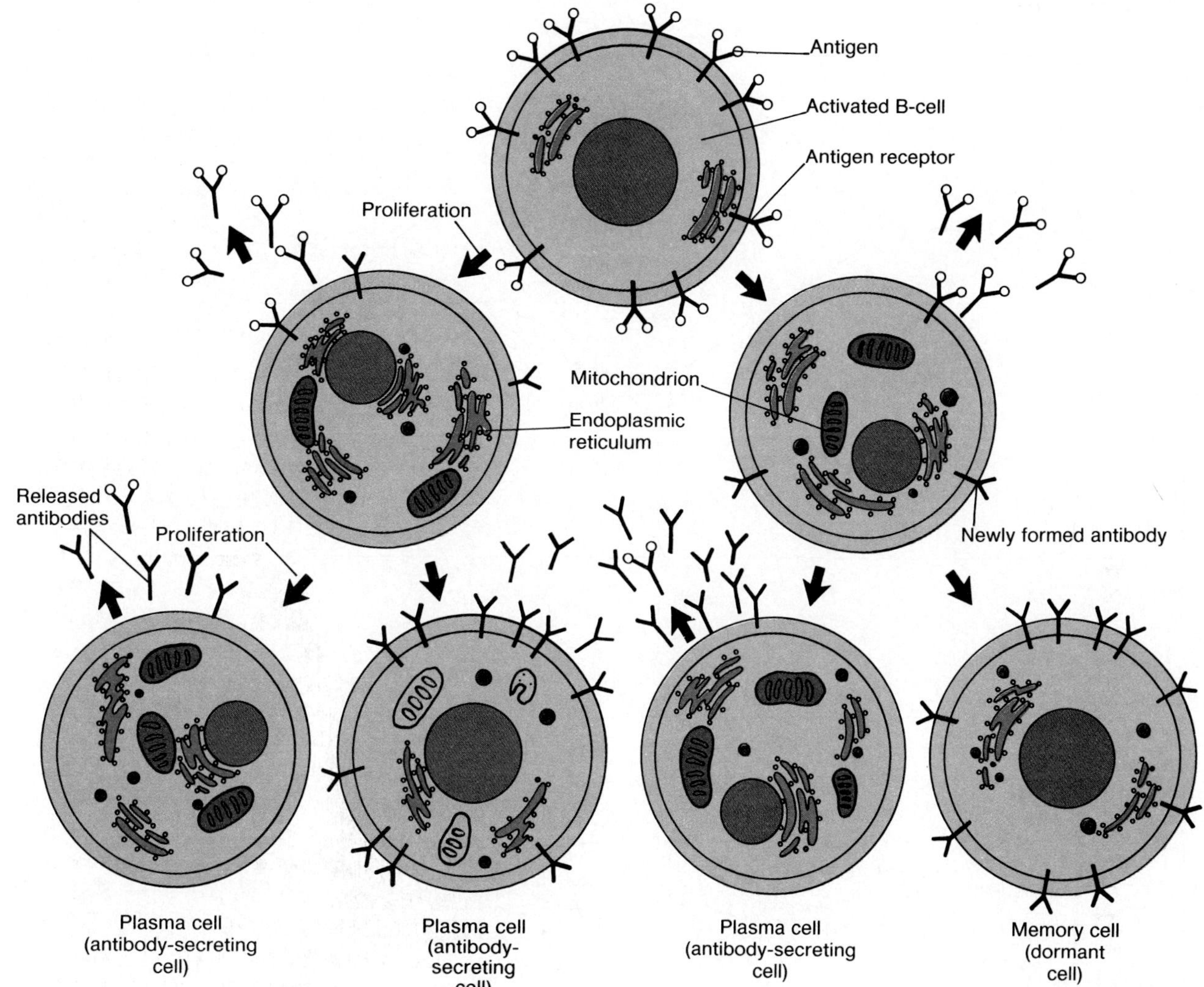

it, and the memory cells do not forget. The pattern of the antigen and the record of what materials were most effective in beating it are retained. Hence, despite the fact that antibody levels are not high when the second attack begins, a first-class defense is nevertheless ready to go. There are memory cells circulating in the blood, and since they recognize the bacteria immediately, it takes fewer of the bacteria to initiate the response. The result is that an immune response begins before any kind of beachhead can develop, and once the response has started, things happen quickly. There is no wait to develop an ideal antibody—the correct one has already been designed, and each memory cell has the necessary blueprints. The production of highly effective, specific antibodies takes a few hours instead of a few days, and because the already-sensitized cells begin proliferation immediately, the response is a great deal stronger than was the primary one. Serum antibody levels that develop during the secondary pattern can be nearly twice as high as those that were produced during the initial exposure to the antigen, and they hit these peaks usually in less than a day. As a result, the disease-causing agents are beaten off before they have a chance to become established. So rapid and thorough is the victory that more often than not, the individual involved is not aware that a conflict ever happened; the causative agents were destroyed before they could produce any symptoms. This accelerated pattern is known as the **secondary immune response** (figure 17.15*b*).

A Mnemonic The pattern has been compared to the mobilization of a reserve army force, and maybe that is a good way to remember it. Reserve forces are the so-called weekend warriors who have normal civilian jobs for most of their lives but have spent some time training for military activity should they ever be needed. It is an important auxiliary to the regular army because many of the preliminaries—including

Figure 17.15 Schematic diagram of the primary and secondary immune responses.

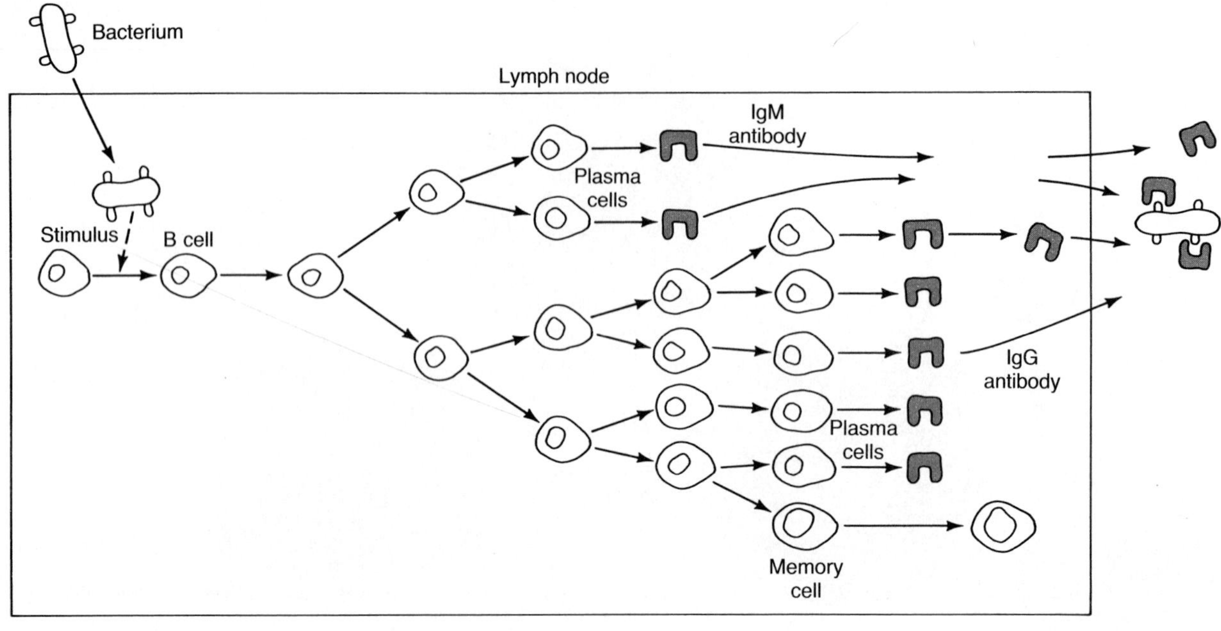

the wash of paperwork—have already been completed, and it is these operations that consume the time. Medical examinations, selection of a specialty, creating new units and providing the soldiers to fill them and officers to command them requires months—sometimes years. But once it is done, once all the basic and specialty training and processing has been completed, the people can be released to their civilian jobs. Like the memory cells, they have not forgotten their military operations. If an emergency for which they were trained should arise, it is not necessary to go through all the laborious, time-consuming preliminaries. That has already been done. The knowledge of where each person has to go and what each will do is already locked away in the memory banks of the military computers. The soldiers are trained and they know their jobs. Preparing a reserve unit for active duty requires a few weeks instead of a few months, and the savings in time can make the difference between victory and defeat. Figure 17.16 and table 17.3 show, in summary outline, the activation of a humoral immune response.

Figure 17.16 (*a*) After digesting antigen-bearing agents, a macrophage displays antigens on its surface; (*b*) T helper cells become activated when they contact displayed antigens that fit their antigen receptors; (*c*) activated T helper cell interacts with B cell and stimulates it to proliferate.

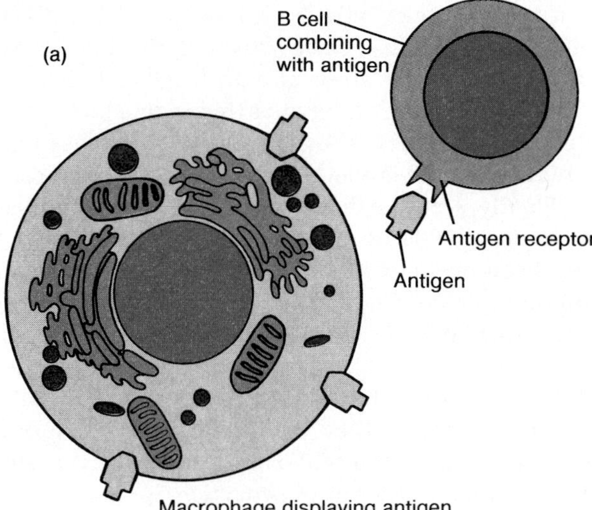

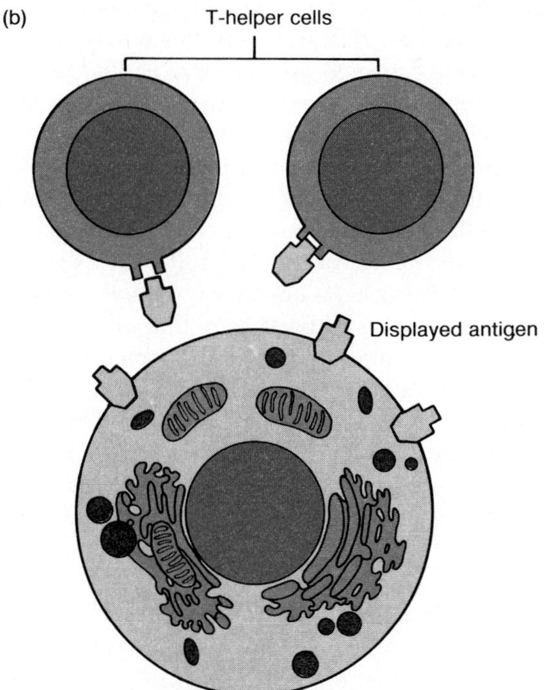

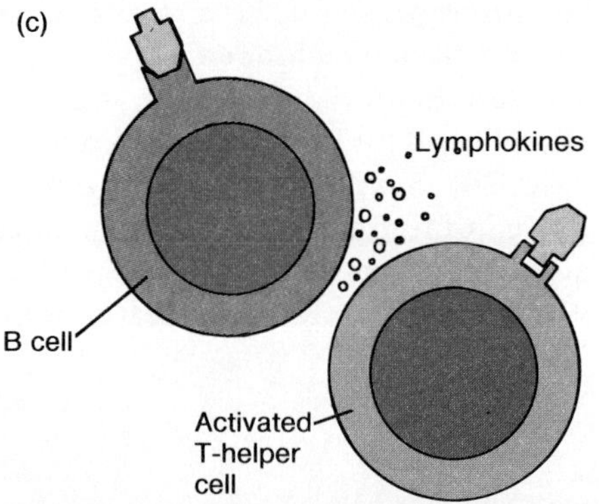

Table 17.3 Steps in the Production of Antibody to a Specific Antigen

1. Antigenic particles enter the body and attract the attention of phagocytic cells and B cells.
2. B cells approach the surfaces of the particles and attach to the antigens. This is the *first signal.*
3. Macrophages ingest particles and display the antigenic portions on their surfaces.
4. T helper cells come into contact with antigens displayed on macrophage surfaces and are activated.
5. Activated T helper cells converge on the B cells that have already contacted the antigens and have received the first signal. This convergence of the two cell types constitutes the *second signal.*
6. The T helper cells release the compound interleukin which stimulates the proliferation and differentiation of the B cells, some of which will become active plasma cells and others, memory cells.

Limitations of Humoral Immunity

Despite its effectiveness, the humoral immune system is not omnipotent. Antibodies can only attack foreign particles if they can reach them, and sometimes they are not able to. Viruses, as we know, live *within* cells, and there are several pathogenic bacteria that also do this. Hiding inside a living body cell works, and as long as parasites remain inside the protective envelope of a host body cell, they are safe from assault by antibodies simply because the antibody cannot get at them.

Some bacteria, such as the one responsible for tuberculosis, have carried this specialization to an incredible degree. Tuberculosis-causing organisms actually hide from antibodies by entering macrophages. Somehow they are able to resist the internal assaults of the macrophages and instead of dying, they thrive. They use the interior of the macrophage as a breeding ground and proliferate with great vigor inside phagocytic cells that are supposed to kill bacteria.

Yet even these parasites are seldom successful—more often than not our bodies are able to fight them off. We know viruses can be beaten because we have all survived repeated attacks of viral diseases (colds, flu, measles, etc.), and we were not helped by antibiotics because there are no antibiotics that will attack a virus. Yet if these parasites are immune to attack by systemic antibodies, what is it that protects us? What is left?

The cellular immune system is what's left, and when parasites hide inside body cells, it comes into play.

The Cellular Immune System

The response patterns of cellular immunity are similar to those of the humoral immune system, although the methods and targets are quite different because the system deals with different problems. As its name implies, this system is mainly concerned with the destruction of *cells.*

Once a cell has been invaded by a parasite, alterations begin to occur. In the beginning, only the cell's construction priorities change, and some internal alterations are made. If that were *all* that happened, the parasites would probably get along beautifully. But sooner or later these internal shifts lead to changes in the molecular patterns on the cellular surface, and that is when the fighting starts. Parasitic attack is not, of course, the only thing that can alter the cellular surface patterns. Sometimes cells will spontaneously develop a flaw in their DNA and cell proliferation may suddenly run wild, threatening the health of the whole organism. Fortunately, such flaws nearly always change the topography of cell membranes, and anything that alters the molecular patterns on the surface of a body cell results in that cell being identified as foreign. That stimulates the cellular immune system, and the slightly changed cells become subject to attack and destruction. Obviously, therefore, the cellular immune system is of vital importance in defending against certain kinds of cancer, viral diseases, and assaults by parasitic protozoans, fungi, or other intracellular intruders.

T Cells and Cellular Immunity

Cellular immunity is mediated by the small lymphocyte known as the T cell. T cells are identical to B cells in appearance, but their chemistry and function are quite different. Even when stimulated by the proper antigen, T cells are incapable of becoming plasma cells. Hence they can neither synthesize nor utilize antibodies in their wars against foreign invaders (see figure 17.7 and accompanying text). They have, nevertheless, very effective ways of dealing with enemy troops.

There are several different kinds of T cells. The most abundant type is known as the **killer** or **K cell.** There are also **helper cells** that are essential as stimulants of the cellular response; **suppressor cells;** and a fourth, recently discovered group known rather picturesquely as **natural killer cells.** Just where these latter come from no one knows, but their surface membranes have characteristics very similar to those of monocytes, an observation that suggests maybe monocytes have even greater versatility than we have already recognized.

The *killer cells* are the ones that physically attack the target cells. Researchers in immunology often refer to them as "angry" killer cells because of the ferocity and relentless nature of their attacks.

Helper cells—also known as **T_4 cells**—are so called because they identify foreign antigens quickly and then induce other cells, both B cells and K cells, to come to full activity. Once activated, the T_4 cells can amplify the effectiveness of both B cells and K cells.

The *suppressor cells* have, as their name implies, an effect opposite that of the helper cells in that they tend to reduce the effectiveness of an immune response.

Finally, we have the *natural killer* or *NK cells.* These are unusual cells, and they could almost be considered a composite of many entities within the human immune system. Classifying them was difficult, and in fact their present classification may not be exactly right. They are not looked upon as B cells because they carry no immunoglobulin on their surfaces as all B cells do. Although they look quite a bit like monocytes, they are not thought of as macrophages because they are apparently not phagocytic.

Thus they became T lymphocytes mainly by default. Once the B cells and phagocytes were eliminated, only the T cells were left. The newly discovered T cells were assigned the adjective *natural* to separate them from K cells, and they are called killers because that's what they do—they kill cells by inducing lysis (bursting) in a manner that is only partially understood. In this respect, they are functionally similar to the K cells, but there are some important exceptions. First of all, the victims of NK cell attack are not just virus-containing cells or other types susceptible to K cell attack, but also tumor cells that are only mildly "foreign" and hence often do not attract the attention of the mainline cellular immune system. Secondly, the method by which lysis is achieved is different from that employed by the K cells. Some workers feel that NK cells may play an enormously important role in the suppression of potentially malignant diseases in humans.

Immune Responses

The primary response of the cellular immune system is, like that of the humoral system, relatively subdued and slow to get under way. Foreign surface patterns on a particular cell or population of cells is usually first detected by macrophages or K cells, and a chemical warning is immediately sounded.

If a K cell makes the initial discovery, it grips the antigenic cell firmly and for several hours a relentless attack takes place. The membrane of the antigenic cell gradually is altered until finally it ruptures, dumping out the cellular contents and killing the cell. Throughout the attack, the K cell releases minute quantities of soluble proteins known collectively as **lymphokines.** T cells produce a fairly large variety of lymphokines, and their release can have a variety of effects. Some of them attract large numbers of neutrophils and macrophages to the combat zone, while another type increases the activity of the phagocytes already there. Still another lymphokine prevents any phagocytes from leaving the area and hence is known as the **migration inhibitory factor.**

Despite the relentless assault carried on by the first K cell to encounter the antigen, it is important for us to realize that the cellular system cannot become fully active without the helper cells. Locating foreign cells and identifying their antigen is merely a first warning. Without the T_4 cells, the K cells can neither proliferate at high speed nor attain maximum efficiency.

Interleukin and the T_4 Helper Cells

The attack of the cellular immune system is augmented by the activity of the T_4 (helper) cells which, working in concert with certain successful macrophages, can magnify the activities of the cellular immune system. Once a macrophage has ingested an invader, it has two means of stimulating the cellular immune system:

1. It displays samples of the invader's antigen on its own surface, and when T_4 cells come into contact with such a macrophage, they immediately combine with the surface-antigen display, thus becoming sensitized to the antigen. Large numbers of helper cells can be activated in this manner.
2. The macrophage may release a compound known as **interleukin-1,** which is carried to the lymph nodes via the circulation. Interleukin-1 is also capable of activating the T_4 cells, this time in the lymph nodes.

These T_4 cells have become sensitized to the invader, and they can now synthesize and release a compound known as **interleukin-2,** which has the ability to make lymphocytic T cells aware of the invaders no matter where they are. Interleukin-2 may be identical to the lymphokine known as **mitogenic factor.** In any case, it carries all the information regarding the nature of the antigenic cells. Under its influence, T cells can be stimulated to proliferate, and they are specifically sensitized to the invaders even if they and the invaders are widely separated (figure 17.17).

Stimulated by interleukin-2, the T cell lymphocytes promptly begin to differentiate and proliferate. Most of them develop quickly into K cells, but not all of them; some differentiate into memory cells similar to those produced by the humoral immune system. Now they leave the lymph nodes and, fully activated, they enter the circulation and are carried to the combat zone. When they find the target cells, K cells attach to them and do one of three things. They either kill them by causing them to burst (lysis), they release more lymphokines, or they do both (table 17.4).

The result of all this diverse activity is a slowly amplifying defensive response to invasion, and presently large numbers of T cells of all kinds are involved in assaulting and killing the foreigners, while equally large numbers of phagocytes ingest the dead and/or dying and generally clean up the mess.

Sometimes, particularly if the population of foreign cells is large, the K cells activate the most drastic weapon of all. They release large quantities of lymphokine toxins throughout the area. These are tremendously powerful toxins, strong enough to kill all the cells they contact without any help from the phagocytes, and they are usually not released except in cases of massive invasion. We will have more to say about this in the section devoted to allergies.

Blood Typing

The ABO Blood Groups

On the surface of each of the erythrocytes in our bodies are places where specific antigens may or may not be present. In humans there are two types of antigens, called **agglutinogens,** that are responsible for producing our major blood types, and these are genetically inherited. Some people possess the first type, which is known as the **A agglutinogen,** and hence have been assigned to blood group *A*. Others possess the second group, which has been designated the **B agglutinogen,** and they belong to blood group *B*. A third group of people have both of these antigens on their erythrocytes and therefore belong to blood group *AB*, while the fourth group possesses neither. Since this latter group has no such antigens—that is, there are zero or 0 antigens present—these people are assigned to the blood group known as *O*. This classification is known as the **ABO blood grouping system,** and it is of great concern when someone needs a transfusion.

When in need of blood, a patient cannot be given any that just happens to be handy. Not everyone has the same agglutinogens on their erythrocytes; thus they present some difficulty when a patient needs blood from an external source. The problem is, as we will see, an immunological one.

People possessing blood types A, B, and O have, in their systems, groups of antibodies called **agglutinins** that are specifically programed to attack

Figure 17.17 Diagrammatic summary of the activation of a cellular immune response.

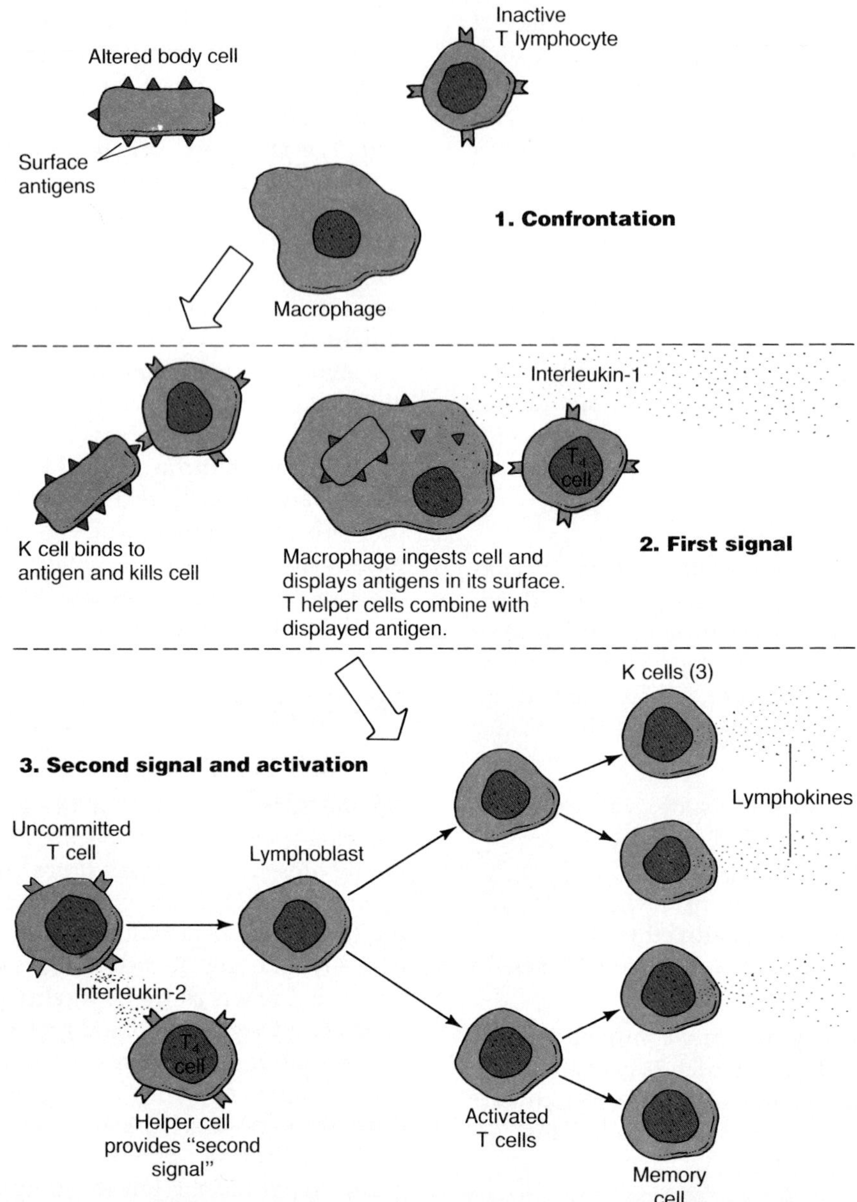

Table 17.4 Steps in the Activation of the Cellular Immune Response

1. Antigen is identified on the surface of a cell by T lymphocytes or by wandering macrophages, or both.
2. K cell binds to the antigen and kills it. Macrophage ingests the debris, including the antigen, and displays the antigen's molecular code on its surface. If a T_4 helper cell contacts these codes on a macrophage, it becomes sensitized. This represents a *first signal.*
3. The macrophage can also release interleukin-1, which is able to carry information about the antigen to the lymph nodes. Here it is presented to other T_4 cells. This is an alternate way of presenting the *first signal.*
4. T_4 helper cells provide the *second signal,* this time in the form of interleukin-2, stimulating the proliferation and activation of K cells and dormant memory cells.
5. K cells leave lymph nodes and travel to target cells, where they either release lymphokines or cause the lysis and death of the target cell.

whichever of the blood agglutinogens they do not have. The possession of these agglutinins is genetically determined (figure 17.18).

Because no one possesses an agglutinin that will attack his or her own blood cells, the question of what "type" blood a person had was of no importance at all until medicine became sophisticated. It was far more common to remove a little blood to "balance the humors" than to provide any. Transfusions, however, are commonplace today, so typing a person's blood is important, especially if that person plans to enter a hospital for some surgical procedure. Obviously, people with anti-B agglutinins in their blood cannot be given transfusions from others who have the B ag-

Figure 17.18 The four blood "types" and the surface antigens with which each is associated. Note that persons lacking a specific antigen *always* possess the antibody capable of attacking the one they lack.

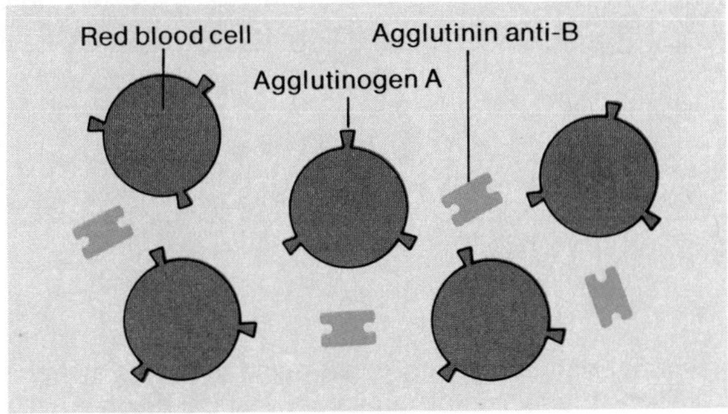

Type A blood

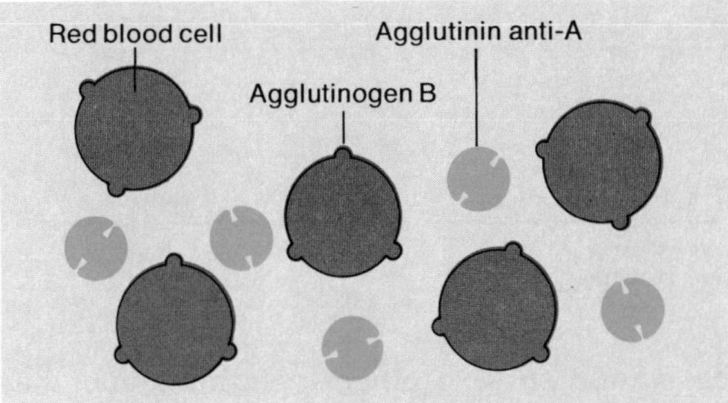

Type B blood

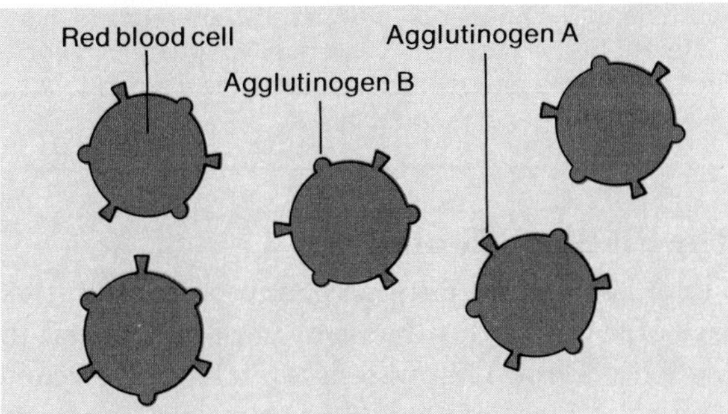

Type AB blood

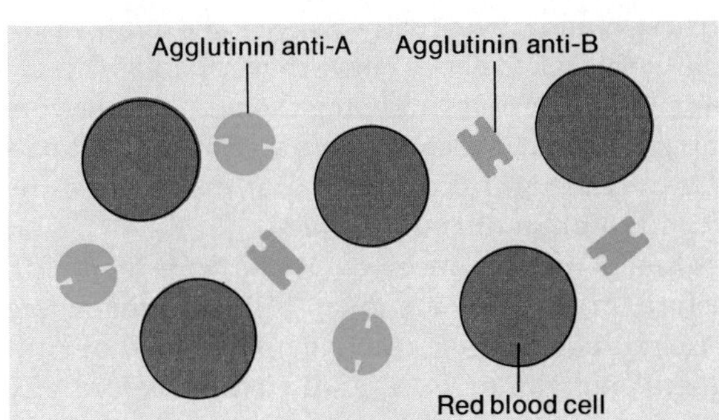

Type O blood

Figure 17.19 (*a*) If red blood cells with agglutinogen A are added to blood containing agglutinin anti-A, (*b*) the agglutinins will react with the agglutinogens of the red blood cells and cause them to clump together and precipitate out of suspension.

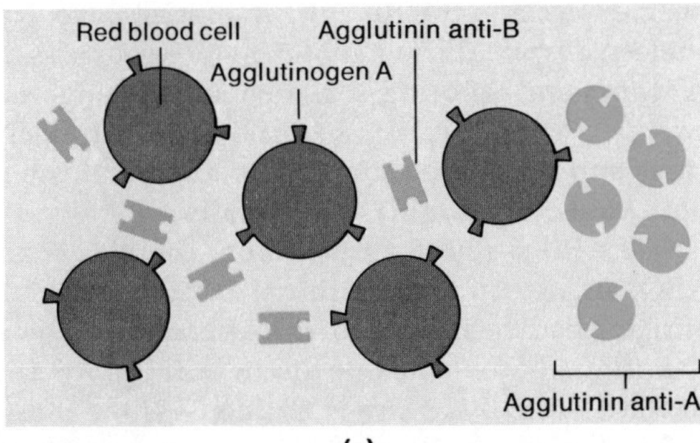

(a)

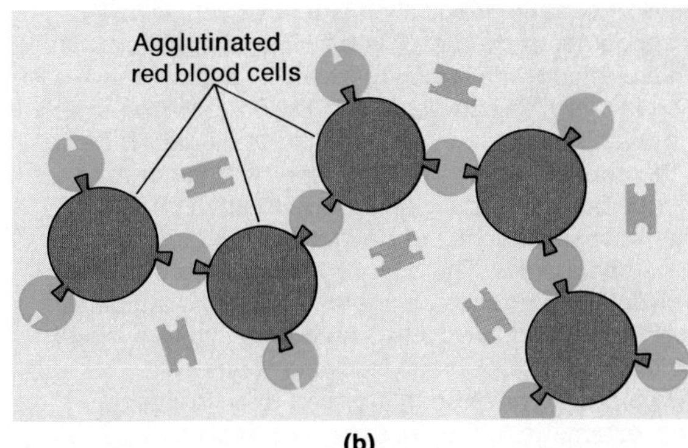

(b)

glutinogen on their erythrocytes. By the same token, an individual with anti-A agglutinins cannot accept blood from a person with the A agglutinogen.

Acquiring the Antibodies

Unlike the development of immunity to infectious diseases, it is not necessary for a person to be exposed to an ABO agglutinogen to develop antibodies against it. People are born with whatever antibody is appropriate (figure 17.18). The antibodies begin to increase in concentration shortly after birth, and they reach their highest concentration in the blood at the age of about 8, after which they begin to decline, although they never actually disappear. People with type A blood will possess anti-B agglutinins, albeit in gradually decreasing numbers, for the remainder of their lives. It is this natural possession of antibodies that is so critical when people are given a transfusion of blood. The wrong type could kill them.

If a person with type A blood (type A agglutinogen on the RBCs, anti-B agglutinins in the plasma) were to be given type B blood (type B agglutinogen on the RBCs, anti-A agglutinins in the plasma), the agglutinins in the recipient's blood would stick all over the outside of the erythrocytes everywhere the agglutinogen was present (figure 17.19). Other eryth-

Table 17.5 ABO Blood Group Summary

Blood Type	Person Has Agglutinogens	Person Has Agglutinins	Can Give Blood to Types	Preferred Donor Type	Acceptable Donor Type
O	none	anti-A and anti-B	O[1], A, B, AB	O	O
A	A	anti-B	A, AB	A	A, O
B	B	anti-A	B, AB	B	B, O
AB	AB	none	AB	AB	O, A, B, AB[2]

1. Universal donor
2. Universal recipient

rocytes would stick to other agglutinins and they would all eventually stick to each other, forming large clumps of red cells.

These clumps eventually become massive—easily visible to the naked eye— hence they can lodge firmly even in large arterioles and plug them up. If this were to happen in a vital organ, whole sections of that particular organ might die, and if that organ were the heart or the brain, it could be fatal.

When a person receives blood from a donor, therefore, great pains are taken to insure that there will be no such adverse reactions. The blood of both recipient and donor is carefully typed before any transfusion is attempted, and hospitals insist that different types not be mixed except in dire emergency. Table 17.5 summarizes the ABO blood groups and how they intermix.

In cases of extreme medical emergency such as one might encounter in combat, it is possible to provide blood of a different type with impunity if care is taken. If the situation is really life-and-death and the correct type simply is not available, a person with, for example, type AB blood could theoretically accept blood from any donor or a type O donor could theoretically give blood to anyone. The important considerations are the *donor's antigens* and the *recipient's antibodies*. The donor's antibodies are of relatively little importance as are the recipient's antigens. Possibly the easiest way to explain why this is true would be to offer the concept in the following way:

When people have been exposed to an antigen and become immune to it, they possess two important items in their blood that can deal with that antigen should it ever show up again: the ability to immediately recognize that antigen, and the blueprints for an effective antibody to combat it. However, until something stimulates the system to begin production, only a few of the antibodies are actually present in the plasma. As long as the blueprints are present, the shortage of antibody is no handicap, because the blueprints can be read easily and fresh antibody can be quickly produced. All this changes when blood is transfused into someone else. There are only very few antibodies actually present because the system has not been threatened, and, because the recipient's body does not know the donor's cellular "language," the blueprints cannot be read and no fresh antibodies can be made. The few antibodies that *are* present in the donor's blood are diluted in the recipient's plasma to a point where they are harmless. It is reasonable, therefore, to consider donor's antibodies to be of limited significance. The concentration is too low to worry about, and a recipient's immune system certainly is not going to produce any. Similarly, the recipient's antigens wouldn't mean anything either, because no matter what they were, the donor's blood does not possess enough antibodies to be a threat and the only system able to read the blueprints is in a different body. That's why a person with type O blood (no antigens, both antibodies) can safely give blood to a type AB (both antigens, no antibodies).

The Rh Blood Groups

There is a second antigen group present on the surface of erythrocytes that is of importance, and that is the **Rh system.** This system is a relative newcomer to medical science. The ABO system was uncovered in 1900, then nearly forty years elapsed before the Rh system was discovered. Probably the biggest reason for the huge hiatus is that anti-Rh antibodies, even under the most ideal conditions, are not spontaneously present in a person's body until they have been exposed to the Rh antigen at least once. Nevertheless, despite the fact that it is not as obvious as the ABO system, ignoring it can be just as dangerous. It was discovered, in fact, because of an extremely serious and once-lethal hemolytic disease of the newborn called **erythroblastosis fetalis.**

The Rh system is much more complex than the ABO; at last count some thirty different types of Rh antigen had been identified. Apparently, however, the original one—the one discovered in 1939 and referred to usually as the D antigen—is the most significant clinically. It may or may not be present on the outer surface of erythrocyte membranes. Those people who have the antigen are designated *Rh positive*, while those lacking it are *Rh negative*. Either situation can exist in any of the normal ABO conditions. For example, people can be type O positive or type O negative, type B positive or type B negative, and so on. Rh positives quite naturally will not possess the anti-Rh antibodies, nor will they possess the ability to produce them. Those who lack the antigens, however, while they do not naturally have anti-Rh antibodies in their blood, do have the ability to make them once they are exposed to the antigen.

Obviously, exposure to the Rh antigen during a transfusion will most assuredly sensitize a person and begin production of an immunity to Rh antigens. Yet

Figure 17.20 (*a*) If an Rh-negative woman is pregnant with a Rh-positive fetus, (*b*) some of the fetal red blood cells with Rh agglutinogens may enter the maternal blood at the time of birth. (*c*) As a result, the woman's cells may produce anti-Rh agglutinins.

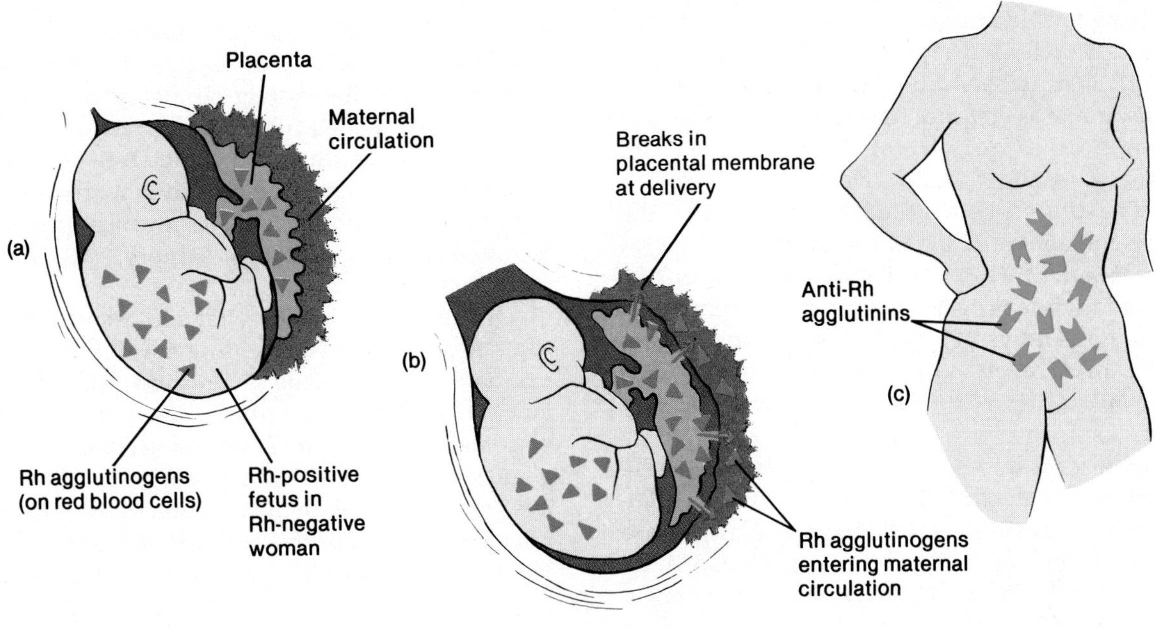

Figure 17.21 If a woman who has developed anti-Rh agglutinins is pregnant with an Rh-positive fetus, agglutinins may pass through the placental membrane and cause the fetal red blood cells to agglutinate.

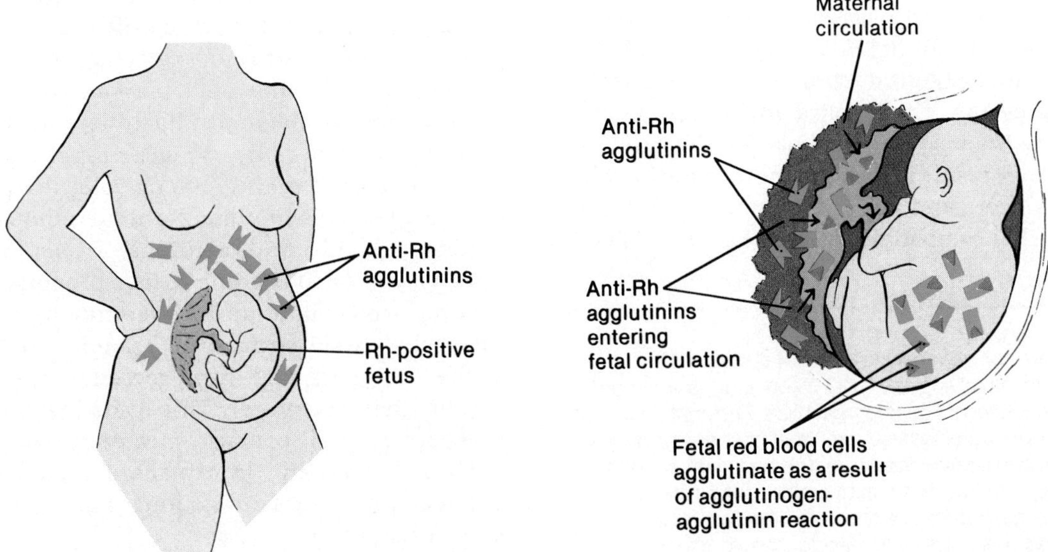

there is another way to become sensitized and it is one that is of great concern to women of childbearing age who possess Rh negative blood.

Should an Rh negative woman become pregnant by an Rh positive man, the fetus has a good chance of being Rh positive also. During the pregnancy, the fetal blood undergoes months of intimate exposure to the maternal circulation and exchange of all kinds of material, including antibodies, occurs freely across the placenta. It is this freedom of exchange that exposes the maternal blood to the Rh antigen and stimulates the mother's system to begin production of the anti-Rh antibody. Production is slow, and the greatest surge usually occurs during delivery, so if the labor is short, the first child can be delivered with impunity (figure 17.20). However should a second Rh positive fetus occupy that woman's uterus at a later date, the situation can be extremely dangerous for the infant. Anti-Rh antibody can reach the fetal blood through the placental circulation, and when it does, it immediately begins to destroy—usually through lysis—the fetal erythrocytes (figure 17.21). In severe cases, the destruction can be so profound that the fetus may die *in utero*, although cases this severe are rare.

On occasion, the infant is born terribly anemic and with gross destruction of RBCs still taking place.

Most of the time, however, the antigen exposure occurs at birth, and the infant can be carefully watched to see if any problem is going to occur. If it does, the solution is to replace the infant's blood with blood that contains no such antibodies. This kind of transfusion is known as *exchange transfusion* and consists of removing a small quantity of the fetal blood and promptly replacing it with "clean" blood from a donor. The process is continued until most of the antibody-contaminated blood is cleared from the infant's circulation. This is a delicate and expensive process, and while it nearly always saves the infant's life, it is not always 100 percent successful. Sometimes the infant, even with prompt treatment, winds up with mental retardation or some sort of sensory loss, such as deafness.

As with most things, the simplest way to handle the problem is to avoid it. If the obstetrician is aware of the situation during the first pregnancy, any future problems can be obviated by injecting RhoGAM, an anti-Rh gamma globulin within seventy-two hours of delivery. Anti-Rh antibody production usually does not start in a brand-new mother until after the delivery of her child, and the injected material is so similar to her own anti-Rh antibodies that her antibody production lines are shut down by negative feedback mechanisms. Since birth has occurred, the fetus is gone, along with its antigens, so there is no stimulus for any new antibody production. Hence the mother never produces any. The injected antibodies are metabolized over the next few weeks and ultimately disappear. The net result is that the mother never does become sensitized, and any subsequent pregnancies are, as far as Rh incompatibility is concerned, all "first" pregnancies.

Although it is not generally known, fetal/maternal incompatibilities involving the ABO blood groups are more common than those of Rh incompatibility. Fortunately, the former are a good deal less severe. In almost every case mentioned in the medical literature, the pregnant woman has been a type O and the most common infant blood type is A—possibly because these are the two most common blood types. Statistics aside, should a woman with type O blood be carrying a fetus with type A, it is quite common for her to begin producing large numbers of anti-A antibodies that enter the fetal circulation and begin to destroy fetal erythrocytes. The reactions are seldom serious enough to kill the fetus, but sometimes red-cell destruction becomes profound enough to produce quantities of bilirubin in the fetal circulation, and it results in jaundice of the newborn. In such cases, exchange transfusions are the most reliable treatment.

Clinical Considerations

A Man-Made Problem with Cellular Immunity

Not all of the things that our cellular immune system can do necessarily benefit us. Sometimes, despite its best intentions, the system winds up making things very difficult indeed for medical practitioners intent on saving the health of a patient. Until this century, it was not anything a person had to worry about, but with the tremendous recent advances in medical technology—particularly in surgery—it has become very important.

When something of vital importance to a person's health stops functioning for any reason, it is mandatory that they be given some kind of replacement. If an endocrine gland has quit working, replacement can take the form of the chemical that the gland secretes. If it's a kidney that has malfunctioned, it is possible to replace the function of that organ with a machine capable of processing the blood (see chapter 16). But if an organ like the liver or the heart begins to deteriorate to the point where it is undependable, there are no mechanical contrivances that can take their place. Under such circumstances, the only replacement that will work is another, similar organ from a human donor, and that is when the cellular immune systems start to cause difficulties.

The cellular system, you will recall, is designed to seek out and destroy any cells that display any hint of "non-self" on the outer surfaces of their membranes. This is a defensive operation of considerable importance, especially considering the number of spontaneously forming tumor cells that can occur during a person's lifetime. Naturally, then, when the system suddenly finds millions of cells that are obviously foreign, it is going to take prompt and drastic action. T cells show up in huge numbers, attaching themselves to the surfaces of "friendly" cells adjacent to the foreigners, and they proceed to kill all the foreigners they encounter. This leads inevitably to the breakdown of all contact between the organ recipient's body and the transplanted organ, and since blood and nutrients can no longer get to it, the organ dies of inanition.

To avoid this, surgeons use chemicals known as **immune suppressants** to prevent the immune system from destroying or *rejecting* the newly implanted tissue. These immune suppressants weaken the T cells' ability to do their job, and hence they give the transplanted organ a better chance of surviving in its new body. As often as not, all the physicians' efforts fail, and the organ is rejected. Even if it is not, suppressing T cell activity leaves the patient tremendously susceptible to infection—especially viruses—and the incidence of certain kinds of cancer is twenty times higher in transplant recipients than it is in the normal population.

Allergy (Hypersensitivity)

The vertebrate immune systems, like all other body systems, are designed to retain homeostasis throughout the organism. The vast majority of the time, they work as they should and produce good results, but every once in a while their efforts, instead of being beneficial, can damage the host.

The phenomenon known as **hypersensitivity** or **allergy** is a case in point.

There are many different kinds of allergic reactions, and people can be allergic to all kinds of things: cat dandruff, heavy metals, pollen of certain plants, some perfumes, plant oils, various chemicals—the list is endless. Nearly all allergies are expressed by traumatic alterations that occur in one of three general body organ systems: (1) the respiratory system, (2) the digestive system, or (3) the skin surfaces.

All the different reactions can be grouped within four main types:

1. **Type I.** These reactions occur immediately upon exposure to the allergic substance. They are **atopic,** meaning that the tendency to be allergic is inherited and is mediated by IgE immunoglobulin. A more detailed discussion follows.
2. **Type II.** These are reactions that occur when an antibody couples to a body cell and exposes it to attack by phagocytes. It is common in drug allergies, but the antigen need not be a foreign particle. Often these reactions are the result of the body's immune system turning on its host. Such assaults are referred to as **autoimmune diseases** because the immune system attacks its own body. Type II reactions are produced by IgG and IgM immunoglobulins, and they can be extremely serious. At least one type—Goodpasture's syndrome, in which the lungs and kidneys are involved—is 100 percent fatal.
3. **Type III.** These are allergies that involve plasma complement. For instance, should an immune complex (antigen/antibody combination) be deposited in a blood vessel, it could activate complement proteins and produce heavy inflammation and often considerable damage to otherwise healthy cells within the vessel. The best-known (and probably the most serious) type III disease afflicts kidney glomeruli and is known as **serum sickness.**
4. **Type IV.** Type IV allergies are all delayed reactions that require hours or even days to manifest themselves. They are due to an unfortunate hyperactivation of the cellular immune system and are caused mainly by the release of cytotoxic lymphokines. For example, when a person is exposed to poison ivy sap, an aromatic fraction of the sap slips through the epidermis and binds covalently to the outer surface of cells in the living dermis. Here it attracts the attention of wandering T cells, and the result is a vigorous assault on all of the cells that exhibit the presence of the sap compound. Because the amount of sap is usually considerable, there are thousands of infected cells in any given area, and this apparently indicates the worst kind of emergency to the T cells. Killer cells rush in, releasing lymphokines of all kinds, macrophages swarm around, ingesting any offensive debris that they can find. Blood vessels dilate, tissue fluids abound and begin to produce blisters in weakened epidermal surfaces, and the whole assault ultimately results in the swelling, heat, and redness of a violent inflammatory response. Then, after the worst assaults are over and all kinds of body cells have been destroyed or damaged, the terrible itching of contact dermatitis begins to manifest itself as tissues start to recover. The worst of the violence is usually over by the third day after exposure to the sap, but repairing the damage often consumes two or three weeks of sleepless, scratching nights and tired, unsightly misery during the days.

Immunoglobulin E and Hay Fever

The concentration of immunoglobulin E in the average person is very small. It amounts to less than 1/40,000 the concentration of IgG; even IgD is one hundred times more concentrated. It probably would have remained undetected even today were it not for the fact that it has an extremely powerful, unpleasant, and all-too-common effect.

IgE antibodies are involved in one of the most uncomfortable hypersensitivity reactions of which we are aware. It is a type I reaction known to the medical community as **anaphylactic hypersensitivity** and to the rest of us as **asthma** and/or **hay fever.** The stimulant (allergen or antigen) responsible is most commonly the pollen of a plant—typically, ragweed or buttercup—and it results in the production of antibodies designed to rid the body of the pollen.

In the average person, this is no problem at all. Plasma cells continue to synthesize antibody from all of the immunoglobulins, including those built on the IgE plan. However the amount of IgE antibody that is produced is generally so small that while it may produce a little discomfort while the person is in the clouds of plant pollen, any adverse respiratory problems disappear pretty quickly once the pollen is no longer present.

Some people, however—often referred to as "allergic types"—have more than their share of IgE. Because they have extra IgE, they produce relatively large amounts of IgE antibody when the immune system is stimulated, and that's the problem. IgE antibody has a particular affinity for *mast cells,* and when it is produced, it promptly anchors to the nearest ones and stays there. Mast cells, as was noted previously, are very similar to basophils—so similar, in fact, that they are often called *tissue basophils,* and they surround tiny blood vessels throughout the body. After the initial contact with the antigen, or **allergen** as it is called in this context, nothing much happens. The IgE antibody is still attached to the mast cells, and as long as the mast cells remain intact, all is well. But the next time the antibody-producing antigen is encountered, the one that stimulated the formation of the IgE antibody in the first place, the troubles start.

As soon as the fresh antigen binds to the IgE antibody, something happens to the mast cell it is attached to, and the result is that the mast cell suddenly releases all of its contents—a process known as *degranulation.* The contents happen to include things like *histamine, prostaglandins, lukotrienes,* and other chemicals that alter normal blood flow locally. These are, as we know, prime motivators in the development of the inflammatory reaction mentioned at the beginning of this chapter. With a sudden flood of such compounds a very powerful, local inflammation begins, including all the unpleasantness that accompanies it. The capillaries leak excess fluids, the areas involved swell with extra blood, higher pressures force tissue edema and considerable weeping through fluid-swollen surfaces, and so on, just as things go during a regular inflammatory reaction (figure 17.22).

Hay Fever When the affected zone is the upper part of the nasal passages, the entire area swells shut, and victims feel horrible things like itching behind their eyes and in the nasal sinuses deep in their heads. The red, tear-filled eyes, eternally plugged-up noses, and continued drizzling of fluids through the nasal passages into the throat and from the external nares are typical of the familiar horrors of hay fever.

Asthma Oftentimes the inflammation includes air tubes deeper in the respiratory tree, and when it involves the bronchioles, the problem can be life-threatening. There are two kinds of asthma: the **ex-**

Figure 17.22 A type I hypersensitivity reaction involving IgE. (*a*) B cells are activated when they contact an allergen; (*b*) an activated B cell becomes an antibody-secreting plasma cell; (*c*) the antibodies become attached to the membranes of mast cells; (*d*) subsequently, when the allergen is encountered, it combines with the antibodies of the mast cell membranes; and (*e*) the mast cell releases substances that cause the symptoms of the allergic reaction.

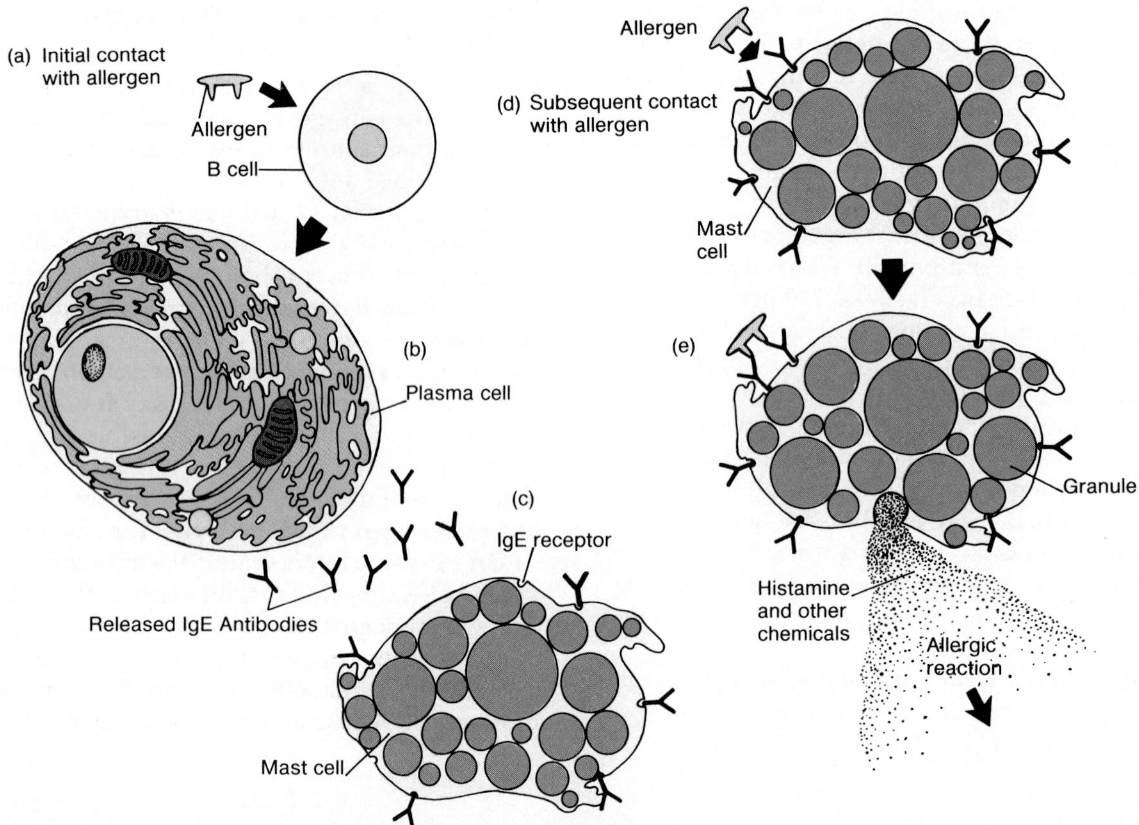

trinsic type, in which the cause (allergen) is known, and the **intrinsic** type, in which the allergen cannot be identified. Asthma is never pleasant, and sufferers experience a great deal more than mere discomfort. On occasion, the bronchioles constrict to the point where breathing is extremely hard, and the victim experiences all the horrors of suffocation, including the terror that accompanies it. No one is really sure what chemicals are responsible for asthmatic attacks, but leukotrienes are certainly involved. Leukotrienes can produce contraction of smooth muscles similar to the type of contraction seen around bronchial tubes during an asthma attack. Furthermore, this contractile effect produced by leukotrienes is not reversed or even reduced by antihistamines, which may explain why antihistamines have no significant effect during asthma attacks. Fortunately, most smooth-muscle relaxants (decongestants) give temporary relief, and often that is adequate to see the victim through the acute phase of an attack.

Anaphylaxis Sometimes, particularly when the allergen is injected into the patient's body, the inflammatory response becomes systemic. The result is a rapidly developing hypotension throughout the body accompanied by powerful constriction of the airways. There is a tremendous movement of fluid from the circulatory system into the interstitial fluid of the body tissues, and while tissues swell with excess fluid, blood volume and pressure can fall so low that the kidneys actually shut down. This condition is known as **anaphylactic shock,** and if treatment is not immediately available, it is often fatal.

Antihistamines Most people who suffer from hay fever are well aware that relief is available in the form of antihistamines. The relief is not complete, because antihistamines, as their name implies, are only histamine antagonists. They have no effect on the other chemicals that are released by the mast cells and stimulate so many phases of inflammation. Even so, the relief they do provide is welcome enough to ignore the problem of drowsiness that antihistamines often produce. Unfortunately, antihistamines are of no value to an asthmatic, because the bronchiolar constriction is not caused by histamines. The culprit is evidently a still-unidentified β-adrenergic blocking agent that inhibits bronchiolar dilation and produces a powerful constriction of the airways.

Desensitization One of the most successful treatments for asthmatics has been **desensitization.** It is only successful in the extrinsic type of asthma, because the allergen must be known if the victim is to be successfully desensitized. Treatment is similar to the Pasteur series of rabies shots which proceeds as follows: In order to build up effective immunity to rabies, weakened rabies virus is injected into the patient in very small quantities at first. Each day, more virus is given, and the virus strength is increased until finally the patient is accepting large doses of full-strength virus with impunity. The same reasoning is behind the desensitization process. The patient is injected with very small quantities of diluted allergen in the beginning, and the injections are gradually increased in concentration and volume until the allergen is no longer effective.

Just why the desensitization process, as it is currently performed in the U.S. today, should be effective in producing an immunity to an allergic reaction is not clear. It represents, after all, an immunity to an immune response. Some think that the answer lies in the fact that such injections stimulate other parts of the humoral immune system. They feel that the gradual introduction of the allergen succeeds in stimulating the IgG synthesizing systems as well as the IgE. Since IgG immunoglobulin is 40,000 times more abundant than IgE, and since it is circulating in the plasma instead of sitting anchored to mast cells, the relatively huge amount of IgG antibody that is available grabs up all the allergen as soon as it comes into the body, leaving none floating around to attach to IgE antibody and release the mast cell contents.

This theory makes good sense, but some researchers disagree. They point out that when an allergen enters the body, the chances are that it will come in at a point that is very close to where the IgE antibody is anchored to the mast cells, and the allergic reaction will occur before the IgG antibodies have a chance to attack. They say that the gradual injections of allergen, instead of involving other aspects of the humoral system, dip into the cellular system's coffers and build up the numbers of T suppressor cells in the blood. As you should recall, these suppressor cells tend to lower the power of an immune response; hence a high level of suppressor cells could substantially reduce the production of IgE antibodies, possibly weakening the IgE immune response to a point closely resembling that of the so-called "non-allergic" person.

Some Observations about Hypersensitivities

The organisms that are alive on the earth today represent the product of eons of evolution. Behind them stand probably a billion years' worth of extinct ancestors that have contributed in one way or another to the current crop of living organisms. We represent what is probably the most successful attitudes and abilities of uncountable predecessors, each of which has contributed its share. Because of this, it is usually pretty hard for anyone in science to understand how any biological system could survive that not only appears to be useless but actually does damage to its host. How can autoimmune diseases exist? Why do allergic reactions occur? Are they of some value?

Most workers are hard pressed to come up with a cogent response when asked these questions, but in some cases they can offer a few. IgE, for instance, seems to be involved in limiting the activity of certain parasitic worms—without it, experimental animals become unusually susceptible to such infestations. Apparently, it works as follows: When IgE stimulates mast cells to degranulate, some of the materials released attract eosinophils, and eosinophils are specifically equipped to help the IgE antibody to deal with both flatworms and roundworms that try to make a home within the vertebrate body. The killing mechanism is believed to be cytotoxic lymphokines released by the eosinophils after stimulation by IgE antibody. The fact that IgE also causes hay fever and asthma may simply be an unhappy by-product of this activity—unfortunate, but better than the worms.

This type of relationship probably exists with the other allergy-causing reactions as well. Certainly it is not hard to understand the violence of the cellular responses that produce the horrid contact dermatitis of poison ivy. The immune system is trying to rid the body of cells that do not belong there. If these were cancerous growths, the damage being done by the lymphokine toxins would certainly be the lesser of two evils, and as far as the cellular immune system is concerned, those non-self cells could be cancerous.

Science doesn't have all the answers yet, but it is generally conceded that all of our immune processes must have a beneficial activity that outweighs the disadvantages in most of the population, or they would never have survived evolutionary pressures.

Interferon

Interferon first came to light in the late 1950s as a material that seemed to increase an organism's ability to resist viruses. As science came to know it better, its importance grew. Actually, interferon is not one chemical but a family of chemicals. They are all globular proteins ranging in size from a molecular weight of 25,000 to nearly 100,000, and there are two major families: those produced following viral infections and those that have generalized effects that include interaction with nonspecific stimulators and the activation of certain types of T cells.

Interferon is produced by different types of cells following an attack by viruses. There are three different kinds of interferon, and lymphocytes, epithelial cells, and macrophages can all produce one kind or another to deal with viral invasions. Interferon first came to the attention of the general public just a few years ago because of its purported effectiveness in dealing with certain kinds of cancer. For a while, injections of interferon appeared to be effective against certain malignant assaults, but its vigor is evidently restricted to just a few types of cancer. Furthermore, it is now felt that its attacks are indirect; that its increased anticancer activity is due to its ability to stimulate natural killer cells, increasing the frenzy of their attacks on certain tumorous growths. Unfortunately, the types of cancer subject to the attacks of natural killer cells are seldom a problem, which may be why natural killer cells exist and why such cancers are rare.

Whatever the reason, the cancer-fighting abilities of interferon have turned out to be less than everyone had hoped. But we should not let that diminish the importance of interferon too much, because it helps us in so many other ways. For instance, it can activate the bacteria-killing activity of macrophages, it can increase the mobility of the body's phagocytes, it can stimulate increased activity in the natural killer cells, and it is one of the most important weapons our bodies have for dealing with viral infections.

Probably its most important capability is antiviral. It has been suggested more than once that when a normally mild viral disease suddenly becomes deadly, it is due to a mutation that provides the virus with greater resistance to interferon. The killer influenza epidemic of 1918 is frequently quoted in this context.

As you know, when viruses attack living cells, the infected cells become the object of a concerted attack by the cellular immune system. And, as is the case with almost every homeostatic mechanism in living systems, there are redundancies that can usually be relied on; viruses entering the human body are subject to attack by several different systems. In addition to the efforts of the cellular system, certain aspects of the humoral system are often able to add their punch to our defenses, but both antibody production and the development of killer-cell defenses requires several days, and this gives the attacker time to become established. In some cases, that extra time is critical. In a way, it is like achieving immunity to bubonic plague by catching the disease—it works, but there are better ways. Interferon is one such better way.

Interferon is a product of our nonspecific immune processes; hence it can go to work without any period of sensitization. It swings into action as soon as the virus begins to assault body cells, and it is apparently intended to contain, that is, to keep the virus within a limited periphery just long enough for the specific systems to mobilize. It operates as follows:

When a cell is attacked by a virus, it apparently recognizes its peril quickly and immediately transcribes a special strand of mRNA that stimulates a short but vigorous production of interferon (figure 17.23). This interferon won't save the cell that makes it, but that is not the intent. It is intended as a dying SOS, a warning and an aid to the cells around it. The cell that is attacked has no way to resist the virus, and

Figure 17.23 The antiviral activity of interferon.

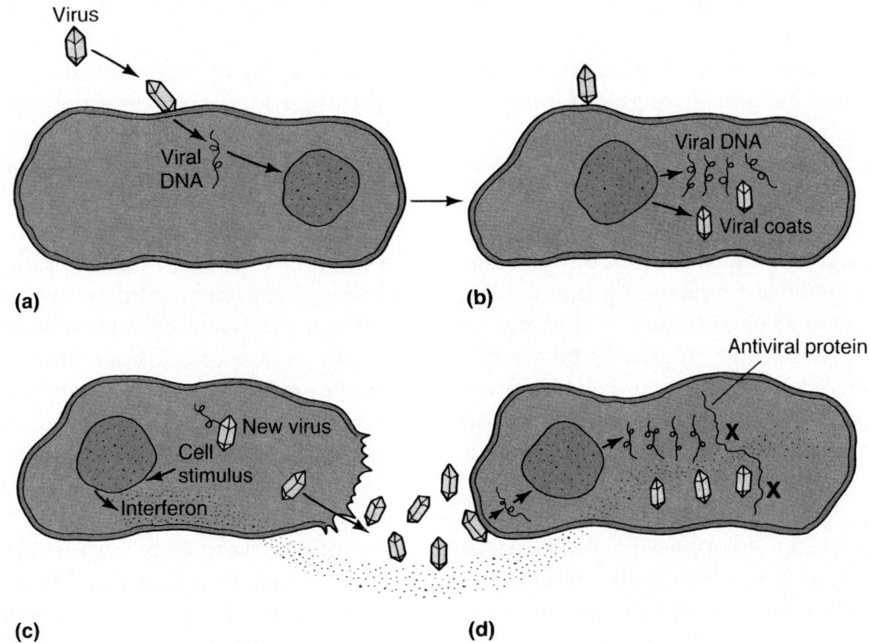

when it ultimately bursts, the interferon is released along with the newly made viruses, travelling with them to nearby, uninfected cells (figure 17.23*c*).

As the viruses attach themselves to these new cells, the interferon sneaks past them into the cellular interiors, where it issues its warning—a warning that produces an antiviral protein. This antiviral protein is not a killer. The newly infected cells still produce viral DNA and make new coating for the viral nucleotide, and the cells still die because they no longer work properly. However, thanks to the antiviral protein, the new viral parts cannot survive. Sometimes they are simply not assembled—the viral DNA is not put inside the protein coats. Sometimes the protective protein coats are incorrectly made. They have holes in them, leaving the DNA exposed and subject to attack. Thus, when the carefully sabotaged viral material is released from its dying victims, instead of infecting other cells it is promptly gobbled up by macrophages. By thus disrupting the efforts of the attacking viruses, interferon prevents rapid, early proliferation of viral material, thereby fighting an effective delaying action until the specific immune systems can swing into action.

Missing Immunity

Everyone is supposed to be born with the ability to resist disease, and most of us are. Our bodies have been designed by millennia of evolutionary effort to provide us with defenses that should be able to withstand many kinds of parasitic assault, ranging from flatworms like lung and liver flukes to objects so simple and tiny that most workers do not even consider them to be alive. Few of us ever stop to consider what the consequences might be if we were born without immunity.

This is not impossible. It is rare, but it happens. And when it does, the victim of the deficiency is subject to attack by organisms that most of the world pays no attention to at all. Recent newspapers carried the story of a young boy, born without any immunities, who had been raised in a sterile plastic bubble until he reached his teenage years and then, unable to take his isolation any longer, demanded and secured his release. He lasted only a few days in the outside world where you and I wander throughout our lives. What happened? What killed him?

Nobody knows for sure! It could have been anything. The world is teeming with invisible organisms that are capable of feeding on the nutrients that we are made of and filled with. We ignore most of their assaults because our immunity works so well that they are never a problem. We really have no idea what they might do if we couldn't resist them.

To give an example, just consider one very common organism—the bacterium known as *Escherichia coli. E. coli* is a common inhabitant of the human intestinal tract, so common and so abundant that it is estimated that approximately 50 percent of the dry weight of human feces is attributable to it. It is of no particular benefit to us, but since it is actually living *outside* of our bodies, and since it does us no harm, our systems simply ignore it . . . a harmless, insignificant squatter. If *E. coli* gets into an area where it does not belong, our immune mechanisms spot it immediately. Should any of the bacteria gain access to our interstitial fluids, they are promptly destroyed, and they last in our circulatory systems for a matter of seconds—time for maybe one pass through our bodies—before they are killed.

But there is one zone in the human body where *E. coli* is never found—the central nervous system. It is excluded from that area by a rather powerful exclusion system known as the **blood-brain barrier,** and should one or two ever survive in the blood long enough to encounter that barrier, they would not be able to penetrate it. As a result, no bodily provisions are made to handle this bacterium should it ever infect the brain. Fractures in the braincase (skull) have, on occasion, let this happen, and experience has shown that when it does, we are faced with a foe of terrifying effectiveness. When *E. coli* gets into the brain, there is no immune system to oppose it; the ability of the animal to resist is almost nonexistent, and the organism runs wild. It feeds voraciously on nervous tissue and the supporting glial cells, leaving vast cavities behind that rapidly fill with pus-like cellular and metabolic debris. Within two or three weeks, the expanding populations can gobble up half of the brain, reducing a previously sentient animal to a vegetable.

That is the kind of thing that can happen when the immune system ignores a normally quiescent bacterium, and we have no way to defeat this kind of assault because we hardly ever encounter it. Unfortunately, the world is filled with organisms about which this is potentially true. They hardly ever bother us, either because we seldom encounter them, or because when we do, we confront them in areas where we can resist them without effort.

But what if we couldn't? What if our immune systems suddenly shut down and we were no longer able to brush these organisms aside or keep them where they belonged? What if we lost our ability to handle the cancers that occur frequently in humans but which our natural killer cells quickly destroy . . . what then?

AIDS – Acquired Immune Deficiency Syndrome

We die, is what! Just as the young boy died when he left his bubble, the person who loses his ability to resist parasitic assault is doomed. That is why the disease known as **AIDS** is viewed as such a scourge. AIDS is an acronym for *acquired immune deficiency syndrome,* and it kills by destroying its victim's immune responses.

AIDS may be caused by a virus—or to be more accurate, a **retrovirus.** The prefix *retro* simply means that instead of a strand of DNA inside a protein coating, the AIDS virus has a strand of RNA. Its targets are the helper T cells—the so-called T_4 cells. Once in the human body, the retroviruses seek out these T_4 cells, drill their way inside, then relax and wait. Their activity is apparently tied to periods when the host cell is active, and they do nothing until that happens. They may lie there dormant for years until some sort of antigenic stimulus energizes their host cells. When it does, they explode into action. The RNA promptly reprograms the cellular DNA; production of new retroviruses is rapid, and when they burst out, they leave behind a dead T_4 cell. As the attacks continue, more and more of the T_4 cells are killed, progressively reducing the victim's ability to resist. The result is unmitigated disaster, because without T_4 cells, the victim loses the services of both immune systems. The cellular immune system does not work at all without the aid of the T_4 helper cells, and the humoral immune system functions at less than one-half efficiency. Specific immunity is suddenly gone, and without specific immunity, the victim dies—in ways most medical practitioners can only surmise. Usually the killer is a rare disease, one that is seldom a problem in other people, like the rare skin cancer known as *Kaposi's sarcoma,* or a type of pneumonia almost unheard-of in normal people. Such rampant infections clearly indicate that the immune systems of the victims are not working anymore.

Retroviruses aren't a new phenomenon. We have known about them for years, and some are just as deadly as the suspected AIDS virus. What makes the AIDS virus so frightening is that it can be transmitted from person to person, an observation complicated by the fact that not everyone is susceptible to AIDS. In some, the humoral immune system is able to respond to the viral invasion rapidly enough to produce antibodies that keep the virus under control . . . not destroyed, just under control. Such people are considered "AIDS carriers" and are like a primed time bomb in society, particularly if they have indiscriminate social habits . . . and in this country, it seems that most AIDS carriers do.

Not all, however. A person does not have to be promiscuous to contract AIDS, but it increases the likelihood. The virus is not transmitted by casual contact. Handling things an AIDS patient has handled will not transmit infection, nor will day-to-day association with a carrier or victim. Contact must be intimate—sexual is ideal—and this has so far restricted its ravages in the U.S. The virus is apparently transferred from one person to another in body fluids, and human semen has turned out to be a perfect vehicle, a fact that has made homosexuals particularly susceptible. Sexual congress between males is often accomplished by anal copulation, and when ejaculation occurs, the virus has only the relatively delicate barriers of the rectum or large intestine to penetrate in order to enter the interstitial fluids of a new victim. Infection is easy and swift.

Transmission during heterosexual congress is more difficult. When the virus is injected into the vagina, it has a pretty tough barrier to penetrate, and the odds are that it won't do it. Infection is therefore less likely, but it should be remembered that if the number of sexual contacts is high and partners are varied enough, the chances of infection increase until, in a socially promiscuous community, epidemic is just a matter of time.

Semen is not the only body fluid that transmits the virus between people. Any body fluid can apparently do it, including infected blood, an unfortunate fact that doomed some transfusion recipients before a means of screening whole blood for AIDS was found. It also means that intravenous drug users are a high-risk group, since they often share hypodermic needles without bothering to rinse them out between "hits."

The whole picture is clouding up like some Dantean nightmare. Staggering statistics are emerging from large population centers across the U.S. Medical workers in New York and San Francisco have surveyed local prostitutes and have discovered that more than 50 percent of them either carry the AIDS virus or have active cases of the disease. All but one or two of the infected women are IV drug addicts, but that merely explains how they probably got the disease; it makes no predictions as to where it will now go. Since prostitution is a female addict's most reliable source of funds and they must have money to support their drug habits, they will surely not change professions. Each can transmit the virus to a customer, and while the probability of infection is low, with enough contacts it is bound to happen. An average street prostitute in New York may handle twenty men on an active night, a very sobering statistic indeed! Any one of these men could contract the disease and transmit it to subsequent companions—male, female, wife, secretary, another hooker . . . who knows?

In this country, AIDS will almost certainly burst out of the minority groups it is now concentrated in and spread into the general population. It will probably remain abnormally prevalent in male homosexuals, intravenous drug users, and drug-addicted prostitutes, but chances are it will not be limited to these groups. In fact, experts believe that in less than ten years AIDS will be the leading cause of death in the 15 to 20-year-old age group, and they may be right. There is solid evidence that the affliction originated in Africa, and many workers feel that we can get some idea of what may happen here by looking at the progress of the disease there.

If that is true, the outlook is grim. In Africa, AIDS is rampant—male, female, heterosexual, homosexual, non–drug addict—*everyone* is susceptible. The number of cases is currently said to be at least twenty million, and every single person that has it will die, but not until many of them have passed the disease on to someone else! There is no cure, and there is no way to immunize against it . . . and if we are correct, Africa is only about five years ahead of us!

Treatment There is no way the disease can be treated—at least, no way of which we are currently aware. There is no cure, no preventive vaccine, not even a reliable means of prolonging life, and once the symptoms have developed, the victim's prognosis is zero. Clearly, the only way a snarling beast like that can be combatted is to keep it carefully caged and never let it go. Sexual contact between uninfected people and those with the disease must be prevented, minimized, avoided . . . something. That is not proving an easy thing to do. The sex drive in human beings is extremely powerful, and casual sexual congress is becoming a norm, particularly among young people. If abstention is not practical, then other means must be found.

Fortunately, there is an alternative. The condom, the thin plastic or rubber tube that is intended to sheath the male organ during coitus, is considered very good protection against transmission or acquisition of the disease, and the reasoning is sound. Since it interposes an artificial and relatively impermeable barrier around the penis, it prevents semen from contacting the vaginal wall while simultaneously blocking vaginal fluids from the penis. If it is put on properly and if it stays on, it is probably as reliable as any protection could be.

Will condoms be used sufficiently to bring the spread of AIDS to a halt? Maybe. It is very hard to say. There has been a tremendous hullabaloo over condoms lately. Television networks, afraid of giving offense to groups they have venerated since their inception, have steadfastly refused to advertise them for any reason. Religious groups object also, on the grounds that nonmarital coitus is evil and should never be condoned. Hence any advice that seems to suggest that illicit sex is OK is anathema, and saying that condoms might ward off AIDS is in effect suggesting that coitus is OK as long as you wear a condom. Their attitude is simplistic and may be unrealistic, but at least it is consistent. What is more, most governmental agencies are listening to them.

To the medical community, this is unfortunate. Of course, as long as the constitution of this country stays intact, everyone one has a right to an opinion and to offer advice, but arm-waving and idealism will not alter facts, and nonmarital sexual activity is a fact. What's more, it is increasing, as the unmarried birthrate clearly shows. Preaching abstinence has not worked up to now, and there is no reason to believe it will suddenly start. It seems obvious that the only realistic answer is to accept the facts and make an effort to educate everyone as to things that need to be done as well as those that should be avoided. Even that may be too late.

Summary

Our Personal Armies

I. The vertebrate immune system is a series of defenses. The first defense consists of the fortress-like walls of various kinds that raise barriers against any kind of invasion.
II. The second defense is an army that is mobilized to protect us against foreign invasions or damage from some internal insurgency.

A Well-Defended Fortress

I. Our bodies have erected passive barriers that are designed to prevent unauthorized invasion of our interior.
II. These barriers, in addition to being passive barricades, have some active defenses as well.
III. Skin. The unbroken skin is our first line of defense against foreign incursion. Not only is it a nearly impenetrable barricade, but it also periodically sloughs off bacteria residing on its surface, thus effectively reducing potentially dangerous populations. Such abilities make it a formidable fortress wall. Unfortunately, there are several breaks in this wall.

Openings Into the Body

I. Any body openings represent a potential door into the body's interior; hence all such entrances must be carefully guarded.
II. Mucous Membranes. These membranes form a mechanical barrier within the openings into our bodies. They also produce many secretions that can actively discourage potential squatters or invaders.
III. The Respiratory Tract
   A. Mucous membranes in the upper parts of the tract are covered with sticky mucus that can trap and hold entering microorganisms.
   B. Cilia on the epithelial cells lining the respiratory tract can move the debris-filled mucus up near the external nostrils where it can be expelled, or to the pharynx where it can be coughed up and swallowed.
IV. Defenses in the Gastrointestinal Tract. The gastrointestinal tract features both passive and active mechanisms designed to prevent the ingress of microorganisms.
   A. The Mouth. Within the oral opening are mucous membranes and constantly flowing and moving saliva. Microorganisms are swept out of the mouth by the saliva. Many are swallowed.
   B. Gastric Defenses
      1. The lining of the stomach is relatively easy to penetrate, but few microorganisms can exist for more than a few seconds in the stomach fluids.
      2. The acid conditions of the stomach make it a most inhospitable breeding ground for foreign invaders.
      3. In addition to the powerful acids that are present, there are also potent protein-splitting enzymes that can tear apart the delicate membranes of microorganisms.
   C. The Small Intestine
      1. The lining of the small intestine is not hard to penetrate, but few microorganisms ever get close enough to the lining to actually get through.
      2. Mucus covers the entire interior of the small intestine, and it tends to trap microorganisms.
      3. Very few microorganisms get close enough to the mucus to get trapped, because materials within the lumen move so rapidly. Fluids are constantly in motion, washing materials into the interior of the tract.
      4. Proteolytic and lipolytic enzymes are present in the fluids in considerable abundance, and they represent another active antibacterial defense in the small intestine.
   D. The Large Intestine
      1. Once again, penetration of the wall is made difficult by the mucus lining the interior of the intestine.
      2. In addition, millions of bacteria are already present. They tend to take up most of the desirable spaces and crowd out new arrivals.
      3. Resident bacteria also secrete unpleasant materials that other bacteria avoid.
V. Defenses in the Urinary and Sexual Openings
   A. The vaginal wall is thick and not easily penetrated. In addition, the interior of the lower reproductive tract is quite acid and is not considered easy access for bacteria.
   B. The walls of the urinary tract are easily penetrated, and there is no mucus to trap invaders. But the constant flushing of the tract by the urine sweeps nearly all bacteria out of the tract. The urine is, therefore, one of the body's defenses against invasion.
VI. External Enzymatic Defenses. The eye and the ear both represent potential entryways into the body. They are well protected by secretions that can kill bacteria.
   A. The eye secretes an enzyme that dissolves bacterial walls, and tears contain a chemical designed to kill bacteria.
   B. Ear wax is a potent means of discouraging microorganisms from entering via that route.

Inflammation

I. This is primarily a protective response to tissue damage or bacterial invasion. Inflammatory reactions result in a greater influx of blood and bacteria-fighting cells. Chemicals are released into the area of inflammation to aid in the fight against microorganisms.
II. Leukotrienes. These are nonsaturated fatty acids that increase the permeability of any capillaries that they contact, thus increasing the outflow of fluid from the blood flowing through the area.
III. Prostaglandins. These chemicals can apparently amplify the effects of many aspects of the inflammatory reaction and can attract bacteria-fighting cells into the area.

IV. The Development of the Inflammatory Response. The inflammatory response is characterized by redness, swelling, heat, and irritation.

V. Inflammation as a Defense Mechanism

A. Inflammation is not a blind response to tissue damage or bacterial invasion. It can act quickly or slowly, depending on the nature of the invader.

B. If the invader is dangerous, it works rapidly and finishes its defenses within a half hour. If the invader is harmless, it may take most of a day to build defenses.

C. When the response is complete, areas that are damaged or under attack are sealed off from the rest of the body, thus preventing any spread of the problem.

VI. Leucocyte Defenses. Leucocytes aid in the defense against bacteria in several ways. One way is by ingesting and digesting the invaders. Another way is by using special chemicals that inspire antibacterial activity by other cells or body mechanisms.

VII. Chemotaxis. Some of the chemicals attract defensive cells into the invasion area. This process is known as chemotaxis.

VIII. Walling Off the Infection Site. The final act of defense is the entry of cells that can deposit connective tissue around the invasion site, thus isolating it.

Our Inner Defenses

I. Defenses in the Lymphatic Circulation. The lymphatic circulation often carries many bacteria from interstitial areas that have been exposed to invasion. As soon as the lymphatic circulation enters a lymph node, the inner defenses begin to assert themselves. Fine filters strain out the invaders, and they are subsequently attacked by blood cells that will ingest and digest them.

II. Defenses in the Blood. The blood contains the most effective armies of all in our war against microbial invasion—the vertebrate immune systems.

Immunity

I. The immune response in humans is highly developed and varied. To begin with, there are two types of immune defense mechanisms available, the specific and the nonspecific.

II. Nonspecific Immunity. This aspect of immunity is so called because it produces general responses. Attacks are directed against any invader, and the assaulting techniques are always the same—the microorganism is ingested and killed. Nonspecific immunity involves mainly the phagocytic leucocytes.

III. The Specific Immune System. The specific immune system involves a certain type of white blood cell—the lymphocyte. Lymphocytes can mediate two entirely different types of responses to microorganic invasion; both result in the production of weapons with highly specific targets.

A. Two Types of Specific Immunity

1. One type of immunity results in the production of highly specific, soluble proteins that are designed to attack and destroy a particular invader.

2. The other type produces cells that seek out and destroy specific invaders.

B. An Indispensable Ability. One thing both types of immunity—specific and nonspecific—possess, is the ability to distinguish between things that are "self" and things that are "nonself." Without this ability, it would not be possible to single out invaders for attack.

C. Antigens. Anything that stimulates the body's immune system to assume an "attack" mode is considered an antigen.

D. Haptens. Haptens are particles that are too small or too insignificant to stimulate the immune system into assuming an "attack" mode, but when they are brought into the body by an antigen, they can be subject to specific attack.

Lymphocytes

I. Lymphocytes are the white blood cells that mediate both types of specific immunity.

II. There are two basic types of lymphocytes, and although they are closely related and have many similar capabilities, they are quite different in their techniques and modes of operation.

A. T Cells. These are lymphocytes that mediate what is known as cellular immunity.

B. B Cells. These mediate what is called humoral immunity.

Humoral Immunity

I. Humoral immunity invokes the assistance of soluble proteins called antibodies.

II. Antibodies. Antibodies are synthesized by plasma cells, which are descendants of B cells. The plasma cells utilize plasma proteins called globulins as substrate for antibody synthesis.

III. The Immunoglobulins. There are at least five different classes of immunoglobulins. They are immunoglobulin A (IgA), immunoglobulin G (IgG), immunoglobulin M (IgM), immunoglobulin D (IgD), and immunoglobulin E (IgE). Each is a variation on a single basic structural theme.

IV. Antibody Structure

A. Antibodies all have the same basic structural plan. Each is composed of units that feature two light protein chains and two heavy protein chains.

B. Each chain has a zone considered to be more or less constant in construction and another zone that tends to vary. All those having the same constant zones are in the same antibody family.

V. Antibody Function. Antibodies are specific. Antibodies that will attack one particular organism will not attack a different one. Usually all antibody types will become involved in attacking a given microorganism. They differ, not so much in *what* they will attack, but rather in *how* they attack.

A. Agglutinates. In this type of attack, antibodies adhere to cells and stick dozens of them together, thus forcing them out of solution. Such precipitates are called immune precipitates.

B. Disrupt Surface Topography. Some antibodies will change the arrangement of chemicals on viral surfaces, thus rendering the virus unable to attack body cells.
C. Inactivating Toxins. Some antibodies attack to toxins and inactivate them.
D. Opsonization. By coating the surface of certain microorganisms with antibody particles, the microorganism is rendered highly susceptible to attack by phagocytic leucocytes.

VI. Complement Activation. Some antibodies can activate a specific plasma protein that has the ability to set off a chain reaction that ends in the destruction of bacteria. The first protein activates another, which in turn activates a third. When the correct number of proteins have been activated, the final one dissolves the bacterial cell wall and kills the cell.

The Humoral Immune Response

I. B Cells and Antibody Production
A. To produce antibodies, a B cell must be able to spot an invader and recognize it as a foreigner.
B. It must then be capable of analyzing the problem and starting operations that will end in the design of a chemical specifically intended to attack that foreigner.
C. Then it must be able to convert itself and stimulate the conversion of other B cells into plasma cells that can produce the specially designed chemical.

II. Primary and Secondary Response. The primary response takes place when the body is invaded by a particular organism for the very first time. The secondary response operates whenever the body is invaded by a microorganism that has attacked before and has been repelled.
A. Plasma Cells. These are the cells that synthesize antibody. They are descended from the B cell.
B. Memory Cells. A memory cell is a special type of lymphocyte that "remembers" the patterns of a given invader and holds the designs for the specific antibody that defeated it.
C. Primary Response. The primary response pattern occupies a time span of from three to ten days, during which time the special anti-invader proteins are being designed. The long duration often is a period of sickness for the victim.
D. Secondary Response
1. The secondary response operates swiftly because all the necessary weapon designs and attack procedures have been prepared and have worked. Often the victims are unaware that they have been invaded.
2. A Mnemonic. The pattern of a secondary immune response is like the calling up of the army reserves. Everyone knows where they must go and what their job is. No training is necessary and all paperwork has been done. Action is quick and decisive.

III. Limitations of Humoral Immunity
A. Many viruses are immune to the attack of the humoral immune system because they enter the body cells and hide.
B. There are bacteria that can do the same thing, thus avoiding humoral immunity.

The Cellular Immune System

I. The cellular immune system is our first line of defense against viral attack and certain types of cancer.

II. T Cells and Cellular Immunity. There are several kinds of T cells: the K cells, the helper cells, the suppressor cells, and the natural killer cells.

III. Immune Responses
A. Like the B lymphocytes, T cells can recognize nonself. K cells perpetually patrol the body's interior, and when they spot nonself, they attach firmly to the invader and kill it.
B. Many chemicals are used in the attack, including lymphokines that can attract phagocytic leucocytes, stimulate them into increased activity, and prevent those already present from leaving the area.

IV. Interleukin and the T_4 Helper Cells
A. It is important to realize that both B cells and T cells cannot produce maximum effect in their operations without assistance from the T_4 helper cells.
B. The T_4 cells release a compound known as interleukin-2, which can sensitize T cells everywhere in the invading microorganisms.
C. Sensitized T cells promptly begin to differentiate and proliferate. Most become K cells, but some become memory cells.

Blood Typing

I. The ABO Blood Groups. These are all due to the presence of two antigens that occupy a site on the surface of a red blood cell. A person's blood type depends on which of these antigens, if any, he or she has.

II. Acquiring the Antibodies
A. Antibodies to the A and B antigens are acquired during the fetal stage.
B. Naturally, a person acquires antibodies only to antigens that he or she does not possess. Acquisition of antibodies to antigens that one possesses would result in the blood attacking itself, which would be lethal.

III. The Rh Blood Groups
A. This is a different category of antigen that, like the A and B antigens, is present on the surface of the red blood cell.
B. Unlike the A and B antigens, people are not born with antibodies to Rh antigens if they lack them. Such antibodies must be acquired, and since they can only be acquired by exposure to the antigen, only women lacking it have any chance of doing so. It is a complication of pregnancy.

Clinical Considerations

I. A Man-Made Problem with Cellular Immunity
II. Allergy (Hypersensitivity)
  A. Type I
  B. Type II
  C. Type III
  D. Type IV. Of all the allergic reactions, only this one involves the cellular immune system.
  E. Immunoglobulin E and Hayfever
    1. Hay fever
    2. Asthma
    3. Anaphylaxis
    4. Antihistamines
    5. Desensitization
  F. Some Observations About Hypersensitivities
III. Interferon. Probably it's most important capability is antiviral.
IV. Missing Immunity
  A. People who lack some aspect of the immune response are unable to resist certain diseases. Those who lack all immune responses are unable to resist anything.
  B. AIDS—Acquired Immune Deficiency Syndrome
    1. AIDS may be caused by a retrovirus. It is transmissible, but not easily.
    2. There is no cure, no immunizing vaccine, nor any reliable means of prolonging life once the symptoms develop.
    3. Condoms may be one of the few practical means of preventing the spread of AIDS.

Review Questions

1. What, essentially, is the function of the vertebrate immune system?
2. What is our first line of defense against attacking parasites?
3. Describe the methods by which the skin avoids attack by microorganisms.
4. Outline the passive and nonspecific defense in:
   a. the respiratory tract
   b. the mouth
   c. the stomach
   d. the small intestine
   e. the large intestine
5. How are the urinary and sexual openings equipped to defend themselves against a microorganic invasion?
6. Describe an example of enzymatic defenses.
7. What is inflammation?
8. List the various processes and chemicals involved in the inflammation reaction.
9. What are leukotrienes? What do they do?
10. What are prostaglandins? What is their function?
11. What are the four most commonly observed phenomena that are observed when inflammation occurs and what is each caused by?
12. What is the purpose of inflammation?
13. Describe the nonspecific reactions that take place in the vicinity of an inflammation.
14. Describe the processes of margination and pavementing. What cells are involved in these processes and what is their purpose?
15. What is chemotaxis?
16. Describe the defenses available in the lymphatic system that protect us against microorganic invasion.
17. What defenses are available in the bloodstream?
18. What is nonspecific immunity? How does it differ from specific immunity?
19. Which of the leucocytes plays the major role in the specific immune reactions?
20. What two types of immunity are available to humans?
21. How is the body's immune system able to respond to foreign invaders without damaging important body cells?
22. Define *antigen* and *hapten* and explain how they differ.
23. Describe the differentiating of lymphocytes into B cells and/or T cells.
24. From what are antibodies made?
25. Name the five classes of immunoglobulins that are present in humans.
26. Which of the immunoglobulins is most abundant in human blood? Which is least?
27. Which immunoglobulin provides us with a defense against invasion through the gastrointestinal system?
28. Which of the immunoglobulins is the largest?
29. Which class of antibodies shows up first in the blood when an infection occurs?
30. Describe the fundamental structure of antibodies. How do the various classes differ from each other?
31. Describe the characteristic known as specificity with respect to antibodies.
32. Describe in detail the process of complement activation.
33. There are at least four other ways (besides complement activation) that antibodies can make war on invading microorganisms. Identify each and describe it.

34. Describe the response of a B cell when an antigen activates it.
35. What is a clone group?
36. Where do memory cells enter into the humoral response? Where do they come from?
37. How does the primary immune response differ from the secondary immune response?
38. How is the humoral immune system limited in what it can do?
39. Identify the four different kinds of T cells and describe their activity to the best of your ability.
40. What are lymphokines? Name some lymphokines and describe how they operate during an immune response.
41. What is present in blood that distinguishes the blood groups? On what is it present?
42. People with type A blood have which antigen? Which antibodies? Answer the same questions for the other blood types.
43. How does a person acquire the antibodies to one of the most common group antigens?
44. Describe the Rh blood factor. How does it differ from the ABO group factors?
45. Describe the three types of humoral allergic reactions. Be sure to identify the immunoglobulin (or other chemical) that is responsible and discuss the treatments that are available.
46. Which of the four types of allergic reactions involves the cellular immune system?
47. Describe the progress of a typical cellular hypersensitivity reaction.
48. With which immunoglobulin is hay fever associated? Describe the immune response and outline what produces the affliction.
49. Suggest some treatments that have been found effective against allergic reactions.

Section VI
Reproduction and Growth

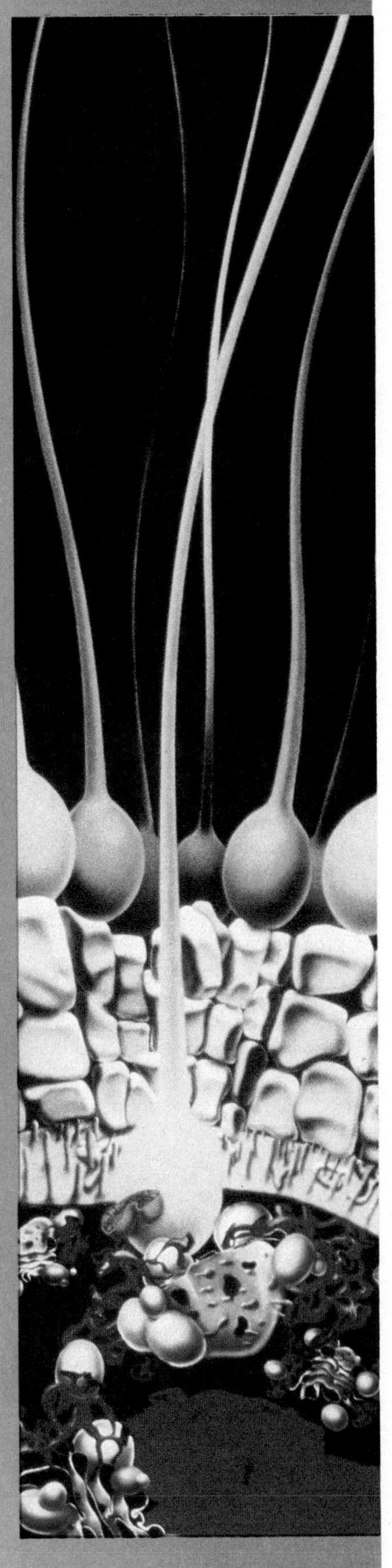

Chapter 18 Mating and Reproduction

Study Hints

When reading, make an effort to view this chapter's subject scientifically. Sex is a volatile subject to most people, and your own views are probably intensely colored by personal experience and background. It is not easy to dissociate yourself from preconceived outlooks, especially ones that can become so emotional, but you should try. Pay particular attention to:

1. the idea that the process of mating has, as its primary object, the procreation of a new being and that this is a matter of species survival.
2. the observation that the basic body plan in mammals is female and that special enzymes are required to alter this plan. The enzymes are genetically programed.
3. the difference between the primary sex characteristics and the secondary sex characteristics. Also be sure you understand the purpose of the latter.
4. the reason why we say people have twenty-three *pairs* of chromosomes instead of simply stating that we have forty-six chromosomes.

Pay particular attention to the endocrinology of the gonads. It is important to learn and remember details of the ovarian and menstrual cycles and how they differ from each other.

A person who is planning to go into some phase of the medical profession should certainly understand the fundamentals of a normal pregnancy. Things like the amniotic sac and the amniotic fluid should certainly be familiar, as should structures like the placenta and the umbilical cord.

It is equally obvious that some of the details of childbirth should be familiar—things like the hormones that stimulate its beginning and help it along and what to expect at the various stages. Also, a knowledgeable professional should know the differences between breast milk and infant formulas as well as the advantages and disadvantages of each.

Details of the menopause should be clear. When a worried woman approaches a nurse or a technician with a typical problem related to her personal climacteric, she places a lot of credence in what she is told, and she is entitled to an accurate answer.

Objectives

When you have finished reading this chapter, you should:

1. be able to describe the development of sexual differentiation in the human embryo, including the source of the sex hormones at each stage and what controls them.
2. be able to describe the secondary sex characteristics and explain the difference between those and the primary ones.
3. know the difference between mitosis and meiosis and be able to explain the process of synapsing and the results of the first meiotic division.
4. be able to describe the development of puberty in both sexes, what causes it, and its results.
5. know what semen is, where it comes from, and what its function is.
6. be able to describe the process of oogenesis and explain how it differs from spermatogenesis.
7. be able to explain the ovarian cycle and the menstrual cycle and know how they differ.
8. know how a human ovum is fertilized and what restricts the movement of spermatozoons through the cell membrane of the ovum.
9. be able to explain the morphological changes that occur in the female when pregnancy occurs.
10. be able to explain the hormonal changes that occur during pregnancy.
11. know the names and the functions of the embryonic membranes.
12. know the roles of the placenta and umbilical cord in maintaining a pregnancy.
13. know how an estrus cycle differs from a menstrual cycle.
14. be able to explain several means of contraception and know the reliability, advantages, and disadvantages of each.
15. be able to describe the physiology of lactation.

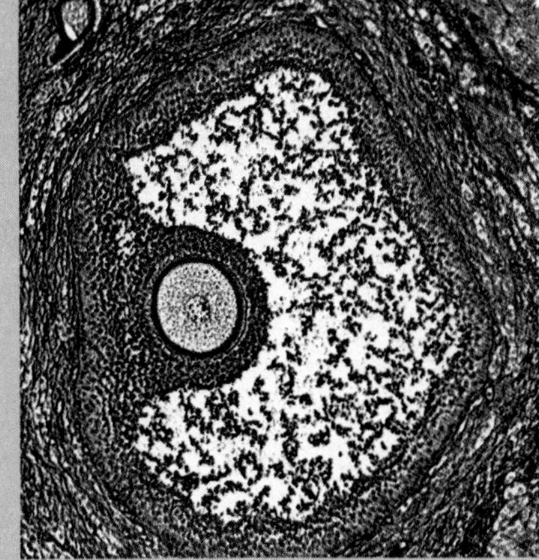

Gravid mammalian follicle.

Introduction

As has been stated repeatedly, the goal of physiological mechanisms in living systems is to maintain homeostasis. There is, however, one system that does not have personal homeostasis as its primary object. It does aim at survival, as do all the others, but not necessarily the survival of the individual organism. It is aimed rather at the survival of the species, and to achieve its ends it will sometimes put the welfare of the single organism in minor jeopardy—something no other properly working system would do.

It is known as the **reproductive system,** and while the name is so deeply ingrained as to be virtually unassailable, it is nevertheless an unfortunate one, because reproduction is not what it accomplishes. Reproduction implies duplication, and duplication occurs when body cells undergo mitosis. Our reproductive system does not duplicate but rather *procreates.* When it is properly activated, the result of its efforts is the production of an entirely new organism, one totally unique, showing characteristics and structures that are only partly similar to those of its parents and sometimes very different indeed.

From the point of view of *species* survival, the reproductive system is the most important of all the body systems. The body's two major control systems go to a great deal of trouble to maintain it, sometimes even to the point of subordinating certain homeostatic efforts to achieve its goals.

Yet the reproductive system contributes very little in terms of day-to-day living. The cells involved in the procreative process have only small roles in homeostasis, as is also the case with the cells that are not directly reproductive but support and maintain those that are. The whole system seems deeply "introverted," mainly concerned with its own goal in life. This is not to imply that it is never involved in homeostatic activity. During pregnancy, many of its mechanisms are equipped to detect any aberrations that may occur and to aid control systems in effecting an adjustment. It is just that the prime goal is to stimulate reproductive activity or to provide protection for a developing new life. So any homeostatic adjustments made by cells of the reproductive areas are directly or indirectly for the support or development of reproductive processes. Aiding control systems is sometimes the easiest way to do this, and the fact that it incidentally helps the individual sometimes seems almost like a by-product of the main effort.

Such a system can seem terribly self-indulgent when viewed in this light, yet it could be that it is fundamentally the most important system in a living organism. When you iron out all the daily wrinkles in living, when you bypass all the laughter, the everyday hassles, and the processes of surviving, it would appear that the only reason any organism exists is to reproduce. Maintaining the survival of the species seems to be the ultimate goal of all life, from bacteria to humans . . . even the viruses seem to be able to do nothing except program a living cell for viral replication. Many insects spend their entire lives preparing for an adulthood that lasts only a few days—sometimes only a few hours—during which reproductive activity becomes frenzied and deadly. Many male insects die shortly after fertilizing their females which, in turn, give up their lives after laying their eggs. Nor is this simplistic pattern apparent only in the invertebrates. Salmon of the Pacific coast will fight their way up the rivers where they were born, never feeding, battering themselves into shattered hulks of their healthy selves, fighting a macabre battle that has only a single ending—frenzied reproduction and prompt death.

In humans the sex drive is not always paramount—a starving man would rather have food than a woman—but it is extremely powerful. Once hunger is satisfied, the woman suddenly becomes tremendously attractive. The drive for racial survival is dynamic in everyone and sometimes is well-nigh irresistible. No one is immune to it. One can assume a position of celibacy or self-denial, and by asserting strength of will can hold to it, but the sex drive is nevertheless always there, waiting to break loose and establish its mastery. Sometimes the celibate wins, sometimes he or she doesn't, but regardless of which is the victor, the fight never ends.

Perhaps it should be pointed out at this time that while it is not a normal (i.e., "average") pattern of behavior, there is nothing unhealthy about celibacy. There is a tendency for many people to view the sex drive as if it were a food drive and to therefore assume that if one does not assuage the former, it could injure one's health. There is no evidence to support this contention, and there is plenty to negate it. There is a huge library of information indicating that celibates often live happy, productive —and quite healthy—lives.

A Touchy Subject

Until recently, the subject of sex was taboo in polite Western society. It was considered to be either "private" or "utterly depraved" and was never discussed or even mentioned in mixed company. Indeed, until the middle of the last century, almost nothing was known about it other than the fact that most people enjoyed it and that it would produce children. Fear-dominated religious attitudes that prevailed in the Middle Ages often focused on sex as a prime target. Sexual fantasies were high on the lists of proscribed mental attitudes, and the penalties for even thinking "impure" thoughts were unbelievably harsh. For instance, **nocturnal emissions** (wet dreams) were not believed to be mere sexual fantasies. They were considered to be genuine acts of sexual intercourse carried out by the devil's spawn while the individual slept, helplessly. The intercourse was between the human and imps or demons, and the folk of that time even had specific names for them—an **incubus** would seduce the female while a **succubus** would have nocturnal intercourse with a male. It may sound like harmless fun, but it was not considered so by the more conscientious evil-fighters. The sufferer was never just an innocent victim. Often the dream was considered to be sufficient evidence to burn the dreamer at the stake for associating with minions of the devil. Can you imagine being killed just for having had a dream?

Western Taboos

More recently—in fact, as late as the early 1900s—several popular and professional medical publications in both England and the U.S. laid down strict rules regarding sexual activity, even between married couples. Men who experienced sexual arousal more than once a month were to promptly subject themselves to large meals, cool baths, or long stints on their knees praying. Women, of course, were even more severely judged. It was firmly believed that women who enjoyed sexual intercourse were depraved, and at least one publication stated unequivocally that if a wife wriggled during intercourse or showed any signs of pleasure, she should promptly undergo *clitoridectomy*—removal of the **clitoris**—an extremely sensitive portion of the female genitalia. Medical authorities issued repeated warnings against unbridled sexual activity and stated flatly that it could result in paralysis, epilepsy, gout, madness, heart disease, bed wetting, sleeping in unnatural positions (whatever that means), and an incredible number of other unexplained afflictions. The most stunning thing to us today is that the men warning of these horrors were not considered cranks or zealots—not during their lifetimes. They were highly respected medical authorities, and people listened to and believed them.

Some of the things these people attributed to sexual stimulation are both laughable and horrifying by today's standards. For instance, masturbators were considered to be teetering on the brink of godless depravity and were obviously becoming insane. Parents were cautioned to be always on the lookout for this deviant behavior and to stamp it out immediately should it ever be observed. Boys who were caught at it should immediately be subjected to a number of absolutely ghastly remedies, among which forty-eight hours without sleep or food, on one's knees, praying, was the mildest. Some medical publications suggest such treatments as cutting off the foreskin with jagged-edged scissors or piercing the penis or foreskin with a darning needle.

Girls who masturbated were (naturally) the worst of all. It was thought they would turn into frenzied prostitutes, have periodic fits of unnatural sexual excitement, and ultimately die in sexual seizures. When they were apprehended masturbating—or even suspected of having done it—they were strapped on the genitals (where they had sinned) or had hot coals or irons applied to the clitoris.

Nocturnal emissions were considered almost as evil and, although no one seriously believed in succubi or incubi any more, the dreams themselves were considered evil. People who experienced them were informed that they were developing a form of sexual insanity and would have to exercise all their will power to bring such dreams to an end. For those who had thus tried to exorcise this "deviation" but couldn't succeed, there were such things as rings with sharp metal spikes inside them to be worn on the penis at night and spiked metal belts for women. One fanatic even devised an alarm system that would ring a bell if the bed moved. Anyone who advocated such horrors today would be viewed as more than a little crazy, and might well be committed for psychiatric evaluation. Yet they were so commonly accepted in the last century that some of those ghastly instruments were advertised in popular national mail-order catalogues.

There are still, today, a substantial number of sects—religious and otherwise—that believe sexual intercourse is vile, even when performed in a marriage bed. To them, the act of procreation is an unpleasant necessity that should be resisted for as long as possible. One should never, under any circumstances, indulge in sexual intercourse for any reason other than procreation—certainly not for *pleasure*—and the earlier the husband and wife can completely eliminate *coitus* (pronounced co-eet-us) from their lives, the better. Yet these same groups object, on the same moral grounds, to external fertilization (test-tube babies), and the inconsistency of maintaining these two positions simultaneously bothers them not at all.

When viewing most of the American population today, it is obvious that sexual attitudes are a good deal less rigid than those of the so-called Victorian Age. We have come a long way in developing a more mature attitude toward sexual activity. Yet a lot of the ignorance and superstition that held sway during the 19th century is still around, albeit a bit less openly. For instance, it is still widely believed that sexual intercourse saps an individual's strength. Managers and coaches of athletic teams continually caution their players against such indulgences the evening before a game or athletic event, fearing that they will not be able to perform up to par. Many men still view women as "spoiled" if they indulge in intercourse prior to marriage, and some even insist that viable sperm from such a dalliance can live within the woman and produce, in later years, an infant that is not her husband's. Despite the wealth of scientific knowledge currently available about sexual activity and procreation, there are still huge numbers of people who believe many of the fables that have their roots in the Middle Ages. The Victorian vision of sexual activity is still very powerful in this country. Most people today are uncomfortable about the subject of sex, and it is never discussed in "polite" society. Children are still sheltered from any thought of sex—girls play with dolls that have no genitalia, siblings of different sexes do not sleep in the same room and are never permitted to see each other's genitalia. Natural curiosity about any observed differences is promptly suppressed as mysterious, undesirable, or "dirty."

The Purpose of Sex

What is all this fuss about? When all the superstitious fervor and the frenzy of the self-elected defenders of public morality are brushed aside, what are we discussing? We are discussing the act of **mating.** A process during which the male and female germ cells are presented to each other in such a way as to produce an offspring; that is what it is all about. Mating is the process that is designed to perpetuate the species and to maintain both variability and adaptability throughout. From a scientific point of view, there is no validity to the claims that procreation without sexual intercourse is "purer," hence more desirable. There is nothing to suggest that artificial insemination is disadvantageous or harmful to anyone, nor is there any reason to believe that sexual intercourse undertaken just for pleasure is depraved or even undesirable. And then, of course, there are the young, the new lives produced by these acts.

Reproduction Without Sex

What about these young? What would they be like without a mating process? Naturally, we cannot know for sure, but there is a lot of evidence to suggest that, without mating, the mixing of genetic material would be severely limited. There is evidently a kind of "stagnation" that is built right into genetic material, and even the simplest organisms go to considerable lengths to "refresh" their personal DNA through the processes of conjugation.

Nor are these ideas particularly new. Records that are four thousand years old indicate that even the ancients knew that there are profound disadvantages to breeding between close family members. They were apparently aware even then that inbreeding often produces severe congenital or inherited defects. Imagine what complete lack of genetic mixing could produce. All the evidence we have accumulated to date suggests that genetic problems we have never dreamed of would show up in the offspring within a few generations. Mutations that are highly undesirable would be passed on to all of the offspring. With no opportunity for any mixing or blending of genetic material, the vigor and versatility of the species would be drastically reduced, and characteristics that enable the species to adapt to environmental changes might never emerge. It seems obvious, viewed in this light, that the whole point of mating is to mix the genetic material, thus increasing versatility and adaptability instead of limiting it. And experience has shown that the more distant the relationship between partners, the better are the chances of subjugating undesirable genetic traits and insuring variability. Most scientists consider sexual reproduction in humans more than merely desirable. To them, it is imperative.

If we accept that contention, then we are obliged to accept the idea that the sex drive is fundamentally sound also. After all, the *ability* to procreate would be of precious little value to anyone if the *desire* to procreate did not accompany it. Thus as each person matures, he or she develops a built-in desire to indulge in sexual activity. In order to augment this desire, certain structural alterations occur in the two sexes when they mature; females and males both undergo changes that, among other things, make them attractive to the opposite sex, thus giving direction to the mating urge. The response to these urges involves all of our systems, but the primary control systems are most deeply involved. The nervous system is heavily motivated to surrender to the sexual attraction it experiences, and these attractions in turn are driven by several groups of endocrine cells present in the hypothalamus, the pituitary and, most of all, the *gonads.*

Some Facts about a Person's Sex

Father Determines the Sex of the Child

The genetic sex of a person depends on the **sex chromosomes.** Each person has two of these, one donated by the father and the other by the mother—and there are two types. One is known as an **X chromosome** and the other, a **Y chromosome.** When people possess two X chromosomes, they are genetically female. If they possess an XY genetic plan, they are male. A person's anatomical sex, then, is genetically predetermined.

What do parents contribute to the sexual nature of their children? What do they pass, in terms of genetic information?

The mother, being a female, has two X chromosomes. These two X chromosomes, along with another forty-four that are not sex chromosomes, are present in every one of her body cells, including the cells in her ovaries. She has no Y chromosome at all, anywhere. Since she lacks Y chromosomes, her only contribution to the sexual plan of her potential offspring is an X chromosome. The father, on the other hand, in order to be a male, has both an X and a Y, and he may therefore donate either one. If he donates an X chromosome, the offspring will have two of them and thus will be a girl. If he delivers a Y chromosome to the female ovum, then the XY plan will produce a boy. Whichever is the case, the genes are the determining factor. They are responsible for producing the forces that ultimately segregate the two sexes and it is the father who contributes the determining gene.

The Y Chromosome

In many animals, the Y chromosome is essentially inert, which is to say, there is very little information on its DNA, and the development of *maleness* is determined not so much by the presence of a Y chromosome as it is by the absence of one X chromosome. In fruit flies, for example, an individual with a single X chromosome is genetically and functionally a male whether or not it has a Y chromosome. This isn't the case in humans. The Y chromosome is not inert, and a human does not achieve maleness by merely lacking one of the X chromosomes. There is a great deal of genetic information on the Y chromosome, including instructions that determine whether or not a genetic male will ever become a man.

The Basic Sexual Plan

In the beginning, and for the first six weeks, males and females are indistinguishable, because during this period there are no gonads. What will one day become the gonadal structure is a simple blob of mesodermal cells known as the **genital ridge,** and snuggled within this undifferentiated mass is a cluster of cells that originated in endodermal epithelium of the embryonic yolk sac. These are the **primordial germ cells,** which will someday produce the ova (eggs) or the sperm.

In humans—indeed, in all mammals—the basic sexual plan is female. The developing human embryo will grow up female if no disruptive influence is imposed by the genes, and if the genetic programing decrees that the embryo is female, there are no disruptions. The genes on the Y chromosome are designed to alter this basic plan.

For the first six weeks of embryonic life these genes are inert, but some time during the seventh week their information is transcribed onto a strip of mRNA that produces a very special protein. This protein is unique. It is known as the **H-Y antigen,** and it is not found in any products of the X chromosome or any of the somatic (nonsex) chromosomes. When it is activated, it imposes a male pattern of development on the embryo. Current evidence indicates that the differentiation process involves the production of a body of specific enzymes and apparently works like this:

In the beginning, the genital ridge is very simple. Its mesodermal components differentiate quickly into two separated layers—an outer *cortex* and an inner *medulla*—and having achieved that, activity ceases briefly. As the seventh week approaches, however, the ridge begins to stir again. If the genes dictate that the embryo will be male, the Y chromosome awakens and produces its H-Y antigen. This antigen stimulates the production of enzymes that galvanize certain parts of the genital ridge into frantic activity. The result is a steady and furious proliferation of medullary cells, while those of the cortex shrink in size and are slowly overwhelmed. Certain cells in the medulla begin the production of small amounts of testosterone—not much, just a little. While this is going on, the cells that migrated into the ridge from the extra-embryonic endoderm in the yolk sac segregate themselves from the mesodermal components and diversify into primordial germ cells that will ultimately give rise to sperm.

If the genes ordain that the embryo will develop into a woman, a subtly different series of enzymes is produced that stimulate the genital ridge into divergent activity. Instead of proliferation of medullary cells, it is the cells of the cortex that begin frenzied mitotic operations, while those of the medulla atrophy. Some cortical cells begin secreting small amounts of estrogen, and the endodermal elements diversify into presumptive egg cells.

Control of the Fetal Hormones

As far as can be determined, there is no pituitary involvement in the early secretion of these steroid hormones. Hormonal secretion during the fetal stage is completely independent of the pituitary-hypothalamic loop. This may be, in fact, why the primordial germ cells remain primordial. The development of germinal tissue into full-blown germ cells—eggs or spermatozoons—requires the presence of FSH (follicle-stimulating hormone), and there is none at this stage. You will recall from chapter 10 that FSH is an adenohypophyseal hormone, and at this stage of development, the adenohypophysis is still a small dimple of tissue inside the embryonic mouth. The cells responsible for the secretion of gonadotrophic hormones have not matured yet. The secretion of the male and female hormones must, therefore, be controlled by something else, and that something else is apparently the genetically operated enzyme system within the fetus and a maternal hormone known as **human chorionic gonadotropin** (hCG).

Human chorionic gonadotropin is secreted by cells of the structure known as a *trophoblast,* and it is almost certainly needed to stimulate steroid secretion by the fetal testes. It also has functions similar to those attributed to LH, and while these operations are aimed primarily at the mother's system, they may also be involved in aiding fetal production of steroid hormones. Under enzymatic and hCG control, the fetal systems continue to operate at "trickle" levels throughout **prepartum** development (development prior to birth), insuring that the child will someday be a fully operating, sexual human being. When birth occurs, these systems shut down for good. The hCG originated with the mother; hence it is permanently lost, and the enzymes never show up again. Their disappearance switches off the steroid-secreting cells of the immature gonads, and the secretion of sex hormones promptly stops. It will not begin again until puberty, when the hypothalamo-hypophyseal control loop initiates its adult operations.

The Gonads

Both the ovaries and the testes originate in tissue in the upper part of the abdominal wall (near where the kidneys will be in the adult), and about two months prior to birth, they descend. The ovaries drift down into the lower abdomen and attach via ligaments to the lateral wall of the pelvis, but the testes do not stop there. They continue to descend from the abdominal cavity of the fetus into the **scrotum** or **scrotal sac,** which dangles below the abdomen. Apparently no one knows what it is that causes the testes to do this, but it is thought to involve testosterone and may be aided by a structure known as the **gubernaculum.** The gubernaculum is a fibrous belt of contractile tissue that extends from the testes to the lower floor of the scrotum. As the fetus grows, the gubernaculum gets shorter, but it is not believed to be strong enough to actually pull the testes out of the abdominal cavity. It has been suggested that it serves to mark the route that the testes must follow from the abdomen into the scrotum, but this is, of course, speculation (figure 18.1).

There are some interesting facts concerning the external positioning of the male gonads. As virtually everyone is aware, their position outside the body renders them vulnerable to all kinds of damage—even a slight blow is extremely painful. As a result, men go to great lengths to avoid such. Athletes in almost every kind of contact sport wear protective steel or plastic cups designed to encase and protect their gonads during sporting events. These protective cups are extremely uncomfortable even when heavily padded and often wear all the skin off the inside of the thighs near the crotch. Yet it would be a very stupid individual indeed who would fail to use this protection. Considering the creative nature of Oriental culture and their tendency to produce answers that vary from the European norm, it is not surprising that the Japanese have devised a way to cope with the problem without resorting

Figure 18.1 The descent of the testes during fetal development. It has been suggested that the gubernaculum pulls them through the inguinal canal into the scrotum, but most workers feel the gubernaculum is too flimsy to exert that much force.

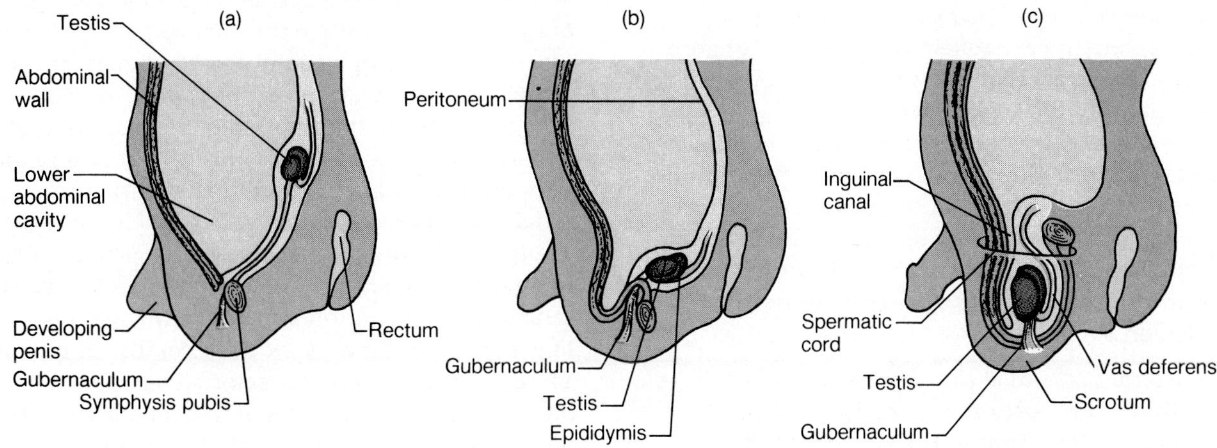

to the steel cups. In Japan, when a family hopes to raise a child to be a Sumo wrestler, the mother sees to it that the inguinal canal is kept open. The inguinal canal (figure 18.1) is the passage through which the testes travel in their move from the abdomen to the scrotum, and it usually atrophies shortly after the descent of the testes. If the testes are forced back up into the abdomen two or three times a day, however, these canals remain patent, and when the child becomes an adult wrestler, he can ignore the "steel jock." Instead, all he needs to do is bind his scrotum with a strap, forcing his testicles back up into his abdomen and out of harm's way.

The gonads are considered to be the **primary sex characteristics,** and they are unusual among endocrine glands for several reasons, not the least of which is the consequence of their removal. If you should lose any of the other endocrine glands—like, for instance, the thyroid, pituitary, parathyroid—you are in big trouble indeed. Unless some replacement therapy were initiated, the situation would be desperate and could be life-threatening. But removal of the gonads does not produce such problems. Not only does it not threaten life, it does not even threaten health! In fact, removal of the male gonads was pretty commonplace in the ancient world and throughout the Middle Ages, not just in the societies of the Middle and Far East, but in Europe as well. There are some structural changes that do not take place when the gonads are removed prior to puberty, and some behavioral changes that normally occur do not happen. For example, a man castrated before puberty would have no interest in any kind of sexual activity when he grew up. His muscles would be weaker than other men's, his body would contain a lot more fat, his voice would be higher, and he would never grow a beard. But if he could tolerate the social problems, his enjoyment of life should not be much different than any other man's; in fact, it might be a lot less complicated. It is all a matter of development.

The gonads of both sexes control two different types of sexuality:

1. *The primary sexual characteristics.* These characteristics are reflected in the type of germ cells **(gametes)** that the individual produces; women produce eggs, men produce spermatozoons. These processes are sometimes referred to as the gonadal **exocrine function** or the **cytogenic function.** In females, all primary sexual activities are carried out in the ovarian follicles; in males they occur within the **seminiferous tubules** and their supporting elements.
2. *The secondary sexual characteristics.* This is tied to hormone production and thus represents the **endocrine function** of the gonads. In women, the **granulosa cells** (follicle cells) of the ovaries handle synthesis and secretion of the hormones, and in men the **cells of Leydig** are responsible. Naturally, being endocrine in nature, these cells have no connection with ducts or tubes of any kind.

The Primary Sex Cells

Production of the primary sex cells—those cells able to unite with an opposite number and produce a new individual—involves a procedure by which the total number of chromosomes in human body cells is cut in half without losing necessary information about any given body structure or characteristic.

As you know, all human body cells contain twenty-two pairs of **autosomes** (chromosomes that are not involved in sex determination) and two sex chromosomes. You will note that the autosomes are not depicted as forty-four chromosomes, but rather as twenty-two *pairs* of chromosomes. It may seem like a hair-splitting distinction to make, but it is not, not at all. Twenty-three of these chromosomes came from the individual's mother; the other twenty-three came from the father. With the exception of the sex chromosomes (the X and Y), each parent contributed information about similar *things* to the offspring, although the information was probably different in each case. For instance, one of the chromosomes from the father might contain instructions to make the offspring's eyes blue, the legs long, and the hair fine and sparse. The matching, or **homologous,** chromosome from the mother might carry information that makes the eyes brown, the legs short, and the hair medium and luxuriant. As you can see, the information provided by each parent is different, but it concerns the same things.

All of these instructions are present in the offspring, and the result is the production of a totally unique individual, one that is truly 50 percent mother and 50 percent father. You could also get a 50-50 amalgamation if the parents contributed all forty-six of their chromosomes to the offspring, but that would mean the offspring would possess ninety-two chromosomes, and that never happens; every normal human being has twenty-two pairs of autosomes and two sex chromosomes. Obviously, then, there has to be some means of sorting out the chromosomal material and segregating it into two clearly separate groups. Each parent must contribute just *half* of his or her genetic material to the new human so that there can be an orchestration of parental information in the new person. But it must not be a totally random half. The chromosomes must be selected so that each parent offers a complete spectrum of information—all that is necessary to produce a complete human.

Figure 18.2 A diagram of the first meiotic division, showing the characteristics of each phase.

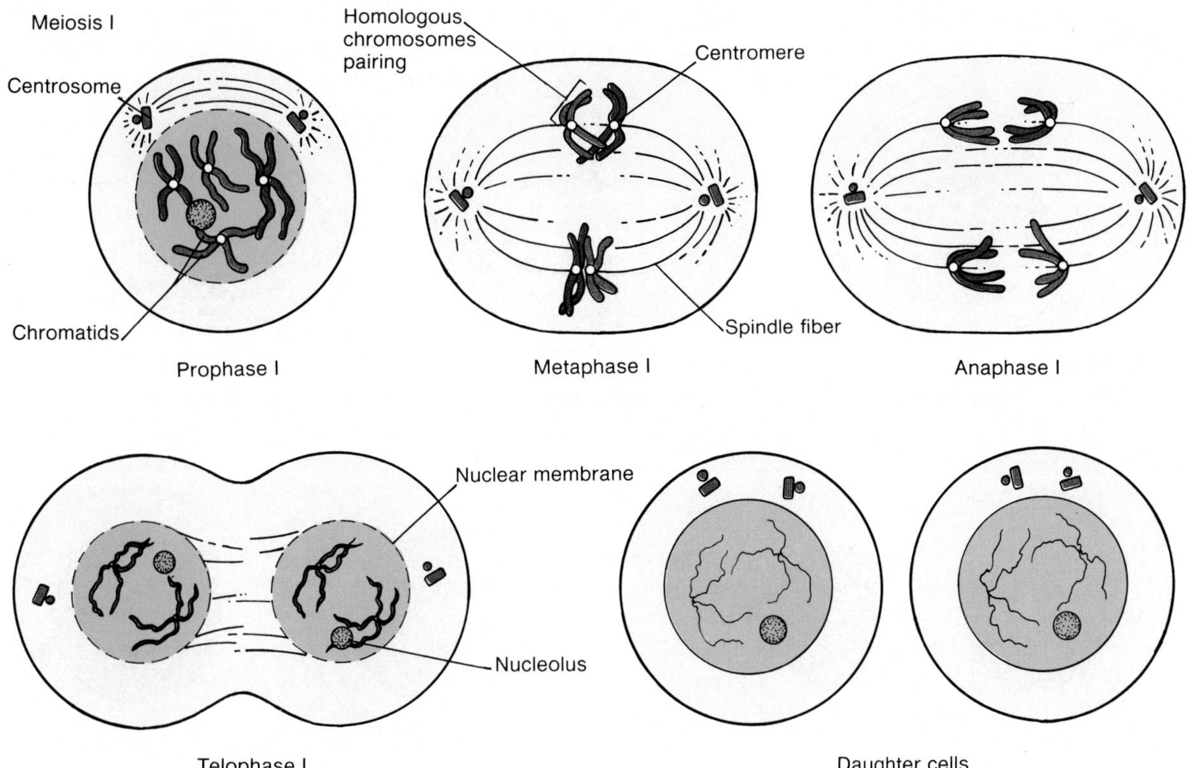

Somehow, this is exactly what happens. No one is sure just what motivates some of the chromosomal arrangements. It is uncertain what the mechanism is that sorts through them and sees to it that each germ cell manages to get all necessary information, but we know it happens, and we can describe the sequence of events. It is accomplished in the gonads by the germ cells and is known as **meiosis.**

Meiosis—also known as **reduction division**—takes place in the seminiferous tubules of the male testes and in the ovaries of the female, and although it differs in certain specifics, the principle is the same in both. It is similar to mitosis (see chapter 5) in that it results in cellular and nuclear division, but since the object is to segregate and reduce the number of chromosomes in the final products, it varies in several important details.

Some Terminology

In order to simplify things, I must introduce some terms of reference. Cells that have a full complement—i.e., twenty-three pairs—of chromosomes are known as **diploid cells.** Hence all human body cells, with the exception of the gametes, are diploid. Even when cells in a given body tissue are multiplying vigorously, only diploid cells are produced, because at the end of each mitotic division, every chromosome present in each daughter cell has a homologous chromosome somewhere else in the same nucleus. Meiosis, however, leaves no such homologies. When reduction division has been completed, each cell contains only twenty-three chromosome strands, and there are no homologies anywhere. Such cells, which exist only in the gonads, are said to be **haploid.**

Meiosis

Meiosis features two separate division patterns. One of them—the second— is similar to mitosis (chapter 5), differing only in the number of chromosomes involved. But the first division is quite different.

The First Meiotic Division

As the first metaphase approaches, the chromosomes move toward the cellular equator just as they do in mitosis, but in meiosis they do not distribute themselves randomly. Instead, some mechanism causes each chromosome to seek out its homologous mate and **synapse** with it. (This is the same term used for a junction of neurons. It is from the Greek *synap,* meaning "a union.") Thus, unlike mitosis, which has a single line of forty-six chromosomes at the equatorial plate in metaphase, during the first meiotic division there are *two* lines, each of twenty-three chromosomes, facing each other (figure 18.2). When anaphase begins and the spindle fibers start pulling on their chromosomes, there is no splitting of the centromeres. Instead of the chromosomes breaking

Figure 18.3 The second meiotic division. Note that after the division occurs, each cell contains half as many chromosomes as the original had when meiosis began.

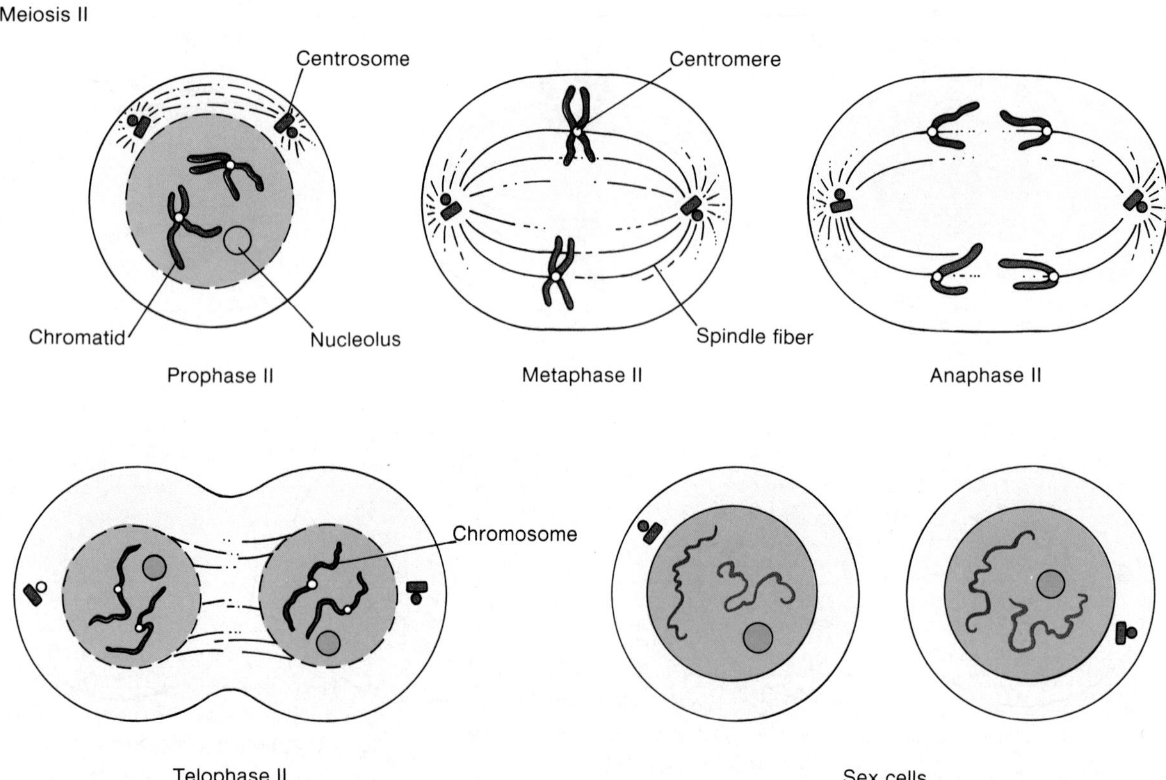

into their separate chromatids, the homologous partners separate and drift into opposite ends of the cell (figure 18.2). When telophase I brings the first meiotic division to a close, each daughter cell contains twenty-three chromosomes, each composed of two chromatids and an intact centromere. There are no homologous chromosomes in any of the daughter cells; hence there is no longer any duplication of information in these cells. Cells elsewhere in the body may contain genes from the individual's mother that indicate blue eyes and short legs and genes from the father that code for brown eyes and long legs. The daughter cells produced by the first meiotic division, however, contain information that will result in blue eyes or in brown eyes; in short legs or long legs. They will not have genes for both.

Interkinesis

An interphase period known as **interkinesis** now occurs, during which the new daughter cells rest and recover from their exertions. It's usually much shorter than a normal mitotic interphase, probably because while it lasts no duplication of genetic material takes place.

The Second Division

The second meiotic division is substantially like mitosis. When the metaphase begins, a single line of chromosomes forms on the equatorial plane (figure 18.3). As anaphase starts and material draws away from the center line, the centromeres split, individual chromatids separate, and single strands of DNA drift, as they do in mitosis, to opposite ends of the cell. When telophase completes the second division, the resultant daughter cells each contain twenty-three chromatids, each of which is a double helix of DNA. The germ cells have been produced.

Puberty in the Male

Throughout the years of childhood, the differences between boys and girls are small. If the two sexes were not dressed or coiffured differently, there would be no way to distinguish them without examining the external genitalia. With the attainment of puberty, however, all this changes. Some time after the age of 10 and almost always before the age of 15, males attain **puberty**—the ability to reproduce. No one really knows what it is that determines when this will take place, but it evidently starts in the brain when something turns on the switch that initiates the necessary hypothalamic activity. The process actually begins with the appearance of the secondary sexual characteristics, and it ends when growth stops. It is not necessarily coincidental with **adolescence** (see box).

Figure 18.4 (*a*) Sagittal section of a testis; (*b*) cross section of a seminiferous tubule.

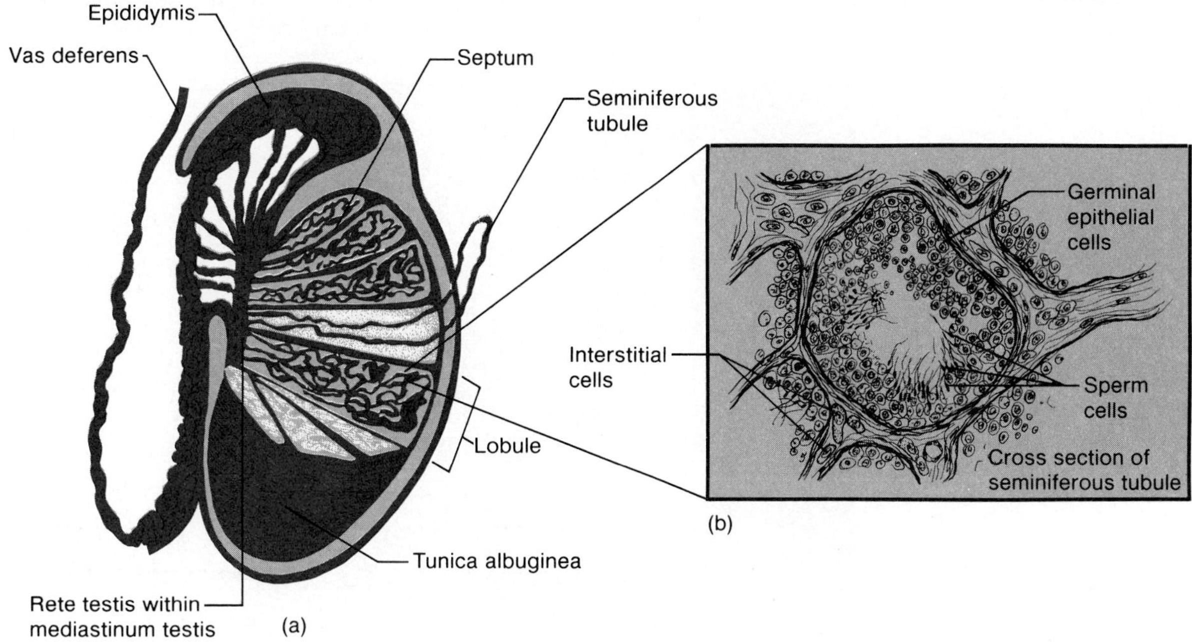

The period of adolescence is, in our society, often considered synonymous with puberty, and it isn't, really. In American society, adolescence is fondly believed to embrace the teenaged years, but since a person's associates pretty well determine the limits, both the beginning and the end of adolescence can vary. The beginning is not definite—it just sort of starts when a person is generally considered no longer a child. The line at the finish is usually much clearer, because it has a solid social and psychological marker—adolescence ends when the individual accepts adult responsibilities. Adolescence is thus a sociological concept that is applied by the culture in which the person is reared, and depending on that culture, it may end prior to the finish of puberty or long after.

Puberty, on the other hand, is a biological phenomenon that pays no attention to cultural morés. No one in our culture would consider 12-year-old girls adults, yet many are perfectly capable of having babies at that age, just as some 12-year-old boys are capable of being fathers. Biologically, puberty begins with the development of the first secondary sexual characteristics. In the U.S., a girl's first menstrual period usually occurs between the ages of 9 and 12, and a boy's first ejaculations take place sometime around the age of 13. Puberty in both sexes ends when the long bones stop growing.

The primary sexual characteristics have always been in place, and now, with the beginning of puberty, the secondary characteristics start to establish themselves. As the gonadotrophins begin to flow from the pituitary, the testes increase their output of testosterone, and once the sex hormones appear, a boy's *maleness* begins to show. The first hint that this is happening is the development of pubic hair, which is shortly followed by a noticeable enlargement of the external genitalia. The scrotum, the testes, and the penis all get larger, and with every enlargement of the testicles comes a still-greater flow of testosterone. Underarm hair usually starts growing at about age 15, and shortly thereafter the beard begins to make a hair-at-a-time appearance. The amount of body fat lessens, the shoulders begin to broaden, and muscle mass visibly increases. About this time the vocal cords begin to lengthen, making the voice crack and break as it shifts uncontrollably from the high soprano of the child to the deepened tenor or baritone of the adult male.

During this period of a boy's life, erections become more and more frequent and are more often than not involuntary . . . indeed, a young man's waking nightmare is being called upon to stand before his high school class or to walk off a bus with an erection bulging in his trousers. Nocturnal emissions are quite common during these years and frequently occur a year or two before the testes are producing any mature sperm; thus boys can experience orgasm while they are yet unable to father a child.

There is usually quite a spurt in growth during puberty. Boys may grow as much as a foot during the first year or so, after which things slow down a bit. Usually about age 21, upward growth ends, although most young men continue to add muscle mass throughout their mid and late 20s.

The Testes

The structure of the testes is illustrated in figure 18.4. The word itself means "witness" and stems from the

Figure 18.5 (*a*) A microscopic photograph of several seminiferous tubules in cross section. (*b*) A line drawing of a cross section in the micrograph. How many structures in the micrograph can you identify through comparison? (*c*) An enlargement of one area of the seminiferous tubule. Spermatogonia undergo a normal mitotic division to produce the primary spermatocytes (forty-six chromosomes). The first meiotic division produces secondary spermatocytes (twenty-three chromosomes).

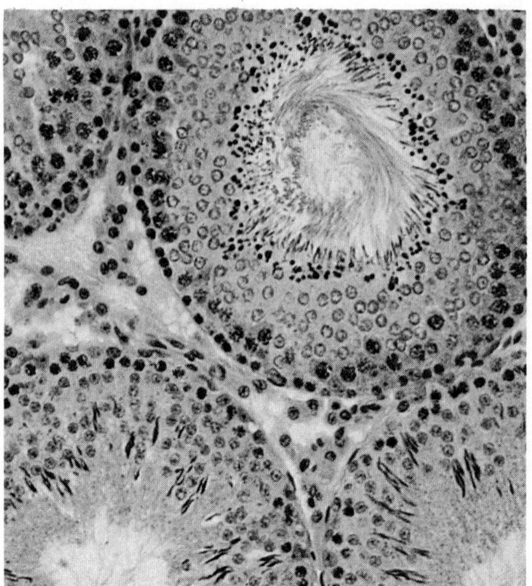

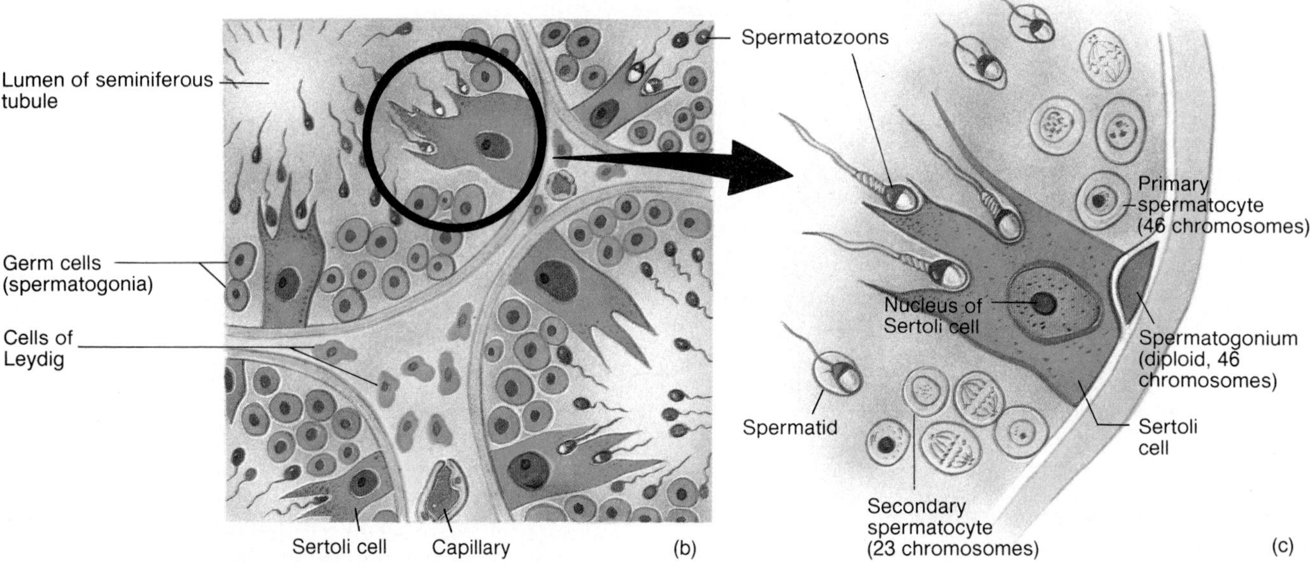

fact that in ancient times, men of some cultures swore to the truth of a statement by placing their hands on their testicles while taking the oath. Testicles resemble very soft eggs about 4 cm long, and within their boundaries both primary and secondary sexual materials are produced.

The production of viable male germ cells—cells that can produce a child— begins at the onset of puberty. It takes place within the seminiferous tubules.

Spermatogenesis

In males, meiosis resulting in germ cell production is the first phase of the process of **spermatogenesis**—sperm creation. It begins in the seminiferous tubules in a layer of cells near the outer margin of each tubule—with cells called **spermatogonia** (figure 18.5).

Spermatogonia are all derived from the original primordial germ cells that were imbedded in the embryonic genital ridge. All are diploid, and they undergo a constant, steady mitosis, so that there will be a perpetual supply of new cells available for the production of sperm. Since they all are diploid when things start, each contains forty-four somatic chromosomes plus the two sex chromosomes—one X and one Y.

Some incompletely understood mechanism selects certain of these cells and they begin to shift position, moving from the periphery of the seminiferous

Figure 18.6 Meiotic division in male germ cells. Because these operations ultimately produce spermatozoons, the process is known as spermatogenesis.

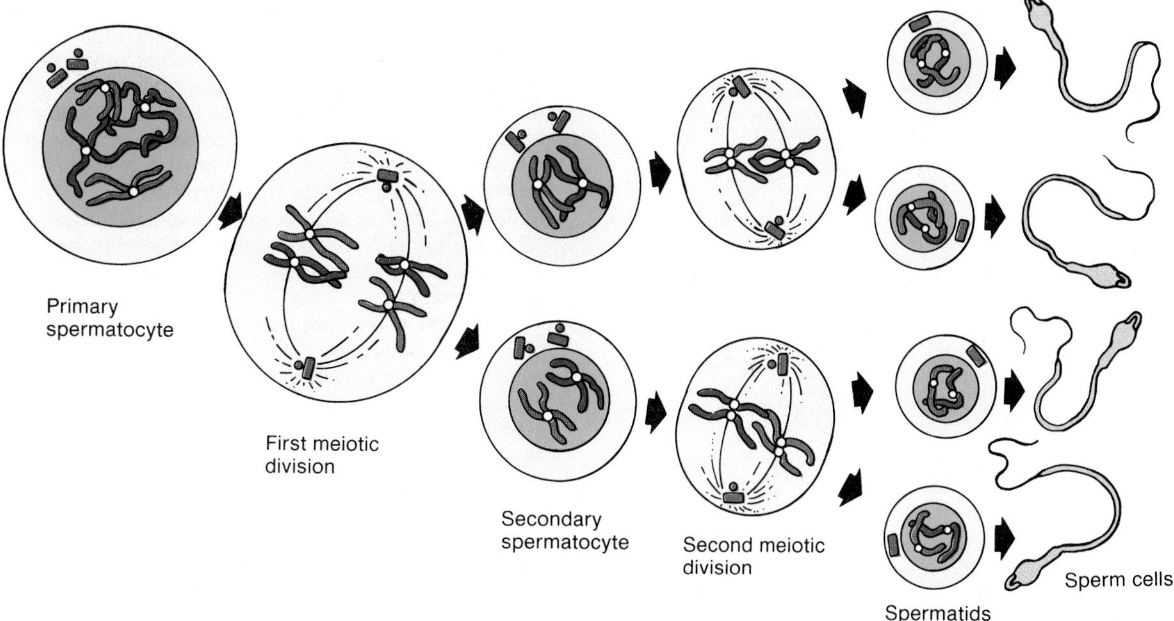

tubule into the hollow center. As they drift into the lumen, they undergo a short burst of development, changing into **primary spermatocytes** in the process. Each then undergoes the first meiotic division, and the daughter cells are **secondary spermatocytes.** Each primary spermatocyte began with forty-four double-stranded chromosomes and two double-stranded sex chromosomes. All the secondary spermatocytes have a reduced number. Each contains twenty-two double-stranded somatic chromosomes, but only half will have Y chromosomes; the other half will have an X.

The second meiotic division alters the secondary spermatocytes into cells known as **spermatids,** each containing twenty-three single-stranded chromosomes. Each single spermatogonium therefore ultimately becomes four spermatids, two of which contain the necessary information to produce a girl child, and two of which contain chromosomes that will produce a boy (figure 18.6).

The spermatids, having undergone the necessary meiotic divisions, now contain the proper chromosome assortments to handle procreation, but they are not yet mature enough to fertilize the egg cell of a female. Before that can occur, each cell must undergo further maturation. The maturation involves the addition of a very active tail and the loss of nearly all cellular cytoplasm. The result is the mature spermatozoan (figure 18.7).

The spermatozoan, tiny as it is, may seem like it should be a relatively simple thing, but it is not. It consists of four separate regions—head, neck, body, and tail—each with its own unique characteristics and capabilities.

The head region is almost all nucleus except for an acorn-like cap on the tip known as an **acrosome.** The acrosome contains a number of enzymes that are designed to aid in penetrating the protective covering of the female egg, should the opportunity arise.

The neck contains a pair of centrioles that apparently provide a kind of "skeletal" anchorage for the contractile proteins in the tail.

The body region is filled with mitochondria that spiral around the upper part of the tail and provide the necessary ATP for the vigorous movement that each spermatozoan produces when shot out of the penis. Almost all of the cytoplasm still present in the cell is in the body region, so whatever glycolytic activity occurs must take place there.

In men, spermatogenesis requires about seventy-two hours to go from start to finish. During this entire time span, the developing germ cells are vulnerable—to mutation or to any kind of physical damage that the external environment might conceivably produce. Such agents might include things like physical disruption or hormonal interference, and if they are encountered during spermatogenesis they can produce mutations. One of the most ubiquitous problems in Western society is excessive heat around the testes. When a man wears pants, the thermal advantages of keeping the testes in a sac outside the body cavity are negated somewhat, and some reputable researchers have speculated that this may have already played a role in weakening the human species.

Figure 18.7 (*a*) The sperm head develops from the nucleus of the spermatid; (*b*) a diagram of a mature spermatozoan.

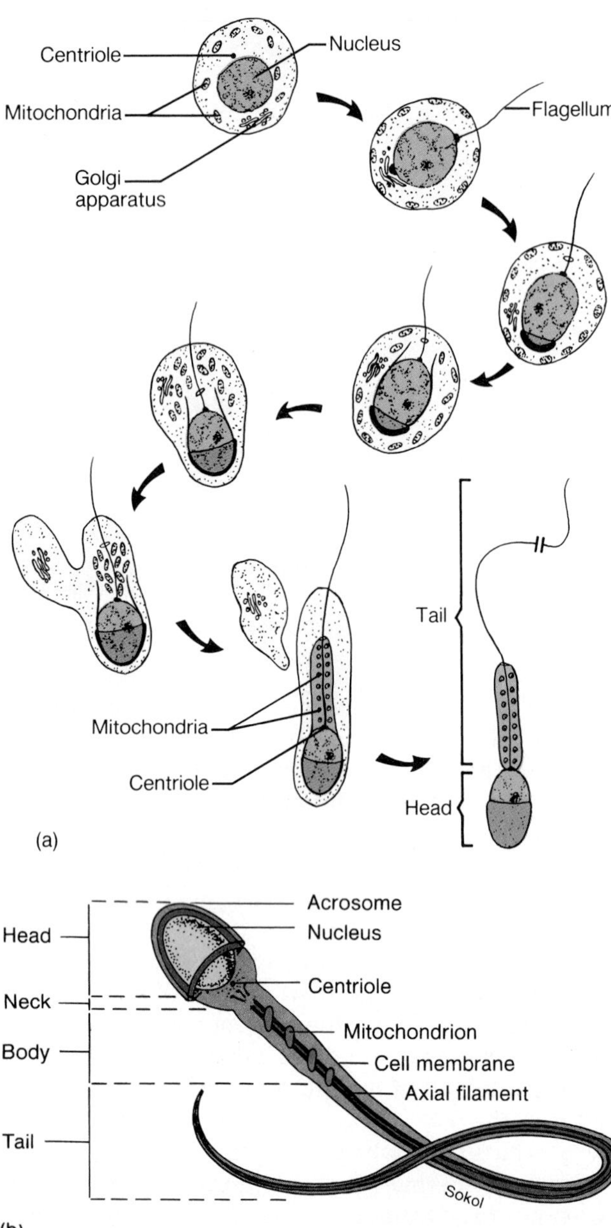

This observation perhaps requires a little explanation. Everyone knows that the ovaries are inside the abdomen while the testes are suspended outside. As we have already indicated, this renders the testes particularly susceptible to damage, a point that is well-known. What is not commonly known is why they are out there. There is a reason for this positioning—a reason that is more important than their unusual vulnerability. It has to do with mistakes, errors that occur during the copying of DNA molecules prior to cell division, errors called *mutations.*

Normally, mutations are expected to occur about 0.01 percent of the time; hence one out of every 10,000 spermatozoons can be expected to contain a mutation. Most mutations are harmful and some are downright lethal, so generally speaking, mutation is highly undesirable. Production of spermatozoons by the testes is an ongoing process that results in literally millions of them every day, which means that at a normal rate, a lot of mutations are going to be produced. A normal ejaculation during coitus injects about 400 million spermatozoons into the female reproductive tract, and if mutations occur at a normal rate, 40,000 of those will contain some kind of mutation. These are not particularly good odds for cells that could produce a new individual. Obviously, if there is a way to reduce that number, it would be desirable, and there is a way. Mutations occur at a lower rate if the cultures are cooled off a little bit, and suspending the testes outside the body does just that, reducing the incidence of mutation by quite a large factor.

Why do women not have their gonads suspended outside the body as well? It is all a matter of numbers. The ovaries produce only one ripe germ cell every thirty days, and the average woman could reasonably expect to produce fewer than 600 during a normal reproductive life. Statistically, then, the odds are nearly 20 to 1 against a woman producing a single mutated ovum in her entire lifetime. Odds that slim are negligible; hence protection from mechanical damage wins out. A woman's gonads are therefore kept inside her body where they are less likely to get hurt.

The Sex Accessory Structures

The sex accessories are structures within the male reproductive system that provide the spermatozoons with a means of getting to the body exterior and in addition provide sustenance for them during their short lives. Like the primary sex organs, the accessories depend for their continued health on the hormones produced by the Leydig cells. They include the following: the **epididymis,** the **vas deferens,** the **ejaculatory ducts,** and the **bulbourethral** (Cowper's) **gland.** In addition, there are two others that are mentioned separately because they are particularly susceptible to a lack of androgens—the **prostate gland** and the **seminal vesicles.**

As you can see in figure 18.8, the epididymides are located on the surface of the testes, and they represent the beginning of the system of ducts and tubes that carries the sperm from the testes to the body exterior.

Superficially, the epididymides resemble a rather diffuse mass of cells loosely pasted on the outer surface of each testicle, but in fact each is an intricately coiled tube that picks up the spermatozoons from within each testicle and leads them into the vas deferens (figure 18.9). Because of its proximity to the testicles, it has been suggested that one of the functions of the epididymis may be the storage of viable spermatozoons for short periods of time. During their stay within the epididymis, the sperm finish the process of maturing and are prepared for ejaculation.

Figure 18.8 Male reproductive organs: (*a*) sagittal view; (*b*) posterior view.

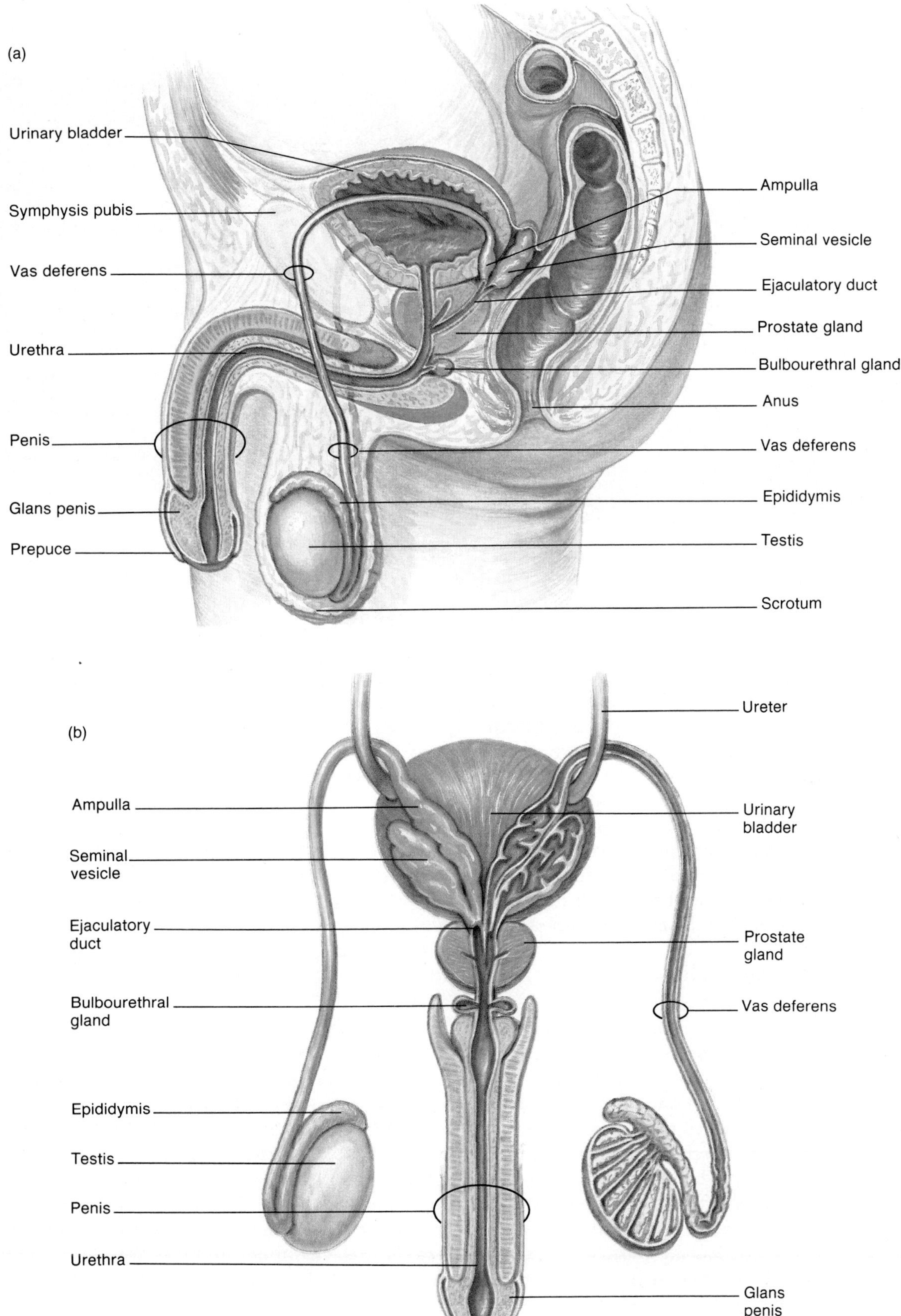

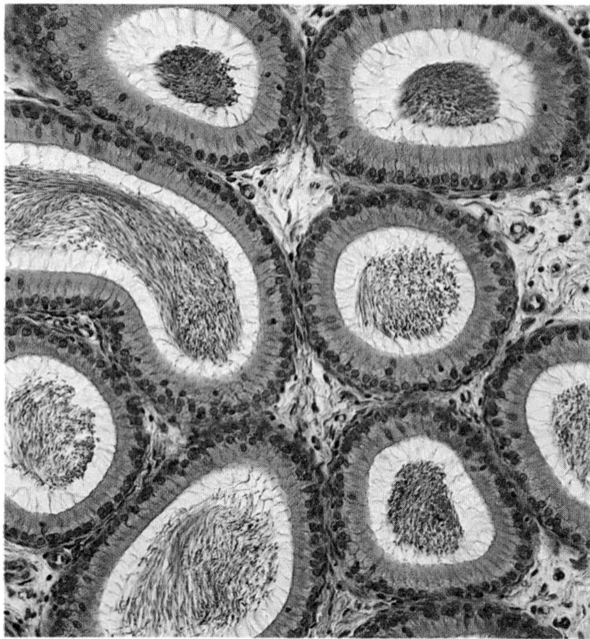

Figure 18.9 Photomicrograph of a human epididymis in cross section.

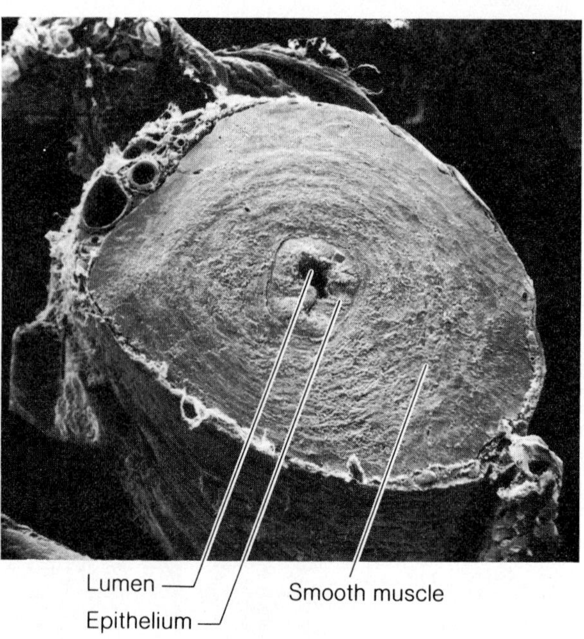

Figure 18.10 Scanning electron micrograph of a cross section of the vas deferens (70×). (*Tissues and Organs: A Text-Atlas of Scanning Electron Microscopy,* by R. G. Kessel and R. H. Kardon. © 1979 W. H. Freeman and Company.)

The *vas deferentia* (figure 18.10) are really much enlarged and straightened-out continuations of the epididymides. These are the vessels that are cut when a vasectomy is performed, and they lead from the outer surface of each testis to the *seminal vesicles.* The ducts from each seminal vesicle join up with a vas deferens, and the two then form a very short *ejaculatory duct,* which passes through the *prostate gland* just before and after the junction with the urethra. The *prostate gland* is about the size and shape of a horse chestnut, and as figure 18.8 shows, it has two channels that open into the two ejaculatory ducts. Shortly thereafter, the *bulbourethral gland* also opens, through a very short duct, into the urethra, which then continues through the penis to the outside of the body.

The External Male Genitalia

The external sexual organs consist of the **penis** and the **scrotum** (figure 18.8). The penis has two main regions—the **shaft** and the **glans** (figure 18.11). The skin covering the shaft is soft, quite loose, and extremely elastic, extending forward in an uncircumcised individual to cover the glans completely. The portion that surrounds the glans is known as the **foreskin** or **prepuce** and is cut away when circumcision is performed. The glans is covered with an extremely thin, shiny epidermis that is loaded with tactile (touch) receptors, two areas of which are particularly sensitive—the **corona** and the **frenum** (see figure 18.11). The shaft itself is much longer than it appears to be. It extends deep into the crotch, a fact which is easily confirmed during erection by simply pressing with your fingers up into the scrotal zone. This internal portion of the shaft is known as the **root** of the penis, and it is connected at its base to the pubic arch.

Figure 18.11 The external anatomy of the penis. The foreskin is shown pulled back from the glans, but is otherwise intact. During circumcision, the frenum is severed and the foreskin removed.

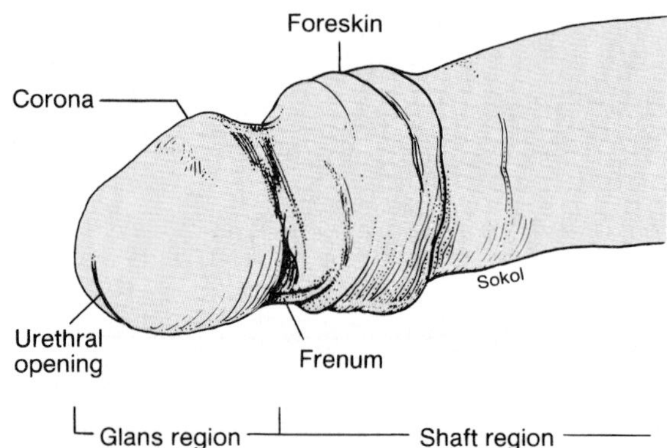

Within the penis, there are three long chambers that form a triangle of spongy tissue with its apex at the bottom (figure 18.12). The two large chambers within the shaft are called the **corpora cavernosa** or **cavernous chambers,** and they terminate at the base of the glans. The smaller chamber—called the **corpus spongiosum**—runs below the cavernosa along the bottom of the shaft, and its swollen end *is* the glans.

Figure 18.12 (*a*) The internal morphology of the penis. (*b*) The penis shaft in cross section. Note the enormous size of the corpora cavernosa. These are the sinuses that fill with blood and become rigid with turgor, thus producing the erection.

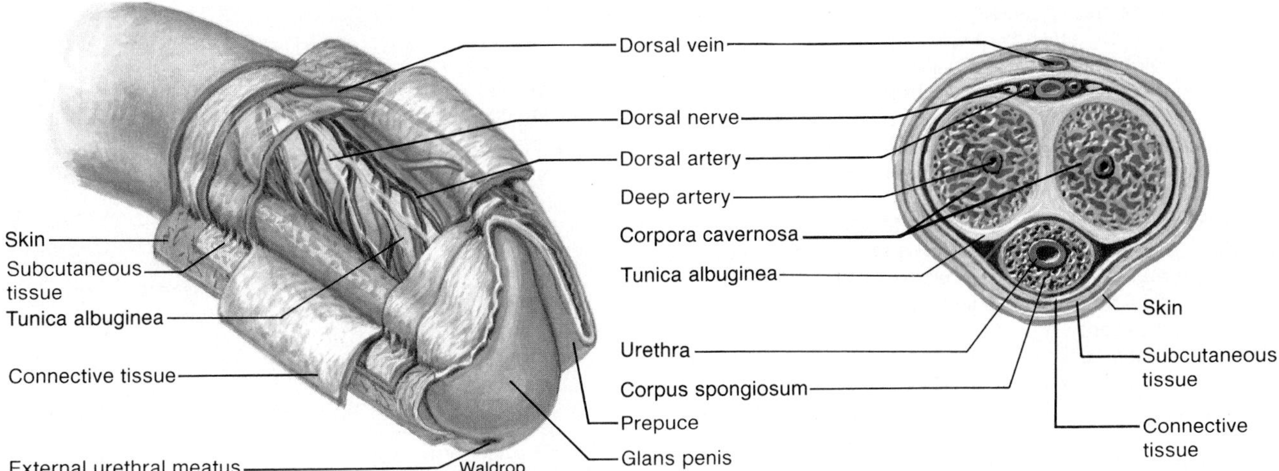

The urethra, which carries both urine and semen, travels down the center of the spongiosum and exits at its tip.

Contrary to what some may think, the penis itself contains no muscle tissue or bone. There are some muscles attached near its base and while they permit some jerking movement, they contribute nothing to the "hardening" of the penis when an erection occurs. Erection is due to engorgement of the mass of blood vessels and cavities within the shaft and glans, and it occurs when the arterial vessels supplying the penis bring in more blood than the veins can carry away. The "hardness" results from turgor pressure within the "blown-up" spongy tissue in the same way that a limp balloon gets rigid when it is filled with air.

Endocrinology of the Testes

There is little doubt that spermatogenesis is regulated at least in part by hormones. But it is a bit difficult to determine just which hormones are involved and when. One of the problems is that the hormonal effects are often different in other species, and in any case, obtaining pure hormones is not always the easiest thing in the world to do. Nevertheless, all current evidence supports the theory that the hypothalamo-pituitary loop is deeply involved in control of the male gonads. (You may want to review chapter 10 before reading this section.)

The hypothalamic gonadotrophin-releasing hormone (GnRH) controls the synthesis and release of the pituitary gonadotrophins luteinizing hormone (LH) and follicle-stimulating hormone (FSH). FSH seems to operate mainly on the Sertoli cells, while LH evidently concentrates on the cells of Leydig (see figure 18.5). The Sertoli cells are the male homolog of the female's ovarian follicle cells, and during spermatogenesis, the Sertoli cells work in very close association with the developing germ cells. The Sertoli cells have several functions. They direct the movement of the developing germ cells toward the lumen of the seminiferous tubules, then they secrete the fluid that both strengthens the acrosome and transports the sperm cells into the epididymis. In addition, although it is by no means a sure thing, it is assumed that the Sertoli cells provide nutrient for the germinal cells, which in turn are driven by FSH. Since the cells of Leydig are responsible for the production of male hormones, this means that FSH concentrates mainly on the production of sperm, while LH exerts most of its effort on controlling the amount of testosterone and other androgens that are released into the bloodstream. The feedback loop is closed by testosterone in the blood. Its presence in the hypothalamus produces a negative feedback effect on the GnRH-producing cells there.

The Male Sexual Response

Sexual responses are driven by both hormones and neural impulses, and the two control systems interact powerfully when the mating urge begins. Probably it all begins in the cerebral hemispheres where conscious thought exists. The mere sight of a cow will induce increased LH secretion in a bull, and there is good evidence that the sight of a sensual woman will do the same thing in a man. The connecting links have not been completely traced, but they are almost certainly neural fibers running from the cerebral hemispheres into the hypothalamus, which then instructs the pituitary to release its gonadotrophs. The gonadotrophs in their turn boost blood levels of testosterone and stimulate increased production of sperm.

A **Male Contraceptive Pill?** Some interesting facts have come out of the investigations into how the releasing factors operate on their target cells in the pituitary. For instance, synthetic analogs of GnRH are available. Some of these analogs are not enough like the real hormone to stimulate the production of gonadotrophic hormones, but they *are* enough like normal GnRH to bind to the receptor sites on the FSH and LH-secreting cells in the pituitary. Thus, by occupying all the receptors on these gonadotrophic cells, they interfere with normal function by preventing natural GnRH from doing its job. This type of interference is known as **competitive inhibition,** and as you might expect, it blocks the release of LH and FSH. This, in turn, reduces the production of male hormones and spermatozoons.

These observations suggested to researchers that they may have, in synthetic GnRH, the nucleus of a formula for a male contraceptive. After all, anything that halts the production of sperm cells would certainly render impregnation unlikely. The idea was tested on human volunteers to see if synthetic GnRH would render men temporarily sterile, and strictly speaking, it worked—it is a very effective contraceptive. But unfortunately it will never sell, because it has a very unpleasant side effect. Synthetic GnRH disrupts the male sex drive, and it does so at the worst possible time during the mating act. Everything goes nicely until penetration occurs, and then the male's erection promptly disappears. This was not an isolated occurrence. It happened to the volunteers consistently, and it jolted them and their spouses so thoroughly that nearly all of them quit within a week.

The initial physical response in men is erection of the penis, which stiffens it to the point where it can be thrust into the female's receptacle. When the sexual congress reaches its climax, there is a tremendous outburst of neural activity, particularly in the limbic system of the brain where the pleasure centers are. These neural outbursts are mainly adrenergic and are associated with sympathetic activity in the pelvic area which stimulates several sets of muscles there into activity. The smooth muscles around the epididymides, the ducta deferentia, the seminal vesicles, and the prostate gland all contract, and their contents are thrust through the ejaculatory ducts into the urethra, near the root of the penis. Simultaneously, a pair of sphincter muscles contract and close up their tubes. One is just below the prostate gland and the other is around the urethra just below its exit point from the bladder. These sphincter contractions thus close off all possible exits from the urethra except the one going through the penis, and the second stage of ejaculation begins. The response up to this point is known as **emission,** and at this stage, most males feel it is an irreversible process, beyond any possibility of control, and they are right.

Once the sphincters close around the urethra, a group of skeletal muscles at the base of the penis begin to forcefully and rhythmically contract, forcing the fluid through the penis to the exterior of the body in a series of spurts, a process known as **expulsion.** A complete ejaculation normally releases in excess of 400 million active spermatozoons from the male genitalia, and the muscles involved contract with sufficient force to shoot the semen a foot or two from the penis, well up into the female reproductive tract.

Table 18.1 Summary of the Mechanisms that Produce Ejaculation

Sexual Arousal

This may take the form of mental arousal or direct physical contact with the genitalia. The first physical manifestation is penile erection.

Sexual Stimulation

This usually (although not always) requires some physical stimulation of the penis. It culminates in:

Orgasm

This consists of an intense sympathetic neural bombardment throughout the brain, particularly in the limbic system and extending to sympathetic motor nerves innervating the pelvic region. It results ultimately in ejaculation. Ejaculation occurs in two stages:

1. Emission
   Smooth muscle contractions:
   a. Production of peristalsis in testicular ducts, epididymides, vas deferentia, and ejaculatory ducts.
   b. Complete (nonperistaltic) rhythmic contractions of seminal vesicles, prostate gland, and bulbourethral gland.
   c. Sphincter muscles close off urinary bladder and ejaculatory ducts.
2. Expulsion
   Skeletal muscle contractions occur through the erectile column at the root of the penis. Seminal fluid is ejected with considerable force from the urethra.

Semen

As was already indicated, there is very little cytoplasm even in the body region of the spermatozoons—certainly not nearly enough to store the amount of energy required for their trip through the female reproductive tract. In fact, the tiny spermatozoons, lacking almost all the cytoplasm present in the original spermatogonia, really do not possess the storage space to hold enough of anything to keep them alive for more than a minute or two. All the necessary raw materials must be supplied, therefore, by the fluid in which they are suspended when they leave the body. This is the seminal fluid, and it has everything necessary to give the spermatozoons a chance to live long enough to complete their mission. The fluid is provided by the sex accessory structures as the spermatozoons pass through them on their way out of the body.

Sperm can be stored within the epididymides for a matter of weeks, and they are activated during their stay there. When ejaculation begins, these activated spermatozoons are thrust into, and through, the vas deferens to the seminal vesicles, where they encounter a thin, watery fluid that is thought to increase their activity. As they enter the ejaculatory ducts, the two short channels leading from the prostate gland introduce a milky, rather alkaline fluid that is synthesized in the prostate. This fluid serves to neutralize the acids produced by the metabolic activity of the spermatozoons and probably also acts to neutralize some of the acid secretions of the vagina, thus giving the spermatozoons a better chance to survive during the time required to swim up to the ovum. The bulbourethral glands provide the last contribution—a clear alkaline fluid that also has a neutralizing effect but which contains, in addition, quantities of fructose that may provide a source of energy for the hard-working spermatozoons.

The entire ejaculatory process is summarized in table 18.1.

The Human Female

As was pointed out previously, when a female fetus is developing, there is apparently no genetically engineered protein to steer it on its way. The basic mammalian body design is female and if left alone, that is what all mammals will become, so the body's developmental adjustment mechanisms simply leave everything alone. In the absence of the H-Y antigen, the developing fetus produces the enzymes that result in internal and external female characteristics. The cortical zones of the genital ridge become dominant during the seventh week of fetal growth, and the germ cells become oogonia instead of spermatogonia.

The total number that develops is truly astonishing. It does not begin to approach the number of sperm cells that are produced in the testes, of course, but there are an awful lot of them just the same. There are nearly seven million oogonia in the first tiny ovaries of the female fetus, and while this number is steadily reduced as growth proceeds, more than two million are still present at birth. By the time puberty is attained, the number has declined to about three hundred thousand, and that is certainly enough . . . far more than any woman will ever be able to deal with during her lifetime. Assuming that a woman has an active reproductive life of about forty years—which is about average—she could have, at maximum, about 520 menstrual cycles. Periods missed for illness or pregnancies reduce that number even more, so that the average woman probably has fewer than five hundred menstrual cycles during her lifetime. Why has she so many potential ova? No one really has a good answer for this. There does not appear to be any kind of internal competition for the process of ripening, although it is possible that there is. The most logical explanation currently available is that it provides whatever mechanism is responsible for making the selection with a larger random choice.

As is the case with male gonads, the follicles operate under the aegis of genetic manipulation until the child is born, and then they become dormant. Throughout childhood they remain quiescent, and they do not awaken again until puberty. At the beginning of puberty, the gonadotrophins begin to flow from the pituitary gland and the menstrual cycles begin.

Puberty in the Female

No one knows why, but puberty usually strikes the female child at a slightly earlier age than it does males. Records suggest a very broad range, some girls starting as early as age 5 (an abnormal condition known as precocious puberty), others showing few, if any, signs of maturity as late as age 16. However, for most girls in the U.S., puberty begins to assert itself shortly after they reach the age of 10. As is the case with boys, a biological "clock" of some kind, probably somewhere in the brain, switches on the GnRH-secreting cells of the hypothalamus and the gonadotrophins begin to flow. Under their influence, the ovaries develop and estrogen secretion begins. The first visible sign of approaching maturity is the beginning of breast growth. The development of milk ducts and deposition of fat in the chest area begins to swell the mammary glands. Simultaneously, the areola (the dark area around the nipples) and the nipples begin to enlarge and protrude. By age 15 or 16 breast development is probably as complete as it will get until pregnancy (figure 18.13).

Some time around the late 1930s the female breast began to assume an extremely important cosmetic role in Western culture, and the general attitude today seems to be that large, firm breasts add a great deal to a woman's physical attractiveness. No matter how one feels about this, it is important to realize that beauty concepts have very little to do with functionality. Contrary to what many seem to believe, the size of the female breast has nothing to do with a woman's ability to produce milk or nurse an infant. When a woman is not pregnant or actually nursing a child, very little of the mammary gland consists of lactogenic tissue; it is mostly fat (figure 18.13). In fact, if it were not for the presence of fat, male and nonlactating female breasts would not be very different in size. Just why some girls tend to have large fatty deposits in the mammary area while others do not is a problem an awful lot of people in this country wish someone would solve. It is no secret that some women can get quite heavy, achieving layer after layer of fatty tissue everywhere except on their breasts, while others tend to have large fatty deposits in the mammary area yet remain essentially lean and fit everywhere else. It is probable that these extremes and all the variations in between are a product of genetic programing and that any alteration one way or another will remain strictly within the realm of the plastic surgeon.

Figure 18.13 Structure of the breast. (*a*) Sagittal section; (*b*) anterior view.

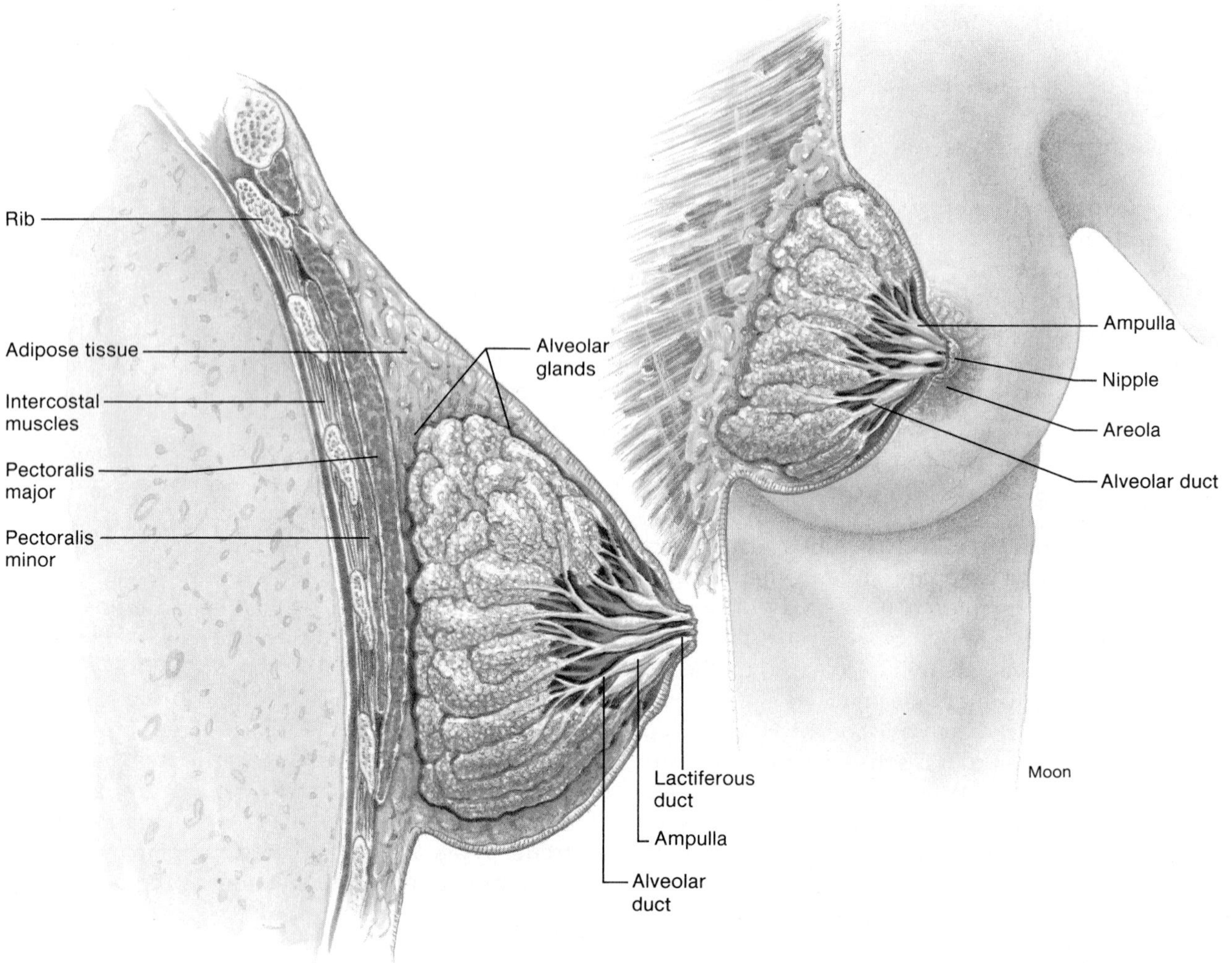

During this time the overall characteristic "female shape" begins to assert itself. Under the influence of the female hormones, fat deposits begin to shift around the entire body, much of it winding up in the hips, buttocks, and breasts. Unlike the male, female shoulders do not become heavily padded with muscle tissue; hence there is very little tendency for the shoulders to broaden. This, coupled with a concomitant widening of the female pelvis, makes a woman's hips about as broad as her shoulders, and the extra fat insures a shape that is usually round instead of the flat or angular aspect of male buttocks.

There is some change in the external genitalia also, although because of their morphology it is not as obvious as it is in the male (figure 18.14). The labia majora tend to grow somewhat, the clitoris enlarges, and pubic hair begins to sprout. Internally (figure 18.15) the lining of the vagina begins to thicken, the ovaries mature, and the uterus begins to enlarge.

Figure 18.14 The external female genitalia.

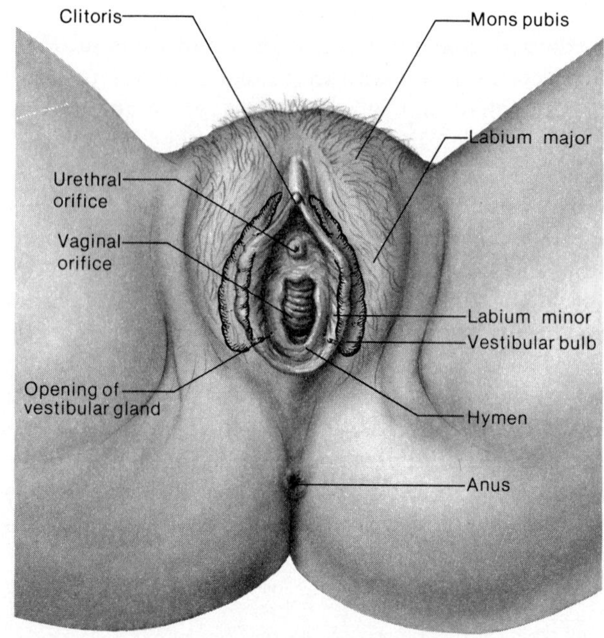

Figure 18.15 A sagittal view of the female reproductive organs.

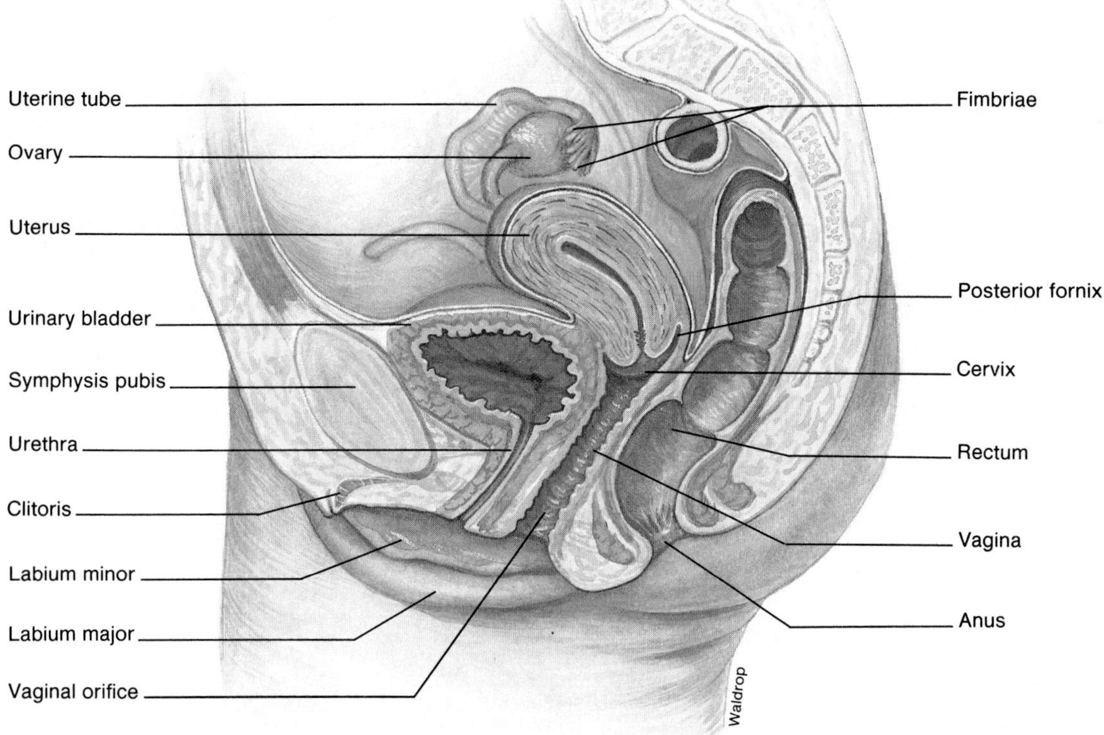

Girls who achieve puberty early are likely to remain fairly short in stature, while those who are late bloomers tend to be tall. Clearly it has something to do with the hormonal flow, and it is obviously independent of other growth characteristics, since women both short and tall show every variation in shape that is conceivable. Most workers feel that it has to do with estrogen/testosterone balance. Estrogens seem to be responsible for braking the growth in height by stimulating the sealing-over of the epiphyseal ends of our long bones. Regarding testosterone, there is plenty of evidence to indicate that it is at least partly responsible for elongation of the long bones and the accompanying increases in height. These two hormones may thus hold the key to the height variations in girls. The adrenal cortices, as we know, produce sex hormones of both kinds, and possibly it is cortical testosterone that produces the increased height in females who mature late in life. Those who mature early produce sufficient estrogen to overwhelm the adrenal cortical testosterone, and thus they close off the long bones and stop growth; late-bloomers would lack the estrogens to oppose this cortical testosterone.

The Gonads

The internal anatomy of the female reproductive organs is shown in figures 18.15 and 18.16. The gonads of the female—the complement of the male testes—are the **ovaries.** They are about the size and shape of walnuts and lie on either side of the **uterus,** connected to it by two quite elastic ligaments. The primary elements within the ovaries are the **oogonia,** which are destined, if things progress as they should, to some day contribute to a new human being.

Oogenesis

Like the germ cells of the testes, the oogonia too must undergo reduction division—meiosis—in order to produce a cell containing the proper number and type of chromosomes to accept fertilization by a spermatozoan. The principles of egg-cell meiosis or **oogenesis** are the same as they are for spermatogenesis, but there are a number of specific differences. The biggest difference is a quantitative one. Meiosis in the testes produces mature reproductive germ cells by the billions, whereas a woman's ovaries normally produce only one every thirty days.

The chromosomal movement patterns are the same in oogenesis as they are in spermatogenesis, but the separation of the daughter cells is quite different (figure 18.17). As you can see from the figure, the division of the cytoplasm during telophase is grossly unequal. One cell—the **secondary oocyte**—gets nearly all, while the other one receives little more than just the chromosomes. This shrunken daughter called the **first polar body**—may or may not undergo a second meiotic division, but it really does not matter, because no matter what it does it will shortly degenerate and be reabsorbed. The secondary oocyte, however, initiates a second meiotic division that will not

Figure 18.16 The female internal reproductive organs. As you can see, the ovary is not attached to the infundibulum of the uterine tube, and when an ovum is released, it must make its way through "open fluid" into the uterine tube.

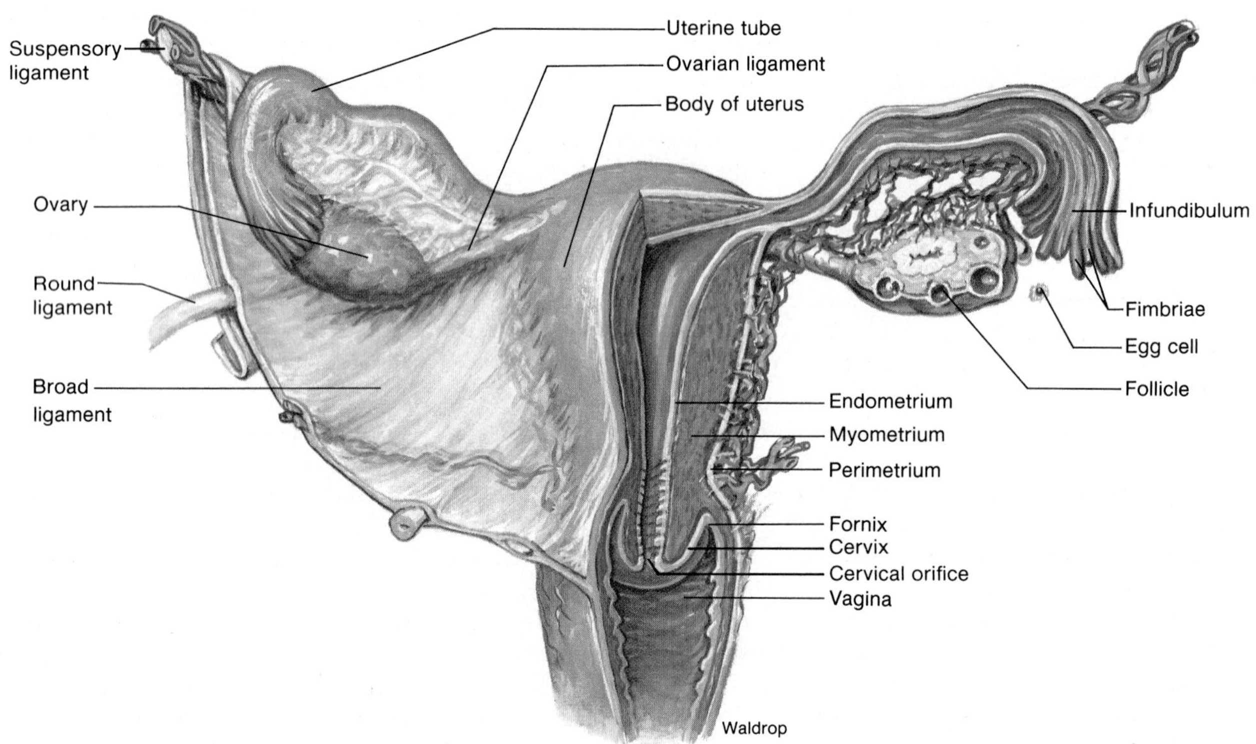

Figure 18.17 Meiosis in female germ cells (oogenesis). The first polar body sometimes undergoes division into two cells, but whether this occurs or not, degeneration of *all* polar bodies is inevitable.

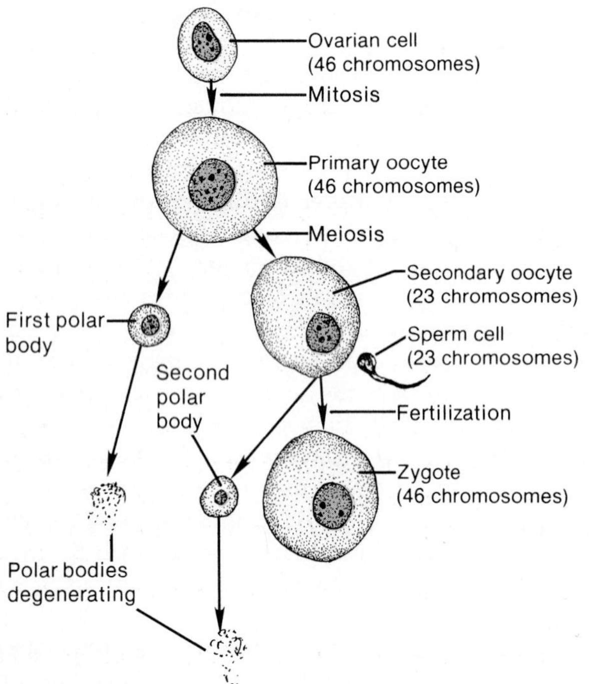

be completed unless the ovum is stimulated by an external agent. That agent is a spermatozoan, and if one actually penetrates into the ovum's interior, the second meiotic division will be completed. Like the first, this second meiotic division features an unequal allotment of cytoplasm, producing an **ovum** and a **second polar body.** The nucleus of the ovum, like the nucleus of the spermatozoan, now contains twenty-three single-stranded chromosomes and is ready to be fertilized.

It is important to be aware that, strictly speaking, the entry of the spermatozoan into the secondary oocyte is not, by itself, considered fertilization. The spermatozoan stimulates the egg to complete the second meiotic division, and only when that division is finally completed can fertilization take place. Fertilization takes place when the haploid nucleus of the ovum fuses with the haploid nucleus of the sperm to produce the progenitor of a brand-new human being—the diploid **zygote.**

Human Cyclical Changes

The word *menstrual* is derived from the Latin *menstru,* which literally means "monthly," and it is appropriate because the human menstrual cycle rotates around a lunar, or monthly, period. This monthly cycle is unique to apes and old world monkeys and differs quite a bit from the ovarian or *estrus* cycles that occur in other mammals (see the section on "Human Sexuality" later in this chapter).

The **menstrual cycle** refers to certain regular changes that take place in the female reproductive system, specifically in the uterus and the lining of the vagina. These alterations coincide with similarly cyclical changes that take place within the ovary and which are referred to as the **ovarian cycle.** Both are regulated by periodic hormonal flow and probably are strongly influenced by neural stimuli. For example, although it is widely believed that human reproductive rhythms cannot be affected by photoperiod (day length), recent observations seem to cast doubt on this belief. In far northern countries, where days are very long in summer and almost nonexistent in winter, studies show that gonadotrophin levels are very much reduced in winter, and menstruation frequently ceases. In slightly lower temperate zones, menstrual cycles appear to elongate in winter and compress in summer months. Births in the northern parts of Norway and Finland occur mainly during February through April, meaning sexual activity accelerated in June. There is reasonably good evidence to suggest that information on photoperiod may be gathered by the pineal gland and relayed hormonally and/or neurally to the hypothalamus, where the GnRH-synthesizing cells are located.

A regular thirty-day menstrual cycle is not invariant, of course. There are many things that can stretch or compress the pattern—or on occasion, stop it entirely for a time. Stress, particularly mental stress, can delay the onset of menstruation—and if it is powerful enough can sometimes stop it completely. Women confined to prison for the first time usually stop menstruating for the first couple of months, and when they finally do start, their periods are irregular until they "settle in." Young girls who worry about being pregnant often are quite late with the period they are agonizing over, and women undergoing divorce proceedings often do not menstruate during the process. Unusual activity or improper nutrition can also interrupt the cycles. During the Second World War, female prisoners in Japanese camps were often fed a bare subsistence diet, and as a result they stopped menstruating completely during their confinement. Most of those who survived didn't start menstruating again until they were liberated and had been properly fed for several months. Also, recent research has revealed that there is a definite correlation between the amount of body fat a female has and the menstrual cycle. A moderate loss of body fat (from 10 to 15 percent of normal) can produce menstrual irregularities, and extreme fat losses will stop menstruation completely. Highly trained female athletes with powerful, lean bodies often miss periods or stop menstruating during training and competition.

Despite the environmental, physiological, and psychological stimuli that seem able to disrupt menstruation, for the average woman, the cycle is surprisingly regular. It is not, however, always a lunar, or twenty-eight-day, cycle. It ranges from twenty-four days to about thirty-two, with the average in the U.S. right around thirty days.

The endocrine trigger is GnRH, released according to instructions from the hypothalamus. Its release stimulates the release of the two gonadotrophins, FSH and LH, from the pituitary. These two trophic hormones control the ovarian cycle, while the hormones they regulate—progesterone and the estrogens—control the menstrual cycle.

The Ovarian Cycle

Since these physiological phenomena are cyclic, it really doesn't matter where one begins. But since everyone else does it, let us, for the sake of uniformity, begin at the end of the previous menstrual period.

The period is over, although the menstrual flow has not completely stopped. At this time, levels of estrogen in the blood are quite low, and progesterone has disappeared. Since increased levels of estrogen inhibit GnRH secretion, the reduced steroid levels remove this inhibition from the hypothalamic receptors, and this allows the hypothalamus to release greater volumes of GnRH. GnRH, in turn, increases the secretion rate of the gonadotrophins, and the gonadotrophins have a direct effect on the ovarian tissue. Levels of both FSH and LH begin to rise, and under their influence some profound changes take place in the ovarian tissue. Although both FSH and LH have general, overlapping effects, FSH seems to concentrate mostly on the selection and maturation of a germ cell and its supporting tissue, while the LH seems to be more involved with the follicle cells—the cells that synthesize the female hormones.

The ovaries consist of cells derived from two different embryonic sources, and they are not scattered randomly but are grouped together in definite patterns. During the late fetal life of a female baby, the oogonia enlarge to form primary oocytes (none form after birth) and begin the first meiotic division. This division freezes in prophase I until puberty, at which time the oocyte enlarges and forms a **primordial follicle.** Each follicle consists of a single germ cell surrounded by a small coating of mesodermal cells that collectively form distinct, organized islands. These are the prime targets of the gonadotrophins which drift in and begin to sort through their enormous numbers. In some mysterious way, twenty or thirty are designated for further development, and under the constant probing of the trophic hormones they begin

Figure 18.18 (*a*) A microphotograph of the surface of a mammalian ovary. (*b*) A sketch of a mammalian ovary showing the stages in the maturation of the ovum.

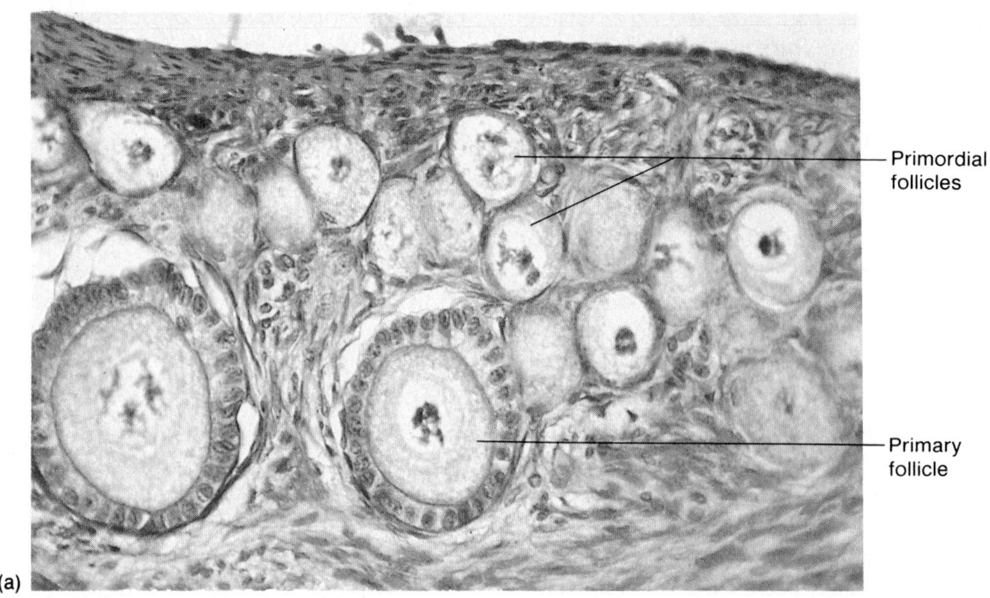

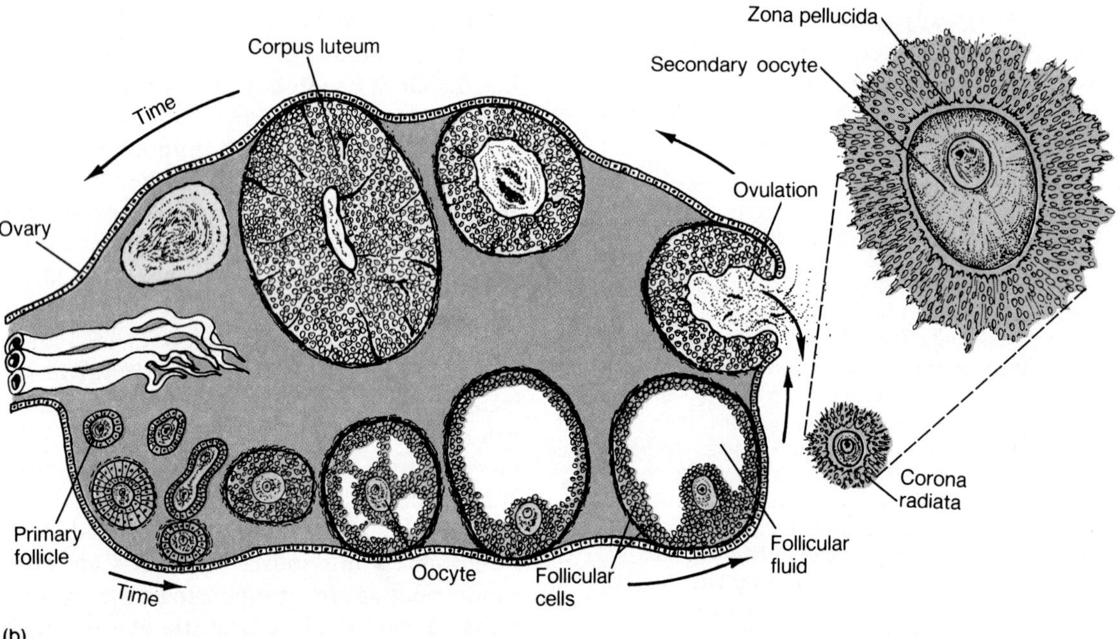

to grow—slowly at first because the amounts of FSH and LH are quite small. As the levels of gonadotrophins begin to rise, they rapidly swell into **primary follicles,** each consisting of several layers of supporting cells surrounding a single oocyte (figures 18.18 and 18.19). These supporting cells are the **follicle** or **granulosa cells,** and in addition to secreting female steroids (mainly estradiol), they provide protection for the oocyte.

For some of the chosen follicles, this is the end of the line. No one really knows what criteria are used to eliminate them, but there is no doubt that some mechanism thrusts them away from the main line of development and shoves them into the background. For the others, steadily increasing levels of gonadotrophins continue to stimulate their growth and expansion, and soon a chamber called the **antrum** (*antro,* a "cave" or "cavity") appears around each oocyte. They are now **secondary follicles.**

Figure 18.19 A microphotograph of a maturing mammalian follicle. Comparing it with figure 18.18*b*, how many structures can you identify?

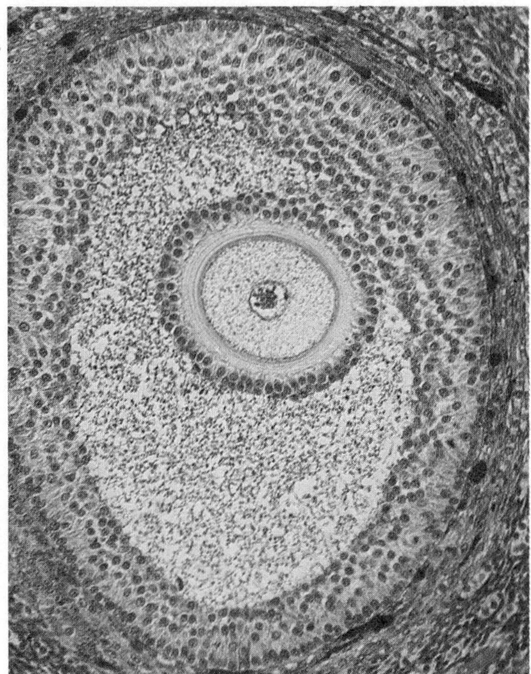

Sometime during this development, the oocytes within each follicle are stimulated to continue the first meiotic division that was begun so many years before (see the previous section on "Meiosis"), and at its completion, the first polar body is extruded. After a brief interphase, the second meiotic division begins, but for some unknown reason stops in the middle of metaphase II. It will proceed no further unless a sperm enters the ovum.

Throughout the second week, the physiological forces driving the cycle have steadily narrowed, and by the thirteenth or fourteenth day they have zeroed in on a single follicle. Its selection may be the result of a careful decision or it could be sheer chance, but whatever the process, one follicle is singled out and stimulated to mature into a **graafian follicle.** As it does, the other follicles change also, but their changes do not represent maturation. Instead of growing, they degenerate and gradually disappear, a process known as **atresia.** Atresia involves both the oocyte and the follicle cells around it—none of them will accomplish anything. They neither participate in ovulation nor are they involved any further in the secretion of female hormones.

In the meantime, the graafian follicle continues to grow, and its granulosa cells rapidly become so numerous and so active that they produce estrogens at a very high rate of speed. At this point, some subtle, unidentified mechanism begins to change the negative feedback system controlling these steroids. Normally, estrogens in the blood have a negative feedback effect on the hypothalamic cells secreting GnRH, but now something—possibly the rapidly increasing rate of estrogen secretion—alters this, and the feedback becomes *positive.* Instead of depressing the activity of GnRH-secreting cells, the estrogens boost it. At the same time, the LH-secreting cells of the pituitary suddenly become unusually sensitive to GnRH. Consequently, there is a sudden surge in blood levels of both FSH and LH, but mainly LH. The sudden burst of LH pouring into the blood produces a flurry of industry within the graafian follicle, a last rush of activity that completes the ripening process then bursts the follicle and initiates **ovulation.** The changes in hormonal secretory rate and the effects these changes have on the ovarian cycle are illustrated in figure 18.20.

Ovulation releases the egg from the follicle and thrusts it toward the entrance to the uterine (fallopian) tube (figure 18.21). There inside the tube, if fate so decrees, it will be fertilized by some lucky and vigorous spermatozoan, finish its second meiotic division, and be swirled into the uterus by beating cilia that line the uterine tube.

Meanwhile, the newly emptied follicle has work to do. Just because the egg has left its confines does not mean that it has suddenly become useless. Estrogens are not the only female hormones produced by the follicle cells. A second hormone—**progesterone**—is exclusively female and is also synthesized by these cells. Up to now its activity has been submerged by the unusually high levels of estrogen, but just prior to ovulation its levels begin to slightly increase. This increased secretion is probably due to the surge in LH, and it has been suggested that progesterone plays a role in weakening the follicle wall, facilitating its rupture and thus making ovulation possible. This may or may not be true, but in either case, with the oocyte now gone, and stimulated by the high levels of LH, the empty follicle begins to fill with granulosa cells. These cells appear bright yellow under a microscope, colored thus by their content of steroid hormones, and when they fill the follicle, they form a brand-new structure. This new structure is a fully functional endocrine gland, and it is called the **corpus luteum** (*corpus,* "body"; *luteus,* "yellow"). The steroid hormones that fill its cells are both estrogens and progesterone, and with the rupture of the follicle, the blood levels of both of these hormones begin to increase rapidly (figure 18.18).

Figure 18.20 Hormonal, ovarian, and morphological changes that occur in the female during a typical menstrual cycle.

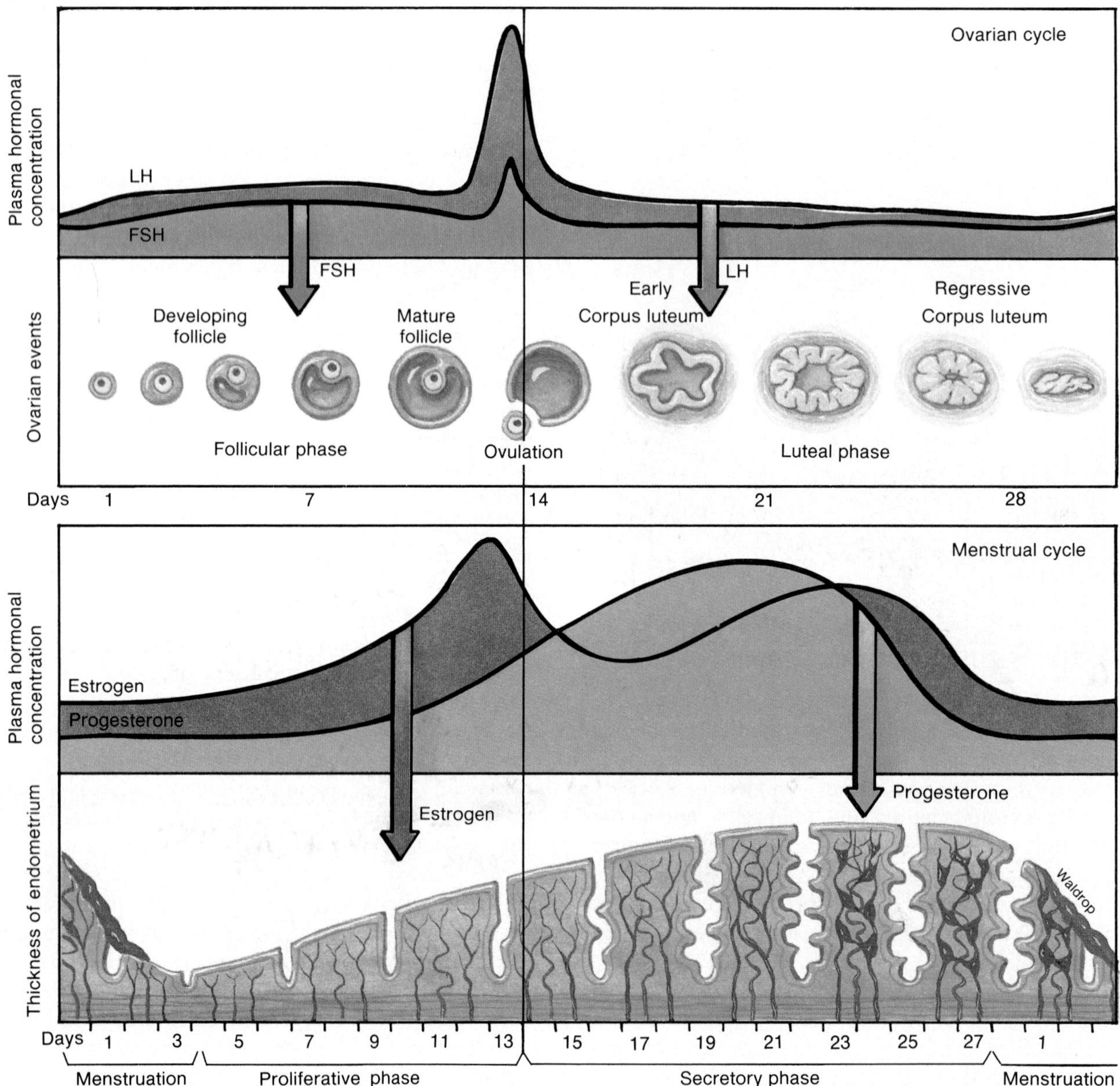

Suddenly, inexplicably, the normal negative feedback relationship between estrogens and the hypothalamus is reestablished. No one really understands why—possibly it is the presence of fairly high levels of both progesterone and estrogen in the blood. Whatever it is, estrogens no longer stimulate the hypothalamus. With the negative feedback loop reestablished, the high estrogen levels work as depressants, and GnRH concentrations begin to fall, reducing secretion of LH and FSH.

The life of the corpus luteum is short. It has about ten days of vigor and then it declines, cutting off production of progesterone, and if the egg has not been fertilized, there is no other source. The loss of the corpus luteum plus the lowered levels of FSH and LH result in a sudden withdrawal of both female hormones. Thus the support for a potential pregnancy is abandoned and the menstrual period begins.

The Menstrual Cycle

The menstrual cycle is directly controlled by the ovarian cycle. Hormones released by the developing follicles are responsible for the development of the genitalia and accessory structures that are intended to support a pregnancy, should one occur. There are four phases to the menstrual cycle: the **proliferative,** the **ovulatory,** the **secretory,** and the **menstrual.**

Figure 18.21 (*a*) A microphotograph of an oocyte escaping from the follicle at ovulation. (*b*) A sketch of an oocyte leaving the ovary and beginning its move toward the mouth of the uterine tube. Note the atretic follicles. These are secondary follicles that fail to develop into graafian follicles.

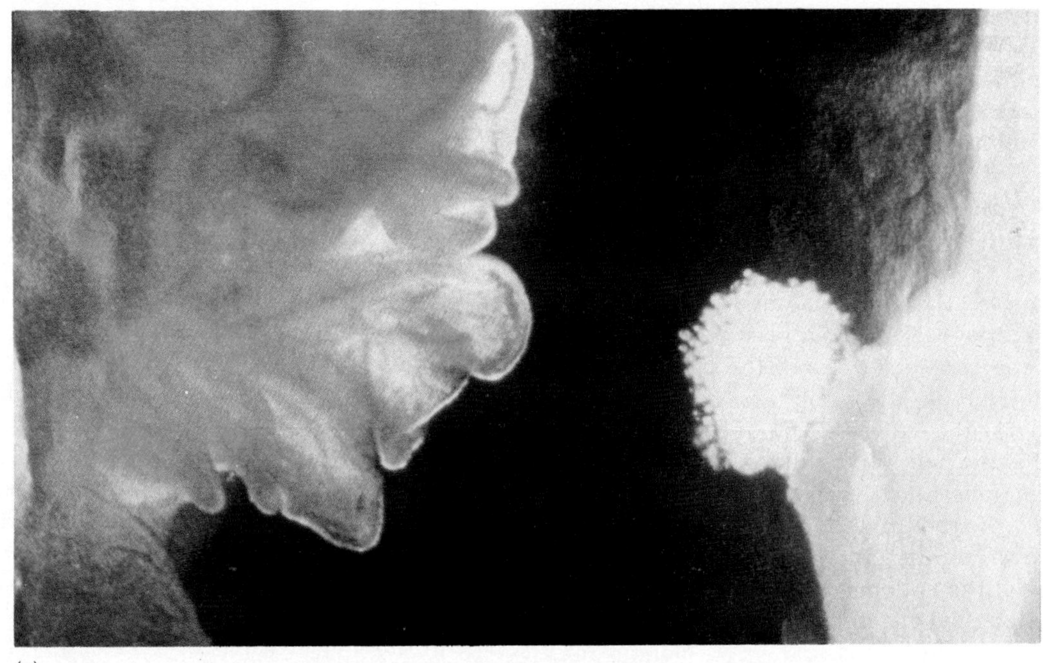

(a)

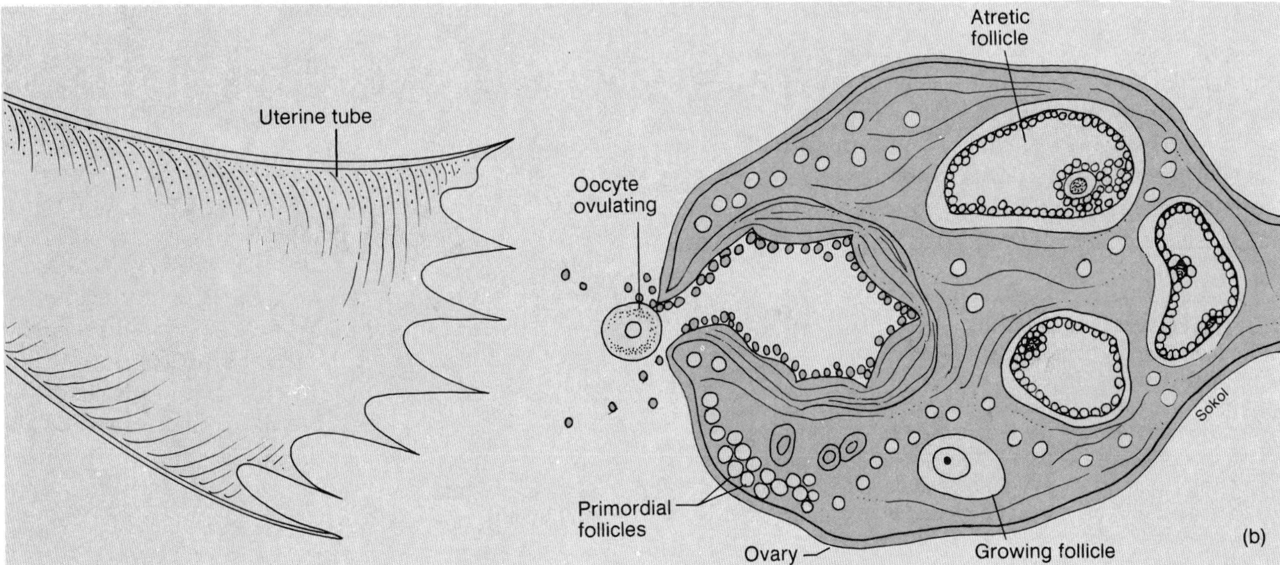

The *proliferative phase* begins when menstrual bleeding stops, and it usually lasts from nine to fourteen days. As we have seen, it all begins when FSH begins to flow and certain ovarian follicles begin to ripen. Ovarian maturation produces increasing levels of estrogens, and the uterus, under their influence, prepares to receive a fertilized ovum. These preparations begin with a thickening of both the uterine wall (the **endometrium**) and of the lining of the vagina (also endometrium). The endometrium actually thickens about 4 mm (1/8 inch), but its preparations are much more complex than merely increasing wall thickness. There is considerable glandular development within this thickening wall—glands that can eventually provide nourishment for a developing embryo. Blood vessels increase in number and distribution, eventually investing the entire endometrium. In the vagina, glands begin producing a mucus similar to intestinal mucin that functions as a buffer and aids in providing a hospitable and nutritious medium for any spermatozoons that might be injected.

Ovulation introduces the short *ovulatory phase*, and the increasing progesterone levels induce the transition to the *secretory phase*. Influenced by progesterone, glandular tissue developing in the uterine endometrium begins synthesizing and secreting glycogen and oils—potential nutrients for a developing embryo and the reason the phase is called "secretory." Nutrient fluids and electrolytes begin to accumulate, swelling the endometrium into a puffy, spongy mass. As a plow turns over and loosens soil for the implantation of a seed, the uterus has been prepared for the implantation of a zygote.

Inevitably, the corpus luteum fulfills its destiny and deteriorates. If the oocyte has not been fertilized, progesterone and estrogen support is thus withdrawn, and the *menstrual phase* of the cycle begins. Lacking progesterone, the straight, abundant blood vessels supplying the endometrial lining of the uterus begin to coil at the base, strangling the blood flow to the upper regions and permitting the cells they nourish to die. As the innermost cells die, the blood vessels coil even tighter, and eventually all but one or two layers of the endometrium succumb to inanition and are sloughed off. Blood vessels rupture as the lining tears free of the uterus, and whole blood is released into the reproductive tract. This blood, coupled with vaginal mucus and the disintegrating tissue that was once endometrium, is the menstrual flow, and while it may sometimes seem like a lot, it hardly ever is. The average woman loses, at most, about 60 ml of blood during a normal period. In perhaps more familiar terms, that amounts to about two fluid ounces (four tablespoons) and is considered negligible.

The appearance of the menstrual flow has had many consequences in human history. During the Middle Ages, Christian Europe considered it to be women's curse, a constant reminder for Eve's having given Adam the deadly apple in the Garden of Eden. To expiate this sin, menstruating women were expected to indulge in "pure" thoughts and/or prayer to "cure" themselves and recover from the bleeding. The Algonquin Indians of eastern Canada and the Navajos of our western states used to provide separate huts or tents where women were obliged to live while having their periods. Even in cultures where menstruating women were not penalized, it is a matter of conjecture just how much moving about they could do with no special means of absorbing the fluids they were passing. It is only in this century that a concerted effort has been made to free women from this trap. In the early 1900s, special, highly absorbent pads were designed to fit inside undergarments, and while they were bulky and somewhat confining, they were better than nothing and are still worn by many women. In the early 1930s the tampon was designed, and despite the fact that it could be worn internally and was enormously convenient, it took more than twenty years for it to be generally accepted by the American public. Objections were conjured up mainly by men, some of whom insisted that the use of tampons prior to marriage would make it impossible for a man to tell whether or not his bride was a virgin. There is some question today about the possibility of tampons producing or aggravating vaginal infections, and young women may want to coordinate their use with a physician's advice, but generally speaking they permit women to enjoy the kind of freedom that men have.

In today's American society, we often talk of sexual coupling as if it were the absolute epitome—the primary goal—of earthly existence. Yet as we have seen, not too many years ago it was viewed as something to be avoided if at all possible. Even today, depending on the people considering it, the act of mating induces emotions that range from disgust to worship. Some still berate it as animal behavior similar to dogs in heat, while others from the opposite extreme describe it as "supersensual" and "spiritual."

Fundamentally, mating is none of these things. It is often hard to see past the emotion and the marvelous pleasure that coitus provides, but when we do we find that the object of it all is nothing supernormal or unearthly. Actually it is quite mundane. The purpose of sexuality is procreation—the production of an offspring—and every species that is alive now or that lived in the past was able to do it. Furthermore, each has done it with considerable efficiency. It all begins with sexual intercourse.

Fertilization

When a man ejaculates, he injects about 400 million spermatozoons into the vagina of his mate. These newly freed spermatozoons now must make the journey from the cervix through the uterus and into the fallopian tubes (figure 18.22). It may not seem like a great distance to us, but to the little sperm it is an obstacle course of prodigious challenge. The mortality rate is enormous. No more than one thousand will survive the trip through the uterus, and fewer than two hundred will ever reach the egg (figure 18.23).

Just what it is that inspires these tiny cells to strive so mightily to reach the female gamete isn't clear. The eggs of some species release materials designed to attract spermatozoons, but that is not believed to be the case in humans. Most workers feel it is a matter of chance, meaning that the spermatozoons swim in whichever direction they are pointed when they are released into the vagina. Spermatozoons are extremely active entities, and they seem to have plenty of stamina, along with a single goal in life. Those that enter the uterus are at least going in the right direction, and as they pass into the fallopian tubes, something in there switches on their egg-fertilizing mechanisms—a process known as **capacitation.**

Figure 18.22 The paths of the egg and sperm cells through the female reproductive tract.

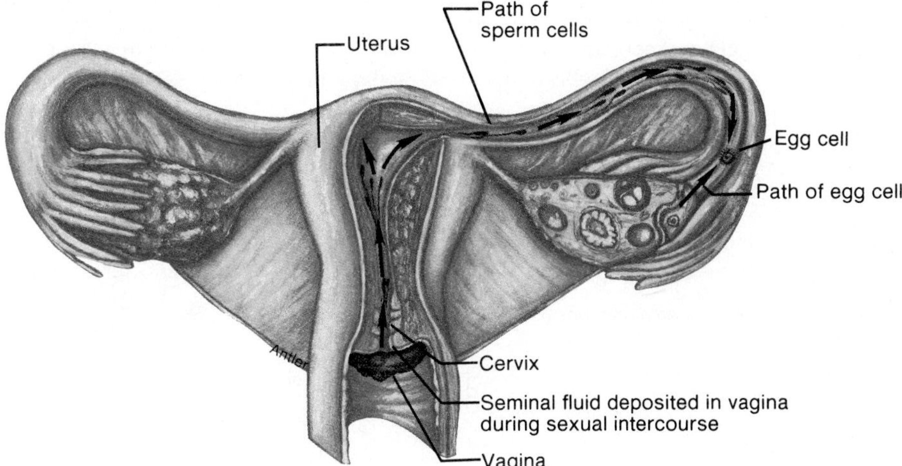

Figure 18.23 A photomicrograph of spermatozoons on the surface of the ovum. Despite their abundance, only one will succeed in penetrating and fertilizing it.

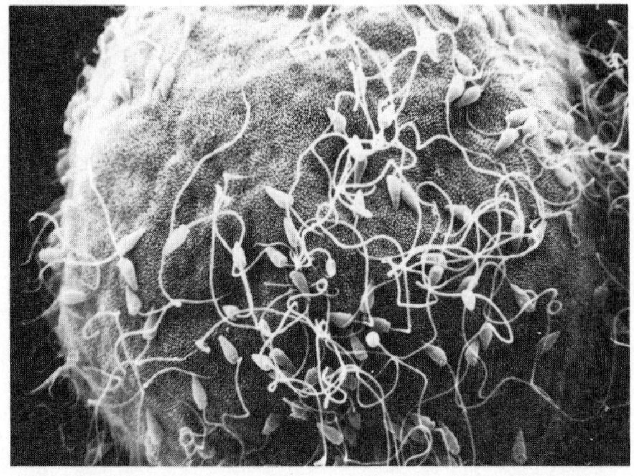

Capacitation provides the spermatozoons with the ability to penetrate two formidable **barriers,** the **corona radiata,** which is a cluster of cells surrounding the egg, and the **zona pellucida,** which is a jelly-like coating that covers the ovum below the corona (figure 18.24).

Each spermatozoan, you will recall, has an outer cover that sits on its head like the cap on an acorn—the acrosome. Within this acrosome are the enzymes that will dissolve both these protective coverings and permit the spermatozoan to perform its function, but these enzymes can't be released unless the sperm has spent some time in the female reproductive tract. The journey it makes from the vagina to the ovum takes just enough time for activation to occur.

As the sperm approaches the egg, some specific and profound alterations start to take place in the acrosome, and modifications known as the **acrosome reaction** begin. The tip of the acrosome covering starts to fragment, and as it does, some of the enzymes within are able to leak out. The first ones to be released appear to break down the cement between the cells of the corona radiata (figure 18.24*a*), permitting the sperms to wriggle between them and get closer to the egg. As it nears the zona pellucida, the whole front of the acrosome opens wide, releasing the final burst of enzymes that digests away the jelly coating and permits the membrane around the sperm head to fuse with and become part of the egg cell membrane (figure 18.24*e*).

The enzyme responsible for digesting away the zona pellucida is called **acrosin.** It is a proteolytic enzyme that is chemically very similar to trypsin (chapter 15), the pancreatic enzyme in our digestive tracts. As is the case with our digestive enzymes, acrosin is stored as **acrosinogen,** which, like trypsinogen, is an inactive molecule. The activation process, which removes a portion of the enzyme, is accomplished by a glycoprotein that is synthesized and secreted in the reproductive tract of the female. Thus we have evidence that the female reproductive tract is more than a series of passive chambers that the male sperm must penetrate; it is an active participant in the fertilization process.

The joining of the sperm cell membrane with the egg cell membrane is like pushing two small soap bubbles together to form a single larger bubble. There is an actual fusion that sees the two separate membranes become the same structure, and this permits the material within the plasma membrane of the spermatozoan, including the nucleus to move into the cytoplasm of the egg, where its presence stimulates a number of important changes.

Figure 18.24 The beginning of fertilization: (*a*) The spermatozoons that have successfully traversed the uterus and uterine tube approach the corona radiata. As they do so, the front of the acrosome begins to fragment, and enzymes able to digest the cement between cells of the corona leak out. (*b*) The sperm, having squeezed between the cells of the corona radiata, now approaches the zona pellucida. (*c*) The acrosome bursts, shedding acrosin. (*d*) The acrosin digests away the zona pellucida, permitting the sperm head to elongate and contact the membrane of the egg cell. (*e*) The sperm cell membrane and the egg cell membrane fuse together, giving the sperm nucleus free access to the interior of the ovum.

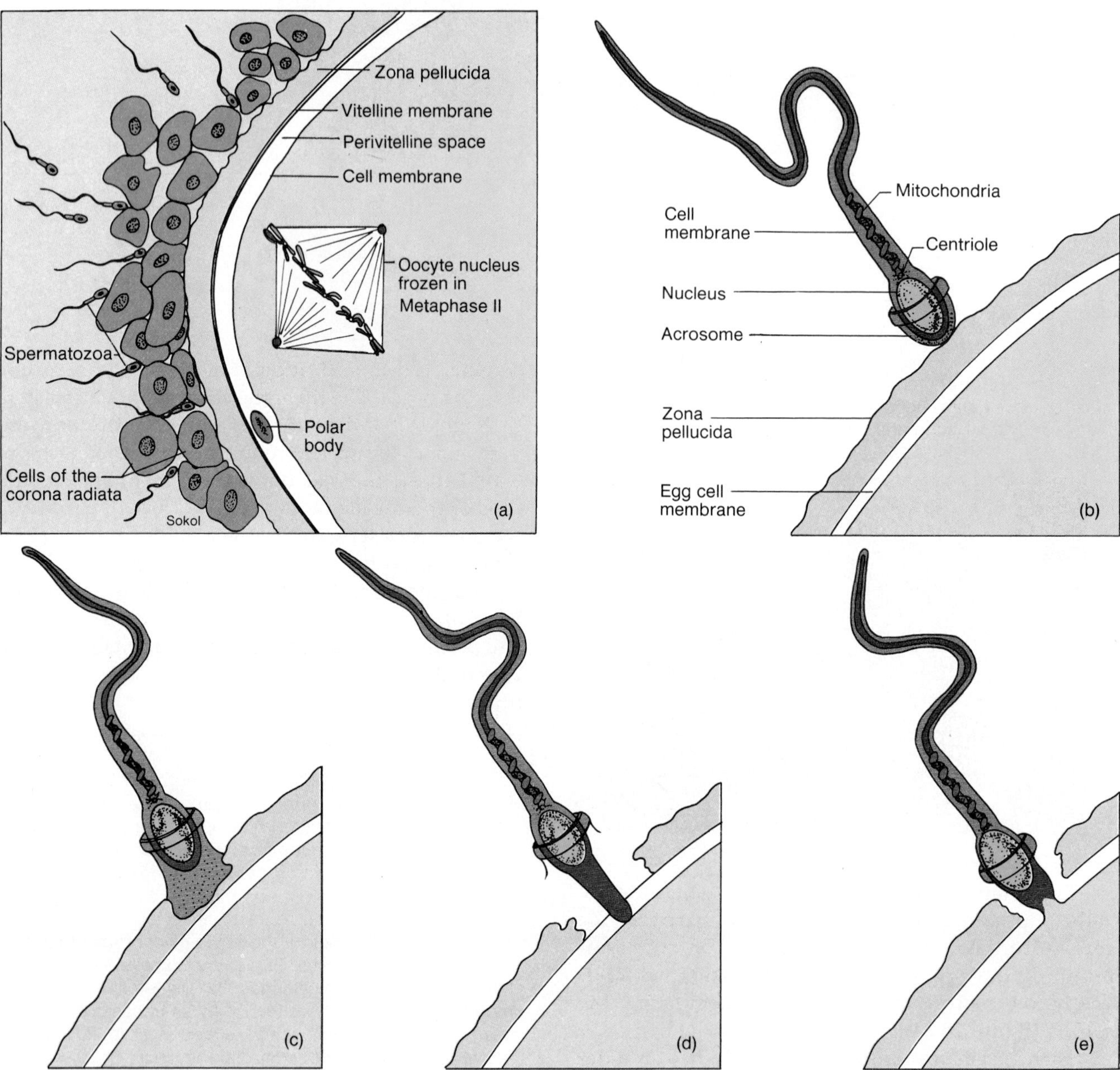

Only One Sperm per Egg

It is important that only a single sperm nucleus be permitted to enter the egg, and animals have a variety of ways to do this. Some—most notably invertebrate types—form what is called a **fertilization membrane** around the egg as soon as the sperm has penetrated (figure 18.25).

This fertilization membrane is composed of hyaline protein and is quite thick. Since there are no enzymes in sperm heads that can break it up, it provides complete protection. For many years, it was thought that the same sort of entity prevented multiple fertilizations in humans, but apparently, mammals have chosen to do things differently. Some are able to alter the electrical potential of the egg cell membrane, changing it from a negative voltage to a positive one, thus keeping extra sperm from fusing with the membrane. Still others will permit many sperm to fuse with the egg cell membrane but will thrust away the extras as soon as one sperm nucleus and its accompanying centriole enter the cytoplasm. The mechanism that

Figure 18.25 Avoidance of polyspermy in a sea urchin egg. (*a*) Egg prior to the approach of sperm. (*b*) The fusion of egg and sperm membranes causes cortical granules to migrate through the cell membrane and thickens the zone between it and the vitelline membrane. (*c*) The new, thick, granule-filled zone becomes the fertilization membrane. In mammals the entire contents of the sperm's plasma membrane enter the ovum, and a different set of mechanisms to prevent polyspermy appears.

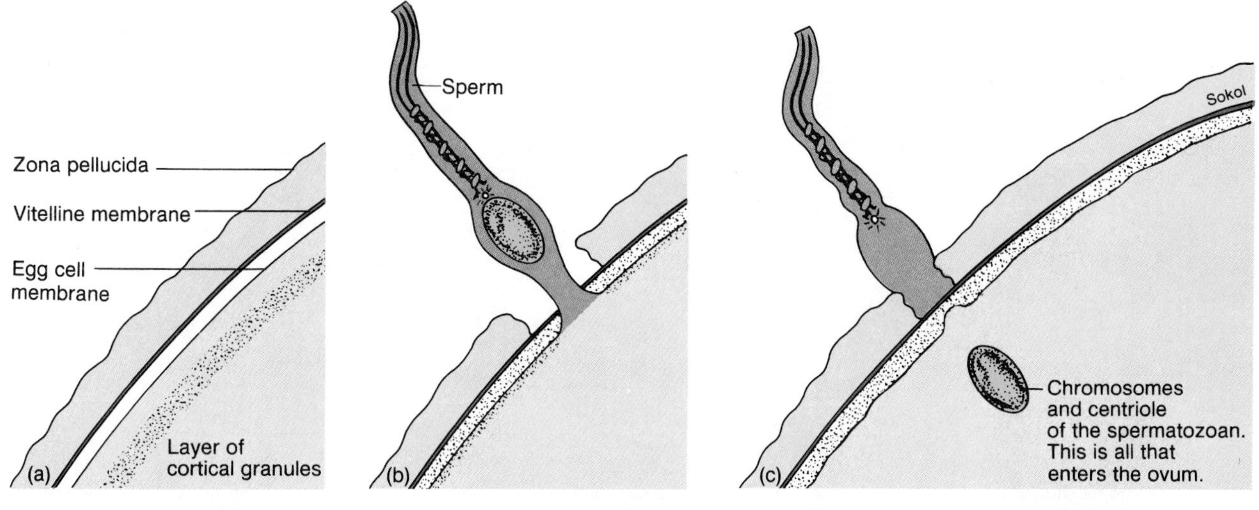

Figure 18.26 The process of penetration (*a, b*) and fertilization (*c*), which produces the zygote of a new individual (*d*).

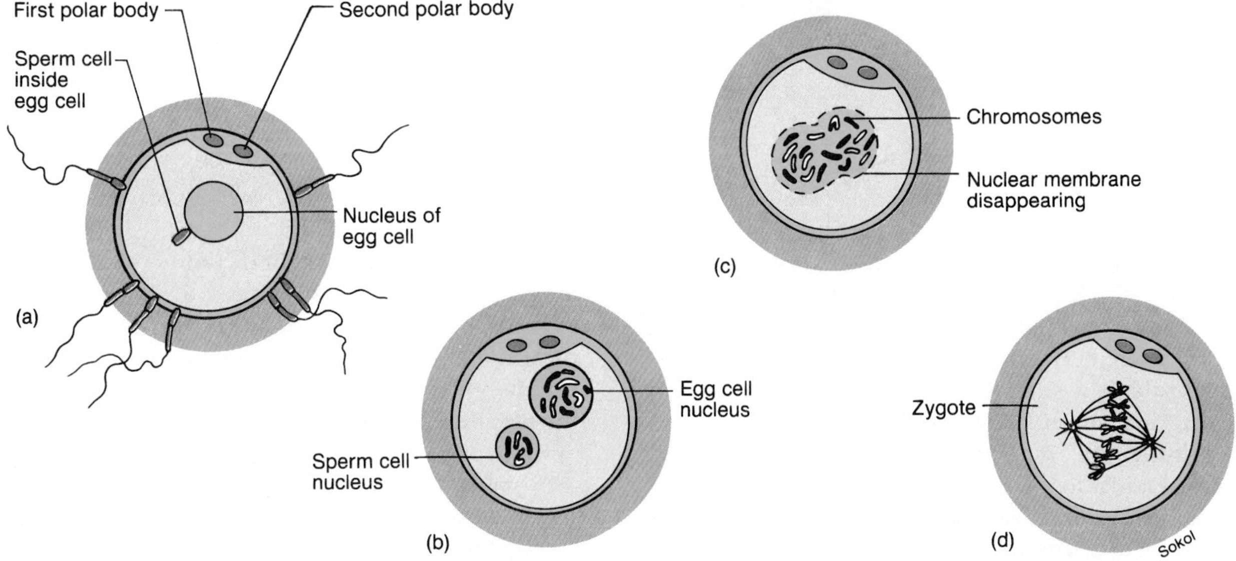

prevents polyspermy in humans is not known, but whatever it is, it works. Triploid or tetraploid nuclei seldom, if ever, occur.

Now the ovum itself becomes the object of primary concern. As soon as the sperm chromosomes and centriole enter the ovum, its own nucleus is immediately energized . . . it no longer sticks, frozen, in metaphase II. The presence of the second nucleus within its membrane produces sudden activity, and meiosis II is completed. With the formation of a completely haploid nucleus and the ejection of the second polar body, fertilization now takes place. The sperm nucleus and the newly prepared egg nucleus fuse into one, forming a complete, diploid nucleus, the zygote (figure 18.26). The creation of a brand-new individual has begun.

Pregnancy

The formation of the zygote induces mitotic division—rapid mitotic division—and as it proceeds, the developing embryo begins to move deeper and deeper into the fallopian tubes, its ultimate destination being the newly thickened lining of the uterus. It is propelled by the beating of cilia lining the tubule walls and some peristaltic tubal contractions. These movements are constant and quite vigorous, but it still takes about three days to complete the trip. On the way, it passes through several stages, two cells, four cells, eight cells, achieving what is called the **morula** stage as it finally enters the cavity of the uterus (figure 18.27). As it moves along, secretions from the cells lining the interior of the uterine tubes provide energy

Figure 18.27 Stages in early human development.

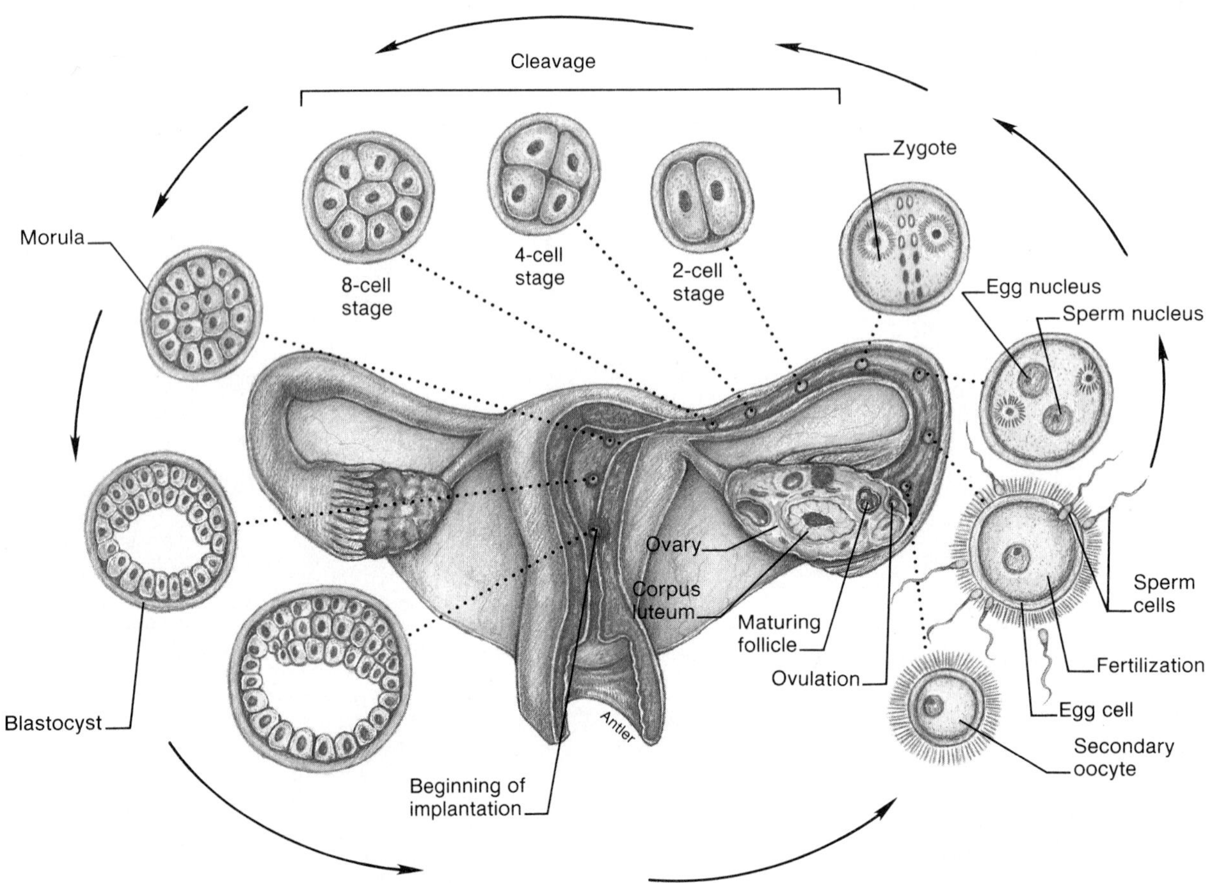

and some essential building blocks, but mitosis proceeds at such a high rate that there is really no time for cells to grow much after dividing. Despite the fact that there are between sixteen and thirty-two cells in the morula, it is still no bigger in total volume than the original, single-celled zygote.

Mitotic divisions continue to occur in rapid succession inside the lumen of the uterus. Three days pass and cell number increases steadily. By now it is a hollow ball of cells—a **blastocyst**—but it is still not significantly greater in mass. Finally, after six days of furious mitosis, it is implanted in the endometrial lining of the uterus (figure 18.28) and true embryonic development can begin. Differentiation begins as some cells migrate into the interior of the hollow ball, thus establishing a separate, interior cell mass, distinctly different from the outer cells.

Finally, as the uterus begins to donate nutrients, the embryo starts to increase in total volume. As time passes, differentiation increases . . . cells from the inner cell mass separate into different embryonic layers and some organization begins to take shape. Not all of the newly developing cells in the blastocyst contribute to the formation of the fetus; in fact, a majority of them do not. While the inner cells line up to form embryonic tissue, the outer, or trophoblast, cells take a different tack. As their numbers increase, they move away from the rapidly dividing inner cell mass and take up positions around the outside, where they form the **chorion.** This is a fetal membrane that will ultimately enclose the developing fetus and become the membranous boundary between it and the lining of the mother's uterus. These chorionic cells also form the embryo's contribution to the **placenta** (figure 18.29). More will be said about that organ shortly.

By the seventh week the genital ridge has differentiated, and as we know, the sex of the embryo is established. There has been considerable cellular differentiation by now. Some tissue formation has occurred, organ systems are beginning to sort themselves out—head, limbs, torso—all are clearly distinguishable. By the end of the seventh week this entire mass of frenzied activity is buried deep in the wall of the uterus and is no longer considered an embryo; it has reached the status of **fetus.**

Endocrinology of Pregnancy

As we know, the corpus luteum normally begins to disintegrate within ten or twelve days of ovulation, and when it does, the uterine lining is stripped away and discharged from the female. With an embryo developing inside, a loss of uterine tissue can't be per-

Figure 18.28 (*a*) The blastocyst adheres to the endometrium on about the sixth day. (*b*) A scanning electron micrograph showing the surface of the endometrium and implantation at twelve days following fertilization.

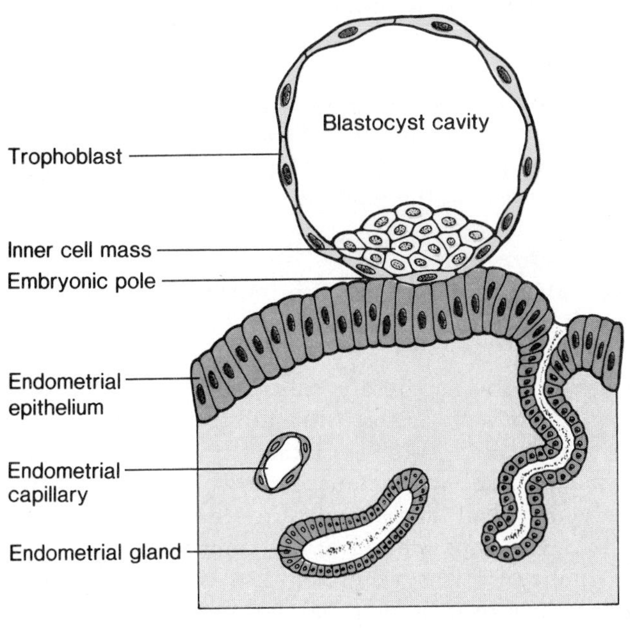

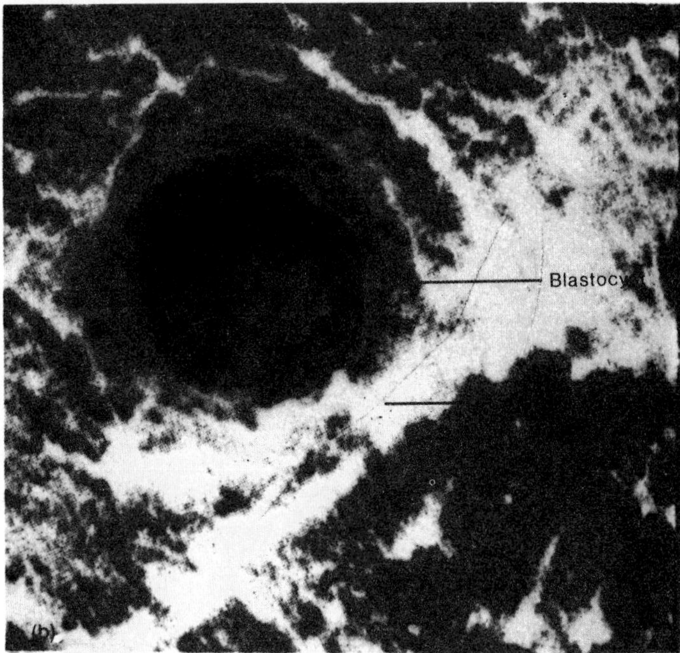

Figure 18.29 Implantation and the beginning of placental development. The inner cells of the blastocyst are presumptive embryo tissue. The outer cells will form the chorionic membrane, which will ultimately enclose the embryo.

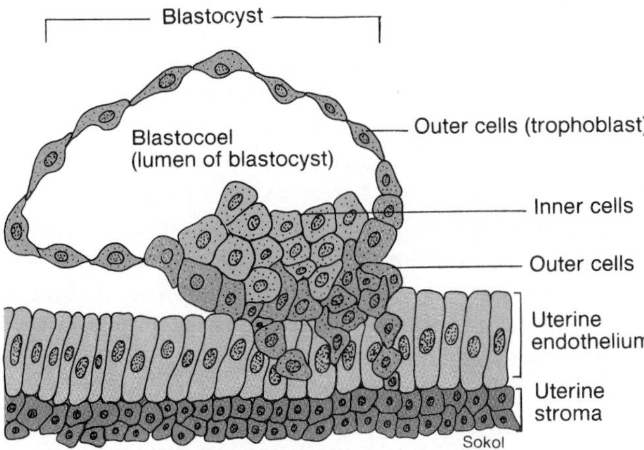

mitted, and in this the embryo aids itself. Some of the cells of the morula can synthesize human chorionic gonadotrophin, and it is the presence of hCG that prevents the corpus luteum from degenerating.

Chorionic gonadotrophin is apparently identical in its effects to LH. With its support, the corpus luteum remains viable and able to secrete enough progesterone and estrogens to prevent menstruation. Normally, the corpus luteum develops, under the influence of hCG, into the corpus luteum of pregnancy and continues to secrete steroids throughout the pregnancy. By the eighth week of fetal life, the placenta has developed into, among other things, a functioning endocrine gland able to synthesize and secrete all necessary hormones, including the steroids. Its secretions soon overshadow those of the corpus luteum.

Hormonal Controls

When hCG first appears, there is apparently nothing present to serve as either a monitor or a secretory control. The embryonic cells that synthesize it are limited in their capacities, and this is evidently the only factor that exerts any governing influence on secretory rate. By the time the placenta has developed to the point where it can assume the duties of hCG secretion, a control mechanism finally appears in the form of a releasing factor synthesized and secreted by the placenta. It has been given the name **human chorionic luteinizing hormone releasing hormone (hCLRH),** and it appears to be exactly the same, chemically, as the hypothalamic factor GnRH.

Human CLRH does determine the release rate of hCG, but despite its presence, there is still no *feedback* control. No matter how high the blood concentrations of estrogen, progesterone, or hCG get, they don't appear to affect the amount of hCLRH that is released, and placental levels of both hCLRH and hCG remain high throughout the pregnancy. As it turns out, this is a good thing, because unusually high levels of all of the hormones are necessary to support the pregnancy in the early weeks. Human CG alone does many things, most of them involved with increasing

Figure 18.30 The relative concentrations of three hormones in the blood during pregnancy.

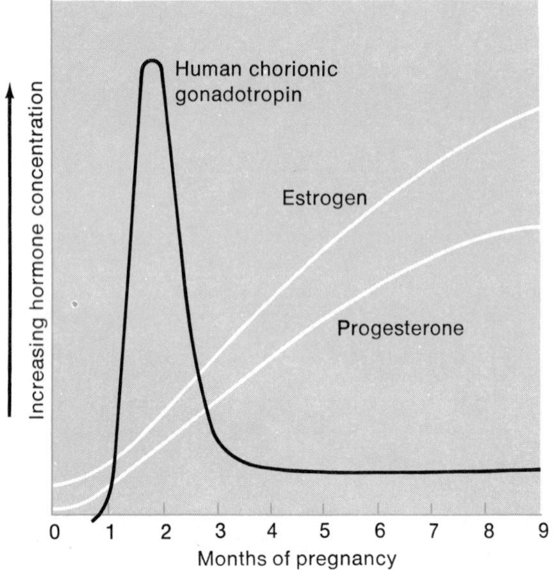

the output of steroids—things like increasing placental utilization of cholesterol, thereby boosting the synthesis of progesterone and estrogens. These high steroid levels, in their turn, add to and maintain the uterine endometrium and begin working on the milk-producing tissue in the breasts. Levels of hCG and hCLRH continue to escalate until the end of the seventh week, at which time some mechanism that has not yet been identified begins operating and reduces them both substantially. They fall steadily during the eighth week and finally level off at new, much lower, levels where they remain steady for the remainder of the pregnancy (figure 18.30).

Steroid levels, on the other hand, continue to climb (see figure 18.30) and are obviously no longer controlled by either hCG or hCLRH. Instead, control seems to switch to other parts of the placenta where unidentified monitors seem to know exactly how much of each is necessary, and they continue to increase output until parturition. Throughout gestation, these steroids keep on working, and their jobs are critical.

Hormonal Roles

Progesterone

Progesterone continues to maintain and add to the endometrial lining of the uterus as the fetus grows. Simultaneously it somehow breaks up the electrical patterns that flow across the uterine surface, preventing the smooth muscles from synchronizing their activity. This tends to keep spurious activity isolated in little twitches, thus preventing a fused contraction of the whole uterus that might expel the fetus before the proper time. In addition, progesterone also regulates many of the secretory activities of other endocrine glands in both mother and fetus.

Estrogens

Estrogens, meanwhile, gradually influence the uterus to accommodate the growing fetus. They also play important roles in the development of fetal endocrine glands and the fetal nervous system.

Other Hormones

Two other hormones are also important in the process of gestation.

Relaxin One of these is called **relaxin (RLX).** Relaxin is not a steroid but a small protein and is involved in aiding both gestation and childbirth. Its primary source in humans is the corpus luteum of pregnancy, and immediately after fertilization, it assists in the implantation of the embryo. During the pregnancy, it is synthesized and secreted by the uterus, where it helps progesterone to inhibit contraction of the uterine musculature (hence its name). As the pregnancy progresses, blood levels of RLX increase steadily, and new functions start to appear. Toward the end of gestation, working synergistically with estrogens, it slowly prepares the pelvic area and the lower abdominal musculature for childbirth. It helps the vaginal canal to enlarge and calms the muscles around the external aperture (vulva). It augments the whole process of "pelvic relaxation" by allowing upper thigh and pelvic muscles to relax and adding to the elasticity of ligaments in the area. Thus it permits pelvic bones more freedom to separate and let the head of the infant through. During the final day of gestation, the blood levels reach a peak and then, just before childbirth, they drop off sharply. It is believed that during that last surge, RLX softens and dilates the cervix, thus facilitating the infant's movement through the birth canal, while the final drop in blood levels removes its inhibitory effects on uterine muscle and permits labor to begin.

Human placental lactogen (hPL) This is a proteinaceous hormone synthesized by cells of the placenta. As the name implies, this hormone is involved in promoting specialization of the lactogenic cells of the female breasts, although it does not appear to play a significant role in milk production. Workers have recently produced evidence that low levels of hPL result in subnormal fetal size, although it is not clear why or how. If this is confirmed, then hPL obviously has another function that is at least as important as its lactogenic operations, one involving fetal development. More work needs to be done to determine whether or not it does this, and if so, how.

Figure 18.31 The formation of the three primary germ layers in the developing embryo.

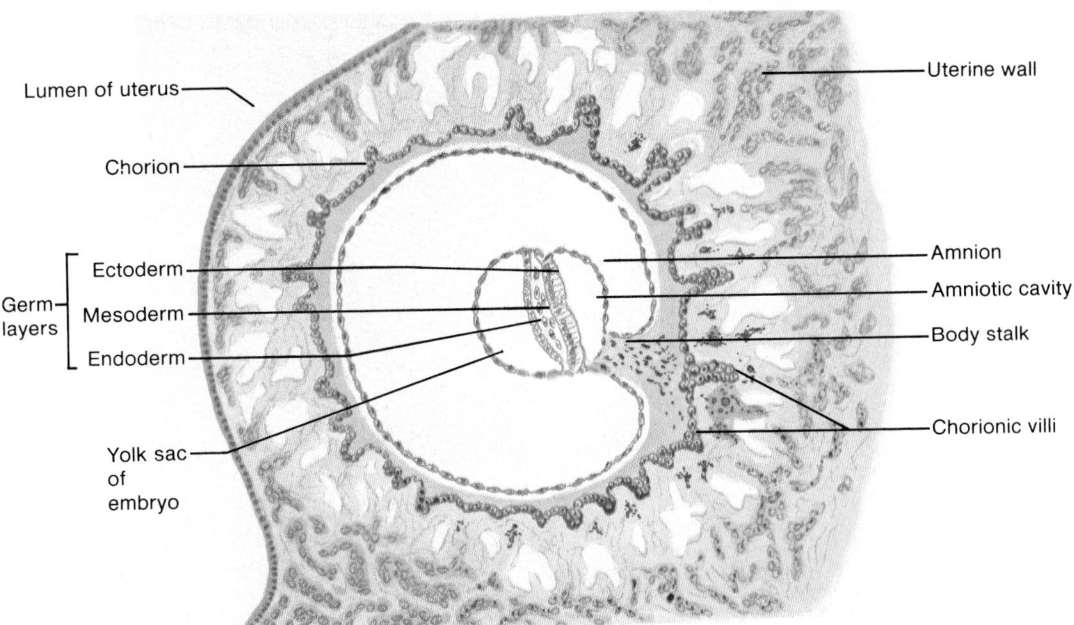

The Placenta

As in all animals, the human fetus must be maintained, and since there is no large food supply provided with the egg (such as the yolk in the eggs of birds and reptiles), all nutrients must come from the maternal circulation. To provide a permissive separation between the mother and the fetus, many of the blastomeric cells develop into special membranes that wrap around the fetus and form an interface between it and the mother. There is a firm fusion of some of these embryonic cells with the endometrium of the uterus, and a complex organ known as the placenta develops.

Viewed from the interior of the uterus, the placenta looks a little like a saucer with its base imbedded in the uterine wall. As time passes, the fetus will fill the interior of this saucer like a steadily growing pat of jello sitting on a plate, and its dependence on the saucer will become absolute. Fetal veins and arteries will coalesce into the large umbilical vessels that plunge into the placental mass searching for the nutrients essential for life and growth. There, they will find everything necessary to fetal prosperity and, in addition, a dumping ground for all waste products.

When the embryo is implanted in the uterus, its outer cells actually invade the endometrium, pushing small turrets or **chorionic villi** deep into the uterine wall (figure 18.31). These projections produce branches of their own as growth proceeds, and the thin **placental membrane** that eventually forms around them becomes a kind of high-surface-area boundary between the mother's uterine tissue and the rapidly dividing embryo cells. As the fetus continues to grow, capillaries, newly born from the umbilical arterioles, twist their way into these villi and take up a position deep in the uterine wall, separated from maternal tissue only by the thin placental membrane. The maternal tissue, meanwhile, develops to interface with the placental membrane. As the villi project outward from the chorionic surface, maternal tissue forms large cavities—*lacunae*, or *sinuses*—around them (figure 18.32). Maternal arteries project into each of these sinuses, and instead of breaking into arterioles and then capillaries, they simply end right there. There are no special ducts built into the sinuses—no channels that direct the blood around specific structures or in a given direction. Blood flowing through the maternal arteries is simply disgorged into the sinuses and flows around the placental membrane, bathing that structure in whole blood.

Positive pressure provided by the mother's heart forces this pooled blood against the placental membrane, stretching it and pressing it back. The placental membrane thus is forced to filter the blood, handling it in much the same way a capillary wall normally would, letting fluid and small solutes squeeze through while turning back the larger particles. Umbilical capillaries on the other side of the membrane now find themselves immersed in a highly oxygenated, rich filtrate, and they can pick up necessary oxygen and other maternally supplied necessities from it. Simultaneously, diffusion gradients provide the energy necessary to move wastes dissolved in these fluids back through the placental membrane (figure 18.33).

Figure 18.32 Fetal nourishment is provided by maternal blood. The placenta is actually tissue of two separate individuals. It consists of the decidua basalis (maternal), the chorion trondosum (fetal), and the chorionic villi that project from the surface of the chorionic cells. Maternal blood is released into the lacunae and bathes the umbilical capillaries that contain the fetal blood supply.

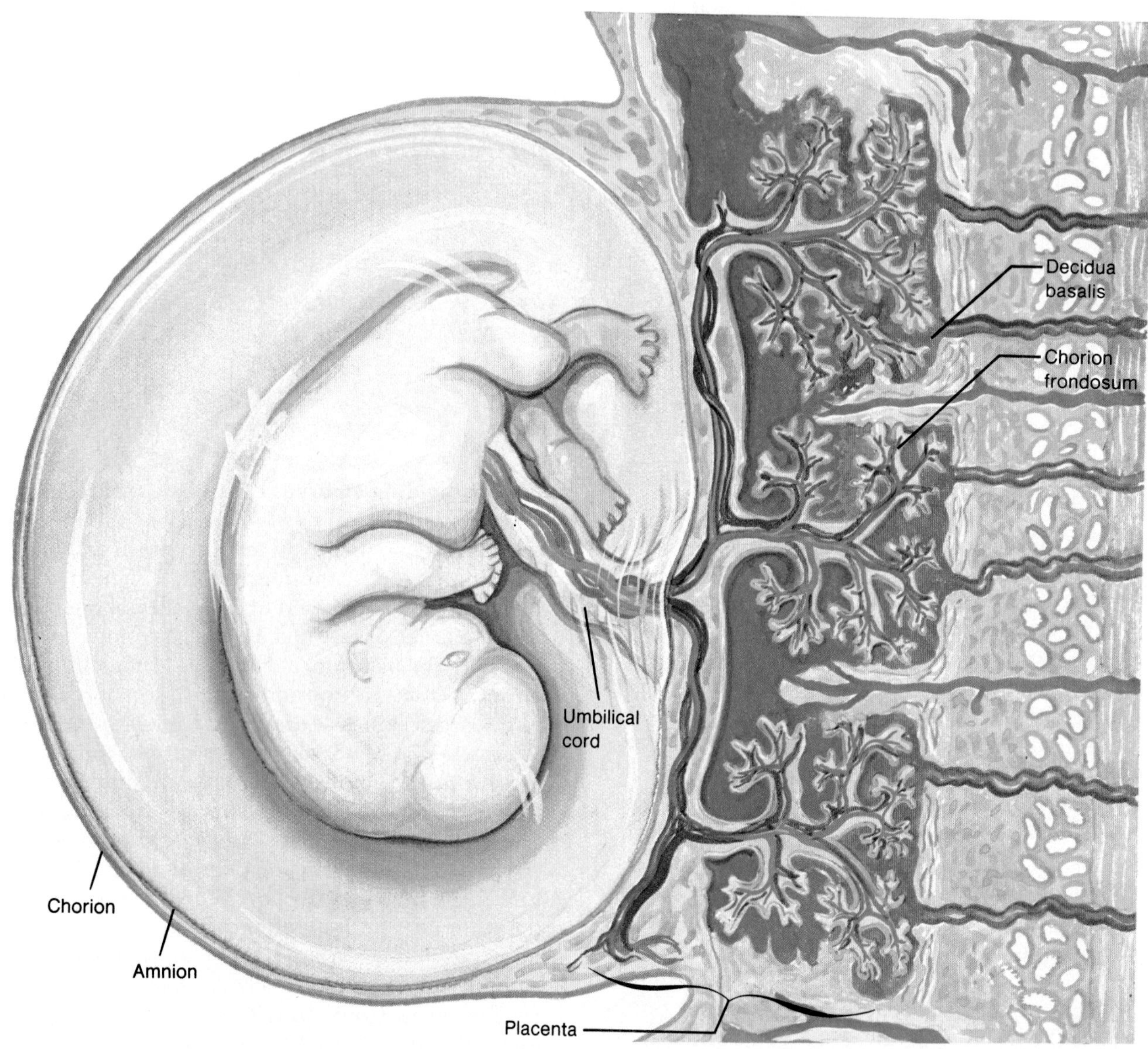

There is one aspect of pregnancy that is of enormous interest to surgeons and immunologists. As we know from chapter 17, every normal person possesses an immune capability that is able to recognize and attack any foreign presence. Hence it is surprising that an embryo can prosper, considering that its cells are foreign to the mother. Granted, half of its genetic material was contributed by her, but we must remember that half also came from the father, and those are foreign genes. To emphasize this, it has been shown repeatedly that unless preventive steps are taken, women reject tissues or organs donated by their offspring. Yet during pregnancy she accepted those foreign cells into her body . . . in fact, she did more than that. She nurtured them, fed them, and helped the embryo to grow. During her pregnancy, she lost none of her resistance to disease—indeed, in some respects it was augmented. Why didn't her immunological responses attack the fetus? Why was it not killed and expelled?

No one really knows, but several theories have been advanced. The most attractive one right now is that the chorion releases certain chemicals that block immunological activity. Some experimental work has produced results that support this concept, although none of the proposed chemicals have been isolated and/or identified, and the evidence is far from complete. More work needs to be done, and certainly there is plenty of financial motivation to find the answer. The benefits to organ and tissue recipients should be obvious. Certainly the surgeon's job would be infinitely easier if he or she did not have to worry about rejection.

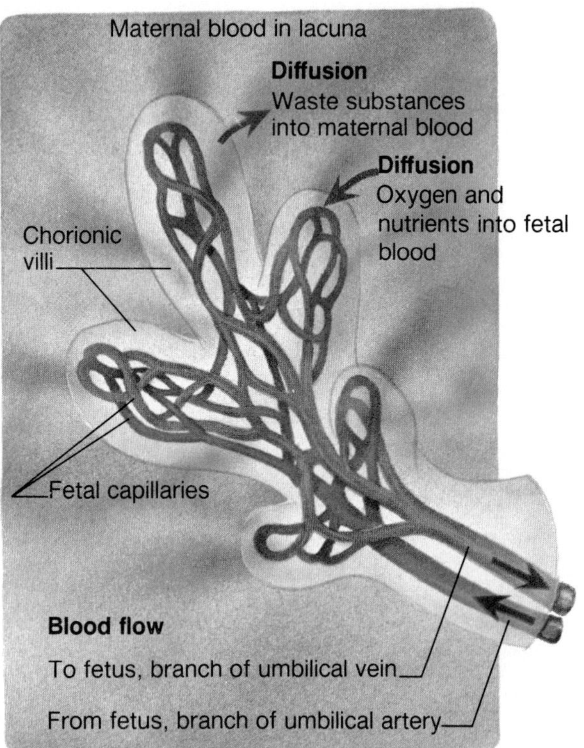

Figure 18.33 An illustration of the capillary circulation of the umbilical blood vessels. Nutrients enter from the maternal blood that fills the lacuna, while wastes are simultaneously released.

Meanwhile, back in the sinuses, continued introduction of additional blood from maternal arteries pushes everything along, forcing the nutrient-depleted fluids with their dissolved wastes down deeper into the sinuses. Here, strategically placed uterine veins pick up these fluids and return them to the mainline maternal circulation (figure 18.32). Thus, there is an exchange of materials between mother and fetus that is as complete and free as any such exchange within the mother's own tissues. Yet it is important to be aware that despite this free exchange, there is no actual mixing of maternal and fetal blood.

Other Fetal Membranes

The formation of the chorion has been outlined, and it is obviously important, but it is not the only fetal membrane. While it is maturing, a second membrane develops inside it and enwraps the embryo. This second membrane, called the **amnion,** fills shortly after it develops with a special fluid, a fluid carefully buffered and adjusted osmotically to favor the rapid growth of the fetus immersed within (figure 18.34). It is called **amniotic fluid,** and in addition to providing complete protection from desiccation, it also

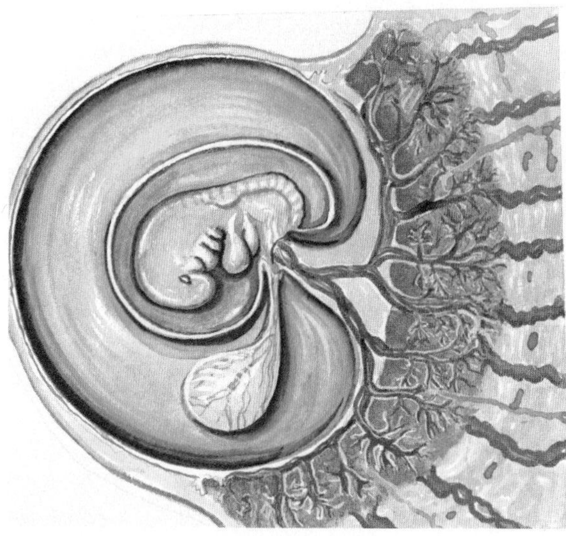

Figure 18.34 The amnion surrounds the developing embryo, and the fluid it holds functions as a shock absorber, providing additional protection for the embryo.

protects against damage that may be caused by the mother as she goes about her normal day-to-day activity. When she bumps into a chair or a desk while at work, a considerable jar is transmitted through her body—a jar that is damped by the amniotic fluid around her baby. Thus amniotic fluid functions as a shock absorber, providing protection against mechanical damage for the tiny life it bathes.

During fetal development, some of the fetal cells are shed into the amniotic fluid. By inserting a needle through the maternal abdomen and into the amniotic sac, a technician can withdraw some of them for analysis—a procedure called **amniocentesis** (figure 18.35). Cells taken in this manner are carefully incubated for two or three weeks. They can then be examined by specialists to determine whether, among other things, there are any genetic defects present. It is an easy and relatively painless method, but it has a big disadvantage . . . it takes a while to make any determinations. In addition to the three-week incubation period, removal of amniotic fluid prior to the sixteenth or seventeenth week is risky because the amniotic sac is small, the volume of fluid it contains is not great, and there is a distinct possibility that the fetus might be pricked. Because of these drawbacks, a second method of achieving the same results is becoming more and more favored. It is called **chorionic villus biopsy,** and it consists of inserting a tube through the vagina and the cervix up into the uterus, where suction can remove some chorionic material. The procedure is a bit more complicated and requires more time, but it is less likely to damage the fetus, is just as reliable, and can provide the necessary information seven weeks earlier than amniocentesis.

Figure 18.35 Amniocentesis. In this procedure, amniotic fluid, together with suspended cells, is withdrawn for examination. Various genetic diseases can be detected prenatally by this means.

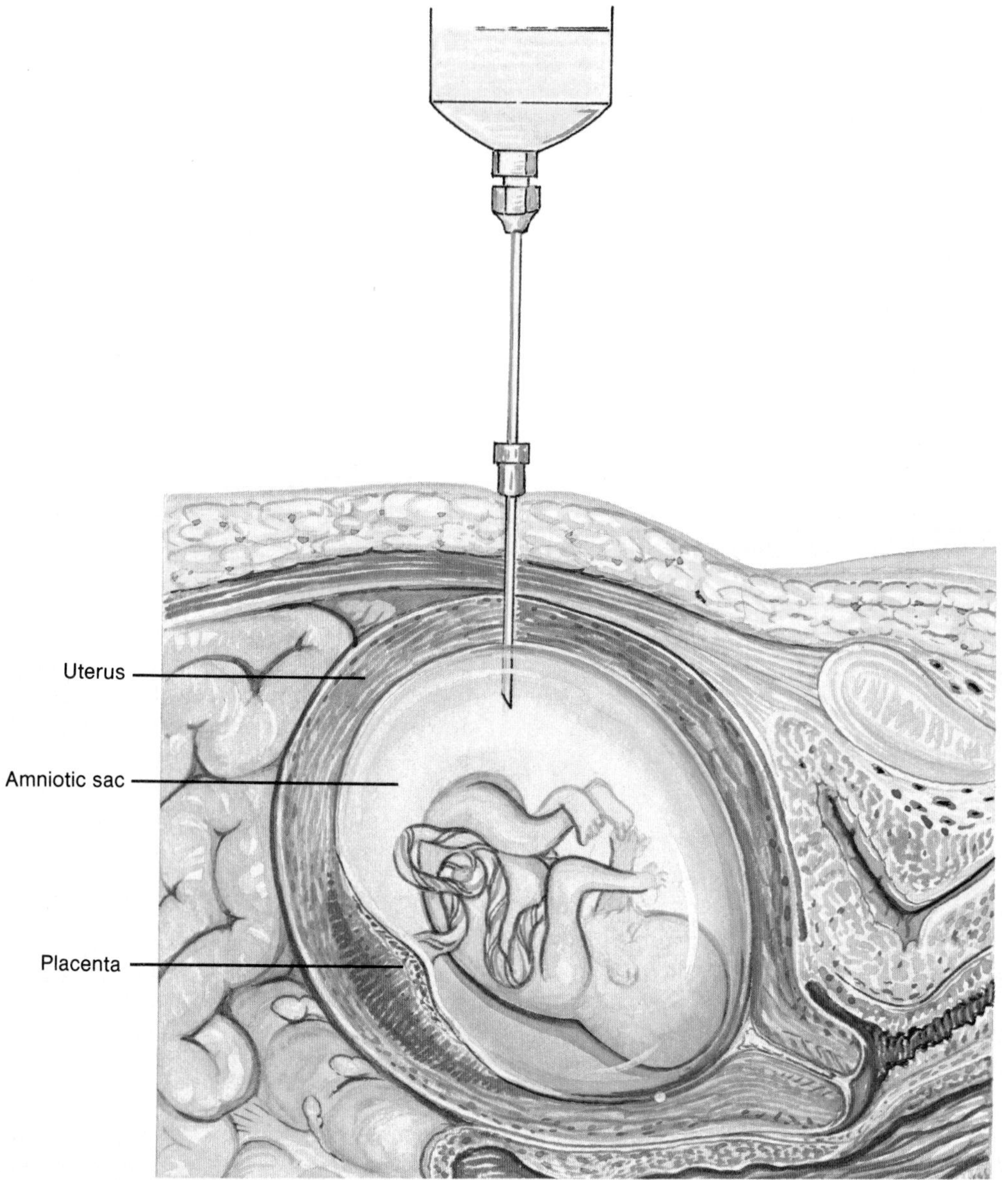

Parturition (Childbirth)

The gestation period of humans is approximately 280 days or ten lunar months. During that time, a single cell changes to a glob of cells which gradually differentiates into tissues, organs, limbs, and finally a fully formed infant human being. Ultimately the day arrives when this new living entity must be expelled from its comfortable home in the uterus and continue its development in a slightly less benevolent environment.

It is not known what initiates the activity that results in childbirth. Some workers believe that the trigger rests in the muscular walls of the uterus. It has been suggested that a woman's uterus is able to stretch only so far, and when it reaches its maximum extent it responds by kindling the mechanisms of labor. If true, this would explain why most multiple births are nearly always premature; a uterus holding two or three fetuses would certainly swell more rapidly than one containing only a single infant. But not everyone subscribes to this idea. Other scientists feel that it is a matter of timing, not size. They say the placenta is programed to last only so long, and then it begins to shut down. One of the first things it is programed to do, say advocates of this theory, is reduce levels of progesterone and relaxin. Estrogens have risen steadily since implantation, and estrogens, as we know, can directly stimulate smooth muscle activity

Figure 18.36 The movement of the fetus through the dilated vagina and cervix at birth.

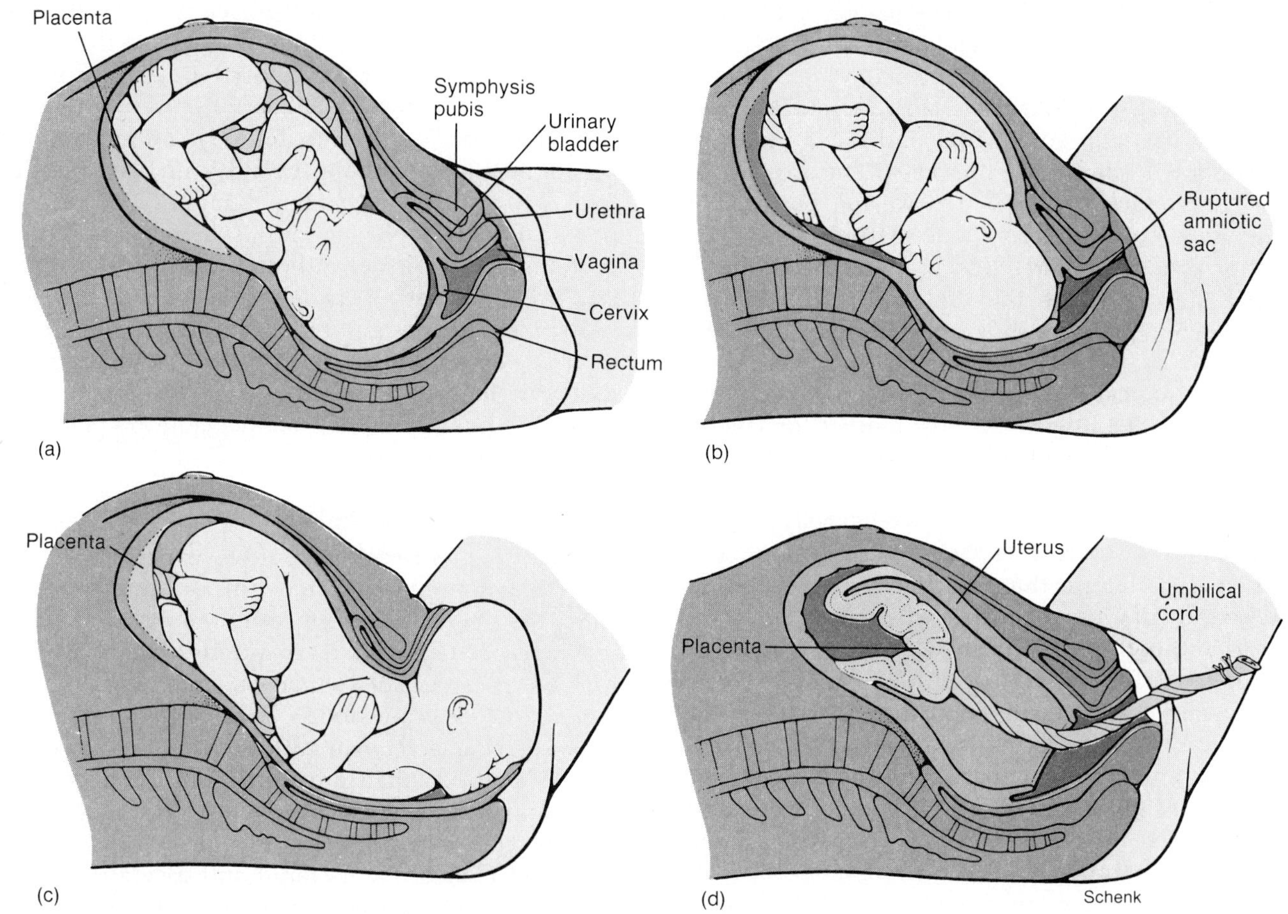

in the uterine wall. Progesterone, like relaxin, opposes this action, but if the placenta shuts down the secretion of the hormones that inhibit uterine contractions, estrogens can work unopposed.

Whatever the trigger may be, when it is pulled, it stimulates a good deal of activity. In addition to increased estrogen levels, other chemicals involved in parturition begin to flow. One of them is *oxytocin,* the octapeptide hormone from the neurohypophysis (chapter 10) and a very powerful stimulator of uterine smooth muscle. In many animals, this hormone is assumed to be responsible for initiating labor. It may or may not do so in humans, but even if it does not, it certainly adds to the force of uterine contractions, and it may be at least partly responsible for breaking the placenta free of the uterine wall after the infant has been expelled. Prostaglandins, which are derivatives of fatty acids and are synthesized throughout the body, have also been implicated in both the onset and the end of labor. They are found in amniotic fluid very early in pregnancy, and their concentration rises steadily, peaking just prior to delivery. It is speculated that they may help to reduce the secretion of progesterone and may help make the uterus more sensitive to oxytocin. It is doubtful if, all by themselves, they initiate labor, but they may be partly responsible for the powerful uterine contractions that accomplish parturition and continue after the placenta has been expelled.

During the last few days of pregnancy, the fetus normally repositions itself so that its head is right at the cervical opening and thus will be the first part of the infant to emerge. As it pushes through the cervix, stretch reflexes stimulate even more powerful uterine contractions, and the body of the infant follows the head down into the birth canal. Reflex impulses produce a strong desire in the mother to contract the skeletal muscles of the abdomen—to push with all her strength—thus consciously aiding the baby's birth (figure 18.36).

After the emergence of the head and shoulders, the remainder is easy—in fact, attending physicians often have to prevent the baby from actually "squirting" out of the vagina at this point. Within ten or fifteen minutes after the infant is born, the placenta or "afterbirth" is expelled. The process of breaking free of the uterus is a violent one, and there is considerable tearing of connective tissue and blood vessels, which creates a situation that could be dangerous were it not anticipated. As usual, the human body leaves little to chance. The danger is foreseen and minimized by the prostaglandins in the circulation and also the action of the neurohypophyseal hormone oxytocin. As we have seen, secretion of oxytocin begins when labor starts, and it continues for many days. In company with some of the prostaglandins, it produces a series of powerful, postpartum contractions of the uterine musculature. These contractions, in addition to reducing the size of the now-empty uterus, reduce the probability of excessive bleeding by squeezing shut the broken blood vessels in the endometrium.

Physiological and anatomical reminders of pregnancy will remain with the new mother for several weeks. Spontaneous bleeding can occur at any time during this period, and although it is seldom serious, it can be inconvenient. The still-swollen belly bothers some women also, as does the slowly shrinking, but still enlarged, uterus that feels like a rough coconut. Ultimately, all these reminders will vanish. Belly and uterus will both gradually shrink in size. A series of uterine contractions will occur at irregular intervals for several weeks and will reduce the protruding belly considerably. The process is known as **uterine involution,** and it is accompanied by the discharge of portions of the thickened endometrium that are still breaking free. By the fifth or sixth postpartum week, both the vaginal and the uterine lining should be back to normal, and the mother should start to feel like a nonpregnant woman again.

Lactation

There is a rapid return to conditions as they were before, both physically and emotionally. Except, of course, for the presence of the new person in the household—a person who needs to be handled with great care and who will change the life of both mother and her mate for years to come. The baby must be changed, bathed, and played with, and of course, father can share in all of these duties. One duty, however, may remain exclusively mother's until the child is weaned—the process of feeding.

Of course, that last statement is not necessarily true. It is not imperative that a baby be breast-fed. In fact, only about 25 to 30 percent of today's mothers do so. Nevertheless, it is the natural state of affairs, and women do have the equipment to provide all the nourishment a child should need for the first several weeks of life.

During gestation, several hormones have been working quietly to ready the mammary glands for the production of milk when the infant is finally born. Progesterone is involved in enlarging the lactogenic glands and getting them ready to work. It is helped in this regard, as we know, by hPL and finally, after the child is born, by prolactin (see chapter 10). The first meals a newborn infant will get from the breast of his mother are mostly **colostrum.** As I noted in chapter 17, colostrum is a rather thin, yellow fluid that fills the breasts just prior to delivery and remains the preponderant fluid there for a day or two after delivery. It contains antibodies, lymphocytes, neutrophils, and macrophages and is extremely rich in proteins and in calories, although there are few lipids and no lactose at all. In addition, it contains substances that are designed to stimulate the newborn's unused gastrointestinal tract into its first vigorous activity. Without colostrum, the babe will get none of these things, and they are not available anyplace but at the mother's breast.

Breast Milk vs. Formula

Human milk, as certainly could be expected, is ideal for consumption by human infants. It contains everything they need and in precisely the right form and quantity. There is milk fat, naturally—about 3.8 percent—almost all of which is monounsaturated, meaning there is one double bond somewhere in the fatty acid chains. Human milk also contains more lactose (7 percent) than any other milk, and human babies possess an abundance of enzymes that digest lactose. The ratio of calcium to phosphorus is very high and is ideal for its rapid and easy absorption. Breast milk contains buffers to maintain ideal intestinal pH in the infant, thereby insuring that a normal, human-type intestinal flora can thrive and protect the infant against gastrointestinal infections (see chapter 17). Maintaining the correct intestinal flora also promotes easy digestion and reduces the incidence of intestinal disturbances in babies. The mother's diet affects both the volume and the content of the milk she produces, but all in all, if her diet is adequate, her milk will provide her infant with everything it will need except fluoride. Fluoride does not dissolve well in milk, so even if the mother consumes supplemental doses, the infant will still need its own supply. Aside from this, there need be no vitamin or dietary supplements.

Cow's milk is nutritionally fine, but it is not exactly like human milk. Its fat and water content are almost the same as human's (4 percent and 87 percent, respectively), but it has more protein and salt and a lot less sugar (lactose). Because of these differences, feeding cow's milk to a newborn sometimes causes intestinal disturbances at first, but babies adapt pretty quickly. Probably the biggest disadvantages are its lack of iron and its calcium/phosphorus ratio. An infant on a cow's milk formula may show signs of iron deficiency by the fourth or fifth month unless iron supplements are provided. As to calcium—the calcium/phosphorus ratio in human milk is normally about 2:1, whereas in cow's milk it is the opposite, about 1:2. As a result, babies on a cow's milk formula sometimes fail to absorb enough calcium, and extra doses must be given to avoid a deficiency. In addition, cow's milk tends to be a bit low in two of the fat-soluble vitamins, A and D; and, of course, fluoride should always be added.

It is a well-documented fact that breast-fed babies suffer from fewer infectious diseases than bottle-fed babies do, and that may account for the upward trend in the number of mothers choosing to breast-feed. So why are there three times as many bottle babies as there are breast babies? The answer is not hard to find. In modern America, working mothers are becoming the norm instead of the exception they were thirty years ago. Babies need to be fed about every four hours, and if the baby is breast-fed, that means mother has to be available six times a day to feed the child. Working mothers simply cannot do this. Add to them the number of women who are psychologically or physiologically unable to nurse, plus those who just will not do it because of the inconvenience, and it is surprising that as many as 25 percent are still breast-feeding.

Human Sexuality

From a standpoint of sexual behavior and overall sexuality, humans are unique among the primates and may be unique among the mammals. Physiologically, the primates are set apart from all other mammals by their menstrual cycle. Mammals other than primates have a **fertility** or **estrus cycle,** and fertility cycles are not much like menstrual cycles. For instance, the internal tissue changes that take place during estrus cycles are very different from those that take place during a menstrual cycle, and their endings are not nearly as violent. In some animals there is a little fluid or blood loss *during* the cycle, when the animal ovulates, but that is associated with unusually high blood levels of estrogen and never includes endometrial tissue loss. In dogs, in fact, what little bleeding they do is called "spotting," which pretty well indicates the extent of it. It is quite a contrast to the bleeding and tissue loss that accompanies menstruation.

The fact that primates menstruate, then, separates them from other mammals. Humans break away from the rest of the primates in breeding behavior and the identification of female fertility. The fertile periods of all nonhuman primates—indeed of nonhuman mammals—are well marked and easily identified by the males. They include both anatomical changes and unusual chemical secretions, and each is designed to attract a mate. Among the old world monkeys and the great apes, the changes are sometimes striking. The zone that alters most, anatomically, is the female buttocks, and when the buttocks change they can be spectacular indeed. When, for example, a female baboon is fertile (or "in season" as it is often called), her buttocks will swell to astonishing proportions and usually turn a brilliant red or bluish-red with a fluorescent yellow or scarlet "bull's-eye" marking her vulva.

This is definitely not the case with humans. As many a young couple has discovered to their chagrin, there is absolutely no way to tell when a woman is fertile. It is not that humans do not display their secondary sexual characteristics when they are fertile, because they do. The problem is that this display is not unusual. Unlike the baboon female, whose secondary sex characteristics diminish remarkably when she is not fertile, a woman's secondary sex characteristics seldom decline and never vanish. For example, the breasts of human females do not swell only when they are fertile . . . they are swollen all the time. No significant anatomical difference is visible anywhere when a woman is fertile.

You cannot tell from the way they behave, either. Most female mammals, including the other primates, will respond favorably to sexual advances only when they are fertile, and those times are often restricted by climate and day length. Mammals living in temperate or arctic zones have their periods of fertility tied to the seasons, and the timing is such that their offspring will be born when food should be relatively plentiful.

During their fertile periods, nonhuman female mammals will do everything in their power to entice males. When potential mates are nearby, female cats will yowl, flip, roll, and perform body gyrations calculated to drive males mad. So will female ferrets, dogs, rabbits, and a host of other species. When they are fertile, these females want males in the worst way, and it is the only time that they do. During periods of infertility, these same animals will resist copulatory advances ferociously. Even animals with frequent fertile periods will not accept males at other times.

In humans, sexual receptivity is a matter of individual peculiarity—meaning each woman is different—but as a whole they are sexually receptive throughout the cycle and, providing the partner is acceptable, may make the first advances themselves.

This unusual human sexual behavior is not limited to women. Male humans are just as unusual. Most male mammals exhibit only a passing interest—or none at all—in nonfertile females. This may be partly because they realize any attempt to mount will result in a horrendous fight, but mostly it seems that they simply are not attracted to these females. In normal humans, this is never true. Men seem to be always on the prowl and are often repulsively aggressive in their pursuit of a mating partner. Since there is no way for a human male to tell when a woman is fertile, the instinct is to attempt fertilization at any time—and if the woman is healthy and her partner acceptable, she is quite willing to let him try.

Humans are unusual in still another respect. Copulation seems to provide more pleasure for humans than it does for other animals. Of course, there is no way of confirming this, but there is plenty of evidence to suggest it is true. Male chimpanzees, for example, will mate with a female when she presents herself. But if, in the midst of the amorous exercise, something interrupts the activity, he will simply disconnect and wander off to check on the interruption. He shows no resentment at being unable to complete the act, nor does he later demonstrate any particular desire to take up where he left off. Male monkeys castrated late in life will never again show interest in sexual activity and will ignore even fertile females.

Men simply do not behave like that. Humans castrated late in life do *not* lose interest in sexual activity. Furthermore, they are able to perform, and do, with vigor and enormous pleasure. Infertility does not result in men and women ignoring each other—in fact, it is more likely to stimulate mating behavior than suppress it. Humans seem always willing to indulge in sexual activity if everything is in proper order . . . and it is clearly not because they anticipate an offspring. Men and women copulate because it feels good, because it is psychologically attractive and intensely pleasurable. Speaking generally, humans enjoy making love and will perform every chance they get.

There is a clinker in all this pleasure, however. In the past, couples who were sexually indulgent could wind up with fifteen or twenty children, and while our ancestors might have accepted this stoically, few Americans today have any desire for that kind of family. Modern couples—married or not—want to plan their families and produce children only when they feel that they are ready and can handle the responsibility.

What all that boils down to is this: couples want to be able to make love whenever the mood strikes them, yet they do not want children every time they do. This attitude is perfectly acceptable, and it should work out nicely except for one thing—it is not possible to tell when a woman is fertile. Sounds like an unbridled passion for life while at the same time being fascinated by Russian roulette, doesn't it?

Contraception

In a way, it is. It has made contraception an extremely popular subject, and it has made the manufacture of reliable contraceptive devices very lucrative indeed.

There is certainly nothing new about contraception. People have been looking for some way to prevent conception since the beginning of recorded history, and it is possible the search extends even further back than that. Unfortunately, until the present day there has been no really dependable method. The last hundred years or so have produced all kinds of paraphernalia that will give some degree of protection—condoms, diaphragms, foam, etc.—but none could combine firm protection with convenience until the advent of the oral contraceptive. Nevertheless, each has its advantages.

Behavioral Contraception

With one exception, the least reliable methods of all are those involving behavioral alterations of normal mating routine. The one exception is, of course, complete abstention. But while a very few dedicated people might be able to achieve this goal, for most people it is very close to impossible. In any case, abstention is not real contraception. Real contraception permits copulation to occur but avoids pregnancy, and most behavioral methods are really bad at this. Nevertheless, for centuries there was no other way, so even though they were unreliable, behavioral methods were better than nothing at all.

The commonest and easiest method was for the male to simply withdraw his penis at the moment of ejaculation so that the sperm would not be injected into his partner's vagina. There are problems with this technique, and some are monumental. From a purely esthetic point of view, it is usually a horrible experience for the male, since it interrupts the act just at the moment of supreme ecstacy. Even so, it might be worthwhile if it worked, but it hardly ever does. The lubricating secretions of Cowper's gland and of the prostate frequently carry sperm with them . . . happy, energetic, fully mature sperm. Those sperm can impregnate as efficiently as the ones discharged during ejaculation, and there's no way to avoid these pre-orgasmic secretions and still perform coitus.

Rhythm

Many branches of the Judeo-Christian tradition teach that the sexual coupling of a man and a woman is inherently depraved unless it is undertaken for the sole purpose of procreation. Hence any kind of contraception is hateful, because it means that coitus is being performed purely for pleasure. At the same time, many church members cannot afford large families, and unchecked childbirth could mean financial and social disaster. In order to squeeze around this seeming impasse, the so-called **rhythm method** was devised. This permits a vague and uncertain form of birth control while still retaining a semblance of philosophical absolution, because nothing artificial is used to prevent conception. It is based on an observation involving hormone flow during the twenty-eight-day cycle. When the graafian follicle bursts and ovulation begins, the woman is fertile. Fertility lasts only a day or so, and the bursting of the follicle releases a surge of steroids that can sometimes cause an increase in a woman's body temperature. If the couple avoids coitus during this fertile period, then there will be no unwanted pregnancy.

There are more problems with this than you can imagine. The increase in body temperature, if it occurs at all, is only a fraction of a degree and is within the range of normal body temperature variations, which means that this is a terribly unreliable method of birth control. Furthermore, sperm can live for two or three days after ejaculation, and if the woman ovulates eight or ten hours after coitus, they can get her. Still, if it is the only thing your religion allows, it is better than nothing—maybe.

Condoms

Early attempts at contraception consisted of placing a barrier between the sperm source and the ultimate goal. Condoms try to do just this. The condom covers the penis in much the same way as a sleeve covers an arm, and if it is put on correctly and doesn't break or slip off, it is effective. Unfortunately, there is no doubt that most condoms interfere with the esthetics of coitus in one way or another. Both males and females complain that they "dull the sensation," or they "disrupt the mood" established by foreplay and refuse to use them. Those condoms that do not appear to affect the feel of coitus are so thin that they often break. Obviously that is no good. The situation is clearly less than ideal.

Diaphragms

The diaphragm needs a bit more attention than a condom does. One cannot, for instance, simply go into a drugstore and buy several. It must be individually fitted, which requires the services of a physician, and to be maximally effective, it must be used with a spermicide. Once purchased and installed, however, it is handier than the condom. For one thing, it can be used over and over again. Secondly, it can be inserted before any sexual activity begins, so it will not interrupt the sexual elevation brought on by foreplay. Furthermore, it is reliable, and if it is positioned correctly, neither partner can feel it. The only real disadvantage is that sometimes love play begins when neither partner expects it and when the diaphragm is not already in place. In such circumstances and in the heat of passion, it is more often ignored than not.

Chemical Contraceptives

It is possible, of course, to use a spermicide without fiddling with the diaphragm. There are also preparations available that have a spermicidal effect and impose a mechanical barrier as well. These are the contraceptive "foams," which are intended to slow the sperm down by forcing it to swim through a viscous material that will kill it. In theory it sounds perfectly reliable, and when first placed on the market the foams were welcomed with glee. Unfortunately their effectiveness, it turns out, is less than 50 percent. No one is quite sure why. Either the foam is displaced during coitus or human sperm are a lot tougher than anyone thought.

The Intrauterine Device (IUD)

The idea of the intrauterine device goes back several millennia. The first record of their use is in writings of ancient Mesopotamia, which relate how caravan drivers used to place stones in the vaginas of their camels so they could not get pregnant on long treks through the desert. During the ascendancy of the Greek civilizations, such devices achieved considerable favor, but they fell into disrepute during the period of the Roman empire because they had gained a reputation for lack of safety and unreliability. The intrauterine devices available today are inserted by physicians, and they can sometimes remain in place for as long as three years without any deleterious side effects. What is more, they have a failure rate of less than 5 percent. When they are used in conjunction with any of the other contraceptive methods, the failure rate should be close to zero.

How do they work? No one knows. It has been suggested that maybe they cause a temporary inflammation of the interior of the uterus, thereby producing noninfective inflammatory reactions—or possibly they disrupt the rhythmic waves of electrical discharge that periodically sweep across the smooth muscle of the uterus. Either of these happenstances would prevent the implantation of a fertile egg.

While their reliability is considerably higher than that of any of the methods outlined above, they do have drawbacks. At least one clinic on the East coast has reported a higher incidence of nonspecific vaginitis and bladder infections in women with intrauterine devices. This is an inconsistent observation, however, and has never been reported anywhere else. It is felt that either they represent the incompetence of the medical staff that inserted the IUDs, or they are in error.

There has, however, been a flurry of reports that are scattered randomly across the country and are thought to be genuine. As many as 20 percent of the women using these devices have reported abdominal pain and unusually heavy bleeding during menstruation. It turns out that the incidence of pelvic inflammatory disease is also very high for those using IUDs. Most of these problems disappear within a month or two, but a lot of women will not put up with that kind of discomfort for a month, and they see no reason why they should. There are other, highly reliable contraceptive methods, and not all of them involve the woman's handling the problem by herself.

Oral Contraceptives

"The pill," as it is called, consists of a physiological dose of female hormones, and it provides protection by inserting an artificial error into the normal hormonal feedback loop. The object is to fool the hypothalamus into thinking that the ovaries are already active and are producing a ripe egg . . . and it works! Normally the subject starts taking the steroids as soon as her period ends. This raises the blood level of steroids before her endocrine system is ready to begin a normal ovarian cycle again. The artificially high estrogen levels inhibit, through negative feedback control, the release of GnRH. Since there is no GnRH, there is no release of FSH or LH, and therefore there is no ovarian cycle . . . no ovum selection, no secondary follicles, and—most importantly—there is no graafian follicle. Since there is no ripened ovum to be delivered into the uterine tubes, there is no possibility of a pregnancy no matter how often coitus takes place or when it occurs.

The contraceptive pill has come in for a lot of attention since its introduction. It seems sometimes that whenever a woman reports feeling badly due to some uncommon affliction, and her physician cannot find a cause, the pill is automatically blamed. It has been cited as a cause of depression, nymphomania, uterine cancer, breast cancer, lung cancer, diabetes, detached retinas—there is no end to the list. These citations are, far more often than not, pure speculation with little foundation in reason.

This is not to imply that taking the pill never produces side effects. There are some. Women occasionally suffer from uncommonly tender breasts, nausea, and high water retention, but these effects can almost always be eliminated with adjustment of dosage. More serious is the observation that women over 35 who are on the pill seem to form a higher number of intravascular blood clots than women not on the pill. This only happens, however, when smoking is also involved. Considering the other things smoking can cause, and since one or the other must be eliminated, dumping cigarettes makes more sense than dropping the pill. Regardless of the number of diseases you may have heard are caused by the pill, the only definitive long-term study that has been completed seems to indicate that oral contraceptives can inhibit uterine and cervical cancer. That, of course, is good, not bad.

Meanwhile, the exogenous steroids are producing an otherwise normal menstrual cycle. The uterine wall thickens as it is supposed to, and so does the tissue lining the vagina. Everything that takes place in a normal menstrual cycle proceeds as usual. The subject continues taking the steroids for three weeks, at which point she stops and the uterine lining is discharged in a normal manner, producing a typical menstrual flow. Sometimes a little subjective adjustment of dosage levels is necessary, but by and large, the system is 100 percent effective and is harmless.

Naturally, the pill can be used only by women, and this has been a sore point with a lot of women's groups. Why, they want to know, are there no solid efforts being made to uncover a male contraceptive? The problem has mainly to do with numbers. A pill to prevent the production of a single germ cell per month seems conceptually a lot simpler than a pill to prevent the production of several million germ cells per day, and while the search goes on, the likelihood of finding a male contraceptive seems to decrease daily.

Vasectomy

This does not mean that a man can do nothing. Aside from the obvious penile accessories that abound in pharmacies, there is a simple surgical procedure known as a **vasectomy** that will provide dependable and convenient contraception. It consists of the severing of the vas deferens and can be done quickly, almost painlessly, and quite inexpensively in a doctor's office. No hospital stay is required (figure 18.37).

The only problem with vasectomy is that once it has been done, it probably cannot be undone. The male who submits to this surgery must resign himself to being permanently sterile. This is an absolute abomination to some men, particularly if they have the idea that they would like someday to be fathers. However for many—especially those who already have families and have no desire to increase them—it is perfectly acceptable and highly desirable.

Tubal Ligation

Women are capable of being sterilized surgically also, and the procedure does not require removal of the ovaries or uterus or anything that drastic. It consists of snipping the uterine tubes just behind the ovaries and tying off the severed ends so that any eggs produced in the ovaries cannot get into the tubes to be impregnated. Even if they did, the spermatozoons could not reach them (figure 18.38). It is a more involved procedure than vasectomy because the abdomen has to be opened for the surgeon to gain access to the reproductive organs, but it is not considered serious. Like the vasectomy, this is usually considered a permanent sterilization.

The Menopause

Menopause, also known as the "change of life," means literally a "pause in menses"—the end of menstruation. It is the final stage in a process known as the

Figure 18.37 Vasectomy, one of the few methods of assuring contraception. In this procedure a section of ductus deferentia is removed, thus preventing viable sperm from entering the seminal fluid. The procedure, once done, is permanent; it cannot be undone.

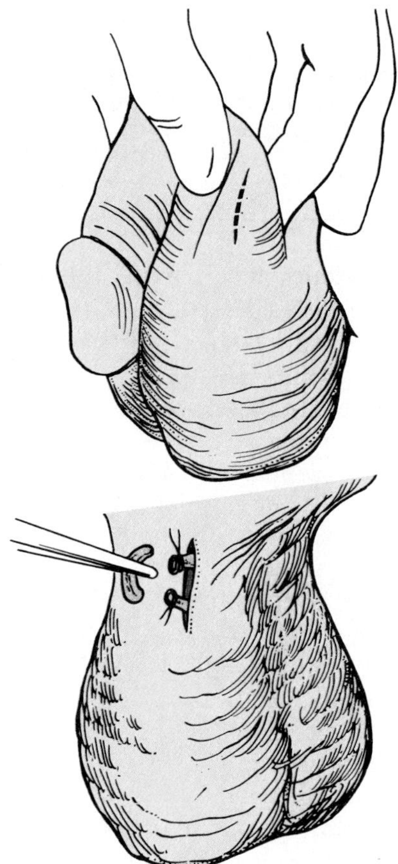

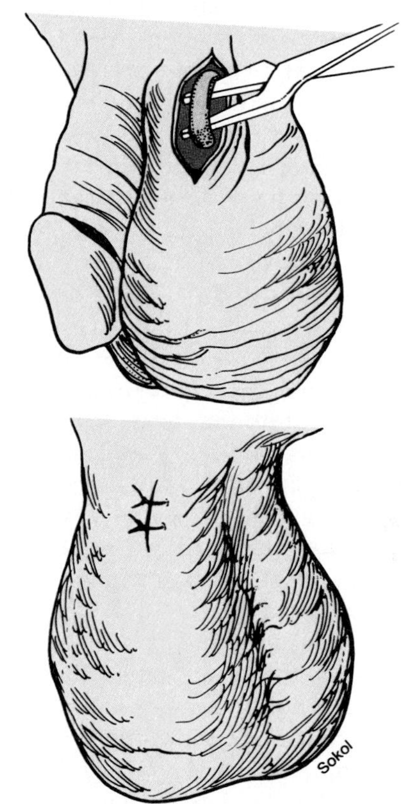

climacteric, which gradually brings to a close a woman's reproductive life. The climacteric generally begins at about age 43 and can last twelve to fifteen years, during which the ovaries slowly deteriorate until they finally stop working entirely. The actual cessation of menses requires a much shorter time, usually starting sometime around age 47 and ending about two years later, although there is a broad range (some women are still fertile in their 50s).

Once menopause is over, the ovaries no longer operate at all; no new follicles develop and those that remain shrink in size. The interstitial cells stop making estrogens, no corpora lutea develop, and the uterus becomes vestigial. It is not known what stimulates this deterioration. But whatever it is, is evidently inherent within the cells of the ovaries, because they seem to lose their ability to respond to the gonadotrophins and simply wear out. The hypothalamus and pituitary continue to function normally, and as you might expect from knowing the feedback loops, their hormone production increases as the ovaries atrophy. With no estrogens in the blood to inhibit them, the feedback mechanisms within the brain crank out ever-increasing quantities of GnRH, causing higher and higher levels of FSH and LH to be released into the bloodstream.

Figure 18.38 Another 100 percent dependable (but permanent) means of contraception. This, known as tubal ligation, involves the removal of a piece of each uterine tube, thus eliminating the possible union of ovum and sperm. It does not eliminate or alter hormonal flow, nor does it reduce sex drive.

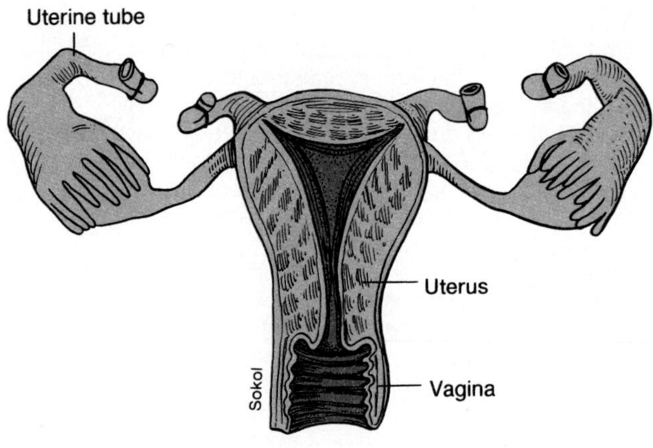

There are some unpleasant physical sensations that result from this hormonal imbalance. Women experience extremely uncomfortable thermal alterations like night sweats and "hot flashes," during which blood vessels in the skin of the face and upper body dilate and the body surface temperature actually goes up four or five degrees. We do not know exactly what causes this. It could be lack of estrogens or the increase in blood concentration of FSH and LH, but whatever it is, it's terribly disconcerting, and most women hate it. Some women get arthritis-like pains in their joints. A few experience psychological changes, particularly depression, which can really upset their loved ones as well as themselves. Pubic and underarm hair thins out and the breasts may get smaller. On occasion, menopausal women will experience skull-cracking headaches and dizziness, but this is quite rare. Usually there is nothing more serious than discomfort. Most of these changes are temporary and will pass with time.

Sometimes, however, there are permanent changes, and when they occur, they can be serious. Most seem to be linked to long-term deprivation of estrogens. Every once in a while, this loss will produce an unusual thinning of the skin, making it more susceptible to bruising or splitting open. Much more common— and just as serious—is the loss of bone calcium that can result in the affliction known as **osteoporosis** (*osteo*, "bone"; *poro*, "softening"). Women have less calcium than men do to begin with, and when estrogens vanish from their bloodstream they start to lose it at a high rate. If nothing is done to slow its loss, as much as 20 percent can disappear. The most obvious indication that this has happened is the appearance of the familiar "widow's hump" that forces the woman's head forward like an arthritic chicken's. This gets more and more pronounced as time passes; the upper spine bends more and more, and it can be more than simply disfiguring. Later in life, as the disease achieves advanced stages, bones get so brittle that they can break merely from the act of walking.

Occasionally, menopausal women will experience some anatomical changes that are definitely masculine. Most often this takes the form of redistribution of hair, particularly facial and body hair. Sometimes small moustaches will grow and/or the woman will develop hair on her chest. Fat begins to redistribute itself, shrinking breast size and imparting a masculine appearance to the silhouette. The cause is probably a slightly higher-than-normal production of sex steroids by the adrenal cortex. As you know, the adrenal cortex normally produces both androgens and estrogens throughout the life of both men and women. While the gonads are functioning, the adrenally produced hormones are simply overwhelmed. However, when the ovaries stop working, the adrenal sex hormones become the only ones in the blood, and they can assume control. Actually, a woman produces just as many adrenal estrogens as she does adrenal androgens, but as the blood circulates through the liver, the estrogens are metabolized at a much higher rate than the androgens are; hence the androgens are the ones that exert their effects.

There are no physiological reasons why this should be any problem, but psychologically it can be devastating. Many women feel that, in addition to losing their ability to reproduce like a woman, they suddenly no longer even *look* like one. There are many things that can be done to alter these unhappy physical changes, and workers have found that once the anatomy is all right again, the psychological discomfort is easy to handle. Psychologists say that the biggest problem is convincing such women that they will not suddenly lose their responsiveness to men and begin to lust after women.

Post-Menopausal Sexual Responsiveness

Happily, sexual interest or responsiveness does not end with the termination of menopause unless the woman wants it to. In fact, with the threat of pregnancy behind them, women often experience an increased sex drive. On the average, the menopause still leaves a woman with a third of her life ahead of her and there is no physiological reason associated with sex that suggests she should not enjoy it.

A Male Menopause?

Unfortunately, the world still views the menopause in a strongly negative way. It is thought to signal the end of youth and vigor and to introduce old age along with all its unpleasant aspects, including senility, irritability, and intolerance. Thus aging men who exhibit a crotchety nature or show signs of mental depression are said to be undergoing a "male menopause" because it fits the stereotype of the menopausal woman.

There are many reasons why this is wrong. To begin with, men cannot go through a menopause; since they never menstruate, how could they suffer from a pause in menses? That, of course, is speaking with scientific precision and is not what people mean when they refer to a male menopause. They are referring to the behavioral changes that old age, illness, or medication can induce in some men, and they attribute this, inaccurately, to a loss of virility because the sex hormones have slowed down or stopped.

Is this possible? Is there a reduction in the flow of androgens in aging men? There may be. Certainly it would not surprise anyone if there were. But if there is, it is probably so small that it has no significant results. There is no reason to believe that there is ever a cutoff point in a man's life when the production of sex hormones stops or is reduced below a critical level. Anyhow, nobody knows what the "critical level" might be. No one has ever produced any figures on just how much testosterone must be present in the blood to produce an erection, nor is there any way to estimate how much hormone the testes must secrete daily to retain a man's interest in women. On the other hand, there is lots of evidence to support the idea that, barring illness, men never lose their virility or the ability to produce viable sperm. There are many confirmed records of 70- and 80-year-old men having fathered children, and there are a few unconfirmed reports that men over 100 have also.

Most researchers are fairly well convinced that healthy men never spontaneously lose the physiological ability to perform coitus with a woman, and that loss of sex drive in otherwise healthy aging men is more a psychological problem than a physiological one. It could be that since the men have been told all their lives that it is supposed to happen, it does. Their friends believe it, their children *demand* it, and the stereotyped attitude of the general public agrees. All this is enough to convince them that it is true and it becomes so—the mind can be a powerful undercurrent on the physiological tide.

Clinical Considerations

Herpes

When considering diseases involving human sexuality and the reproductive organs it is impossible not to begin with diseases transmitted while engaging in coitus. The most terrifying one today, of course, is AIDS, and for a discussion of that affliction I refer you to the previous chapter. Just a few years ago, however, AIDS was unheard of, and the big problem in the singles crowd was **herpes.** The infection is so named because it is caused by *Herpes hominis II*, a virus closely related to *Herpes simplex*, the virus responsible for things like cold sores.

Genital herpes usually starts with unusually heavy itching of the genitals, changing presently to pain and finally into small, superficial ulcers in the mucous membranes of the external genitalia. If it is ignored and some other organism manages to get into these small sores, the result can be the formation of some huge, really painful ulcers, but this seldom happens if reasonable care is exercised. Usually the glans or foreskin of the penis is the site of infection in men, while the labia, clitoris, and vagina are the main targets in women. It can be quite painful, particularly while the victim is urinating. Sometimes merely walking can hurt. The disease seems to run in rhythmic surges. There will be long periods of quiescence followed by a sudden outbreak of miserable activity which gradually subsides into quiescence again.

Until AIDS reared its murderous head, herpes was the problem most feared by sexually active single people in this country, and with good reason. The infection is spread from person to person by sexual contact, and while it is not the killer that AIDS is, it can lead to lethal intrauterine disease, and it most certainly can kill a fetus if the mother is infected. Generally, however, it is simply a great inconvenience and discomfort. What makes matters infinitely worse is, there is no cure for genital herpes and once you have it, you do not recover—it never goes away.

Syphilis

Before the advent of effective antibiotics, **syphilis** was an extremely dangerous and often lethal infection. In fact, until the early part of the twentieth century, syphilis was fatal nearly 100 percent of the time. It did not kill quickly. Sometimes it took thirty years to do its lethal work, but it killed relentlessly. Thousands of people died from it, including Sir Francis Drake and Winston Churchill's father, the Duke of Marlborough. It varied without pattern in its deadliness. It could kill in a reasonably short period—history indicates that Drake contracted it less than two years before it did him in—or it could lay dormant for decades and then take out its victims with a funny kind of "heart disease" or unexpected stroke.

It has had dozens of names. The English and Germans called it the "French Sickness," the French called it the "Italian Sickness," and Italians called it the "Spanish Plague." No one knows for sure when it started. There are records that suggest that it was unknown in Europe until Cuban Indians gave it to the Spaniard conquistadores. Yet medical writings made by Middle Eastern physicians indicate that it may have been present in the ancient world. In any case, we have it today, and it is essentially a disease of humans. It is caused by a type of bacterium called a **spirochete.** This is a microorganism that resembles a corkscrew, and like a corkscrew it seems able to "screw" its way into unbroken skin. Its specific name is *Treponema pallidum*, and it is acquired through sexual contact with an infected person. Tales of people having caught syphilis from toilet seats or from other fomites touched by an infected person are almost certainly just tales. Although it lives very nicely in the warm, nutritious fluids of the human body, *T. pallidum* cannot live more than moments outside. It probably could not survive more than a minute or two on a person's skin, and it certainly could not exist on the cold hardness of a toilet seat. During sexual intercourse, however, it moves freely from person to person, entering wherever it can. It will certainly penetrate a sore, if one is present in the vagina or on the penis, but it can get in easily without one, apparently burrowing right through any damp, warm mucous membranes it encounters. Once in a new territory, it establishes itself locally, gets a colony growing, then migrates gradually into the bloodstream.

Indications of *primary syphilis* are fairly direct. About the fourth week a wet, unsightly ulcer or **chancre** appears, usually where the organism first entered, which is generally somewhere on the genitals. It does not hurt, doesn't bleed, and lasts about a month, during which time it gradually gets smaller until it goes away. If the victim ignores this sign, the disease incubates for about three months; then signs of *secondary syphilis* appear.

Secondary syphilis usually features bright red, cutaneous rashes scattered over the body. Sores often appear in the mouth, nose, and on other mucous membranes and give great difficulty. Lymph nodes swell and get sore, and the victim experiences all the systemic symptoms of a slowly developing influenza, including fever and sometimes jaundice for good measure.

If the disease is still ignored, it drifts into a period of latency that can last from two to twenty years, after which it will suddenly flare up as *tertiary syphilis.* Tertiary syphilis often begins with a series of horrid ulcers as soft, gooey, and unpleasant as their name: **gummas.** They are found in the mouth, on the tongue, inside the nose—even in the throat—but mostly they appear on the skin surface. They tend to stay in one place, but this is not something you can depend on. Sometimes they will completely infiltrate an organ or a tissue and make the whole thing sore. They are unpleasant enough on the skin surface, but they can find worse places to develop. Sometimes they appear beneath the skin in connective or muscle tissue and will swell into subcutaneous lumps that eventually break through the skin surface and slough off quantities of viscous liquid, leaving behind large craters with lifeless, leathery interiors that turn slowly into deep scars.

The organism can invade any tissue. It frequently enters cardiac muscle where it causes deep damage that is extremely serious and usually fatal. Invasions of nervous tissue can also be disastrous, producing sudden outbursts of epilepsy or convulsions with no immediately apparent cause. Often the victim shows uncontrollable trembling in hands, arms, or face—sometimes the whole body trembles. The urine is often filled with *T. pallidum,* which invades testicular tissues, rendering the victim both primarily and secondarily impotent. The organism will even invade bone joints, where it can disrupt function in a manner similar to arthritis but without the pain of the latter.

Until early in this century, a diagnosis of syphilis was a sentence of isolation and eventual death; there was nothing anyone could do. About the turn of the century a German scientist named Erlich uncovered an arsenic compound that would kill the organism and could cure the disease. Unfortunately, the cure was sometimes as dangerous as the disease. Being arsenic, the curative compound was toxic, occasionally to the patient as well as to *T. pallidum.* Several deaths were recorded as directly attributable to the treatment.

Today, treatment is reliable and swift. Penicillin is the drug of choice, and it kills *T. pallidum* quickly and surely. Syphilis caught in the primary or secondary stages can be completely cured within three weeks, and even those with tertiary syphilis can be treated. Damage already done by the spirochete cannot be corrected with antibiotics, of course, but further damage can be prevented.

Gonorrhea

Gonorrhea is a common and well-known disease throughout the world. In this country, everyone hears about it, usually from "the gutter," before they reach puberty, and people in the military service are particularly familiar with it. Thousands of dollars have been spent by the U.S. military since 1916 trying to warn G.I.s about its depredations and without much success, which testifies to the power of the "mating urge." It has starred in more movies than Robert Redford and has been the chief protagonist in comic books, speeches, and military courts martial for a hundred years. Known familiarly as "the clap," it has been a ubiquitous scourge throughout recorded history. Every G.I. or stranger in town who has ever visited a brothel has watched for its appearance with a certain dread. Jokes referring to "clap" are bandied about with childish glee, and a colleague who suddenly "comes down with it" is more an object of hilarity than sympathy. Yet, in fact, it is nothing to laugh at.

It is caused by a bacterium of the genus *Neisseria,* which includes some pretty deadly pathogens—like, for example, the organism responsible for meningitis. It is a venereal disease, which means it is spread by intimate contact with infected persons, and the bacterium, like the syphilitic spirochete, cannot live for more than a few moments outside the human body. The most commonly experienced symptom is a sharp pain in the urethra when urinating and a purulent discharge or "drip" from the urethral opening. Although it usually restricts itself to the urogenital tract, it has been known to become chronic, invading the bloodstream and spreading into the interstitial areas. Women are as susceptible to it as men, but unfortunately, they often experience no symptoms, and if they are sexually active they can spread the disease widely before they know they have it. Women who become pregnant while suffering from undiagnosed gonorrhea often infect newly born offspring as they pass through the infected maternal genital tract. A common effect of this infection was blindness in the newborn. The problem became so widespread during the early years of this century that it became routine for physicians to place silver nitrate in the eyes of newly born infants to kill any *Neisseria* that might happen to be there. Indeed, some older obstetricians still do it, and in fact, there are a few states where it is required.

The most common problems, however, involve the urogenital tract, and if untreated the disease can render the sufferer sterile. If it invades the blood and is spread throughout the body, it can cause heart problems, liver difficulties, and meningitis, any of which can be fatal.

Penicillin is still the drug of choice, although many strains of *Neisseria* are highly resistant to it. Tetracyclines will usually work if penicillin fails. Cures are complete and require only a short period of time (five days), and the social stigma attached to gonorrhea is nothing compared to what it once was—even the military no longer punishes itinerant soldiers for catching it. It should be clearly understood, however, that no one possessing natural immunity has ever been found, and recovery from an attack does not confer immunity to subsequent attacks.

The Prostate

Hyperplasia

The prostate gland is the site of frequent difficulties. Prostatic hyperplasia (enlargement of the gland) is common in men over 50 and can be a real problem. As you know from earlier in this chapter, the prostate gland wraps around the urethra, and if it enlarges, it can clamp down on it, making it smaller and causing the victim considerable difficulty in urinating. A reliable sign that the gland is enlarging is an increase in the frequency of urination and a loss of urine flow pressure, but sometimes this is hard to spot. The growth of the gland is slow, so the restriction of urine flow is gradual—so gradual that often it isn't spotted until it becomes really severe.

As is the case with tubal pregnancy, the only cure for an enlarged prostate is surgical removal of part of the gland.

Prostatic Cancer

Cancer of the prostate is the most common form of cancer in men over the age of 65, and while it can be effectively treated, like other cancers it is difficult to cure. Surgical removal of the prostate or heavy radiation therapy has produced remissions and life extensions of more than ten years in some cases, but such long-term remissions usually include castration, and not every man—even 70-year-old ones—views that with favor.

The reason castration is utilized is quite simple. Testosterones are produced by the testes, and testosterone aggravates the cancer and stimulates its growth. By removing the source of the hormone, the progress of the growth can be substantially slowed. However it is a fact that the disease is very slow in developing and slow in progressing, and as is the case with benign prostate enlargement, it sometimes produces signs so gradually that people do not notice them until it is too late. If the cancer metastasizes before treatment begins, there is little that can be done.

Dysmenorrhea (Menstrual Cramps)

Menstrual cramps are one of the most common problems associated with the reproductive tract. Yet because some women do not suffer from them (and of course, men *never do*), they are often discounted as "imaginary female troubles." More than one high school student has reported unsympathetic high school teachers—female as well as male—who consistently refused to accept monthly cramps as a legitimate illness, claiming a little self-discipline would dispel them.

Yet they are real enough and when severe can be crippling. No one knows what causes them, but it is believed to be uterine contractions or an inadequate blood flow to the awakening uterine endometrium as the menstrual cycle begins. If the pain were restricted to the lower abdomen it would be bad enough, but it frequently involves lower backache, nausea, diarrhea, and sometimes skull-bursting headaches.

There is seldom any problem with the reproductive organs, and it is usually a good idea to assure adolescents of this fact. Treatment with over-the-counter analgesics like aspirin, acetaminophen, or ibuprofen may work, although none of them are reliable in severe cases. The most reliable painkillers are prescription antiprostaglandins, of which the most effective has proven to be mefenamic acid.

The medical profession used to believe that dysmenorrhea was primarily an affliction of adolescence and that age or pregnancy dispelled it, but this idea is beginning to pass. Achieving maturity usually does not signal an end to dysmenorrhea, and childbirth usually eliminates the problem only temporarily. Evidence is beginning to accumulate to suggest that exercise and plenty of regular sleep can help reduce the intensity if not eliminate cramps entirely, but this doesn't always work. For those who have tried every preventive without success, antiprostaglandin preparations are the only resort.

Ectopic (Tubal) Pregnancy

Every once in a while, a fertilized egg will be implanted in the wall of a uterine tube instead of being propelled down into the uterus. (Remember, the egg is fertilized in the uterine tube and is not implanted in the uterine wall for two or three days.) When this occurs—and it is not particularly rare—the embryo proceeds to develop inside a structure that is not able to properly handle it and cannot contain its growth.

This problem is commonly known as a **tubal pregnancy,** and it can cause real trouble if not properly treated. The victim experiences terrible pain in the lower abdomen and often suffers from shock, and hemorrhage from the vagina is frequently heavy. If not properly handled, the fallopian tube containing the embryo will burst sometime during the third month of pregnancy, seriously endangering the mother's life.

Surgery is the only treatment for tubal pregnancy. Even if it is recognized early and caught before the tube can burst, surgery is still the only cure. The afflicted tube and usually the ovary associated with it are removed.

Eclampsia (Toxemia of Pregnancy)

No one really understands why it happens, or what causes it, but in about 5 percent of otherwise normal pregnancies, the potential mother will develop what was once called **toxemia of pregnancy.** This usually begins as a mild hypertension and progresses to a swelling of the skin around joints of the lower extremities and an accumulation of fluid within (edema). In this stage, it is considered **preeclampsia,** and if recognized promptly and properly treated, it remains in this stage or regresses to normalcy. About one patient in every two hundred, however, will suddenly develop a severe and sometimes fatal form of the disease in which, among other things, the placenta separates from the uterus and spontaneous abortion occurs.

Swollen ankles and knees, along with protein in the urine, usually warn of the presence of preeclampsia, and a blood pressure higher than 140/90 can quickly confirm. Treatment should be started immediately. Until recently, such patients were immediately placed on low-salt diets and given large quantities of diuretics, but this is no longer considered effective. Salt intake should remain normal and diuretics, since they do not work anyway, should be avoided. Even if the affliction is mild and the woman is allowed to remain at home, she must be cautioned that lots of rest is essential, and her physician should check her carefully at least three times a week. If blood pressure continues to increase during this time, the patient is usually hospitalized immediately. Fortunately, hospital treatment seldom fails, and a perfectly normal childbirth usually occurs. Even then, however, the patient must be watched for three or four days, as relapses often happen during this period. The problem gradually lessens with the passage of time and is usually gone by the end of the second postpartum month.

Breast Cancer

The cause of breast cancer is, as is the case with nearly all cancers, not known. But there are some factors that definitely influence a person's susceptibility. For example, women are one hundred times more likely to develop breast malignancies than men are, and there is fairly good evidence that it runs in families, so obviously both sex and heredity play a role. It is a statistical fact that women who had children before age 25 have a lower incidence of breast cancer than those whose children came later, but it is not known why. About all anyone can say is, these factors play a role.

There are several fairly good signs. Nipple discharge or crusting is very important and should never be ignored. Breast examination should be carried out at least once a month and any unusual lump or mass should be immediately examined by a physician. Confirmed malignancies should be promptly excised.

The most common treatment has been and still is total mastectomy—complete removal of the breast and its attendant lymph nodes. However, even with such radical surgery, fewer than half of the patients survive more than ten years, and this statistic can be matched with much less radical surgery. One technique used with success has been to cut below the breast and skin it, then remove the offending tissue beneath and take out the necessary lymph nodes. The entire area can then be restructured, and when the skin is placed back down over the newly molded breast all normal external sensations will still be there. Another, even simpler, procedure is known as a **lumpectomy** (removal of just the malignant lump). Many surgeons insist that this is not the treatment of choice, but statistical evidence indicates that these less-radical procedures produce survival rates as high as total mastectomy, and both recovery rate and life quality are certainly better.

Toxic Shock Syndrome (TSS)

Until 1978, no one had ever heard of toxic shock syndrome. That year, the first case was described in a 17-year-old girl who died from the disease. And suddenly, there were dozens of cases everywhere—there were nearly a thousand in 1980. Most of these involve young women (less than 35 years of age) and are nearly always associated with the use of tampons during menstruation. This quite naturally led the medical community to conclude that the use of tampons was somehow associated with the development of the disease, an assumption that is still prevalent.

It is still not known what causes TSS. The association between it and certain kinds of tampons has been confirmed in a vague kind of way, but it is weakened considerably by the observation that about 15 percent of all TSS cases involve men. The only pathogenic organism that has been found in association with TSS is *Staphylococcus aureus*—the common "staph" bug—but it is not always present. TSS sometimes occurs without involving a staph infection.

Do tampons cause it? Obviously they do not, or men would not get TSS at all, but they may contribute to it. It has been suggested that super-absorbent tampons may eliminate some of the vagina's normal resident flora, thus permitting the causative organism—whatever it may be—to become established. Other people suggest that maybe consistent use of tampons causes breaks in the vaginal lining and permits the infectious organism to get into the bloodstream. Either, or both, of these hypotheses may be true, but they cannot explain the incidence of TSS in men, nor its occurrence in women who do not use tampons. The simple truth is that no one knows what causes it. But most physicians can recognize it when they see it.

The earliest signs of the disease are: sudden, and very high, fever (as high as 105 °F), headache, sore throat, bloodshot eyes, obvious mental confusion, and gastrointestinal disruptions. The fever is persistent, and within a couple of days a redness begins to appear on the skin—not a rash, more like a spotty sunburn—and the patient may drift into severe shock—hence the name toxic *shock* syndrome. This disease is no joke. Upwards of 10 percent of those who become infected die of it.

The medical profession certainly considers it a deadly disease. Once it is diagnosed, the patient is hospitalized in intensive care immediately. In addition to antibiotic therapy, it is essential to replenish water losses and to carefully balance electrolytes in the body fluids. Intensive care is often maintained for as long as a week, and patients must be carefully watched for three or four months following their release from the hospital. Most are warned not to use tampons for at least a year, but this advice is considered more prudent than anything else and may or may not be of value.

Summary

A Touchy Subject

The subject of sexual congress has been anathema in polite society for decades.

I. Western Taboos
   A. Until well into the twentieth century, sex was considered by most Americans to be a necessary evil that one never indulged in frivolously.
   B. Recently, these Victorian attitudes have receded considerably. Sex, especially in marriage, is no longer viewed as something to be avoided.

II. The Purpose of Sex
   A. Biologically, the purpose of sexual intercourse is to produce a thorough mixing of two different kinds of genetic material and the production of an offspring.
   B. Reproduction Without Sex
      1. Many people, even today, still feel that sexual intercourse is both depraved and inherently evil. To these groups, natural reproduction without sex, if it were possible, would be the ideal process. Sex could then be permanently discarded.
      2. Simultaneously, most such people also reject artificial insemination on moral grounds. Inconsistency is not a consideration.
      3. Regardless of one's attitude toward sexual intercourse, there is simply no way that natural procreation can occur without it. And in any case, sexual procreation has enormous benefits for the species.

Some Facts about a Person's Sex

I. There are two kinds of sex chromosomes—the X chromosome and the Y chromosome. An individual with two X chromosomes is a female, while a person with one of each type is a male. Since all females have only X chromosomes, the only way a variation can be introduced into an offspring is through the father, thus:

II. Father Determines the Sex of the Child.

III. The Y Chromosome
   A. In many animals, the Y chromosome is essentially inert, genetically. In such animals, maleness is determined not by the presence of a Y chromosome, but by the absence of one of the X chromosomes. If such an animal possessed a single X chromosome and lacked a Y completely, it would still be a functional male.
   B. In most of the vertebrates, this is not the case, and certainly it is not true of humans. In humans, the Y chromosome is loaded with genetic information and is absolutely essential if an individual is to show "maleness."

The Basic Sexual Plan

I. In mammals, the basic sexual plan seems to be female. If no disruptive influence is imposed by the genes, developing embryos will all be female.

II. Control of the Fetal Hormones
   A. By the seventh week of embryonic life, the genital ridge of humans is sufficiently well-developed to produce sex hormones. These hormones begin to flow at about this time and are able to undertake the necessary anatomical modifications for production of whatever sex has been programed into the genes.
   B. Hormonal activation is stimulated by enzymes that are produced in the embryo according to the instructions programed on the chromosomes.

The Gonads

Whether the gonads are ovaries or testes, they are considered the primary sexual characteristics of the individual.

I. The Primary Sexual Characteristics. They begin their development at the embryonic age of seven weeks. Ovaries develop in female embryos, testes in males.

II. The Secondary Sexual Characteristics. Secondary characteristics are those anatomical variations that make a woman look like a woman and a man look like a man. Sexual body differentiation is controlled by the male and female hormones and the gonadotrophic hormones of the pituitary. It does not occur *in utero,* since gonadotrophins do not appear until puberty.

The Primary Sex Cells

I. Production of the sex cells or gametes in humans involves a process known as meiosis, or reduction division. This process is as carefully programed as mitosis, but its objects are different. It is designed to produce cells with twenty-three chromosomes instead of twenty-three *pairs* of chromosomes.
II. Some Terminology. Diploid cells contain twenty-three pairs of chromosomes. Haploid cells contain twenty-three chromosomes.

Meiosis

I. The First Meiotic Division. The first meiotic division is essentially a reduction division. It differs from mitotic divisions in that the centromeres of the chromosomes are not split. Instead, it separates homologous chromosomes, placing them in different cells.
II. Interkinesis. This is a pause between meiotic divisions.
III. The Second Division. The second meiotic division is similar to mitosis in that centromeres are being split and separated; chromatids are pulled into opposite ends of the daughter cells.

Puberty in the Male

At puberty, males begin to show characteristics of maleness. Broad shoulders, narrow hips, growth and distribution of body and facial hair. Enlargement of both testes and penis. The ability to father a child also appears.

The Testes

I. The testes are suspended outside the body in the scrotal sac. They produce viable reproductive cells and the sex hormones.
II. Spermatogenesis. The meiotic processes in males leading to production of spermatozoons.
III. The Sex Accessory Structures. These are the epididymis, the vas deferens, the ejaculatory ducts, the bulbourethral gland, the prostate gland, and the seminal vesicles.
IV. The External Male Genitalia. These are the penis and the scrotum.
V. Endocrinology of the Testes. The interstitial cells of Leydig are responsible for the synthesis and secretion of the male hormones (androgens). They are stimulated by gonadotrophic hormones of the pituitary gland.

The Male Sexual Response

Semen. Semen is a complex fluid produced by a variety of structures in the male reproductive tract. This is the fluid vehicle that carries sperm and provides them with nourishment and sustenance.

The Human Female

Puberty in the Female

Puberty in females begins with the first menstrual period. It results in the broadening of the hips, the appearance of axial hair, but none elsewhere on the body, including the face. It also results in the production of fertile ova.

I. The Gonads. These are the ovaries. They are contained within the abdominal cavity.
II. Oogenesis. Oogenesis is the process that can result in the production of a fertile ovum.

Human Cyclical Changes

Cyclical sexual changes in humans are pretty well restricted to women.

I. The Ovarian Cycle. This is a series of cyclical changes that occur within the ovary every thirty days or so.
II. The Menstrual Cycle. This refers to regular changes that take place in the female reproductive system that coincide with the cyclical changes that occur within the ovaries.

Fertilization

I. The process of fertilization occurs when the egg nucleus fuses with the modified nucleus of a spermatozoan. It is preceded by a series of chemical and physical events that reach their climax when the sperm nucleus manages to enter the fertile ovum.
II. Only One Sperm per Egg. It is not possible for more than one sperm to enter the ovum and fuse with the ovarian nucleus. Great physiological pains, not all of which are understood, are taken to prevent such a thing from happening.

Pregnancy

I. Once the egg and sperm nuclei have fused, the fertilized egg (zygote) is implanted in the wall of the uterus, and pregnancy begins.
II. Endocrinology of Pregnancy
   A. The early stages of pregnancy are not significantly different from the latter stages of a menstrual cycle. Hormonal changes are the first to occur.
   B. The corpus luteum maintains the pregnancy until the placenta develops, at which time it takes over the job of synthesizing and secreting the necessary steroids.
III. Hormonal Controls. The first hormone, unique to pregnancy, is human chorionic gonadotrophin. It is controlled by a special hormone released by the placenta.
IV. Hormonal Roles. During pregnancy, the normal female hormones have special jobs to do, and they are different from their day-to-day jobs.
   A. Progesterone. Progesterone desynchronizes electrical activity of the uterus, thus preventing a coordinated contraction of that organ that might expel the embryo.
   B. Estrogens. Estrogens help the uterus to become accustomed to the presence of a growing fetus.

C. Other Hormones
   1. Relaxin. Relaxin is a small protein secreted by the corpus luteum. It aids in the implantation of the zygote, and when the time comes to expel the infant, it helps relax the muscles and tissues around the vulva and vagina, permitting dilation to occur.
   2. Human Placental Lactogen (hPL). This hormone is produced in the placenta and is deeply involved in preparing the breasts for the synthesis and secretion of milk.

The Placenta

I. The placenta is made up of both embryonic and maternal tissues. It is the interface between the fetus and the mother. All exchanges between the two individuals must take place across the placenta. In addition, the placenta is the source of most of the hormones of pregnancy.
II. Other Fetal Membranes. The chorion and amnion both provide protection and sustenance for the developing embryo.

Parturition (Childbirth)

Birth usually occurs after 280 days of intrauterine development. It is a much more involved process than it may appear to be—it requires the activity of several hormones as well as both autonomic and somatic neural processes.

Lactation

I. Synthesis and secretion of milk begins in earnest as soon as parturition has taken place. Lactation is also under both hormonal and neural control.
II. Breast Milk vs. Formula. The pros and cons of breast feeding are discussed, and cow's milk is compared with human milk.

Human Sexuality

I. The sexual behavior of humans is unique in the animal world. Humans may be the only animals that undertake sexual activity for the sheer pleasure of it.
II. Contraception. Since sexual activity is a pleasurable act, humans often want to indulge in it without having to worry about the possibility of pregnancy and procreation.
   A. Behavioral Contraception. This is the least dependable method of contraception.
   B. Rhythm? This is a form of behavioral contraception.
   C. Condoms. This is a more dependable contraception method than behavioral ones, but there are many disadvantages.
   D. Diaphragms. Diaphragms are more dependable than condoms, but they are not foolproof.
   E. Chemical Contraceptives. These are, like the diaphragm, not foolproof.
   F. The Intrauterine Device. This device works, and it has advantages over both diaphragms and condoms, but there are unpleasant side effects.
   G. Oral Contraceptives. These are the most dependable and convenient contraceptives.
   H. Vasectomy. This is a 100 percent dependable technique, but it is permanent.
   I. Tubal Ligation. Like vasectomy, this has the disadvantage of being permanent.

The Menopause

The end of menses. It doesn't exist in men.

I. Post-Menopausal Sexual Responsiveness. In humans, there are seldom any changes in sexual desire after menopause.
II. A Male Menopause? Scientifically, this doesn't exist. Behaviorally it sometimes occurs, but there is no empirical evidence to suggest that it should.

Clinical Considerations

I. Herpes
II. Syphilis
III. Gonorrhea
IV. The Prostate
   A. Hyperplasia
   B. Prostatic Cancer
V. Dysmenorrhea (Menstrual Cramps)
VI. Ectopic (Tubal) Pregnancy
VII. Eclampsia (Toxemia of Pregnancy)
VIII. Breast Cancer
IX. Toxic Shock Syndrome

Review Questions

1. From a biological point of view, what, precisely, is the purpose of sexual intercourse?
2. What advantages does sexual intercourse offer humanity as a species?
3. Which of the sexes determines the gender of the offspring? Why is this so?
4. Describe the Y chromosome.
5. How does the Y chromosome adjust the basic sexual plan in humans?
6. Describe the development of the reproductive organs in embryos up to six weeks of age.
7. How does the H-Y antigen affect these organs?
8. At what period of development does sexual differentiation begin in humans?
9. Describe the output of sex hormones in these early stages. Be sure to mention the source of each and the control system.
10. Describe the movement of the testes from the abdominal cavity of the fetus into the scrotal sac.
11. What constitute the primary sex characteristics of an individual?

12. What are the secondary sex characteristics? What system is primarily responsible for providing humans with secondary sex characteristics?
13. What is the normal chromosome count in humans? Would it be correct to state that men have twenty-three pairs of chromosomes? How about women?
14. What is meiosis? What is its purpose?
15. Describe the first meiotic division; if necessary, make sketches of the primary stages.
16. Describe the second meiotic division.
17. Describe the onset of puberty in the male. How does puberty differ from adolescence?
18. Describe the process of spermatogenesis. How much time does it consume?
19. Describe the morphology of a mature spermatozoan.
20. Name the male sex accessory structures. Why are they called accessory structures?
21. What force is responsible for the stiffening process that occurs when a man attains an erection?
22. Discuss the endocrinology of the testes.
23. What is semen? Describe its constituents, their source(s), and their function(s).
24. Describe the processes that take place during the development of femaleness in a child.
25. Describe the maturation process in girls.
26. Describe the process of oogenesis. Be sure you clearly describe the differences between it and the process of spermatogenesis.
27. Describe the ovarian cycle in as much detail as you can.
28. Describe the menstrual cycle. Be sure to correctly name the phases.
29. Describe the process by which a spermatozoan traverses the distance between the cervix and the waiting ovum.
30. Outline the processes by which a sperm penetrates the protective layers of the ovum and succeeds in fusing with the ovarian membrane.
31. The penetration of male germ cell material into the ovum triggers a process that must take place before fertilization can occur. What is it?
32. At what point does the process of fertilization actually take place?
33. Describe the implantation of a fertilized ovum into the uterus.
34. What is hCG? Describe its source and early control mechanisms.
35. Outline the role of progesterone in pregnancy. How does its action differ from that of estrogen?
36. Discuss the roles of relaxin and hPL.
37. Describe the placenta. Be sure to include both fetal and maternal tissues involved in its formation.
38. How is the fetus nourished? Describe the morphology and physiology of the exchange system that exists in the placenta.
39. What is the amnion? From what is it formed?
40. Describe the process of parturition.
41. Outline the differences between cow's milk and human milk. Describe colostrum.
42. How does the estrus cycle differ from the human ovarian and menstrual cycles?
43. It has been hypothesized by some scientists that the reason the human race is having troubles with overpopulation is the presence of a menstrual cycle instead of an estrus. Can you suggest why this might be so?
44. Describe some of the other contraceptive processes and describe their reliability.
45. What is the most reliable of the temporary contraceptive processes?
46. Outline the endocrinological and morphological changes that occur during menopause.
47. In view of the fact that the adrenal cortex usually produces equal amounts of male and female hormones, why is it that adrenal androgens sometimes produce physical changes in post-menopausal women?

Chapter 19 Maturity and Aging

Study Hints

When reading this chapter, try to remember that age is a collective process, embracing an enormous panorama of events that seems to sweep across living systems. We can see the results of aging when we look at old people, but there is a great deal that we cannot see that has been inferred—often incorrectly.

1. Try to enter this chapter with an open mind. Make an effort to discard the stereotyped version of the aged person.
2. Try to view the aging process as a series of individual events that may detract from a person's physical (and to a lesser extent, mental) capabilities but which do not lessen their worth as human beings.
3. Remember that aging does not always cause serious mental deterioration. Old people have had a tremendous number of experiences and have compiled a huge library of facts that they can relay to their younger colleagues.
4. There is no way to avoid aging, but gerontologists tell us that there are ways to avoid or postpone some of its ravages. Try to remember as many of these avoidance tactics as you can, particularly those that you can start on now. If you become a health professional, you will be asked about many of them, and you should not only be able to list them, you should also be able to explain why they are good or bad.

Objectives

When you have finished reading this chapter, you should:

1. be able to explain the difference between life expectancy and life span.
2. be able to outline how aging affects such things as the skin, the brain, the circulatory system, the skeleton, and the sensory organs.
3. know which physiological processes inevitably deteriorate with age and which need not do so if proper care is exercised
4. know how to help prevent the loss of those faculties that might be saved.

Introduction

Aging and death are aspects of living that everyone is aware of. We make repeated references to dying and the fact that "everyone does it, sooner or later." Yet somehow, in our eternal optimism, none of us like to believe we will ever experience it personally. We accept in a vague, dreamy sort of way the prospect of getting old, yet no one really believes that it will ever happen . . . until it does.

And it will—it is as inevitable as the sunrise. If we manage to survive the rigors and trauma of youth and the struggle to achieve the state of relaxed independence that categorizes the middle years, we will all—finally—grow old. Aging has been described by some as a disease to which everyone is susceptible. They have suggested that every body cell has the disease built right into it, and each will lose its ability to resist as time passes. There are even those who have gone so far as to attribute age to the efforts of a devious and as-yet-undiscovered virus.

It is certainly possible that age is a disease, and it would be nice if it were true, because there is always the hope that a disease can be cured, and finding a cure for age would make someone a lot of money. Most workers, however, tend to believe that it is not disease that ages a person but something much more fundamental . . . basic, but unfortunately probably not curable. Something that happens to everything that we manufacture or build, something that happens to the mountains and valleys, rivers and coastlines, something that can overtake the crust of the earth itself. The system simply wears out.

On a cellular level, there is evidence in abundance to support the latter idea. The most obvious support is to merely check the average age of human beings over the last several millennia and see just how much it has changed as a result of our medical advances and increased scientific knowledge. Surely, one would think, with all we know today, we *must* have increased humankind's life expectancy by dozens of years, but have we?

The average life expectancy of an American man today is about seventy-three years. During the so-called Dark Ages in Europe, the *average* life expectancy of a human male was less than thirty years. By that standard, we have improved the human life expectancy by fifty years, and we may feel that this reflects progress in defeating the process of aging. We must, however, remember that we are comparing ourselves to people who were poorly nourished, who often lived miserably,

Atherosclerosis is an arterial disease that can result in a stroke.

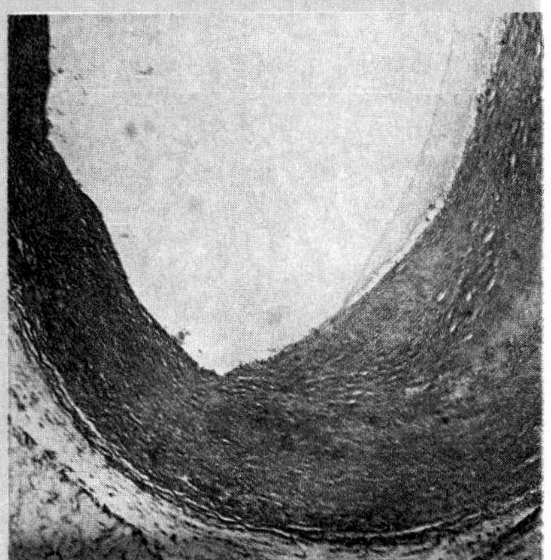

and who felt they were fulfilling laws of good hygiene by not defecating in the village well. Fewer than 50 percent of the children born to the average peasant of those centuries survived to 3 or 4 years of age, and of that group, only about 60 percent managed to reach age 10. Adult peasants were worked so hard and lived in such squalor that most were considered middle-aged at 26, and only a very few (less than 5 percent) survived to be 40. Compared to those unfortunates—our ancestors—we are indeed long-lived, but is that really a valid comparison? Are we really comparing the human ability to resist aging and senescence with such figures?

Definitely not! We are making comparisons that reflect mainly cultural differences rather than the ability of human beings to resist age. We note the life spans of these people. Then we average them all together and calculate the mean, which we announce is the life expectancy of the average person living in that culture. Life expectancy statistically reflects, therefore, the number of years the average individual lived under a given set of circumstances. Our *averages* today are higher because so few children die young and because we have the means to prevent or fight diseases that, in the Middle Ages, used to kill thousands of people a year. But averages are not a true reflection of what has been done to extend the *individual* human's absolute life span, and absolutes are what we need to view. When we talk of fighting age, we are referring to fending off the aging process. We are talking about maintaining an individual's youth for a longer period of time and permitting people to achieve greater age than they could a hundred or a thousand years ago. To make this kind of comparison, we have to examine whole populations and separate out those who succeeded in living long lives. How long could a really old person survive two thousand years ago? Do people today live any longer?

It certainly does not seem so. When we check records of ancient Egypt, ancient Greece or the Roman empire, we find that peasants and slaves often lived miserably and died young, but the average patrician lived a life that was about as long as the average person has today. In fact, thorough checking into various literary and historical sources reveals that when it comes to staving off old age, we have not progressed a great deal in the four or five-thousand years since human civilizations began to keep records. It is not the human life span that has improved in the last half-dozen centuries, but the *average person's life expectancy*, and that is not the same thing. To those working today to uncover the mystery of aging, it seems that people four thousand years ago had the potential to live just as long as anyone today. And when modern men and women reach 90 years of age, they look and feel just as old as citizens of ancient Egypt who achieved the same age. Not very many people lived to be 90 years of age then, and not very many do so today, either. Those who do are *old*. They look old, they act old, and it is obvious to everyone who sees them that they are at or near the end of their lives. A 90-year-old man was a very old man four thousand years ago and is a very old man today.

What all this tells us is that the number of years it is possible for a human being to live probably has not increased at all. This suggests that our bodies only have so many years in them, and when those years are gone, things give out—or in more modern jargon, the human body is programed to wear out in just under 100 years, and there isn't really anything that a person can do to prevent it. So it seems to most scientists who are working on the physiology of aging that even if our civilization suddenly gained the ability to cure cancer, clean up sclerotic blood vessels, effect permanent repairs on a damaged heart, and eliminate all problems with infectious diseases, people still would not be able to live much longer than ninety to one hundred years.

The process is apparently fundamental. It is evident even in individual cells, and it is probably built right into the DNA. Workers have grown cell cultures sampled from all kinds of human tissues, and they note that every single one of them has a definite limit to its life span. From constant checking with cells taken from different kinds of tissues in all kinds of experimental animals, it appears that a given cell has an absolute limit to the number of times it can reproduce. Each is able to divide a specified number of times, and when this limit is near, mitosis slows down. Finally, it stops. At this point, all the cells—the entire tissue preparation—begin to deteriorate, and shortly afterward, they die. As we have seen, all of us are composed of individual cells, and if our components wear out, so will the whole engine. If our body's cells are wearing out at a predetermined rate, ultimately our whole body will deteriorate . . . it is ineluctable.

The Aging Process

We know that as people approach old age, vulnerability to almost everything increases. The ability to rebound from accidental damage is reduced. Diseases that people would have thrown off with ease in their youth may suddenly get a foothold and cause severe and debilitating illness that can steal a few years. This increased frailty is the reason the average person expects to live seventy-plus years instead of ninety-plus.

But what about people who defy the averages? Not every man dies at age 73. There are a lot of people who manage to avoid all these problems and who remain healthy throughout their declining years. What about them?

Even there, we can still observe specific changes occurring, and since none of them are pathological, they must be due solely to age—to the process of wearing out. Some of them are pretty familiar.

1. Graying of the hair seems to happen universally. Sometimes a person will have gray hair by the time he is 25 while others are still dark-haired at 40, and some people never do get completely gray. Obviously, it does not always happen at the same age, but if the person lives long enough, it happens. It is a hallmark of age.
2. The skin on the body surface loses its elasticity, and instead of stretching tightly over the underlying muscles and bones as it did in youth, it begins to sag and wrinkle—another characteristic of age.
3. As time passes, the thick, cartilaginous pads that separate the individual elements of the vertebral column get thinner and lose some of their elasticity. This actually makes the person shorter in stature—not more than an inch or so, but it is noticeable.
4. In some people—particularly women—calcium loss from the skeleton can weaken the pectoral support and result in a noticeable hump across the shoulders or a bent-over appearance.
5. The ears and nose increase in length, and the end of the nose may become bulbous.
6. The hairline recedes, and hair in both sexes becomes thinner.
7. The skin becomes dry and flaky.
8. Nail growth slows noticeably, and heavy, longitudinal lines begin to show up, sometimes causing the nails to bend around the fingertips.
9. Hearing almost always degenerates, and the lens of the eye begins to lose its elasticity. Thus, the ability of the eyes to focus deteriorates, making bifocal or even trifocal glasses necessary.

These changes are obvious and can be spotted pretty easily. They are characteristics of old age, and when we see them, we immediately recognize them for what they are. Yet they are really only superficial manifestations of other, more deep-seated, changes . . . changes that often produce unseen internal depreciation as well. Sometimes the decline of a single system will trigger or exacerbate a series of events that will produce an insidious feedback loop that circles back and aggravates the initial cause. Let's view just one of the systemic attenuations that crop up in elderly people and consider its myriad consequences.

Circulatory Attrition

Cause

As age advances, the circulatory system begins to deteriorate. It seems to languish everywhere. The propulsion systems are usually the first to go. Neither the venous nor the arterial pumping mechanisms are able to work as hard as they once could. This is probably just as well, because for many reasons the blood vessels of aged people are smaller and less elastic than they used to be. The overall result is a reduced flow of blood through the body.

Effect

Now, recall the mission of the circulatory system. Remember how intimately it is tied into virtually every homeostatic and control mechanism in the body and you can imagine the consequences this kind of attenuation can produce. Let us consider a few of them:

1. *Homeostatic alterations,* which once responded so quickly to change, lose their smoothness. Old people tend to heat up uncomfortably in temperatures that younger ones can easily handle. Part of this is due to the loss of sweat glands and some body insulation, but the major cause is diminished circulatory capacity. Because there is a reduction in blood flow through skin surfaces, heat exchange between the body and the environment is less efficient. The body is thus unable to lose internal heat even when the ambient temperature would favor it.
2. *Cold temperatures* are just as difficult to deal with. Older people have a lower metabolic rate than they had when they were young, which means their body's *basic* heat production is less than it used to be. In addition, the reduced circulatory capacity slows overall blood movement. Hence heat distribution within the body is not as even as it once was. Hot spots and cool spots occur more often—hands, legs, feet, and arms get cold, and the impaired blood flow simply cannot keep up with it.

3. *The production of heat by the muscles* is probably the body's main source of intrinsic heat, yet the aged muscles do not get as much blood as they once did and so don't work as well. For this reason it is difficult for an oldster to get warm once he has cooled off—even shivering doesn't help much.
4. Since blood vessels that supply the epidermal skin layers have decreased in number and capacity, the skin's ability to repair damage is reduced. Sores that once healed in a day or two suddenly take a week, and bruises occur much more easily.

Consequences

All these problems can produce monumental erosion of a person's overall health. Probably the biggest reason is because, taken collectively, they can reduce the old person's ability and the desire to obtain adequate exercise . . . just consider the additional motivation:

1. Because work or even pleasant exercise can result in bumps or scrapes, elderly men and women may avoid any unnecessary activity since they know they do not heal very well.
2. In warm weather, because they cannot cool off with the efficiency they once could, they tend to avoid any operations that might increase their heat load.
3. In cold weather, since their muscles produce less heat than they used to, their outdoor activity is reduced, and they tend to stay inside their houses.

Feedback

The reduction in overall activity has, in its turn, a definite and very profound effect on the already-declining circulatory system.

1. It has powerful effects on the heart, reducing its pressure, lowering the pumping capacity, and usually reducing efficiency throughout the entire arterial system.
2. Alterations in pressure, can reduce the rate of exchange in the capillary beds, resulting in some tissues being deprived of adequate nourishment and rendering them less *able* to be active.
3. The reduced skeletal muscle activity also directly affects the venous return, since the energy for that is provided mainly by skeletal muscle movement.

Thus we have come full circle. The weakened pumping capacity, the lower pressure, and the smaller, less elastic vessels all combine to produce effects in the organ systems that they supply. These, in their turn, exacerbate the deterioration that is occurring in the circulatory system. And because of this system's ubiquity, breakdown of the entire body accelerates a little bit.

As you can easily see, if circulatory deterioration were the only problem that an aging person had to face, it would be enough. But it is not. Circulation is not the only system to deteriorate with age. Internal organs get smaller and less active, a fact that is most obvious to observers by changes in elimination patterns. The urinary bladder of an elderly man holds less than half of its youthful capacity and, unfortunately, in both men and women, indications that it is filling do not come as soon. Young people receive a warning from bladder sensory nerves when the bladder is about half-full and so can take their time looking for a rest room. But old people are not warned that their bladder is filling; there is no indication that a problem is building. Usually the first warning is also the last, because when it comes, the bladder is already full. This quite naturally creates a sudden air of urgency. The knowledge that the bladder must be emptied is accompanied by the knowledge that it must be emptied immediately—a characteristic of age.

Tissue Elasticity

This partial loss of sensation is probably directly related to a dwindling of bladder elasticity. Stretch receptors simply do not respond until the walls of the bladder stretch, and with elasticity lost, they do not stretch until they are full. And the problem is not restricted to the bladder. Loss of elasticity is universal throughout the body. It occurs in every tissue, and it has a multiplicity of causes. First of all, the number of elastic fibers diminishes. That alone would significantly reduce resilience, but in certain body areas it is exacerbated by the infiltration of inflexible protein and sometimes by the deposition of calcium salts. The protein that usually infiltrates is **collagen.** This is a rather stiff, unmalleable albuminoid that in young people lends support to tendons, connective tissues, and cartilage—and it is fine as long as it stays in these rather stubborn, unyielding tissues. But as age creeps up, it begins to move into other parts of the body, and the total amount of body collagen inexorably increases. It begins slipping surreptitiously into tissues where it really doesn't belong, and it increases rigidity wherever it goes. As the deposits thicken, areas that used to indent easily and quickly rebound suddenly stiffen like the rubber on the sole of a shoe. You cannot deform them easily, but when you do, they tend to remain longer in the new shape. Calcium salts sometimes percolate into the collagen deposits, converting areas that were like resistant rubber into petrified, bony masses. The main targets are skeletal junctions, chest areas, and the spine. As a result, there is a thickening of body joints, an increased rigidity in the chest, and a loss of suppleness in the vertebral column, particularly the neck and shoulder zones.

Reaction Time

Something also happens to the nervous reflexes—something that no one really understands. Reaction time slows dramatically, a phenomenon that begins in the twenties and is obvious in most people by the early thirties. As we all know, a highly trained athlete is old when he or she is 35, and very few people who play in professional sports continue actively to that age. Those who do, do so because they have acquired considerable knowledge to make up for their lost physical attributes, but sooner or later, even the extra knowledge is overwhelmed by their physical decline and they must quit. As age advances, reaction time slows to the point where many of the motor skills learned in one's youth are no longer possible.

Exactly what happens to reactions is not really clear. It may be a neural problem, but it does not appear to be. Most of the work done to date suggests that it is either a delay at myoneural junctions (researchers suggest that synthesis of neurotransmitters may be slowing) or some sort of change that has taken place within the body of the muscle itself. Generally speaking, the feeling is that it is probably the latter. Careful electrical measurements show that there is no loss in neural conduction speed; hence, the problem must be at the synapse or within the muscles, but precisely what it is or what causes it is not known.

Special Sense Organs

We know what causes some of our sensory problems—or maybe a better way to put that would be to state that we know what happens to certain sensory structures as they age. We do not, of course, know *why* it happens.

Eyes

As far as the eyes are concerned, probably the first sign is the discovery that your eyes don't seem to focus as quickly when they shift from distant objects to things nearby. The lens is to blame. Like all other tissues, the lens has lost its flexibility; hence no matter how hard the ciliary muscles tug, it takes more effort and more time to change its shape. The difficulty is amplified by a loss of power in the ciliary muscles themselves. Eventually we arrive at the point where, between the hardening of the lens and the weakening of the ciliary muscles, the eyes simply will not focus. The clear focal length moves farther and farther away as time passes until even a nearsighted person cannot see nearby things clearly and cannot read fine print without glasses. The person has suddenly become *presbyopic* (see chapter 9).

To make vision even more difficult, the lenses begin to fog up a little, mainly with color. It seems that the capsule enclosing the lens thickens and turns yellowish, thus altering the ability of elderly people to clearly discern those colors on the high end of the visible spectrum. Purples, blues, and sometimes even blue-greens lose their enchantment, which may explain why, as artists age, we see fewer blues and purples in their work.

The lacrimal (tear) gland begins to malfunction. In some people it produces too many tears, while in others it secretes too few. Thus the aged person is afflicted either with excessive tearing or a drying cornea.

Ears

Hearing is also characteristically affected. Usually the problem is conductive (see chapter 9) and can be corrected with hearing aids and/or surgery. But as we have already seen, the overall body loss of elasticity includes the basilar membrane. As this membrane stiffens, the ear's ability to respond to high frequencies diminishes; hence older people have difficulty detecting high notes and voices. Children, especially when they are playing, are difficult to hear, and sometimes old people are accused of ignoring their grandchildren when in fact they cannot hear their squeaky, excited voices.

Olfaction and Taste

The ability to taste and/or smell things also appears to weaken with age, although this may be more the result of environmental assault than an inevitable result of the aging process. After years of inhaling tobacco smoke or puffing on a pipe, a person probably loses a considerable number of both taste buds in the mouth and olfactory receptors in the nasal epithelium. However it is generally agreed that even those who have never smoked must experience some attenuation from the odors and pollution of our cities. Some medical records have been compiled that suggest that people who have spent their lives in the clear air of the countryside, and have never smoked, never do lose their ability to clearly detect odors and to enjoy most of the flavors they appreciated as children. There are, however, few people lucky enough to have spent their lives in such a place, just as the number of such places is diminishing.

Eating Habits

Possibly part of the reason older people seem to have lost their appreciation for good food is because their digestive system has changed—especially their mouths. Throughout the 1930s, the 1940s, and well into the 1950s it was standard practice for dentists to pull out every one of a person's teeth once the gum disease known as **pyorrhea alveolaris** (compound periodontitis) was diagnosed. By today's standards, many of these extractions were premature. We are aware of causes and preventive measures today that no one in the 1930s could possibly have known. Nevertheless, as a direct result of this practice, many of our oldest citizens no longer have their own teeth and have been without them for several decades. This undoubtedly has changed many eating habits. There is also some evidence that the gastrointestinal organs responsible for synthesizing digestive enzymes lose their efficiency as time passes and secrete fewer and fewer enzymes. Hence foods that a person once ate with considerable relish may cause gastrointestinal upset that is just not worth risking.

The Circulatory System

As we noted earlier, probably the system that is most affected by the loss of tissue elasticity is the circulatory system. As the elastic fibers decrease in number, all the vessels become stiffer, and this includes even the heart itself. As the heart valves lose their pliancy, heart murmurs and regurgitations may occur, especially in the valves controlling the high-pressure flow on the left side of the heart. The overall stiffening also affects the arteries that feed the heart muscle, and their loss of resilience makes it harder to get adequate nutrient into the myocardium. This further reduces myocardial efficiency. All these things put together substantially decrease cardiac output, a circumstance that produces physiological changes elsewhere, some of which we have already examined.

The Respiratory System

The respiratory system doesn't escape the aging process. As with all the systems, the most common problem involves erosion of flexibility. In the intercostal areas, this, coupled with a loss of power in the respiratory muscles, can seriously impair breathing. It is especially noticeable in the ability of elderly people to recover from strenuous exercise or other stresses. The bronchi and bronchioles are often heavily invaded by collagenous fibers that can harden them to the point where they are nearly inflexible, thus further reducing the vital capacity of the lungs. If these fibers infiltrate alveolar areas as they sometimes do, it can result in the functional loss of those parts of the lungs. This leaves them highly susceptible to infectious diseases like pneumonia or tuberculosis.

Sexuality and the Reproductive Organs

Although there is no evidence to suggest that the sex drive ever completely disappears, there is clear evidence that the sex organs undergo a certain amount of attrition, which can sometimes substantially affect an individual's ability to perform. Particularly in men, this can lead to psychological blocks that may never vanish. For one thing, the prostate gland almost always hypertrophies, often requiring some surgical correction. Medical records further indicate that by the time men reach the age of 90—if they ever do—there is *always* some evidence of prostatic cancer, although the actual disease may never become active. We have already seen how age affects the urinary bladder, and there is little doubt that the kidneys lose some of their efficiency as well. And women are not immune. The incidence of calculi (stones) in the urinary tract increases enormously, particularly in women, and renal infections occur much more frequently.

Endocrine Glands

The endocrine system comes in for its share of problems, although more difficulties occur with target organs and secretory mechanisms than with the hormone synthesizers themselves. The thyroid gland, however, is one endocrine gland that definitely loses both size and efficiency. There is a general decrease in serum levels of T_3 hormones (see chapter 10) and a loss of tissue sensitivity to what little there is. As a result, oxygen consumption at the tissue level is reduced substantially, and this, as we have already seen, produces some pretty far-reaching effects throughout the elderly body. Also, the incidence of myxedema in the aged is quite a bit higher than it is in the general population.

Aged people also lose some of their ability to metabolize glucose, and the problem seems to be mainly tied in with insulin. Although no one is really sure why, old people seem unable to tolerate glucose loading the way they could when they were young. It has been suggested that insulin production in aged people drops as the years advance. While this may be true for some, in most cases it seems that the target tissues themselves lose their sensitivity to the hormone.

All this is part of growing old. The physical and mental erosion is, unfortunately, inevitable and this can lead a person to believe that the so-called golden years are contaminated with more than a little brass.

Table 19.1 Changes Brought On by Aging

Skeletal Changes

Spinal column shortens.
- Sometimes produces curvature in the upper part of the spine.

Bones in arms and legs may decalcify a little, but do not shorten.

Pectoral girdle narrows.
- Older people are thinner through the chest, from side-to-side, than they were when they were younger.
- The chest deepens. Older people are wider from front-to-back than they were when they were younger.
- Pelvic girdle widens.
- Bones become less dense.
- Bone porosity increases and calcium salts are lost.

General Tissue Changes

Atrophy occurs generally.
- Number of smaller blood vessels is often reduced.
- Brain shrinks slightly.
- Kidneys are reduced in size.
- Total body water is reduced.
- Many blood vessels are reduced in size.

General Appearance

Ears and nose become slightly longer.

Nose often broadens.

Hair thins and hairline recedes.

Hair lightens. Often turns white or gray.

Loss of body hair.

Nail growth slows.

Increase in skin folds. Sagging and wrinkling occur.

Physiology

Digestive system
- Less hydrochloric acid produced.
- Fewer enzymes produced.
- Visceral muscles weaken.
- Mucosal lining atrophies.

Nervous system
- Some atrophy of central nervous tissue due to loss of neurons.
- Tendon reflexes begin to lose efficiency.

Urinary system
- Loss of elasticity in urinary bladder.
- Little warning given that bladder is full.

Respiratory system
- Membranes in alveoli thicken slightly, making gas diffusion less efficient.

Circulatory system
- Loss of elasticity results in increased diastolic pressure.
- Loss of some smaller vessels reduces efficiency of nourishment in some areas.

Skin
- Atrophy of sweat glands. Thermoregulation becomes less efficient.
- Melanin deposition occurs at random, producing "age spots."
- Connective tissues thicken. Fingernails thicken and show heavy longitudinal ridging . . . may curl over at tips.

Sensory organs
- Reaction time slows. Particularly noticeable in pupillary reflex.
- Hearing is often affected, although this seems to depend to an enormous extent on long-term exposure to noise.
- Sense of touch diminishes.
- Ability to perceive pain is reduced, particularly in peripheral areas.
- Taste and smell may diminish somewhat. This is dependent to a great extent on how much insult has been delivered to these receptors during the individual's lifetime. Smokers usually experience enormously reduced senses. Nonsmokers may not experience any diminution of these senses.

Sociologists tell us that the attitude in many people today seems to be that if all we have to look forward to after a lifetime of labor is increased loss of ability to enjoy the last few years, it may not be worth it. Add to this the uncertainty about a person's financial status during these years and there are an awful lot of people beginning to wonder if a "ripe old age" isn't vastly overrated.

It is hard, even in a physiology text, to ignore the financial status of elderly people in this country. The way the U.S. ignores the financial plight of its old people is a national disgrace. The state and federal governments of this country have done very little to ease the financial problems of old people. So little, in fact, that we are all confronted with one enormous, and very depressing, truth. As things currently stand in this country, everyone of us—unless we drop dead suddenly or are independently wealthy—will, before we die, lose everything we own to some member of the medical community. Health inevitably dwindles in the elderly, and care becomes increasingly necessary and more intensive. Unfortunately, Medicare and state financial assistance programs do not help much as long as the patients have any ability at all to pay. A chronic illness means, beyond a shadow of a doubt, that the victim will be reduced, by medical bills, to abject poverty, after which the government will begin to pay all of his overpowering medical expenses.

This is not a suspicion or a possibility—it is a *certainty.* With medical costs skyrocketing as they are, a two-week stay in a hospital can cost $20,000, 20 percent of which—$4,000—the elderly patient must pay himself. Any fees for things like surgery or intensive care are extra, as are physician's fees. Hospital stays are not unusual for old people. Surgery is reasonably certain at one point or another, and the probability of a lingering illness is high. As a result, there are very few elderly people in this country who are not completely dependent on Social Security or their children for support. When many of these people retired they had reasonable bank accounts—not a lot of money, but enough to keep them in relaxed comfort. Most owned their own homes, had a decent car, and looked to the future with a certain amount of optimism. One or two illnesses, and their homes have been sold, their bank accounts are nonexistent, and any optimism is shattered forever.

Table 19.1 shows the major alterations that occur in humans as age begins to set in.

Immortality

It is intriguing, is it not, to think that someday, before we die, someone might discover a means of stopping or even reversing the aging process? People throughout history have dreamed of achieving eternal youth. The Egyptians wrote of it. We know that Greek mythology included records of normal humans that were granted this boon, and Ponce DeLeon, the intrepid Spanish explorer, spent years of his life tramping through the swamps and jungles of the Florida peninsula during the 1500s, searching for the Fountain of Youth. Is it possible that such a thing may someday be found . . . not a fountain as such, but something that can restore youth and vigor to people?

It is certainly possible. Research into the process of aging has been going on a long time, and today it is reaching a scientific crescendo. Several theories are available to explain the process of aging, and some of them have considerable empirical support. As I indicated at the beginning of this chapter, there are good reasons to believe that the process of aging is built right into cellular DNA. The evidence is impressive. Cells taken from certain body tissues have been seen to divide a predetermined number of times, toward the end of which they slow down, then finally stop and die. Let us say such cells, provided with sufficient nutrient, oxygen, and everything else that they need for life, can divide one hundred times before they age and die. If these cells are permitted to divide twenty times and are then frozen for a year or two, when they are taken out of the freezer and revitalized, they will divide eighty more times and then die. If they are frozen after sixty divisions, they will divide forty more times when thawed out, and then they will die. The number of divisions seems to be predetermined, and as far as is known, the only place it could be programed is on the DNA.

There are other observations, a little less direct, that support the idea that aging is DNA-linked. Children of long-lived parents seem to be long-lived also, whereas those offspring of parents who died young seem also to have short lives. This, of course, could be due to a programed susceptibility or resistance to certain diseases or to anatomical or physiological infirmities, but even if that's true, the programing must be on the DNA.

Switches on the DNA?

Some workers are looking for on/off switches that may control the workings of certain cell functions. It has been theorized that, as life progresses, our DNA has areas that switch on, do what it is they are supposed to do, and then switch off, permanently. This certainly fits in with the process of growth, but it is hard to reconcile with the systems that manage day-to-day tasks throughout our lives. Many of these latter may slow down as the years pass but they never actually shut off.

An Age Center in the Brain?

Gerontological researchers have hypothesized that there may be areas in the brain that can switch certain controls on or off as time passes. The idea is speculative, but it is nonetheless an *educated* guess. It is certainly consistent with what we have been able to uncover so far regarding puberty, and it could include the process of aging. It has been said many times that a person is only as old as he or she feels, and there is little doubt that many people tend to look a good deal younger than they actually are until some catastrophe occurs in their lives, after which they age and deteriorate rapidly. The observations are nearly all medical reports and are admittedly subjective, but they are reported with such consistency that researchers feel there is at least a grain of accuracy in them. Could it mean that the cerebral hemispheres have some measure of unconscious control over the "age center," wherever—and whatever—that may be?

Reasoning further on this hypothesis, where could such a center be? Most workers feel that the most logical place to look is in the hypothalamus. Certainly there are a lot of other controls there, and while no direct evidence suggests the presence of an "aging" clock ticking away in the hypothalamus, circumstantial evidence hints that there may be. The suprachiasmatic nucleus, for instance, certainly acts as at least one element in a daily biological clock. The pineal gland, which responds to day length and is known to control periodic adjustments in many animals, is closely associated, both neurally and endocrinologically, with the hypothalamus. No one will deny the existence of cellular mechanisms that control all kinds of biorhythms that exist in humans as well as nearly every other organism on earth. If there are cells that can count hours and record day length, and if there are others that operate on a weekly or a monthly schedule, why couldn't there be a group of cells that count the years of a person's life and click on an "aging center" when a certain number have passed?

Miscellaneous Ideas

There are other hypotheses also, all of which have their advocates and certain evidences for their existence. Some are based on empirical evidence, some on deductive logic and philosophical reasoning. It has been suggested, for instance, that the pituitary gland synthesizes and secretes an "aging hormone." Others are convinced that the cause of aging lies in environmental pollutions that have been extant since time immemorial—things like ultraviolet radiation and radioactive carbon present in the foods we eat. Still others say that the process of aging is extremely complex and that there is no single cause. It may be a combination of DNA programing, an "aging center" in the brain, and environmental factors. If things turn out the way they usually do in biological research, this final hypothesis, being the most complex, has a better chance of being right than the others do.

One thing is fairly certain—there is no reason to believe that research into the process of aging is a wasted effort. It is entirely possible that someone may stumble onto the key to eternal youth during our own lifetimes. There is certainly a lot going on and progress being made. Workers are uncovering interesting facts about the process of aging and how to slow it down a little. For instance, scientists discovered fifty years ago that young rats, fed a bare subsistence diet, lived 50 percent longer than littermates who were fed abundantly. This observation has since been extended to other animals, and there is reason to believe that humans who are fed sparsely when young tend to live longer.

One of the most striking experiments was done by workers at Monsanto in the early 1960s. Newly hatched chickens and very young mice were fed a diet deficient in the amino acid *tryptophan,* and their normal growth suddenly stopped. What is more, as long as their diets remained deficient in this amino acid, they stayed underdeveloped and immature. They were maintained in this state of arrested development for a full year, then a normal diet was offered. Development and growth promptly picked up again and proceeded as it does in normal animals. That doesn't sound like much, but what makes it intriguing is that *the year of suspended growth was added to their total life spans.* All those that managed to survive disease and fatal injury lived an extra year—which for a mouse represents a life expansion of nearly 100 percent. Would it not be wonderful if humans could be arrested in development during their formative years? Education could proceed at normal rates and be all over by the time the individual was permitted to resume normal development. The years of struggling and making horrible mistakes would all be over, and the person would still be vigorous and youthful while possessing knowledge and experience only possible in people 35 and 40 years old today.

Other Organisms

Are there any animals that have unusually long lives? Humans and certain birds seem to have the longest life spans of the warm-blooded animals, but there are some other vertebrates that may, for all we know, have tremendously long lives. For example, many species of fishes—sharks, for instance— grow continually for as long as they live, and this is also true of some reptiles, most notably the crocodilians. How long can these animals live? No one seems to know. No one has ever reported having detected significant signs of aging in these eternally growing organisms . . . overall body deterioration typical of old age never seems to set in. Obviously these animals die, because it is their corpses that we are studying, but when they are found dead in nature, there is no evidence to suggest that they died because of age. No significant deterioration is visible in any of the systems studied, and the consensus is that they probably died of disease or from injury, not from old age. Is there something in their brains that prevents the "age center" from being switched on? People are certainly trying to find out.

Botanists also have subjects that could be investigated in the hope of unlocking some of the secrets of longevity. Most people do not tend to think of plants as being "living" in the sense that animals are living, but in fact, they are just as alive. Their individual body cells have some pronounced differences, and their tissue and body designs are certainly at variance with ours, but many of their biochemical operations are identical to our own, and some of them live to incredible ages. Certain trees, like the giant sequoias and redwoods of the west coast, were upwards of four thousand years old when they were cut down, and it is a fact that the *General Sherman Tree,* which probably was a fairly large tree when Julius Caesar was tramping through Gaul, is the fastest-growing tree in California's Giant Forest. It is showing no signs of deterioration or age, and no one knows why it is not.

What if immortality is possible? What if someone actually does stumble upon such a secret and the ability to retain youth forever becomes a fact, what then? Will it prove a blessing or a curse?

This is the kind of question that could stimulate debate and hassle the likes of which none of us have ever encountered before. One thing we must ask ourselves is, "is there a reason for aging and dying?" Most scientists and philosophers contend—objectively, of course—that death is a survival factor. It is important because it clears an older generation out of the way to make room for the next. Knowing this, would *you* turn down youth if it were offered to you? Would an extended life span for humans offer anything that we do not already have?

Some advantages are easy to see. Wouldn't it have been wonderful to keep men like Einstein or Abraham Lincoln with us for a few thousand years instead of losing them after less than 100? It is such a shame to waste the intellect of people who have spent fifty years learning about a certain field of science or medicine just when they are arriving at a point where they can be superbly productive. Things are becoming so complex today that it seems, when a person finally manages to learn enough about a given field to be able to make a real contribution to science or literature, he or she gets old and dies. Who knows what Mozart, Goethe, or Shakespeare might have written with a thousand extra years?

On the other hand, what might Genghis Khan or Jack the Ripper have done with a few extra centuries? Would you want immortality for people like that? What about the everyday, ordinary person? There are an awful lot of ordinary people knocking about this world. Do we make them immortal? Obviously we could not make *everyone* immortal and still permit unrestricted childbirth, so who gets the gift and who doesn't? Who makes that decision?

You see the problem? Most scientists do not know how they would evaluate the person who finally unlocks the mystery. Do you?

Prolonging Health—Realistically

Until someone manages to uncover this "Fountain of Youth," we must, all of us, face the inevitability of age. We can anticipate some degenerative changes in our bodies as the years advance, and we must confront the fact that there will be an increased propensity toward chronic illness. With all this pessimism almost inherent in such an outlook, is there any way to avoid these problems?

Obviously there is no way to avoid the physiological alterations that take place. Yet with any kind of luck at all, it would appear that there are ways to avoid becoming crippled or bedridden by age. Gerontologists are striving very hard to find out just what one must do to retain as much vigor as possible when aging sets in. How are they doing this? One way is to find populations of aged people who are vigorous and healthy. If these populations are scattered, see if they have anything in common, and if they do, note what they are. From such facts, often a great deal can be learned about what to avoid and what to do as the years pass.

And such populations do exist. In areas out of the normal run of civilization, it is not unusual to find large numbers of vigorous people, healthy and alert, who are in their nineties or even hundreds. Nearly all such populations are restricted to isolated areas, particularly high mountain valleys, and in these areas, longevity and vigorous old age are the rule rather than the exception. One such is in the Himalayas of Pakistan. Here, in a valley essentially isolated from the outside world, there is a population of people who call themselves the Hunnars. Their longevity so impressed one group of anthropologists a few years ago that an entire book was devoted to describing them, their life-style, and their homeland. Another such area is in the Andes of Ecuador. A third is located in the mountains of southern Russia and a fourth in the Rhodope Mountains between Greece and Bulgaria. These areas are widely separated and there is no possibility that the peoples have mixed, genetically. Furthermore, their diets are usually different and their occupations vary widely.

Do they have anything in common? Yes, they do. They live in areas where the climate is on the cool side of temperate and the air is crisp and clear. Generally speaking, they are isolated from the mainstream of the modern world—isolated not just from other populations but also from the pollutants that fill the atmosphere in our cities, towns, and most of our countryside. These areas are self-sufficient, so obviously a large segment of the population works the land. They do so without many of the work-saving conveniences we utilize; hence their lives include a lot of vigorous physical exercise, much of it outdoors. Roads are mostly cart trails or footpaths, so the people walk everywhere they want to go. All of these areas have a large population of active, healthy, alert 80-, 90-, and 100-year-olds.

The *Los Angeles Times* reported in 1987 that in the Smolyan district of Bulgaria, there were more than 430 people between 90 and 100 years old and sixty more that had passed the century mark. The Smolyan district is in the Rhodope Mountains in southern Bulgaria. It is a primitive area pretty well isolated from the rest of the world. The people who live there avoid extremes in their daily lives. They seem to believe, as did their ancient ancestors, that moderation in all things is the key to life, and based on their life spans, they could very well be right. They have not discovered a magic ingredient that retains youth or anything like that, for they age just as people everywhere do. The main difference between oldsters here and old people in the rest of the world is that these are healthy and physically vigorous, their minds are sharp, and they enjoy life to the fullest. The only doctor in the area reports that they seldom get sick, and since age never seems to cripple them, they tend to live longer. They are not immune to death; it is just that they do not break up a bit at a time as so many aged folk do in this country. When they finally do die it's much like Oliver Wendell Holmes' "Wonderful 'One-Hoss Shay' "—everything in their bodies collapses at once and they just drop dead—a termination that would certainly appeal to me, and I suspect to almost everyone.

What's the secret of their astonishing accomplishment? As far as their overall health—particularly their sensory abilities—are concerned, their isolation may be the single most important thing. Get people away from the screams of traffic and modern machinery and although age steals some ability to hear, their ears seldom deteriorate significantly. When free sugar in the diet is reduced, gum diseases due to plaque formation do not occur, so the teeth remain strong and healthy. Constant viewing of scenery nearby and then rapidly flicking the eyes upward to focus on some object twenty miles away provides constant eye exercise and thus keeps eye lenses flexible and ciliary muscles taut. Air pollution seldom, if ever, invades these high mountain valleys; hence respiratory illnesses are almost unheard-of. Vigorous and constant outdoor exercise, featuring lots of walking, places plenty of stress on the bones, and this apparently reduces calcium loss from the skeleton. It also maintains muscle tone and helps retain flexibility in the aging circulatory system and the heart muscle, making further exercise possible and perpetuating a circle of health instead of breakdown.

All by itself such a life would tend to maintain vigor, but there are several other things that must be taken into account to explain the incredible longevity. Psychologically, things tend to be supportive—there is very little mental stress in such a life. The diet is exactly what it should be, lots of vegetables, with meat and fish supplements once or twice a week. Since there are few or no cars in the area, one gets around by walking, so exercise is an unavoidable part of life which, coupled with the moderate diet, insures that overweight people will be almost nonexistent.

Then—and this may be nearly as important as isolation—there is the genetic component. Due to their isolation from mainstream civilization, and the difficult lives they had to lead, only the strongest people moved in and only the strongest remained. Over the centuries, there would be further selection pressure to eliminate all but the toughest individuals. Those who did not have the genetic makeup to handle the rugged life seldom survived past childhood, and if people made it past puberty, the only thing that could kill them would be a bullet. There can be little doubt that this would strengthen the overall population by removing the weaker individuals from the genetic pool. Those people who were genetically incapable of resisting the diseases and problems inherent in their part of the world are gone. Those who remain are the cream of the physical crop, the long-lived, hardy stock with the toughest genes.

What Can We Do?

What about the rest of us—those of us who live in the mainstream of civilization with an ancestry that maybe did not face this kind of physical weeding-out? The kind of life that these people live, regardless of its promise of longevity and health, is not for everyone. I certainly would not want to spend my life isolated from the rest of the world in a high mountain valley, cut off from theater, music, and social relationships I have come to value, and I doubt if many of us would. Is there anything that we can do to help retain our health against the onslaught of age?

Medical scientists assure us that there is! Researchers and physicians who have studied the problems of aging have offered all kinds of suggestions, and we are told that if we followed most of them, we would probably do pretty well in our so-called declining years. As has often been said, it is never too late to start taking better care of yourself. If you are young and gravitating toward a sessile existence, it is probably a good idea to start right into a program of vigorous exercise and to begin cultivating good health habits—habits that you can retain as age begins to set in. There is no particular boundary inaugurating the period known as middle age, nor is there a hard, fast bifurcation between middle and old ages. If you are 20 and have been slowing down physically, start reversing the trend. Get yourself into a solid program of exercise and keep at it. If you are 50 and have never exercised, it is a good idea to start. Do it slowly and according to a doctor's advice, but do it. Watch your diet and be careful of excesses.

What can you do specifically? Let us consider those attributes that seem to degenerate stereotypically—those mentioned above. While experts agree that it is not possible to stop the deteriorations of old age, they also are unanimous in their contention that you can certainly slow them down.

Teeth

Loss of teeth, for instance, is not an inevitable consequence of age. In fact, older people have, surprisingly, a distinct advantage over children in one respect. Resistance to tooth decay seems to increase with age, and that's good, obviously. Unfortunately, as the cavities decrease in number, susceptibility to periodontal disease increases. Most toothless people over the age of 55 lost their teeth to such disease. Yet it can be prevented with a little care. A substance known as **plaque** is the culprit in these cases; hence the single most important thing is to keep the teeth clear of plaque. Plaque forms as a result of bacterial action on free sugars in the mouth. These sugars often concentrate around the base of the teeth, and if the mouth is not washed out right away, they form tiny, stagnant pools around the base of the teeth. Bacteria convert these sugars into lactic acid and other residues, which means there is a pool of unpleasant materials around the base of each tooth. Within hours, these form a gummy, bacteria-filled coating that sticks to the enamel, right at the point where the teeth penetrate into the gums. This is plaque, and at this stage, it can be scraped off the teeth without much effort by dental floss. However, if left undisturbed, it will ultimately harden into a thick coating called **tartar,** and tartar can be removed only by a professional. If it is not removed, if it is just left in place, it loosens the grip that the gums have on the teeth, making them wobble in their sockets and eroding bone from their anchor points in the jaw. Ultimately, this bone loss permits the jawbone to recede from the teeth, and they become loose and may fall or tear out. At this point, periodontal disease is pretty well advanced, and often all that a dentist can do is pull the offending teeth.

One way to prevent this from happening is to avoid free sugar in any form. The dental profession agrees that this would be optimal, but also that it is almost impossible to do. It would mean giving up everything that contains free sugars—not just cakes, pies, and sweet things, but bakery products of all kinds—breads and other such staples—as well as sweet melons, freshly picked corn, and all kinds of fruits. Obviously, that just is not practical. A much more reasonable preventive is to interrupt the cycle by "flossing" daily. As noted above, careful cleaning with dental floss removes plaque before it can harden, and a daily scrubbing with a toothbrush with the assistance of some fluoride-containing mouthwash or toothpaste can help enormously. Obviously, this must be coupled with regular professional attention, and it should be started in early childhood. But even if you are in your fifties, if you still have some teeth left, it is probably not too late to begin.

Nutrition

If the teeth are bad, certain foods become difficult to eat, and people with sore mouths often concentrate on bland, soft foods that do not hurt to chew. Unfortunately, such diets are almost always low in essential proteins, vitamins, and minerals, and deficiency diseases often appear. Even if the teeth are in good shape, nutritional intake may need to be adjusted a little once middle age approaches. Those requirements that are most important are listed below.

Fiber

Older people need an abundance of fiber in their diet, and vegetables high in complex carbohydrates have plenty. Beans, broccoli, cauliflower, and lettuce all are high in fiber, but most nutritionists agree that if the diet contains lots of vegetables, you will probably get all the fiber you need. For people over 50, the current recommendation is about 25 grams of pure fiber daily.

Protein

Protein intake should constitute at least 15 percent of the total caloric intake, a figure that is about the same when you are 50 as it is when you are 30. The best sources, according to nutritionists, are skinless poultry, very lean beef or pork, and especially fish—in fact, the more that comes from fish, the better. Fish is not only very high in protein, it also contains oils that can prevent formation of plaque inside blood vessels. For those who do not particularly care for animal protein, there are plenty of vegetables that are high in protein, and many low-fat dairy products have all that you need.

Lipids

As we have seen, fat is a dietary ingredient that we cannot do without, but everyone—particularly older people—should be careful not to get too much. Nutritionists recommend that no more than 30 percent of our caloric intake come from fat, and less than 10 percent of that should be saturated.

There are ways to reduce fat intake that should probably become habit for most of us. For instance, it is a good idea to trim all excess fat off meats—including poultry—before it is cooked. Since most of the fat in poultry is in the skin, it is not hard to do—just skin it before cooking. Skinning the bird before baking is easy to do, but it may not be esthetically pleasing. We are all accustomed to drooling over a browned, well-roasted Thanksgiving turkey, and the prospect of a naked bird somehow is depressing. Nevertheless, we should do it just the same. A skinned bird can be kept moist by basting with polyunsaturated margarines or cooking oils instead of pan drippings. Also, before making the gravy, lay some tough paper towels across the surface of the drippings for a while. Fats are less dense than water, remember, and floating paper towels on top of gravies and soups can absorb lots of melted fats without picking up any water-soluble nutrients. When you throw away the towels, you toss away a lot of saturated fat. If you decide to save leftover soups or gravies, you can get rid of even more. The fats will separate from the water-soluble materials in the refrigerator and as they cool down will form a hard crust on the upper surface that is easily removed later.

The cheapest cuts of meat are almost invariably those that contain the least fat. They are also the toughest and often the least flavorful, and so they require some imagination to make them appealing. This is admittedly a pain, but over the long haul, it is worth it.

Vitamins, Minerals, and Other Nutrients

People who eat a well-balanced diet should not have any need to take vitamin supplements even when they are old. However, menopausal women often tend to lose calcium from their skeletons at accelerated rates and for that reason, they might consider a supplement. Calcium alone, however, does not appear to be the answer. Taken by itself, it will *not* prevent osteoporosis if the woman is susceptible to it. The problem involves estrogen, and at menopause estrogens simply stop flowing (see chapter 18). Estrogens are involved in incorporating calcium into skeletal cells. Without them, calcium metabolism just does not seem to work right. The obvious answer, then, is to take a little estrogen daily. That seems simple and it is—*too* simple. The problem is that estrogen, taken at physiological levels (0.6 mg/day, at least), has side effects that can be undesirable—even unhealthy—so such estrogen supplements over long periods of time may be a poor idea indeed. Recent research, however, has shown that when the estrogen intake is reduced to half a normal daily dose, or even less than half, it will prevent calcium loss *if it is supplemented with calcium.* Less than 0.3 mg of estrogen daily coupled with extra dietary calcium apparently will prevent skeletal calcium loss. At such dosage levels, adverse side effects are almost nonexistent, and so this regimen is recommended, under the supervision of a doctor.

"Youth" Pills

One precaution that nutritionists and physicians emphasize is to avoid any tablets, capsules, powders, or dietary supplements that claim to impede or reverse the effects of aging. The chances are that they are nothing more than simple vitamin and mineral supplements or herbs that could be purchased in any health food store. As such, they will not harm you, but since they are sold at inflated prices they will lighten the pocketbook, and most elderly people do not need any help doing that. In addition, you must consider the fact that anyone who advertises that their preparation will counter aging is clearly lying, and that dishonesty could carry over into the material that they are selling. The preparation could easily be contaminated, be of questionable purity, or contain an untested and potentially harmful ingredient.

Smoking

A great deal has been said about how smoking contributes to cancer, respiratory disease, and cardiovascular problems, and any one of these is very good reason for the elderly to avoid it. However, it should probably be mentioned, for the sake of fairness, that people over the age of 60 evidently do not increase their risk of heart attack by smoking. It seems a little contradictory to say this, but it is apparently true (see chapter 13). Statistics show quite clearly that smokers over the age of 60 do not show any greater predilection for cardiovascular problems—especially heart attacks—than their contemporaries who are nonsmokers. This observation, however, is not a medical absolution for the aged smoker to continue using tobacco, and it is certainly noteworthy that tobacco is unknown in the mountain valleys where longevity is so common. We must remember that heart attack is only one of the problems the elderly person must be wary of. Smoking definitely does cause cancer and it certainly reduces the ability of the respiratory surfaces to effect the necessary gas exchanges. No elderly person should smoke—in fact, *nobody* should, old or young.

Alcohol

Alcohol, regardless of how it is packaged, is still essentially a toxin. Its effects on the CNS are pretty well known, as is its ability to destroy essential liver cells. If alcohol is an integral part of a person's life—that is, if one depends on it—that person may be in trouble and should probably stop drinking entirely. Social drinking, however, does not appear to be a problem if it is done in moderation. In fact, there is even some evidence that it can be good for a person. Nutritionists recommend that one never indulge in more than a couple of drinks a day. That's two 12-ounce beers, two standard glasses of wine, or two shots of hard liquor. Taken this way—never to excess—alcohol seems to have a beneficial effect on the cardiovascular system. Nobody is really sure why, but one or two drinks per day, when accompanied by a sensible diet, seem to reduce the risk of heart attack. Even so, it is well to remember the point made at the beginning of this paragraph—alcohol is a poison. It probably does more damage than it does good, and most practitioners advise that if you do not drink, it is probably better if you don't start.

Exercise

No one should become inactive just because it is a little harder to move around and performance has deteriorated. Sure, it was wonderful to run across fields and leap up over small fences—sometimes it felt like flying— and the old person cannot do that anymore. Often old people will hesitate to pull on exercise clothes because they sag now in places where they never used to sag and they sometimes bulge where they shouldn't. The number of elderly people who refuse to exercise because they are embarrassed to be seen performing poorly is surprisingly high. Yet exercise is essential and should never be avoided. The *kind* of exercise one should undertake should, of course, be discussed with a professional, but certainly some form of physical activity should be a regular routine. Running is definitely a good exercise if you can do it, but it should never be started without talking things over with your family physician. There are lots of reasons why running or jogging might be damaging instead of helpful—maybe your feet can't take it, or your knees are too delicate; maybe your heart just is not up to it. If you cannot run, you can always walk, and walking is a wonderful exercise.

Obesity

Obesity is a chronic problem in America today—in fact, in the entire Western world. There was a time when being fat and comfortable was highly desirable in old people and was considered a *sine qua non* for the successful businessperson. No more! It is not that the extra body fat or the extra weight by itself is much of a problem, because it isn't, necessarily. The problem is that overweight people are usually inactive, and inactivity can be lethal as maturity proceeds. There is a lot that is not known about what causes a person to be overweight, but there is little doubt today that obesity is rampant in America. There are many reasons, but the most common are:

1. As people age, their metabolism slows down and they require less food, yet most people do not alter their caloric intake to compensate.
2. In addition, they usually slow down physically as the years pass and they require less food—but they seldom eat less.
3. They quit smoking. This needs some elaboration.
   a. It seems that smoking increases the basic metabolic rate. When smoking ceases, the metabolism slows down spontaneously.
   b. In addition, it is commonplace for smokers to end their meal with a cigarette. When they no longer smoke, the cigarette is not there anymore to put a period to eating, and they feel that something more is essential. It is usually dessert. A newly reformed ex-smoker can gain weight by leaps and bounds . . . it is astonishing how much and how quickly.

There are more reasons why weight gain occurs so commonly once youth has passed, but these are the primary ones. Whatever the reason, however, you can ultimately narrow it to a single cause—people eat too much. Maybe it is a little too simplistic to look at the problem this way, but it is nevertheless true. When you ingest more calories than you use, the excess is stored as fat. The cure really is very simple: eat less!

If you do all of these things, will you live any longer? Will all these healthy things increase the life expectancy of the average person?

It might. But even if it does, it won't be more than a couple of years at most. That is not really the goal. The purpose of living and eating as this list suggests is to increase the likelihood that an average person will be healthy, motile, and alert during their last years instead of limping around in a walker or being confined to a wheelchair.

Longevity

What are *your* chances of living to be 100? Well, according to the latest statistics, the average American male will live to be 73 and the average female will live about five years longer. However, we must remember that this is an *average* figure. It includes all the people that die before puberty and all those who have been killed in their youth by traffic, disease, and what-have-you. A 30-year-old has already managed to bypass some of these statistics, and as he ages, his life expectancy improves. An American male who lives to be 50, we are told, has a good chance of living another twenty-eight years, while a woman of 50 should live to be 82. A person who reaches the age of 70 has a good chance of living to be 85, and if you manage to live to 85, you will probably celebrate your ninety-first birthday. American statistics do not go beyond that, because one generation might have several thousand nonagenarians while the next may have only a dozen or so.

All these figures, however, are averages and are based on past records. We are more aware today than we have ever been about the infirmities of age and how to avoid—or at least, slow down—most of them. We may not be able to eliminate the aging process, but we can certainly learn to enjoy every year that we have. That in itself means a longer life, and we may be part of the generation in which centenarians are not all that unusual.

Clinical Considerations

Since aging is mostly clinical, it should come as no surprise to discover that we have broadly surveyed quite a bit already. There is, however, one affliction that never seems to strike anyone under the age of 50, and hence must be considered a disease that is restricted to the aged. We did not investigate it before because it is not an inevitable consequence of the aging process.

Senility

Like people everywhere, Americans tend to stereotype a little too much, and our view of old people is no exception. Our stereotype of the aged person is that of a forgetful or confused antiquarian who blames everything on someone else and sometimes forgets where he is and what he is doing. We imagine benevolent but confused old dowagers calmly giving away their valuables to an obvious con man or leaving the pot roast on the front lawn to cool. The mental confusion—called **senility**—was believed to be an inevitable consequence of age, and most of us still have this picture of old people.

Yet it is not an accurate picture according to most current findings. Old people who have managed to retain their health may never approach this stereotypical confused senility. There are some aspects of mental function that apparently do weaken, but they are pretty specific—things like remembering faces or shapes. Memory of things read or heard does not slacken, nor does the oldsters' ability to express themselves coherently and intelligently. Furthermore, their ability to perform sensitive, highly complicated tasks does not deteriorate significantly—witness the number of successful writers who continue to produce wonderful works well into their eighties.

The extensive memory losses and confused thought patterns of the stereotype are usually caused by disease of one kind or another, not by passing years. And the most common of these diseases is Alzheimer's disease.

Alzheimer's Disease

Alzheimer's is one of the most depressing and inexorable diseases we know of. It creeps up on one and steals memories, family, pride, and finally, life. The first thing to vanish is memory—the most recent things vanish first, and then, slowly but surely, the older patterns follow. Victims forget where they are, then they forget acquaintances, friends, their spouses, their children, and finally who they themselves are. It is hard to believe, but it's not unusual for victims of Alzheimer's disease to look into a mirror and wonder who that ugly old man or woman is that keeps staring at them. Both conscious and reflex control of body functions presently disappears, and the individual slips into a vegetative state that finally lapses into death. The mental anguish the patient must experience is intense, but it vanishes fairly early in the disease as he or she promptly forgets what is going on. For the patient's family things do not end quite so soon. Watching what once was a fine mind or a glorious personality gradually vanish into a miserable, blubbering void is heartbreaking. There is no pattern of attack, and no group seems to enjoy any kind of selective immunity. In this regard, Alzheimer's is quite democratic. It strikes with a fine impartiality, taking out the high-powered intellects as readily as the popular and gorgeous: Dr. John French, the head of the Brain Research Institute at the University of California, Los Angeles, went down that road, as did the sex goddess and movie star Rita Hayworth. There are many thousands more, in between, somewhere.

No one knows where Alzheimer's comes from. It almost certainly has something to do with the process of aging, because no one under the age of 50 has ever gotten it, and most of the time it does not appear until the age of 70 or so. Furthermore, its incidence appears to be increasing as the population ages, although it is hard to tell if that is true because until the patient dies and the brain can be examined, the diagnosis is never certain.

Recent work has associated it with a genetic defect on the chromosome that is implicated in Down's syndrome (mongolism)—another cause of mental deficiency. Does the fact that there is a chromosomal defect present mean that Alzheimer's disease is passed from one generation to the next? Maybe . . . probably. Many Alzheimer's patients have had ancestors who died of it, and if it runs in families, it obviously can be inherited. Yet the majority of the cases to date show no familial inheritance patterns, and if those records are correct, then heredity is not always involved. For a while, it was suspected that a virus might be the cause, but that idea has disappeared because there doesn't seem to be any infectious pattern. Because anxiety or physical trauma can accelerate the progress of the disease, workers have speculated that some sort of stress might be responsible for its existence in the first place, but records that are available do not seem to support this idea. Several years ago, workers noticed that Alzheimer's patients had unusually high levels of aluminum in their brains, and it was theorized that aluminum might somehow contribute to its development. This could still be a cause, but it's beginning to look like it is just another dead end, because aluminum seems to show up in high concentrations in the brains of all aged people.

Figure 19.1 The human brain with the temporal lobe removed to show the hippocampus in relation to other structures.

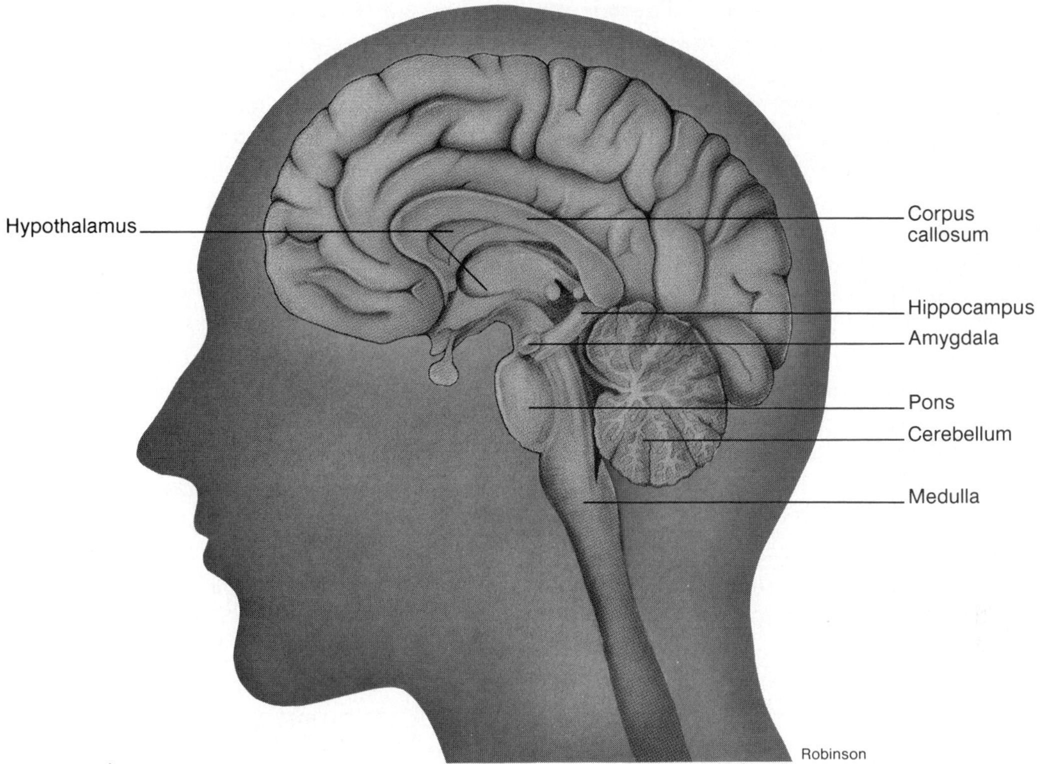

Posthumous inspection of the brain has yielded a few answers. Acetylcholine is abundant in the brains of normal people, yet it is almost completely absent from the limbic system of Alzheimer's victims. It seems reasonable, therefore, to assume that they have somehow lost the ability to synthesize this neurotransmitter, and its lack is at least partly responsible for the mental and physical deterioration. Subsequent research suggests that this is true—lack of acetylcholine is responsible for some of the problems, but there is almost certainly more to the disease than the absence of a single neurotransmitter.

Scientists have uncovered evidence that glucose metabolism is impaired in the Alzheimer brain, but why and how is unclear. That problem may be linked to a proteinaceous compound known as **amyloid.** Postmortem examinations of Alzheimer's brains have shown that amyloid is present in abnormally large quantities, and earlier research has already confirmed that it is involved in the mental retardation of Down's syndrome. Since amyloid is implicated in one form of retardation, could it somehow contribute to Alzheimer's? It is certainly reasonable to assume so.

Some experiments suggest that maybe amyloid is responsible for altering the brain's blood vessels, and if the carrying capacity of these vessels is reduced, it could slowly starve whatever nerve cells they feed. That would reduce glucose metabolism quite effectively, but it would do more than just that. Partially starved cells would not be able to synthesize much neurotransmitter either, an observation that hints that maybe all three basic theories are right. Maybe all these defects are linked somewhere deep in the brain, producing the syndrome we call Alzheimer's. One thing is reasonably certain: there is nothing simple about the etiology of Alzheimer's disease, and the consensus among workers is that medical research has only scratched the surface so far.

As to what the disease does to the brain when it strikes, there are apparently a few things that are known and many things that are not. In every case, there has been significant deterioration of nerve fibers leading into and from the zone known as the **hippocampus,** which is below and slightly behind the hypothalamus (figure 19.1). Nerves that normally course into and out of this brain region have degenerated into tangled masses of directionless fibers projecting everywhere and nowhere. In addition, large, abnormal deposits of proteinaceous material seem to clog all the entrances to and exits from the hippocampus, effectively isolating it from the rest of the brain. Since the hippocampus has been implicated in the development and retrieval of memory patterns, its isolation would eliminate any possibility that the patient could learn anything new or retrieve memories that were already there. The big question is, of course, why do these aberrations occur? There is no answer to that, and aside from these few facts, little else is known.

As far as treatment is concerned, there really is nothing that can be done aside from providing for the patient's comfort and subsistence. The discovery that Alzheimer's disease is associated with a chromosome may provide us with a means of identifying potential victims of the disease, but unfortunately, it does not offer any new hope that a cure will be found in the near future. Certainly there is none now. Several times, the news media have optimistically reported a breakthrough in its treatment, but the announcements have turned out to be premature. In 1984 a drug called **bethanechol chloride** was injected directly into the brains of four or five Alzheimer's patients with remarkably good results. Relatives were ecstatic at the apparent improvement in the patients, a fact that the NBC television network somehow discovered and optimistically reported. Unfortunately, the "cure" turned out to be temporary—and its effectiveness diminished with each dose, leaving patients back where they started in a very short period of time. To make matters worse, there were occasionally some horrid side effects. More recently, a new drug known as **tetrahydroaminoacridine (THA)** was used experimentally on a group of a dozen patients, and it produced very good results. Those receiving the drug were all suffering mild to moderate disability due to the disease, and after treatment their mental processes improved measurably. At the time of this writing, workers emphasize that tetrahydroaminoacridine is very definitely still in the developmental stages, and they caution that since it merely prolongs a patient's sentience, it certainly cannot be considered a cure.

Alzheimer's disease is a killer. Those who get it simply waste away, gradually deteriorating both mentally and physically until they die. Nevertheless, research is not standing still—progress is being made and researchers are beginning to hint, cautiously, that they are finally on the road to producing some practical results.

Summary

The Aging Process

It seems that every system in the body is affected by the aging process. Some systems age more visibly than others; discolored hair and inelastic skin, for example, have become hallmarks of aging. Other systems age invisibly, but inexorably, and contribute to the overall deterioration of the body. Some systems age earlier and more profoundly than others, although in that respect, much depends on the individual.

- I. Circulatory Attrition. One of the first systems to show signs of aging is the circulatory system.
  - A. Cause. One of the first circulatory changes involves the propulsion systems. Blood vessels are all profoundly affected, shrinking in size and elasticity.
  - B. Effect. Because the blood is omnipresent, anything that affects the blood can be expected to affect almost every part of the body, and it does.
    1. Homeostasis alterations: adjustments to sudden changes in body conditions are forced to slow and thus lose effectiveness.
    2. Cold temperatures are not easily tolerated. Ability to adjust to decreases in temperature is reduced because blood flow, particularly into the periphery, is less than optimal.
    3. Heat production is reduced. Muscles cease to provide extra heat when it is needed because they no longer have the blood supply they used to have; thus they can no longer work as hard as they used to.
    4. Blood vessels are reduced in number and capacity. Reduction in the capacity of the blood vessels reduces the body's ability to shift homeostatic or nutritional priorities swiftly and effectively.
  - C. Consequences. These circulatory changes are thus able to alter the effective operation of virtually every system in the body. As a result, many problems arise.
    1. Inactivity
       - a. Muscles cannot work as hard as they once could because of the reduced blood supply.
       - b. The reduced blood flow into the surface areas means that individuals cannot reduce the increased heat load resulting from hard muscular activity.
       - c. As a result, oldsters tend to suffer from inactivity, which hastens the aging process throughout the body.
    2. Hot weather is poorly tolerated.
    3. Cold weather is also poorly tolerated.
  - D. Feedback. These problems, taken together, further reduce the aged person's ability to retain vigor.
    1. The heart is affected by the overall reduction in activity. The inability to exercise effectively reduces the demands on the heart, and it begins to deteriorate even more rapidly than it should.
    2. This can affect capillary beds and nutrient delivery. Reduced cardiac output and pressure

further reduces the ability of the circulatory vessels to carry blood; thus overall circulatory efficiency suffers.

3. Reduced skeletal muscle activity reduces venous return.

II. Tissue Elasticity. Tissue elasticity is reduced throughout the body.

III. Reaction Time. Reaction time is severely compromised.

Special Sense Organs

I. Eyes

A. The lens of the eye becomes discolored, reducing the ability of the aged to discern blues and purples.

B. The lens of the eye hardens, reducing the ability of the ciliary muscles to pull nearby objects into focus, necessitating the wearing of bi- or trifocal lenses.

II. Ears. The basilar membrane stiffens, making high-pitched sounds hard to hear.

III. Olfaction and Taste. There is a general deterioration of both olfactory and gustatory receptors. This deterioration is almost certainly accelerated by smoking or by inhaling the noxious fumes of modern-day civilization.

IV. Eating Habits. Because food can no longer be appreciated as it once was, its attraction slowly vanishes, and aged people frequently suffer from malnutrition.

V. The Circulatory System. The systemic effects partially brought on by faulty circulation further exacerbate the circulatory problems. Thus a positive feedback process has come into existence.

VI. The Respiratory System. The loss of skeletal muscle activity, plus an overall loss of tissue elasticity, can reduce the ability of the respiratory system to function optimally.

VII. Sexuality and the Reproductive Organs

A. The reproductive organs undergo a certain amount of attrition. In women, menopause ends their reproductive life.

B. The sex drive. Unlike other animals, humans do not lose the desire for sexual intercourse as they age.

VIII. Endocrine Glands. The endocrine glands, like everything else in the body, deteriorate somewhat. Much of what happens to these glands is incompletely understood.

Immortality

People have thought about eternal youth since recorded history began. Is it possible?

I. Switches on the DNA? There are certain portions of DNA that switch on and off and control certain aspects of the process of living. It is hypothesized that there may be such a switch to turn on the aging process.

II. An Age Center in the Brain? It has also been suggested that there may be such a switch in the brain. Workers are searching for it, mainly in the hypothalamus.

III. Miscellaneous Ideas

A. Other suggestions regarding aging include the possibility that the pituitary secretes an "aging" hormone or that the foods we eat cause aging.

B. Some research suggests that the cause of aging may someday be found and a means to prevent it will be discovered.

IV. Other Organisms. Do other vertebrates possess a kind of immortality? Some animals grow all their lives, and there is no indication that such organisms ever age.

Prolonging Health—Realistically

Until someone actually discovers how to prevent aging, there are things that we can do as individuals that will slow down the aging process.

I. What Can We Do? There may not be any way to increase a person's life span. There seem, however, to be many things that can increase quality of life during the so-called declining years.

II. Teeth. Until the 1960s, gum disease often resulted in the removal of all of a person's teeth. Hence many old people today have had dentures for decades.

III. Nutrition

A. The loss of one's teeth and the wearing of dentures almost certainly affects a person's appreciation of food; hence nutrition suffers.

B. This is something that can be slowed—possibly even prevented—by taking care of one's teeth.

C. It is also necessary to watch one's diet. The following materials must be ingested on a regular basis:

1. Fiber. Lots of foods contain both soluble and insoluble fiber. It is not possible to consume too much of this valuable nutrient.
2. Protein. The same is true of protein.
3. Lipids. Fats and oils are usually present in more abundance than necessary in the modern diet. Care should be taken to get only the amount you need. And whatever fats you do ingest should be the right kinds.
4. Vitamins, Minerals, and Other Nutrients. If the diet is carefully watched and all the necessary foods are consumed, supplements of minerals and vitamins should not be necessary.

D. "Youth" Pills. Any tablets or preparations that claim to prolong life or return the aspects of youth should be avoided. Nothing will do this, and a person who claims his preparation will is almost certainly lying and should not be trusted.

IV. Smoking. It is a fact that smoking, after the age of 60, does not appear to increase the incidence of heart disease. However, smoking causes so many other problems that it is certainly not a smart habit to indulge in.

V. Alcohol. Alcohol is not, apparently, all bad. There is some evidence that a cardiac patient who has a couple of drinks a day will fare better than a teetotaler. However, this is not a license to drink wantonly, and it is suggested that those who do not have cardiovascular problems would be well advised to leave alcohol alone.

VI. Exercise. Exercise is a *sine qua non* at any age. It is never too late to start, and it should be indulged in whenever possible.

VII. Obesity. Overweight individuals seem to die younger and to have a lower life quality than those who are not overweight.

Longevity

We know that certain life-styles seem to prolong life . . . things like semistarvation, or living in super-rural, isolated, and rather primitive parts of the earth.

Clinical Considerations

I. Senility

II. Alzheimer's Disease

Review Questions

1. Outline the changes that occur in the circulatory system as aging progresses.
2. Discuss the effects that the circulatory changes perpetrate on other organ systems and tissues.
3. How does aging affect the skeletal system?
4. What effects does aging have on special sensory organs?
5. How much degeneration of our sensory systems is ascribed to environmental stresses?
6. Have our life spans actually increased in the last three or four thousand years?
7. What evidence is available to suggest that humanity has a built-in age-limiting factor?
8. Suggest some techniques for avoiding the infirmity of old age.

Section VII
Contemporary Topics

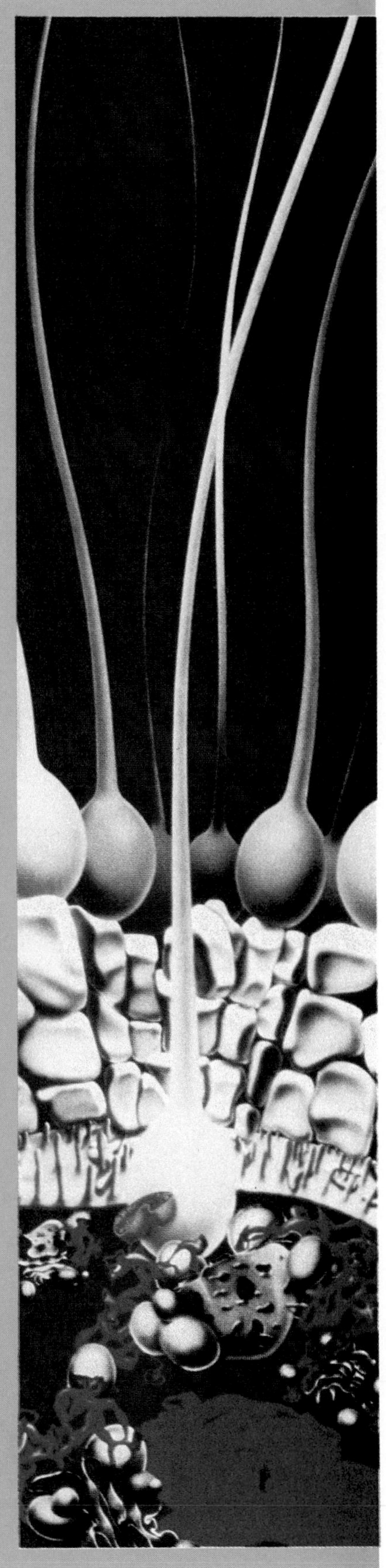

Chapter 20 The Physiological Effects of Euphoric Drugs

Study Hints

It is really not possible to suggest study techniques or points to concentrate on without sounding like I am either preaching or ranting, and there is no place for either in this book. In any case, if you are not aware of America's drug problem, you must have spent your developmental years on a small Pacific island inhabited only by monkeys, insects, and small birds. I will not tell you what to concentrate on or what to believe and disbelieve. The facts speak for themselves.

Objectives

When you have finished reading this chapter, you should:

1. have some idea of what the various kinds of drugs do in the human nervous system.
2. know the difference between the physiological actions of "uppers" (stimulants), "downers" (depressants), and the hallucinogenic drugs.
3. know why so many medically oriented people are against the legalization of any drugs.

A beautiful killer: cocaine crystals on a thin blade of glass.

Introduction

The use of narcotic and/or hallucinogenic drugs was once restricted to the underprivileged dregs of our cities or to a neurotic social minority that soon found their way there. Unfortunately, such restrictions no longer apply. Drug use has spread so rapidly through all levels of society that today its roots grow everywhere. Unrestricted, rampant drug use probably began among unattached teenage "drop-outs," then quickly found its way into the high schools and colleges and has now infiltrated even our grade schools. There is no area or cultural zone today that is safe from its ravages. Even parents whose children attend the most expensive, well-regulated schools that money can provide are confronted by problems that were once unique to Skid Row.

How could this have happened? What has taken place in society that has seen its people unleash, voluntarily, such a defervescing plague? Is there some deep-rooted reason for this seemingly sudden descent from the All-American boy image so prevalent in the early decades of this century into the dazed, semiconscious world of today's drug user?

Obviously a question of this sort is so all-embracing that it has many answers—a whole panorama of cause-effect patterns, none of which is complete by itself. We cannot begin to explore them all. However there are some fundamental aspects of drug use that we *can* deal with. First of all, I think it is important for everyone to realize that the problem has always been with us, in all cultures and throughout the social structures in those cultures. There is nothing particularly novel about the use of euphoric drugs in human society. We have anthropological evidence that indicates that some drugs were associated with humans before writing was invented. The chewing of coca leaves (from the plant *Erythroxylem coca*—the source of cocaine) was common more than fifty centuries ago in the Andes of modern Peru and Ecuador. The Indians who inhabited this area when the Spanish conquest began considered it a holy plant, and its use, while regulated, was universal throughout their empire. The *peyote* mushroom (source of mescaline) was, and still is, used by certain Mexican Indians in ancient religious rites, and the inhabitants of China knew about the narcotic effects of their poppies while the ancestors of modern Europeans were still living in caves and painting themselves blue.

Yet even then, Indo-European cultures had their own drugs. The oldest is alcohol, and its use has been noted in records going back forty-five centuries. We have written notes describing an alcoholic, beer-like drink that was used socially by the Egyptians as early as the twenty-second century B.C., and its use then was so widespread that it must have been around for a long time. Wine was as common as water in ancient Greece, and historians insist that there is good reason to believe that Alexander the Great was an alcohol addict whose habit killed him. Neither wine nor beer were strangers to Italy, and both remained in use throughout Europe long after Rome's empire had crumpled and fallen. In the early seventeenth century, the still was invented, and hard liquors became cheap and common. Their use became so widespread, in fact, that for a brief period of British history there was real fear in governing circles that indulgence in gin and whiskey would obliterate industry and destroy the nation. If that sounds familiar, it is because our American culture is not the first to experience a sudden pandemic of drug use and to fear its results.

We are afraid of drugs today for the same reasons our ancestors feared them long ago—they cause behavior that we do not understand, which is completely unpredictable and is sometimes downright dangerous. Furthermore, drugs demolish the people who use them, they damage or snuff out families, attack the most promising youth—and could, conceivably, uproot whole cultures. The incidence of drug use in our student population today is astonishingly high, and we are all beginning to realize what a few social workers realized long ago—once addicted, the cure is difficult, drawn-out, and all too often impossible.

The Addictive Personality

Is everyone a potential addict?

There are several schools of thought in response to that question. The earliest one theorized that some people had what was called an "addictive personality." It was suggested that such people were generally "subordinate" types, who tended to be followers, and they were characterized as introverted, uncomfortable at parties or other large gatherings. They were said to hate responsibility; in fact, they refused to be responsible for anything, especially themselves. It was further suggested that these addictive personalities, if they did not get caught up in drugs, often became religious or political fanatics, unreasonably—often violently—faithful to a given cause or person. When introduced to the drug scene, they gave their loyalty to the drug instead of to an individual or an ideal.

It was a well-developed theory and was deeply ingrained in literature dealing with social behavior—so deeply imbedded, in fact, that a large number of responsible people today still believe it. It has, however, lost favor among most professionals, simply because the evidence for it is unconvincing—there are too many exceptions to the rule.

The discovery that the concept of an addictive personality was wrong led to the development of a second theory, one that suggested that there is no such thing as a susceptible type and that everyone has an equal chance of becoming an addict. This school became entrenched because there did not seem to be any predictive method of determining just what an addictive personality might be. It was most popular until recently.

The Addict

Today the evidence seems to suggest that both of these theories were partially right and partially wrong. Workers are convinced that there most assuredly is a type of individual having an unusual susceptibility to drugs and that this type is indeed at greater risk of addiction than the average. But these people do not possess, as the earliest theory suggested, addictive personalities. The susceptibility is, unfortunately, not that easy to spot. It is a set of genetic instructions, passed from generation to generation and quite invisible even to the trained eye. Human chromosomes evidently have certain zones or genes that control susceptibility to drugs. They exert this control on certain parts of the brain, and their instructions determine whether or not the individual concerned can be easily addicted. Unfortunately, these genes offer no morphological or behavioral trait that can serve as a label. There is nothing overt that can warn when a given person is inordinately prone to addiction. As a result, those so predisposed are seldom aware that they are.

The only warning sign currently known is parental addiction, and if neither parent drinks or uses drugs of any kind, susceptible children may be completely oblivious to their danger.

Parental addiction is, however, an admonition that is dependable and should never be ignored. If a parent is an alcoholic, the chances are pretty good that at least one of the children—and probably all of them—will be an addictive type. This is the kind of information that raises a bright red flag to wave in the face of temptation. However, as anyone who has ever raised a child knows, such warnings will probably not be enough. Peer pressure is tremendous and usually decisive. Few children have the ability to say no when confronted by the unanimous demands of their friends, and the young tend to be essentially optimistic about their own survival and health. In a gathering of experimenting drug novices, no one heeds parental warnings about addiction, and when youngsters see several friends enjoying alcohol, cocaine, or marijuana without ill effects, they feel that they can too.

For some of them—fortunately just a few—it could be the end of their relaxed, happy lives. One type of inherited susceptibility is so vulnerable to the lure of drugs that those who have it can become hopelessly addicted after a single experience. What is more, they remain powerfully attracted, psychologically, to their drugs. Even if they succeed in breaking free, they will be perpetually fighting temptation, and their lives will never be simple and easy again.

Obviously, not everyone who tries drugs becomes addicted to them, even if social and physical conditions seem ideal. Just as some people are resistant to certain bacterial diseases, it seems that there are those who are also resistant to drug addiction. Some people are apparently able to use drugs recreationally for a while; then, as they get older and mentally more mature, they get sick of the feelings induced by drugs and tend to discard them. As with those who are terribly susceptible, such resistant people represent a small percentage of the population and are luckier than they will ever know.

The majority of people are somewhere in between the two extremes. "Average" people may not have a powerful predisposition for addiction, but they do not have any particular resistance, either. Drugs have a powerful grip and, taken frequently and regularly for a long enough period of time, can probably nail anyone. The country is filled with people who are not particularly susceptible to drug addiction yet are dedicated smokers, thoroughly addicted to nicotine. There are probably a lot of alcoholics who became hooked because they drank so much, socially, so often. These people do not really have a high predilection for addiction and will almost certainly "dry out" permanently, someday. One can only hope they have not destroyed their lives before they do.

Addiction

Drug addiction is a disease—a tremendously complex and devastating illness that can damage people's health and cripple them socially. There are two separate aspects to drug dependence: physical addiction and psychological addiction.

Physical addiction, which we once thought was irresistably powerful, has turned out to be the weaker of the two. True, the addict's body can become habituated and, depending on the drug, withdrawal can certainly produce powerful physical discomforts and ghastly illness. But those who treat addicts consider physiological dependence a relatively minor worry. The major problem is psychological. Addicts are addicts because they want to be, and that is a psychological state. They take their drugs because the euphoric or relaxed state is more attractive than real life, and they are happy under the influence. And drugs seem able to offer attractions to warm any personality. The dreamy effect of heroin provides a feeling of warmth and security. It lets people retreat from a world they cannot handle into a world essentially similar to the womb, where problems leave no imprint. Wrapped comfortably in their drug-induced blanket, mundane cares drift past . . . let someone else deal with them. For them there is nothing that can approach this feeling—not eating, not sleeping, not even sex. For others, this kind of addiction would be less attractive. They prefer the vigor-increasing, superhuman euphoria offered by stimulants like amphetamines or cocaine. Still others like to wander in never-never lands of LSD-induced hallucination where visions that emerge from deep in their own minds are displayed in vibrant, inchoate colors on whatever background they choose to imagine. Whatever the attraction, every drug has its own particular group of advocates.

Therapists have offered lists of characteristics to help determine whether or not a drug can be considered addictive. The list includes criteria like "tolerance for the drug," "powerful physiological responses to its removal," and so on. These lists have their uses, particularly for the government agency that is charged with determining which drugs can be sold over the counter and which will have to be prescribed. Yet, as was suggested earlier, a far more important aspect of drug addiction is the psychological dependency that becomes fixed in the addict. Everyone knows that a heroin addict will slowly become tolerant of his drug. A "junkie" who may start with two or three small bags of the drug per day will shortly require two or three such bags for a single dose, and it is not at all unusual for a heroin addict to require $500 a day to support his habit. Eventually, the tolerance becomes so great that it is not possible for the addict to obtain enough money, at which time he will often enter a treatment clinic where he will "kick" (undergo withdrawal). When he leaves the clinic, he promptly goes back to heroin in small doses, and the cycle begins again.

It may continue for decades if the junkie lives that long. Every time he enters a clinic, the addict eliminates the physiological hold. He knows he will suffer through a period of misery and illness, but he is willing to do that. He is willing to endure, not to rid himself of the drug forever, but to rid himself of his built-up tolerance so that he can return to his drug's embrace on a much less expensive level. He obviously does not consider the physiological hold very significant, and today, neither do most drug therapists. Even when dealing with drugs that get a firm physiological hold and can produce terrible withdrawal symptoms, most workers feel that the physical grip is nothing compared to the psychological one.

The strength of the psychological hold is probably impossible for a nonaddict to comprehend. Addicts will go through almost anything to obtain their drug. They have no pride and there are no restrictions. High school girls have no compunctions at all about selling sexual favors for money to buy drugs—in fact, becoming a prostitute is one of the least demeaning ways of getting money. Addicts will steal from family and friends; they will lie furiously to anyone at all including their spouses, children, and clergymen; they will completely subordinate themselves to their desire for their drug, and naturally violent addicts may even kill to obtain it.

Early Depictions of Addiction

Movies, books, and radio programs from the 1930s and 1940s depict marijuana addicts, heroin addicts, and every other kind of drug addict in the same manner. All are sex-crazed, maniacal killers hopelessly ensnared by their drug, utterly incurable and only half-sane even when they are not "high." That picture was, in fact, unquestioned by the generations that grew up during those years, and it probably played a major role in discouraging an awful lot of teenagers from using drugs. Unfortunately, it is not an accurate picture.

It is not possible to develop a characteristic picture of the heroin addict, marijuana addict, or cocaine addict because every person is unique. People respond to stimuli in their own way, and while there is often a relationship between responses to a given stimulus, there are always exceptions. A common example of this is the typical neighborhood bar. We have all been in bars where alcohol is liberally dispensed, and we have all seen the varying results of alcohol intoxication. Neighborhood bars have one thing in common and that is the drug that is used. It may be whiskey, it may be wine, or it may be beer, but it is all alcohol, and it is dispensed in whatever volumes the buyers wish. Some people will take one or two drinks and never overindulge. Others will stop after four or five and spend the rest of the evening at that particular level of inebriation, while still others will drink all that they can and get "smashed." This latter type, as we all know, includes many different personalities. Some people will be happy and pleasant, others will be talkative, some will cry, and others will become argumentative. Inevitably, some will become unpleasant, aggressive, and want to pick a fight. Most people are not like that when they get drunk, but "mean drunks" are by no means rare. They get to be pretty well-known after a while, but the point is that there is a personality that has this reaction to intoxication

There is no reason to believe that other drugs will not produce effects that are just as varied. You cannot stereotype a drug user's behavioral response to a drug today any more than you could fifty years ago. It has been said many times that heroin addicts aren't really violent. All they want is their drug. They don't want to fight and they don't want to kill—yet it's well known that they have no use for anyone or anything that interferes with their obtaining drugs. A heroin addict who is caught breaking into someone's home might try to talk his way out of his problem; in fact, most available evidence suggests that nearly all will. But the one you catch might not be an average one and he might kill, because the person who caught him is standing between him and his heroin. The drug known as STP (2,5-dimethoxy-4-methylamphetamine) has a reputation for making people vicious, twisting their personalities into unrecognizable beastiality, and making them unpredictably violent. Sometimes it will do this, but usually it does not. There are people who use it regularly and who don't become particularly active, let alone violent. Yet some people go berserk when they take STP. How a person will behave when under a drug's influence depends on the person, the drug, and maybe the time of day, month, or overall social atmosphere.

The Attraction

As to why people let themselves be entrapped by drugs, the reasons are probably just as varied. The psychologists who hypothesized the addictive personality were not completely wrong. Some people need to have a crutch to hold them upright. These people simply cannot exist without someone who believes in them and upon whom they can lean. They need someone to tell them what to do and someone or something to shoulder all responsibilities. These are the personalities that became the disciples of Charles Manson and committed a mass murder for him in 1968, or who followed the Reverend Jim Jones into self-destruction in 1978 when given a verbal order to do so. When people with this type of personality discover a drug that will permit them to drop into a warm and secure embrace, sheltered from the horrors of the world around them, they will adhere to it with a loyalty that knows no bounds.

But there aren't very many people in the world who will commit murder or suicide just because someone has told them to. The majority of people are not like that, nor are the majority of addicts. What is it, then, that attracts the ordinary person? Whence do they glean their philosophic absolution for such self-destructive indulgence?

A Drug-Oriented Society

The most important absolution may be supplied by us. We, by our own behavior, provide our children with an example that might absolve them of any personal guilt should they wander astray. We live in a drug-oriented society. Our magazines and radio and television airwaves are loaded with persuasive advertisements suggesting that we take pills, powders, or elixirs for illnesses we have never heard of and probably never will have. Familiar aches and pains are talked about until some people get such an ache just to oblige the advertisers. Headaches, stomachaches, backaches, nose aches, sinuses, ears . . . you name it, there's a pill or a powder available to cure it. Even if you are not sick, advertisers see to it that you think you are. We laugh today at depictions of old salesmen who used to peddle things like *Injun Joe's Snake Oil* or *Dr. Wampum's Magic Elixir* and we get a real kick out of the gullibility of our ancestors. After all, who could really believe that one medicine could do everything from curing warts to removing paint from walls?

Yet our sophistication today is only marginally greater. Advertisers know that if they mention a hoard of symptoms, some of us will recognize a couple of them. Then they think up catchy afflictions, things no one ever heard of before, like "tired blood" or

"B.O."—to be the cause of all these symptoms. After convincing us that we have this new disease, an actor clad in a doctor's white hospital coat then reveals to us (confidentially, of course) that we can be cured by simply taking their patented medicine for it. When we take it, we discover it works, probably because we never had anything wrong with us in the first place. Our medicine cabinets at home are jammed full of drugs about which most of us know nothing, yet there they are and we take them whenever we do not feel good. And sometimes we take them when we do feel good but we want to feel better.

Feeling Better than Good

Now we approach the marrow in the bone. It is not enough, it seems, to simply feel healthy and happy anymore. What you need to do is try to feel *super* happy and *super* healthy. Ninety percent—even 100 percent—is no longer enough; you now have to give 110 percent (which, of course, you cannot) to be successful, and you cannot give 110 percent unless you feel better than good.

When they are young, children are given vitamins rampantly. Overly concerned parents will often decide a child who does not feel good needs a laxative or an antihistamine or a decongestant and provide one or all of them with abandon. These same children see their parents taking pills to feel better, pills to help them sleep, and pills to keep them awake. When the parents relax, they and their friends use alcohol to help them unwind. Children see their father or mother, drunk and out of control, and everyone laughing at them, having a good time. It is not much of a step from this kind of example to actively using drugs. Americans are so accustomed to pills and powders that taking another one—no matter who provides it—is not any big deal. What could be wrong, after all, with indulging in a little grown-up activity? And besides, the highs really feel good.

Drugs and the Brain

But the psychology of addiction is, for the most part, beyond the scope of this book. What I want to develop is a broad view of the physiological aspects of addiction—to survey what it is that drugs do to the brain and how the body develops tolerance. Much of this is unknown, because it takes years to work out the long-term effects of drugs, especially on organisms as long-lived as humans. Nevertheless, we do have some answers. Before we get into specifics, however, let's take a broad, cursory look at the overall effects that drugs have on the brain.

We have been studying homeostasis, and by now you should certainly be familiar with its basic idea, that of providing resistance to any changes that steer the organism's internal environment away from normal tolerance ranges. These normal tolerance ranges embrace every aspect of the living organism, including its behavior. Behavior, no matter how complex, is a response to some internal need, and humans, like other organisms, are designed to maintain homeostasis. Regardless of the parameter involved, whenever our internal detectors sense a movement away from normal, some part of us is informed. Speaking broadly, anything that pushes us away from normal tends to make us uncomfortable and that discomfort has a purpose; it is designed to make us find a way back to normal.

We seldom need any instructions as to what these stimuli mean. When we get too hot, our internal sensing mechanisms send out signals, and their interpretation is automatic. We instinctively know from the way we feel that the problem is too much heat. We do, however, need a little experience as to the best way to alleviate the problem, and that is where cultural training takes over. Ten thousand years ago, the response may have consisted of taking a dip in a pool or finding a shade tree to sit beneath. Today we may stand in front of a fan or head for an air-conditioned room. When people got hungry 10,000 years ago, they got the same hunger signals that we get today, and they interpreted them in the same way. But they would go out and search for berries, roots, or seeds or maybe, if they were lucky, they'd kill a deer or rabbit. Today, we go to a restaurant or head for the refrigerator. The stimuli are all the same, although the behavior changes with the times and the culture. Even so and regardless of the changed responses, whatever we do is intended to adjust some aspect of our bodies that will help return things to normal.

If the behavioral mechanisms do not succeed in making things normal again, there are physiological mechanisms that will lend a hand. If we are walking in the sunlight and we get too hot, we may not be in a position to do anything behaviorally that will reduce our heat load, so physiological mechanisms take over and we begin to sweat. As we continue to sweat, our bodies become "used to" the heat, and we begin to feel less uncomfortable. In other words, we have become "tolerant" of the heat—we have adapted to it. Now if we suddenly plunge into an air-conditioned theater or restaurant we will feel cold, cold enough to shiver. The body, having become acclimated to the heat load of the sunlit outdoors, suddenly finds that it is losing heat at too high a rate of speed, and our discomfort can become acute until things readjust. Physiological mechanisms that were all tuned to cool us off suddenly have to do the opposite, and shifting gears like that requires some time.

When we are afflicted by a disease, things are more complex, of course. But viewing it broadly and somewhat simplistically, we can state that we feel miserable because certain parameters within our bodies have been forced out of their normal tolerance ranges. The discomfort we feel has its normal homeostatic function, which is to say, our body is trying to make us, behaviorally, do something that will help get things back where they belong. Unfortunately, when we are sick we often do not know what we have to do to make things feel good again. It isn't like jumping in a pool when we are too hot or leaning against a heater when things get too cold. We do not know instinctively how to fight against bacterial or viral invasions. The only behavioral weapon we have is rest, and usually we feel better when we lie down and try to sleep.

In the meantime, our bodies are trying to win a war against a ferocious invader, and physiological mechanisms of all kinds are struggling to return our disturbed parameters to normal. The fight is fierce and the efforts often involve everything the body has to give. When the fight is won, the victim frequently feels unusually good for a time. A person awakening after a painful bout with fever or pain may experience the most marvelous feeling of dreamy relaxation and comfort. Sleep becomes easy and delightful, and one hates to wake up, or move, or anything. This feeling of dazed euphoria is a result of our body's arduous efforts to make things better. For days or even weeks, most of our homeostatic mechanisms have been straining to force things away from "sickness" toward "normal," and the sudden surrender of the invading bacteria results in a rebound—an effect related, in a way, to the feeling of uncomfortable cold when the air-conditioned theater is entered (figure 20.1). The body is struggling to push things toward normal but is encountering resistance and so has to push without restraint. When that resistance suddenly vanishes, the pressure forces things over into an unreal, euphoric zone of pleasure that one normally visits only occasionally.

It is this unreal pleasure zone that the euphoric drugs thrust us into.

The first time people take a euphoria-producing drug, the body is not braced for it, and the feeling of pleasure is intense. The novice users drift around in an ecstatic cloud—a cloud they have encountered

Figure 20.1 (*a*) In a normal individual, the body's physiological mechanisms always push toward the "normal zone." As long as the body's parameters are in the normal zone, the mechanisms are quiescent. (*b*) When a person gets sick, the body struggles to return things to normal. Physiological mechanisms (*arrow*) fight hard against the disrupting bacteria (*triangles*). (*c*) Sometimes, when the illness leaves suddenly, the patient will experience a dreamy euphoria, because the body was pushing so hard it pushed right through normal when resistance vanished. (*d*) Drugs can push a person into the euphoric zone artificially, and in the beginning, they can overwhelm physiological efforts to return things to normal. (*e*) Eventually, however, the body's physiological mechanisms become used to the drug and begin to push harder. It becomes more and more difficult to achieve euphoria. (*f*) Soon the body becomes so used to the drug that it is exerting pressure toward the "sick zone" all the time. In the absence of drugs, it wins, and the addict is sick when he is not "high".

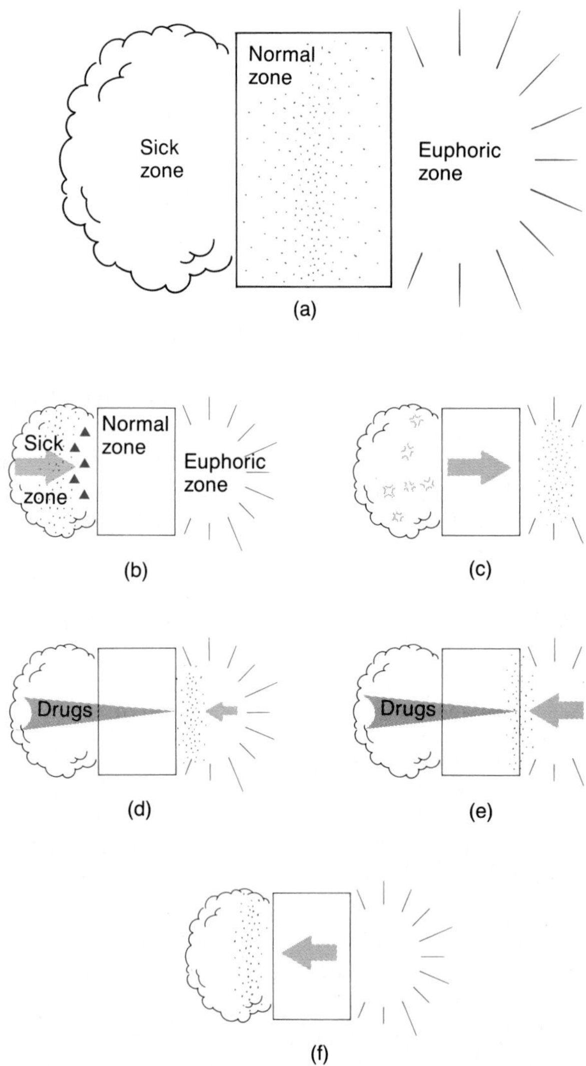

before, but only sporadically, and only for short periods of time. If the intervals between drug ingestions are fairly long, the feeling of euphoria will probably be intense every time and tolerance will be slow in developing. The chances are, however, that long intervals will not satisfy, and the drug will be experienced as often as possible. As the intervals shorten, the body adjusts to the drug's interference and begins to take steps to minimize it. It fights against the drug's pressure to push things away from the normal range, and as its resistance increases, more and more drug is required to achieve the euphoric state. Tolerance is beginning to develop and an addiction is forming.

For some strange reason, drug tolerance, when achieved with alcohol, is considered very *macho* in our society. People who order lemonade in a bar are subjects of ridicule and are often depicted as flimsy little characters who are afraid to indulge in a "man's drink." It is a mark of achievement to be able to "hold your liquor," and a person who gets drunk on one or two drinks is considered a wimp or a nerd. Movies, television, and stage plays commonly depict the hero as being a person who can still stand after a night-long drinking bout has rendered everyone else in the place unconscious, as if the fact that he is able to drink more is an indication of strength.

I cannot explain why this should be. A newborn baby, offered a teat, knows how to drink, so it cannot be skill at consuming fluids that is appealing. Any idiot can become tolerant of alcohol, if he drinks heavily enough, often enough. If we extended the same logic to eating, it would be equally reasonable to make a hero out of a person who is able to choke down more food than his companions, but it doesn't work that way. I have no idea why not.

If an addiction is indeed beginning, the pattern now is predictable. Each dose gets larger and the interval between doses gets shorter and shorter as the body learns about its enemy and how to combat it more effectively. Eventually, the body becomes so accustomed to the presence of the drug that its efforts to reduce the effects become constant. Now the user is in a quandary, because the body's pressures keep on working when there is no drug in his body at all. He doesn't ever feel normal any more. When he has his drug, he feels euphoric. When he does not have the drug his body pushes him into the discomfort zone and he feels sick. The feeling really is that of being ill, just the way people feel when they have a miserable case of the flu. Heroin addicts actually use the word "sick" to describe the misery they endure when they are not high. Since the normal world no longer exists and since drugs are expensive, the addict is usually sick.

Kicking the Habit

When one is thoroughly addicted, the process of getting things back to normal can be pretty bad. Heroin addicts who kick their habits (undergo withdrawal) go through about a two-week period during which they feel stomach cramps, nausea, muscle spasms, and all the misery of a really bad case of the flu. Alcohol addicts have the same sorts of problems: night sweats, unbelievable stomach cramps, gastrointestinal disruptions, horrible visual hallucinations, and ghastly nightmares—all this is typical. Recovery from barbiturate addiction is even worse. All the horrors mentioned above are experienced, but with magnified intensity, and medical personnel report that sudden withdrawal from barbiturates can cause rebound reactions powerful enough to kill.

Not all drugs develop tolerances in their victims and so not all of them produce the physical illnesses I have described. Nevertheless, for the most part the cycle described is accurate and is one that is best avoided.

Some Specific Drugs

A great deal has been written about the various hallucinogenic and euphoric drugs that are loose in our society. It would be folly to try to discuss all of them in this type of book, yet a few are so pervasive that they deserve some comment, if only for the sake of thoroughness.

Marijuana

It seems that the problems all began with the use of marijuana (*pot, weed, grass, reefer,* etc). This is not to imply that using marijuana leads to the use of other, heavier, drugs—although it sometimes does—but that marijuana was the first drug, widely acknowledged as highly undesirable, that became universally popular.

Marijuana is obtained from the plant known scientifically as *Cannibis sativa.* The common name is *hemp,* and in the heyday of the great sailing ships it was renowned as the source of the finest rope fiber that was available. During the Second World War both the U.S. and Great Britain set aside large areas to grow hemp for that very reason, and it still has considerable value for that purpose. Now, however, it is seldom grown for hemp fiber. Its leaves and flowers have an even greater cash value thanks to the presence of the psychoactive material they contain.

There is nothing particularly new about this material. In one form or another it has been known and used for centuries throughout northern and southern Africa, the Middle East, and southeast Asia. Legend has it that one Middle Eastern ruler used *hashish* in conjunction with other drugs to drive men to commit political murders, hence the name *assassin* (hashishin). The natives of India were drinking it as a tea called *bhang* long before the English invasions. It is new only to American culture and even there, it is not completely new. We were well aware of it fifty years ago, although it was not a problem then, and our attitude toward it could not have been more mistaken.

In the 1920s, 1930s, and 1940s, the person who smoked marijuana was pictured as a giggling, goggle-eyed sex fiend who would kill for the sheer joy of killing and was hopelessly and permanently insane. Movies depicting this kind of drug addict are now viewed as "camp" and are considered hilariously funny, but the people who made them were deadly serious. And most people believed the depictions. Unfortunately, this was the picture that was presented to our young people in the late 1950s and 1960s, and its rampant inaccuracies contributed to the drug's popularity. Perhaps if authority had told young people the truth, the weed would not have taken hold as quickly as it did, but the question is certainly academic now. Students of the 1960s could see for themselves that marijuana did not cause any of the problems they had been told it would. On the contrary, it seemed to be perfectly harmless, and it was certainly no worse than the alcohol their moms and dads used with such abandon. Marijuana never made a person stagger and fall down, and none of them had ever heard of marijuana addicts. Furthermore, once they got used to it, they needed less and less to get high, which meant no tolerance was developing. It was eminently clear that their parents, school principals, and police had either lied to them about marijuana or were mistaken in what they believed. Nothing authority had claimed to be true had turned out to be true. As a result, the kids of the 1960s believed nothing of what they were told, if it involved drugs. Drugs in general and marijuana in particular became the *cause célèbre* of the children of the sixties.

From the parents' standpoint, it was not so much that they were lying to their children as it was that neither they nor anyone else really knew anything about marijuana. Until the 1960s, the simple truth was that no scientific attention had ever been paid to it. Most people believed the stories they were told in the thirties and forties, and the people who were children then were the scientists of the sixties. They had not researched it earlier because they thought they already knew what it would do. When its use began to spread, it became obvious that marijuana did not do the things they thought it did. Most assumed it probably was a dangerous drug, but no one was really sure about that, and knowledge was so sparse that no statements of any authority could be made.

A lot of years have passed since then. Some long-term and short-term studies have been completed, and we have a much better handle on marijuana now than we had thirty years ago.

Even so, I don't want to give the impression that researchers know all there is to know about marijuana. Its physiological effects are still being examined, and, as has already been indicated, the psychology of drug addiction is enormously complicated and still largely unknown. But workers have some facts now, and there is plenty of evidence to back them up. To begin with, scientists are reasonably sure that there is more than one psychoactive material in marijuana. To date only one—the primary one—has been positively identified.

It is a substance known as **tetrahydrocannabinol** or **THC.** THC is not a very complex molecule (figure 20.2). As you can see from figure 20.2, it is a lipid, similar in some ways to cholesterol; hence it will dissolve in fats or fat solvents. The fact that it is soluble in fats explains why, as one becomes accustomed to it, it seems to require less of the drug to produce the desired high. It is able to dissolve in the phospholipid of cell membranes, and it stays there in solution for long periods of time. When it is picked up by blood flowing through the lungs it quite naturally dissolves in the membranes of the erythrocytes and any other cellular or fatty material available. Since it is delivered to other body areas, it finds its way into the cell membranes there as well, and because the brain gets an enormous flow of blood, there is quite naturally a good deal of the drug delivered to brain cells.

The first few times a person smokes pot, a lot of the THC dissolves in the membranes throughout the body and only a small amount remains free to produce its psychoactive effects. Once the body cells have become saturated with the drug, however, only a very little is necessary to produce the high that the user craves. Hence, for a brief period, it appears that there

Figure 20.2 The chemical structure of tetrahydrocannabinol, the psychoactive fraction of marijuana.

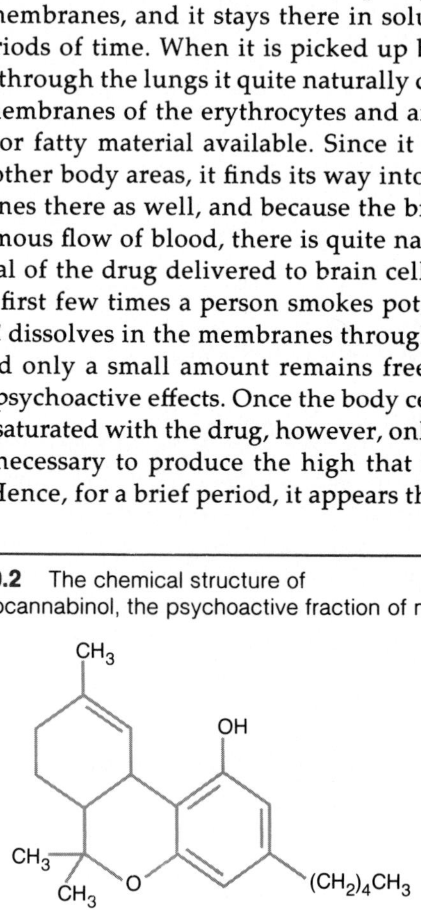

is actually a reverse tolerance building up, because the user requires less, instead of more, to produce the effect he or she wants. But this is an illusion. Once the body cells are saturated with the drug, each subsequent high requires a little bit more, indicating that a positive tolerance is indeed developing.

Addictive?

How addictive is it? Well, most of the research to date seems to indicate that if it is, it is only mildly so, at least physiologically. Some mild, short-lived withdrawal symptoms have been noticed when chronic, heavy users are forced to kick their habits, but there is no evidence to suggest that it creates the kind of physical dependence that the narcotic drugs can produce. Its psychological hold is also usually quite weak, although in some cases it can be as strong as that of nicotine.

What Harm Does It Do?

Lung Damage There is as yet not enough empirical evidence to confirm the contention that marijuana smoking damages the lungs. We must remember, however, that medical researchers warned for years about the dangers of tobacco smoking before confirmatory evidence was available. When it came, however, it came in quantity. Marijuana smoke contains a lot of the same chemicals that tobacco smoke does, and physicians are convinced that it is at least as damaging to lung and respiratory tissue as tobacco, and it may be worse. If it turns out that it is worse, it will be due at least in part to the method of smoking pot. Unlike tobacco smokers, who inhale the smoke and then immediately blow it out, marijuana smokers hold the smoke in their lungs for a while before exhaling it. This, quite naturally, means that delicate respiratory surfaces in the lungs suffer prolonged exposure. The feeling is pretty unanimous that future research will confirm the harmful effects of marijuana smoking on pulmonary structures and function.

Nervous Effects Marijuana seems to exert most of its autonomic effects on the sympathetic nervous system. Characteristically, the user will show increased heart rate (tachycardia), gentle, cold sweat, and heavily bloodshot eyes. If the subject is really high, the pupils will dilate and will not react to a light shone directly into them. In addition, there is at least one general nervous experience that occurs with consistency. It is called "the munchies," and as the name implies, it involves food. Not everyone who gets high on marijuana gets hungry, but most people do, and not only do they want to eat greater quantities of food, but the food they eat tastes better to them. This is a relatively harmless effect unless, of course, one is on a diet.

Nerve Damage As far as the nervous system is concerned, it is hard to determine how severe or permanent any damage might be. There were some disquieting reports of brain atrophy and ventricular enlargement in 1974, but confirmation has not been forthcoming, and the research has been justifiably criticized as lacking adequate controls. Nevertheless, it is hard to believe that any substance that can short-circuit certain nerve pathways and augment or depress synapses does not have some deleterious effects, and most workers are convinced that it does. Whether or not these effects are permanent is currently being researched.

Sensory Effects Marijuana's short-term effects, however, are pretty well known and they have been confirmed. Probably the most potentially dangerous effect it produces is distortion of sensory perception. Sixty miles per hour may seem like 10 or 15 mph, five minutes may seem like an hour, and twenty feet may seem like a hundred. Obviously, effects like these make a marijuana-intoxicated driver tremendously dangerous. In addition, researchers have discovered that it affects peripheral vision to the extent of eliminating it entirely when the user is really high, and subjects see only that which is directly in front of them. Since objects in the periphery are no longer visible, all visual stimuli come from that which is directly ahead. Because they are not being distracted by things that are going on beside them, users get the impression that they are concentrating with unusual clarity on what is ahead and they feel able to deal with it more effectively. Are they correct? Can they really handle the world around them with more clarity and perception than normally?

Well, since their vision is tunnelled, obviously they are not going to be able to handle much of it. They are not going to be aware of what is happening right beside them, and that is a mighty dangerous situation if they are operating in or around machinery. As to things directly ahead of them that they feel they see so clearly, users cannot handle them very well either, despite what they think. Carefully controlled experiments have shown pretty conclusively that many skills are lost, even those that are deeply ingrained. Typing skills, for example, are drastically reduced, suggesting that the subjects are not really concentrating as hard as they think they are. Because it reduces motor coordination as well as perception, marijuana use often reduces driving ability to a point equal to that of a thoroughly drunk individual.

Repeated experiments also have revealed that marijuana reduces a person's ability to learn and react. Short-term memory is drastically impaired, and if a person cannot get information into short-term memory, it will never be transferred into long-term memory banks. Thoughts that intoxicated people put down on paper, and which they feel are really profound, turn out to be pretty silly when viewed in the light of sobriety. Users' ability to comprehend what they read is reduced, and the attention span is much shorter than normal. To make things worse, there is a raft of evidence showing that habitual pot users have lost their motivation to improve themselves physically, mentally, or socially. Students who have fought their way to the top of their classes in high school and college and were steady A and B students have, as a result of heavy marijuana smoking, lost their desire to continue learning. Often they become content to detach themselves from ambience and laugh as they watch the world roll past. From society's and especially parents' points of view, this is a terrible waste.

Its Effect on the Genes As far as can be demonstrated, marijuana does not have a significant effect on the germ cells—sperms or eggs. It does not appear to affect fertility, nor does it appear to reduce the sex drive. Early reports that it turns users into uncontrollable satyrs or nymphomaniacs are in error.

Is it Good for Anything?

Yes, it is. Marijuana has been used with considerable success in treating the eye affliction known as **glaucoma,** and it is still prescribed in acute cases. Apparently none of its beneficial effects are permanent, however, and it is debatable whether the improvement in vision is worth the possible deleterious effects it may have as a drug. It may have clinical applications in cases of asthma and several spastic nervous conditions, although this is not confirmed. It has definitely proven to be of benefit as an antiemetic (anti-vomiting) agent, and cancer patients on chemotherapy have often used it in this capacity. It has the additional advantage of affecting such patients in much the same way as it does anyone else; it makes them hungry, which is also a good thing. Patients on chemotherapy often are so nauseated that they fail to eat properly, which complicates an already critical situation. By stimulating the munchies, marijuana can alleviate this. As of this writing, marijuana is dispensed legally, by prescription, in thirty-three states. It is available in dried form for smoking or as a THC-containing gelatin capsule called **Marinol** for those who do not wish to smoke.

Is It Worse than Alcohol?

Young people have contended for decades that marijuana is no worse than alcohol and may, in fact, be better. For that reason alone, many of them contend it should be legalized since, after all, alcohol is.

Is marijuana less of a problem than alcohol? That is a hard question to answer. In a way, it is like asking if cancer is worse than AIDS . . . since both have the same result, it becomes a matter of opinion. Some facts, however, can be stated:

1. Alcohol is a toxin. It can inflict irreversible damage on liver cells and can destroy brain cells.
2. It is powerfully addictive, and alcohol addicts have horrible withdrawal symptoms while "drying out."
3. It can (although it seldom does) produce serious genetic defects.

As far as can be determined right now, marijuana does none of these things. However, it is not harmless. For one thing, it is ten thousand times more intoxicating than alcohol, molecule for molecule. Also, there is no doubt that it can be addictive, although it is apparently much less powerful in this regard than alcohol. It is fat-soluble and hence is not eliminated from the body as rapidly as alcohol—in fact, its presence can be detected in a person's body as long as three months after he or she last smoked it. Finally, as was already pointed out, it can almost certainly damage the lungs, maybe more than tobacco smoking can. Clearly, neither drug is particularly desirable from either the individual point of view or from society's.

Cocaine

Cocaine is what is known as an "upper," meaning that it is a stimulant like amphetamines instead of a heroin-like depressant. It is probably the most popular of the so-called recreational drugs and is rapidly becoming common in our modern "yuppie" culture. Narcotics enforcement officials say it is even displacing some of the other drugs as the narcotic of choice within the drug community. People who use it claim that it is a harmless intoxicant and that they would not dream of throwing a party without offering their guests a "line" (a small amount of powdered cocaine arranged in a straight line) to "snort" (inhale into a nostril through a straw). Alcohol and heroin addicts seem to come from all walks of life, particularly low-income areas and cultures. Not so with cocaine. It is not used with any regularity in lower-income groups simply because it costs too much—at least $100 a gram—yet despite the expense, its popularity is soaring. The most recent figures released by the National Survey on Drug Abuse indicate that there may be as many as twenty million users in America today. That's more than five times the 1984 estimate and nearly ten times the number estimated to be regularly using cocaine in 1976.

When it is sniffed into the nose, cocaine can cross the nasal membranes, enter the bloodstream and get to the brain in less than three minutes. Heavy users often cannot wait that long and "mainline" the drug into a vein, whence it can hit the brain in less than fifteen seconds. Advocates of this latter technique claim that the "rush" derived this way is sometimes intense enough to cause temporary blackout. Others say it is just a different way of experiencing the high, but they have all tried it just the same.

Its attraction is collosal. Unlike the feeling of restful, warm security afforded by heroin, cocaine wakes a person up with an enormous bang. It exerts its effects in the pleasure centers of the brain (the limbic system, principally the **amygdala**), and by manipulating both catecholamine production and its effects on nerve endings, it turns everything there on to "high." EEG recordings made during a cocaine rush resemble somewhat the patterns that appear during orgasm, with a few important differences. The most obvious one is the duration of the effects. Natural orgasm lasts only a very short time—usually less than a half-minute—whereas the cocaine high can extend to three or four times that long.

Both orgasm and cocaine turn things on in the brain's pleasure centers by activating sympathetic centers. Orgasm usually turns on these centers gradually, using a certain amount of restraint. The excitement begins slowly and builds exponentially, straining toward a maximum sensation that approaches with increasing intensity. But when it reaches its peak, natural orgasm does something that cocaine does not do. As the emotional intensity experiences its crescendo, parasympathetic neural centers are gradually activated and begin swinging into action. Their activity increases and the amount of acetylcholine they release slowly increases in abundance. Cholinergic neurons begin awakening and respond smoothly, soothing the jittery adrenergic synapses that have been banging away, gradually bringing them back to quiescence. To complement this softening of sympathetic stimuli, the parasympathetic nerve centers spread a calming effect, like a great, soft blanket over the cerebral cortex. A feeling of tranquillity slowly begins to rise and its soothing influence leaves the subject with an air of dreamy satisfaction and calm fulfillment.

This does not happen with cocaine. None of the sensations are gradual.

Its effects are explosive. When cocaine hits the brain, it immediately increases catecholamine production. Dopamine, epinephrine, and norepinephrine squirt all at once into susceptible synapses, and sympathetic pleasure zones snap on with shocking suddenness. Adrenergic and dopaminergic centers in the brain suddenly flare into life, and conscious areas in the cortex are literally bombarded without warning by their impulses. Users say they feel as if they have literally burst open, that pleasure suddenly assails them almost violently. They feel healthier than they have ever felt, like they could conquer the world; problems that they couldn't handle simply do not exist anymore, and an orgasmic torrent of joy rushes through their system as a powerful undercurrent on a tide of unbelievable rapture. It hangs on and on. Feelings get more and more intense. They keep reaching higher, stretching a last little bit, searching for the ultimate experience, and just as they seem certain to reach the peak, everything suddenly stops.

The end is shattering, like a piece of heavy, soft lead hitting pavement—no resounding crash, just a mushy thunk. The parasympathetic nervous system does not switch on, and there is no gradual reduction of emotion. There is no feeling of satisfaction or fulfillment. Instead of experiencing a relaxed joy and satisfied pleasure, they remain edgy, irritable. They almost—but not quite—reached some important pinnacle that suddenly disappeared. But maybe they can get it back. Maybe, if they try right away, they can reach the top this time. So they reach again for cocaine and once again the vast arena of intense bliss opens up . . . only to close with a thud again when the rush wears off. With this sort of pattern, small wonder that the experience is repeated so frantically and the addiction rate is so high.

Cocaine can snare, with ridiculous ease, even those people who have used other drugs and have resisted addiction. One addict in California noted that he had used marijuana, amphetamines, heroin, alcohol, and LSD and had not been particularly attracted to any of them, but when a friend introduced him to cocaine he was instantly caught. That case is a bit extreme, but it illustrates the incredible power of cocaine. For the average person, officials say it takes only two to three years of regular (once or twice per week) use to create a dedicated addict. And once addiction occurs, the subject may be trapped for life; and remember, that is the average person. Some people try it just once and are hooked.

Addiction to Cocaine

For some, cocaine may never be a problem. Most authorities feel that of all those who use cocaine, only about 10 to 15 percent will ever become addicted. But if twenty million people are trying cocaine, soon there will be two million devoting their lives to it, and that is a terrible waste. And when it effects a capture, it rapes its victims both physiologically and psychologically.

When their drug is taken away, cocaine addicts definitely experience physical discomfort and illness. In fact, there is a rebound effect even after a single "hit." Knowing the overall effect drugs have on the brain, you might predict that the user who has "come down" will feel exactly the opposite of the way he felt when he was high, and you would be right. Instead of feeling like he can lick the world, he feels weak and his muscles hurt. Instead of feeling healthy, he feels sick and his stomach aches. His sensory processes are working at less than half capacity, so the impact of the world around him is reduced. Things that used to provide pleasure don't stimulate pleasure centers any more. The ability to produce dopamine and the other adrenergic transmitters is reduced, and the antagonistic cholinergic centers are running at full power. Instead of feeling pleased with himself, he feels depressed, and worst of all he isn't satisfied. All his pleasure is gone and there is nothing to show for it. Everyone is against him, and there is a feeling of intense paranoia, which often leads to anger and violence.

All in all, it is a miserable feeling, but it's minor compared to the agonies of alcohol or heroin withdrawal. And compared to cocaine's crushing psychological grasp the physical problems are meaningless. Cocaine's psychological talons are at least as strong as heroin's, which means the addict will steal, lie, cheat—maybe even kill—to get it. Yet there are people who persist in believing that because it does not produce a powerful physical addiction that it is essentially a harmless drug.

What Harm Does Cocaine Do?

One of the reasons that cocaine usage is climbing today is that the all-embracing opinion on the street is that it is essentially harmless. It is not and it never was, even when it was used only in medicine.

Cocaine was the first local anesthetic ever discovered, and in that role it is still effective, but most medical personnel prefer not to use it because it is too dangerous. Even in carefully supervised medical situations with experienced physicians in attendance and all necessary life-saving equipment immediately available, it is a killer just under 1 percent of the time.

Many of its most dangerous effects are well-known. The worst involve the heart and its attendant blood vessels, and cocaine's actions there are often fatal. It produces arrhythmias in the heart's pacemaker and can cause spasmodic vasoconstrictions of coronary arteries—vasoconstrictions so powerful that cardiac infarctions sometimes result. As many as 70 percent of the teenagers and young adults using cocaine regularly have reported frequent, recurring chest pains, and people in this age group should *never* need to worry about such things. In 1986, cocaine killed two highly publicized sports figures—Len Bias of the University of Maryland's basketball program, and Don Rogers of football's Cleveland Browns—indicating that even being in top physical condition will not necessarily help. The number of young adults who have quietly and invisibly died from cocaine-induced heart attacks may never be known. Its effects on the brain can sometimes be nearly as dangerous. Epileptic-like seizures are common, give no warning, and can cause complete respiratory collapse. In addition, cocaine can produce hallucinations that are so pure they seem utterly real. An addict responding to a cocaine-induced vision might do anything—even kill.

Freebase, Rock, or Crack

Cocaine, as it is bought on the street, is in the form of a soluble salt—cocaine hydrochloride—and it is never pure. Usually it is cut with dextrose, mannitol, or quinine and offered for sale at about 30 percent purity. In this form, it dissolves quickly and easily in water so it can be sniffed or injected with equal ease and effectiveness. Drug peddlers will seldom consider selling cocaine in amounts smaller than a gram, which pretty well restricts the buyers—especially amateurs—to middle- or high-income groups. However, when it is properly treated, cocaine can become a much more dangerous drug and can be obtained quite cheaply.

By cooking relatively impure "street" cocaine in a little water, using ammonia or baking soda as a catalyst, one can remove the impurities and dissolve away the chloride, leaving behind solid, hard lumps of almost insoluble and 90 percent pure cocaine. When the cooking is finished, the bottom of the vessel that was used will be littered with cocaine particles that look like little rocks; hence the name *rock*. This material is packaged and sold in much smaller amounts than street cocaine is peddled, and that brings more buyers into the marketplace. It is not unusual to be able to buy rock in amounts costing only ten or fifteen dollars, which puts it well within the range of the average high school student. That, coupled with its tremendous effects, makes it terribly dangerous.

Since it will not dissolve in water, rock cannot be sniffed or injected. However, it will change from a solid directly into a vapor when it gets hot enough, and burning tobacco is exactly the right temperature. So in common usage, it is placed in pipes or stuffed into a tobacco cigarette and smoked. When it burns, it crackles like a green log on a fire, which is where the name *crack* comes from. In this form, its effect is mind-shattering. The user experiences an immediate, tremendously intense high that lasts from five to seven minutes and then drops him with a thunk.

Addiction to Crack Crack's addictive ability is incredible. Where alcohol takes a decade of heavy drinking to produce an addict, where even heroin requires a year or so of steady "chipping" (intermittent use), crack can take a victim by the throat in one or two trials. As is the case with most drugs, the pattern of usage is unique. There is no such thing as a "recreational" user of crack. Where heroin and cocaine users often stretch out the intervals between highs so they can think about the pleasure that is to come, the crack user never does. The crack high is so intense and the drop so precipitous that the user feels like part of his life has been suddenly taken away. After coming down from a crack high, he has a sense of urgency bordering on desperation. He cannot wait to regain the pleasure that was so surprisingly and so completely stolen. If there is any crack available, it will be used immediately. Only when it is all gone will the user be forced into a pattern of recovery.

What Harm Does Crack Do?

Anything cocaine does, crack can do, but more so. Recent statistics from narcotics addiction treatment centers have yielded some sobering results about crack. In 1986, nearly 20 percent of the teenagers who used crack experienced seizures similar to epileptic seizures, 35 percent experienced hallucinations that required restraint by hospital authorities, 30 percent were hospitalized for attempting suicide, and nearly 20 percent had been jailed for crack-related traffic accidents or offenses.

Of the total number of people who used crack, nearly 30 percent became addicted, and of that group, nearly 50 percent of them stole from their families or friends to support their habits. Seventy percent of the girls gave sexual favors for money, nearly 40 percent of users became crack dealers to support their habits, and *all* of them had been deserted by their oldest friends and had fallen in with new companions, all of whom were addicted, like themselves, to crack.

The psychological damage crack can do is immeasurable. Most workers are convinced that there is no permanent cure for cocaine/crack addiction. Once an individual is hooked, he is hooked for life. He may get free of the drug, but if he ever relapses and tries it even once, he may as well never have taken the cure, because he will have to do it all again. As is the case with the alcoholic, there is no possibility of ever being able to take it socially again, and there is no way to ever be completely free. The urge will never leave. In this respect cocaine addiction, indeed, addiction to most drugs, is ultimately lethal.

Is Cocaine Any Good?

Aside from its limited medicinal use, cocaine appears to have no value. Until recently, it was felt that it did not produce particularly harmful long-term effects in body cells or tissues, but very few workers believe that now. Its effects on the brain may be irreversible. It may permanently reduce the hormone production of some endocrine glands, and there are indications that it can produce irreversible damage in certain cells of the immune system. For addicts who prefer to snort the drug, there is also abundant evidence that it produces permanent tissue damage in the nasal epithelium and external nares.

Alcohol

The drug that is abused more than any other in our society is almost certainly alcohol. That is mostly because it is legal, so it is relatively easy to get, and there is no penalty if you are caught possessing some. In addition, almost everybody in the country drinks, so police, judges, lawyers, jury members—everybody—having had experiences with alcohol, tend to be lenient with a drunk. Yet alcohol is probably as deadly as any drug of which we are aware.

Many people tend not to consider alcohol as a drug simply because it is in liquid form. If it were a powder like cocaine and heroin, or in a solid chunk like crack or marijuana, they would have no trouble with the identification, but since it is in the form of a liquid they seem to think it's somehow different. It is not! It's a drug, just as cocaine, heroin, and all the others are drugs. It is just as damaging and every bit as deadly.

One of the most discouraging facts about alcohol is that more teenagers are involved with it than with any other drug, and this includes even marijuana. Parents who would quail at the knowledge that their offspring was smoking marijuana will often ignore a developing problem with alcohol. When they realize that their children are stealing liquor or beer from their own stocks, parents will often rationalize it away with the observation that "kids will be kids" or something equally inane. Teenagers can find latent permission for drinking almost everywhere. Modern "teenaged movies" more often than not show high school students guzzling beer with or without their parents' permission and obviously with the approval of the script writers. Children see their parents enjoying drinks of various kinds and sometimes are even invited to "take a sip and see what you think" when a parent gets a slight buzz from the drinking.

Once they begin drinking on a regular basis, they become members of an enormous statistical club. Alcohol is responsible for more than ninety-eight thousand deaths each year in this country, and nearly a third of them are teenagers involved in fatal traffic accidents. The down-and-outers that can be seen in any city's skid row district are nearly all alcohol addicts. The homeless bums wandering city streets and the people found dead in doorways almost every morning are probably alcoholics, too. Liver cirrhosis resulting from chronic alcoholism kills about thirty-thousand people every year; alcohol psychoses and alcohol-related brain damage kill another five thousand. There is no way to determine how many people die five or ten years earlier than they would have had they stayed free of alcohol, but there can be no doubt that they number in the tens of thousands. Even those who tend to be moderate, sporadic drinkers or those who do not drink at all are brought into these statistics by being forced to pay for the problems of those who do. Hospitals and clinics for the treatment of alcohol addiction cost taxpayers in this country millions of dollars. More than 519,000 people spend time in hospitals every year because of alcohol-related illnesses, and they occupy anywhere from 25 to 50 percent of the bed space and professional time, most of which they are unable to pay for. What is more, as long as we keep finding half-dead drunks lying all over the downtown streets and in our parks, these expenses are going to continue. Even teetotalers are not free from the costs of alcohol.

So why do people drink? In the beginning, of course, it is peer pressure. Everywhere you go, liquor is offered, and as long as you are not a mean drunk or have an alcohol-related traffic accident, the chances are that no one will admonish you for heavy drinking. It is nearly impossible to find a party nowadays that does not include alcohol in one form or another. In fact, how many movies or television shows have you seen in which nonalcoholic parties are presided over by prissy, stereotyped "old maids" who hate to see anyone having fun? And how many of those movies show one of the heroes or heroines rushing over to fill the punch bowl with alcohol, thus livening up an otherwise dull party and ultimately being responsible for making it a success? How many movies have you seen in which the stars got drunk and the whole scene was terribly amusing and harmless? How often is the hero a macho-type man who can drink his buddies under the table without half-trying, and how often have you heard the line "throw away that kid's stuff and have a *man's* drink"? It happens all the time, doesn't it? So why are we surprised when most of our children drink regularly before they are out of high school and alcohol is our biggest drug problem?

Is childhood drunkenness a really big drug problem? According to recent statistics compiled by the National Institute on Drug Abuse, it's bigger than any other, and it can begin as early as age 9 or 10. More than a third of all fourth graders who were asked said that they had been pressured by their peers to take a drink, and the pressure increases as they get older. In our high schools, drinking is as common as dancing. Two out of every five high school students in this country confess to drinking heavily and more than a third of the seniors, girls included, say they get drunk at least once a week.

What Harm Does It Do?

Fables about alcohol and its lack of effect on the body abound, especially among those who drink more than they should, and like it. Drinkers love to glean a measure of absolution by pointing to a statement made by an alcoholic physician in the late 1920s. This physician, warned by friends of horrible liver damage, insisted that the liver breakdowns so common in alcoholics were not the result of drinking, but rather of their inadequate diets. He never permitted himself to get that run-down, he insisted, hence he would never have such liver trouble. I do not know what ultimately happened to that physician, but I can tell you that it is not the poor diet that causes cirrhosis, it is the alcohol. What's more, the liver cell destruction is irreversible, which is why the cirrhotic invasion occurs.

Put quite simply, *alcohol is a poison—it kills body cells.* Its lethal effects are concentrated in the liver because that is where it is metabolized, but it kills cells everywhere it goes. Brain cells are destroyed by the thousands, and it is axiomatic that once a nerve cell is gone, it is gone forever. Alcohol is toxic to bone marrow cells, which can result in profound primary anemias. Alcohol breaks down myoneural coordination, interferes with hormone production, and can severely damage the immune system. It also produces some rather fundamental damage at the cellular level. Being a fat solvent, alcohol can dissolve in the fats of the cell membrane. It does not appear to stay there long, but while it is there it can damage the membrane, and the damage may be permanent. By interfering with the membrane's ability to control the movement of materials into and out of its cell, alcohol can disrupt the function of every cell in the body.

Kidney cells, gastrointestinal cells, and blood cells are all affected, and current evidence shows that once they are killed, they are not replaced.

Its mental effects are more complex but are just as disruptive and potentially just as deadly. Much as a shotgun splatters shot all over the targets it is pointed at, alcohol alters memory and motor skills in a blurred, scattered fashion. The outside world becomes rather hazy to alcoholics, and they often have little use for people other than drinking buddies. Natural emotions are weakened, sex drive is damaged, and the sense of balance is nearly eliminated.

Alcohol's physical hold is quite strong, every bit as powerful as that of heroin. It takes all a person's strength to go through the cramps and agonies of physical withdrawal, yet the psychological grasp can be even stronger. When all the pain is gone, it still takes a lot of determination to handle the burning desire for alcohol that follows. Drunks report that they see the well-lit, cheery bar at the top of every staircase they climb and behind every door they open. One recovering alcoholic, after abstaining for nearly a year, received a bottle of twelve-year-old whiskey as a gift and had to call a friend to throw it away for him. He reports that he tried to pick it up and pour it down his sink a dozen times, but couldn't bring himself to touch the bottle. He was both horrified and enchanted by it, and completely lacked the strength to handle it. One never survives alcoholism. Ultimately, it dies with you.

Addiction

About one out of every six people who drink on a more or less regular basis will wind up addicted. But you don't have to be a heavy drinker to be taking a chance. Those who are taking their first drink have about a 10 percent chance of winding up alcoholics, and if either parent is a drunk, the probability is nearer to 40 percent. In many ways, alcohol addiction is not very different from heroin addiction. Alcohol is more toxic than heroin, but its intoxicating effects are roughly similar. Both are depressants. Both tend to reduce neural activity in the cerebral cortex and underlying brain areas, and both will put the user to sleep if enough is taken. The strength of the physical grip is roughly the same, which means withdrawal produces roughly similar symptoms.

People often refer to the "happy alcoholic," and movies portray him or her as a benign, rather ridiculous but utterly harmless slob, usually flat on his face or with his nose buried in a glass on a bar. The picture is ludicrous in the extreme, because the happy alcoholic is a myth. Like any addict, alcoholics live from drink to drink, and when they are sober, they are not happy, they are desperate. In the beginning, they are almost always overweight, probably because they tend to be self-indulgent where food is concerned, thanks to the will-depressing effect of alcohol. As the alcoholism advances and they lose their jobs, families, and friends, they slowly lose weight, too. This is because their ability to buy enough food is gone. Their earning power has dropped, and anyhow, they tend to devote most of the money they earn or steal to the purchase of alcohol. They can be seen in public parks and streets all over our larger cities, sitting quietly by themselves or in the company of one or two cronies, disheveled, dirty, undernourished, and sick, gulping cheap wine from gallon jugs and wondering where they are going to get money to buy more.

Is It Any Good?

There are some good things to be said about alcohol, although they do not begin to balance the bad. Statistical analysis seems to show that patients who have suffered cardiac infarctions and are on low-fat diets fare better if they have one or two drinks a day than if they abstain. No one has yet figured out why. Also, West Coast workers say that smokers who drink are less likely to develop emphysema than are those smokers who do not drink. They hasten to point out, however, that they are not advocating that heavy smoking teetotalers take up drinking. The damage elswhere in the body from alcohol cannot possibly offset the slight benefit it may offer in this regard.

Tobacco

Tobacco has been with us for so long that very few people look upon it as an addictive drug, but it most assuredly is. In fact, it is one of the most powerful addictive drugs known to science.

Probably the biggest reason it is not viewed in the same light as alcohol, heroin, cocaine, and the others is because people do not lose their minds under its influence. It is not hallucinogenic, and it is neither a strong depressant nor a powerful stimulant. It does not impair judgment, nerve-motor coordination, eyesight, or anything else, and people can function normally when completely under its influence.

Addiction

Yet one can become addicted to it as fast as to any of the other drugs. Those who smoke a single pack of cigarettes are probably completely hooked, and it may require tremendous will power to get them unhooked. It is not unusual for the dedicated smoker to go through two or three packs of cigarettes a day, and this may go on for years.

It is not an expensive habit, not when compared to the others. Even a heavy smoker probably won't spend more than $25 a week on it, and that, relatively speaking, is peanuts. It is a remarkably persistent habit, however, and very hard to break. The physical grip is not particularly powerful when one considers the mild withdrawal symptoms the new abstainer must endure. Yet when taken in conjunction with the psychological grasp, its overall power can be shocking. Everyone today is aware that Jews in Nazi concentration camps, if they survived at all, were beaten, worked half to death, malnourished, and on the brink of starvation. Yet there are reliable reports that many would surrender a meager meal for an extra half-cigarette and would smoke it greedily when it came. And there are people all over this country who have tried unsuccessfully to quit smoking again and again without success.

What Harm Does It Do?

Why bother? If smoking does not damage reflexes, upset behavior, or interfere with one's ability to live normally, what's the point of quitting?

We all know the answer to that question by now. Statistics compiled by the American Medical Association are enough to make the most dedicated tobacco farmer blanch. Heart disease caused by smoking kills nearly a quarter of a million people every year. Cancer resulting from smoking takes another 150,000. Other respiratory diseases and cardiovascular problems caused by smoking will kill 75,000 more. Even if disease doesn't get the smoker, he or she may fall alseep while smoking and set the bed on fire. Statistics indicate fires like that will take the lives of more than 4,000 people every year. Even nonsmokers aren't safe from tobacco. Inhaling tobacco smoke from other people's cigarettes will probably contribute to the deaths of 80,000 adults, while 4,000 newly born infants and/or unborn fetuses will die because their mothers smoked while carrying them.

Those numbers are appalling. We know how deadly the automobile is, and most people are horrified to note that thousands of people die every year in non-alcohol-related traffic accidents. We are overwhelmed at the prospect of losing American soldiers in foreign wars and will complain bitterly to our elected representatives if a division or two is placed in jeopardy. We would crucify any general who had a half-million of his men killed in combat in a year—in fact, we might crucify him if he lost that many in ten years. America didn't lose that many G.I.s in the Korean and Vietnamese conflicts put together. Yet we lose more than 600,000 Americans each year to tobacco and continue to say nothing about it.

Is It Any Good?

There is nothing of which I am aware that suggests a clinical or therapeutic use for tobacco. In fact, if there is anything suggesting it might have some social or psychological value beyond the fact that it makes millions of dollars a year for those who grow and process it, I have never heard of it. It does have an effect that some might consider beneficial although I do not choose to. It increases a person's basic metabolic rate, which means that smokers can eat a little more than nonsmokers without putting on extra poundage. This is one reason why people often gain weight when they quit smoking. They may eat no more than they did before, but now that amount of food will put on weight.

Other Drugs

There are myriad other drugs available to people in this country, if they are fool enough to try them. Even things that have never been considered drugs are often used. One hospital in New York reported a brief flurry of early teenage admissions due to their having intravenously injected the oil squeezed out of banana peelings in an effort to get high. Children and teenagers, pressured by peers to try something, have attempted all kinds of things. Some of the more common ones follow.

Sniffing glue (toluene mostly) was a favorite twenty years ago, but when some children died from its effects, it began to lose favor. Toluene, in any concentration sufficient to cause a high, can dissolve nervous tissue, including the brain.

LSD (lysergic acid diethylamide) or **acid** was very popular in the drug culture of the 1960s and is beginning to make a comeback in the late 1980s. As a hallucinogenic drug, it has few equals. LSD-induced hallucinations are astonishingly brilliant and effective, and LSD has the additional virtue of making the user aware that he or she is hallucinating. Its visions are realistic and often in full color. Users say that they can hear appropriate sounds from their hallucinations and can smell the right smells. LSD-induced hallucinations seem to make sense up to a point, but sooner or later distortions of reality insert themselves and the user becomes aware of them. When, for instance, a subject becomes suddenly aware, beyond a shadow of a doubt, that he and he alone is holding up a 300-foot cliff in the Grand Canyon with his shoulder, common sense quickly informs him that his experience is hallucination and is not real. Nevertheless, any effort to move away from the cliff might bring ominous rumblings and a cascade of rocks crashing down around him, and he dares not move, even in illusion. Merely knowing that an experience is not real does not necessarily free the victim from its grip.

LSD users who have undergone a disastrous experience (called a "bad trip") are shaken and often badly stirred up mentally, but nevertheless they were aware throughout that it was really nothing more than a hallucination that would ultimately disappear. Yet sometimes, knowing their visions are unreal is not enough. Sometimes the visions fill users with emotions that overwhelm common sense. (See box on page 264). To make matters worse, LSD use always leaves open the possibility of "flashbacks" (spontaneous occurrence of hallucination, not brought on by drugs). Because of the danger it represents, its use tends to be self-limiting.

PCP (angel dust) is extremely popular on the West Coast, not so much in the East or America's heartlands. Its name is not an acronym based on its chemical identity (phencyclidine hydrochloride) but rather is condensed from its 1960s drug culture-derived identity (*P*ea*C*e *P*ill). It is a dissociative anesthetic, meaning it removes the user from reality almost completely, and in addition it operates as a painkiller. Between these two effects, users represent a tremendous danger both to themselves and society. Their behavior is utterly unpredictable. A mild-mannered individual may suddenly become a violent, half-mad killer in the true mold of the 1930s "reefer maniac." Anyone who gets in such a user's way can and will be attacked with any weapon at hand. Exacerbating this is the fact that users cannot be hurt—literally. Those who try to subdue a person who has become violent after using angel dust are in for the fight of their lives. Twisting an arm up behind the user's back has no effect at all, even if the arm is broken. Pain has no meaning for him. Since pain is responsible for a large part of the effectiveness of a blow to the head, you have to half-kill such a person to calm him down. Only repeated blows to the head or overwhelming numbers can succeed.

Space Base

A ghastly problem that has surfaced in California and is rapidly spreading east is a mixture known as "ghost buster" or "space base." This is crack and PCP mixed, and when crack is smoked simultaneously with PCP, the result is frightening in its intensity and ramifications. Users report that the high is unbelievable, even greater than that obtainable with pure crack. While lost in its throes they feel as if they have tremendous energy. They are sure no physical act is beyond them, and they are ready to try anything. For about twenty minutes, there is absolutely no way to predict what the subject will try or will do. The hallucinative reality of cocaine is combined with the wild fanaticism and dissociative effects of PCP. A user who is ghost-busting may see any number of enemies nearby and, knowing that nothing can stop him, he may decide to wipe them all out. That they are all his friends is not something that he would recognize, and remember, PCP renders the user insensitive to pain. The addictive nature of space base is greater than that of crack. Much of the time a single experience will be enough to make experimenting users want more, and three or four experiences will nail them.

Is There Any Solution?

For years people have argued that the simplest and quickest solution to the drug problem would be to legalize all of the problem drugs. The argument notes that there is so much money to be made in illegal drugs that we will never be able to control them. The government cannot begin to pay law officers as much money to catch drug dealers as the dealers can pay them to lay off, and bribery is so rampant that a lot of our drug enforcement programs—especially those involving foreign governments—aren't worth pursuing. If the drugs were legalized, this money would not be forthcoming, and with the huge profits gone, the illegal activity would gradually dry up. That is, after all, what happened to the bootleggers and illegal alcohol barons of the 1920s. And just think of all the educational programs that could be financed with the taxes that could be applied to these legal drugs.

The arguments seem reasonable, and should be answered. Let us consider what would happen if all drugs were legal.

Would it dry up the illegal trade? Probably! Most of it anyway, and if illegal alcohol is any indication, only minor problems of that nature would remain.

Would the taxes collected really help educate people about the evils of drugs? How much of the tax money on liquor and tobacco collected today is spent on educating people about the evils of either of them? Do you honestly believe that government officials would spend a windfall of this sort on education?

Would it solve any of the other problems? Well, abstainers would still be fighting a losing battle against *very* big money indeed. It does not take much experience to see that the alcohol and tobacco industries are not hurting for money. All of them are extremely wealthy, and through judicious distribution of these monies they can adjust laws to suit themselves and to make sure that we do not hear too much about all the lives they destroy and the deaths they cause. As for the other troubles, just consider the two drugs that *are* legal in our society and ask yourself, honestly, if you think they are adequately harnessed. From the statistics you have read, does it appear to you that alcohol and tobacco are firmly under control? Are you ready for TV commercials that advertise the hallucinatory power of "Lucky Hit Marijuana Cigarettes" or the purity of "Driven Snow?"

Of course, not everyone wants to legalize drugs. There are other equally simplistic and equally impractical views. One group, for example, feels that people repeatedly arrested for addiction should simply be eliminated. It is pointed out that habitual addicts are completely lost anyway and are of no value to society. In fact, since they must steal to support their habits and can be downright dangerous when they are high, they are *worse* than useless. Further argument notes that recovery is statistically close to impossible. Very few addicts, in fact, bother to try. Of those who do—and less than a third ever *really* try—fewer than 20 percent will ever rejoin society and become worthwhile citizens again. That means that of the millions of addicts walking the streets today, fewer than 6 percent will ultimately recover, and only after the expenditure of millions of dollars in taxpayers' money. With a success rate that low, rehabilitation of drug addicts is not worth the time or the money. To these people, elimination is the clear and simple answer.

Killing them off would certainly dilute the problem temporarily, but it would reduce our population rather more than anyone realizes and would swallow a good many people who might otherwise be saved.

Fortunately, very few people subscribe to that violent a solution. Most are responsible enough to realize that there is no simple answer. The fear of death has not stopped young men from joining the military services, and the knowledge that cocaine can kill does not prevent kids from trying it. Besides, some addicts are potentially very useful people, and the list of recovered addicts today includes many influential and very familiar names.

Treatment

Most experts agree that addiction is an illness, just as is diphtheria or bubonic plague, and should be treated as such. Business people realize too that just getting rid of a drunken or addicted employee is not necessarily a good answer. They know, of course, that drunken employees are potentially damaging, but most of them agree that dedicated and well-trained employees are worth saving and are willing to try. Insurance companies are also aware of this, and most large companies offer group policies to businesses, insuring the company executives against the possibility that one or more of their employees might become drunks. Now, instead of simply firing the drunks, these policies provide for the treatment of employees with a drinking problem. These policies cover all drugs, of course, not just alcohol. Most companies in the business of insuring are as aware of the spreading drug problem as anyone else.

Yet very few people who undergo treatment at the centers provided for them ever fully recover. Statistics show that 65 percent of those who leave the centers after treatment will return to their drug almost immediately, and another 15 percent will relapse within a week or two.

Why does this happen? People who go to these centers are usually worthwhile, sensible people. They realize they are addicted, and most of them want to rid themselves of their habit. They are supported by their families and by their employers. Those who run the treatment centers are experienced, knowledgeable people who know what they're doing and how to handle addicts.

So why are their success rates so low?

Workers in the treatment centers think they know, and their opinions are reflected by those in narcotics law enforcement.

"They're turned loose too early," one officer reported. "Programs that are sponsored by most businesses keep the patient for only twenty-eight days, and that's not nearly enough time to free them from addiction—even if they're really serious about breaking loose."

Why are these programs all limited to twenty-eight days, despite the fact that such a period of time obviously is not adequate to do the job it is intended to do?

"Because," replied this same officer, "the insurance companies have a standard limit of twenty-eight days written into their policies, and they will not pay for treatment that lasts past that."

This is an unfortunate situation, but in our society there is not much we can do about this. Money is, after all, critically important. Even the most dedicated people must eat, and food is not free. And we all know that it is not reasonable to expect nurses, doctors, and orderlies to work in a center that does not pay them a decent salary.

Yet if it is to be successful, treatment must be prolonged. This fact was recognized half a century ago by the instigators of the **Alcoholics Anonymous** programs. They knew it took most people several months and that some alcoholics would fight it for years before winning. But they were willing to finance it themselves or with contributions from people who cared, and it has worked. Today there are similar programs for cocaine addicts, heroin addicts—even for those addicted to gambling.

But real success probably doesn't lie in treatment after addiction has occurred. It lies rather in prevention. A person who is never addicted to any of these drugs does not have to fight off either physical or psychological discomfort and can only be happier for it. But how is it possible to prevent a person from trying these drugs and running the risk of getting hooked?

Education is certainly part of the answer, and a very critical part. But educators *must be very careful not to lie* to their audiences. Children are quick to pick up on half-truths or outright lies, and if they uncover one, that person will be discredited forever. Even if the educators are believed, the chances are that they will be ignored. As we all know, horrible things like accidents or robberies always happen to somebody else, and children in particular are prone to this kind of logic. The glamor of drugs and their use has got to be expunged, and this is terribly hard to do.

How do you tell a child that it is wrong to drink when he sees movies and TV shows featuring heroes and heroines who guzzle booze as if it were water? Even a show as innocent as *M*A*S*H** showed the leading characters constantly sucking in alcohol and staying as drunk as possible. Movie characters are often shown smoking marijuana cigarettes, "for the sake of realism," argue their producers and writers, and that is a valid point in some cases. Rock musicians are probably more maligned than they deserve, yet it is a fact that a great many of them use drugs to extremes, and it seems that few people attend rock concerts today without getting high on marijuana either before or during the performance. As long as teenage idols smoke pot, drink alcohol, and sniff cocaine, it is going to be terribly hard for even the most obedient child to ignore the pressure of his peers to experiment.

Kids often confide that they have committed an indiscretion "because my friends told me to." The standard answer to that has been and still is: "If they told you to jump off a cliff, would you do it?" Not a good answer. First of all, friends would not ask anything that insane, and even if they did, the child would have to be mentally disturbed to attempt it. He can see clearly that it will kill him. But this is not the case with drugs, and he knows that, too. He knows that trying it once or twice probably will not kill him, so he is less reluctant to take a chance. Under those circumstances, what can you say?

Maybe the best argument is one that I heard a recovering cocaine addict give in a drug treatment center in Los Angeles a few years ago.

"It's like standing on the mainland," she said, "looking across a small bay at an island where people are laughing, playing, and having an incredible time. You want to get to that island really badly, but there are no boats and the water in the bay is filled with sharks—big, nasty ones with huge mouths and lots of teeth. Your friends are calling to you to come across. They're arguing that what everyone says about sharks simply isn't true. Sharks aren't really all that dangerous and you'll probably get to the island without being bitten . . . and when you get there, look at the fun you'll have . . . !"

Summary

The Addictive Personality

I. It was suggested years ago that there was a certain type of personality that was particularly susceptible to addiction. There are a lot of people today, including psychiatrists and psychologists, who still believe this.

II. The Addict. Nearly all evidence to date suggests that this is not so. There is a certain type of person who is unusually susceptible to addiction, but personalities give no indication of this characteristic. The only visible warning sign is one's parents' response to drugs.

Addiction

Addiction is generally considered to be a disease. There are two aspects.

I. One aspect is physical dependence. The body adjusts to the presence of certain drugs and tends to thrust physical conditions into illness without them.

II. The other aspect is psychological addiction. It is much more powerful than physical dependence.

Early Depictions of Addiction

I. Popular forms of communication throughout the early part of this century depicted the use of certain drugs in a totally inaccurate manner. Because of this, people gave their children misinformation. As a result, their children believed nothing told to them by those in authority.

II. We have lots of information about drugs today, but today's adults are those who distrusted authority, and they still disbelieve. Many of them still use illegal drugs. To make matters worse, they have passed their disbelief and their love of drugs on to their children.

III. The Attraction. The attraction of drugs is obvious. People take them to feel good, just as they indulge in eating or sexual intercourse to feel good. Why they permit themselves to become dependent on drugs is currently under investigation.

IV. A Drug-Oriented Society. Western culture is more dependent on drugs than it should be. Advertisers peddle drugs persistently on all media outlets, and people take them with abandon. Why, children reason, should they not do what their parents do?

V. Feeling Better Than Good. Besides, certain drugs make people feel *wonderful.*

Drugs and the Brain

I. One thing we do know about drugs is that they tend to disrupt the body's homeostasis. Certain brain centers that adjust how we feel to the condition of our bodies are thrust into abnormal pleasure zones.

II. When pushed into abnormal pleasure zones, the brain's mechanisms, being homeostatic, recognize that they are out of adjustment and begin to push back against the mechanism that is causing the maladjustment. When the drug is finally gone, this results in a rebound effect that causes the "let-down" feeling.

III. If indulgence in the drug is continued, the rebound pressure becomes a constant, and the person feels sick when the drug is not present. Now pleasure is only part of the desire for the drug. Now the person must take the drug in order to feel normal.

IV. Kicking the Habit
   A. Once one is physically addicted, removing oneself from drug dependence can be painful and miserable. Nevertheless, addicts often will voluntarily undergo withdrawal in order to reduce their body's demand for drugs.
   B. After undergoing withdrawal, they can get high on a much lower dosage and remain high for a longer period of time.

Some Specific Drugs

I. Marijuana
   A. Addictive? How addictive is marijuana? Not very, apparently, but addiction *can* happen.
   B. What Harm Does It Do?
      1. Lung Damage. It is a virtual certainty that it will have effects on the lungs that are roughly similar to the effects of tobacco; in fact, because of the techniques used in the smoking of marijuana, these effects may be even worse.
      2. Nervous Effect. It has sympathomimetic effects.
      3. Nerve Damage. If it does any, it is minor and temporary.
      4. Sensory Effects. These are more profound and can drastically affect a person's ability to perform at any given time. Furthermore, continued use of marijuana seems to dull a person's ambition drastically.
      5. Its Effect on the Genes. Marijuana does not appear to have any lasting genetic effects.
   C. Is It Good for Anything? Yes. It is used to stimulate appetite in cancer patients and to reduce the effects of glaucoma.
   D. Is It Worse Than Alcohol? In some ways it is. It is not as toxic as alcohol, but it can damage the lungs, and its long-term effects are not pleasant.

II. Cocaine. This may be the most popular of today's recreational drugs. It is also a killer.
   A. Addiction to Cocaine. Fewer than 15 percent of today's users will become addicted. Some can use cocaine repeatedly for years before becoming dependent. Others become dependent after a single experience.
   B. What Harm Does Cocaine Do? It is a killer. It can produce cardiac problems, including spasmodic constrictions of coronary arteries that result in cardiac infarctions (heart attacks). Teenaged users have reported frequent, recurring chest pains, which indicate that minor infarctions are occurring. Such infarctions have already killed some professional athletes, indicating that physical condition is no deterrent to cocaine's lethal effects.
   C. Freebase, Rock, or Crack
      1. This is a pure form of cocaine that is particularly addicting. In addition, it is cheap; thus it is available to even young children.
      2. Addiction to Crack. Addiction to cocaine in any of its forms is unbelievably easy to achieve. Crack is especially addictive. Sometimes one experience will do the job.
   D. What Harm Does Crack Do? Crack is much worse than cocaine in its overall effects. It causes quicker and stronger addiction, and the addicts have no honor, no restrictions, and no qualms about anything they must do to support their habits. Even if you have never known anyone involved with crack, you could easily be the victim of an addict who must steal to obtain his crack or cocaine.
   E. Is Cocaine Any Good? Cocaine has limited medical value as a local anesthetic. Otherwise, it is of no value at all.

III. Alcohol. Alcohol is one of the two most consistently abused and ubiquitous drugs in our society. It is responsible for nearly one hundred thousand deaths each year in this country. In addition, the homeless bums who require constantly recurring medical care in our rehabilitation hospitals cost taxpayers millions of dollars. Childhood drunkenness is one of our biggest problems.
   A. What Harm Does It Do? It is a poison. It kills body cells, mainly liver and central nervous cells. It is physically addicting, and its withdrawal symptoms are as powerful as those of the narcotic drugs.
   B. Addiction. Alcohol's addiction rate is about 16 percent, and one needn't be a heavy drinker to get caught. Statistics show that the average person

taking his or her first drink has about a 10 percent chance of becoming addicted. If either parent is an alcoholic, the percentage is closer to 40.

C. Is It Any Good? It has been shown that heart attack victims fare better if they have one or two small drinks a day than if they do not indulge. Other than that, alcohol is of no value.

IV. Tobacco. Tobacco is the second of the two most abused and ubiquitous drugs in this country.

A. Addiction. It is one of the most powerfully addicting drugs in our society. A single pack of cigarettes will frequently trap the user.

B. What Harm Does It Do? It causes cancer, emphysema, strokes, and heart attacks. All in all, it is responsible for more than 500,000 deaths per year in this country. In two years, it kills more Americans than were killed in the Second World War.

C. Is It Any Good? Tobacco has no redeeming features whatever.

V. Other Drugs

A. Sniffing Glue

B. LSD

C. PCP

D. Space Base

Is There Any Solution?

I. There are some alternatives to continuing as we are. Two of these are considered.

II. Treatment. Some of the methods of treating addiction are mentioned, along with some of the problems.

Chapter 21 Facts, Theories, Myths, and Fallacies

Objectives

This section is not devoted to laying out a series of facts, but rather to impress you with a general feeling of what science is all about. When you are finished, I hope you will:

1. understand that science has not presented us with unalterable "facts."
2. have a better understanding of the word *theory*.
3. have a feel for what the scientist does and how it is accomplished.
4. comprehend the value of "pure" research.
5. be able, from a simple set of observations, to suggest a problem, formulate a hypothesis that may solve the problem, then design an experiment to test the hypothesis.

This chapter represents an exercise in critical thinking.

Scanning electron micrograph of a nerve cell growing on a silicon chip: A biohybrid circuit.

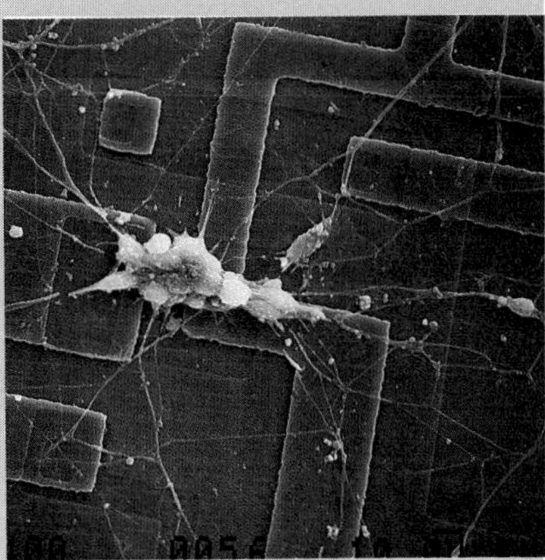

Introduction

For the last twenty chapters, we have examined the workings of the human body. We have viewed its control systems, delivery systems, and reproductive operations, and I am sure you will agree that physiologists have a large number of facts at hand just as they have a good many mysteries. The information that we do possess was gleaned through the efforts of science, as you all know, and because the source was scientific, probably none of you doubted any of the facts that you were offered.

Some of this information was uncovered by scientists who were trying to discover precisely what they *did* discover. Other such facts were accidently uncovered while searching for some related mechanism, still others are spin-offs from research not even remotely connected to physiology. All of them have been tested and retested and are accepted by the majority of the scientific community.

Yet you should understand that these "facts" are not inviolable, and they are not necessarily correct. Some of them are; just as many of them are either incorrect or will be modified in the future. None were given with intent to mislead. As of this writing, everything within this textbook is as accurate as I can make it and is, for the most part, as conclusive as any scientific information can be. Why, then, will so much of the information be modified in the future?

It is the nature of science.

Science

Everyone is familiar with the word *science,* and everyone seems to have an idea of what it means. One authoritative survey recently reported that a good many people consider science a "thing"—some sort of entity, rather than a process of thinking or a procedure for investigating the world around us. To many, it denotes the ultimate in knowledge and hence is viewed almost with reverence. Some, while acknowledging its contributions, distrust or dislike it because it contradicts or interferes with their fondest beliefs. Others are suspicious or afraid of science because they, like the nineteenth century writers of supernatural mysteries, feel that scientists are delving into things that "man was never meant to meddle with." Still others dislike science because scientists are difficult to understand.

As to the scientists themselves, there are variant views of them, too. Unlike medical doctors, all of whom are presumed to be supremely intelligent, scientists are often not regarded in this light. People often view scientists as bookworms who totally lack "common sense," whatever that is. A surprising number of people think that all scientists are *idiot savants,* brilliant in a single field but unable to add 2 plus 2 or otherwise use the type of everyday intelligence that every nonscientist has in abundance. Have you never heard that Albert Einstein was unable to balance his bank account despite his acknowledged genius in advanced mathematics?

The attitude of the general public toward scientists has always been suspicious and generally negative. Most scientists are not trusted by the public. Everyone suspects the scientists' motives and generally feels that science will ultimately change something that people do not want changed. This attitude is not peculiar to American society. It was with the tribes of Israel in the desert and has been a part of Western culture since the fall of Rome. A few examples:

Galileo was kicked out of the University of Pisa when he announced his theory that a feather and a cannonball would fall to the earth at similar speeds in a vacuum. He maintained that it was the air that slowed up the descent of the feather, but no one believed him. In fact, his theological colleagues were so angered at his disputing their philosophical principles that they tried to have him arrested.

Copernicus knew that the earth was not the center of the solar system, but he was so afraid of what ecclesiastic members of society might do that his work was not published until after he had died.

Andreas Vesalius published a textbook of human anatomy that he compiled from dissections he had done himself, and he came close to being arrested for disagreeing with current views. A colleague of his, Miguel Servetus, was burned at the stake for publishing a work that refuted the accepted ideas of how the respiratory system worked.

Actually, none of these views is accurate. The thing that makes scientific endeavor a little different is the thinking process. Science is a bit more methodical than most logic sequences, and it demands that all opinions be confirmed before they are accepted. As to the scientists—science is populated by the same kind of people that are found in other professions. There are mediocre scientists who will probably never amount to very much, and there are others who would succeed, and succeed big, in anything they set their minds to. In general, scientists are highly intelligent (not *idiot savants*) with a great deal of knowledge at their fingertips. Nevertheless, they share the same likes and dislikes that everyone has, and they are merely another group of professional people in this wide world. If anything sets them off from the members of most other professions, it is an insatiable curiosity . . . a desire to *know.*

Science and its technical spin-offs have been so successful in remaking the modern world that scientific research is looked upon generally as the ultimate way to uncover facts. Our television sets and modern magazines are overrun with people in white laboratory coats, holding test tubes or otherwise trying to look "scientific" while assuring us that the product they advocate is the universal specific. Science has forced its way into everything; cooking, transportation, medicine—it is ubiquitous. To gain instant approval for a new product, all an advertiser has to do is state that it was tested "scientifically." How many times have you heard the assurance that *Super Fizz* is "scientifically proven effective" in cleaning your plumbing, or "clinical proof" is available that *Gurgle Drops* will prevent acne and polish your shoes?

Presenting an actor in a white coat to tout a patent medicine is one of the most common ploys used by advertisers to get the gullible public to buy their products. Anything that will convince a person that the product is scientifically tested or is approved by doctors is the key to the magic kingdom of success. Actors have been seen, dressed in white coats, announcing to the world that: "I am *not* a doctor—but I *play* one on T.V. . . ." as if that meant something, as if it gave them an air of authority. One must be extremely careful when listening to advertising, even on network television. It is a mistake to assume that all advertising must be accurate or it would not be permitted. Advertisers will often make false claims about their products, swearing to "clinical tests" that "prove" their product is finest without knowing—or caring—whether or not what they say is true. It may take years for the Food and Drug Administration (FDA) or the Federal Communications Commission (FCC) to get around to telling them to cease their false or misleading claims.

Unfortunately, most of these attitudes are the wrong attitudes, and since you have just spent twenty chapters delving into some of the secrets of scientific discovery, it seems to me that you, at least, should get it right.

Let us be quite clear about one thing: there is nothing particularly mystical about science, nor is there anything sacrosanct about scientific research or "scientific facts." Science is a way of thinking. It is a method of processing information that permits the questioner to get the most correct answer possible—and it doesn't always yield nothing but the truth. We hope when you are finished reading this section, you will have a better idea of what science can do and what its limitations are. (Incidentally, Einstein could handle any intellectual exercise with ease. His bank account, in his lifetime, never contained an error.)

Answering the Question "Why?"

Throughout human history, there have always been those who are curious, and curiosity is the essence of science. People need to have their questions answered, and in many instances, science provides the best way of getting them.

Long before humanity had begun its long climb upward from savagery to its present pinnacle, people were curious about why they died and what happened to them when they did. The problems of dying were probably not difficult to deal with when a companion was torn apart by a predator or fell off a high cliff, because the cause was both familiar and obvious. But it must have been hard to handle when an invisible force shattered strong, vigorous individuals in the prime of life, sometimes running through whole tribes or villages. Plagues could leave people crippled even if they didn't die and could mark them with visible scars. Yet there was never anything around to suggest what was causing the problems. It must have been easy to ascribe these disasters to vindictive supernatural beings whom the victims had somehow offended. To complicate things for early humans, even if they did everything right and survived predation, starvation, and natural disasters (including the whims of disease), sooner or later changes would occur in the body that converted it from a vibrant, confident entity into a trembling physical wreck in which even hair color deteriorated. Probably most people never wondered why this occurred; they merely accepted it. But in every group there was bound to be one or two who were not happy with simple acceptance. They wanted to know why.

In the earliest years, the explanations were probably superstitious meanderings, and for people whose waking hours were concerned with gathering sufficient food to stay alive, this was enough. As civilization evolved, however, agriculture and villages appeared, and people began to find time for pursuits other than the acquisition of food. The haphazard spiritual traipsing of their ancestors was not enough any more. Something a bit more systematic was necessary, and the unreasonable snake trails of semi-logic began to change into disciplined, channeled logic patterns. Inevitably, someone insisted on testing the ideas they came up with to see if they were right or wrong, and it was this inspiration, the concept of *testing*—so logical to us today—that marked the labor pains of the philosophical pattern we call **science.**

Scientific Philosophy

Looking back, rich in hindsight, we find it difficult to understand why it took so long to decide that testing was necessary. Very few of us would accept an explanation that was obviously speculation without testing it somehow. The idea is so deeply ingrained in our way of life that when someone suggests an answer to a question, the most common response is "how do you know?" Testing explanations, theories, or ideas seems almost to suggest itself, but it was not always so.

I do not mean to imply that people never thought of testing anything. In some cases, testing is obvious. Any fool has enough sense to know that before you trust your life to a bridge over a gulley you first make sure it will hold your weight; even monkeys have enough sense to do that. But testing *ideas* or *theories*—that is different. Despite the sophistication of the ancient Greek philosophers and the engineers of Egypt or Rome, the idea of scientific experimentation was never grasped.

There are many reasons for this failure. Probably the most important one is that during great bites of cultural history, progress in uncovering the mysteries of the natural world was encumbered by restraints imposed by custom and ecclesiastical authority. In the writings of ancient philosophers we can sometimes see glimmerings of a desire to experiment with natural phenomena, but for a lot of reasons nothing of the sort was ever done. It is hard to blame them. During much of the vast span of history it was worth a person's life to suggest that even the most absurd superstition, if it was the official state position, might be in error. In this context, the Judeo-Christian tradition was a particularly powerful antagonist and still is. The anti-evolutionist movement in this country is more powerful than it has ever been—not in the scientific community but among the general population—and their objections are based in religious dogma. In Britain there is an organization called *The Flat Earth Society* whose members are convinced that the earth is flat, not spherical. No modern observations can persuade them that they are wrong . . . not astrophysics (which they neither understand nor accept) or the extraterrestrial expeditions of

NASA, which they label elaborate hoaxes. For years, biological research in Russia stood quite still because Stalin approved of archaic dogma levied by a fanatic whom he believed. None of these confrontations is unusual. Science is constantly encountering nonscientific challenges that seem absurd but cannot be dispelled.

From about 500 A.D. to the middle of the eighteenth century, scientists lived extremely precarious lives. People were so afraid of challenging custom that intellectuals didn't dare work publicly in their universities; they formed secret societies where they could gather and discuss their interests. The names they chose reflect the secret nature of each society, names like the *Academy of the Lynx-Eyed* and the *Academy of Secrets of Nature* in Italy, the *Invisible College* in England, and the *Academy of Secret Science* in France. Things had not changed an awful lot even by the nineteenth century. Writers in the early decades of the 1800s assured everyone that they would sicken and die if they opened windows on trains going faster than 30 miles per hour. People cannot breathe air moving more than 30 miles an hour, they were told; hence they would suffocate. The fact that people managed to live during hurricanes and gales when the wind whipped around at up to 100 miles an hour was skillfully ignored.

People were scared to death of the first automobiles, and bizarre laws were passed to stifle their use. Electricity was the biggest horror of all, and all kinds of ghastly results were predicted if its use became common. In the early 1940s and 1950s, nuclear experts tried desperately to sell suspicious naval officials on nuclear power and nearly had to resort to trickery to finally get permission to test it on submarines. Today we still have such problems. Consider the incredible resistance that is developing to animal research and genetic engineering. Workers in California had enormous difficulty obtaining permission to test a newly developed frost-resistant bacterium on crop plants because of local public outcry.

Such objections are not always simple fanaticism. Sometimes they are justified. New things are often accepted before they have been adequately tested and investigated, but this is not necessarily so. The next time you read an emotional appeal against a newly discovered item, read it carefully. Don't be fooled by overuse of the word *theory,* and ask yourself if it sounds like the objections are really knowledgeable. You may be surprised.

I do not intend to explore the evolution of scientific thinking, but be assured it was a process filled with traps and quicksand. Let me just state that the actual birth occurred when one logic sequence developed the idea of controlled testing and careful observation, and if there is any magic in science, that's what it is. Science enjoys its smashing success because it incorporates a system of confirmation before accepting the results of a logic process, a constraint that is not a part of the other techniques of disciplined thinking.

Definition of the Scientific Method

Stated in words, the scientific method looks like a plodding logic sequence and few scientists consciously adhere to it. Nevertheless, usually without realizing it, all of us follow it in our research. Generally speaking, it goes like this:

Let us assume you have just visited a rocky island that was packed with breeding birds. You noticed that these birds didn't build nests of twigs or fabric of some kind but incubated their eggs by holding them on their feet. Stating that simple fact constitutes an

Observation

This is self-explanatory except for one important point. That is, the observations must be made without any preconceived notions or interpretations. This is a major flaw in what is known today as "creation science," and it is one of many reasons why creation science is not recognized as genuine science. One cannot enter into a scientific effort with the idea that the answers are already known, because doing so can color observations until workers think they see things that are not happening. To be scientifically satisfactory, the observations must be open-minded—in a word: *objective.*

Recording

All observations must be put down on paper in as much detail as possible. This process must be undertaken during the period of observation and must be done with great care. Memory can fail or err, and subjective evaluations made during or after the events take place can sometimes color a person's memory of what actually happened. Objective, systematic recording of the events eliminates both as variables.

Identification of a Problem

This really is not very hard. It amounts to merely asking "why did that happen?" or "why didn't something prevent that from happening?" Considering your observation made on the rocky island, you might formulate the following question: "Why are the birds holding their eggs on their feet?" Workers seldom have any difficulty with this aspect of science.

Hypothesis

Hypothesis consists of formulating an educated suggestion that might answer the questions posed by the problem. For example, considering those same birds, you might suggest several reasons why they hold their eggs on their feet. You might say "they hold their eggs on their feet because otherwise the eggs might break on the hard rocky surface," or "they hold their eggs on their feet to prevent the cold rocks from cooling them and delaying their development." You can formulate any number of hypotheses to answer your questions.

Prediction

Predictions usually precede any experimental testing, and they are nearly always put in the form of an "if . . . then" statement. For example, you might decide that the most logical hypothesis regarding the birds and the eggs is that the eggs are held on the feet to prevent them from getting too cool. Then you would make a prediction like this: "*if* the birds hold their eggs on their feet to keep them warm and help them develop more rapidly, *then* if we take them away from the birds and incubate them on the rocks, they should take longer to hatch."

Testing

This is the kernel—the *soul*—of the scientific method. Science demands experimentation, and this "obvious" step represents a huge advance over the methods once used to explain natural phenomena. Intellectual giants of the past, men like da Vinci and Galileo, often advocated a kind of scientific experimentation to test the accuracy of their theories, but they left no record of ever actually having done so.

It is surprising how widely experimental observation can vary from common sense. For instance, our earliest assumptions about the vertebrate nervous system were derived from common sense. Once it was determined that nervous energy was electricity, common sense predicted that this electricity was generated and conducted in the same manner as our man-made electricity. If we had not tested this hypothesis experimentally, we would never have discovered how wrong that was. Experimental results are often very different from common sense predictions, and the reason is quite simple. Common sense is generally based on things with which we are familiar, and when we step into an uncharted realm, it lets us down more often than not. It seldom plays much of a role in science simply because it is wrong so often.

Modern Science

Modern scientists actively engaged in research do not attack problems in the stepwise fashion outlined above—at least, not consciously. But all adhere to the basic pattern pretty closely. When the idea of experimentation was new, laboratories were rough, techniques were primitive, and there were as many methods of approach as there were scientists. Not any more. Today, science is refined to a polish that would astound researchers of a century ago. Along with this polish, some fairly firm principles have emerged involving science, and they include some limitations that might surprise you.

Nothing in Science Is Ever Proven

When the evolution of the scientific method was complete, it became evident to all its adherents that *science is not capable of proving anything.* We cannot perform every possible experiment under every possible set of conditions, and so we can never be *certain* that a theory is correct. Also, we cannot dismiss the possibility of human error. Even the best scientist may miss some vital fact, or may even ignore it if it doesn't seem important at the time. Also—and this is happening more and more often—we often cannot see everything that is going on. Hence, if the result of the experiment agrees with a prediction, we will often accept our theory even when we could not observe each step. Each experiment that agrees with our theory provides us with support, but we never actually obtain proof.

Science is, in a way, like the architecture of the U.S. Constitution. The intellectuals who developed each of these instruments realized that their efforts were not perfect at birth and would become less perfect as knowledge increased. So the ability to change things around without disruption is a fundamental part of both instruments. The Constitution accomplishes necessary changes by way of amendment. Science accomplishes the same thing by possessing a built-in uncertainty, an inability ever to be sure.

Theory vs. Hypothesis

This simple fact does more than merely surprise people; it also attaches tremendous importance to the word **theory.** To most people, a theory is at best an educated guess, and many equate it to scientific fancy. Even today there are a good many who will denigrate a scientific principle because it's "just a theory" and "is not proven." Such doubters are correct, but not for the reasons they think they are. The theory is not proven because nothing scientific is ever proven. A theory is not "merely an idea." "Merely an idea" is called a **hypothesis.** When a scientist wishes to offer an explanation for a certain phenomenon he has observed, he will offer a hypothesis. Then he will experiment to test his hypothesis. After a hypothesis has undergone a certain amount of experimental verification, it may blossom into a full-fledged theory, and there, as far as certainty is concerned, it stops.

A theory is probably the highest level of certainty that science can achieve. Electricity is a theory, light is a theory, evolution is a theory, the existence of cells as the basic units of life is a theory—in fact, when you get right down to it, the existence of the universe is "just" a theory. We have no proof that any of these things is real or correct, simply because science is not capable of proving that *anything* is correct. It is possible to obtain *support* for a theory. We can perform experiments by the score, each one providing more and more evidence that a given theory is correct, but we will never be sure. A given theory may stand for years and be assumed to be correct by most of the world's scientists, yet one series of contradictory experiments can blow it all away. When that happens, a new theory emerges from the ruins of the old. This is not bad. It is the way science is supposed to work.

For many decades it was assumed that while no theory could ever be proven to be correct, it was possible to prove that one was incorrect. Actually, the philosophical foundation of science may be even more tenuous than that. There are a lot of workers today who feel that it is no more possible to disprove a theory than it is to prove it. Often theories that many thought were safely disproven have come back to haunt us. Probably uncertainty is the only real certainty in science.

Whatever view one takes there seems very little doubt that those professionally involved with science look upon it as blessedly unsure, that science is constantly changing its face, that it is, to put it picturesquely, *dynamic!*

Early Science

Spontaneous Generation

Probably the best way to illustrate the value and limitations of science is to present an example of research that began in the earliest days of objective thought and is still a wide-open question, even after hundreds of years of arguing and presentation of "proofs" of every kind. The controversy over the *principle of spontaneous generation* is the perfect vehicle, so let us pursue this.

First of all, let's define the term. Spontaneous generation, as conceived in the beginning, stated that many organisms in this world—particularly those that are termed *vermin*—could arise from piles of debris or garbage, literally *begotten* by the trash in which they were found. For millenia this principle was generally accepted by the entire world. It was common knowledge that piles of old rags and other rubble could serve as the raw material for the conception of rats, burrowing beetles, cockroaches, and similar pests, while decaying vegetables or meats would generate maggots and subsequent clouds of flies. No eggs were laid. Parents were considered unnecessary because a normal life cycle required a period of growth, and the rats that showed up in the piles of trash and litter around ancient and medieval settlements were full-grown and able to make themselves maximally offensive immediately.

To appreciate the significance of this example, it is necessary to view it with a completely objective set, and this can serve, in a way, as an initial experience in scientific thinking. Try not to cloud your mental processes with current knowledge and try instead to place yourselves in the position of the people who firmly believed that this sort of thing happened. There was no question in the minds of most early people about the accuracy of the theory. Custom stated that it was true, everyone accepted it, no one thought to question it.

Nor was this outlook restricted to the average citizen. Aristotle, a man recognized today as one of the reigning intellectuals of the ancient world, believed it with such sincerity that he produced a classification scheme in which he reserved a special category for those organisms that appeared from thin air. He called it *Animalia Sponte Hascentia,* and it was a catch-all for the organisms that did not seem to fit anywhere else. Throughout the centuries, people never questioned his idea—intellectuals, religious philosophers, nobles, and the common man—all agreed it was real. It lasted well into the last century, and some people still believe it today.

The "Sacred Cow"

Such principles crop up in science every once in a while. They are known euphemistically as **sacred cows** and are really more traditions than principles. They can be defined as an inference or conclusion that has been accepted for years without challenge. Usually these conclusions are unchallenged because at the time they are offered, they have been logically worked out and are supported by unimpeachable authority. Acceptance is so broad that no one bothers to question the logic, or, if experimentation has been done, to repeat the experiments. Sacred cows are not particularly rare. They emerge, are quickly accepted, and become established. After a few unchallenged years they become so firmly ingrained in both nonscientific and scientific lore that they are unquestioned by everyone, including scientists and educators. No one thinks to doubt them until suddenly a newly emerging sequence of facts fails to coincide, at which point someone, usually with new techniques or instruments at their disposal, suggests that maybe that unassailable principle was not right after all.

A Sacred Cow Assailed

Even in earlier years, a few thinkers realized that the spontaneous appearance of animals from nothing at all did not make an awful lot of sense. But it was not until near the end of the seventeenth century that someone really tried to "test" it. Francesco Redi, a poet, physician, and generally curious resident of Florence, Italy, determined in 1690 to demonstrate its fallacy. In the process he performed about as perfect a scientific experiment as can be designed.

Figure 21.1 Redi put meat scraps in both sets of flasks. Set *a* he stopped up, while set *b* was left open to the air. Soon, flies entered the open flasks, and within a day or two, maggots appeared in the meat. The stoppered flasks showed no sign of maggot infestation.

He put meat scraps in several flasks, divided the flasks into two groups, then sealed one group, leaving the second one open to the air. In the succeeding days, he observed flies entering the unsealed flasks, after which maggots appeared in the meat. Neither flies nor maggots appeared in the sealed flasks (figure 21.1).

For a time period as scientifically naive as the seventeenth century, this was a remarkable experiment. Redi did not try merely to *confirm* his ideas, but to genuinely *test* them, and in the process he avoided several problems that often afflict student researchers today. To begin with, he did not try to check everything he could think of, as novices so often do. Instead, he restricted himself to confronting a **single variable,** an extremely important aspect of experimental design. It means that the two groups being compared were exactly the same except for one thing. In this case, one group was sealed and the other was not. Thus he had both an **experimental group** and a **control group,** although Redi would not have called them that, and his **controlled experiment** was enough to convinced him that he was right, that maggots could not spontaneously appear in decaying organic garbage. To us this is sheer logic, but let me remind you that it was not so in Redi's world and, complete though his experiment was, far more people criticized it than accepted it.

As the years passed and science slowly increased in sophistication, so did the conflict. By the mid-nineteenth century, the idea of flies and maggots spontaneously generating in garbage had matured into a more sophisticated belief involving microorganisms. People had pretty well accepted the idea that maggots had fly parents because microscopes permitted them to see the eggs that the flies laid on the garbage. Spontaneous generation thus became cosmopolitan. Instead of fiddling with smelly piles of garbage as early "scientists" had, researchers graduated to various kinds of nutrient broths where they searched for bacteria and other "animalcules" that spontaneously generated there. Sometimes the contentions of those opposing the doctrine were supported, but equally often, despite careful treatment and precise preparation, all sorts of microorganisms would appear within jars that had been carefully sealed. An intense polarization of opinion was developing among researchers, and the ensuing squabbles became harsh and furious, with neither side able to claim any real advantage.

Probably the most significant altercation to emerge during the eighteenth century involved Lazzaro Spallanzani, an Italian professor, and John Needham, an English cleric. About mid-century, Needham undertook to prove that bacteria would spontaneously generate given the right set of conditions. He boiled a quantity of beef broth and poured it quickly into jars before it could cool. Then, using special resins, he carefully sealed his jars and allowed them to stand for several days. When they were opened, the broth in both his experimental and control jars teemed with microorganisms. Had Needham stopped his research at that point, his experiments would not really have softened the controversy much, because he was merely adding to an already significant library of similar experimental findings. He was well aware of this, so he followed with a volley of similarly designed studies, involving other materials, like garbage, feces, and similar organic debris. In every one, swarms of organisms appeared in airtight, sealed jars containing carefully boiled nutrient.

The proponents of spontaneous generation rejoiced! The cause they championed had teeter-tottered back on top. They were convinced that they now had proof that their theory was correct.

At this point, an objective evaluation could reasonably conclude that the advocates of spontaneous generation had the most support. In the face of such findings today and lacking substantial evidence to the contrary, we would not be wrong to concede the point. In science, however, interpretations made by one worker are often modified by others, and that was as true in the 1700s as it is now. Spallanzani did not feel that Needham had proven his theory to be correct. He had worked extensively with microorganisms, and he suggested that Needham's cultures had never really been sterilized, and hence they were contaminated when they were sealed within their jars. If that were true, it would, of course, make the conclusions invalid—so much for Needham's proof. Needham naturally asked how that could be when he had carefully inspected the broth before boiling it and sealing it in the jars, and it had been devoid of microscopic life. Spallanzani answered that the life had been in the form of "eggs" or reproductive spores of some kind, and these had "hatched" or developed after the jars had been sealed.

"Why," he was asked quite reasonably, "did the boiling not kill the eggs? How could *anything* remain alive in boiling broth?"

Spallanzani replied that the eggs were more resistant to heat than adult bacteria and the broth had not, in his opinion, been boiled long enough to kill them. He then ran a series of experiments, using broths boiled for varying periods of time, and his results were so beautifully quantitative that they were hard to dispute. He continued to quantify his experiments until he was able to state that if nutrient broths were boiled for between thirty and forty-five minutes, they would remain sterile.

In the conflict between Spallanzani and Needham, we can see the incredible flexibility of science, and we should be able to further appreciate the value of testing. If you think about it objectively, Spallanzani's arguments sound like he was groping for reasons to reject an obviously good piece of work. Such survival mechanisms as spores were unheard of in the eighteenth century, and it was terribly hard for even the most reasonable people to accept the idea that anything could survive boiling. When you think about it, how *could* anything remain alive in boiling water for fifteen minutes? How many people that you asked today would believe an organism could live in rapidly boiling water for a half hour? The whole thing sounds absurd. Common sense (not experimentation) suggests very strongly that we accept Needham and reject Spallanzani—yet as we are aware, Spallanzani was right. When confronted with difficult living conditions, many bacteria can compress themselves into entities known as *spores*. These are highly resistant vegetative cells that can withstand dessication, heating, freezing, and total lack of nutrient.

Now the discussion began to heat up. Needham, in his turn, promptly criticized Spallanzani's work. He insisted that the extended boiling destroyed what he called the "germinative force" within the broth and may even have damaged the air above it. Consequently, in his opinion, Spallanzani's experiments did not disprove anything at all about spontaneous generation. They merely demonstrated that prolonged heating would damage the broth and its accompanying air so that the normal generation of microorganisms could not occur. In the light of modern-day knowledge, we may laugh smugly at such suggestions, but in the eighteenth century Needham found plenty of support. What is more, he was not being obtuse. He and his supporters sincerely believed that spontaneous generation was possible, and to them such a thing as an undefined and easily damaged "germinative force" might well exist within unboiled broth. It was not illogical to postulate that Spallanzani was damaging this, as well as some vital property of the air, with all that heat. Without more evidence they could not logically reject a doctrine they had accepted all their lives. For the time being, both sides paused to regroup.

It may be worth mentioning that by viewing the experiments done by both Spallanzani and Needham, we can see examples of how theories that pass tests are not necessarily proven, and those that fail tests are not necessarily disproven. It can logically be argued (as both Spallanzani and Needham did so often) that the tests themselves are inappropriate, inadequate, or otherwise unsuitable as experimental vehicles. What Needham clearly implied in his criticisms of Spallanzani's experiment with the boiling broth is that if a test falsifies a theory, maybe it is the test that is at fault and not the theory. It suggests that we cannot even be sure we are right when we prove something is wrong, and it emphasizes still more the dynamic nature of science.

The next logical step—to demonstrate that air is not damaged by heating—was not attempted until the middle of the nineteenth century. Theodor Schwann, a German scientist of exceptional ability, presented air heated over boiling broth to experimental animals to breathe, reasoning that if such air would support life, its vitality could hardly have been destroyed. Of course, it did all that air is supposed to do. It was breathable and it supported combustion, so Schwann stepped back to await comments.

One might assume that this would reduce at least the intensity of the argument, and it did. By 1859, only a very few diehards still clung to the timeworn concept of spontaneous generation, but despite its waning popularity there had never been a final period put to the dispute. During all the years, and through all the experiments, nothing had ever been undertaken that would set at rest all of the objections from both camps. Maybe it was just too hard to let go of a universally accepted doctrine after so many centuries. Whatever the reasons, its adherents remained unconvinced.

The French Academy's Contest

By the middle of the nineteenth century, the French Academy of Science realized that the question had never been settled and that both points of view boasted some pretty illustrious scientists as proponents. Hopeful of settling the controversy permanently one way or the other, the academy offered a prize for the best treatise on *Origins of Life.* Initially there were a large number of entrants, but they were gradually whittled down until it became an experimental duel between two of the most renowned scientists of the period—Felix Pouchet, a naturalist who championed the spontaneous generation doctrine, and Louis Pasteur who attacked it.

Pouchet offered his side of the story in 1859. His case was presented in the form of a treatise called *Heterogenie,* which consisted of a list of case histories. Each case was elaborately detailed and documentation was generous, but collectively they were nothing more than recountings of personal experiences. Upon investigation it turned out that most of the quoted "authorities" were not recognized as reliable scientists, other witnesses were not credible, and no experimental support was offered at all. Overall, it was impressively long, but unconvincing.

If history were to base its opinion of Pouchet on *Heterogenie,* he would undoubtedly be classified as a bungling, amateur scientist. This evaluation would be wrong. Pouchet was not a bungler. His work as a descriptive naturalist was generally pretty good. He was recognized throughout Europe as a good worker, but his science was of the classical type. He was trained as naturalists had always been trained, and his work depended on accurate descriptions and careful observation. In this, Pouchet excelled, but naturalists of that era were seldom required to test observations, and it is suspected that he really did not understand the process of controlled experimentation. In any case, in Pasteur, his opponent, he was thoroughly outclassed.

Pasteur was a master of experimental design. He had worked for years with microorganisms, and he was an excellent chemist and a first-class researcher. Furthermore, his work with fermentation and wine chemistry had made him (although few knew it at the time) the world's foremost authority on bacteria, and he was certain that even bacteria had to have a parent of some kind.

He had a good deal of convincing to do. Few people had worked at length with microorganisms, so there were many eminent scientists who were not so sure. Very little was known about bacteria. However, it was known that they could do a lot of things multicellular organisms could not do. What animal or plant, for instance, could survive being boiled for fifteen minutes? Maybe those teeny little things *could* condense out of thin air! Maybe the air really *was* damaged by being subjected to boiling temperatures for long periods of time, and if air could be hurt, so could broth. Schwann's experiment, they pointed out, may have merely shown that previously heated air would not do any harm to already-living organisms. It did not show that the germinative force in the air had not been damaged. After all, they argued, since all living things need air, it must contain something critical, and anything critical could be damaged.

Pasteur picked up the gauntlet. It was something he had to know.

He set about settling things in a stepwise fashion. The first thing he had to demonstrate was that bacteria were all around us, floating on dust particles in the air. Pasteur maintained that the bacteria and molds that seemed to come from nowhere were actually colonies that were established in exposed nutrients by nomadic organisms in the air. This was not easy for even broad-minded types to accept. People were just beginning to get used to the idea that fatal diseases could be caused by things that were invisible but alive, and it was terribly hard for them to accept the notion that these "killer bugs" were floating around in the air they breathed. Most of his critics felt he was suggesting that the air was a kind of germ soup, a patently ridiculous concept!

Yet to settle the argument in his favor, he had to establish a solid theoretical foundation. He had to demonstrate that bacteria *were* floating around in the air. His experimental apparatus consisted of two separate groups of guncotton air filters and two flasks with pumps to draw the air through the filters.

One group consisted of just a single filter, while the second group featured double filters (figure 21.2). Through both groups he passed fresh, clear air. He then pulverized all the filters, soaked them in water, poured the solutions onto nutrient plates and incubated them for two days. Then he checked the results under a microscope. In the residue from the single filters he found all kinds of evidence of life in the form of rods and spheres mixed in with the fibers of guncotton. In the cultures prepared from the primary filters of group 2 he got the same result. But in the cultures made from the secondary filters nothing grew; there was only guncotton fiber and water.

Note the careful pattern of investigation. Pasteur designed his experiments so that not only did his results support his preliminary contention but they also established a foothold for the central investigation. Confirming the abundance of life in the air swirling around us showed that it was possible that the bacteria, mold, and other tiny life forms that appear in uncovered foods were carried there by dust particles in the air, and that was all he was trying to establish.

Figure 21.2 Pasteur's experiment to show that microorganisms abound in the air. Arrows indicate the direction of air movement.

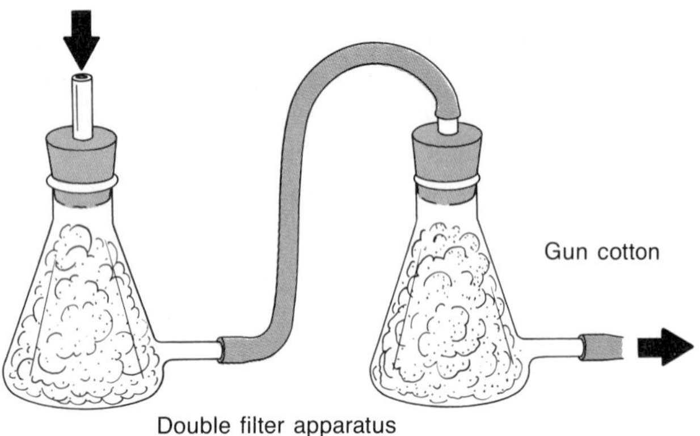

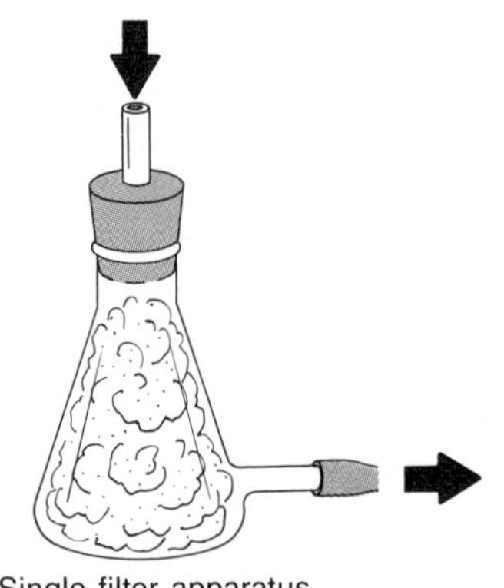

Pasteur's Classic Experiment

Bearing all the objections in mind, Pasteur proceeded to design his final experiment. In the beginning his nutrient broth would have to be sterile, or the experiment would have no meaning. At the same time, this broth had to be left exposed to ordinary fresh air because of the possibility that there might be vital ingredients in the air that would be damaged by heating. There could be no obstructions anywhere that would significantly interfere with air diffusion, and this meant there had to be a continuous airway through the tubes and over the broth.

At the same time, however, he could not permit a free flow of air. There had to be some means of getting rid of dust particles that the bacteria and other microorganisms rode on. It was an interesting problem and one that required unique containers. After some careful thought and some very creative design efforts, he finally settled on the flasks illustrated in figure 21.3. The dip in the entry tube was an inspiration, and it solved his biggest problem—how to stop dust from entering the broth without interfering with the free diffusion of air through the tubes. Dust particles are heavier than air, and they can remain suspended only because of convection currents. They ride these convection currents from place to place, and bacteria hitchhike on the dust, so if you stop the dust, you stop the bacteria. The S-shaped tube was the answer. Since there was no way the air could flow completely through the flask, there could be no convection currents. Any dust that floated into the tubes would, along with its wayfaring bacteria, sink to the bottom of the curve and stay there, yet air could still freely diffuse into and out of the flask. When everything was ready, Pasteur sterilized the broth by the simple expedient of boiling it, in the flasks, for 45 minutes. He noted that if the air above the broth were indeed damaged by heating, it could still diffuse out and be replaced by undamaged air. The spout, being open, would not interfere with diffusion.

Then he cooled all the flasks and placed them in large cabinets. The cabinets were kept closed so the air within would be still but there were plenty of cracks and leaks to permit air to diffuse in and out. Then, everyone waited and watched.

For the first few days, the flasks were inspected daily. As time passed, weekly inspections became the rule, then monthly inspections. Still, the broth remained sterile. Finally satisfied that life would never show up under existing conditions, Pasteur proceeded to demonstrate that the broth had not been damaged by the long process of boiling. He cut the necks of the flasks and removed the S-shaped tubes (figure 21.3). Open now to the dust, the broth rapidly took on thriving communities of microscopic life, effectively silencing any who might contend that boiling had destroyed the germinative force.

This experiment is still fondly viewed as having destroyed forever the doctrine of spontaneous generation. The French Academy was satisfied, Pasteur received his prize, and the doctrine ultimately tumbled into the category of utter nonsense where, as far as most people are concerned, it resides today.

Yet it is important to remember that we can prove nothing in science, and to suggest that something is proven false or correct is probably a fallacy. Pasteur's classic experiment spawned a sacred cow. It resulted in the contention that the idea of spontaneous generation has been proven wrong. Yet has it?

Apparently not. Paleontologists and biochemists interested in the origin of life on Earth are challenging its more sweeping aspects, and in so doing they are underscoring the contention that science remains forever in the realm of theory. Researchers no longer view the doctrine of spontaneous generation as utter nonsense. Pasteur demonstrated that spontaneous generation of fully formed organisms is not possible under the conditions he established for his experiment. There is no argument with Pasteur's conclusions as long as we realize the context in which he

Figure 21.3 Pasteur's flasks and their S-shaped entry tubes.

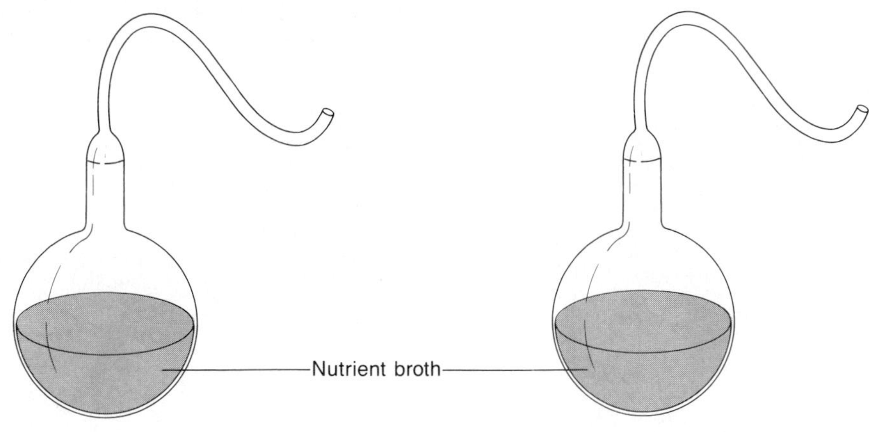

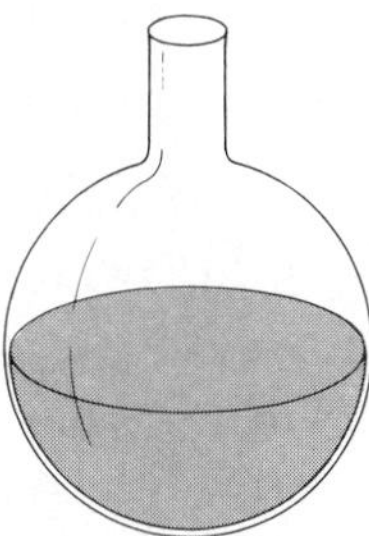

Flask with tube cut away. Such flasks grew colonies of microorganisms that were visible to the naked eye in less than a week.

made them. Pasteur's experiment is considered a scientific classic. Its design was so clean and it so completely anticipated or answered every objection that even the most devout disbelievers could find no reason to question it.

But he did not prove that the doctrine of spontaneous generation is wrong. Workers involved today in the investigation of life's origins are convinced that life arose in earth's ancient oceans from an amalgam of simple inorganic materials. These materials were pressed into more complex—ultimately organic—forms using energy from several sources, including unfiltered, hard radiation from the sun, high temperatures, and abundant, violent discharges from the never-ending electrical storms that afflicted the young earth. What these scientists are clearly suggesting is that over a towering span of centuries a spontaneous generation of organic molecules occurred in earth's ancient oceans and moved inexorably to a spontaneous generation of living molecules. What is more, there is plenty of experimental evidence to support many of their contentions.

Another Sacred Cow

There are plenty of other sacred cows in science. For instance, it was established early in this century that the hearts of the mammals and birds were fully developed, four-chambered hearts. Not so the other vertebrates. Workers in the early 1900s were still hagridden with the concept of a "ladder of evolution" at the top of which were the mammals. Reptiles, being less perfectly evolved, had less perfect hearts. The reptilian heart was viewed as a four-chambered heart, on the way to becoming a mammalian type, but not yet there (figure 21.4). These early anatomists had a hypothesis that this would prove to be the case, and when they looked at a turtle heart, sure enough, there was a hole in the septum between the two ventricles.

Amphibians (frogs, newts, etc.) were below the reptiles on the evolutionary ladder; hence their hearts would be slightly less well evolved than the reptilian one. Investigation by anatomists in the early 1900s showed that these hearts were simple, three-chambered hearts with a single ventricle to pump

Figure 21.4 The "sacred cow" of heart anatomy. (*a*) The four-chambered mammalian heart. Separation of arterial blood and venous blood is 100 percent. (*b*) The early concept of the imperfect reptilian heart. The hole in the septum between the two ventricles was thought to permit mixing of the arterial and venous bloods. (*c*) The actual, five-chambered reptilian heart. It doesn't work much like a mammal's, but investigations indicate that the separation of arterial and venous blood is complete.

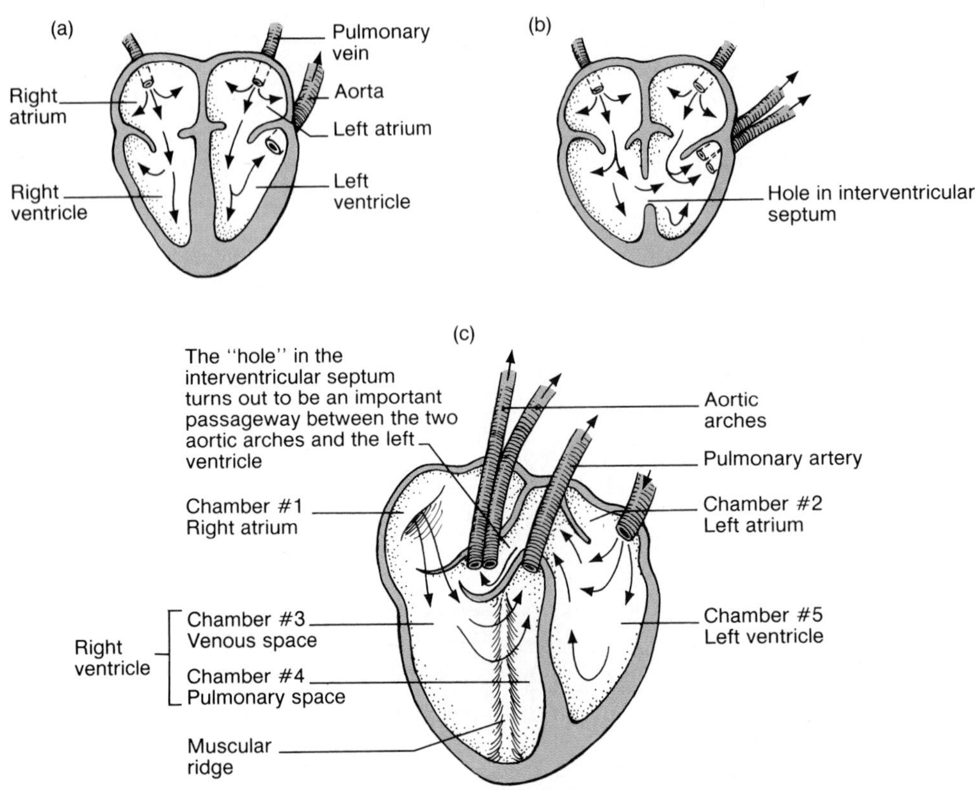

both pulmonary and systemic blood. They had found what they expected, and they went no further in their investigations.

White's Discovery

This view of animal hearts became a sacred cow very quickly, and for sixty years, no one challenged it. But in 1960, a scientist named Fred White noticed that the blood emerging from the heart of a turtle and heading out into the systemic circulation was fully saturated with oxygen. If the prevailing view of the reptilian heart was accurate, this was simply not possible. With a hole in the septum between the two ventricular chambers, mixing of venous and arterial blood was inevitable; hence complete saturation of the blood by oxygen was not possible.

Yet there it was—saturated. This drew White into a thorough investigation of the reptilian heart, and the results of his work killed another sacred cow. He found that there was indeed a hole in the intraventricular septum of the reptilian heart, but that it was a functional hole. The reptilian heart, instead of being less perfect and more primitive than the mammalian heart, turned out to be even more advanced. Reptilian hearts are five-chambered hearts. The oxygenated and nonoxygenated bloods are kept separated just as smoothly and completely as they are in mammalian and avian hearts, and the circulation through the reptilian heart is every bit as perfect as it is in mammals. This work was published in 1961, yet so thoroughly had the early sacred cow impregnated the scientific community that anatomy books published in the late 1970s and early 1980s still carried the old view of the turtle heart.

Conclusions

So the theories that make up science are constantly being altered or tossed out, and as a result, science continually changes. Concepts that seemed in perfect tune with "everyday common sense" suddenly become foolishness because we did not have the information yesterday that we have today. Needham did not make a foolish interpretation of his experimental results. *We* know that microorganisms can encapsulate themselves in tiny, almost indestructible spores, but Needham didn't know this, and his interpretations were not foolish to his contemporaries. The way research is headed, it may turn out that while he was indeed wrong, he was less wrong than we thought.

What this research also illustrates is that scientists tend to think on plateaus. The mind-set that prevails today transcends the capabilities of many researchers of the nineteenth century because we *begin* at a point they didn't know existed. It is not just the absolute facts of science that are dynamic, but also the attitudes that underlie its foundation. The result is that the scientific toeholds from which modern hypotheses are reached could not even be seen from the rungs occupied by earlier researchers. It is reasonable to assume that the scientific plateaus from which future hypotheses will spring are equally invisible to us.

Pure Science

One question frequently asked of scientific researchers today is, "what good is your research?" This is an almost universal comment, and it is typical of our technically oriented culture. When a scientist uncovers a new fact, the first thing the average person wants to know is, "is it any good?" If it doesn't show promise as a medical breakthrough or represent a potential money-maker, questioners are then led to wonder why anyone would spend money on research that does them no good. Especially since tax money—their tax money—is often involved in this research.

More than one politician has taken advantage of this public attitude to advance his or her career. And it is easy to launch attacks on scientists because they seldom fight back. As a result, there are a lot of political attacks on scientific research. One senator from a northern state wanted to know why a California researcher was fiddling around with the immune system of cockroaches. He insisted that trying to figure out how a bug fought off disease was a gross waste of taxpayers' money. When a group of NASA researchers spent about $15,000 trying to reduce the pH of a monkey-astronaut's urine, the question was again raised. "Who cares what it takes to make monkey-pee acid?" one congressman asked.

Theoretically, one is not supposed to need an excuse to pursue what is called "pure" research ("pure" in the sense that it is being pursued for the sake of knowledge only). Yet all too often we find scientists attacked because the facts they have uncovered are tremendously interesting if you happen to be a bug or a penguin, but are seemingly of no value to human beings. When knowledge is pursued for its own sake, almost any scientist would agree that it is worthwhile. Unfortunately, scientists in this country do not make the priorities—politicians make them—and if politicians cannot see some sort of political or financial profit, they seldom see any reason to spend money.

Are they right? Is it a mistake to spend money for the pursuit of sheer knowledge when no immediate, profitable application is evident?

Suppose we take a look at some of the pure research that has been done in the last ten years and examine any practical applications that have spun off.

Our NASA researchers who were trying to reduce the pH of monkey urine found what they were looking for. It was a simple dietary ingredient, and not only did it make monkey urine acid, it proved to be a practical, cheap preventive for the formation of kidney stones in paraplegic patients. That was not the object of the research. No one expected to produce a practical result, but they did just the same.

The California physiologist who is studying the immune system in insects has pointed out that insects never suffer from cancer. For some reason, their immune systems break up malignant growths before they can get properly started. Who knows where that kind of information may lead?

And on the subject of practical results from "miscellaneous" research operations, try some of the following:

Water hyacinths (*Eichhornia crassipes*) grown by NASA scientists to help retain a constant earth-like environment for long-term astronauts may turn out to be one of the most important ecological discoveries of the 1980s. It seems that these hyacinths are super-cheap, easy to grow, and will remove all kinds of debris from whatever water they are growing in. Not only will they break up the organic pollutants, they can clear even heavy metals from polluted water. No one expected that when the research began. Workers just wanted to see if the hyacinths would clear CO_2 from the atmosphere and replace it with lots of O_2.

Simple mussels—*Mytelus edulis, Mytelus californicus*, and myriad other types of bivalves that anchor to rocks and pilings along seawater docks, do so by means of a powerful glue. There is no doubting the strength of this glue, since it can hold the mussels firmly in place on rocks that are being pounded by the surf. A great deal of work produced the nature of this glue, and an alert orthopedic surgeon noted that it retained its remarkable adhesive qualities even though immersed in salt water. Using this observation as a base, he tried gluing prosthetic hip joints to bone substrates with mussel glue, and in the process he found that it seems to enhance the ability of bone cells to grow onto the metal of the prostheses. The glue is nontoxic, will set in saline solutions, and may actually permit bone cells to become firmly attached to metal replacement parts in a person's body. The dental profession is looking into the possibility of using it to glue teeth to jawbones.

There is a frog that lives in Australia that is known as the Australian Gastric Brooding Frog. This animal hatches its eggs in its stomach, nurtures them there as tadpoles, and gives birth to fully developed young through its mouth. No one has any idea how the eggs and the emerging tadpoles can withstand the digestive juices or acidity of the frog's stomach, but they do. Researchers have been investigating these phenomena for no other reason than to discover how they do it, but an alert gastroenterologist in Brisbane has suggested that just maybe it may have a medical application. If they can figure out how the tadpoles can swim and live in enzymes that should digest them, maybe they can learn a few new methods of treating gastric ulcers in human beings.

An instrument that was developed to ascertain the visual acuity of astronauts has proven to do the same for almost everybody. Today the so-called eye computer is used in optometric and ophthalmological offices across the country to help diagnose visual abnormalities and prescribe corrective lenses.

The ceramic shield on NASA's space shuttle was originally designed to reduce the heat created on the surface of the shuttle when it reentered the earth's atmosphere. These ceramic tiles permit the shuttle to probe the atmosphere at very high speeds and actually use the friction that results to slow it down. Without these tiles, the metal of the spacecraft would melt, and the passengers would all be killed. The original research was done to produce a material with very high fire resistance and strong insulating properties. The resulting product was never considered to be any good for anything else.

It turns out, however, that this particular ceramic makes magnificent false teeth. Normally a dental patient about to get a bridge made must choose between strong but relatively ugly metal and brittle but prettier porcelain. As it happens, the ceramic shield material is better than either. It is as strong as metal, yet unlike metal it is an insulator, and so will help avoid pain when eating ice cream or other cold foods. There is no possibility of generating a mild voltage in contact with the solutions in the mouth as there sometimes is with metal. Certainly it looks better than metal—in fact, since it is easier to keep clean, it is even better in this regard than porcelain. It can be X-rayed and metal cannot, patients have less gum disease with caps made of this ceramic, it does not require a metal backing as porcelain does, and it is easier to mold than either metal or porcelain. Furthermore, it is cheaper. Maybe in company with the mussel glue a person could have a whole new set of teeth glued to his jawbone and never have to worry about the hassle of normal false teeth.

A prescription drug called *Minoxidil* has been used for years in the treatment of hypertension, a very commendable ability. In addition, it may someday make a million for its inventor for an entirely different reason: it grows hair.

People who criticize the Endangered Species Act are abundant and vocal. They cannot understand why a tiny fish like a snail darter should prevent the building of a dam or the pollution of a river. Maybe the following will suggest a good reason:

An alert zoologist, working with a certain type of African toad, noticed that when the toad suffered a cut, it healed almost immediately. Subsequent experiments have shown that this toad secretes a material from its skin that is antiviral in its activity (no antibiotic in use today can attack viruses) and stimulates healing so powerfully that, when it is placed on a cut, you can almost see the cut healing.

A very similar material is secreted from the skin surface of several American amphibian species, and this material, besides speeding healing, is a potent blood coagulant. The often-maligned common Mississippi catfish has a skin secretion that is a powerful antibacterial and antiviral agent, a discovery made, by accident, while investigating some of the breeding habits of this animal.

You never know what a pure scientific investigation might turn up, and you cannot tell what irreplaceable animal or plant might house a life-saving secret somewhere in its physiology.

Even the field of criminalistics can benefit from pure science. It seems that some laboratory techniques designed for use in genetics research may be as good as fingerprints in identifying criminals. In England, using a technique that involves isolating chromosomes from blood and saliva samples, detectives were able to identify the rapist/murderer of two young girls and bring him to justice. In the process, they cleared a 17-year-old boy who had been arrested earlier as the most likely suspect in the killings. It's actually a fairly simple process. It is not necessary to analyze the DNA; you merely need to see the chromosomes. Workers say that the bands are as distinctive as a fingerprint and can be isolated from tissue under fingernails or from dried blood as much as five years old.

There are many more such cases. I have cited just a few, and it should be obvious that even if one sees no value at all in pure science, one must still acknowledge its potential. There is no way of predicting what practical discoveries might spin off from research undertaken for the sake of pure knowledge. The most unlikely things might produce some of the most valuable medical discoveries or money-making objects ever found.

Summary

Science

What it is, how it works

I. Answering the Question "Why?" What is it that has made science so successful?
II. Scientific Philosophy
III. Definition of the Scientific Method
   A. Observation
   B. Recording
   C. Identification of a Problem
   D. Hypothesis
   E. Prediction
   F. Testing
IV. Modern Science
V. Nothing in Science is Ever Proven
VI. Theory vs. Hypothesis

Early Science

I. Spontaneous Generation:
II. The Sacred Cow. Throughout history, the theory of spontaneous generation had been viewed as unassailable and correct.
III. A Sacred Cow Assailed. In the eighteenth century, it was questioned.
IV. The French Academy's Contest. Louis Pasteur vs. Felix Pouchet to settle forever the validity of the theory of spontaneous generation.
V. Pasteur's Classic Experiment:
VI. Another Sacred Cow. White's Discovery: The old view of the reptilian heart is wrong, yet it prevailed from 1903 until 1961.

Conclusions

Pure Science

Some investigations into the realm of pure science have produced medically valuable and financially lucrative discoveries.

Appendix The Metric System

There is nothing mysterious about the metric system. In fact, when you become familiar with it, you will find it is strikingly easier to work with than our English system of weights and measurements. Basically, everything is either a multiple of ten or a quotient of ten, so to change from one metric unit to a different one requires only the moving of a decimal point.

Linear Measurement

The basic unit of linear measurement is the *meter.* A meter was originally one ten-millionth the distance from the North Pole to the equator. Since no one believed that such a distance would ever change, it was considered a stable unit.

The various multiples and divisions of the meter were expressed by using Latin prefixes.

Mega = 1,000,000	micro = 1/1,000,000 (one-millionth)
Kilo = 1,000	milli = 1/1,000 (one-thousandth)
Deka = 10	deci = 1/10 (one-tenth)

You may have noted that *multiples* of a meter all begin with a capital letter, whereas prefixes denoting *fractions* of a meter begin with lowercase. This is standard procedure.

Since the metric system is the only measuring system used in science, you should become familiar with the abbreviations used. You'll probably see a lot of them. In biology, most of the linear measurements listed in table A.1 are common.

As we pointed out, conversion from one metric unit to another involves merely shifting the decimal point. Consider an object that is 11.64 m long. To change this to smaller units, we need only shift the decimal point to the right. In cm, the same length would be 1,164, which in turn is equal to 11,640 mm. To go the other way—change small units to larger ones—the decimal is shifted to the left. 11.64 m is 1.164 dekameters or decameters (a unit seldom used) or 0.01164 Km.

There is one other unit of linear measurement that should be mentioned, because it's of great value in disciplines like microbiology and cellular physiology. It's the *angstrom unit,* symbol Å. It's used to designate objects that are extremely small—too small to use the micrometer (micron) practically. There are 10,000 Å in a single micron, and anything smaller than 1,000 Å is, for all practical purposes, unresolvable in a light microscope. To give you some perspective, amino acid molecules range from 5 to about 7 Å in size.

Volume Measurement

We do not use the meter as a standard for volume measurement, and there is a good reason for deviating from that linear standard. A cubic yard represents more than 203 gallons, and a meter is slightly larger than a yard, so obviously a cubic meter would be an inconvenient unit for everyday use. Instead we use a unit fairly close to the U.S. quart. It is called a *liter* (L), and it was defined originally as 1,000 cubic centimeters. Volumes in laboratories are measured in several ways. Beakers are sometimes graduated, but they are not as accurate as graduated cylinders, which can measure to the nearest ml. Please notice that despite the similarity in prefixes, a cubic milli*meter* (mm^3) is not the same as a milli*liter.* A mm^3 is the unit used in blood counts, and students often get confused because it sounds equal to a ml, but it's not. A ml is roughly equal to a cubic centimeter, and that's 1,000 times larger than a cubic millimeter.

Mass Measurement

Please note that we use the term *mass* instead of *weight.* Weight is a property of matter often confused with mass, but it's not the same thing. Weight measures gravitational attraction for an object, and that means that weight can change with altitude. If you weighed an object at 10,000 feet you'd find it was lighter than it is at 10 feet altitude, and if you got beyond the gravitational pull of the earth, it would be weightless.

Table A.1 Linear Measurements Used in Biology

Name	Abbreviation (Fraction of a Meter)	Comparison with English Unit
Kilometer	Km (1,000 m)	About ⅝ or .6 mile.
Dekameter	Dm (10 m)	Almost the equivalent of two rods (11 yds). Used mostly to describe land plot sizes in cities.
meter	m (1 m)	40 inches, a little more than a yard.
decimeter	dm (0.1 m)	About 4 inches.
centimeter	cm (0.01 m)	A bit less than ½ inch.
millimeter	mm (0.001 m)	Usually the smallest unit on a metric ruler.
micrometer or micron	μm (0.000001 m)	Used in light microscope work.
nanometer	nm (0.000000001 m)	Used in electron microscope work.
angstrom unit	Å (0.0000000001 m)	Used in electron microscope work.

Mass, on the other hand, never changes. It is defined as the amount of *inertia* (resistance to a change in motion) possessed by a material object. The unit of mass is the *gram.* A gram is about 1/28 of an ounce, so 1,000 g or one Kilogram (Kg) equals about 2.2 lbs. Mass is measured, not on typical scales (which measure weights, hence are too variable for scientists), but on *balances,* which compare the mass of the object being measured with objects of known mass.

Temperatures

Temperature is actually a measurement of the energy content of a system. We are most familiar with the Fahrenheit (F) scale. On this scale, pure water freezes at 32° and boils at 212°. In science we use neither the Fahrenheit scale nor the Fahrenheit degree.

Instead we use the *Celsius* or *Centigrade* (C) scale and the Celsius degree. On this scale, pure water freezes at 0° and boils at 100°; again, like everything in the metric system, it is based on a system of tens. In the Celsius temperature system, our normal body temperature would be 37° instead of the 98.6° F that we are used to, and normal temperatures in our home freezers (0° F) would be slightly less than −18° C. There are 1.8 Fahrenheit degrees in every Celsius degree.

There is a third temperature scale that is not popularly used because its zero designation is so low, but in cryogenetic research it is extensively used, and since it is used in biological science on occasion, it won't hurt to acquaint you with it. It is called the *Kelvin* scale, and its zero point is the lowest temperature attainable in our universe. When Lord Kelvin of England began to design his thermal measuring scale he decided to use the Centigrade degree rather than the Fahrenheit, because the latter appeared to be restricted to England and the U.S., and the Centigrade scale was used everywhere else in the world. His zero point was, and still is, unattainable here on earth, simply because it is the temperature of intergalactic space. It is known as *absolute zero* because it is believed that lower temperatures simply do not exist. It is defined as the temperature at which all molecular motion ceases. Its Centigrade equivalent is 273 degrees below zero, and its Fahrenheit value is −459°.

In our laboratories here on earth, the closest to 0° K we have managed to come is liquid helium, which is a little less than 1° K.

Time

In this system you will encounter nothing new. We use the same system as everyone else all over the world. It's defined in terms of the *second* which is 1/86,400 of the time it takes for the earth to rotate once (one day). Unlike everything else used for scientific measurement, this is not a metric tool; hence, it is not based on a decimal system.

The metric system has undergone considerable revision as methods of measurement have increased in precision. The meter, for example, is no longer defined in terms of the earth's quadrant but is now measured in terms of wavelengths of electromagnetic radiation, and it is known with extreme precision. It's still close to, but is not exactly, one ten-millionth the distance from the north pole to the equator. Similarly, the gram was intended to be, and very nearly is, the weight in a vacuum of one cubic centimeter of pure water at maximum density. You will recall that originally, the liter was defined in terms of linear units. It was later found that greater accuracy could be obtained by comparing volume to mass rather than to linear units. So the liter was redefined as 1,000 grams of pure water weighed at maximum density, at sea level, in a vacuum. This volume was found to be slightly more than 1,000 cc—1,000.027 cc, to be precise. A cc, therefore, is slightly more than one one-thousandth of a liter, hence the origin of the unit, milliliter. Obviously, for our purposes, a cc equals one ml, but in analytical cases where extremely small volumes are involved and very high precision is required, the cc is no longer used, and it is gradually being phased out as a metric unit. Today, the only art in which it is still used regularly is medicine.

Glossary

A

A band Part of the recurring striation pattern of skeletal muscle fibers. It is the darker region in the middle of the sarcomere and equals the entire length of the thick filaments (myosin). It gets its name from the fact that it can polarize light; it is *anisotropic*.

ablation technique A way to discover how certain parts of the central nervous system work by selectively eliminating those parts one at a time. It is considered only a rough determinant.

absolute refractory period The period immediately following an action potential when a neuron will not fire, regardless of stimulus intensity.

absolute zero The temperature at which all molecular motion ceases. It is known as zero degrees Kelvin (0° K), which, on more familiar scales, is equal to −273° C or −459° F.

absorption The movement of a substance through a membrane, such as the movement of oxygen through the membrane of a red blood cell into the hemoglobin.

acceleration An increase in rate of movement, change, or other activity. In mathematics, it is the derivative of velocity.

accelerator nerve A nerve devoted to carrying information about increases in rate of movement or activity.

acetate A small organic ion (CH_3COO^-) that is present in a large number of biochemicals.

acetic acid The smallest of the fatty acids; its formula is CH_3COOH. Six percent acetic acid is known commercially as vinegar.

acetoacetic acid An organic acid that forms when the concentration of acetyl coenzyme A, a product of cellular metabolism, increases to above-normal levels. This occurs most frequently when fatty acid metabolism is rapid.

acetone A volatile ketone formed as a breakdown product of acetoacetic acid. It diffuses from the blood into alveolar air and is present in large concentrations in the exhaled air of untreated diabetics.

acetylcholine A neurotransmitter formed of choline and the acetate ion. It is the most common neurotransmitter in the peripheral nevous system of vertebrates.

acetylcholinesterase The enzyme designed to hydrolyze the neurotransmitter acetylcholine and render it ineffective. It is present in large quantities in the synaptic zones of skeletal neuromuscular junctions and is a particular target of the so-called nerve gases. The destruction of this enzyme results in uncontrollable tetanus convulsions and rapid death from respiratory paralysis.

acetyl coA An abbreviation for acetyl coenzyme A, referring to the substance that serves as an intermediate between the glycolytic pathway and the citric acid cycle.

acid Any substance that donates protons (hydrogen ions) to an aqueous solution. Those that release large numbers of protons are termed strong acids, while those that release fewer are considered weak acids.

acidosis A disease condition in which the body fluids become more acid than is normal or desirable.

acinar cell An acinus is a cluster of cells that form a goblet or sac-like structure. An acinar cell is involved in the formation of such a structure.

acquired immunity A condition that exists as a result of having been vaccinated against a specific disease or having suffered from the disease and recovered.

acromegaly A serious and terribly disfiguring endocrinological disease caused by hypersecretion of the hormone somatotropin from the adenohypophysis (pituitary gland).

acrosome The structure, shaped like half of a tiny sphere, that caps the head of the spermatozoan. It encloses an enzyme that enables the sperm to penetrate the ovum.

actin A globular protein that polymerizes in muscle tissue to form the long, fibrous thin filaments. It is one of the main substances involved in muscle contraction.

action potential A wave of voltage change that sweeps along nerve or muscle fibers when the system is activated. In nerves, it carries information, while in muscle tissue it initiates the contractile process.

active transport A process by which molecular or atomic-sized particles are concentrated in given areas. It requires considerable expenditure of energy.

actomyosin A complex consisting of the contractile proteins actin and myosin. It is intimately involved in muscle contraction.

acuity Refers to sharpness or acuteness. It is used in this book with reference to vision.

acupuncture A technique pioneered in China centuries ago that consists of inserting a needle into a specific body zone in order to deaden pain in another zone.

adaptation A nervous phenomenon. It represents a reduction in the sensitivity of a neuronal receptor during the presentation of a sustained stimulus. It is manifested as a reduction in action potential frequency. It is what occurs when a person "gets used to" hot water or a slight, steady pressure.

Addison's disease An endocrinological disease resulting from insufficient secretion of hormones from the cortex of the adrenal gland.

adenine One of the four nucleotide bases that make up nucleic acids. It is a double-ring purine.

adenohypophysis The entire non-neural portion of the pituitary gland, including the infundibulum, the intermediate lobe, and the anterior lobe. It means "a glandular growth beneath," which refers to the fact that the pituitary gland dangles from the floor of the brain.

adenosine diphosphate (ADP) One of the molecules that remains when the body's high-energy compound ATP is split to provide energy. The other molecular by-product is phosphate.

adenosine monophosphate (AMP) The molecule that is formed when an entire pyrophosphate molecule is removed from ATP. It is an important substrate for cyclic AMP, which is an intermediate in many endocrinological reactions.

adenosine triphosphate (ATP) The most abundant and universal high-energy compound in living cells. It consists of adenine, the five-carbon sugar ribose, and three phosphate molecules attached in a single line to the ribose molecule.

adenyl cyclase The enzyme responsible for catalyzing the breakdown of ATP to cyclic AMP.

adequate stimulus The stimulus that a receptor is specialized to receive and transduce. In the case of the eye, the adequate stimulus would be visible light, in the ear it would be sound waves, and so on.

adipose tissue Fatty tissue consisting of cells each of which contains a drop of oil. It is a connective tissue and represents a major energy-storage system for the body.

adrenal A multiple endocrine gland located on the dorsal surface of each kidney. It features an inner "core" or medulla and an outer "peel" or cortex.

adrenal cortex The outer three layers, considered the "peel," of the adrenal gland. These are the layers responsible for the synthesis and secretion of the steroid hormones.

adrenal corticotrophic hormone A proteinaceous secretion of the adenohypophysis. It is a trophic hormone that stimulates certain layers of the adrenal cortex into increased activity.

adrenalin *See* epinephrine

adrenal medulla The inner zone or core of the adrenal gland. It secretes a mixture of the catecholamine hormones epinephrine (75 percent) and norepinephrine (25 percent).

adrenergic nerve A neuron that releases epinephrine from its terminal buttons or whose dendritic receptor zones respond to that neurotransmitter. The term *adrenergic* is also used to describe chemicals that mimic the physiological action of epinephrine.

adsorption The adhering of one substance to the surface of another.

aerobic That which takes place in the presence of molecular oxygen.

aerobic exercise Exercise during which the subject breathes steadily.

afferent That which transports or conducts something toward a reference point, usually some centrally located region.

afterloaded muscle An experimental condition in which a muscle is not required to lift or move its load until after the contraction has begun.

agranular leucocyte A type of leucocyte thats lack clearly visible granules in its cytoplasm. Lymphocytes and monocytes are in this group.

AIDS Acquired immune deficiency syndrome; a recently elaborated viral disease in which the T4 (helper) cells of the immune system are destroyed. It appears to be infectious only through sexual contact or direct contact between the body fluids of an infected person and those of the subject. There is no known cure, no preventive vaccine, and the mortality rate is 100 percent.

albumin The most abundant of the plasma proteins.

aldosterone A steroid hormone secreted by the adrenal cortex. It exerts its effects on the kidney and is responsible for maintaining correct electrolyte balance in body fluids.

alkaline Anything that accepts, or reduces the number of, protons from an aqueous solution. It is the opposite of an acid in that the two tend to neutralize one another.

allergen That which is responsible for the development of an allergy.

allergy (hypersensitivity) A response mediated by the immune system that is capable of damaging the subject. It is usually caused by a substance that doesn't affect the average person.

alpha cells Cells within the pancreatic islets of Langerhans that synthesize and secrete the hormone glucagon. They are the largest cells in the islets.

Alzheimer's disease A progressive brain disease affecting the basal ganglia, specifically the structure known as the putamen. It apparently restricts its attacks to persons 50 years of age or older, and although its cause is not known, it is suspected to be at least partly genetic. Its mortality rate is 100 percent.

amebocyte Any body cell that can move independently throughout the body. Its motion resembles that of the ameba, hence the name.

amenorrhea The absence of menstrual flow. In a mature woman of childbearing age, it is one of the most reliable indications of pregnancy.

amine group A functional organic chemical group. It is one of the three hydrides of nitrogen—NH_2.

amino acid A relatively simple organic compound containing at least one amine group and one carboxyl group (COOH). Amino acids are the building blocks of proteins.

aminopeptidases (peptidases) Any enzyme capable of hydrolyzing peptide bonds and releasing free amino acids.

amniocentesis A process by which fetal cells are collected by hypodermic from within the pregnant woman's body. The process is used when a congenital disorder in the fetus is suspected.

amnion A tough fetal membrane that forms the amniotic sac and encloses the amniotic fluid in which the fetus is immersed.

ampere A unit of electrical current flow. Theoretically, it is the amount of current that can be pushed through one ohm of resistance by one volt of potential.

amphetamine A drug capable of stimulating certain brain centers. It can increase one's energy levels and make one feel remarkably healthy; hence it is often abused.

amphipathic A term that describes the ability of some chemical structures to simultaneously exhibit different properties. The phospholipids of cell membranes, for instance, feature both hydrophilic and hydrophobic groups on the same molecule.

amphoteric Refers to molecules that feature opposite characteristics. Amino acids, for instance, are simultaneously acidic (COOH can donate protons) and alkaline (NH_2 will accept protons).

ampulla A dilation of a tube or duct that produces a sac-like structure.

amputation neuroma A tangle of neuronal fibers often found growing through an amputation stump. The fibers are produced by neurons that once innervated the lost structure.

amyotropic lateral sclerosis Also known as Lou Gehrig's disease. It is a progressive deterioration of muscles and nerves, often characterized by a loss of neurons in the ventral horn of the spinal cord.

anabolism Metabolic operations that synthesize or build up tissues, hormones, or enzymes. It is the opposite of catabolism.

anaerobic metabolism Energy-producing metabolic reactions that do not require molecular oxygen.

analgesia Loss of perception of pain without loss of consciousness.

anal sphincter muscle The circular muscle around the anus.

anaphase A characteristic phase of mitotic division. During anaphase, the chromosomes that lined up on the equatorial plane begin to split into their component chromatids, which move to opposite ends of the dividing cell.

anaphylactic shock A serious, exaggerated hypersensitivity response resulting from systemic exposure to an allergen, usually caused by injection.

anemia Reduction to below-normal levels of red blood cell number, hemoglobin quantity, or packed cell volume in the blood. Any similar affliction that reduces the ability of the blood to carry adequate quantities of oxygen.

anesthesia Strictly speaking, a loss, partial or complete, of feeling or sensation. Usually used with reference to a loss of the ability to perceive pain.

angina pectoris A sudden, intense pain in the middle of the chest, often extending down the left arm to the hand and frequently accompanied by a feeling of suffocation. It may or may not be indicative of an impending cardiac infarction (heart attack).

angioma A tumor made up of blood or lymphatic vessels.
angiotensin I A small peptide (ten amino acids) broken off angiotensinogen by the action of renin. It is further modified to angiotensin II by enzymes in the lungs.
angiotensinogen A plasma protein formed by the liver from α globulin.
angstrom unit A measurement used in defining extremely small things, common in descriptions of cellular ultrastructure. It is symbolized by Å and is, by convention, one ten-thousandth of a micrometer.
anion A negatively charged particle.
anorexia nervosa A pathological and dangerous central nervous syndrome usually arising from self-induced starvation in an attempt to lose weight.
antagonistic muscle A muscle that operates in such a way as to oppose the actions of a given muscle.
anterior root Also known as the ventral root of the spinal cord. It is the zone in the spinal cord from which the motor nerves spray out to all parts of the body's periphery.
antibody Soluble proteins produced by specialized lymphocytes (plasma cells) and intended to provide specific immunity to a given antigen.
antidiuretic hormone (vasopressin) An octapeptide (eight amino acid) secretion of the neural lobe of the pituitary gland. Its target is the kidney; it increases the absorption of water from the kidney filtrate prior to its excretion as urine.
antigen Any substance that can elicit an immune response.
antigen/antibody complex A complex formed when antibodies attack the antigen for which they were created. It develops when antibody molecules stick to large numbers of antigens, removing them from solution and making them more susceptible to attack by phagocytic cells.
antigenic determinant The region on the surface of an antigen by which it is recognized by elements of the immune system. This is the site to which antibodies bind.
anuria The absence of urine.
aorta The large artery that carries newly oxygenated blood from the left ventricle of the heart to the systemic circulation.
aortic bodies Chemoreceptors in the arch of the aorta that detect changes in the oxygen concentration of the blood. They appear to exert their influence only when a lack of oxygen is life-threatening.
aortic semilunar valve The heart valve that guards the opening between the left ventricle of the heart and the aorta.
aplastic anemia Anemia resulting from a loss of the body's ability to regenerate red blood cells.
apnea Pertaining to an absence of breathing.
apneustic center A cluster of neurons in the hindbrain (the pons) which, when properly stimulated, produce a prolonged and deep inspiration.
appendicitis An inflammation of the vermiform appendix.
aqueous humor A watery, crystal-clear fluid that fills the anterior and posterior chambers of the eye.
aqueous solution Any solution that features water as the solvent.
arachnoid mater The fine, threadlike membrane that lines the inner surface of the dura mater. It is the middle element of the meninges of the central nervous system.
arachnoid villi Processes of the arachnoid mater that extend like fingers into the cerebrospinal fluid within the superior sagittal sinus of the brain.
arteriole A small arterial blood vessel barely visible to the unaided eye. Arterioles contain a greater percentage of smooth muscle than any other blood vessels, and thus they have more to do with the manipulation of systemic blood pressure than any other vessels.
arteriosclerosis The hardening of the walls of arterial vessels.
arthritis The inflammation of a skeletal joint.
artifact A product of an artificial nature resulting from human efforts. In the preparation of tissues for microscopic examination, an artifact is usually an apparent structure that resulted from the preparation techniques.
aspiration pneumonia An inflammation of the alveolar sacs of the lungs caused by the inhalation of some foreign material.
asthma A disease thought to be autoimmune in origin and characterized by sudden episodes of difficulty in breathing because of spontaneous constriction of the walls of the breathing tubes.
atherosclerosis *See* arteriosclerosis
atom The smallest particle of organized matter. All matter in the universe is made up of atoms.
atomic mass unit A number representing the sum of the protons and neutrons in an atom. Physically, it is defined as one-twelfth the mass of the commonest isotope of carbon.
atomic number A number representing the number of protons in the nucleus of an atom.
atomic weight A number representing, in grams, the weighted average of atomic mass units in all the isotopes of a given element.
atopic allergy An allergy that seems to have been inherited.
atrioventricular node A mass of specialized cardiac muscle cells located at the juncture between the right atrium and the right ventricle of the vertebrate heart. This is the only point at which any electrical impulses can be transmitted from the atria to the ventricles.
atrium Literally, a chamber that leads into another chamber. Most commonly used in reference to the atria in the heart.
auditory meatus The canal leading from the external ear (pinnae) to the eardrum.
auditory nerve The auditory branch of the vestibulocochlear (VIII cranial) nerve.
autoimmune diseases A disease characterized by the host's production of antibodies against one of his own tissues.
autonomic nervous system The portion of the nervous system that operates without any voluntary controls or interference. It is based on function rather than anatomy and thus includes elements of both the central and peripheral nervous systems.
axon An extension of the cell body of a single nerve cell that usually carries information away from the cell body. The "transmission line" of a neuron.
axon hillock The slight swelling on the body of a nerve cell from which the axon arises.

B

barbiturates Small, usually two-ringed compounds capable of producing behavioral depression. Their psychological effects are roughly similar to those of alcohol, and they are often abused.
base *See* alkaline
basilar membrane A very thin membrane separating two compartments within the inner ear. It supports the organ of Corti, which is the primary receptor of sound waves.
basophil The rarest of the white blood cells. Basophils appear to be more important for what they contain than for what they do. Their main constituents are histamine, serotonin, and heparin.
B cell A specialized lymphocyte which, under the proper stimulus, can develop into an antibody-secreting plasma cell.
beta cell The most abundant type of cell within the islets of Langerhans of the pancreas. Beta cells synthesize and secrete the hormone insulin.
bile salts The primary digestive secretion of the liver. Bile salts render ingested fats soluble in water, thus enabling them to react with the water-soluble enzymes designed to hydrolyze them.
bilirubin The liver secretion also known as bile pigment, bilirubin is the major breakdown product of red blood cells. It is primarily responsible for the dark brown color of the feces.
biliverdin One of the earliest breakdown products of red blood cells. Biliverdin is a green pigment that can be converted to bilirubin.

bioelectricity Electrical current created and used by living systems. It takes various forms but is usually a movement of inorganic ions, mainly sodium and potassium.

bionics Pertaining to a combination of living tissues and artificially manufactured devices.

bipolar cell Neurons located in the retina of the vertebrate eye. They are activated by the receptor cells (rods and/or cones) and transfer their information to the ganglion cells whose axons form the optic nerve.

black lung A severe respiratory disease caused by breathing fine particles of coal dust, common among coal miners.

blastocyst A nearly hollow mass of cells resulting from the early cleavages of a fertilized ovum.

blind spot (optic disc) The area of the retina where the axons of the ganglion cells cluster together and leave the eyeball to form the optic nerve. It contains no visual receptor cells; hence it is insensitive to visual stimuli.

blood-brain barrier An anatomical and physiological obstruction to the free movement of materials from the blood into the nervous tissue of the brain.

blood dust *See* chylomicra

Bohr effect A reduction of hemoglobin's ability to combine with molecular oxygen caused by an increase in carbon dioxide or a reduction in pH. It represents a homeostatic mechanism to deal, on a cellular level, with varying oxygen requirements.

bolus An oval-shaped, semisolid mass of food that has been chopped up and mixed with saliva in the mouth and is now ready for swallowing.

borborygmus A sophisticated gentleman's way of saying that his stomach is growling.

botulism A highly dangerous form of food poisoning caused by a neurotoxin released by the bacterium *Clostridium botulinum* when enclosed under anaerobic conditions. Possibly the most toxic substance ever discovered.

bouton (end button) The terminus of a neuron—the portion that transmits the information contained in an action potential to the next neuron or neurons in line. In chemical synapses, the bouton is the site of neurotransmitter assembly and secretion.

Bowman's capsule The portion of the renal corpuscle that enwraps the glomerulus or capillary ball from which the kidney filtrate is squeezed. Bowman's capsule is the beginning of the nephron and is essentially a blind end of the nephridial tube.

bronchiole An extremely narrow (usually less than 1 mm in diameter) respiratory tube branching from larger elements of the respiratory tree. The smallest bronchioles terminate in the alveoli.

bronchus One of the larger elements of the respiratory tree. Bronchi are cartilaginously supported tubes that branch off from the trachea.

Brunner's glands Mucus-secreting glands located in the upper reaches of the small intestine. They provide extra mucous coverings for the duodenum where the highly acid secretions of the stomach first enter the small intestine.

brush border A free tissue surface consisting of epithelial cells covered with microvilli.

buffer A chemical designed to resist significant changes in pH when acids or alkalines are added. In biological systems, buffers are usually weak acids or bases and salts of those acids or bases.

bulbourethral (Cowper's) glands A pair of small secretory glands that surround the urethra at the base of the penis. They secrete fluid that appears during sexual arousal and may serve to lubricate.

bundle branch block Pertaining to the inability of one of the three branches of the bundle of His to conduct electrical signals properly.

bundle of His A specialized cluster of modified cardiac muscle cells between the A-V node and the interventricular septum. It accepts electrical signals from the node and transfers them to its branches.

C

calciferol A steroid hormone that stimulates the absorption of calcium in the small intestine.

calcitonin A recently discovered hormone of the thyroid gland that is involved in calcium metabolism.

calmodulin One of the contractile proteins of smooth muscle; it is totally absent in skeletal muscle. Like troponin, its analog in skeletal muscle, it has an extremely high affinity for ionic calcium.

carbonic acid A weak acid formed when carbon dioxide is dissolved in water. It has the molecular formula H_2CO_3.

carbonic anhydrase An enzyme abundant in red blood cells that catalyzes the formation or the breakup of carbonic acid. It speeds up the reaction $CO_2 + H_2O \leftrightarrow H_2CO_3$ in either direction.

carbuncle A cluster of boils that have coalesced into a single mass.

carcinogen Any substance that is known to stimulate the formation of a malignant tumor (cancer).

cardiac cycle A period of time extending from the beginning of one heartbeat to the beginning of the next.

cardiac output The volume of blood pumped from either ventricle of the heart in a given period of time.

carotid body A specialized receptor located at the point where the common carotid artery splits into the internal and external carotid arteries. It responds primarily to lack of oxygen.

carotid sinus A small swelling in the internal carotid featuring large numbers of baroreceptors (pressure receptors) imbedded in the wall. It is intended to monitor arterial pressure of the blood entering the brain.

carrier enzyme A protein constructed to physically transport materials from one place to another across membranes or through special structures.

carrier-mediated diffusion *See* facilitated diffusion

catabolism The portion of metabolism devoted to the breakup of structural materials or foodstuffs.

catalyst Anything that speeds up a chemical reaction and is itself not consumed by that reaction.

cataract An opaque eye lens. Loss of lens transparency is usually slow and is generally not difficult to arrest.

cathartic A laxative. Anything that increases the activity of the GI tract or adds to the fluidity of the feces, thus increasing the tendency to defecate.

cation Any positively charged molecule or atom.

cell cycle The reproductive and living cycle of any cell. In most body cells it includes periods of normal activity and the process of mitosis by which cells are able to replicate themselves.

cell division A phase of the cell cycle during which the cell undergoes a series of characteristic changes that ultimately result in the production of two identical cells where there used to be just one.

cell furrow The indentation in the cell membrane that occurs after the chromatids have separated during mitosis and have been pulled to opposite ends of the cell.

cell theory A hypothesis advanced by Schleiden and Schwann in the mid-nineteenth century that stated that all life was cellular and that all cells came from preexisting cells.

cellular immune system One of the two types of immunity present in humans.

cellulose The most abundant of the carbohydrates. It is an indigestible polymer of glucose.

central lacteal An element of the lymphatic circulation that projects, as a blind sac, into the villi of the small intestine. Almost all digested fat particles enter the central lacteal.

central nervous system An anatomical division of the nervous system. It comprises the brain and the spinal cord.

centrifuge An instrument designed to spin containers, usually tubes, at very high rpm, thus producing extremely high gravitational forces within the containers.

centriole Cylindrical organelles composed of twenty-seven microtubules organized into nine parallel clusters of three each. There are two centrioles per cell, arranged at right angles to each other. They migrate to opposite ends of the cell during mitosis; the contractile fibers of the mitotic spindle extend from them.

centromere A constricted portion of the chromosome where the two chromatids of which it consists are joined.

cephalic Pertaining to the head.

cerebellum A portion of the brain involved in the coordination of motor operations. It is a two-lobed, heavily striated mass perched, in humans, on the posterior cranial fossa, posterior (but not caudal) to the brain stem.

cerebral cortex The outer layer of the cerebral hemispheres of the brain. It consists of a layer of cells about 3 mm thick and is believed to be the site of conscious thought and reasoning processes.

cerebral hemisphere Large, paired structures that, in humans, occupy most of the braincase. *See* cerebral cortex

cerebral hemorrhage Bleeding from blood vessels supplying the brain into subdural areas of the cerebrum.

cerebrospinal fluid (CSF) A watery, serous fluid produced in the lateral and third ventricles of the brain. It completely covers both the inner and outer surfaces of the central nervous system and apparently serves mainly as a shock absorber.

cerebrum *See* cerebral hemisphere

charley horse A deep muscle bruise, usually in the outer part of the thigh.

chemical digestion The breakup of food particles into their smallest molecular units, usually through the action of enzymes.

chemical property A property of matter dealing with the ability of one element or molecule to combine with another element or molecule.

chemical synapse A neuron-to-neuron communication point at which contiguity is accomplished through the mediation of a chemical called a neurotransmitter.

chemoreceptor A neuronal sensor that responds primarily to chemical changes in its immediate environment.

chemotaxis Movement in a living entity that is determined by the presence of a chemical. Positive chemotaxis means that the living material is attracted to the chemical; negative chemotaxis means the living material is repelled by it.

chlorolabe One of the three visual pigments in cone cells of the vertebrate retina. Chlorolabe is most sensitive to wavelengths of light in the green range.

cholecystokinen (CCK) An endocrine secretion of the upper portion of the small intestine. CCK is secreted in response to the presence of acids or fats in the duodenum.

cholesterol A four-ringed organic compound with a long side chain that is classified as a lipid because of its solubility in lipid solvents. Normally synthesized in the liver, it is a component of plasma cell membranes and the core molecule for all steroid hormones, including vitamin D.

cholinergic nerve A neuron that releases acetylcholine from its terminal buttons or whose dendritic receptors respond to that chemical. The term *cholinergic* also applies to muscle fibers that are responsive to acetylcholine and to chemicals that can mimic acetylcholine.

chorion Of the three fetal membranes surrounding a developing infant, the chorion is the outermost one.

chorionic gonadotropin (hCG) A hormone secreted by developing embryonic cells. Its action is similar to that of the luteinizing hormone; hence, it indirectly prevents menstruation in early pregnancy and is responsible for the maintenance of the corpus luteum and the continued secretion of progesterone.

choroid coat The thin, darkly pigmented and heavily vascularized tissue layer immediately behind the retina of the eye. It encloses more than 80 percent of the eyeball.

choroid plexus A thick network of specialized capillaries that project into the ventricles of the brain. These blood vessels and their surrounding membranes are responsible for filtering the cerebrospinal fluid from the blood that flows through them.

chromatic aberration A visual phenomenon that produces a loss of visual acuity in a light microscope at high magnification due to the different wavelengths of various colors.

chromatid A fully developed double helix of DNA wrapped around its nucleoproteins and connected at the centromere to a precise duplicate of itself.

chromosome A chemical strand consisting of nucleic acids and protein. In animal and plant cells, chromosomes are restricted to the nucleus, except during mitosis. They contain all the information necessary for the process of living.

chylomicra Extremely small globules of lipid attached to protein carriers. They represent the form in which lipids are transported from their area of absorption to storage or utilization zones.

chyme The semiliquid mass of nutrients that food becomes as the bolus is gradually broken up in the stomach by mechanical and chemical digestive processes.

cilia Hairlike protoplasmic extensions that reach outward from the free surfaces of certain cells. They usually occur in large numbers and are able to beat rhythmically, thus moving materials across their surfaces.

ciliary body A swelling along the anterior edge of the choroid coat of the eyeball. It includes the ciliary muscles, which stretch the lens to provide the eyes with focusing power.

circular folds Inpocketings that occur along the inner surface of the intestinal tract and form ripple-like folds projecting into the lumen. They serve mainly to increase the surface area of the gut.

cirrhosis A disease most often associated with the liver, in which normal tissue is destroyed or lost and is replaced by fibrous, nonfunctional masses of tissue. Liver cirrhosis is usually caused by excess alcohol consumption.

citric acid A six-carbon structure that is built from oxaloacetic acid and acetic acid at the beginning of the metabolic operation known as the *Krebs cycle*.

citric acid cycle *See* Krebs cycle

climax Synonymous with orgasm, the climax is the period of most intense neural excitement associated with sexual intercourse.

clitoris The female counterpart of the male penis, the clitoris is an elongated, relatively small mass of erectile tissue in the female external genitalia.

cocaine A small (17-C) molecule derived from leaves of the coca plant (not cacao, from which chocolate is obtained). It acts physiologically as a powerful central nervous stimulant, affecting mainly the cortex and the brain stem, increasing mental awareness but not physical strength. It is also a powerful local anesthetic.

cochlea The tightly coiled, snail-shaped and fluid-filled tube in the inner ear that contains the receptors that permit us to hear—the organ of Corti.

coenzyme A nonprotein, organic compound that must combine with a protein fraction known as an *apoenzyme* in order to produce a complete, active enzyme. Coenzymes are often derived from vitamin substrates, and they often transport materials from one location to another.

coenzyme A A nonprotein molecule known chemically as pantothenic acid, coenzyme A serves to transport acetyl molecules from the end of the glycolytic chain across the mitochondrial membranes and into the mill of the Krebs cycle.

coitus The process of mating; the insertion of the penis into the vagina.

collagen A protein compound characteristic of connective tissues, collagen mainly provides support in areas where rigidity is required but little or no elasticity.

collateral ganglia The chain of sympathetic synapses that run down the middle of the back just lateral to the vertebral column.

collaterals Small branchings of a main stream, typical of neurons and blood vessels. If a clot or other object plugs the main stream, the plug can be bypassed through the collaterals.

collecting ducts Tubes in the kidney into which the distal tubules of many nephrons pour their treated contents for excretion. The final concentration of urine, which is under the control of vasopressin, is believed to occur within these ducts.

colloid A dispersion in which the size of the solute particles is between 10 Å and 1,000 Å.
colloid osmotic pressure The differential osmotic pressure between interstitial fluid and blood plasma. COP occurs mainly because of the presence of dissolved proteins in blood plasma; it draws fluids from the interstitial compartment back into the blood.
colostrum A watery, yellowish secretion of the mammary glands that is present usually during only the first postpartum day or so. It is rich in immunoglobulins and prepared antibodies for use by the newborn infant.
common goiter A disease state usually caused by inadequate dietary iodine. The thyroid gland swells to enormous size in an effort to capture enough iodine to synthesize the thyroid hormones.
competitive inhibitor A molecule that occupies a receptor site intended for some other molecule. By occupying the receptor, the inhibitor prevents the subject molecule from exerting its influence on its target tissue.
complement A group of plasma proteins that are activated by certain antigen/antibody complexes, almost always those involving bacterial cells. The proteins are activated in succession and ultimately destroy the invading cell.
compound A group of two or more elements held together by chemical bonds and possessing its own, unique properties.
compound microscope A light microscope with more than one objective lens.
concentration gradient A variation in concentration between two zones in a fluid matrix.
concha A structure shaped like a shell. The most obvious example is the bony structures that project into the nasal cavity—the *nasal conchae.*
condom A thin rubberoid film worn over the penis during intercourse to contain the emission of sperm. Its popularity waned with the introduction of oral contraceptives, but it is making a comeback as a device to prevent infection by the AIDS virus.
conductive deafness Reduction in hearing due to fusion or partial fusion of one or more of the bones of the middle ear.
conductor When used in the context of electricity, this term refers to a material that offers little resistance to the flow of electrical current.
cones Retinal receptors responsible for visual acuity and color vision.
conjunctivitis Once known as *pink eye,* conjunctivitis is an inflammation of the conjunctiva, the membrane that lines the inner surface of the eyelids and covers the cornea of the eyeball.
constipation A lack of defecation, for whatever reason. Infrequent or very difficult elimination of feces.
contact receptor A sensory receptor that responds to physical contact.
contraception The prevention of conception; anything that prevents a spermatozoan from fertilizing an ovum.
contractile period The period of time during which a muscle is active.
contractile protein Any of the proteins capable of utilizing energy to shorten with power.
control group In an experiment, the entity or group of entities that is treated exactly the same way as the experimental group, with the exception of a single variable.
cornea The epithelial covering over the external portion of the eye. It protects and aids to some extent in focusing light correctly on the retina.
coronary artery The Latin word *corona* translates as "encircling, as with a chaplet or crown," and the term *coronary artery* pertains to the arterial blood vessels that infiltrate and nourish the heart muscle.
coronary sinus A large venous vessel located on the outer surface of the myocardium between the left atrium and the left ventricle of the heart. The blood it collects is fed directly into the right atrium.
coronary thrombosis A disease condition in which a clot has formed and is plugging the coronary arterial circulation. Because collateral circulation is not always present in coronary patterns, such plugs can result in the death of large chunks of heart muscle and are often fatal.
corpora cavernosa A pair of dorsally located masses of erectile tissue in the lateral aspects of the penis.
corpus luteum A mass of cells that develops as a result of stimuli delivered by the luteinizing hormone of the adenohypophysis. These cells develop to fill the ovarian follicle that emptied when ovulation occurred and the unfertilized ovum left.
corpus spongiosum A mass of erectile tissue, smaller than those of the corpora cavernosa, in the ventral aspect of the penis through which the urethra passes.
cortisol A steroid hormone of the adrenal cortex that is involved in glucose metabolism. It is frequently used in ointments and injectables as an anti-inflammatory agent.
countercurrent A system in which exchange is effected between vessels that run parallel to each other and carry fluids that move in opposite directions.
countercurrent multiplier The loop of Henle, a part of the nephron in mammalian kidneys, is the only multiplier system in the body. By means of its closed-loop countercurrent circulation, it can build up a high concentration of salt in the immediately surrounding kidney zone with a minimum of energy spent on active transport mechanisms.
covalent bonds Chemical bonds formed when two or more elements share electrons.
Cowper's glands *See* bulbourethral glands
cranial nerves Nerves originating in the brain and sometimes extending well out into peripheral body areas. In humans, there are twelve pairs of cranial nerves.
creatine phosphate A high-energy compound used mostly as an energy storage depot in skeletal muscle tissue.
cretin A prepubescent individual who is suffering from an inadequate supply of iodinated thyroid hormones. The term is also appropriately applied to individuals who are brain damaged because they lacked thyroid hormones at a critical period in their central nervous development.
crista An invagination of a structural element that results in the development of a series of partitions that divide a large space into several smaller ones. The cristae of the mitochondria divide the interior (matrix) of those organelles into several separate "rooms."
curare A poison made originally from crushed insect larvae by certain primitive tribes in South America. It competitively inhibits acetylcholine from transmitting neural instructions to skeletal muscles, and the victim dies of suffocation.
current When used in an electrical context, *current* refers to the movement or flow of charged particles.
Cushing's disease A serious endocrinological affliction resulting from a hypersecretion of the glucocorticoid hormones of the adrenal cortex.
cutaneous Pertaining to the skin.
cyanacobalamin A true vitamin (B12), involved in DNA replication, hence essential for mitosis and cell proliferation.
cyanide An extremely toxic poison capable of interrupting the movement of electrons. Cyanide prevents these subatomic particles from linking up with oxygen after running through the cytochrome system within the mitochondria.
cyanolabe One of the three visual pigments involved in color vision, cyanolabe is sensitive to visual radiation in the blue part of the spectrum.

cyanosis A bluish tinge that is imparted to the lips, skin, and mucous membranes when the blood is deprived of oxygen.

cyclic AMP (cAMP) A nucleotide monophosphate formed from ATP by the action of the enzyme adenyl cyclase.

cytochromes Clustered iron-containing proteins that are capable of rapid and easy oxidation and reduction.

cytochrome system (electron transport system, respiratory chain) A system, present on the inner surface of the innermost mitochondrial membrane, that consists of cytochromes arranged in sequential patterns. Electrons are passed through successive cytochromes to extract the energy necessary to phosphorylate ADP to ATP.

cytoplasm The materials within a cell membrane. The cytoplasm includes all the fluid material (cytosol) plus all the intracellular organelles immersed in that fluid.

cytosine One of the nitrogen-containing nucleotide bases found in DNA and RNA. It is a single-ring pyrimidine.

cytosol The aqueous dispersion enclosed by the cell membrane, but not including the intracellular organelles.

D

Dale's law A physiological principle, now known to be incorrect, that stated that a neuron was only able to secrete a single neurotransmitter.

decibel A measurement of sound. Zero decibels is defined as the faintest audible sound, and each ten-unit step represents a tenfold increase in sound volume.

decremental transmission When used in an electrical context, this refers to a loss of potential energy as electricity is transmitted from one point to another.

dehydration synthesis The process of producing large molecules out of two or more smaller ones through the removal of a water molecule.

delta cells A group of cells within the islets of Langerhans of the pancreas. The delta or D cells synthesize and secrete the hormone *somatostatin.*

denature To disrupt a protein's quaternary, tertiary, or secondary structure without breaking any of the peptide linkages that produce the primary structure. The protein is not destroyed, but its function is suppressed.

dendrite A protoplasmic extension of a neuronal cell body. Unlike axons, which are likewise extensions of the cell body, dendrites normally carry information *toward* the cell body.

deoxyribonucleic acid (DNA) The nucleic acid that makes up the nucleotide portion of cellular chromosomes. DNA is also present in mitochondria.

deoxyribose One of the building blocks of DNA, deoxyribose sugar is the central element to which both the phosphate group and the nitrogen-containing nucleotide bases are attached.

depolarization The loss of charge, voltage, or electrical potential energy. Used in physiology to describe the process by which an action potential is developed.

diabetes insipidus A severe endocrinological disease caused by the near or total absence of the hormone vasopressin (antidiuretic hormone). Untreated patients suffering from D.I. produce enormous amounts of urine.

diabetes mellitus A common and, if untreated, fatal endocrinological disease caused by lack of the pancreatic hormone insulin. Patients with diabetes mellitus usually have blood sugar levels so high that the kidney cannot reabsorb it all.

dialysis A process by which a person's blood can be cleansed of its impurities and its pH, mineral content, and other homeostatic parameters adjusted through the use of a special piece of medical equipment. Essential for patients who have lost their kidney function.

diaphragm The large, flat sheet of skeletal muscle that serves as the floor of the thoracic cavity. Contraction of this muscle reduces the pressure within the thorax and initiates the process of breathing in.

diastole The term used to describe the relaxation phase of the cardiac cycle.

diffusion The movement of materials down a concentration gradient without any use of exogenous energy. The energy comes from the random movement of the particles involved and is always from a higher to a lower concentration.

digestion The mechanical and chemical processes that result in the breakdown of large food particles into their smallest component molecular parts.

digestive tract The tubular system enclosed by the body in which digestion of food occurs.

diploid The possession of two complete sets of chromosomes, one from each parent, designated $2n$. In humans, the diploid number of chromosomes is 46 (23 pairs).

dipolar bond A bond formed between two particles having opposite charges. These charges are not full charges; hence, dipolar bonds are quite weak.

disaccharide A sugar molecule that is formed of two simpler sugar molecules through the process of dehydration synthesis.

dispersion A dispersion is created whenever particles of one kind are scattered through particles of another kind. For our purposes, the words *dispersion* and *mixture* can be considered synonymous.

distal Pertains to that which stands apart or at a distance from a reference point. Anything that stands apart from the central nervous system, for instance, would be distal to the CNS.

distal convoluted tubule The convoluted tubule that is farthest away from the initial segment of the nephron in the vertebrate kidney. More specifically, it is the portion of the nephron between the ascending part of Henle's loop and the collecting duct.

distance receptor Sensory receptors that are capable of detecting stimuli that originate some distance away from the individual. In humans, they would be the eyes, the ears, and the nose.

disulfides Sulfur compounds that are linked to two organic molecules are known as sulfides. Disulfides are organic sulfides containing two sulfur atoms held together as S—S, a type of bonding known as *disulfide.*

dopamine The catecholamine precursor of norepinephrine. Like its successor, dopamine is a neurotransmitter; unlike its successor, it is restricted to the CNS.

ductless glands Secretory glands that have no obvious exit routes for their products; instead they secrete them into the interstitial fluids, where they can be picked up by the blood. Endocrine glands are often referred to simply as ductless glands.

duodenum That portion of the small intestine closest to the stomach. In actual distance, it encompasses about the first 25 cm of the small intestine.

dura mater The outermost of the three meninges of the brain and spinal cord. The dura mater is extremely tough and fibrous, providing considerable protection for the delicate tissues it encloses.

dynamic equilibrium The maintenance of balance and equilibrium when an individual is accelerating or decelerating. Dynamic sensors can detect motion and acceleration, while static sensors are designed to indicate the body's position in space.

dysmenorrhea Difficult or painful menstruation, known in the vernacular as cramps.

dyspnea Labored breathing.

E

eardrum The fine membrane that separates the auditory meatus from the middle ear. The eardrum initiates the processing of pressure waves in the atmosphere into impulses we can detect as sound.

eclampsia A disease state that sometimes occurs during pregnancy. It is manifested as convulsions and coma and usually occurs in patients suffering from toxemia of pregnancy. Its cause is not known.

ectopic Anything out of the ordinary. Ectopic heartbeats are arrhythmic beats; ectopic pregnancy usually refers to the implantation of the fertilized ovum in the fallopian tubes instead of the wall of the uterus.

effective filtration pressure The net pressure forcing fluids out of the blood into the interstitial fluids. It is the algebraic sum of the blood pressure provided by the heart and the colloid osmotic pressure of the plasma.

effector organ The last organ in a sequence of events or structures. Skeletal muscle is the effector organ in a simple motor reflex, since it performs the final operation.

efferent neuron Any neuron that follows a reference event or structure. The motor neuron innervating a skeletal muscle is always an efferent neuron, since it is invariably the last neuron involved in reflex or voluntary activity.

eicosapentaenoic acid A nutrient, present in fish oils, that aids in the prevention of cardiovascular problems. It can reduce the body's production of thromboxane, which results in platelets that are less likely to stick to irregularities in blood vessel walls.

ejaculation The ejection of semen from the penis.

ejaculatory duct A pair of small tubes (about 2 mm long) that result from the anastomosis of the vas deferens and the tube emerging from the seminal vesicle. They enter the prostate gland and emerge as one tube, the *prostatic urethra.*

electrical synapse A point of contiguity between two neurons in which the action potential is transferred directly from the afferent to the efferent neuron without the mediation of a chemical neurotransmitter.

electrocardiogram (EKG, ECG) A recording made of the electrical potential developed by the heart muscle during a normal cardiac cycle.

electroencephalogram (EEG) A recording made of the brain's electrical activity. The wave forms produced are recorded from electrodes placed in standardized spots on the skull and probably involve many millions of neurons.

electrolyte Any mineral that, when added to water, increases the solution's ability to conduct electricity.

electromotive force (EMF) A difference in electrical potential energy between two points. EMF is measured in volts.

electron A subatomic particle, the electron is the smallest known particle in terms of mass. Its total absolute mass is 9×10^{-28} grams, which is less than 1/1,800 the mass of a proton. Electrically, it is recorded as the smallest unit of negative charge that has ever been measured.

electron microscope An instrument that directs a beam of electrons through the object being viewed and creates a picture of that object on a photographic plate. Theoretically, electron microscopes are capable of diagraming objects as small as 0.5 Å units in diameter.

electron orbital A purely statistical entity. The electron orbital is the zone occupied more often than any other zone by an electron circling an atomic nucleus.

electron transport system *See* cytochrome system

element Matter that is composed of atoms that are all the same.

embolus A blood clot, often several centimeters in length, that formed on the inner surface of a blood vessel and has broken free. It can create a blockage in the circulatory system.

emphysema A respiratory disease caused by the stretching of alveolar walls or destruction of the walls between alveoli. Either condition results in the enlargement of individual alveoli and a reduction in total internal surface area of the lungs involved.

emulsion A mixture of two liquids that normally do not mix. Oil cannot be mixed with water under ordinary circumstances, but when detergent is added to an oil/water mixture, the two become miscible and form an emulsion.

end button *See* bouton

endocardium The glassy-smooth sheath of connective tissue that lines the inner chambers of the heart. It protects and minimizes frictional losses as blood rushes across its surfaces.

endocrine system One of the body's two major control systems, the nervous system being the other. The endocrine system's instructions are carried by special chemicals that are transported from their places of origin to target zones by the blood.

endocytosis The process by which materials too large to penetrate the cell membrane are able to get into the cell.

endolymph A highly specialized fluid that fills the membranous labyrinth of the inner ear.

endometrium The sheet of mucous membrane that lines the interior of the uterus.

endoneurium The layer of connective tissue that enwraps individual neurons in peripheral nerves, thus isolating them electrically from each other.

endoplasmic face The surface of the Golgi apparatus on the side closest to the endoplasmic reticulum.

endoplasmic reticulum A series of membranous tubes and flattened sacs that winds back and forth through the cellular cytosol, occasionally fusing to the plasma membrane and thus communicating with the interstitial fluid. Rough ER is involved in the synthesis of proteins for extracellular use. Smooth ER is usually involved in the synthesis and export of lipid-based molecules.

endorphin A morphine-like secretion of certain cells in the brain. Endorphins are similar in activity to morphines and are responsible for the ability of the CNS to sometimes ignore painful stimuli through autosuggestion.

endothelium The epithelial lining of the blood and lymphatic vessels. It features a glossy, highly polished surface, thus reducing frictional losses as fluids stream through the vessels. It is continuous with the endocardium.

end tuft *See* bouton

energy Energy is usually defined as the ability to do work. It is an essentially immortal entity that, like matter, can neither be created nor destroyed.

engram The name sometimes used to describe a memory pattern stored in the brain. It is difficult to define because it is not known what memory is or in what form it is stored.

enterogastric reflex A simple reflex that begins in the small intestine and ends in the stomach. When food enters the duodenum it stretches the walls and the stretch receptors of the reflex. Parasympathetic impulses to the stomach are inhibited, and digestive activity in the stomach slows.

enterokinase An enzymatic secretion of the small intestine, enterokinase is responsible for converting the pancreatic secretion *trypsinogen* into the proteolytic enzyme *trypsin,* thus activating it.

enzymes Stereospecific proteins synthesized by living systems to perform certain tasks. Generally, they serve as catalytic agents in both anabolic and catabolic biochemical reactions, although some function to carry particles from place to place.

eosinophil A type of white blood cell in vertebrates. Eosinophils are so called because they readily take up the acid stain *eosin.* They are granulocytes (polymorphonucleocytes) and have been associated with immune reactions.

epicardium The glossy-smooth, glasslike sheet of connective tissue that enwraps the entire outer surface of the vertebrate heart. As is the case with the endocardium, it serves both as a protective layer and a friction-free surface.

epididymis Part of the male reproductive system, the epididymis is a fine, tubelike structure that traces a serpentine path on the surface of each testicle, then enlarges to eventually form a junction with the vas deferens. It stores newly matured spermatozoons.

epilepsy A central nervous affliction that features either short periods of complete blackout (*petit mal*) or randomly intermittent episodes of violent muscular convulsions (*grand mal,* once called "fits") followed by short periods of unconsciousness, then a long sleep session.

epinephrine Also known as *adrenalin,* epinephrine is a catecholamine hormone and neurotransmitter synthesized and released by elements of the sympathetic nervous system. It is a powerful vasoconstrictor and cardiac stimulant.

epistaxis Bleeding from the nose.

EPSP A voltage applied to the postsynaptic element that tends to depolarize that element. It is an acronym for *e*xcitatory *p*ost*s*ynaptic *p*otential.

equipotentiality Pertaining to equality in potential energy content or potential ability to do or obtain something. May also refer to a voltage across a membrane that holds the ion species involved in electrochemical equilibrium.

erythroblastosus fetalis A hemolytic complication of pregnancy and/or childbirth caused by an immunological attack instigated by antibodies in the blood of the mother.

erythrocyte Red blood cell. Erythrocytes are biconcave, anucleate discs about 7 μm in diameter and filled with the respiratory pigment *hemoglobin.* Their primary function is the transport of molecular oxygen.

erythrolabe A visual pigment present in the retinal cone receptors; erythrolabe is sensitive mainly to radiation in the red band.

erythropoietin A glycoprotein formed mainly in the kidney. When present in the blood, it stimulates synthetic elements in the bone marrow to increase the production of red blood cells.

estradiol A steroid hormone produced by the interstitial cells of the ovarian follicle. It is the most active of the female hormones.

estrogen The family of hormones produced by the interstitial cells of the ovary, in smaller amounts by the adrenal cortex and, during pregnancy, by the placenta. Estrogens are responsible for the development of the female secondary sex characteristics.

estrus cycle The analog of the human menstrual cycle, estrus occurs in nonprimates and many of the primates. It is characterized by an annual increase in the secretion of estrogens, which makes females both fertile and receptive to males of the same species.

eupnea Normal, relaxed breathing patterns.

eustachian tube A small (less than 1 mm in diameter) tube that runs from the pharynx to the middle ear.

exocrine gland A secretory gland that releases its secretions into ducts that connect with specific target zones.

exocytosis A process by which materials, usually wastes, that are too large to cross the plasma membrane are eliminated from the cytosol.

exogenous insulin Insulin synthesized by an organism other than the recipient.

exophthalmos A marked protrusion of the eyeballs.

exoplasmic face The surface of the Golgi apparatus that faces the plasma membrane, away from the ER.

experimental group *See* control group

expiratory reserve volume One of the conventionally prescribed lung volumes. The expiratory reserve is the volume of air that can be forcefully expelled from the lungs after a normal expiration.

external ear The portion of the ear that protrudes from the side of the head plus the tunnel (meatus) that extends from the outside to the eardrum (tympanic membrane).

extracellular compartment A conventionally agreed-upon fluid compartment of the body, the extracellular compartment represents all the fluid within the body that is not within or bounded by a cell membrane.

extrinsic pathway Pertaining to one of the biochemical pathways that ends in a blood clot.

extrinsic protein A membrane protein that "floats" on the outer hydrophilic zone of the lipid bilayer that makes up the cell membrane. These proteins may or may not circulate onto and from the cell membrane.

F

facilitated diffusion A mysterious and little-understood means by which certain particles, too big to easily penetrate the plasma membrane, are carried into the cell without any expenditure of energy. Also known as *carrier-mediated diffusion.*

fallopian tubule A tube in the female reproductive system extending from the ovary to the uterus. Also called *uterine tubule.*

farmer's lung A lung disease in which the alveoli of the lungs become inflamed and swollen. The cause is not known, but it is fairly common in workers exposed to moldy hay or grain.

fasciculus Literally meaning "a small bundle," a fasciculus is a cluster of muscle fibers or neurons wrapped in a fibrous sheath of connective tissue.

fatigue Inability to continue working. In muscle fatigue, the biochemical processes that provide the energy for contraction are loaded with by-products, and energy production must stop until some of them are removed.

fatty acid An organic acid consisting of methyl groups (CH_2) linked to each other to form chains of from fourteen to twenty-two such groups.

fecalith A hardened ball of fecal material that has jammed in the vermiform appendix, forming an irritation site that often becomes infected, producing the inflammation known as appendicitis.

feces Materials composed of metabolic waste products plus the indigestible debris left over from the mechanical and chemical food-breakdown operations performed in the gastrointestinal tract.

fenestrae Literal meaning, "a window"; most often refers to the extra- large openings present in glomerular capillaries of the kidney.

ferritin A large organic molecule fairly abundant in the liver and spleen. It serves mainly to store iron for future erythrocyte synthesis.

fertilization membrane A membrane that forms around certain mammalian (not human) ova after a spermatozoan has entered for the purpose of fertilization.

fiber Any chemical strand that is longer than it is wide. The term has broad application.

fibrin An insoluble protein that forms when thrombin reacts with fibrinogen. Fibrin's fibers adhere to each other and form a netlike mass that traps cells and large proteins, thus preventing their loss when a blood vessel is damaged.

fibrinogen A fairly abundant, soluble plasma protein synthesized in the liver. In the presence of thrombin, fibrinogen is broken up into its insoluble monomers (fibrin) in the final, and only visible, reaction of the clotting process.

fibroblast A cell found in connective tissue that is capable of differentiating into any one of several different kinds of connective tissue cells.

fight, flight, fright response Also called the three-F reaction, this response results when the sympathetic nervous system is suddenly stimulated. It is designed to help a person to deal with an external emergency.

filtration The passage of fluid through a membrane that restricts the passage of dissolved materials on the basis of size.

first heart sound A sound produced by the mammalian heart when the ventricles contract. It is caused mainly by the slamming shut of the A-V valves.

first polar body A daughter cell resulting from the first meiotic division of female germ cells. It is eventually broken up for its spare parts and plays no role in the reproductive process.

fixation The process by which specimens are prepared for slicing and presentation for viewing on a microscope slide.

flagellum Literal meaning, "whip" or "whiplike"; to a physiologist, it refers to the long protoplasmic extensions from cell surfaces that serve to provide the cell with motion.

flaxedil A synthetic curare, used in surgery as a muscle relaxant.

fluid-mosaic model Currently the most widely accepted version of cell membrane structure, the fluid-mosaic model envisions the membrane as a lipid bilayer in which proteins are imbedded.

folic acid A water-soluble vitamin important in the replication of DNA.
follicle Literally, a "small bag." The term *follicle* refers in biology to several structures, most commonly the structures in the ovaries that contain the ova and the structures in the thyroid gland in which the iodinated thyroid hormones are stored.
follicle-stimulating hormone A proteinaceous hormone secreted by the adenohypophysis that serves to stimulate maturation of both male and female germ cells.
fovea A cluster of tightly packed cone cells in the retinal zone where light strikes most often. This is the zone of greatest visual acuity in humans.
free electrons Electrons that are not tied tightly to any given nucleus but instead tend to wander from atom to atom.
functional group A small molecule, sometimes only one or two atoms, with a specific arrangement that occurs repeatedly in organic molecules and imparts specific chemical and physical properties to the larger molecule. Also called an *organic radical.*

G

gallstones A disease state in which biliary secretions, chiefly cholesterol, have become impacted and densely concentrated in the gallbladder or the bile duct, thus preventing normal flow of bile from the liver.
gamete A fully mature reproductive cell, in humans a spermatozoan or a mature ovum.
gamma efferents Specialized motor nerves that innervate the intrafusal fibers of skeletal muscle spindles.
ganglion A swelling that occurs on nerves in the periphery caused by clusters of neuronal synapses or aggregations of nerve cell bodies.
gap junction A specialized contact point or point of contiguity between two cells. When used in the context of neurons, it refers to an electrical synapse.
gap one (G1) A period in the cell cycle during which the cell undertakes normal daily activity.
gas phase The high-energy state of matter. In this state, the atoms of a substance are so loosely confined that they will assume the shape and size of any container into which they are placed.
gastric gland A gland in the mucosa of the stomach that is made up of specialized secretory cells and secretes enzymes, mucus, and/or hydrochloric acid into the lumen.
gastrin A hormone released by the mucosa of the stomach into the bloodstream when food is present in the stomach. It serves to stimulate the gastric glands to increased activity.
general anesthetics Anesthetics capable of inactivating conscious portions of the brain and inducing sleep or unconsciousness.
generalized cell A hypothetical cellular structure drawn from a composite of many different cell types and containing all organelles that show up in any of them.
generator potential A membrane depolarization that occurs mainly on a postsynaptic neuronal element and is graded according to the strength and duration of the stimulus. It is not self-propagating.
germ cells The cells present in the endodermal tissue of the gonads from which mature ova and/or spermatozoons arise.
gingival margin The section of the gums contacting the enamel of the teeth.
gland Any multicellular structure that secretes a product.
glaucoma A relatively common visual disease in which Schlemm's canal is blocked, producing unusual and damaging pressure in the anterior chamber of the eye.
glial cells A collective term used to describe non-neuronal structural cells within the central nervous system.
globin The protein fraction of the hemoglobin molecule, globin is the structure that encloses the iron-containing fraction and helps prevent it from becoming oxidized by the cytosol of the erythrocyte.
globulin The second most abundant of the plasma proteins, globulin occurs in three forms: alpha, beta, and gamma. All three are involved in providing substrate for the synthesis of antibodies.
glomerular nephritis A kidney disease in which there is inflammation in the glomerulus.
glomerulus A ball of capillaries enclosed by Bowman's capsule of the nephron. The glomerulus is the site where the kidney filtrate is formed.
glucagon A fairly large polypeptide hormone produced by the alpha cells of the islets of Langerhans; it opposes the activity of insulin.
glucocorticoids A group of steroid hormones produced by the middle layer (zona fasciculata) of the adrenal cortex. The most active of the glucocorticoids is *cortisol* (hydrocortisone).
gluconeogenesis The conversion of amino acids or certain lipid molecules into glucose.
glucose The most abundant sugar in the body. Glucose is also known as "blood sugar." It is synthesized by the liver into a bushlike polysaccharide called glycogen or animal starch.
glycerol A three-carbon compound that is generally viewed as an alcohol, glycerol is the backbone of our storage fat molecules.
glycocalyx An ultrastructural projection arising from the surface membrane of intestinal cells, the glycocalyx is a carbohydrate fraction of an acid mucopolysaccharide or glycoprotein.
glycogen The chief storage form of glucose in animals, glycogen is a bushlike polymer consisting of hundreds of glucose molecules.
glycolipids Organic molecules consisting of lipid and carbohydrate.
glycolysis The anaerobic phase of intermediary metabolism; also known as the *Embden-Meyerhoff-Parnas pathway.* It takes place in the cellular cytosol and produces only four ATP molecules while consuming two each time a glucose molecule enters the pathway.
glycoprotein An organic molecule consisting of protein and carbohydrate.
goblet cell A large, flask-shaped cell found within the epithelial layers of many of the body's tubular structures. It secretes mucus.
Golgi apparatus A cluster of saucer-shaped membranous saccules stacked together within the cell, usually near the nuclear envelope. The Golgi apparatus puts the finishing touches on newly synthesized proteins.
Golgi tendon organ A stretch receptor located in muscle tendons. It is designed to respond when its tendon is stretched either by muscle activity or passive stretching.
gonadotrophic hormone A collective noun referring to any of the proteinaceous hormones of the adenohypophysis that are involved in stimulating gonadal activity.
gonads The reproductive organs of any organism, male, female, or hermaphroditic.
gonorrhea A bacterial disease capable of causing serious damage in the body, particularly in the reproductive tract and the heart. It is considered a venereal disease.
gout A form of arthritis, gout is usually characterized by an excess of uric acid in the body fluids. It customarily assaults joints, especially in the foot.
graafian follicle The follicle within the ovary that is about to shed its gravid (ripe) ovum into the fallopian tubes, a process known as *ovulation.*
gram atomic weight The relative mass of an atom, expressed in grams.
gram molecular weight The relative mass of a molecule, expressed in grams. Gram molecular weight is the sum of the gram atomic weights of the elements of which the molecule is made.
granular leucocyte Means literally "white cells containing granules." They are also known as *polymorphonuclear* leucocytes. There are three subclasses: *neutrophils, eosinophils,* and *basophils.*
granulosa cells A layer of cells within the ovarian follicle that surround the oocyte.
Graves' disease A disfiguring endocrine disease the symptoms of which are the result of the hypersecretion of iodinated thyroid hormones.

gray matter Usually refers to the portion of the cerebral cortex containing mainly neuronal cell bodies.

GTP Guanosine triphosphate; the high-energy form of the nucleotide base *guanine*. It is produced within the mill of the Krebs cycle and is involved mainly with lipid metabolism.

guanine A double-ringed nitrogen-containing purine base present in both RNA and DNA.

gumma A soft tumorous growth. When used without modifiers, the word refers to the gummy tumorous growths typical of tertiary syphilis.

gustation One of our five senses, gustation is the sense of taste.

H

Hand-Schuller-Christian's disease A disease characterized by an unusual proliferation of fixed macrophages (histiocytes). It usually begins in childhood and can affect any body organs, although the lungs and bones are most often attacked.

hapten A substance, usually of 8,000 daltons or smaller, which by itself is not antigenic. When linked to a protein carrier, however, it can produce an immune response, and when the pure hapten later appears, it can be specifically attacked.

hay fever A hypersensitivity aggravated by the pollen of certain plants, usually pine and ragweed.

H band A segment occupying the middle of the skeletal muscle sarcomere. The H band begins at the inner ends of the thin actin filaments and consists solely of the thick filament, myosin.

heart block A disease in which the A-V node fails to properly transmit the atrial depolarization into the bundle of His.

heart murmur A sound produced by turbulence as blood flows through the heart valves. If the sound is caused by unusual narrowing of the valvular openings, it is considered a disease state and can be life-threatening.

heat capacity A measure of the ability of a given substance to absorb energy without altering its physical state.

heat of vaporization The amount of energy that must be absorbed by a given mass of liquid at its boiling point in order to change all of that liquid into a gas.

helix A corkscrew-like shape. The secondary structure of all DNA molecules is helical, as is the secondary structure of many proteins.

helper cells The T4 elements of the cellular immune system of human beings. They stimulate both B cells of the humoral system and killer cells of the cellular immune system to maximum activity when disease strikes.

heme The prosthetic (nonprotein) portion of the hemoglobin molecule. Heme consists of an iron molecule within a circle of four pyrrole rings.

hemoglobin The respiratory pigment of mammalian blood that carries oxygen from the lungs to the deep body tissues. It is composed of a protein fraction and a prosthetic group containing iron.

hemoglobinopathy A disease characterized by an alteration of the hemoglobin molecule as a result of some genetic disorder. Sickle cell anemia is the most commonly occurring one in this country.

hemohistioblast A cell that may or may not actually exist, the hemohistioblast is a theoretically derived progenitor of all blood cells, white and red.

hemophilia An inherited disease in which the victim's blood will not clot. Usually due to a defect in the intrinsic clotting pathway, the hemophiliac suffers continually from subcutaneous bleeding, often caused by minor bruising.

hemorrhage Bleeding. A loss of blood from the blood vessels.

hemorrhagic anemia Anemia caused by blood loss due to hemorrhage.

hemorrhoids An evagination or dilation of veins in certain zones of the rectum and anus that results in the protrusion of part of the rectum, sometimes through the anus to the outside.

hemotoxin A poison that specifically attacks some part of the blood.

heparin A metabolically produced anticoagulant that is abundant in the lungs and the liver of humans. When extracted from the tissues of animals, it is used as an anticoagulant in the treatment of thrombosis.

hepatitis An inflammation of the liver.

Hering-Breuer reflex The periodic activity of afferent and efferent nerve fibers that results in the cyclic activation of the muscles that cause a person to inhale.

heroin A morphine derivative with enormous painkilling powers and a tremendous potential for abuse.

herpes virus One of the most ubiquitous of all human viruses; it occurs in several forms. Herpes type 1 causes cold sores and sores within the mouth. Herpes type 2 causes the venereal infection commonly known as "herpes."

heterocyclic compound A compound forming a ring in which not all of the elements at the ring corners are the same.

hexose A six-carbon sugar.

histamine A base formed by the decarboxylation of histidine. It is present in all cells, but it is particularly concentrated in basophils, mast cells, and platelets.

histone A small protein that is attached to DNA, thus forming *chromatin*.

homeostasis The fundamental goal of all physiological operations. Homeostasis is the retention of all chemical, osmotic, and physical parameters of the body within strictly defined tolerance limits.

homologous chromosomes Chromosomes possessing genetic information that is not necessarily the same but deals with similar characteristics and similar traits.

hormone A chemical secretion of the endocrine system that carries a specific message in the blood to its target cells and tissues.

human chorionic gonadotropin *See* chorionic gonadotropin

humoral Pertaining to body fluids, or to materials carried in solution in the body fluids.

H-Y antigen The compound present in males that becomes active in the seventh week of embryonic development and alters the basic body plan of the embryo from female to male.

hydrocarbon A name given to any organic compound that consists solely of carbon and hydrogen molecules.

hydrogen bond The strongest of the dipolar bonds; a weak attraction that exists between a hydrogen atom that is part of a covalent molecule and a nearby negative zone on a neighboring molecule.

hydrogen ion (H^+) A free proton.

hydrolysis The process of breaking a polymer into its component monomers through the addition of a water molecule.

hydrophilic Literally, "water loving." A hydrophilic molecule absorbs water or dissolves easily in a watery matrix. Generally speaking, any molecule that is polar (charged) is hydrophilic.

hydrophobic Literally, "water fearing." A hydrophobic molecule will not absorb water. Hydrophobic molecules are characteristically nonpolar (electrically neutral throughout their entire mass).

hydroxyl ion The negatively charged particle that is produced when water is split into its component ions, H^+ and OH^-. It is present in all alcohols and hence is often referred to as the "alcohol group."

hyperglycemia An overabundance of glucose in the blood, a condition characteristic of diabetes mellitus.

hyperopia Farsightedness; a condition usually caused by a foreshortened eyeball, which forces the lens to focus objects nearby at a point behind the retina of the eye.

hyperplasia A condition in which there is an increase in the number of normal cells in their normal tissues.

hyperpnea Rapid, deep breathing as a result of reflex activity.

hyperpolarization An abnormally high charge (voltage) across a given membrane or between two terminals. In biological systems, it would mean an increase in the negativity of cellular cytoplasm.

hypertension A disease state that features a chronic increase in systemic blood pressure.

hypertonic A relative term that means the subject solution has a greater osmotic pressure than the reference solution.

hyperventilation Rapid, deep breathing that is not caused reflexly but rather is being done voluntarily.

hypodermic Injected beneath the skin. It has become a general term referring to anything that can inject materials into the body, whether through the skin or not.

hypoglycemia A condition in which the glucose content of the blood is below normal range.

hypophysis The Greek word meaning pituitary gland, the master endocrine gland dangling from the floor of the brain. The pituitary is a multiple gland, producing a number of trophic hormones as well as nontrophic hormones, and it is critical to continued life.

hypothalamo-hypophyseal portal system A collection of blood vessels featuring a capillary bed at both ends and connecting the hypothalamus with the adenohypophysis.

hypothalamo-hypophyseal tract A cluster of nerve fibers running from several nuclei in the hypothalamus into the neurohypophysis (the posterior lobe of the pituitary). They carry the hormones vasopressin and oxytocin in various stages of synthesis and activation.

hypothalamus A subcortical brain structure, located just above the roof of the mouth, that controls and integrates most endocrine secretions and is responsible for integrating a great deal of endocrine and autonomic neural activity with conscious zones of the brain.

hypotonic A relative term meaning that the solution in question has a lower osmotic pressure than a reference solution.

I

I band One of the striations of skeletal muscle fibers. It gets its name from the fact that it will not polarize light; hence it is *isotropic*. The I band extends from the end of one thick band to the end of another and includes only thin filaments.

ignition temperature The temperature at which a given substance will begin to burn.

ileocecal valve The sphincter-like muscle that guards the opening from the small intestine into the large intestine.

immune agglutinates Immune agglutinates form when antigens and antibodies stick together, forming a large mass of cells that precipitate, thus becoming vulnerable to attacks by phagocytes.

immune suppressants Reagents designed to reduce the effectiveness of certain aspects of the immune system. They are used by surgeons to reduce the likelihood that an implanted organ or tissue will be attacked and rejected by the recipient's immune system.

immune system The tissues and cells that protect a person from disease by rendering the person resistant to assault by microorganic parasites or their products.

immunoglobulins Antibodies. Immunoglobulins are specific, soluble proteins synthesized by plasma cells using plasma globulins, chiefly the gamma fraction, as substrates.

incisura (dicrotic notch) The brief, spikelike pattern visible on the distal side of ventricular pressure waves.

incus Literally, "anvil-like." The incus is one of the tiny bones of the mammalian middle ear. It is involved in the amplification and transmission of sound waves from the tympanic membrane to the inner ear.

inertia One of the properties of matter, inertia is that quality which tends to resist a change in state.

infarction The process of depriving an area of an organ or a tissue of its normal blood supply, thus causing severe damage or the death of that area.

inflammation A characteristic response to a local injury. When a tissue becomes inflamed, there is an increase in total blood flow and an unusually high fluid accumulation in the affected area. The temperature throughout the area increases.

infrared radiation Electromagnetic radiation in a frequency range just below the zone of visible light. To our senses, it manifests itself as pure heat.

inner ear The portion of our ears containing the sensory endings of the cochleovestibular (VIII cranial) nerve. The senses of static and dynamic equilibrium and of hearing are transduced from mechanical stimuli into neural impulses in the organs of the inner ear.

inorganic chemistry The branch of chemistry that deals mainly with noncarbon and nonhydrocarbon compounds.

inspiratory reserve volume A standardized volume of air, the inspiratory reserve volume is the amount of air that can be forcefully inspired after a normal inspiration has been made.

insulin A double-chained polypeptide hormone synthesized by the β cells of the islets of Langerhans. Insulin is a primary anabolic hormone and is the only one whose prime function is to reduce glucose levels in the blood. A lack of insulin causes the disease diabetes mellitus.

insulin-dependent diabetes A severe form of diabetes mellitus that requires the victim to take injections of insulin for the remainder of his or her life.

integral proteins The protein portions of a cell membrane that are permanent residents of the membrane. They always penetrate through the hydrophilic portion of the lipid bilayer into the hydrophobic zone, and some go all the way through the membrane.

integrator/controller The fraction of any homeostatic feedback loop that accepts information about a stimulus and decides whether things are outside tolerance limits. If so, it sends instructions that will bring conditions back in line.

intercalated discs Unusual and irregular contact points between cardiac muscle cells.

interferon A specific protein produced intracellularly when a cell is assaulted by a virus. Interferon stimulates reactions in nearby cells that interfere with the ability of the virus to replicate.

internuncial A neuron that connects two separate neurons, or relays information from one neuron to another. Internuncial is a synonym for interneuron or connecting neuron.

interphase The period of time during a normal cell cycle when the cell is neither preparing for, nor undergoing, mitosis. This is the phase during which the nuclear envelope is present and the chromosomes are not visible.

interstitial Pertaining to areas outside cells but still within a tissue. It refers to intercellular fluids.

interstitial cell-stimulating hormone (ICSH) *See* luteinizing hormone

intervertebral disc A layer of fibrocartilage separating two bony elements of the vertebral column.

intracellular compartment Pertaining to that which is inside the cell; all fluids that are inside body cells.

intravascular clots Clots inside blood vessels.

intrinsic factor A glycoprotein secreted by the lining of the stomach that can bind to vitamin B_{12} and protect it (the vitamin) from the destructive action of stomach acids and enzymes.

intrinsic pathway A biochemical pathway leading to the formation of a clot. Whereas the extrinsic pathway is stimulated by substances released by damaged cells, the intrinsic pathway is stimulated in the absence of cell damage by the contact between the blood and a foreign surface.

intrinsic protein *See* integral proteins

invertebrate An animal lacking a vertebral column. Any animal not belonging to the phylum Chordata.

ion A charged particle. It may be atomic or molecular in size.

ionic bond A chemical bond formed between a metallic ion and a nonmetallic ion.

ionization potential The energy necessary to strip an electron or electrons away from the outermost orbit of an element with the subsequent formation of an ion.

ion (sodium/potassium) pump The energy-consuming cellular machinery that is responsible for pumping sodium ions out of, and potassium ions into, a given cell, thus maintaining the correct ion imbalance between the intracellular and interstitial fluids.

IPSP Inhibitory postsynaptic potential. A permeability change in a postsynaptic membrane that tends to hyperpolarize rather than depolarize, thus inhibiting the development of an action potential in that neuron.

iris The pigmented tissue that surrounds the pupil of the eye and is responsible for widening or narrowing the pupil to conform to varying intensities of light.

irritable membrane A plasma membrane that features a solid link between the voltage that is developed across it and the membrane's permeability to sodium.

ischemia An inadequate blood flow to any given zone in an organ or tissue, regardless of the cause.

islets of Langerhans Clusters of cells and blood vessels that are scattered throughout the pancreas. Cells within the islets are all secretory cells and are probably chemoreceptive cells as well. There are three types of these cells: α cells, which secrete glucagon, β cells, which secrete insulin, and δ cells, which synthesize and secrete somatostatin.

isomers Compounds having the same molecular formula but different structures and properties.

isometric contraction Activation of muscle tissue that results in a change in muscle tension but no change in muscle length.

isotonic contraction Activation of muscle tissue that results in a change in muscle length but no change in tension.

isotope An elemental form in which there is a variation in the number of neutrons in the nucleus of an element but no variation in proton number. Isotopes have the same atomic number, but a different mass.

IUD (intrauterine device) A small structure, usually a coil of fine wire or plastic with a fine thread attached, that is inserted into the uterus as a contraceptive agent.

J

jaundice A disease state in which the skin takes on a yellowish hue. It is caused by a plug of some sort in the common bile duct, which produces a backup of bilirubin into the blood.

juxtaglomerular apparatus A group of cells from two separate structures, the macula densa and the juxtaglomerular cells of the circulatory system. These structures are found in close proximity to each other in the kidney.

K

kidney A large paired organ in the back near the shoulder blades, the kidney is responsible for maintaining homeostasis in our body fluids.

killer cell The name given to activated T cells of the body's cellular immune system. They are called killer cells because they attack and literally kill invading (foreign) cells.

kinetic energy Energy of motion—energy actually performing work.

Krebs cycle The aerobic aspect of intermediary metabolism. Fuel that has been broken down to some extent by enzymes in the cell cytoplasm is fed into the mitochondria, where the first of the oxidative reactions takes place.

L

lactate The negatively charged form of lactic acid. This is the form in which lactic acid exists in all aqueous solutions.

lactation The synthesis and secretion of milk into the storage ducts of the mammary glands.

lactose The disaccharide found in milk, lactose is formed of glucose and galactose.

large intestine The last segment of the digestive tract. It includes the colon and rectum, where water is withdrawn from the indigestible fragments of food and the feces are formed for disposal.

larynx The voice box, the zone in the pharyngeal area where the vocal cords are located.

latent period The period of time between the stimulus (electrical activation) and the beginning of contraction in muscle tissue.

lateral line organs The organs that run down along the side of a fish's body and produce a perceptive awareness that corresponds to hearing in mammals.

LATS *See* long-acting thyroid stimulant

Legionnaires' disease A lethal, pneumonia-like affliction caused by bacteria. It was first diagnosed among members of the American Legion during a convention held in Philadelphia in 1976.

lens A pliable biconvex structure immediately behind the pupil of the eye. It can alter its shape slightly to focus visual images onto the retina.

leprosy A chronic bacterial disease, known today as Hansen's disease, that selectively attacks sensory endings of peripheral nerves, eliminating all sensory input from body surfaces.

leucocyte White blood cell.

leucocytosis An increase in the number of white blood cells in the circulation, usually the result of an infection. Leucocytosis is diagnosed whenever the WBC count reaches 15,000 per mm^3 or higher.

leukemia A malignant disease, possibly autoimmune in nature, that attacks the bone marrow and results in the uncontrolled proliferation of white blood cells.

leukotrienes A group of chemicals that have been identified as antagonists in some of the body's allergic reactions.

ligament The tough, fibrous connective tissue holding elements of the skeletal system together. Although composed of essentially the same tissue as tendons, they are more elastic than tendons.

limbic system The portion of the brain between the cerebral structures and the hindbrain.

lipid Any organic chemical that will not dissolve in water, but is soluble in any nonpolar fat solvent such as alcohol or ether.

lipid bilayer The double-layered, dynamic structure that forms spontaneously when phospholipids are stirred into water.

lipoprotein A complex organic molecule that combines proteinaceous and fatty fractions. Following the hydrolysis of lipids in the gut, the free lipids are linked to proteins in the absorptive cells of the intestine and are carried in the blood as miscible lipoproteins.

liquid phase A phase assumed by matter, the liquid phase contains more energy than the solid phase, but less than the gaseous phase.

liver The largest single organ in the abdominal cavity, the liver is responsible for a huge number of things, including the metabolism of all types of foodstuffs.

liver cirrhosis *See* cirrhosis

local anesthetics Chemicals capable of eliminating the ability to perceive pain in certain discrete body zones without interfering with consciousness.

long-acting thyroid stimulator (LATS) A compound derived from immunoglobulins that can imitate the activity of the thyroid-stimulating hormone (TSH) without being subject to any of the feedback limitations that control the latter.

long-term memory One of two types of memory; it seems to have no capacity limits and can last for decades.

loop of Henle A portion of the kidney nephron, the loop of Henle features the countercurrent multiplier that makes it possible for the medullary portion of the kidney to possess unusually high concentrations of salt.

Lou Gehrig's disease *See* amyotropic lateral sclerosis

LSD An acronym for lysergic acid diethylamide, LSD is a powerful hallucinogenic drug with an enormous capacity for abuse.

lumen A cavity, hollow, or passageway with a tube or saclike organ.

luteinizing Literally, "yellowing." Pertains to the luteinizing hormone.

luteinizing hormone (LH) One of the two gonadotrophins released by the adenohypophysis. LH is involved mainly with the gonadal cells responsible for the synthesis and secretion of steroid hormones. Called ICSH in males.

lymph A pale yellow ultrafiltrate of the blood, formed when interstitial fluid is squeezed into the vessels of the lymphatic circulatory system.

lymphatic system The system of tubes and nodes that make up the lymphatic circulatory system.

lymph node An expansion or swelling that occurs periodically in vessels of the lymphatic circulatory system. The lymph nodes contain a fine-mesh filter and large numbers of T cells.

lymphocyte A granulocytic white blood cell, the most polymorphic of all white blood cells.

lymphokines A series of incompletely known organic compounds that are synthesized and released by killer cells of the cellular immune system.

lysosome An intracellular digestive organelle, membranous in origin, that contains quantities of enzymes capable of hydrolyzing lipids, carbohydrates, nucleic acids, and proteins.

M

macrocytic normochromic anemia A type of anemia characterized by the appearance of abnormally large erythrocytes.

macrophage A large phagocytic leucocyte found throughout the body's connective tissues; never present in the circulatory system. The macrophage is a modified monocyte.

macula densa A zone in the distal tubule of the kidney nephron located at the point where contact is made with the afferent arteriole as it leaves the glomerulus.

macula lutea A zone within the retinal layer of the eye that is about 1 mm in diameter. Within this disk is the fovea centralis, which represents the area of greatest visual acuity.

malleus Literally, a "hammer." One of the three middle ear bones that amplifies and transmits mechanical sound waves from the tympanic membrane into the receptor areas of the inner ear.

maltase An enzyme produced in the mucosa of the small intestine that can hydrolyze maltose into its two component glucose monomers.

maltose A disaccharide composed of two glucose molecules linked together by means of dehydration synthesis.

mammary gland One of the distinguishing characteristics of mammals, the mammary glands are clusters of milk-secreting glandular tissue located on the ventral (anterior) surface.

mammography A specialized X-ray process designed specifically for inspecting the interior of the breasts, usually for tumorous growths.

Maple Bark disease An occasionally fatal type of pneumonia caused by mold spores that grow under the bark of maple trees.

marijuana The common name given to *Cannabis sativa* or hemp. Grown for rope fiber in years past, the plant is now better known for the euphoric effects it produces when smoked, because it contains tetrahydrocannabinol.

marker protein A protein that identifies a cell or other structure as belonging to "self" or "non-self," depending on the conditions.

mass One of the properties of matter, mass is that which has inertia and is defined mathematically in terms of force and acceleration: mass = force × acceleration.

mass number A number relating, in grams, the total number of nucleons (protons and neutrons) present in a given element.

mast cell A connective tissue element found in large numbers around arterioles and other small blood vessels. When properly stimulated, mast cells release histamine, serotonin, and heparin.

master gland A name frequently applied to the pituitary gland because of its ability to control so many other endocrine glands.

masticate To chew.

masturbation Literally, "to pollute oneself," although current outlook doesn't agree with the nomenclature. It refers to the achievement of orgasm through manipulation of one's own genitalia.

matter The material stuff of the universe, matter is that which has mass, inertia, and occupies a point in space that no other material can occupy at the same time.

mechanical digestion The process by which complex chunks of food are physically battered, smashed, and chopped into smaller chunks so that the mass can be further attacked by aspects of chemical digestion.

mechanoreceptor A specialized sensory receptor designed to respond optimally to some sort of mechanical distortion of its surface.

medulla The interior of an organ or structure, as opposed to the cortex, which represents the "peel" of the organ.

medulla oblongata A cone-shaped mass of cells in the brain stem between the spinal cord and the pons.

medullary respiratory center An area in the medulla oblongata containing cells involved in the control of breathing.

meiosis A type of cellular division restricted to the germ cells of the gonads, meiosis undertakes to segregate homologous chromosomes, sort them randomly, and then reduce the total chromosomal content of the cell to half that of a normal body cell.

Meissner corpuscle A specialized somatosensory receptor.

megakaryocyte An unusually large cell in the blood-cell manufacturing area of the long bones. The cytoplasm of the megakaryocyte periodically breaks into fragments called platelets.

melanin A dark brown pigment found in certain dermal cells and frequently in tumors.

melanocyte A cell commonly present in the dermis that synthesizes melanin. When stimulated by ultraviolet light, these cells spread out and migrate toward the upper zones of the dermis, producing a tan.

melanocyte-stimulating hormone (MSH) A hormone secreted by the intermediate lobe (part of the adenohypophysis) of the pituitary gland, MSH specifically stimulates the expansion and migration of melanocytes.

membrane Generally, refers to any thin sheet or filament that is used to cover a given surface. In biological contexts, membrane refers to the lipid/protein film that separates the cytoplasm of a cell from the interstitial fluid that bathes it.

membrane potential The voltage, sometimes known as "resting potential," that is normally present across the membrane of a living cell. If the interstitial fluid is reckoned as the "zero" value, the interior of the cell has a voltage ranging from −30 to −110 millivolts.

memory cell A specialized lymphocyte produced during the accelerated division of cells that occurs when stimulated by an antigen. Memory cells neither kill nor produce antibody but rather retain the recognition pattern of the antigen as well as the genetic information for production of an effective antibody.

menarche The beginning of menstruation in a young girl.

meninges Singular *meninx*. The three membranes that enwrap the central nervous system. The innermost meninx is the pia mater, the middle one is the arachnoid mater, and the outermost one is the dura mater.

menopause The cessation of menstruation. Usually occurs in humans between the ages of 45 and 55.

menstrual cycle The cyclic process that takes place in women and prepares them for pregnancy. Mainly an endocrinological operation, menstruation produces changes in the lining of the uterus and vagina and stimulates the development of a germ cell into a mature ovum that is capable of fusing with the nucleus of a mature spermatozoan.

Merkel's discs Specialized somatosensory receptors, Merkel's discs are moderately slow-acting touch receptors.

messenger RNA (mRNA) A type of nucleic acid responsible for obtaining information from nuclear DNA and carrying it into the cytoplasm, where synthetic mechanisms are available to obey the instructions it carries.

metabolic water Water produced by the union of subatomic debris spinning out of the respiratory chain and the oxygen that is breathed in.
metabolism The sum total of all biochemical and mechanical operations taking place in the body. It includes both the anabolic (constructive) and catabolic (destructive) aspects.
metaphase One of the phases of cellular mitosis. During metaphase, the chromosomes that appeared during prophase line themselves up on the cellular equator preparatory to splitting apart.
metarteriole A blood vessel that joins capillaries to arterioles. Like arterioles, metarterioles can constrict or dilate in response to the body's commands.
micelle A microscopic globe formed of amphipathic molecules in a water solution. The molecules of the globe are arranged so that the hydrophilic ends face the watery matrix while the hydrophobic ends are huddled in the middle of the globe.
microcytic hypochromic anemia A form of anemia featuring unusually small erythrocytes, each of which contains a smaller-than-normal amount of hemoglobin.
microfilament A cluster of contractile proteins arranged into a filament and responsible for stiffening the plasma membrane when necessary.
microtubule A hollow cylindrical structure composed of specific alignments of microfilaments. Microtubules are responsible for a cell's independent motility and for its ability to move materials back and forth within the cytoplasm.
microvilli Extensions of the cell membrane, microvilli are hollow tubes that poke out, usually from a single cell surface, and are particularly abundant in cells that line tubules or glandular structures. They increase the surface area of the cell.
micturition The process of urinating.
middle ear The portion of the ear that connects the tympanic membrane to the oval window of the inner ear. It is a hollow, air-filled cavity containing the three bones known as the middle ear ossicles.
migraine A particularly painful, recurring type of headache with an unknown cause and a very uncertain cure.
milieu interieur The internal environment. The phrase *milieu interieur* was coined by Claude Bernard in the last century to refer strictly to conditions that exist in the cytosol, interstitial fluids, and body tissues.
mineral In a biological context, one of the essential inorganic elements that are present in trace or larger amounts, such as calcium, sodium, phosphorous, and iron.
mineralocorticoids Steroid hormones secreted by the outermost layer of the adrenal cortex that control relative concentrations of mineral electrolytes in body fluids.
minute volume The volume of air moved in and out of the lungs in a single minute. Minute volume equals the tidal volume × respiratory rate.
mitochondrion An organelle of membranous origin that contains the necessary oxidative enzymes for the final processing of fuel molecules into free energy that the cell can use. The matrix of the mitochondria encloses the Krebs cycle operations as well as those of the respiratory chain.
mitosis The duplication of nuclear chromosomal material and the subsequent production of two brand-new cells where there was once only a single cell.
mitotic spindle A structure that forms in cells undergoing mitosis, the mitotic spindle is a spindle-shaped amalgam of microtubules, chromosomes, and centrioles that apparently serve to provide the traction and motive power necessary to pull centromeres apart.
mitral valve The valve between the left atrium and left ventricle of the heart.
mixed nerve Any nerve containing both sensory and motor fibers.
mixture *See* dispersion
mobile receptor A chemoreceptor present in the cytoplasm of cells that is designed to accept and respond to certain steroid hormones.
molal solution A standardized chemical unit. A molal solution exists whenever one mole of a substance is dissolved in one kilogram of solvent.
molar solution Another standardized chemical unit. A molar solution exists whenever there is one mole of a given substance per liter of solution.
mole A standardized concept, a mole exists whenever a given substance contains the same number of basic particles as there are atoms in 12 grams of pure carbon.
molecule A combination of two or more atoms resulting from a chemical interaction.
monoamine oxidase (MAO) An enzyme capable of oxidizing the neurotransmitters epinephrine and/or norepinephrine.
monocyte An agranular leucocyte. Monocytes change dramatically when they leave the circulatory system, becoming the enlarged and voraciously phagocytic cells called macrophages.
monomer A compound capable of combining with itself repeatedly to form a larger molecule.
monosaccharide A simple sugar. Monosaccharides strictly obey the basic structural carbohydrate formula $C_x(H_2O)_x$, with 'x' being a small, whole number. Most monosaccharides cannot be broken down into simpler sugars.
motor nerve Always efferent, motor nerves innervate muscles and provide the necessary stimuli that move the muscles they innervate.
motor unit A motor neuron and all the muscle fibers that it innervates.
mucin A glycoprotein synthesized and secreted by specialized cells of the gastrointestinal tract. Mucin-secreting cells are particularly abundant in the esophagus, stomach, and duodenum.
mucous (neck) cells Cells specialized in the synthesis and secretion of mucin.
mucus A combination of the glycoprotein mucin, inorganic salts, and, occasionally, leucocytes, mucus is secreted by cells lining certain tubular or glandular structures. It serves a protective function.
multiple sclerosis A neurological disease in which the myelin sheathing is stripped from neurons in apparently random patches and replaced with fibrous masses. The cause is unknown.
multiunit smooth muscle A type of smooth muscle. The other type is visceral.
muscle fatigue *See* fatigue
muscle spindle A stretch receptor located at strategic intervals in skeletal muscles. Muscle spindles are part of a feedback system designed to keep the skeletal muscles under constant tension.
muscle twitch An experimental event, the twitch is a single, rapid muscle contraction that results from one electrical stimulus.
myasthenia gravis A neuromuscular disease characterized by a rapidly developing and unusual fatigue in certain muscles, eventually progressing to paralysis. It is caused by a gradual loss of functioning acetylcholine receptors in the motor end plate of the muscles involved.
myelin sheath A fatty sheath surrounding the axons of certain peripheral nerves. Myelin is produced by extraneuronal cells called Schwann cells and serves as a protective agency as well as a means of speeding the propagation of action potentials along the nerve involved.
myocardial infarction Necrosis of a portion of the myocardium due to lack of adequate blood flow.
myocardium The heart muscle.
myofibrils The contractile elements within muscle fibers.
myofilaments The contractile proteins of which myofibrils are made, myofilaments consist of four contractile proteins arranged in parallel register. When the muscle contracts, the proteins interdigitate and slide past one another the way fingers do when the hands are clasped together.
myoglobin A hemoglobin-like structure found in skeletal muscle. Whereas hemoglobin contains four iron molecules, myoglobin has only one.
myoneural junction The point at which the motor neuron infiltrates the muscle it innervates.
myopia Commonly known as "nearsightedness," myopia is usually caused by an abnormally elongated eyeball.

myosin One of the contractile proteins, myosin molecules grouped together make up the thick filaments of the myofibril.

myotactic reflex A simple reflex that is stimulated when a muscle is abruptly stretched.

myringotomy An incision made in the tympanic membrane, usually to relieve excessive pressure caused by the accumulation of fluid in the middle ear.

myxedema Literally, "a swelling due to mucus," myxedema is an affliction of adults caused by an inadequate production of iodinated thyroid hormone.

N

naked nerve endings Somatosensory nerve endings lacking specialized receptor organs. Naked nerve endings are probably responsible for thermal sensitivity and pain reception, as well as fine tactile reception.

nasal septum The cartilaginous sheet that runs longitudinally down the middle of the nose, separating the two nostrils.

natural killer cell A specialized T cell. Natural killer cells are apparently involved almost exclusively in attacking and destroying certain types of cancer cells.

negative feedback loop A feedback system in which the effect produced by the effector opposes the original stimulus. Negative feedback loops are the primary control loops involved in homeostasis.

nephron The functional unit of the kidney, the nephron consists of a renal corpuscle, proximal convoluted tubule, loop of Henle, distal convoluted tubule, and a portion of the collecting duct.

nerve A cluster of neuronal fibers outside the central nervous system. Nerves may be specialized into motor or sensory nerves, or they may be mixed nerves, which contain both kinds of fibers.

nerve ganglion A cluster of nerve cell bodies outside the central nervous system.

nerve impulse The action potential.

neuroendocrine cell A highly specialized cell capable of functioning as both a neuron and a secretory endocrine cell.

neurohypophysis The lobe of the pituitary gland that consists of neural tissue, mainly axonal fibers extending from two pairs of hypothalamic nuclei. It secretes vasopressin and oxytocin.

neuron The functional unit of the nervous system.

neuropeptide A proteinaceous neural secretion.

neurosecretion A compound synthesized and secreted by a neuron.

neurostenin One of the contractile proteins in the end buttons of a neuron that is responsible for secreting the neurotransmitter.

neurotransmitter A chemical assembled and secreted by the end button of a neuron when an action potential arrives. It carries the message of the action potential from one neuron to another.

neutral fat A glycerol molecule linked via dehydration synthesis to three fatty acid chains. The term is synonymous with triglyceride.

neutron One of the three prime subatomic particles. Neutrons have a mass approximately equal to the mass of a proton, but they lack an electromagnetic charge.

neutrophil The most abundant of all the leucocytes, neutrophils are classified as phagocytic, granular polymorphonucleocytes.

nicotinamide adenine dinucleotide (NAD^+) A coenzyme capable of undergoing oxidation and reduction, NAD is involved, among other things, in transferring electrons from fuel molecules in the Krebs cycle into the respiratory chain.

Nissl (tigroid) substance Rough endoplasmic reticulum in the soma of neurons. It was given the name tigroid substance by British researchers who likened its patterns in nerve cell bodies to the stripes on a tiger.

nitrogen-containing organic base (nucleotide base) One of the purine or pyrimidine bases that make up the repeating units of nucleic acids.

noble gas An electrically neutral element with a stable electron arrangement in its valence shell.

nociceptor A specialized sensory receptor designed to perceive pain.

nocturnal emission An orgasm, occurring usually in recently matured males, as the result of an erotic dream. Known euphemistically as a wet dream.

nodes of Ranvier Zones of exposed neurilemma that appear periodically in myelinated nerve fibers. The nodes are the sites of axonal depolarization in myelinated neurons.

non-insulin-dependent diabetes Once called adult-onset diabetes, non-insulin-dependent diabetes is a form of diabetes mellitus in which the victim often produces enough insulin, but for some reason the target tissues have lost their sensitivity to that hormone. Usually controllable with careful diet.

nonspecific immune system Defense mechanisms of the body that are designed to attack, or resist invasion by, any non-self antigen. The skin, mucous membranes, and phagocytic leucocytes are all considered part of the nonspecific immune system.

norepinephrine A precursor of epinephrine.

normal flora When used in a microbiological context, it refers to bacterial colonies that are permanent guests in a given body zone.

nuclear envelope The outer boundary of the nucleus. The nuclear envelope is similar to strips of smooth endoplasmic reticulum, and it differs from the plasma membrane in that it lacks cholesterol molecules and is double-layered.

nucleic acid A long string of repeating nucleotide units. Nucleic acids are either ribonucleic acids (RNA) or deoxyribonucleic acids (DNA). The repeating units consist of a pentose sugar, an organic phosphate group, and either a purine or a pyrimidine nucleotide base.

nucleolus Literally, "a diminutive nucleus," the nucleolus is a cluster of ribosomal material—both RNA and ribosomal protein—that has been synthesized but has not yet left the nuclear envelope.

nucleus In biological science, (a) the core of an atom, consisting of protons and neutrons; (b) the membrane-wrapped organelle containing the cellular DNA; or (c) a cluster of nerve cell bodies located within the central nervous system.

O

Oddi's sphincter The muscle wrapped around the common bile duct just below the point where the cystic duct from the gallbladder enters. Normally, Oddi's sphincter is contracted between meals, and is relaxed by the presence of the hormone cholescystokinen.

ohm A unit of electrical resistance.

olfactory Pertaining to the sense of smell, one of the five primary senses.

olfactory epithelium The layer of epithelial tissue within the nasal cavity between the internal and external nares.

oogenesis A specific type of meiosis that is peculiar to female germ cells and results in the formation of a mature ovum. *See* meiosis

opsonization A phenomenon associated with the activity of the specific immune system; this is a process that renders bacterial cells and/or other foreign cells especially susceptible to attacks by phagocytes.

optic chiasma A point located just beneath the floor of the hypothalamus where the optic nerves cross over one another and distribute their fibers to both sides of the brain.

optic nerve Axonal processes from ganglion cells of the retina that have clustered together into two nerves, one from each eye. The optic nerve is considered the second cranial nerve.

organelle A subcellular structure analogous to a body organ and having a specialized structure and function.

organic chemistry The branch of chemistry that deals exclusively with carbon compounds.

organ of Corti The snailshell-shaped organ within the inner ear that contains the receptors responsible for transducing the mechanical energy of sound waves into neural impulses.

organs of equilibrium The utricles and saccules of the inner ear. These organs are responsible for detection and transduction of energy produced by movement of the whole organism.
orthopnea A condition in which the victim experiences considerable difficulty in breathing when in any position except upright.
osmoreceptors Specialized receptors capable of detecting changes in osmotic pressure in the surrounding fluids.
osmosis Movement of water through a semipermeable membrane in response to a concentration gradient that exists between the solutions separated by that membrane.
osmotic pressure The amount of water pressure that is generated by osmosis.
ossicles The three bones of the middle ear. *See* incus; malleus; stapes
osteoclast A skeletal cell that specializes in disrupting the protein matrix of bone tissue, thus freeing the calcium salts that impregnate that area of the bone.
otoliths Calcareous crystals that are present in the utricle and saccule of the middle ear and are part of the stimulus involved in static equilibrium.
oval window The membrane-covered opening in the organ of Corti that forms a junction with the bones of the middle ear.
ovarian cycle The periodic maturation and release of an ovum from the ovary.
ovary The female gonads. The ovaries make up the primary reproductive organ in females. The feminine counterpart of the male testicles.
ovulation The release of an ovum from the ovaries.
oxaloacetate The final compound to form during the breakdown of fuel molecules in the Krebs reactions. It joins with acetate to form citric acid, which initiates the Krebs reactions again.
oxidation Any chemical reaction that leaves the original atom with an increased positive charge. This usually involves the loss of electrons, but it can involve the flow of protons or whole hydrogen atoms.
oxidative (aerobic) metabolism The name given to the catabolic reactions that take place within the confines of the mitochondria.
oxidative phosphorylation A series of reactions that take place in the respiratory chains of the mitochondria. It refers to the extraction of energy from a chain of moving electrons and using that energy to link phosphate onto ADP molecules.
oxygen debt The amount of oxygen required to eliminate the lactic acid formed during intensive, anaerobic exercise. It is a systemic phenomenon and is not restricted to the muscle tissue in which the lactic acid was generated.
oxytocin An octapeptide that is synthesized in certain hypothalamic cells and released by the neurohypophysis. Oxytocin is a powerful smooth muscle stimulant, exerting most of its effects on the muscles of the uterus and those surrounding the lactating glands in the breasts.

P

Pacinian corpuscle A somatosensory receptor, the Pacinian corpuscle is a very rapidly adapting, deep pressure sensor believed to be capable of detecting vibration.
pancreas A large, diffuse, and rather elongated visceral organ that wraps around the intestinal tract just behind the stomach. It is both an exocrine and an endocrine organ.
pancreatic amylase A starch-splitting enzyme produced by acinar cells of the pancreas and released into the small intestine.
pancreatic lipase A pancreatic enzyme that specializes in the hydrolysis of fats.
pancreatic nuclease A pancreatic enzyme that splits nucleic acids into their component molecules.
pancreatic polypeptide (PP) A peptide secreted by cells outside the islets of Langerhans, PP appears to oppose the activity of cholecystokinin, inhibiting the gallbladder and stimulating constriction of the sphincter of Oddi.
pancreatitis An inflammation of the pancreas.
pancreozymin *See* cholecystokinin
pancytopenia A general, abnormal reduction in numbers of all the formed elements of the blood.
paralysis An inability to move; the term is usually restricted to muscle tissues. Paralysis may be *spastic,* in which case the involved muscles are in a constant state of contraction, or it may be *flaccid,* in which case the muscles are completely relaxed.
parasympathetic A branch of the autonomic (involuntary) nervous system. The parasympathetic system is usually involved with day-to-day involuntary operations. It generally opposes the activity of the sympathetic nervous system.
parathormone The polypeptide hormone synthesized and released by cells of the parathyroid glands. Parathormone is a critical manipulator of ionic calcium and phosphates in body fluids.
parathyroid gland The smallest of the endocrine glands, located in and/or near the thyroid gland.
paraventricular nucleus A cluster of neuronal cell bodies located in the hypothalamus adjacent to the third brain ventricle. This is the nucleus responsible for the synthesis of oxytocin.
parietal Pertaining to the walls of a gourd or cavity. Used in a biological context, the word generally refers either to a lobe of the brain next to the parietal bones of the skull or to cells in the stomach that are responsible for the isolation and secretion of hydrochloric acid.
parotid gland One of the structures in the mouth responsible for the synthesis and secretion of salivary fluids.
pars intermedia The intermediate lobe of the pituitary gland. Part of the adenohypophysis.
partial pressure The pressure contributed by a single gas in a mixture of gases. The partial pressure of a given gas is proportional to the percent composition of that gas.
parturition Live childbirth, as opposed to hatching from an egg. Parturition is the process by which the fetus is expelled from the mammalian uterus.
passive Pertaining to that which is not active but rather is acted upon. In a medical context, it often refers to passive immunity, which is immunity provided by antibodies synthesized by some other person.
patellar reflex A commonly tested simple reflex. It is tested by tapping the patellar tendon (the tendon just below the kneecap) and noting the reflex contraction of the thigh muscle.
penicillin One of the first of the antibiotic substances to be isolated from microorganisms. It is extracted from the molds Penicillium and Aspergillus. It destroys bacteria by eliminating their ability to grow cell walls.
pentose sugar A five-carbon sugar.
pepsin The active fraction of pepsinogen, pepsin is a protein-splitting enzyme secreted by the gastric mucosa.
peptic (chief) cell One of the secretory cells of the gastric glands. Chief cells are responsible for the synthesis and secretion of pepsinogen.
peptide bond The type of chemical bond that holds amino acids together, thus making possible the formation of amino acid polymers—the peptides and proteins. The peptide bond is formed by dehydration synthesis.
peptide hormone Any hormone that consists of two or more amino acids.
pericardial sac The highly polished, glossy-smooth connective tissue sac in which the heart is suspended. The pericardium is continuous with the epicardium (*see* epicardium).
perikaryon (soma) The cell body of a neuron.
perilymph The fluid between the bony and the membranous labyrinths in the equilibrium organs of the inner ear.
perineurium The connective sheet that wraps bundles of neurons, thus isolating them from other, similar bundles, in a peripheral nerve.

periodic table of elements A table of the elements arranged in such a way as to relate those having similar chemical properties.
peripheral nerve A nerve in the peripheral nervous system.
peripheral nervous system Any nerves outside the brain and spinal cord.
peripheral protein *See* extrinsic protein
peristalsis The wavelike contractions of smooth muscles typical of the intestinal tubes, where peristalsis moves foods and fluids through the gastrointestinal tract.
peritubular capillaries (vasa recta) The mass of capillaries that arises from the efferent arteriole of the glomerulus and envelopes the other elements of the nephron. The peritubular capillaries ensure that any materials pumped from inside the nephron into the interstitial spaces will be promptly picked up by the blood.
pernicious anemia A primary anemia manifested by an abnormally low erythrocyte count. It is usually caused by a deficiency of vitamin B_{12}, usually because the victim is unable to synthesize and secrete effective intrinsic factor from the stomach.
pH A standardized means of communicating acidity or alkalinity, pH describes the concentration of hydrogen ions $[H^+]$ in a solution. Mathematically, $pH = -\log_{10}[H^+]$.
phagocytic cell A blood cell that literally "eats" unwanted debris and/or invading bacteria and antigens.
phasic receptor A sensory receptor that responds mainly to change in its adequate stimulus.
phospholipid A lipid in which two of the glycerol's available OH^- groups are linked to fatty acids, while the third is bonded to a phosphate group, which in its turn is linked to a nitrogenous molecule. The portion of the molecule containing the nitrogen and phosphate groups is often referred to as the hydrophilic (water loving) portion, while the other portions are said to be hydrophobic (water fearing).
photoreceptor A sensory receptor capable of responding to electromagnetic radiations in the visible spectrum.
physical properties Characteristics of elements or compounds that do not involve their ability to combine with other elements or compounds.
physiological saline A mixture of salts and buffers intended to osmotically simulate normal body fluids.
pia mater The innermost meninx of the meninges of the brain. The pia is extremely thin and fragile and is so closely associated with brain tissue that some workers consider it part of the brain and not a meninx at all.
pigment Any chemical compound that reflects a specific group of light rays.
pineal gland A little-known structure near the third brain ventricle believed to be a functioning endocrine gland.
pinnae The major portion of the external ears of mammals. The pinnae are the cartilaginous ear structures that project from the sides of the human head.
pituitary *See* hypophysis
pituitary dwarf A disease state that produces an abnormally tiny individual. This is due to an inadequate amount of somatotropin available during the years of growth.
pituitary giant A disease state that produces an abnormally large individual. It results from hypersecretion of the pituitary hormone somatotropin before puberty.
placenta An organ that develops from both maternal and fetal tissue in the uterus of pregnant mammals. It serves as a zone of nutrient and waste exchange between the maternal blood and that of the fetus.
plasma The liquid fraction of whole blood. Plasma is a yellowish, transparent fluid rich in protein.
plasma cell A type of B cell lymphocyte responsible for the synthesis of antibodies.
plasma membrane *See* cell membrane
plasmin A protein capable of attacking and hydrolyzing fibrin, plasmin is a clot-dissolving enzyme.
plasminogen The inactive form of plasmin.
platelet A formed element of the blood produced when the cytoplasm of megakaryocytes in bone marrow is fragmented.
platelet plug A mass of platelets with adhesive surfaces, all sticking together and jammed as a unit into a hole or slice that has been cut into a blood vessel. Platelet plugs form when a blood vessel is damaged and blood is leaking from the circulatory system.
plexus A thick network or mat of capillaries, nerve fibers, or lymphatic vessels.
Plummer's disease A form of toxic goiter, Plummer's disease is a relatively gentle form of hyperthyroidism, usually caused by a hypersecreting nodule on the thyroid gland.
pneumonia An inflammation of alveolar and bronchiolar tissue in the lungs, with the subsequent secretion of exudates (usually phlegm) and exfoliation of tissue.
pneumotaxic center A cluster of nerve cells located in the pons of the hindbrain that are involved in the process of breathing. This is the center that depresses the activity of the apneustic center during the respiratory cycle.
podocyte Specialized cells that develop from epithelial cells in Bowman's capsule. Extensions of these cells enwrap the glomerular blood vessels and receive the first blood ultrafiltrate that enters the kidney nephron.
polar covalent bond When covalent bonds form between different types of atoms, there is always an imbalance in the distribution of the shared electrons. Inevitably, they will tend to gather around the atomic nucleus with the greatest positivity, thus creating zones of electrical charge. Such bondings are said to be polar covalent bonds.
polar molecule Any molecule that has an unequal distribution of electrical charge.
polygraph An instrument designed to measure many electrical characteristics of a living body, including skin resistance, electroencephalography, ECG, respiratory rate (ZPG), muscle movement, and so on. Often referred to as a lie detector.
polymer A large molecule constructed by linking together smaller, repeating units. *See* monomer
polysaccharide A large, complex sugar molecule constructed by linking together chains of smaller sugar molecules.
polyuria Elimination of large volumes of urine.
pons One of the structures of the hindbrain. It forms a contact between the medulla oblongata and the mesencephalon or middle brain.
positive feedback A homeostatic loop in which the product of the effector tends to support or increase the stimulus. Positive feedback loops are inherently unstable, and there are very few in living systems.
posterior chamber When used in reference to the eye, the term pertains to the chamber between the lens and the iris.
posterior root Called the dorsal root when not referring to human beings, this is a bundle of sensory neurons entering the central nervous system between the bony elements of the vertebral column.
postsynaptic element The receptor zone (often dendritic) of any neuron in a position to receive information from a preceding neural element.
postsynaptic potential (PSP) Any voltage change that is initiated on a postsynaptic element as a result of information transmitted from a precedent neuron.
potential electrical energy Electrical energy that is available for work but is not yet doing anything. An electrical charge, or voltage.
potential energy Energy that is available, but is not yet doing anything.
PQRST wave The designation given to an electrocardiographic pattern taken from lead 2 of a polygraph.
prepuce (foreskin) The normally retractable sheath of skin that covers the glans penis in males and the clitoris in females. This is the tissue that is removed during circumcision.

presbyopia A loss of elasticity in the lens of the eye that normally occurs with age. It renders the subject incapable of adjusting visual focus through a very broad range.

presynaptic element A neuronal end button in a synapse. The portion of the synapse that precedes the synaptic cleft.

presynaptic fiber The neuronal axon that ends in the presynaptic element.

primary follicle The cluster of cells within the ovary that surround the potential ovum.

primary immune response The immune system's response to its first encounter with an antigen.

primary sensory neuron Neuron featuring specialized receptors and axons that carry the messages from that particular receptor.

primary sexual characteristics The testicles of a man or the ovaries of a woman.

primary spermatocyte A developing male germ cell that is derived from the spermatogonium. The primary spermatocyte possesses a full complement of chromosomes and must undergo meiosis to reduce the number.

primordial A word referring to that which is the very first or the oldest of any given type.

P-R interval The time interval between the beginning of an ECG P wave and the beginning of the R wave.

progesterone The hormone synthesized and secreted by the corpus luteum or by the placenta of a pregnant woman. Progesterone is a steroid hormone that stimulates cellular and glandular proliferation of the uterus and lactogenic cells of the breasts.

prolactin A peptide hormone of the adenohypophysis, prolactin stimulates milk production in postpartum female mammals. In nonmammals, it is thought to stimulate parental behavior.

prolapsing The downward displacement, or drop, of a body part, usually referring to some large abdominal organ.

prophase The first phase of mitosis, characterized by a dissolution of the nuclear envelope and the appearance of the chromosomes.

proprioceptor Sensory receptors involved with the perception of movement. In humans, the proprioceptors are buried in tendons, muscle tissue, and inner ear organs of equilibrium.

prostaglandins A group of recently discovered fatty acids that occur naturally in all humans. They can cause pain and abnormal muscle contractions and relaxations, and they are capable of changing the operations of some hormones. Anti-prostaglandins are often used as analgesics.

prostate gland A mass of male glandular tissue through which the urethra passes. The prostate secretes a milky white fluid that is injected into the urethra when ejaculation is about to occur.

protein A large polymer of amino acids. The difference between a peptide and a protein is tenuous, but generally speaking, any amino acid polymer larger than 10,000 daltons could be considered a protein.

proteinaceous hormone A peptide or protein hormone. Any hormone made up of amino acids, the protein's building blocks.

proteolytic enzymes Enzymes that are designed to break up protein molecules into their component structures.

proton The positively charged nuclear particle in an atom.

proximal convoluted tubule The portion of the nephron immediately adjacent to the Bowman's capsule. The proximal tubule connects the capsule and the loop of Henle.

ptyalin The starch-splitting enzyme produced by the salivary glands.

puberty The point at which a person achieves adulthood—the ability to produce an offspring.

pulmonary circulation The portion of the circulatory system that carries the blood from the heart, through the lungs, and back to the heart again.

pulmonary veins Vessels carrying blood from the lungs back to the heart.

pulmonic semilunar valve A valve in the right ventricle of the heart that opens to permit blood to flow into the pulmonary artery.

pulse pressure The difference between the systolic pressure and the diastolic pressure. If systole is 125 and diastole is 60, pulse pressure is 65.

pupil With reference to the eye, the pupil is the opening between the anterior chamber and the lens.

purine A heterocyclic, double-ringed, nitrogen-containing compound. Two of the purines are nucleotide bases (adenine and guanine).

Purkinje fibers Modified myocardial fibers that branch from the bundle of His and spread through the ventricle. They carry the depolarizing impulses from the bundle to the ventricular muscle cells.

pyloric sphincter The sphincter muscle that sits between the stomach and the small intestine.

pyorrhea A disease of the oral cavity that manifests itself with reddening and swelling of the gums that ultimately progresses to bleeding. Bone deterioration and loss of all the teeth is the inevitable result if the disease is not checked.

pyrimidine A heterocyclic, single-ringed nitrogen-containing compound. Three of the pyrimidines are nucleotide bases (thymine, cytosine, and uracil).

pyruvate The final form of the fuel molecule as it progresses through the glycolytic reactions. Pyruvate is the structure that forms before the fuel is decarboxylated and linked to coenzyme A for transport into the mitochondria.

Q

QRS complex The portion of an electrocardiogram that shows the electrical stimulation of the ventricles.

quantum A quantity or amount of something, usually specified.

quantal transmission The theory that neurotransmitter is released from the presynaptic endings in discrete bundles or packets containing an unspecified number of neurotransmitter molecules. The bundles or packets are referred to as quanta.

R

radioactive Materials that emit electromagnetic radiation or subatomic particles as they disintegrate are said to be radioactive materials. Such materials have considerable value in medicine and scientific research.

rapid ejection phase A phase of the cardiac cycle that begins immediately after the semilunar valves in the ventricles open to permit outflow.

receptive field A zone surrounding a sensory receptor that can, if stimulated, cause some depolarization of the receptor.

receptor (a) Any sensory ending capable of converting ambient energy into neural impulses. (b) Molecules arranged into a shape designed to be fit onto molecules with a specifically complementary shape.

receptor potential The slow depolarization of nerve endings that results from the stimulation of a specialized receptor. These depolarizations are usually quite small and spread decrementally from their source.

rectifier An arrangement of electrical elements that permits current flow in only a single direction. Neural synapses and myoneural junctions are neuronal rectifiers.

redox reactions Oxidation reactions usually involve the loss of electrons, and those electrons must go somewhere. The elements that accept the electrons are said to be reduced. Such reactions are always coupled, and redox is an abbreviation of reduction/oxidation.

reduced ejection phase A phase during the cardiac cycle immediately following the rapid ejection phase, when blood is still leaving the ventricles and entering the great arteries, but the outflow is relatively slow.

reduction A chemical reaction that is linked to oxidation. Reduction occurs when an element or molecule receives electrons, protons, or hydrogen atoms.

refractory period A period when the stimulus normally required to fire a neuron is inadequate to do so.

Reissner's membrane A fine membrane in the organ of Corti, sometimes called the vestibular membrane. It separates the cochlear duct from the scala vestibuli.

relative refractory period A period immediately following the absolute refractory period when the neural axon is capable of being fired, but requires a much greater stimulus than normal to do so.

relaxation period The period during a muscle twitch immediately following the peak of the contraction, when tension on the muscle is decreasing.

relaxin A polypeptide hormone produced by the corpus luteum that inhibits smooth muscle contractions of the uterus until the time is right for parturition to begin.

releasing hormones Hormones produced by the hypothalamus, most of which exert their effects on some part of the pituitary gland.

renal corpuscle The initial portion of the kidney nephron. It consists of a circulatory factor—the glomerulus—and a renal factor—Bowman's capsule.

renin An enzyme produced by the juxtaglomerular apparatus of the kidney. Through the activation of a series of subsequent enzymes and hormones, renin is ultimately capable of producing an increase in systemic blood pressure.

respiratory chain *See* cytochrome system

respiratory pigment The pigment in blood cells that bonds to molecular oxygen, thus enormously increasing the ability of the blood to carry oxygen. In vertebrates, this pigment is hemoglobin.

respiratory rate The number of breaths taken in a minute.

respiratory system The organ system that begins with the external nares (nostrils) and ends with the alveolar sacs in the lungs.

reticuloendothelial system The complex cellular system that protects by phagocytizing cellular debris or any foreign materials that might enter the body. All phagocytic cells are part of the reticuloendothelial system.

retina The light-sensitive part of the eye. It is where the light waves entering the eyeball are transduced into electrical impulses and sent along nerve axons to the brain.

retinal (retinene) A metabolic product of beta carotene, retinal is one fraction of the visual pigment of the retinal receptors known as rods.

retrovirus A virus that possesses no DNA but carries all necessary information on strips of RNA instead.

rhinitis An inflammation of the mucous membranes of the nasal cavity and/or nasal sinuses.

rhodopsin A visual pigment of retinal receptors. It breaks down when exposed to light, separating into the prosthetic group, retinal, and the protein scotopsin.

rhythm method A highly unreliable method of contraception often practiced by couples whose religion forbids copulation for any reason other than procreation. It advocates undertaking copulation only during those periods when the female is infertile.

ribonucleic acid (RNA) A strip of nucleic acid, differing from DNA in its shape, length, and some of its chemical constituents. There are several kinds of RNA.

ribose A five-carbon sugar. One of the subunits making up the repeating monomers of nucleic acids.

ribosomal RNA (rRNA) A type of ribonucleic acid that is part of a ribosome on which proteins are synthesized.

ribosome A subcellular organelle consisting of RNA and protein, on which proteins are assembled according to instructions from nuclear DNA.

rods Visual sensory receptors in the retina of the eye responsible for our being able to see in very dim light.

rough ER *See* endoplasmic reticulum

round window A small, membrane-covered opening in the organ of Corti that distends when the oval window is pushed in and pooches in when the oval window is drawn out. By moving when the oval window moves, the round window permits movement of the fluid within the organ of Corti.

Ruffini's end organ Slow-acting somatosensory receptors believed to be mainly responsive to slow pressure changes.

S

saccule Literally, "a small bag." One of the two chambers in the vestibular part of the labyrinth of the inner ear.

salt One of the products of a neutralization reaction between an acid and a base.

saltatory conduction Saltation means to leap, and it refers to the movement of information along a myelinated nerve. Because of the insulating effect of the myelin, action potentials can only appear at the nodes of Ranvier that occur periodically along such fibers; hence the signal appears to jump from node to node.

sarcolemma The plasma membrane of a muscle cell.

sarcomere A repeating unit of skeletal muscle. It is measured between striation patterns from Z bar to Z bar.

sarcoplasm The cytoplasm of a skeletal muscle fiber.

sarcoplasmic reticulum The endoplasmic reticulum of a skeletal muscle fiber. In muscle cells it forms a repeating pattern of tubes and small sacs around each myofibril. It contains the ionic calcium that triggers muscle contractions, releasing it into the sarcoplasm when properly stimulated.

scala tympani The lower portion of the fluid-filled cochlear canal. Pressure waves are transmitted to the round window through the scala tympani.

scala vestibuli The upper portion of the cochlear canal. Sound waves are transferred from the oval window to the fluid in the scala vestibuli and thence to the basilar membrane.

Schwann cell A type of glial (non-neuronal) cell associated with neurons outside the CNS. Schwann cells are responsible for the sheath surrounding neuronal axons and serve as guides for axonal regeneration as well as protective coverings. In addition, some Schwann cells form the myelin sheath.

scotopsin The protein fraction of visual pigments present in rod cells of the retina.

secondary immune response The response given by the immune systems to an invasion of the body by an organism or foreign substance with which the system is familiar. It is much more rapid than the primary response.

secondary sensory receptor A neuron featuring a specialized receptor but no axon. To transmit its transduced neural signals into the nervous system, a secondary receptor must synapse with other neurons possessing axons.

secondary sexual characteristics The body configurations, produced by the sex hormones, that make people attractive to members of the opposite sex. In women, such characteristics include breast development and broadening of the hips; in men it would be manifest in broad shoulders, narrow hips, and facial and body hair.

second heart sound The sound produced by the heart when ventricular diastole begins, believed to be produced primarily by the semilunar valves banging shut.

second messenger Proteinaceous hormones cannot penetrate cell membranes, so they deliver their messages to the outside of the membrane, and the messages are carried into the cell by another chemical, usually cyclic AMP. This relaying chemical is known as the "second messenger."

secretin A polypeptide hormone secreted by the mucosal cells of the duodenum whenever there is acid in the duodenal lumen. It stimulates the production and outflow of large quantities of a bicarbonate-rich buffer into the small intestine.

selectivity The ability to distinguish between multiple stimuli applied simultaneously.

semen A milky, rather thick fluid that serves as a matrix to carry mature spermatozoons out of the male reproductive system when ejaculation occurs. It is synthesized in the seminal vesicles, prostate gland, and Cowper's gland.

semicircular canals Three hollow tubes in the vestibular apparatus of the inner ear, arranged at right angles to each other. They are responsible for the maintenance of dynamic equilibrium and for the detection of acceleration and movement.

seminal vesicle Paired glands located lateral to the urinary bladder in males. They synthesize and secrete the major bulk of the fluid known as semen.

semipermeable membranes Membranes that permit the free passage of some materials but restrict the passage of others.

serotonin A central nervous neurotransmitter whose chemical name is 5-hydroxy tryptamine.

serum A fluid fraction of the blood, serum is obtained by permitting a clot to form, then removing the clot and all the formed elements that adhere to it. It differs from plasma in the fibrinogen content—serum has none.

serum sickness A serious hypersensitivity reaction, most often a reaction to penicillin or some related antibiotic. It is characterized by high fever, skin rashes, and swollen lymph nodes.

short-term memory One manifestation of the process of remembering. *See* long-term memory

sickle-cell anemia An inherited condition to which anyone is susceptible, but which occurs most often in black Americans. It is caused by an abnormal hemoglobin molecule that changes its shape when oxygen tension is low. As a result of this shape change, it tends to jam in small blood vessels and can cause severe abdominal and joint pain.

silicosis A type of pneumonia caused by the deposition of silicon particles on the alveolar surfaces of the lungs.

sinoatrial node (S-A node) A cluster of highly modified myocardial cells imbedded in the wall of the right atrium near the point where the great veins enter. They initiate the electrical signals that depolarize the atrial musculature and begin contraction. The S-A node is also known as the pacemaker.

sinus A cavity, expanded hollow, or basin-like depression. In biology, it refers to things like the hollows in the skull near the nose and sudden expansions in the diameter of blood vessels.

sinusitis An inflammation of the mucous membranes of the nasal sinuses.

skeletal muscle One of the three major types of vertebrate muscle. Skeletal muscle is voluntarily controlled and is anchored to bones.

small intestine The portion of the gastrointestinal tract extending from the stomach to the large intestine. Most digestion and nearly all nutrient absorption take place in the small intestine.

smooth ER *See* endoplasmic reticulum

smooth muscle One of the three major types of vertebrate muscle. There are two kinds of smooth muscle and both types are under autonomic control. One type enwraps the entire length of the gastrointestinal tract, and the other appears in places like the iris of the eye.

sodium inactivation A partially understood process that occurs when the action potential along a neuron reaches its peak. It renders the neurilemma impermeable to sodium ions. The duration of absolute refraction is determined by the period of sodium inactivation.

solute Substances that are dispersed throughout a matrix. In biological systems, solute particles are usually dispersed in a water matrix.

solution A dispersion in which the solute particles are smaller than 10Å units.

solvent Any substance that forms a matrix through which some other substance is dispersed. In biological systems, the solvent is almost always water, and the dissolved particles are broadcast throughout the water matrix.

somatic nervous system The voluntary nervous system. The peripheral and central neurons that are involved in conscious thoughts and which we can manipulate consciously.

somatostatin A hormone that appears to be produced mainly in the hypothalamus and the cells of the pancreas. It is thought to be involved in the regulation of both glucagon and insulin operations, and it is known to inhibit the activity of thyroid-stimulating hormone and somatotropin, both hormones of the adenohypophysis.

somatotropin (STH) An adenohypophyseal secretion once known as the growth hormone. In addition to its heavy involvement with the process of growing, STH functions in adults to alter metabolic priorities, particularly during periods of fasting and starvation.

space base Also known as ghostbuster, this is a combination of crack (a nasty type of cocaine) and PCP or "angel dust" (phencyclidine hydrochloride). It is thought to be capable of producing a schizophrenic paranoia in users.

spatial summation The blending of a series of stimuli from different sources that have arrived at the same time on the same structure. It refers to an algebraic addition across space.

special senses A term normally reserved for the eyes, ears, nose, tactile, and gustatory senses. Some authors leave out the tactile sense.

specific heat The amount of energy necessary to raise the temperature of one gram of a substance (usually water) one degree Celsius.

specific immune system The system that identifies specific antigenic particles and prepares defenses to attack that particular antigen. It involves lymphocytes of both the humoral and the cellular immune systems.

spermatid Male germ cells that have completed their meiotic divisions and are ready to be modified into spermatozoons.

spermatogenesis The process of converting male undifferentiated germ cells into mature gametes (spermatozoons).

spermatogonia Undifferentiated male germ cells located in the basal layer of the seminiferous tubules.

spermatozoan The mature male gamete.

sphygmomanometer The instrument used to determine a person's systemic arterial blood pressure. It consists of an air-filled bag that is wrapped around the upper arm and then inflated, and a barometer that indicates the air pressure within that bag.

spinal cord Part of the central nervous system. The brain is actually an enormously swollen end of the spinal cord.

spinal nerve A peripheral nerve that originates in the spinal cord.

spirochete A type of bacterium. The most widely known is a member of the genus *Treponema*, which is responsible for the venereal disease syphilis.

spontaneous generation A theory, once widely accepted, that flies, rats, and many other pests could generate without any parents, from piles of garbage and trash. Nowadays it often refers to current theories about the appearance of proteins, lipids, and other large molecules in the waters of ancient oceans.

spore A reproductive or protective structure. In molds and the more primitive plants, spores are the germ cells from which new plants can grow; in bacteria, the spore is a heavily walled structure into which the living chemicals of the cell retreat when environmental conditions are unsuited for continued survival.

stable octet A name given to the eight-electron configuration of an atom's valence shell. Achieving such a configuration makes the atom very stable chemically.

stapes Also known as the *stirrup*, this is the third bone of the middle ear (*see* incus; malleus).

starch The second most abundant organic compound on earth, starch is an edible polymer of glucose.

Starling's heart law A series of observations made in the early 1900s and compiled into a group of rules by the British physiologist E.H. Starling. The most widely known states that the energy associated with cardiac contraction is a function of the length of the myocardial fibers during diastole.

static equilibrium The position of a body in space. Acceleration and velocity are not involved with static equilibrium. The utricle and saccule of the inner ear are responsible for this sensing ability in humans.

steatorrhea The presence of unusually large amounts of fat in the feces.

stenin One of the two contractile proteins involved in the secretion of neurotransmitters from presynaptic nerve endings.

stenosis A narrowing or constriction of a tube or an opening. Often used in reference to blood vessels, heart valves, or the GI tract.
steroids Hormones built on a cholesterol nucleus. They include all the sex hormones, hormones of the adrenal cortex, and cholecalciferol (vitamin D).
stimulus Anything capable of producing a response, usually in a receptor.
stroke A disease condition, usually sudden and severe, that usually refers to a bursting blood vessel or a plugged artery or arteriole in the brain. They produce brain infarctions that often deprive the victim of such things as speech, reasoning power, and motility.
stroke volume The volume of blood squirted into the aorta with a given ventricular systole.
sublingual glands One of the three pairs of salivary glands, the sublingual glands are located, as the name implies, beneath the tongue.
submandibular (submaxillary) glands One of the three pairs of salivary glands, these glands are located on the floor of the mouth, just medial to the jawbone.
succus entericus A collective term used to describe all enzymatic secretions of the small intestine.
sucrase One of the secretions of the small intestine, sucrase is an enzyme that splits sucrose into its two component monosaccharides, fructose and glucose.
sucrose A disaccharide composed of fructose and glucose. Ordinary table sugar.
supraoptic nucleus (SON) One of the two pairs of hypothalamic nuclei that supply hormone for the neurohypophysis, the SON is the site of vasopressin synthesis.
suppressor cells A special group of lymphocytes whose efforts are directed toward reducing the effectiveness of the killer lymphocytes.
surface active agent A substance capable of rendering water miscible with oils. *See also* surfactant
surface tension The attractive force between molecules that exists on the surface of a liquid.
surfactant A compression of the term "surface active agent." The term usually refers to a phospholipid substance secreted onto the alveolar and bronchiolar surfaces in the lungs. When present, it reduces surface tension throughout these zones, thus rendering alveolar surfaces more pliable.
sympathetic chain A chain of nervous ganglia that are immediately lateral to the spinal column and extend from the uppermost thoracic vertebrae to the upper lumbar region. They contain the cell bodies of postsynaptic sympathetic neurons.
sympathetic system One of the two branches of the autonomic nervous system, this is involved with preparing the body to face and cope with an external emergency. *See* fight, flight, fright response
sympathomimetic Anything that mimics the operations of the sympathetic nervous system.
synapse The junction between two or more neurons where information can be passed between them.
syncitium A concatenation of similar cells that have blended to form a single cell. A group of similar cells that cooperate so completely that the movement of all of them is a single coordinated operation.
synthetic phase (S1) The period immediately preceding mitosis when the cellular machinery is replicating its nuclear DNA.
syphilis A disease caused by a spirochete (*Treponema pallidum*) and spread through sexual contact. It occurs in three clearly separated stages: primary, secondary, and tertiary. Tertiary syphilis is not always fatal, but it is often crippling or disfiguring. Syphilis is effectively treated with penicillin.
systemic circulation The portion of the blood circulatory system that does not include the pulmonary circulation.
systole A contraction of the myocardium. The entire cardiac cycle consists of two phases, the systolic (contraction) phase and the diastolic (relaxation) phase.

T

tactile receptor *See* contact receptor
tapetum A reflective sheet of tissue present in the eyes of most nocturnal mammals, the tapetum reflects light waves that have already stimulated retinal receptors back across the same receptors, thus giving them a double stimulus with a single light wave. It is the tapetum that makes the eyes of cats seem to glow in the dark.
target tissue A group of cells that are specifically responsive to the information carried by a given hormone.
taste bud A collection of chemoreceptors arranged into a single, goblet-shaped gland with a tiny opening onto the surface of the tongue. Such receptors are responsible for our ability to perceive flavors.
Tay-Sachs disease An inherited defect in lipid metabolism that produces malignant mental degeneration, paralysis, and ultimately, death. It is most prevalent in children whose ancestry is Jewish, mainly from eastern Europe. There is no known treatment, and the mortality rate is 100 percent.
T cell One of the two broadest categories of lymphocytes, the T cell is the mediator of the cellular immune response.
telophase The final phase of mitosis. It is characterized by the formation of a cleavage furrow in the cell membrane that continues to deepen until it finally pinches the cell into two parts.
temporal summation An increase in response due to: (1) an increase in the frequency of subthreshold stimuli applied to a neuron, or (2) an increase in the frequency of above-threshold stimuli applied to a muscle.
temporary suspension A dispersion in which the solute particles are too massive to remain in suspension, and thus they will ultimately settle to the bottom of the mixture.
tendon A tough, inelastic strip of connective tissue connecting muscle to bone. *See also* ligament
tertiary stucture The curled or coiled shapes assumed by long strands of protein that already possess a primary and secondary structure. Often tertiary shapes curl back over themselves repeatedly and are linked together at these sites by disulfide or sulfhydryl bonds.
testes The male gonads.
tetanus A state of constant contraction. Tetanus is the type of contractile phenomenon that produces the smooth movements of *in vivo* muscle operations.
thalamus A subcortical brain structure, the thalamus forms the greater portion of the walls of the third brain ventricle. It is an important relay center for our special senses.
thin filament A cluster of specific contractile proteins in muscle tissue, made up of strings of actin monomers and linked troponin/tropomyosin complexes.
threshold voltage The minimum voltage necessary to produce an action potential in a neuron or muscle fiber.
thrombocyte *See* platelet
thrombus A blood clot.
thymine One of the two pyrimidine nucleotide bases present in DNA molecules. In a completed DNA molecule, it always links with the purine adenine.
thymus gland A large, diffuse mass of glandular tissue located in the upper medial part of the thorax. It is involved in the maturation of T cells and is responsible for the secretion of a hormone that is also involved with the immune system.
thyroid A large, diffuse glandular structure wrapped around the larynx. The thyroid is responsible for the synthesis and secretion of iodinated hormones associated with metabolic rate and neural development, and also a peptide hormone, calcitonin, that is involved in calcium metabolism.
thyroid-stimulating hormone (TSH) A glycoprotein hormone synthesized and secreted by the adenohypophysis. It is involved in stimulating the production and secretion of the thyroid's iodinated hormones.

thyroid storm A particularly lethal phase of hyperthyroid disease or toxic goiter.
thyroxin A hormone of the thyroid gland containing four iodine molecules. It is the most abundant, although not the most effective, of the iodinated hormones.
tidal volume The volume of air moved into or out of the lungs during relaxed, reflex breathing.
tinnitus The perception of a constant whistling or humming sound that has no apparent external source.
tissue factor (thromboplastin) A factor usually released by a damaged cell that is capable of initiating the formation of a blood clot.
TMJ (temporomandibular joint) The joint between the temporal bone of the skull and the mandible (the lower jaw).
tonic receptor A type of receptor able to indicate constant values in a given stimulus.
total lung capacity The maximum volume of air that can be crammed into a pair of lungs.
toxic goiter A disease condition caused by the hypersecretion of iodinated thyroid hormones. It manifests itself in two forms: (1) Plummer's disease and (2) Graves' disease.
trace element Any element present in the body that represents less than 0.01 percent total body weight.
trachea The windpipe. A tube, supported periodically by cartilaginous rings, that extends from the pharynx to the bronchi.
transcription The transfer of information from DNA to any one of several different kinds of RNA.
transducer Anything capable of changing energy from one form into another.
transferrin A type of β-globulin that is involved in the transport of iron.
transfer RNA (tRNA) A small chunk of specialized RNA that can pick up a specific amino acid molecule and carry it to any ribosome where protein synthesis is occurring. Once there, tRNA hooks its amino acid onto the protein chain and leaves to pick up another, similar amino acid molecule.
tricuspid valve The fleshy heart valve that guards the opening between the right atrium and right ventricle.
triglyceride A neutral fat. A glycerol molecule with three fatty acids attached.
triiodothyronine (TRIT) An iodinated thyroid hormone that contains three iodine atoms per molecule and is the most active of all the thyroid hormones.
triose A three-carbon sugar.
trophic hormone Any hormone of the adenohypophysis that exerts control over another hormone or endocrine gland.
tropomyosin One of the contractile proteins of muscle. In company with troponin and actin, it forms the thin filaments of skeletal muscle.
troponin One of the contractile proteins of muscle. It complexes with tropomyosin, then lies along the actin polymer. It is not present in smooth muscle.
T-system A specialized system of membranous tubes running mainly perpendicular to the myofibril orientation in skeletal muscle. It is responsible for carrying action potentials deep into the muscle fiber.
tuberculosis A chronic bacterial disease caused by the organism *Mycobacterium sp.* Although it can attack any organ, it usually invades the lungs, where it produces lesions and tubercles in alveolar spaces and bronchioles. In previous centuries it was almost always fatal; today the mortality rate is about 10 percent.
tubular secretion The process of actively transporting unwanted waste products from interstitial fluids directly into the proximal tubule of the nephron.
tumor A growth of tissue caused by uncontrolled proliferation of slightly altered cells. The cells are usually sufficiently different to be functionally useless. If they remain where they are, they can be encapsulated and are considered benign. But if they can circulate through the body, starting new growths elsewhere, they are usually adjudged malignant.
T wave One of the elements of the electrocardiogram, the T wave is generally viewed as representing repolarization of the myocardium of the ventricles.
tympanic membrane *See* eardrum

U

ulcer Necrosis in a tissue that results in the development of a crater. Ulcers can appear anywhere but are most common on the skin surface and in the gastrointestinal tract.
ultrafiltrate A solution that is formed by passage through a filter with extremely fine pores.
ultraviolet radiation Electromagnetic radiation of a frequency just a little too high to be seen. The shortest visible wavelengths appear violet; hence those just a little shorter—almost, but not quite visible—are termed ultraviolet.
unipolar That which has only a single pole or a single charge. In a biological context, it refers to neurons having an axonal process leading in only one direction from the cell body.
unsaturated The ability to take more of a given thing than is already possessed. Unsaturated fat refers to the fatty acid chain, and it means that the chain could hold more hydrogen atoms than it has.
uracil One of the nucleotide bases. It is a single-ring pyrimidine and is peculiar to RNA. Uracil's counterpart in DNA is thymine.
urea A one-carbon organic compound, urea is the major nitrogenous waste product of protein metabolism. It forms in the liver and is carried by the blood into the kidney, where it becomes the major nitrogenous waste product of urine.
ureter The tube carrying urine from the urinary bladder to the body's exterior.
urethra The tube carrying urine from the kidney to the urinary bladder.
uric acid A nitrogenous waste product that is excreted in the urine. It is an end product of the breakdown of nucleotide bases.
urinary alkaline tide A phenomenon that results from the production of hydrochloric acid by the parietal cells of the stomach. Since the acid must come from the blood, when it is extracted it leaves behind an excessively alkaline plasma. The excess alkalinity is adjusted by the kidney, and it produces an unusually alkaline urine. The phenomenon usually occurs just after a meal begins and lasts for about twenty minutes.
urinary bladder A large sac formed mainly of transitional cuboidal epithelium and smooth muscle tissue, located in the pelvic cavity. Urine produced by the kidneys is stored in the bladder until it can be eliminated.
uterus A heavily muscled sac in the pelvic cavity of female mammals that opens through the cervix into the vagina. It serves to hold the developing embryo and fetus during pregnancy.
utricle One of the two divisions of the membranous labyrinth of the inner ear. The utricle is the larger of the two and is capable of sensing linear acceleration.
uvula A bag-shaped fleshy mass that dangles from the soft palate.

V

vagus nerve The tenth cranial nerve. It functions in the body as a parasympathetic nerve and sends both sensory and motor fibers throughout the thorax and the abdomen. It innervates all the important organs, including the heart and lungs.
valence The number of electrons that a given atom must either obtain or lose in order to achieve overall electrical neutrality. It involves only the outermost electron shell.
varicose vein A vein that has been stretched to a point where a permanent weak spot in the wall has been produced.
vasa recta The capillaries that surround the deep loops of Henle. They form a U-shaped mass of hairlike vessels around each loop in the kidney medulla.
vas deferens Tubular organs in males that extend from the epididymis to the ejaculatory duct.

vasectomy The surgical transection of both vas deferens tubes. A certain birth-control method.
vasopressin *See* antidiuretic hormone
venule A small blood vessel that accepts blood from capillaries and carries it into the larger veins.
ventilation Breathing.
ventricle One of the two large chambers of the vertebrate heart. The ventricles are distinguished from the atria by the presence of heavy muscular walls, particularly in the left ventricle.
ventricular bundle. *See* bundle of His
vermiform appendix A tubular evagination of the cecum of the large intestine. Its function is only partially understood.
vertebrate Any of the group of animals possessing a backbone.
vestibular organs The organs of equilibrium (balance) in the inner ear of mammals. They include the utricle, the saccule, and the semicircular canals.
vestibule A collective term referring to the utricle and saccule of the inner ear.
villi Small tubular projections extending outward from the outermost surface of a membrane, usually functioning to increase cellular surface area.
viscosity A physical property of a liquid. When viscous liquids begin to move, forces arise within them that oppose the flow. A viscous liquid is a "thick" liquid. The more syrupy a liquid is, the more viscous it is.
visual acuity Pertaining to keenness of vision. It is defined as the minimum distance between objects that still permits their perception as separate objects.
visual pigment A pigment in the retinal receptors of the eye that changes chemically when exposed to certain electromagnetic wavelengths.
vital capacity A standardized lung volume. It is defined as the volume of air that can be inhaled with maximal effort after a maximum expiration.
vitamin B_{12} *See* cyanacobalamin
vitamin D *See* calciferol
vitreous humor The transparent, gelatinous material that fills the eyeball between the retina and the lens.
volt A measure of the electrical potential energy content of a point or object. It is also known as electromotive force or EMF.
voltage drop The amount of electrical potential that is lost during the flow of current through a resistance.

W

wavelength Electricity flows in waves like the waves on the surface of the ocean. Wavelength is measured from a point on one wave to the identical point on the immediately succeeding wave.
weight A measure of gravitational attraction. It is a force that changes significantly with altitude.
white matter Portions of the central nervous system that appear white, as opposed to the gray matter. White matter is made up of myelinated nerve fibers. Gray matter is composed mainly of cell bodies.
work Physically, work is force multiplied by distance moved. If there is no motion, there is no work.

X

X ray A method of producing photographic plates that show only the densest organs in the body.

Z

Z bar A thick bar at both ends of a skeletal muscle sarcomere. It consists of a dense latticework of protein from which the actin filaments arise.
zygote A single cell formed from the nuclear fusion of male and female gametes. Simplistically, it could be referred to as a fertilized egg.

Credits

Tables and Text

Chapter 1

Figure 1.1: From Kent M. Van De Graaff and Stuart Ira Fox, *Concepts of Human Anatomy and Physiology.* Copyright © 1986 Wm. C. Brown Publishers, Dubuque, Iowa. All Rights Reserved. Reprinted by permission.
Figures 1.4, 1.6, 1.8, 1.10, 1.11, 1.12, 1.13, and 1.14: From John W. Hole, Jr., *Human Anatomy and Physiology,* 3d ed. Copyright © 1984 Wm. C. Brown Publishers, Dubuque, Iowa. All Rights Reserved. Reprinted by permission.

Chapter 2

Figures 2.11, 2.17, 2.20, and 2.21: From John W. Hole, Jr., *Human Anatomy and Physiology,* 4th ed. Copyright © 1987 Wm. C. Brown Publishers, Dubuque, Iowa. All Rights Reserved. Reprinted by permission.

Chapter 4

Figures 4.18, 4.19, 4.30*b*, and 4.31*b*: From John W. Hole, Jr., *Human Anatomy and Physiology,* 4th ed. Copyright © 1987 Wm. C. Brown Publishers, Dubuque, Iowa. All Rights Reserved. Reprinted by permission.
Figure 4.29*b*: From Leland G. Johnson, *Biology,* 2d ed. Copyright © 1987 Wm. C. Brown Publishers, Dubuque, Iowa. All Rights Reserved. Reprinted by permission.
Figures 4.36 and 4.37: From Stuart Ira Fox, *Human Physiology,* 2d ed. Copyright © 1987 Wm. C. Brown Publishers, Dubuque, Iowa. All Rights Reserved. Reprinted by permission.

Chapter 5

Figure 5.1: From Leland G. Johnson, *Biology,* 2d ed. Copyright © 1987 Wm. C. Brown Publishers, Dubuque, Iowa. All Rights Reserved. Reprinted by permission.
Figure 5.5: From Stuart Ira Fox, *Human Physiology,* 2d ed. Copyright © 1987 Wm. C. Brown Publishers, Dubuque, Iowa. All Rights Reserved. Reprinted by permission.
Figures 5.6, 5.16, and 5.17: From John W. Hole, Jr., *Human Anatomy and Physiology,* 4th ed. Copyright © 1987 Wm. C. Brown Publishers, Dubuque, Iowa. All Rights Reserved. Reprinted by permission.

Chapter 7

Figure 7.1: From Kent M. Van De Graaff, *Human Anatomy,* 2d ed. Copyright © 1988 Wm. C. Brown Publishers, Dubuque, Iowa. All Rights Reserved. Reprinted by permission.
Figures 7.3 and 7.14: From John W. Hole, Jr., *Human Anatomy and Physiology,* 3d ed. Copyright © 1984 Wm. C. Brown Publishers, Dubuque, Iowa. All Rights Reserved. Reprinted by permission.
Figures 7.4 and 7.20: From John W. Hole, Jr., *Human Anatomy and Physiology,* 4th ed. Copyright © 1987 Wm. C. Brown Publishers, Dubuque, Iowa. All Rights Reserved. Reprinted by permission.

Chapter 8

Figures 8.2 (*left*), 8.32, 8.33, 8.34, 8.35, 8.36, and 8.38: From John W. Hole, Jr., *Human Anatomy and Physiology,* 3d ed. Copyright © 1984 Wm. C. Brown Publishers, Dubuque, Iowa. All Rights Reserved. Reprinted by permission.
Figures 8.2 (*right*), 8.3, 8.22, 8.23, 8.37, 8.39, and 8.41: From John W. Hole, Jr., *Human Anatomy and Physiology,* 4th ed. Copyright © 1987 Wm. C. Brown Publishers, Dubuque, Iowa. All Rights Reserved. Reprinted by permission.
Figure 8.8: From Kent M. Van De Graaff and Stuart Ira Fox, *Concepts of Human Anatomy and Physiology.* Copyright © 1986 Wm. C. Brown Publishers, Dubuque, Iowa. All Rights Reserved. Reprinted by permission.
Figures 8.9 and 8.30: From T. L. Peele, *The Neuroanatomic Basis for Clinical Neurology,* 2d ed. Copyright © 1961 McGraw-Hill Book Company, New York, NY. Reprinted by permission of the publisher.
Figure 8.12*c*: From Leland G. Johnson, *Biology,* 2d ed. Copyright © 1987 Wm. C. Brown Publishers, Dubuque, Iowa. All Rights Reserved. Reprinted by permission.
Figure 8.18: From Stuart Ira Fox, *Human Physiology,* 2d ed. Copyright © 1987 Wm. C. Brown Publishers, Dubuque, Iowa. All Rights Reserved. Reprinted by permission.
Figure 8.28: From John W. Hole, Jr., *Essentials of Human Anatomy and Physiology,* 3d ed. Copyright © 1989 Wm. C. Brown Publishers, Dubuque, Iowa. All Rights Reserved. Reprinted by permission.
Figure 8.44: From Kent M. Van De Graaff, *Human Anatomy,* 2d ed. Copyright © 1988 Wm. C. Brown Publishers, Dubuque, Iowa. All Rights Reserved. Reprinted by permission.

Chapter 9

Figures 9.9, 9.15, 9.24, and 9.37: From John W. Hole, Jr., *Human Anatomy and Physiology,* 4th ed. Copyright © 1987 Wm. C. Brown Publishers, Dubuque, Iowa. All Rights Reserved. Reprinted by permission.
Figures 9.12 and 9.13: From Kent M. Van De Graaff and Stuart Ira Fox, *Concepts of Human Anatomy and Physiology.* Copyright © 1986 Wm. C. Brown Publishers, Dubuque, Iowa. All Rights Reserved. Reprinted by permission.

Chapter 10

Figure 10.1: From Stuart Ira Fox, *Human Physiology,* 2d ed. Copyright © 1987 Wm. C. Brown Publishers, Dubuque, Iowa. All Rights Reserved. Reprinted by permission.
Figures 10.5, 10.15, 10.20, 10.21, 10.22, 10.24, 10.25, and 10.27: From John W. Hole, Jr., *Human Anatomy and Physiology,* 4th ed. Copyright © 1987 Wm. C. Brown Publishers, Dubuque, Iowa. All Rights Reserved. Reprinted by permission.

Figures 10.10, 10.11, and 10.30*a* and *b*: From Kent M. Van De Graaff and Stuart Ira Fox, *Concepts of Human Anatomy and Physiology*. Copyright © 1986 Wm. C. Brown Publishers, Dubuque, Iowa. All Rights Reserved. Reprinted by permission.
Figures 10.12 and 10.19: From John W. Hole, Jr., *Human Anatomy and Physiology*, 3d ed. Copyright © 1984 Wm. C. Brown Publishers, Dubuque, Iowa. All Rights Reserved. Reprinted by permission.

Chapter 11

Figures 11.2 and 11.25: From Kent M. Van De Graaff and Stuart Ira Fox, *Concepts of Human Anatomy and Physiology*. Copyright © 1986 Wm. C. Brown Publishers, Dubuque, Iowa. All Rights Reserved. Reprinted by permission.
Figures 11.5*b*, 11.16, 11.31, and 11.32: From John W. Hole, Jr., *Human Anatomy and Physiology*, 3d ed. Copyright © 1984 Wm. C. Brown Publishers, Dubuque, Iowa. All Rights Reserved. Reprinted by permission.
Figures 11.10, 11.12, 11.18, 11.26, and 11.27: From Stuart Ira Fox, *Human Physiology*, 2d ed. Copyright © 1987 Wm. C. Brown Publishers, Dubuque, Iowa. All Rights Reserved. Reprinted by permission.
Figures 11.24 and 11.29: From John W. Hole, Jr., *Human Anatomy and Physiology*, 4th ed. Copyright © 1987 Wm. C. Brown Publishers, Dubuque, Iowa. All Rights Reserved. Reprinted by permission.

Chapter 12

Figures 12.4, 12.6, 12.7, 12.11, 12.13*a*, 12.15, 12.16, 12.18, 12.19, 12.22, 12.23, and 12.24: From John W. Hole, Jr., *Human Anatomy and Physiology*, 4th ed. Copyright © 1987 Wm. C. Brown Publishers, Dubuque, Iowa. All Rights Reserved. Reprinted by permission.
Figure 12.5: From Kent M. Van De Graaff, *Human Anatomy*, 2d ed. Copyright © 1988 Wm. C. Brown Publishers, Dubuque, Iowa. All Rights Reserved. Reprinted by permission.
Figures 12.10 and 12.14: From Stuart Ira Fox, *Human Physiology*, 2d ed. Copyright © 1987 Wm. C. Brown Publishers, Dubuque, Iowa. All Rights Reserved. Reprinted by permission.

Chapter 13

Figures 13.2, 13.3, 13.5, 13.7, 13.9, 13.14*b*, and 13.29: From John W. Hole, Jr., *Human Anatomy and Physiology*, 4th ed. Copyright © 1987 Wm. C. Brown Publishers, Dubuque, Iowa. All Rights Reserved. Reprinted by permission.
Figures 13.4, 13.21, and 13.24: From Kent M. Van De Graaff, *Human Anatomy*, 2d ed. Copyright © 1988 Wm. C. Brown Publishers, Dubuque, Iowa. All Rights Reserved. Reprinted by permission.
Figures 13.11 and 13.13: From Kent M. Van De Graaff and Stuart Ira Fox, *Concepts of Human Anatomy and Physiology*. Copyright © 1986 Wm. C. Brown Publishers, Dubuque, Iowa. All Rights Reserved. Reprinted by permission.
Figure 13.14*a*: From Stuart Ira Fox, *Human Physiology*. Copyright © 1984 Wm. C. Brown Publishers, Dubuque, Iowa. All Rights Reserved. Reprinted by permission.
Figures 13.26 and 13.28: From John W. Hole, Jr., *Human Anatomy and Physiology*, 3d ed. Copyright © 1984 Wm. C. Brown Publishers, Dubuque, Iowa. All Rights Reserved. Reprinted by permission.
Figure 13.31: From Stuart Ira Fox, *Human Physiology*, 2d ed. Copyright © 1987 Wm. C. Brown Publishers, Dubuque, Iowa. All Rights Reserved. Reprinted by permission.

Chapter 14

Figures 14.2, 14.3, and 14.10: From Kent M. Van De Graaff, *Human Anatomy*, 2d ed. Copyright © 1988 Wm. C. Brown Publishers, Dubuque, Iowa. All Rights Reserved. Reprinted by permission.
Figures 14.4, 14.6, 14.7, 14.9, 14.14, 14.15, 14.18, 14.20, 14.27, 14.36, and 14.37: From John W. Hole, Jr., *Human Anatomy and Physiology*, 4th ed. Copyright © 1987 Wm. C. Brown Publishers, Dubuque, Iowa. All Rights Reserved. Reprinted by permission.
Figure 14.17: From Stuart Ira Fox, *Human Physiology*, 2d ed. Copyright © 1987 Wm. C. Brown Publishers, Dubuque, Iowa. All Rights Reserved. Reprinted by permission.
Figure 14.24: From Kent M. Van De Graaff and Stuart Ira Fox, *Concepts of Human Anatomy and Physiology*. Copyright © 1986 Wm. C. Brown Publishers, Dubuque, Iowa. All Rights Reserved. Reprinted by permission.
Figures 14.25 and 14.40: From Stuart Ira Fox, *Human Physiology*. Copyright © 1984 Wm. C. Brown Publishers, Dubuque, Iowa. All Rights Reserved. Reprinted by permission.
Figure 14.41: From John W. Hole, Jr., *Human Anatomy and Physiology*, 2d ed. Copyright © 1981 Wm. C. Brown Publishers, Dubuque, Iowa. All Rights Reserved. Reprinted by permission.

Chapter 15

Figures 15.3 and 15.21: From Kent M. Van De Graaff, *Human Anatomy*, 2d ed. Copyright © 1988 Wm. C. Brown Publishers, Dubuque, Iowa. All Rights Reserved. Reprinted by permission.
Figure 15.4: From John W. Hole, Jr., *Essentials of Human Anatomy and Physiology*, 2d ed. Copyright © 1986 Wm. C. Brown Publishers, Dubuque, Iowa. All Rights Reserved. Reprinted by permission.
Figure 15.7: From John W. Hole, Jr., *Human Anatomy and Physiology*, 3d ed. Copyright © 1984 Wm. C. Brown Publishers, Dubuque, Iowa. All Rights Reserved. Reprinted by permission.
Figures 15.11, 15.14, 15.16, 15.17, 15.23, 15.24, and 15.30: From John W. Hole, Jr., *Human Anatomy and Physiology*, 4th ed. Copyright © 1987 Wm. C. Brown Publishers, Dubuque, Iowa. All Rights Reserved. Reprinted by permission.
Figures 15.15, 15.39, and 15.42: From Kent M. Van De Graaff and Stuart Ira Fox, *Concepts of Human Anatomy and Physiology*. Copyright © 1986 Wm. C. Brown Publishers, Dubuque, Iowa. All Rights Reserved. Reprinted by permission.

Chapter 16

Figures 16.2, 16.4, 16.15, 16.20, 16.21, 16.22, 16.24, and 16.25: From John W. Hole, Jr., *Human Anatomy and Physiology*, 4th ed. Copyright © 1987 Wm. C. Brown Publishers, Dubuque, Iowa. All Rights Reserved. Reprinted by permission.
Figure 16.3: From Kent M. Van De Graaff, *Human Anatomy*, 2d ed. Copyright © 1988 Wm. C. Brown Publishers, Dubuque, Iowa. All Rights Reserved. Reprinted by permission.
Figure 16.16: From Kent M. Van De Graaff and Stuart Ira Fox, *Concepts of Human Anatomy and Physiology*. Copyright © 1986 Wm. C. Brown Publishers, Dubuque, Iowa. All Rights Reserved. Reprinted by permission.
Figures 16.17 and 16.27: From Stuart Ira Fox, *Human Physiology*, 2d ed. Copyright © 1987 Wm. C. Brown Publishers, Dubuque, Iowa. All Rights Reserved. Reprinted by permission.
Figure 16.23*a*: From John W. Hole, Jr., *Human Anatomy and Physiology*, 3d ed. Copyright © 1984 Wm. C. Brown Publishers, Dubuque, Iowa. All Rights Reserved. Reprinted by permission.

Chapter 17

Figures 17.1, 17.2*a*, 17.6, 17.8, 17.14, 17.16, 17.18, 17.19, 17.20, 17.21, and 17.22: From John W. Hole, Jr., *Human Anatomy and Physiology*, 4th ed. Copyright © 1987 Wm. C. Brown Publishers, Dubuque, Iowa. All Rights Reserved. Reprinted by permission.
Figure 17.4: From Kent M. Van De Graaff and Stuart Ira Fox, *Concepts of Human Anatomy and Physiology*. Copyright © 1986 Wm. C. Brown Publishers, Dubuque, Iowa. All Rights Reserved. Reprinted by permission.

Chapter 18

Figures 18.1, 18.2, 18.3, 18.6, 18.7*a*, 18.8, 18.14, 18.15, 18.17, 18.18*b*, 18.20, 18.22, 18.27, 18.30, and 18.33: From John W. Hole, Jr., *Human Anatomy and Physiology*, 4th ed. Copyright © 1987 Wm. C. Brown Publishers, Dubuque, Iowa. All Rights Reserved. Reprinted by permission.
Figure 18.4: From John W. Hole, Jr., *Essentials of Human Anatomy and Physiology*, 3d ed. Copyright © 1989 Wm. C. Brown Publishers, Dubuque, Iowa. All Rights Reserved. Reprinted by permission.

Figures 18.12, 18.13, 18.16, and 18.36: From Kent M. Van De Graaff and Stuart Ira Fox, *Concepts of Human Anatomy and Physiology.* Copyright © 1986 Wm. C. Brown Publishers, Dubuque, Iowa. All Rights Reserved. Reprinted by permission.
Figure 18.28*a*: From Kent M. Van De Graaff, *Human Anatomy,* 2d ed. Copyright © 1988 Wm. C. Brown Publishers, Dubuque, Iowa. All Rights Reserved. Reprinted by permission.
Figures 18.31, 18.32, 18.34, and 18.35: From Stuart Ira Fox, *Human Physiology,* 2d ed. Copyright © 1987 Wm. C. Brown Publishers, Dubuque, Iowa. All Rights Reserved. Reprinted by permission.

Photographs

Chapter 1

Opener: © From the works of Andreas Vesalius of Brussels by J. B. de C. M. Saunders and Charles P. O'Malley, p. 109, Dover Publications, Inc., N.Y. 1973.

Chapter 2

Opener: © Michael C. Webb/Visuals Unlimited.

Chapter 3

Opener: © D. W. Fawcelt/Photo Researchers, Inc.

Chapter 4

Opener: © Andrew Staehelin, Dept. of Molecular, Cellular and Developmental Biology, University of Colorado.
Figure 4.1*a*: © Billings Microscope Collection, Armed Forces Institute of Pathology; ***b*:** © National Library of Medicine.
Figure 4.2: Courtesy of Cambridge Instruments, Inc. Optical Systems Division.
Figure 4.4*a*: Courtesy of Bausch and Lomb; ***b*:** © Dr. Ned Feder, National Institute of Arthritis, Diabetes, and Digestive and Kidney Diseases, NIH; ***c*:** © Carl Zeiss, Inc.
Figures 4.4*d*, 4.10, 4.14*a*, 4.15*a*: © Dr. Keith Porter.
Figure 4.16*a*: © Gordon F. Leedale/BioPhoto Associates.
Figure 4.20*a*: © Dr. Keith Porter.
Figure 4.21: © James A. Lake, Journal of Molecular Biology 105, 131–159 (1976), © Academic Press, Inc. (London) LTD.
Figure 4.22*a*: © Dr. Keith Porter.
Figure 4.23: © Sandra L. Wolen.
Figure 4.25: © Dr. Joseph Gall, Reproduced from *Journal of Cell Biology* 31 (1966). Copyrighted permission of Rockefeller University Press.
Figure 4.27*c*: © Dr. Keith Porter.
Figure 4.28: © Reproduced with permission of the American Lung Association.
Figure 4.29*a*: Visuals Unlimited/© David Phillips.
Figure 4.30*a*: © Gordon Leedale/Biophoto Association.
Figure 4.31*a*: © Stephen L. Wolfe.

Chapter 5

Opener: © David Scharf/Peter Arnold, Inc.
Figure 5.2*b*: © E. J. Dupraw.
Figure 5.14*b*: © H. Fernandes-Moran.

Chapter 6

Opener: Courtesy of AT&T Bell Laboratories.

Chapter 7

Opener: © Manfred Kage/Peter Arnold, Inc.
Figure 7.21: © H. Webster from *The Vertebrate Peripheral Nervous System,* John Hubbard, editor.

Chapter 8

Opener: © Manfred Kage/Peter Arnold, Inc.
Figure 8.12 (*both*): © MacMillan Journals, LTD.
Figure 8.15: © E. R. Lewis, University of California, Berkeley/BPS.
Figure 8.42: © Monte Buchsbaum, University of California.
Figure 8.43: © Tom Hollyman/Photo Researchers, Inc.

Chapter 9

Opener: © Frank Werblin, University of California, Berkeley.
Figure 9.16: © Per H. Kjeldson, University of Michigan, Ann Arbor.
Figure 9.27*d*: © Manfred Kage/Peter Arnold, Inc.
Figure 9.38: © Edwin A. Reschke.

Chapter 10

Opener: © Carolina Biological Supply Company.
Figure 10.6*b*: N. S. Halmi, from Weiss, Leon, *Histology,* 5th ed. Elsevier Biomedical, 1983.
Figures 10.16, 10.30: © Edwin A. Reschke.
Figures 10.33, 10.34: © Green, R. *Human Hormones.* Copyright 1970 by World University Library. Reprinted with permission of publisher.
Figure 10.35: Courtesy WHO photo by Paul Almasy.
Figure 10.36: © Courtesy of F. A. Davis, Co., Philadelphia, and Dr. R. H. Kampmeier.
Figure 10.37: © Lester V. Bergman and Associates.

Chapter 11

Opener: © Manfred Kage/Peter Arnold, Inc.
Figure 11.3: © Edwin A. Reschke.
Figure 11.9*b*: Kessel, R. G., and Kardon, R. H. *Tissues and Organs: A Text-Atlas of Scanning Electron Microscopy.* © 1979 by W. H. Freeman and Co.
Figure 11.33 (*both*): © Avril Somylo, Ph.D.
Figure 11.34*a*: A. Abrahám.

Chapter 12

Opener: © Warren Rosenberg/New York University Biology/BPS.
Figure 12.3: © Carolina Biological Supply Company.
Figure 12.13: © Bill Longcore/Photo Researchers, Inc.
Figure 12.25*a*: © Eric Grave/Photo Researchers, Inc.; ***b,c*:** © Bill Longcore/Photo Reseachers, Inc.

Chapter 13

Opener: © Dr. Gregory J. Highison, Ph.D., University of Nevada, School of Medicine.
Figure 13.6*c*: © Dr. Thomas F. Robinson.
Figure 13.12: © Bob Coyle.
Figure 13.26*a*: © Courtesy of Eastman Kodak; ***b–f*:** © Martin M. Rocker/Tauras Photos.

Chapter 14

Opener: © Peter Andrews, Ph.D., Imagery.
Figure 14.5 (*both*): © Courtesy of Eastman Kodak.
Figure 14.8: © West, J. B. *Respiratory Physiology: The Essentials.* © 1979 Williams and Wilkins Co., Baltimore.
Figure 14.11: © From *Tissues and Organs: A Text-Atlas of Scanning Electron Microscopy,* R. G. Kessel and R. H. Kardon.
Figure 14.19*a*: Courtesy of Warren E. Collins, Inc., Braintree, MA; ***b*:** © Ken Sherman/Bruce Coleman, Inc.

Chapter 15

Opener: © Biophoto Associates/Science Source/Photo Researchers, Inc.
Figure 15.18: © Edwin A. Reschke.
Figure 15.34: © Dr. Keith Porter.
Figure 15.44*a*: © Carroll Weiss/RBP; ***b*:** © Sheril D. Burton.

Chapter 16

Opener: © Manfred Kage/Peter Arnold, Inc.
Figure 16.8: Courtesy the Eppley Institute for Research in Cancer/R. B. Wilson, M. D./The University of Nebraska Medical Center.

Chapter 17

Opener: © David M. Phillips/Visuals Unlimited.
Figure 17.2: © Edwin A. Reschke.

Chapter 18

Opener: © Carolina Biological Supply Company.
Figure 18.5*a:* © Biophoto Associates/Photo Researchers, Inc.
Figure 18.9: © Edwin A. Reschke.
Figure 18.10: © From *Tissues and Organs: A Text-Atlas of Scanning Electron Microscopy,* R. G. Kessel and R. H. Kardon. © 1979 W. H. Freeman and Company.
Figure 18.18*a:* © Manfred Kage/Peter Arnold, Inc.
Figure 18.19: © Edwin A. Reschke/Peter Arnold, Inc.
Figure 18.21: © Dr. Landrum B. Shettles.
Figure 18.23: "Sea Urchin Sperm-Egg Interactions Studied with the Scanning Electron Microscope," Tegner, M. J. and Epel, D. *Science,* Vol. 179, pp. 685–688, 16 Feb., 1973.
Figure 18.28*b:* © Dr. Landrum B. Shettles.

Chapter 19

Opener: © Edwin A. Reschke.

Chapter 20

Opener: © F. J. Dias/Photo Researchers, Inc.

Chapter 21

Opener: © Science Photo Library/Photo Researchers, Inc.

Index

B

F

G

T

U

V

W

X

Y

Z